NON-LEAGUE CLUB DIRECTORY 2021-22

(44th Edition)

EDITORS
MIKE & TONY WILLIAMS

NON-LEAGUE CLUB DIRECTORY 2021-22
ISBN 978-1-869833-02-2

Editors
Mike Williams
(Tel: 01548 531 339)
mwpublishing@btconnect.com
Tony Williams
Email: t.williams320@btinternet.com

Published by MW Publishing
(Tel: 01548 531 339)
Email: mwpublishing@btconnect.com

Printed by
CPI William Clowes - Suffolk

Sales & Distribution
MWPublishing (01548 531 339)

Front Cover: Cuxton's Stuart West (hoops) clears against Chipstead during his side's 3-0 victory in the Sevenoaks Charity Cup. Photo Alan Coomes.

EDITORIAL

Well, here we go again. As the book goes to the printer, the start of the 2021-22 season kick's off for some tonight (30th July) and they, along with most of the Non-League Pyramid, will be hoping to complete a full season for the first time in two years.

Once again this year's book looks back at a COVID disrupted season, recording every league and FA cup match played by those teams playing in Steps 1-4, whilst league tables act as a record of the games played by the Step 5-7 clubs. Every result from the FA Cup, Trophy and Vase is also included plus reports from last year's Non-League finals.

Going forward the new National League System's club allocations for 2021-22 have reshaped the Non-League Pyramid and it will be interesting to see how teams fare in the new geographical structure.

Despite the lack of football, it has felt as though we have had a glut of the sport as television has been broadcasting, almost daily, the 'professional' game over the last 12 months. Don't get me wrong, it's been great to watch something, Euro 2020 was the highlight for me, not just because of England's performances, every game was played in a great spirit, the officiating was top class and atmospheres were back! And it's the lack of the latter that, for me, made the rest of the year's viewing underwhelming. As a player even playing in front of one man and his dog gave you extra out on the pitch. Maybe that's why the Euro's were a success, players had their 'live' audiences back. If it is, we could be in for a great season ahead.

England reaching the final of Euro 2020 stirred up memories from 1966, not for me I was four years from existence, but Dad was there. Working as a steward his position in the stadium had him looking along the line of the goal mouth that has been under so much scrutiny ever since - for the record Dad says the ball was over the line in the air and that the spin took it back down on to the line.
He has lots of memorabilia from that World Cup, as well as many other football publications and of course scrap books of cuttings and statistics from his own playing days (836 apps 697 goals).
He often refers to them just to remind himself of the clubs he played for and against, the stadiums he played at and the players he played with over the years. I don't know if players today at our level keep scrap books in the same way but if not this Directory has been keeping a record now for 44 years and I would like to think it will bring the same enjoyment Dad gets from looking back over his seasons.

Good luck for the season ahead, let's hope next year's Directory is packed with chamionship winners, promotions and relegations!

Mike Williams

CONTENTS

THE 2020-21 SEASON

STEP 1

NATIONAL LEAGUE 9
- LEAGUE TABLE
- MATCH FACTS

STEP 2

NATIONAL NORTH 77
- LEAGUE TABLE
- MATCH FACTS

NATIONAL SOUTH 129
- LEAGUE TABLE
- MATCH FACTS

NATIONAL LEAGUE PLAYERS DATABASE 173

STEP 3 & 4

ISTHMIAN LEAGUE 255
- LEAGUE TABLES
- MATCH FACTS

NORTHERN PREMIER LEAGUE 297
- LEAGUE TABLES
- MATCH FACTS

SOUTHERN LEAGUE 329
- LEAGUE TABLES
- MATCH FACTS

STEP 5/6

LEAGUE TABLES 371

STEP 7+

LEAGUE TABLES 385

ENGLAND C 408

FA COMPETITIONS

THE FA CUP 412
THE FA TROPHY 431
THE FA VASE 445
THE FA YOUTH CUP 467
THE FA WOMEN'S CUP 472
THE FA DISABILITY CUP 478

GROUNDS OF GREAT BRITAIN AND CLUB INDEX 844

THE 2021-22 NATIONAL LEAGUE SYSTEM CLUB DIRECTORY

STEP 1

NATIONAL LEAGUE 482

STEP 2

NATIONAL NORTH 494
NATIONAL SOUTH 505

STEP 3 & 4

ISTHMIAN LEAGUE
PREMIER 516
NORTH 527
SOUTH CENTRAL 537
SOUTH EAST 547

NORTHERN PREMIER LEAGUE
PREMIER 558
EAST 570
MIDLANDS 580
WEST 590

SOUTHERN LEAGUE
PREMIER CENTRAL 602
PREMIER SOUTH 613
DIVISION ONE CENTRAL 624
DIVISION ONE SOUTH 634

STEP 5/6

COMBINED COUNTIES LEAGUE
PREMIER NORTH 644
PREMIER SOUTH 650
DIVISION ONE 657

EASTERN COUNTIES
PREMIER 663
DIVISION ONE NORTH 670
DIVISION ONE SOUTH 674

ESSEX SENIOR LEAGUE 679

HELLENIC LEAGUE
PREMIER 686
DIVISION ONE 693

MIDLAND FOOTBALL LEAGUE
PREMIER 698
DIVISION ONE 705

NORTH WEST COUNTIES
PREMIER 710
DIVISION ONE NORTH 717
DIVISION ONE SOUTH 721

NORTHERN COUNTIES EAST
PREMIER 727
DIVISION ONE 734

NORTHERN LEAGUE
DIVISION ONE 740
DIVISION TWO 747

SOUTH WEST PENINSULA LEAGUE
PREMIER EAST 753
PREMIER WEST 758

SOUTHERN COMBINATION
PREMIER 763
DIVISION ONE 770

SOUTHERN COUNTIES EAST
PREMIER 775
DIVISION ONE 782

SPARTAN SOUTH MIDLANDS LEAGUE
PREMIER 787
DIVISION ONE 794

UNITED COUNTIES LEAGUE
PREMIER NORTH 799
PREMIER SOUTH 806
DIVISION ONE 815

WESSEX LEAGUE
PREMIER 819
DIVISION ONE 826

WESTERN LEAGUE
PREMIER 831
DIVISION ONE 838

FA Vase Second Qualifying Round action between Brimscombe & Thrupp v AFC Aldermaston.
Photo Peter Barnes.

Houghton (Peterborough) clips the Portsmouth bar during the Amputee final at the FA Disability Cup weekend.
Photo by Keith Clayton.

As always I'd like to say a special thank you to **'OUR TEAM' OF PHOTOGRAPHERS**, Peter Barnes, Keith Clayton, Alan Coomes and Bill Wheatcroft, who, despite everything, managed to travel from ground to ground getting their shots. Above I've selected one of my favourite photos from each of them.

VCD keeper Nick Blue clears from the onrushing Cray Valleys Francis Babalola, during this FA Cup Preliminary Round tie. Photo by Alan Coomes.

Walsall Wood keeper Wren saves in the penalty shoot out in their Firth Round FA Vase tie vs Anstey Nomads. Photo by Bill Wheatcroft.

CONTRIBUTORS: Scott Bolton (FA Competitions Department), Craig Pottage, Richard Rundle (Football Club History Database), and the many league and club officials that have been kind enough to supply the necessary information, thank you one and all.

FOR THE NLS

2021-22

STEP 1

NATIONAL

STEP 2

NATIONAL NORTH

NATIONAL SOUTH

STEP 3

ISTHMIAN
PREMIER

NORTHERN PREMIER
PREMIER

SOUTHERN PREMIER
CENTRAL / SOUTH

STEP 4

ISTHMIAN
NORTH / SOUTH CENTRAL / SOUTH EAST

NORTHERN PREMIER
EAST / MIDLANDS / WEST

SOUTHERN
CENTRAL / SOUTH

STEP 5/6

COMBINED COUNTIES
EASTERN COUNTIES
ESSEX SENIOR
HELLENIC

MIDLAND FOOTBALL LEAGUE
NORTH WEST COUNTIES
NORTHERN COUNTIES EAST
NORTHERN LEAGUE

SOUTH WEST PENINSULAR
SOUTHERN COMBINATION
SOUTHERN COUNTIES EAST
SPARTAN SOUTH MIDLANDS

UNITED COUNTIES
WESSEX
WESTERN

STEP 7 - REGIONAL NLS FEEDER LEAGUES

NATIONAL LEAGUE

		P	W	D	L	F	A	GD	Pts
1	Sutton United	42	25	9	8	72	36	36	84
2	Torquay United (Play-off finalists)	42	23	11	8	68	39	29	80
3	Stockport County	42	21	14	7	69	32	37	77
4	Hartlepool United (Play-off Winners)	42	22	10	10	66	43	23	76
5	Notts County	42	20	10	12	62	41	21	70
6	Chesterfield	42	21	6	15	60	43	17	69
7	Bromley	42	19	12	11	63	53	10	69
8	Wrexham	42	19	11	12	64	43	21	68
9	Eastleigh	42	18	12	12	49	40	9	66
10	Halifax Town	42	19	8	15	63	54	9	65
11	Solihull Moors	42	19	7	16	58	48	10	64
12	Dagenham & Redbridge	42	17	9	16	53	48	5	60
13	Maidenhead United	42	15	11	16	62	60	2	56
14	Boreham Wood	42	13	16	13	52	48	4	55
15	Aldershot Town	42	15	7	20	59	66	-7	52
16	Yeovil Town	42	15	7	20	58	68	-10	52
17	Altrincham	42	12	11	19	46	60	-14	47
18	Weymouth	42	11	6	25	45	71	-26	39
19	Wealdstone	42	10	7	25	49	99	-50	37
20	Woking	42	8	9	25	42	69	-27	33
21	King's Lynn Town	42	7	10	25	50	98	-48	31
22	Barnet	42	8	7	27	37	88	-51	31
23	Dover Athletic were unable to complete the season - record expunged.								

		1	2	3	4	5	6	7	8	9	10	11	12	13	14	15	16	17	18	19	20	21	22	23
1	Aldershot Town		2-1	2-1	3-3	2-3	0-1	2-1		1-3	1-3	1-3	1-1	0-0	1-0	1-3	1-2	1-2	1-4	2-0	0-2	3-0	3-0	2-0
2	Altrincham	1-2		2-3	2-3	0-1	3-2	0-1		1-1	0-1	1-1	3-0	2-0	1-1	0-2	1-1	0-4	0-0	2-0	0-0	1-0	1-2	4-3
3	Barnet	3-1	1-2		0-3	1-3	0-2	0-2		1-5	2-1	0-0	0-2	2-0	1-4	0-2	1-2	2-0	0-2	0-0	1-0	0-2	0-2	1-4
4	Boreham Wood	3-2	0-1	0-0		1-1	0-0	0-1		1-2	0-0	2-2	5-1	1-4	2-2	2-2	0-3	0-0	0-0	3-1	1-0	1-0	2-3	2-3
5	Bromley	2-0	3-1	2-2	1-1		1-2	1-0		1-2	1-2	1-0	2-0	2-2	1-0	1-0	0-2	1-3	1-2	2-2	3-2	2-2	1-1	1-2
6	Chesterfield	0-0	1-0	6-0	0-0	1-2		2-1		1-0	1-2	1-2	4-1	1-2	2-3	1-0	1-2	0-1	0-2	0-0	1-0	4-0	2-1	3-0
7	Dagenham & Redbridge	0-2	0-1	1-2	2-2	1-0	2-2			2-0	3-0	0-1	3-2	2-1	0-0	3-2	0-2	1-2	1-0	1-0	1-1	3-1	1-1	0-0
8	Dover Athletic																							
9	Eastleigh	2-2	1-1	3-0	1-0	1-2	0-1	3-0			1-0	2-1	0-1	0-1	2-0	1-1	1-0	1-0	2-1	2-0	0-0	0-0	1-1	1-0
10	Halifax Town	1-0	3-2	5-2	0-1	1-2	1-2	2-0		3-1		1-1	4-2	2-3	1-1	1-0	0-1	2-2	1-2	0-1	3-2	1-0	0-4	1-1
11	Hartlepool United	2-1	1-1	1-0	1-2	0-0	3-1	2-1		0-0	3-1		2-0	2-4	2-0	2-0	4-0	1-0	0-5	3-1	4-0	1-0	0-1	2-1
12	King's Lynn Town	4-4	2-0	5-1	0-3	1-4	1-2	0-3		2-1	1-1	2-2		0-0	0-1	1-1	0-4	0-1	0-0	2-3	2-2	3-2	0-2	2-2
13	Maidenhead United	2-4	0-1	0-0	0-1	2-2	2-0	2-1		0-1	1-2	0-4	2-3		0-4	3-1	0-0	0-3	4-1	4-0	0-1	2-1	2-2	4-2
14	Notts County	0-1	3-1	4-2	0-1	2-2	0-1	3-1		0-1	1-2	0-1	2-2	2-3		2-0	1-0	3-2	0-0	3-0	3-0	1-0	1-0	2-0
15	Solihull Moors	1-0	4-0	1-0	1-0	0-1	2-1	0-1		2-0	2-1	2-0	5-0	1-1	2-1		0-5	0-0	1-2	3-0	2-1	2-1	1-0	5-1
16	Stockport County	0-0	2-2	2-1	1-1	0-0	2-0	1-1		3-0	2-1	1-1	4-0	2-2	0-0	0-0		0-2	2-2	4-0	1-2	1-1	2-0	1-0
17	Sutton United	3-1	2-2	1-0	2-0	3-2	0-1	1-1		3-0	1-0	3-0	5-1	3-0	0-1	4-1	1-1		0-1	4-1	2-0	3-2	0-0	2-1
18	Torquay United	2-1	1-2	2-2	1-1	0-0	2-1	0-1		3-1	2-3	0-1	1-0	2-1	2-2	2-0	1-0	0-0		1-1	2-1	1-0	3-1	6-1
19	Wealdstone	3-4	1-0	5-1	1-0	0-1	3-2	0-5		0-0	1-2	2-7	3-1	0-6	0-1	1-4	2-5	3-3	1-2		2-1	0-1	4-3	0-2
20	Weymouth	0-3	2-1	0-2	1-3	2-1	1-2	2-3		1-1	1-5	1-0	2-1	2-1	0-1	0-0	1-0	0-1	3-4	4-0		0-1	2-3	0-3
21	Woking	0-1	1-1	4-1	0-0	3-4	1-4	2-0		0-0	0-0	3-0	3-0	0-0	2-4	2-1	1-4	0-1	0-2	2-4	2-4		0-4	1-1
22	Wrexham	1-0	0-1	0-0	2-1	3-0	0-0	2-2		2-2	0-0	0-0	5-3	0-1	0-1	2-1	0-3	4-0	0-1	4-1	2-0	2-0		3-0
23	Yeovil Town	3-0	2-0	3-1	1-0	1-2	0-1	1-0		1-3	0-3	1-3	3-1	0-0	2-2	3-0	0-1	1-2	2-1	2-2	3-1	2-1	0-1	

ALDERSHOT TOWN MATCH RESULTS 2020-21

Date	Comp	H/A	Opponents	Att:	Result		Goalscorers	Pos
Oct 3	**NL**	**A**	**Hartlepool Town**		**L**	**1 - 2**	**Tanner 63**	**20**
6	NL	H	Sutton United		L	1 - 2	Bettamer 74	21
13	NL	A	Dover Athletic		**W**	5 - 0	Panayiotou 32 Bettamer 35 85 Rees 45+1 58	15
17	NL	A	Eastleigh		D	2 - 2	Tanner 45 Whittingham 61	13
24	**FAC4Q**	**H**	**Woking**		**L**	**1 - 2**	**Bettamer 7**	
27	NL	H	Torquay United		L	1 - 4	Tanner 8	17
Nov 7	NL	H	Notts County		**W**	1 - 0	Panayiotou 64	13
14	NL	A	Altrincham		**W**	2 - 1	Edser 13 Kandi 79	11
17	NL	H	Maidenhead United		D	0 - 0		10
21	NL	A	Wrexham		L	0 - 1		15
Dec 1	NL	A	Chesterfield		D	0 - 0		15
5	NL	H	Dagenham & Redbridge	920	**W**	2 - 1	Bettamer 7 Panayiotou 31	13
8	NL	H	FC Halifax Town		L	1 - 3	Bettamer 36 (pen)	16
12	NL	A	Boreham Wood	650	L	2 - 3	Ogie 29 Fyfield 53 (og)	17
19	**FAT3P**	**A**	**Welwyn Garden City**		**W**	**5 - 1**	**Fondop-Talum 20 (pen) Finney 55 Ogie 73 Bettamer 75 Kandi 90+1**	
26	NL	H	Woking		**W**	3 - 0	Panayiotou 32 Anderson 34 38	16
28	NL	A	Yeovil Town		L	0 - 3	(RC 2xY - Anderson 87)	16
Jan 2	NL	A	Woking		**W**	1 - 0	Miller 72	12
19	**FAT4P**	**H**	**Solihull Moors**		**W**	**3 - 2**	**Bettamer 30 (pen) 74 Edser 37**	
23	NL	A	Wealdstone		**W**	4 - 3	Nouble 7 Anderson 39 Kandi 42 Rees 76	9
26	NL	H	Weymouth		L	0 - 2	(RC - Walker 17)	12
30	NL	A	Bromley		L	0 - 2		15
Feb 2	NL	H	Barnet		**W**	2 - 1	Seniles-White 61 Bettamer 72	12
13	NL	A	Stockport County		D	0 - 0		12
16	NL	H	Solihull Moors		L	1 - 3	Rees 87	13
20	NL	H	Wrexham		**W**	3 - 0	Nouble 26 46 Anderson 68	11
23	NL	A	Maidenhead United		**W**	4 - 2	Miller 6 Rees 27 39 90+5 (RC 2xY - Colombie 70)	9
27	**FATQF**	**H**	**Hereford**		**D**	**1 - 1**	**Rees 90+3 (Lost 3-5 on pens)**	
Mar 13	NL	H	Altrincham		**W**	2 - 1	Nouble 43 Kandi 88	12
16	NL	A	FC Halifax Town		L	0 - 1		14
20	NL	H	Boreham Wood		D	3 - 3	Edser 54 Rees 63 78	13
23	NL	H	Chesterfield		L	0 - 1		15
27	NL	A	Solihull Moors		L	0 - 1		16
30	NL	A	Notts County		**W**	1 - 0	Panayiotou 4 (pen)	15
Apr 2	NL	H	Stockport County		L	1 - 2	Rees 74	16
5	NL	A	Dagenham & Redbridge		**W**	2 - 0	Bettamer 43 (pen) Nouble 46	12
13	NL	A	Weymouth		**W**	3 - 0	Rees 34 89 Panayiotou 56	12
17	NL	A	Barnet		L	1 - 3	Panayiotou 37	12
20	NL	H	King's Lynn Town		D	1 - 1	Miller 31	12
24	NL	H	Wealdstone		**W**	2 - 0	Panayiotou 34 Kandi 90+5	11
27	NL	A	Torquay United		L	1 - 2	Lyons-Foster 17	11
May 1	NL	A	Sutton United		L	1 - 3	Miller 23	14
11	NL	H	Yeovil Town		**W**	2 - 0	Kandi 51 Panayiotou 83	15
15	NL	H	Hartlepool Town		L	1 - 3	Bettamer 86 (pen)	15
18	NL	H	Eastleigh		L	1 - 3	Panayiotou 52	16
22	NL	H	Bromley		L	2 - 3	Panayiotou 71 83	16
29	NL	A	King's Lynn Town		D	4 - 4	Edser 19 Kandi 37 Lyons-Foster 61 71	15

Goalcorers	LGE	FAC	FAT	SG	CSG	HAT	PEN	1Q	2Q	45+	3Q	4Q	90+	T
TOTALS	**64**	**1**	**9**			**1**	**6**	**9**	**24**	**2**	**15**	**20**	**4**	**74**
Rees	12		1	8	2	1			3	1	2	5	2	13
Bettamer	8	1	3	9	2		4	2	4			6		12
Panayiotou	12			11	2		1		6		3	3		12
Kandi	6		1	7	1				2		1	2	2	7
Nouble	5			4	1			1	2		2			5
Anderson	4			3	1				3			1		4
Edser	3		1	4	1			2	1		1			4
Miller	4			4	1			1	2			1		4
Lyons-Foster	3			2	1			1			1	1		3

	LGE	FAC	FAT	SG	CSG	HAT	PEN	1Q	2Q	45+	3Q	4Q	90+	T
Tanner	3			3	1			1		1	1			3
Ogie	1		1	2	2				1			1		2
Finney			1	1	1						1			1
Fondop-Talum			1	1	1		1	1						1
Opponent	1			1	1						1			1
Sendles-White	1			1	1						1			1
Whittingham	1			1	1						1			1

Senies-White J	Finney A	Lyons-Foster K	Ogie S (L)	Rees J	Edser T	Fowler G	Bettamer M	Tanner C	Nouble J	Panayiotou H	Colombie K	Rowe J	Whittingham A	Hall R (Gk)	McCormack R	Wylie R	Kandi C	Rabbetts J	James B (Gk) (L)	hillips G (L)	Hungbo J (L)	Fondop-Talum M	Anderson J	Miller R	Shroll B	Gillela D (L)	Kinsella L	Hinds K	No.
x	**x**	**xs**	**x**	**x**	**x**	**x**	**xs**	**x**	**xs**	**sx**	**sx**	**sx**	**s**	**s**															1
x	x	xs	x	x	xs	x	x	x	xs	s	sx	sx	sx	s															2
x	xs	sx	x	x	sx	x	x	x	s	xs		xs	x		sx	s													3
x		x	x	x	sx	x	x	x	s	xs	s	xs	x	s	sx														4
c		**c**	**c**	**c**	**sc**	**c**	**c**	**c**	**sc**		**cn**	**cs**	**cs**	**cn**	**cs**	**cn**	**sc**	**cn**											5
x	sx	x	x	xs	sx	x	x	x	s		sx	xs	x	s			x												6
x		x	x	x	sx	x	x	x	s	xs	s	s	x				x		x										7
		x	x	x	x	x			s	xs	s	sx	x				sx		x	x	xs	x							8
		x	x	x	x	x	sx		s	xs		s	x				xs		x	x	sx	x							9
		x	x	x	xs	x	x		sx	x	s	sx	xs				sx		x	x	xs								10
sx		x	x	x	x	x	xs		s	xs	s		x				x		x	x	sx								11
sx		x	x	x	xs	x	x		s	x		xs					xs		x	x	sx		sx						12
s		x	x	x	x	x	x			xs		xs					xs		x	x	sx	sx	sx						13
s		x	x	x	x		x		s	xs	x	xs					x		x	x		sx	sx						14
t	**t**	**tn**	**t**	**ts**	**ts**		**st**		**t**		**t**		**st**				**t**		**tn**	**tn**		**t**	**t**						15
xs	s	sx	x	x	xs	x	x		sx	x			sx				xs		x	x			x						16
	x	s	x	x	x	x	x		sx	x	s		s				xs		x	x			x						17
	s	x	x	x	x	x	x		xs	x		s	x				sx		s	x				sx					18
	t	**t**	**t**	**t**	**t**	**t**	**t**		**ts**		**tn**	**tn**	**st**			**tn**	**ts**		**tn**				**t**	**st**	**tn**				19
s	x	x	x	x	x	x	x		xs		sx	s	sx				xs		s				x						20
x	x	sx	x	x	x		x		xs	s	xs	s	sx				xs		sx				x						21
s	x	x	x	x	xs		xs		xs	x		sx	x	s			sx		x				x	sx					22
x	x	x	s	x	x		sx		x	xs		s	s				sx						x	xs		x			23
x	x	x	s	x	xs		x		x	sx		s	s				sx						x	xs		x			24
x	xs	x	sx	x	xs		x		x	s		sx	s				sx						x	xs		x			25
x				x	sx		sx		xs	sx	x	x	x	s			xs						x	xs	x	s			26
x		sx		x	sx		sx		xs	s	x	x	x	s			xs			x			x	xs					27
tn		**t**	**t**	**t**	**st**		**st**		**t**			**ts**	**t**	**tn**			**ts**	**tn**		**t**			**t**	**t**	**tn**	**tn**			28
sx		x	s	x	x		xs		xs	sx	x		x	x		s	sx			x			x	xs					29
s		x	s	x	x		xs		x	sx	x		x	x		s	sx			x			x	xs					30
s		x	sx	x	x		sx		x	xs	xs	s	x	x			sx			x			x	xs					31
s		x	x	x	x	xs	x		xs	xs	s		sx				sx			x			x	sx					32
s		x	x	x	x	xs	sx		x	sx		xs	s				sx			x			x	xs					33
x		sx	x	x	x	s	sx		xs	xs		s	x				xs			x			x				sx		34
x		s	xs	x	x	sx	xs		x	x		s	xs							x			x				sx	sx	35
x		x	x	x	x	x	xs		x	xs	s	s											x	sx			sx	s	36
x		x	x	x	xs	x		sx	x	xs		s					xs						x	sx			sx	s	37
x		x	x	x	x	xs	sx	sx	x	xs		s					xs						x	sx			s		38
x		x	s	x	x		sx	sx	xs	xs	x	sx											x	xs			x	s	39
x		x	s	x	xs	x		sx	x	xs		s					sx						x	xs			x	sx	40
x		x	s	x	x	x	sx	s	xs	x							sx						x	xs			x	s	41
x		x	s	x	xs	x	sx	sx	x	xs							s						x	xs			x	sx	42
x		x	s	xs	x	x	sx	x	sx	x							xs						x	s			x	sx	43
x		x	s		x	x	sx	xs		x			s			sx	xs						x	xs			x	sx	44
x		x	s		x	x	xs	xs	x	xs			s				sx						x	sx			x	sx	45
x		x	s		x	x	sx	xs	x	x			sx	x		s	sx						xs				x	xs	46
		x	x		xs	x	x	xs		xs			x	s		sx	x	sx						sx			x	s	47
27	10	36	30	40	27	28	20	8	16	11	7	2	17	4	0	0	6	0	11	19	0	3	30	1	1	3	9	0	x
1	2	2	1	3	12	3	8	4	14	20	2	9	3	0	1	0	16	0	0	0	2	0	1	14	0	0	0	1	xs
3	1	5	2	0	8	1	16	5	5	6	4	7	8	0	2	2	17	1	1	0	4	2	3	9	0	0	4	6	sx
9	2	3	12	0	0	1	0	1	9	4	10	15	8	10	0	6	1	2	4	1	0	0	0	1	2	2	1	5	s

OALKEEPERS	CS	CCS
alker	10	2
mes	3	1

x/c/t - Played full 90 minutes
xs/cs/ts - Substituted off
sx/sc/st - Substituted on
s/cn/tn - Non-playing sub

TECHNIQUE

Chesterfield 0 - 0 Aldershot Town - 01/12/2020

Photos Bill Wheatcroft

ALTRINCHAM MATCH RESULTS 2020-21

Date	Comp	H/A	Opponents	Att:	Result	Goalscorers	Pos
Oct 3	NL	H	Weymouth		D 0 - 0		11
7	NL	A	Notts County		L 1 - 3	Mooney 77	18
10	NL	A	Eastleigh		D 1 - 1	Ceesay 11	18
24	**FAC4Q**	**A**	**AFC Fylde**		**L 1 - 2**	**Peers 60**	
27	NL	A	Hartlepool United		D 1 - 1	Peers 85	23
31	NL	A	Dover Athletic		**W** 1 - 0	Adarabioyo 11	19
Nov 7	NL	A	Wealdstone		L 0 - 1		20
11	NL	H	Solihull Moors		L 0 - 2		
14	NL	H	Aldershot Town		L 1 - 2	Peers 89	21
17	NL	H	Chesterfield		**W** 3 - 2	Adarabiyo 29 Hancock 69 (pen) 89	16
21	NL	A	Boreham Wood		**W** 1 - 0	McDonald 87	14
24	NL	H	Bromley		L 0 - 1		14
28	NL	H	Maidenhead United		**W** 2 - 0	Hancock 63 (pen) Peers 80	10
Dec 1	NL	A	Wrexham		**W** 1 - 0	Sutton 44	4
12	NL	A	Dagenham & Redbridge	773	**W** 1 - 0	Moult 39	4
19	**FAT3P**	**H**	**Chester**		**W 2 - 1**	**Senior 45+3 Peers 54**	
26	NL	H	Stockport County		D 1 - 1	Ceesay 25	7
28	NL	A	FC Halifax Town		L 2 - 3	Hancock 31 Mooney 70	9
Jan 2	NL	A	Stockport County		D 2 - 2	Ceesay 71 Colclough 75	7
9	NL	A	Sutton United		D 2 - 2	Mullarkey 16 Hampson 90+4	5
23	NL	A	Barnet		**W** 2 - 1	Kosylo 35 Hancock 90+1	5
26	NL	H	Wealdstone		**W** 2 - 0	Hancock 39 Smith 79	4
Feb 2	NL	A	Torquay United		**W** 2 - 1	Hancock 33 (pen) Colclough 45 (RC 2xY - Moult 86)	4
9	NL	H	Wrexham		L 1 - 2	Colclough 51	6
13	NL	A	Yeovil Town		L 0 - 2		6
20	NL	H	Boreham Wood		L 2 - 3	Kosylo 58 Peers 86 (RC 2xY - Hampson 29)	9
23	NL	A	Chesterfield		L 0 - 1		10
27	NL	A	Bromley		L 1 - 3	Moult 36	11
Mar 2	NL	H	Woking		**W** 1 - 0	Kosylo 69 (RC - Hannigan 34)	8
9	NL	H	Hartlepool United		D 1 - 1	Colclough 45+1	11
13	NL	A	Aldershot Town		L 1 - 2	Hancock 48 (pen)	13
16	NL	A	Woking		D 1 - 1	Hancock 90+2 (pen)	13
20	NL	H	Dagenham & Redbridge		L 0 - 1		15
23	NL	H	King's Lynn Town		**W** 3 - 0	Hancock 16 57 Hardy 59	11
29	NL	A	Maidenhead United		**W** 1 - 0	Colclough 64	11
Apr 5	NL	A	King's Lynn Town		L 0 - 2		13
10	NL	H	FC Halifax Town		L 0 - 1		13
17	NL	H	Sutton United		L 0 - 4		17
24	NL	H	Barnet		L 2 - 3	Colclough 4 Smith 16	17
May 1	NL	H	Notts County		D 1 - 1	Smith 24	17
3	NL	A	Solihull Moors		L 0 - 4		17
15	NL	A	Weymouth		L 1 - 2	Colclough 50	17
22	NL	H	Yeovil Town		**W** 4 - 3	Kirby 18 Mooney 45+7 Peers 85 Hancock 90+2	17
25	NL	H	Eastleigh		D 1 - 1	Colclough 78	17
29	NL	H	Torquay United		D 0 - 0		17

Goalcorers	LGE	FAC	FAT	SG	CSG	HAT	PEN	1Q	2Q	45+	3Q	4Q	90+	T
TOTALS	47	1	2			0	5	7	10	4	11	14	4	50
Hancock	12			10	3		5	1	3		3	2	3	12
Colclough	8			8	2			1		2	3	2		8
Peers	5	1	1	7	2						2	5		7
Ceesay	3			3	1			1	1			1		3
Kosylo	3			3	1				1		2			3
Mooney	3			3	1					1		2		3
Smith	3			3	2			1	1			1		3
Adarabioyo	2			2	1			1	1					2
Moult	2			2	1				2					2

	LGE	FAC	FAT	SG	CSG	HAT	PEN	1Q	2Q	45+	3Q	4Q	90+	T
Hampson	1			1	1								1	1
Hardy	1			1	1						1			1
Kirby	1			1	1			1						1
McDonald	1			1	1							1		1
Mullarkey	1			1	1			1						1
Senior			1	1	1					1				1
Sutton	1			1	1				1					1

White A	Moult J	Densmore S	Hannigan T	Williams S	Hancock J	Mullarkey T	Ceesay Y	Peers T	Kosylo M	Miller C	Richman S	Clayton M	Hampson C	Sutton R	Mooney D	Senior J	Potter D	Gould M (Gk)	Adarabioyo F	Robbins J (L)	Sass-Davies B	Salmon L	Hall W	Roache R	Dales A (L)	Smith A (L/P)	McDonald J	Colclough R	Holgate H (L)	Howarth G	Blyth J	Harrison B	Piggott J	Hardy J	Ogle R (L)	Zouma L (L)	Gibson M (L)	Bell N (L)	Kirby C (L)	No.
x	x	x	x	x	xs	x	xs	x	xs	sx	sx	sx	s	s																										1
x	x	x	x	xs	x	x	xs	x	xs	sx	sx		s	s	sx																									2
x	x		s	xs	x	x	xs	x	x	s	sx		s	x	sx	x																								3
cn	c	c			c	c	cs	cs	c	sc	sc		c	c	sc	cn	cs	cn																						4
x	x	s	x		xs	xs	x	x	sx		xs		s	sx	sx	x			x																					5
	x	sx	x		x		sx	sx	xs	s			x	x	xs	x		s	xs	x																				6
s	x	s	x		x		xs	sx	x	sx			x	xs		x			xs	x	sx																			7
	x	s	x		x			x	x	sx			x		xs	x				x	x	s	s	s																8
	x	s	x		s			x	x	sx			x			x			xs	xs	x				xs	sx	sx													9
	x	x	x		x				x	sx			x	sx		s			xs	s	x				xs	x	s													10
	x	s	x		xs		sx		x				x	s		x			xs	sx	x				xs	x	sx													11
	x	x	s		x		xs		x				xs	x		sx			xs	s	x					x	sx	sx												12
x	x	sx	x		xs		xs	sx	x	s				x		x			xs	s						x		sx												13
x	x	sx	x		xs		xs	sx	x	s				x		x					sx					x	s	xs												14
x	x	sx	x		x		xs	sx	x		sx			xs		x		s				s				x		xs												15
ts	t	st	t		ts		t	t	t		st		st			t		tn				tn	tn			ts			t	tn										16
		s	x		x		xs	x	xs		x		x		sx	x							s	s		x			x		sx									17
	x	s	x		x		xs	xs	xs		s		x		sx	x										x		sx	x		sx									18
	x	s	x		sx	sx	x	sx			s		x	xs	xs	x										x		x			xs									19
s	x		s		xs	x	xs		x		s		x	x	sx	x										x		x				sx								20
sx		s	x		x	x	sx	sx	x		s		xs	x	xs	x										x						xs								21
s	x		x		x	x		sx	xs		s		x	s	x	x										x		sx				xs								22
sx	x		x		x	x	sx	s	x	s			xs		xs	x										x		sx				xs								23
x		s	x		x	x	sx	s	x		s			xs		x										x		x				xs	sx							24
x	x		x		x	x	sx	xs	xs		s			s		x										x		x				s	sx							25
sx	x	s	x			sx	x	sx	xs				x	x		x										x		xs				xs	s							26
xs	x	sx	x			x	x	xs	x		s			s		x										x						xs	sx	sx						27
	x	sx	x	s		sx	x	sx	x		s		xs	x		x										x						xs		xs						28
	x		x			sx	xs	sx	x				sx			x										x		xs				s		s	x	x	xs			29
	x			s		x	xs	sx	xs				s		sx	x										x		x						sx	x	x	xs			30
	x		s	s	xs	x	x	x					s			x										x		x				s		sx	x	x				31
	sx		x	x	x	x	sx	s	xs							x												x					xs	s	x	xs		sx		32
	x		x	x	x	x	xs	sx			sx			s		x												x					xs	s	xs			sx		33
	x		x	sx	xs	x	s	s			xs					x										x		x					xs	x	sx			sx		34
	x		x	sx	xs	x	s	sx					x			x										x		x					xs	xs	s			sx		35
	x		x	xs	x	x	sx	sx			sx		x			x												x					xs	xs	s			s		36
	x		x	x	xs	x	x	s			s					x		s										x					xs	sx	x			sx		37
	x		xs	x	xs	x	x	s			sx				sx	x										s		x					xs		x			sx		38
	x			s		x	sx	sx			s			x	xs	x										x		x						s	x			xs	x	39
	x			s	sx	x		sx						x	xs	x										x		x						s	x	s		xs	x	40
		sx		x	x	x	x	x		s	x			s		x		x	sx														xs	xs		x			sx	41
	x	s		xs	sx	x		sx	sx						xs	x		s								x		x							x			xs	x	42
	x	s	s	sx	x	x		sx	xs						xs	x										x		x						sx	x				xs	43
	x	x	x	sx	xs	x		sx	sx						xs	x										xs		x						s	s				x	44
	x	x	x		xs	x		sx	xs						xs	x			s							x		x						sx	s				sx	45
9	40	7	33	6	21	27	10	10	19	0	2	0	15	12	1	40	0	1	1	3	5	0	0	0	0	28	0	19	3	0	0	0	0	1	10	4	0	0	4	x
2	0	0	1	4	14	1	15	4	12	0	2	0	4	4	11	0	1	0	7	1	0	0	0	0	3	2	0	4	0	0	1	7	8	4	1	1	2	3	1	xs
3	1	8	0	4	3	4	9	21	3	7	9	1	2	2	9	1	0	0	1	1	2	0	0	0	0	1	3	5	0	0	2	1	3	6	1	0	0	6	2	sx
4	0	13	5	5	1	0	2	6	0	6	11	0	6	8	0	2	0	6	1	3	0	3	3	2	0	1	2	0	0	1	0	3	1	6	4	1	0	1	0	s

OALKEEPERS	CS	CCS
hompson	11	3

x/c/t - Played full 90 minutes
xs/cs/ts - Substituted off
sx/sc/st - Substituted on
s/cn/tn - Non-playing sub

Chesterfield 1 - 0 Altrincham - 23/02/2021

Photos Bill Wheatcroft

BARNET MATCH RESULTS 2020-21

Date	Comp	H/A	Opponents	Att:	Result	Goalscorers	Pos
Oct 3	NL	H	Eastleigh		L 1 - 5	Fonguck 39	24
6	NL	A	Dagenham & Redbridge		**W** 2 - 1	Hooper 85 (pen) Richards 88	14
10	NL	A	Notts County		L 2 - 4	Hooper 45+1 75	15
13	NL	H	Weymouth		**W** 1 - 0	Fonguck 45	10
24	**FAC4Q**	**A**	**Leiston**	**600**	**W 3 - 2**	**Petrasso 15 84 Hooper 45+6 (pen)**	
27	NL	A	Wrexham		D 0 - 0		14
Nov 8	**FAC1P**	**H**	**Burton Albion**		**W 1 - 0**	**Fonguck 10**	
14	NL	H	Bromley		L 1 - 3	Petrasso 68	17
17	NL	H	King's Lynn Town		L 0 - 2		20
21	NL	A	Woking		L 1 - 4	Petrasso 89 (pen)	20
24	NL	H	Hartlepool United		D 0 - 0		18
29	**FAC2P**	**H**	**Milton Keynes Dons**		**L 0 - 1**		
Dec 2	NL	A	FC Halifax Town		L 2 - 5	Faal 68 Effiong 85	20
5	NL	H	Wealdstone		D 0 - 0		20
8	NL	H	Stockport County		L 1 - 2	Mason-Clark 48	20
12	NL	A	Chesterfield		L 0 - 6		20
Peter Beadle steps down as manager. Tim Flowers is named as the new man in charge.							
19	**FAT3P**	**A**	**Dorking Wanderers**		**L 1 - 3**	**Fox 35 (RC - Fox 73)**	
Jan 2	NL	H	Boreham Wood		L 0 - 3	(RC - Judd 29)	22
23	NL	H	Altrincham		L 1 - 2	Hooper 14	22
26	NL	A	Dover Athletic		L 1 - 3	Petrasso 59	23
30	NL	H	Torquay United		L 0 - 2		23
Feb 2	NL	A	Aldershot Town		L 1 - 2	Petrasso 53	23
16	NL	H	FC Halifax Town		**W** 2 - 1	Petrasso 33 Wordsworth 45	22
20	NL	H	Woking		L 0 - 2		22
23	NL	A	King's Lynn Town		L 1 - 5	Hooper 28	22
27	NL	A	Hartlepool United		L 0 - 1		22
Mar 2	NL	H	Yeovil Town		L 1 - 4	Hooper 15 (RC 2xY - Adeloye 33)	22
9	NL	H	Wrexham		L 0 - 2		22
Tim Flowers departs, Gary Anderson takes over with the help of England C manager Paul Fairclough.							
13	NL	A	Bromley		D 2 - 2	Baker-Richardson 14 (pen) Petrasso 63 (RC 2xY - Dunne 82)	22
16	NL	A	Stockport County		L 1 - 2	McQueen 63	22
20	NL	H	Chesterfield		L 0 - 2	(RC - Richardson-Everton 90+2)	22
29	NL	A	Yeovil Town		L 1 - 3	Kefalas 67	22
Apr 2	NL	H	Solihull Moors		L 0 - 2	(RC 2xY - Kefalas 86)	22
5	NL	A	Wealdstone		L 1 - 5	Baker-Richardson 46 (RC - Baker-Richardson 57)	22
10	NL	A	Maidenhead Town		D 0 - 0		22
17	NL	H	Aldershot Town		**W** 3 - 1	Hooper 30 Mason-Clark 71 (pen) Adeloye 90+4	22
20	NL	A	Boreham Wood		D 0 - 0		22
24	NL	A	Altrincham		**W** 3 - 2	Baker-Richardson 45+2 Mason-Clark 88 Adeloye 89	22
27	NL	A	Sutton United		L 0 - 1		22
May 1	NL	H	Dagenham & Redbridge		L 0 - 2		22
3	NL	A	Weymouth		**W** 2 - 0	Richards-Everton 34 Adeloye 78 (RC - Wordsworth 55)	22
8	NL	H	Notts County		L 1 - 4	Petrasso 89 (pen)	22
15	NL	A	Eastleigh		L 0 - 3		22
19	NL	A	Solihull Moors		L 0 - 1		22
22	NL	A	Torquay United		D 2 - 2	Petrasso 37 (pen) Kefalas 54	22
25	NL	H	Maidenhead Town		**W** 2 - 0	Taylor 57 Wordsworth 65	22
29	NL	H	Sutton United		**W** 2 - 0	Simpson 61 (og) Walker 90+1	22

Goalcorers	LGE	FAC	FAT	SG	CSG	HAT	PEN	1Q	2Q	45+	3Q	4Q	90+	T
TOTALS	**38**	**4**	**1**			**0**	**6**	**5**	**7**	**5**	**11**	**13**	**2**	**43**
Petrasso	8	2		9	2		2	1	2		3	4		10
Hooper	7	1		7	2		2	2	2	2		2		8
Adeloye	3			3	1							2	1	3
Baker-Richardson	3			3	1		1	1		1	1			3
Fonguck	2	1		3	1			1	1	1				3
Mason-Clark	3			3	1		1				1	2		3
Kefalas	2			2	1						2			2
Wordsworth	2			2	1					1	1			2
Effiong	1			1	1							1		1

	LGE	FAC	FAT	SG	CSG	HAT	PEN	1Q	2Q	45+	3Q	4Q	90+	T
Faal	1			1	1							1		1
Fox			1	1	1				1					1
McQueen	1			1	1						1			1
Opponent	1			1	1						1			1
Richards	1			1	1							1		1
Richards-Everton	1			1	1				1					1
Taylor	1			1	1						1			1
Walker	1			1	1								1	1

No.	Nugent B	McQueen A	Binnom-Williams J	Preston M	Taylor H	Dunne J	Fonguck W	Richards E	Hooper J	Mason-Clark E	Duffus T	Pavey A	Azaze A (Gk)	Vasiliou A	Pascal D	Walker J	Tompkins J	Connors J	Hernandez L	Petrasso M (L)	McBurnie A	Callan J (Gk)	Granville S	Wordsworth A	Faal M (L)	Effiong I (L)	Mohsni B	Parrat D	Fox B (L)	Judd M (L)	Daly L	Richards-Everton B	Kefalas T (L)	Baker-Richardson C (L)	Taylor R	Adeloye T	Vaughan L	Beard S (L)	Skeffington S (L)	Parkes A (Gk) (L)
1	x	x	x	xs	x	x	x	xs	x	x	sx	sx	s	s	s																									
2		x	x	x	x	x	x	xs	x	xs	sx	sx	s	s	s																									
3	x	x	x	x	xs	x	xs		x		x	sx	s	s	s	sx																								
4	x	x	x	s	x	x	x		x	x	x	xs	s	sx	s		s																							
5					c			c	c				c	c	c	c	cn	c	c	c	c	cn	cn																	
6		x		x	x	x		x	x			sx	x	s	x	x		x	s	xs	s	s																		
7	c	c	c	c	c		c	cs	cs	c		sc	cn	cn	sc			cn	sc	cs	cn																			
8	x	x	x		x		xs			xs		sx	s	sx	x			s		x	sx			x	xs															
9	x	x	x	x	x		xs		x	x			s	sx	s					xs	s			x	sx															
10	x	xs	x		x		xs		x	x			s	sx				xs	s	sx	x			x	sx															
11	x	x	x		x	x	sx		x	x			s		s			s		xs	xs			x	sx															
12	c	c	c		c	c	cs		c	c				sc	cn		cn	cn	cn	cs		cn		c	sc															
13	x	x	x		x	x	x			x			s	s	sx			s						xs	x	x	s													
14	x	x	s		x	x	x			x			s	sx	s			x						x	xs	x	s													
15	x	x	s		x	x	xs			x			s	s	s			x						x	sx	x	x													
16		x	x		x	x	s		sx	x			s	s	s			x							xs	x	x	x												
17	t	st	t		t	t			ts	t			tn	tn	ts	st		ts							st	t	tn	tn	t											
18	x	sx	x		x	x				xs		xs	s	sx		xs									s	x	x	sx		x										
19	s	xs	x		x	x			x	xs		x	s					s		sx					sx						x	x	x							
20		s	x		x	x			x	x		xs	s					s		sx					sx					x	x	x	xs							
21			x		x	x			x	xs		sx	s							sx	sx			xs						x	x	x	s	xs						
22			x		xs	x			x	sx			s							xs	sx			x	s					x	x	x	s	x						
23			x		x	x			xs	sx			s							xs	sx			x	sx					x	x	x	s	xs						
24		sx	xs			x			x	sx	s		s							xs	xs			x	sx					x	x		x	x						
25		sx			x	x			x	sx			s					xs		x	sx			xs	s					x	x		x	xs						
26		x			x	x			x	sx			s							xs	s									x	x	x	s	sx	x	xs				
27		x			x	xs			xs	sx			s							xs	s				sx						x	x	sx			x				
28		x			sx	xs			x	sx			s							s				xs	sx						x	x	x	xs	x		x			
29		x	x		x	x				xs			sx								s				sx						xs	x	sx	x	s		x			
30		x	x		x					x			x	s						x	sx	s			xs						x	x	s	x	s		x			
31		xs	x	s	x					x			x	sx						x	sx	s			x							x	x	xs	sx		xs			
32	s			x	x				xs	xs			x	sx						x	x	s		s	sx						x		x			x	x			
33		x		x	x				x	x			x	sx						xs	sx	s		xs	s						x		x			sx	xs			
34	s	xs		x	x				sx	x			x	xs							xs	s		x	sx						x			x		sx	x			
35	sx	x		x	x				x	x			x								s	s			s						x		x			s	x	xs	x	
36	s	x		x	xs				xs	x			x								s	s									x	sx	x			sx	x	x	x	
37	s	x		x	xs					x			x								s	s			sx						x	sx	x			xs	x	x	x	
38		x		x	x					x			x							sx	s	s									x	sx	xs	xs		sx	x	x	xs	
39		x		x	x					x			xs							sx	s	sx									s	x	x	xs		sx	x	x	xs	
40	sx	x		x	x					xs				sx						xs	s	s										x	x	x		sx	x	xs		x
41	x	x		s	x					xs				s						sx		s		x								x	x	sx		xs	x		x	x
42	x	x		xs	x				s	x				s						sx	sx	s										x	xs			x	x		x	x
43	x	xs								x				s						sx	s	s										x	x		x	x	x	x	x	x
44	x	s			x					x				sx						xs	sx	s										x		xs		x	x	x	x	x
45	x				x					xs				s		sx				xs	sx	s										x	x			x	x	x	x	x
46	x				x					x				s		sx				sx	sx	s		xs								x	x			xs	x	x	xs	x
47	x				xs					x				s		sx					sx	s		x								x	xs	sx		xs	x	x	x	x
x	21	28	22	14	39	22	6	2	20	27	2	1	11	1	3	2	0	5	1	6	3	0	0	13	2	6	3	1	1	8	18	20	16	6	3	6	18	9	9	8
xs	0	5	1	2	5	2	6	3	6	10	0	3	1	1	1	1	0	3	0	14	3	0	0	6	4	0	0	0	0	0	1	0	4	8	0	5	2	2	3	0
sx	2	4	0	0	1	0	1	0	2	7	2	7	1	12	2	5	0	0	1	10	13	1	0	0	16	0	0	1	0	0	0	3	2	3	1	6	0	0	0	0
s	5	2	2	3	0	0	1	0	1	0	1	0	25	16	10	0	3	7	3	1	13	20	1	1	5	0	3	1	0	0	1	0	5	0	2	1	0	0	0	0

OALKEEPERS	CS	CCS
oach	4	1
zaze	3	1
arkes	3	2

x/c/t - Played full 90 minutes
xs/cs/ts - Substituted off
sx/sc/st - Substituted on
s/cn/tn - Non-playing sub

BOREHAM WOOD MATCH RESULTS 2020-21

Date	Comp	H/A	Opponents	Att:	Result	Goalscorers	Pos
Oct 3	NL	A	Wrexham		L 1 - 2	Murtagh 60	17
10	NL	H	FC Halifax		D 0 - 0		20
13	NL	A	King's Lynn Town		**W** 3 - 0	Rhead 28 Tshimanga 32 (pen) 63	13
17	NL	A	Solihull Moors		L 0 - 1		15
24	**FAC4Q**	**H**	**Wimborne Town**		**W 2 - 0**	**Fyfield 60 Tshimanga 90**	
27	NL	H	Woking		**W** 1 - 0	Mafuta 33	12
Nov 7	**FAC1P**	**H**	**Southend United**		**D 3 - 3**	**Fyfield 8 Ricketts 51 Tshimanga 93 (pen) (Won 4-3 on pens)**	
10	NL	H	Dagenham & Redbridge		L 0 - 1		13
14	NL	A	Torquay United		D 1 - 1	Thomas 45+1	13
17	NL	A	Bromley		D 1 - 1	Thomas 6	15
21	NL	H	Altrincham		L 0 - 1		16
30	**FAC2P**	**A**	**Canvey Island**		**W 3 - 0**	**Tshimanga 8 Smith 28 Rhead 83**	
Dec 5	NL	A	Hartlepool United		**W** 2 - 1	Mafuta 36 69	16
8	NL	A	Notts County		**W** 1 - 0	Fyfield 71	15
12	NL	H	Aldershot Town	650	**W** 3 - 2	Tshimanga 13 (pen) Mafuta 22 Thomas 87	10
Jan 2	NL	A	Barnet		**W** 3 - 0	Tshimanga 19 30 (pen) Champion 43	10
9	**FAC3P**	**H**	**Millwall**		**L 0 - 2**		
12	NL	A	Dover Athletic		D 1 - 1	Tshimanga 14 (RC 2xY - Mafuta 85)	10
19	**FAT4P**	**H**	**Torquay United**		**L 0 - 4**	**(Received a walkover in the Third Round against Yeovil Town)**	
23	NL	A	Stockport County		D 1 - 1	Tshimanga 60	11
26	NL	H	Chesterfield		D 0 - 0		9
30	NL	H	Eastleigh		L 1 - 2	Smith 12	14
Feb 2	NL	H	Weymouth		**W** 1 - 0	Tshimanga 72	11
6	NL	A	Maidenhead United		**W** 1 - 0	Marsh 51	7
13	NL	A	Sutton United		L 0 - 2		9
16	NL	H	Yeovil Town		L 2 - 3	Tshimanga 48 (pen) Mafuta 78	10
20	NL	A	Altrincham		**W** 3 - 2	Smith 7 Tshimanga 29 Whiteley 47	8
23	NL	H	Bromley		D 1 - 1	Marsh 30	8
27	NL	H	Solihull Moors		D 2 - 2	Tshimanga 40 (pen) Morias 54	8
Mar 2	NL	A	Wealdstone		L 0 - 1		9
6	NL	A	Dagenham & Redbridge		D 2 - 2	Whitely 44 Coulthirst 49	10
9	NL	A	Woking		D 0 - 0		10
13	NL	H	Torquay United		D 0 - 0		10
16	NL	H	Notts County		D 2 - 2	Marsh 2 Tshimanga 55	11
20	NL	A	Aldershot Town		D 3 - 3	Phillips 14 (og) Whitely 56 Tshimanga 59 (pen)	10
Apr 2	NL	H	Sutton United		D 0 - 0		12
5	NL	H	Hartlepool United		D 2 - 2	Marsh 5 Whitely 26	11
10	NL	H	Wealdstone		**W** 3 - 1	Fyfield 73 Tshimanga 85 90+4	11
13	NL	A	Chesterfield		D 0 - 0		11
17	NL	A	Yeovil Town		L 0 - 1		11
20	NL	H	Barnet		D 0 - 0		11
24	NL	H	Stockport County		L 0 - 3		13
May 3	NL	H	King's Lynn Town		**W** 5 - 1	Mafuta 6 Tshimanga 52 59 74 Smith 67	13
8	NL	A	FC Halifax		**W** 1 - 0	Ilesanmi 67	13
15	NL	H	Wrexham		L 2 - 3	Smith 18 Tshimanga 45 (RC 2xY - Champion 74)	13
18	NL	A	Weymouth		**W** 3 - 1	Marsh 22 Smith 33 Whitely 85	12
22	NL	A	Eastleigh		L 0 - 1		13
29	NL	H	Maidenhead United		L 1 - 4	Marsh 48	14

Goalcorers	LGE	FAC	FAT	SG	CSG	HAT	PEN	1Q	2Q	45+	3Q	4Q	90+	T
TOTALS	**53**	**8**	**0**			**1**	**7**	**15**	**13**	**2**	**18**	**10**	**3**	**61**
Tshimanga	19	3		17	2	1	7	4	4	1	7	3	3	22
Mafuta	6			5	1			2	2			2		6
Marsh	6			6	1			3	1		2			6
Smith	5	1		6	1			3	2		1			6
Whitely	5			5	1				2		2	1		5
Fyfield	2	2		4	1			1			1	2		4
Thomas	3			3	2			1		1		1		3
Rhead	1	1		2	1				1			1		2
Champion	1			1	1				1					1
Coulthirst	1			1	1						1			1
Ilesanmi	1			1	1						1			1
Morias	1			1	1						1			1
Murtagh	1			1	1						1			1
Opponent	1			1	1			1						1
Ricketts		1		1	1						1			1

Fyfield J	Ricketts M	Ilesanmi O	Smith K	Murtagh K	Champion T.	Rhead M	Tshimanga K	Whitely C (L)	Thomas S	Coulthirst S	Stephens D	Mafuta G	Mingoia P	Francis-Angol Z	McDonnell A	Woodards D	Huddart R (Gk)	Brennan M (Gk)	Morais J (L)	Pearce K	Marsh T	Green D (Gk)	Jallow M	No.
x	x	x	x	x	x	x	x	xs	x	sx	s	s	s	s										1
x	x	x	x	xs	x	sx	x	sx	x	xs	s	sx	xs	s										2
x	x	x	x		x	xs	x	xs		sx	sx	x	sx	x	s	s								3
x	x	x	x		x	x	x	x		sx	s	x	s	xs	s	s								4
c	**c**	**sc**	**c**	**cn**	**c**	**sc**	**c**	**cn**	**sc**	**cs**	**cs**	**c**	**c**	**cs**	**cn**		**cn**							5
x	x	x	x	sx	x	x	xs	x	x	s	s	x	s				s							6
c	**cs**	**cs**	**c**		**c**	**c**	**c**	**cs**	**c**	**sc**	**sc**	**c**	**sc**	**cn**	**cn**	**cn**	**cn**							7
x		x	x		x	sx	x		x	xs	sx	x	xs	sx	xs	s	s							8
x		x	x		x	x	xs		x	sx	s	x	x	s	x	s	s							9
x		x	x		x	x	x		x	s	sx	x	x	s	xs	s	s							10
x		x	x		x	x	x		x	sx	s	x	x	s	xs	s	s							11
c		**c**	**c**	**cs**	**c**	**c**	**c**		**c**	**cn**	**cn**	**c**	**cn**	**c**	**sc**	**cn**	**cn**							12
x		x	x	xs	x	x	x		x	s	s	x	s	x	sx		s							13
x		x	x	x	x	x	x		x	s	s	x	s	x	s			s						14
x		x	x	xs	x	x	x		x	s	s	x	s	x	sx	s								15
x		x	xs	x	x	x	xs	x		sx	s	xs			sx	sx	s							16
c		**c**	**c**	**cs**		**cs**	**cs**	**sc**	**c**	**sc**	**c**	**cs**	**sc**		**sc**	**cn**	**cn**		**cs**					17
x		x	x	x		sx	xs	x		s	x	x	xs		sx	s	s		x					18
t	**ts**	**t**	**t**	**t**		**t**	**ts**	**t**		**st**	**ts**		**st**	**st**		**tn**	**tn**		**t**					19
x	x	x	x	x	s	s	x	sx		s		x		xs			s		x	x				20
x	x	x	x	xs	sx	sx	xs	sx		s		x		xs			s		x	x				21
x	xs	x	x	sx		x	s	x		sx	s	x		xs			s		x	x				22
x		x	x	x	xs	sx	xs	x		sx	s	x		sx			s		xs	x				23
x		x	x	x		sx	x	s			s	x		x	s		s		xs	x	x			24
x		x	x	x		sx	x	sx		s	s	x		xs			s		xs	x	x			25
x		x	x	x		xs	x	x		s	s	x				s	s		sx	x	x			26
x		x	x	x			x	x		sx	s	x				s	s		xs	x	x			27
x		x	x	x			x	x		sx	s	x		s	s		s		xs	x	x			28
x		x	x	x			x	x			s	x		s	s	s	s		x	x	x			29
x	s	x	x	x			x	x		sx	s	x		s			s		xs	x	x			30
x	xs	x	x	sx		s	x	x		xs	s	x		s					sx	x	x			31
x	x	x	x	x		s	x	x		sx	x	xs		sx					s	s	xs			32
x	x	x	x	xs			x	xs		sx		x		sx		s	s		s	x	x			33
x	x	x	x	x			x	x		s		x	s	s		s	s			x	x			34
x	x	x	x	xs		sx	x	x				x	s	sx		s	s			x	xs			35
x	x	x	x	xs	x	sx	x	x			s	x	s		s		s				x			36
x	x	x	x	xs	x	sx	x	x			s	x	s		s		s				x			37
x	x	x	x	x	x	s	x				s	x								s	x	s	s	38
x	x	x	x	xs	x	sx	x	x			s	x								s	x	s	s	39
x	x	x	x	xs	x	sx	x	x			sx	x				s				s	xs	s		40
x	x	x	x	s	s	x	x	x			s	x								x	x	s	s	41
xs	x	x	x	xs	x	sx	x	x			s	x								sx	x	s	s	42
xs	x	x	x	x	sx		xs				sx	xs				s				x	x	s	sx	43
x	x	x	x	x	x		x	x			sx	s				s				x	s	s	xs	44
x	x	x	x	xs	x		x	x			sx	x				s				x	s	s	s	45
x	x	s	x	x			x	x			x	x				x				s	x	s	s	46
x	x	s	xs	x	x		x	x			x	x				sx				s	x	s	s	47
s	x	s	x	x	x		x	xs			x	x				sx				xs	x	sx	sx	48
45	25	43	46	22	26	15	38	26	13	0	6	40	4	6	1	1	0	0	6	19	20	0	0	x
2	4	1	2	14	1	3	9	5	0	4	2	4	3	6	3	0	0	0	7	1	3	0	1	xs
0	0	1	0	3	2	14	0	5	1	16	8	1	4	6	6	3	0	0	2	1	0	1	2	sx
1	1	3	0	2	2	4	1	2	0	12	27	2	11	11	10	22	29	1	2	6	2	10	7	s

OALKEEPERS	CS	CCS
shmore	16	2

x/c/t - Played full 90 minutes
xs/cs/ts - Substituted off
sx/sc/st - Substituted on
s/cn/tn - Non-playing sub

BROMLEY WOOD MATCH RESULTS 2020-21

Date	Comp	H/A	Opponents	Att:	Result		Goalscorers	Pos
Oct 6	NL	H	Dover Athletic		W	4 - 1	Cheek 24 90+3 Holland 52 Williamson 72	6
10	NL	H	Torquay United		L	1 - 2	Webster 18	13
13	NL	A	Hartlepool United		D	0 - 0		12
24	**FAC4Q**	**A**	**Sutton United**		**W**	**1 - 0**	**Cheek 35 (pen)**	
27	NL	H	Weymouth		W	3 - 2	Cheek 35 (pen) L'Ghoul 47 Williamson 67	11
31	NL	H	Eastleigh		L	1 - 2	Alabi 85	11
Nov 7	**FAC1P**	**H**	**Yeovil Town**		**L**	**0 - 1**		
14	NL	A	Barnet		W	3 - 1	Kizzi 12 Alabi 26 Cheek 57	10
17	NL	H	Boreham Wood		D	1 - 1	Cheek 45	9
21	NL	A	Maidenhead United		D	2 - 2	Hackett-Fairchild 59 Bush 90+5	13
24	NL	A	Altrincham		W	1 - 0	Alabi 4	7
28	NL	H	Wrexham		D	1 - 1	Cheek 45+9	8
Dec 1	NL	A	King's Lynn Town		W	4 - 1	Alabi 22 Cheek 42 Trotter 45 Hackett-Fairchild 55	3
5	NL	H	Stockport County		L	0 - 2		5
8	NL	H	Yeovil Town		L	1 - 2	Cheek 70	6
12	NL	A	Solihull Moors		W	1 - 0	Cheek 45+1	3
22	**FAT3P**	**H**	**Hemel Hempstead Town**		**W**	**2 - 0**	**Forster 23 60**	
Jan 19	**FAT4P**	**H**	**Woking**		**D**	**1 - 1**	**Cheek 49 (pen) (Lost 6-7 on pens)**	
23	NL	H	FC Halifax Town		L	1 - 2	Cheek 15 (pen) (RC - Trotter 67)	14
26	NL	H	Woking		D	2 - 2	Roberts 30 Wakefield 62	14
30	NL	H	Aldershot Town		W	2 - 0	Bridge 21 Cheek 79	10
Feb 6	NL	A	Weymouth		L	1 - 2	Kizzi 33 (RC 2xY - Bush 55, RC - Wakefield 79)	13
9	NL	H	King's Lynn Town		W	2 - 0	Duffus 40 68	11
16	NL	A	Dagenham & Redbridge		L	0 - 1		11
20	NL	H	Maidenhead United		D	2 - 2	Coulson 12 Cheek 34	13
23	NL	A	Boreham Wood		D	1 - 1	Duffus 55	12
27	NL	H	Altrincham		W	3 - 1	Cheek 5 41 (pen) Kizzi 38 (RC - Bush 90+2)	9
Mar 2	NL	A	Sutton United		L	2 - 3	Cheek 14 Duffus 65	11
6	NL	A	Eastleigh		W	2 - 1	Holland 65 Duffus 85	8
13	NL	H	Barnet		D	2 - 2	Trotter 8 Cheek 61 (pen) (RC - Kizzi 12)	9
16	NL	A	Yeovil Town		W	2 - 1	Cheek 57 Reid 90+4 (og)	8
20	NL	H	Solihull Moors		W	1 - 0	Kizzi 78	7
23	NL	H	Sutton United		L	1 - 3	Bridge 79	7
Neil Smith is sacked as manager.								
29	NL	A	Wrexham		L	0 - 3		10
Andy Woodman is named as the new manager.								
Apr 2	NL	H	Wealdstone		D	2 - 2	Webster 25 Cheek 74	10
5	NL	A	Stockport County		D	0 - 0		10
10	NL	H	Dagenham & Redbridge		W	1 - 0	Cheek 32 (RC - Coulson 90+3)	10
13	NL	A	Woking		W	4 - 3	Bridge 3 Cheek 79 Alabi 83 Cook 88 (og)	9
17	NL	A	Chesterfield		W	2 - 1	Cheek 19 Kizzi 85	9
24	NL	A	FC Halifax Town		W	2 - 1	Cheek 14 (pen) Alabi 90+1	6
27	NL	H	Chesterfield		L	1 - 2	Arthurs 68	8
May 3	NL	H	Hartlepool United		W	1 - 0	Arthurs 41	7
8	NL	A	Torquay United		D	0 - 0		9
11	NL	A	Wealdstone		W	1 - 0	Kizzi 61	8
15	NL	A	Notts County		D	2 - 2	Ellis 27 (og) Campbell 75	8
22	NL	A	Aldershot Town		W	3 - 2	Cheek 28 Alabi 75 Kizzi 90+5	8
29	NL	H	Notts County		W	1 - 0	Williamson 64	7
Jun 6	**NL PO QF**	**A**	**Hartlepool United**		**L**	**2 - 3**	**Alabi 48 Webster 90+3**	

Goalcorers	LGE	FAC	FAT	SG	CSG	HAT	PEN	1Q	2Q	45+	3Q	4Q	90+	T
TOTALS	69	1	3			0	7	13	17	4	17	16	6	73
Cheek	23	1	1	23	4		7	5	8	3	4	4	1	25
Alabi	8			8	1			2	1		1	3	1	8
Kizzi	7			7	1			1	2		1	2	1	7
Duffus	5			4	2				1		2	2		5
Bridge	3			3	1			2				1		3
Opponent	3			3	1				1			1	1	3
Webster	3			3	1			1	1				1	3
Williamson	3			3	1						2	1		3
Arthurs	2			2	2				1			1		2

	LGE	FAC	FAT	SG	CSG	HAT	PEN	1Q	2Q	45+	3Q	4Q	90+	T
Forster			2	1	1				1		1			2
Hackett-Fairchild	2			2	1						2			2
Holland	2			2	1						2			2
Trotter	2			2	1			1		1				2
Bush	1			1	1								1	1
Campbell	1			1	1							1		1
Coulson	1			1	1			1						1
L'Ghoul	1			1	1						1			1
Roberts	1			1	1				1					1
Wakefield	1			1	1						1			1

Webster B	Bush C	Roberts K	Kizzi J	Forster H (L)	Bingham B	Holland J	Williamson B	Raymond F	Cheek M	Alabi J	Trotter L	Vincent L	Purrington T	Maloney T	L'Ghoul N	Coulson L	Kyprianou H (L)	Hackett-Fairchild R	Edwards K (Gk)	Arthurs J	Najia T (Gk)	Duffus C	Bridge J	Wakefield C	Fox C	Mitchell A (L)	Campbell T (L)	No.
x	x	x	x	x	x	x	xs	x	x	sx	s	s	s	s														1
x	x	x	x	x	xs	x	xs	xs	x	sx	sx		s	sx	s													2
x	x	x		xs		xs	x	x	x	sx	x	s	s	sx	xs	sx												3
c	c	c		sc			c	sc	c	cn	c	cn	cn	cs	cs	cs	c	sc	cn									4
	x	x		xs		s	x	s	x	sx	x		s	x	xs	x	x	sx										5
	x	x	s	xs		x	x	sx	x	sx	x		s	xs	xs		x	sx										6
	c	c	c	c	sc	sc	cs	c	c	sc	cs		cn		sc		cs	cs		cn	cn							7
x	x	x	x		x	s	x	x	x	x		s	s		s		sx	xs										8
x	x	x	x		x	s	x	xs	x	x	sx		s		s		s	x										9
x	x	xs	x		x	sx	xs	xs	x	x	sx		s		sx		s	x										10
x	x	x	x	s	x	sx	x	s	x	xs	x		s			sx		xs										11
x	x	x	x	sx	x	s		s	x	xs	x		s		s	x		x										12
xs	x	x	x	sx	x	sx		sx	xs	x	x		s		s	x		xs										13
x	x	xs	x	sx	x	sx		s	x	xs	x		s		s	x		x										14
x		xs	x	sx	x	x	sx	sx	x	xs	x		s		s	x		x										15
x	x	x	x	s	x	sx	xs	sx	xs	sx	x		s			x		xs										16
t	t	t		t	ts	tn	t	t		ts	t	st	st	tn		t					tn							17
t	t	t	ts	t	t	tn	t	st	t	tn	t	tn	tn	tn							tn	t						18
x	x	x	x	xs	x	s	sx	sx	x	s	x											xs	xs	sx				19
x	x	x				sx	x	x	x	s		s	s	x						x		sx	xs	xs				20
x		x	x			sx	xs	x	xs	sx			s	x						s		sx	xs	x				21
x	x	x	x			sx	xs	x	x	sx		s	s	xs								sx	xs	x				22
x		s	x		x	x	sx	x	xs	sx	x	sx	xs	s								xs	x					23
x	x	s	xs	xs	sx	x	sx	xs	x	s	x					sx						x	x					24
x	x	sx	x		x	x	sx	s	x	sx	x	s				xs						xs	xs					25
	x	s	x		x	x	s	x	x	s	x					x				s		x	xs	sx				26
	x	s	x		x	x	sx	x	xs	sx	x	s				xs						x	x	s				27
x		s	x		x	x	sx	x	xs	sx	x		s			xs						x	xs	sx				28
x		s	x			x	s	x	x	sx	x	s		x		x						xs	xs	sx				29
x		s	x			x	sx	x	xs	sx	x		s	x		x						xs	xs	sx				30
x		sx	x			xs	s	x	xs	sx	x		s	x		x						x	xs	sx				31
xs	x	sx	x				s	x	x	sx	x		s	x		x						xs	x	s				32
	x	xs	x				sx	x	xs	sx	x	s	s	x		x						xs	x	sx				33
x	x		x			s	sx	xs	xs		x	sx	s	x		xs				sx		x	x					34
x	x		x				xs	sx	x	sx	x	x		xs		sx				xs	s		x	s				35
xs	x		x				x	x	x	s		xs	s	x		sx				sx	s		x		x			36
	x		x			xs	xs	x	x	sx		xs		x		sx				sx		s	x	s	x			37
	x	s	x				s	sx	x	sx	xs	sx		xs						x		x	x	xs	x			38
	x		x		x		x	sx	xs	sx		xs								xs		sx	x	s	x	x	s	39
	x		x		x		x	s	xs	sx	sx	s				x				xs			xs		x	x	sx	40
	x		x		x		xs	sx	x	sx	s	s				xs				x			x		x	x	s	41
	x		x		x	sx	xs	xs	x	sx	sx					s				x			xs		x	x	s	42
	x		x		x	s	x	sx	xs	sx	x					xs				xs	s				x	x	sx	43
	x		x	sx	x	sx	xs	x	x	sx	s									x			xs		x	xs	s	44
	x		x	sx	x	s	xs	s	x	sx	x									xs			xs		x	x	sx	45
	x		x	sx	x	s	xs	s	x	sx	x									xs			xs		x	x	sx	46
	x		x	sx	x	s	xs	xs	x	sx	sx									xs			x		x	x	s	47
sx	**x**		**x**	**xs**	**x**		**xs**	**s**	**x**	**sx**	**s**									**x**			**x**		**xs**	**x**	**sx**	48
7	41	19	40	5	27	12	14	20	34	4	29	1	0	11	0	14	3	5	0	6	0	8	14	2	12	9	0	x
3	0	4	2	6	2	3	16	7	13	5	2	3	1	5	4	7	1	5	0	7	0	7	15	2	1	1	0	xs
1	0	3	0	9	2	11	10	12	0	31	6	4	1	2	2	6	1	3	0	3	0	4	0	7	0	0	5	sx
0	0	8	1	2	0	12	5	9	0	7	4	13	27	4	7	1	2	0	1	3	6	1	0	5	0	0	5	s

LKEEPERS	CS	CCS
sins	14	3

x/c/t - Played full 90 minutes
xs/cs/ts - Substituted off
sx/sc/st - Substituted on
s/cn/tn - Non-playing sub

CHESTERFIELD MATCH RESULTS 2020-21

Date	Comp	H/A	Opponents	Att:	Result		Goalscorers	Pos
Oct 6	NL	H	Hartlepool United		L	1 - 2	Denton Tom 54 (pen)	19
10	NL	H	Woking		**W**	4 - 0	Denton Tom 4 Rawson 84 90 Kiwomya 87	12
13	NL	A	Torquay United		L	1 - 2	Denton Tom 43	16
17	NL	H	Stockport County		L	1 - 2	Cropper 36	21
20	NL	A	Wealdstone		L	2 - 3	Denton Tom 3 (pen) 83	21
24	**FAC4Q**	**A**	**Stockport County**		**D**	**1 - 1**	**Butterfield 85 (Won 6-5 on pens)**	
31	NL	A	Yeovil Town		**W**	1 - 0	Denton Tom 69	17
Nov 4	**FAC4Q**	**A**	**Stockport County**		**L**	**0 - 4**	**(Tie played again due to Chesterfield playing an ineligible player)**	
14	NL	H	Maidenhead United		L	1 - 2	Boden 30	19
17	NL	A	Altrincham		L	2 - 3	Boden 13 Cropper 63	21
John Pemberton steps down as manager. John Dungworth takes over as caretaker.								
21	NL	H	Notts County		L	2 - 3	Smith Jon 33 Denton Tom 78	21
Former Gloucester City manager, James Rowe, is confirmed as the new man in charge.								
28	NL	A	Weymouth		**W**	2 - 1	Asante 45+2 Denton Tom 60	17
Dec 1	NL	H	Aldershot town		D	0 - 0		16
8	NL	A	Sutton United		**W**	1 - 0	Hollis 39	17
12	NL	H	Barnet		**W**	6 - 0	Asante 40 74 79 Boden 56 Hollis 64 McCourt 89	15
19	**FAT3P**	**H**	**Brackley Town**		**D**	**0 - 0**	**(Won 4-3 on pens)**	
Jan 2	NL	H	Solihull Moors		**W**	1 - 0	Whelan 43 (RC 2xY - Carline 82)	16
5	NL	A	Solihull Moors		L	1 - 2	Denton Tom 34	17
20	**FAT4P**	**A**	**Boston United**		**D**	**1 - 1**	**Hollis 75 (Won 4-1 on pens)**	
23	NL	H	Wrexham		**W**	2 - 1	Asante 9 89	13
26	NL	A	Boreham Wood		D	0 - 0		13
30	NL	A	Dagenham & Redbridge		D	2 - 2	Evans 17 Asante 40 (RC - Whelan 10)	13
Feb 20	NL	A	Notts County		**W**	1 - 0	Gunning 32	15
23	NL	H	Altrincham		**W**	1 - 0	Asante 49	13
27	NL	A	Stockport County		L	0 - 2		16
Mar 2	NL	H	Eastleigh		**W**	1 - 0	Asante 86	13
6	NL	H	Yeovil Town		**W**	3 - 0	Asante 48 Whelan 68 McCourt 78	9
13	NL	A	Maidenhead United		L	0 - 2		14
16	NL	H	Sutton United		L	0 - 1		15
20	NL	A	Barnet		**W**	2 - 0	Whelan 11 Yussuf 48	11
23	NL	A	Aldershot town		**W**	1 - 0	Whittle 27	10
29	NL	H	Weymouth		**W**	1 - 0	Whelan 38	7
Apr 2	NL	A	Eastleigh		**W**	1 - 0	Mandeville 61	6
10	NL	A	King's Lynn Town		**W**	2 - 1	Tyson 74 Whelan 75	6
13	NL	H	Boreham Wood		D	0 - 0		5
17	NL	H	Bromley		L	1 - 2	Maguire 74	7
20	NL	H	FC Halifax Town		L	1 - 2	Mitchell 71	7
24	NL	A	Wrexham		D	0 - 0		8
27	NL	A	Bromley		**W**	2 - 1	Clarke 51 Carline 77	6
May 1	NL	A	Hartlepool United		L	1 - 3	Kerr 61	7
3	NL	H	Torquay United		L	0 - 2		8
8	NL	A	Woking		**W**	4 - 1	Gunning 7 Dinanga 20 Carline 40 Clarke 88	8
11	NL	H	King's Lynn Town		**W**	4 - 1	Yussuf 28 Carline 34 Yarney 47 Rowe 54	6
15	NL	H	Wealdstone		D	0 - 0		7
22	NL	H	Dagenham & Redbridge		**W**	2 - 1	Rowe 38 87 (pen)	7
29	NL	A	FC Halifax Town		**W**	2 - 1	Mandeville 14 Tyson 79	6
Jun 5	**NL PO QF**	**A**	**Notts County**	**4000**	**L**	**2 - 3**	**Rowe (Fk) 28 Mandeville 42**	

Goalcorers	LGE	FAC	FAT	SG	CSG	HAT	PEN	1Q	2Q	45+	3Q	4Q	90+	T
TOTALS	**62**	**1**	**1**			**1**	**3**	**9**	**18**	**1**	**13**	**22**	**1**	**64**
Asante	10			7	2	1		1	2	1	2	4		10
Denton Tom	9			8	3		2	2	2		2	3		9
Whelan	5			5	3			1	2			2		5
Rowe	4			3	1		1		2		1	1		4
Boden	3			3	2			1	1		1			3
Carline	3			3	1				2			1		3
Hollis	2		1	3	1				1		1	1		3
Mandeville	3			3	2			1	1		1			3
Clarke	2			2	1						1	1		2
Cropper	2			2	1				1		1			2
Gunning	2			2	1			1	1					2
McCourt	2			2	1							2		2
Rawson	2			1	1							1	1	2
Tyson	2			2	1							2		2
Yussuf	2			2	1				1		1			2
Butterfield		1		1	1							1		1
Dinanga	1			1	1			1						1
Evans	1			1	1			1						1
Kerr	1			1	1						1			1
Kiwomya	1			1	1							1		1
Maguire	1			1	1							1		1
Mitchell	1			1	1							1		1
Smith Jon	1			1	1				1					1
Whittle	1			1	1				1					1
Yarney	1			1	1						1			1

Letheren K	Buchanan D	Evans W	Maguire L	Yarney J	Cropper J	Smith Jon	Weston C	Butterfield M	Boden S	Denton Tom	Mandeville L	Rawson L	Rowley J	Sharman J	Wharton D (Gk)	Kiwomya A	Denton Tyler	McKay J	Hollis H	Tyson N	Hutchinson R	Addai C (Gk) (L)	Asante A	Taylor J	McCourt J	Carline G	Whelan T	Dinanga M (L)	Clarke J (L)	Smith M	Przybek A (GK) (L)	Whittle A	Gunning G	Smith G (Gk)	Yussuf A (L)	Kerr F	Oyeleke E (L)	Mitchell K	Montgomery J (Gk)	Rowe D	No.
x	x	x	xs	x	x	x	xs	x	x	xs	sx	sx	sx	s	s																										1
x	x	x	xs		x	x	x	xs		xs	sx	sx		x	s	x	sx	s																							2
x	x	x	x		x	x	x	sx		xs	xs	sx		x	s	xs		sx	s																						3
x	xs	x	x		x	x	xs	sx		x	x	xs		x	s	sx	s			sx																					4
x		x		sx	x	x	x	s	sx	x	xs	sx		xs	s		x		x	xs																					5
c	cs	c	c	c	c	cn	c	c	cn	c	sc	sc		cn	cn	cs	sc			cs																					6
x	xs	x	x			xs	x	x		x	sx	sx		x	s	x	sx		s	xs																					7
	c	c	c	c			sc	c	c	sc	cs		c	cn	c	cn	cs	sc		cn	cs	cn																			8
x	x	x	x		x	s	x	x	x	x		sx	xs	xs	s	sx			s																						9
	xs	x	x	x	x	xs	x	x	xs	x		sx	sx		s		sx		s			x																			10
	x	x	x	x	x	x	x		x	x	s	s			s		x		s		s	x																			11
x	x	x	x	sx	xs	x	x		sx	x	sx		xs				s		x			s	xs																		12
x	x	x	x	s	x	x	x		sx	x	x		s						x				xs																		13
x		x	x	s	sx		xs		sx	x	sx		s						x				xs	xs	x	x	x														14
x			x	x	sx	s	x		xs	sx	sx						s		x				xs	x	x	xs	x														15
t	tn	t	t	ts	tn	ts	st		t		ts		tn				tn		t				st	st	t	t	t														16
x		x	x	sx		sx	x		s	xs	sx		s						x				x	x	xs	x	xs														17
x		x	x	x	s	s	x			xs	sx								x				x	x	x		xs	sx	s												18
		t	t	t			t				ts		t		t				t		tn		st		st	t	st	ts	tn	ts											19
		x	x	sx		s	x				sx		sx						x				x		x	x	xs	xs			x	xs	s								20
		x	x	s			x				sx		xs						x				x		x	x	xs	s		s	x	x	sx								21
		x	x	s			x				sx								x				x	s		x	x	xs	s	sx	x	x	xs								22
		x	x	s			x				sx								x				xs	x	x	x		xs	sx	s			xs	x	sx						23
		x	x				x				xs								x				x	sx	x	x		sx	sx	s		xs	s	x	xs						24
		x	x				x				sx								x				x	x	xs	x		xs	s	sx		s	xs	x	sx						25
		s	x				x				sx									sx			x		sx	x	xs	s	xs	xs		x	x	x		x					26
		s	x				x				xs									sx			xs	sx	x	x	x		sx	s		xs	x	x		x					27
		x	x								xs									sx			x	sx	x	x	x		s	xs		xs	x	x	sx	s					28
			x				x				s								sx	sx			x	x	x	x	xs	s	x			sx	xs	x		xs					29
			x	s			x				sx		sx						x	sx			xs			x	xs	sx	x	s		x		x	xs	x					30
			x	s			x				sx								x	s			xs			x	sx	sx	xs	x		x		x	xs	x					31
			xs	sx			x				sx		s						x	xs			x			x	xs	sx		x		x		x	s	x					32
				x			x				sx		sx						xs	sx			x			x	sx	s	sx	x		x		x	s	x					33
			x	s			x				xs									sx			x			x	sx	s	sx	xs		x	x	x	xs	x					34
			x	s			x				sx									sx			xs			x	xs		s			x	x	x	sx	x	x	x			35
			x	x			xs				xs									sx				s		x	sx	s	xs	sx		x		x		x	x	x			36
			x	s			x				xs									sx				sx		x	xs	s	sx			xs	x			x	x	x	x		37
			x	s			x				s									sx				x		x	sx		xs				x	x	s	x	x	xs		x	38
			x	sx							s									sx				x		x	sx		xs	x		s	xs	x		x	x	xs		x	39
			x	x			x			x	sx		sx							xs				xs		x	s		xs	s				x		x	x	sx			40
			x								xs		s												s	x	sx		sx	xs		x	x	x	sx	x	x	xs		x	41
			x				x				sx		xs							s					sx	x	xs	x	sx				x		s	xs	x		x	x	42
		sx	x	x							s														xs	x	sx	sx	x			xs	x		xs		x	s	x	x	43
		x	x	x							xs														xs	x	sx	sx	x	s		s			xs		x	sx	x	x	44
		x	x				xs				xs		sx							s				x	sx	x	sx		xs				x		s		x		x	x	45
		x	x				x				xs									sx				xs	sx	x	s		x			sx	x		s		x		x	xs	46
		x	x				x				x									sx				sx	sx		s		x			xs	x		s		xs		x	xs	47
16	8	29	42	12	10	8	36	6	4	11	3	1	1	5	1	2	2	0	18	0	0	2	13	9	11	31	6	1	6	4	3	11	13	18	0	14	12	3	7	7	x
0	4	0	3	1	1	3	5	1	2	6	14	1	4	2	0	3	0	0	1	6	0	0	9	3	4	1	11	5	7	5	0	7	5	0	6	2	1	3	0	2	xs
0	0	1	0	6	2	2	1	2	5	1	21	8	7	0	0	2	5	1	1	15	0	0	2	6	6	0	11	7	8	3	0	2	1	0	5	0	0	2	0	0	sx
0	1	2	0	11	2	5	0	1	2	0	5	1	7	2	11	0	4	1	6	3	3	1	0	2	1	0	3	7	6	7	0	3	2	0	7	1	0	1	0	0	s

GOALKEEPERS	CS	CCS
Smith G	10	4
Letheren	7	5
Montgomery	1	1
Przybek	1	1

x/c/t - Played full 90 minutes
xs/cs/ts - Substituted off
sx/sc/st - Substituted on
s/cn/tn - Non-playing sub

Chesterfield 4 - 1 King's Lynn Town - 11/05/2021

Photos Bill Wheatcroft

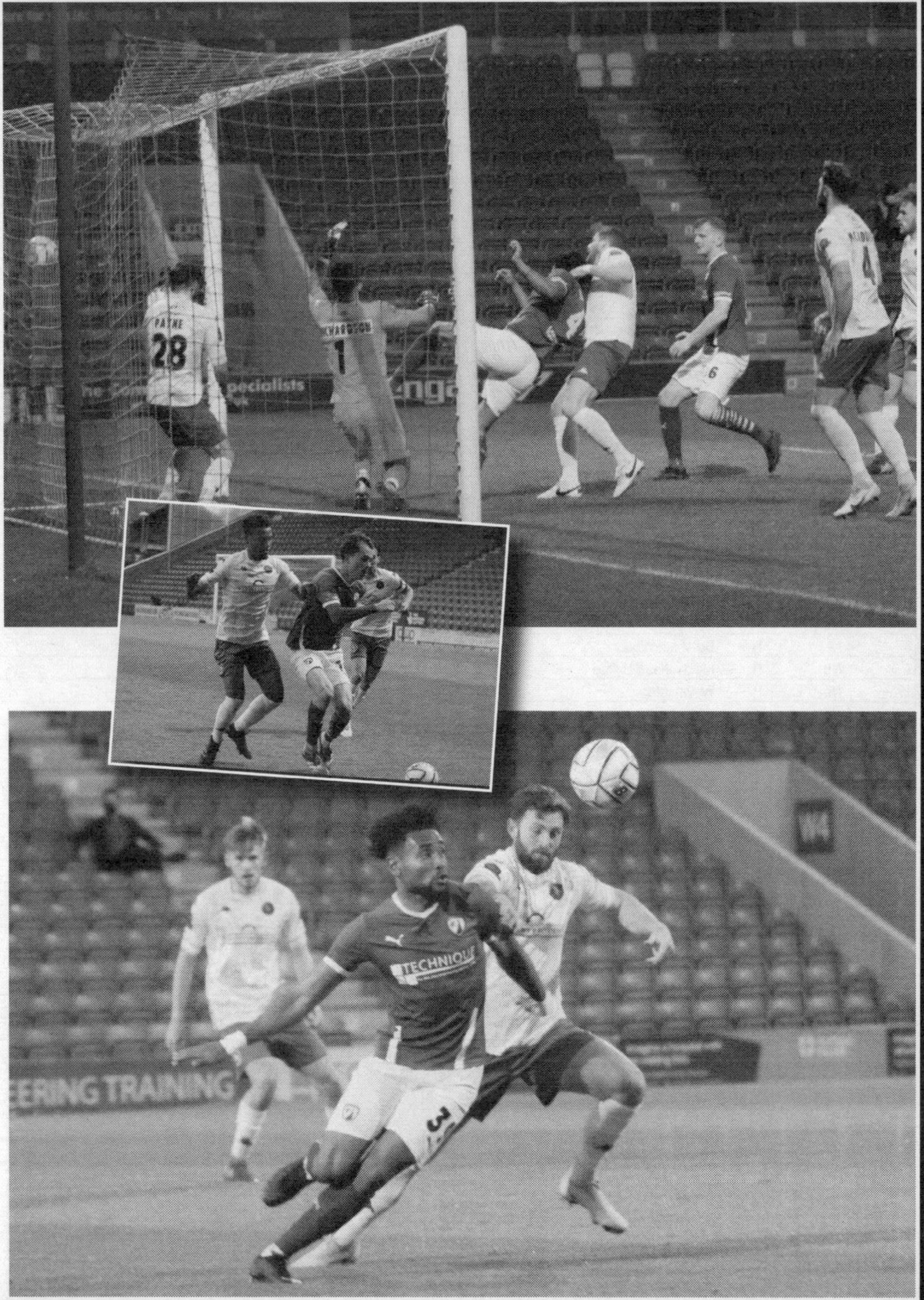

DAGENHAM & REDBRIDGE MATCH RESULTS 2020-21

Date	Comp	H/A	Opponents	Att:	Result		Goalscorers	Pos
Oct 3	NL	A	FC Halifax		L	0 - 2		22
6	NL	H	Barnet		L	1 - 2	Balanta 30	22
10	NL	H	Wealdstone		**W**	1 - 0	Balanta 65	14
13	NL	A	Woking		L	0 - 2		18
17	NL	H	Yeovil Town		D	0 - 0		19
24	**FAC4Q**	**H**	**Hartley Wintney**		**W**	**1 - 0**	**Brundle 14 (pen)**	
27	NL	A	Maidenhead United		L	1 - 2	Deering 45+1	20
Nov 7	**FAC1P**	**H**	**Grimsby Town**		**W**	**3 - 1**	**Wilson 10 90+1 Brundle 90+6**	
10	NL	A	Boreham Wood		**W**	1 - 0	Weston 58	17
17	NL	A	Sutton United		D	1 - 1	McCallum 66	17
29	**FAC2P**	**A**	**Mansfield Town**		**L**	**1 - 2**	**McCallum 19**	
Dec 2	NL	H	Notts County		D	0 - 0		19
5	NL	A	Aldershot Town	920	L	1 - 2	Rance 89	19
8	NL	A	Weymouth		**W**	3 - 2	Brundle 26 70 (pen) McCallum 27	19
12	NL	H	Altrincham	773	L	0 - 1		19
15	NL	A	Torquay United		**W**	1 - 0	McCallum 14 (RC - Brundle 41)	18
19	**FAT3P**	**H**	**Ebbsfleet United**		**W**	**5 - 2**	**McCallum 16 Balanta 20 Reynolds 44 McQueen 64 66**	
26	NL	A	Dover Athletic		**W**	1 - 0	Balanta 47	17
Jan 16	**FAT4P**	**A**	**Sutton United**		**L**	**1 - 3**	**Bouzanis 86 (og)**	
19	NL	H	Stockport County		L	0 - 2		18
23	NL	H	King's Lynn Town		**W**	3 - 2	Reynolds 72 Eleftheriou 78 Brundle 90+3	16
26	NL	A	Eastleigh		L	0 - 3		17
30	NL	H	Chesterfield		D	2 - 2	Wilson 20 Deering 53	17
Feb 6	NL	A	Wrexham		D	2 - 2	Robinson 76 Rance 90+5	17
9	NL	A	Notts County		L	1 - 3	Robinson 90+1	17
16	NL	H	Bromley		**W**	1 - 0	Gordon 25	16
23	NL	H	Sutton United		L	1 - 2	Gordon 62	18
27	NL	A	Yeovil Town		L	0 - 1	(RC 2xY - Reynolds 88)	18
Mar 2	NL	A	Solihull Moors		**W**	1 - 0	McCallum 57	17
6	NL	H	Boreham Wood		D	2 - 2	Balanta 73 89	17
9	NL	H	Maidenhead United		**W**	2 - 1	McCullum 14 16	16
17	NL	H	Weymouth		D	1 - 1	Gordon 43	16
20	NL	A	Altrincham		**W**	1 - 0	Wright 79	16
23	NL	H	Hartlepool United		L	0 - 1		16
29	NL	H	Torquay United		**W**	1 - 0	Balanta 79	15
Apr 2	NL	A	Hartlepool United		L	1 - 2	Robinson 32	17
5	NL	H	Aldershot Town		L	0 - 2		17
10	NL	A	Bromley		L	0 - 1		17
13	NL	H	Eastleigh		**W**	2 - 0	Balanta 23 McCallum 64	16
17	NL	H	Solihull Moors		**W**	3 - 2	Saunders 29 Balanta 41 (pen) Robinson 49	13
24	NL	A	King's Lynn Town		**W**	3 - 0	McCallum 16 Balanta 39 Robinson 46	14
May 1	NL	A	Barnet		**W**	2 - 0	McCallum 38 Robinson 56	11
3	NL	H	Woking		**W**	3 - 1	McCallum 8 27 (pen) Balanta 81	11
8	NL	A	Wealdstone		**W**	5 - 0	Balanta 2 Robinson 4 90+1 McCallum 21 36	11
11	NL	A	Stockport County		D	1 - 1	McCallum 43	11
15	NL	H	FC Halifax		**W**	3 - 0	Vilhete 34 McCallum 45+1 Balanta 55	11
22	NL	A	Chesterfield		L	1 - 2	Gordon 29 (RC 2xY - Jones 77)	12
29	NL	H	Wrexham		D	1 - 1	McCallum 51	12

Goalcorers	LGE	FAC	FAT	SG	CSG	HAT	PEN	1Q	2Q	45+	3Q	4Q	90+	T
TOTALS	54	5	6			0	4	14	17	2	15	11	6	65
McCallum	16	1	1	15	6		1	8	5	1	4			18
Balanta	12		1	12	3		1	2	4		3	4		13
Robinson	8			7	2			1	1		3	1	2	8
Brundle	3	2		5	1		2	1	1			1	2	5
Gordon	4			4	2				3		1			4
Wilson	1	2		2	1			2					1	3
Deering	2			2	1					1	1			2
McQueen			2	1	1						2			2
Rance	2			2	1							1	1	2

	LGE	FAC	FAT	SG	CSG	HAT	PEN	1Q	2Q	45+	3Q	4Q	90+	T
Reynolds	1		1	2	1				1			1		2
Eleftheriou	1			1	1							1		1
Opponent			1	1	1							1		1
Saunders	1			1	1				1					1
Vilhete	1			1	1				1					1
Weston	1			1	1						1			1
Wright	1			1	1							1		1

Justham E	Clark K	Reynolds C	Brundle M	Eleftheriou A	Rance D	Johnson E	Robinson M	McQueen D	Balanta A	McCallum P	Croll L	Deering S	Clifton A	Brown K (L)	Wright W	Weston M	Adams C	Strizovic J (Gk)	Thompson-Brissett J	Saunders G	Ogogo A (L)	Wilson S	Clements B (L)	Jones J	Gordon L	Sagaf M	Smith T (L)	Vilhete M	Khan S (L)	No.
x	x	x	xs	x	x	x	xs	xs	x	x	sx	sx	sx	s	s															1
x	x	x	x	sx	xs	x	sx	sx	x	x	x	xs	s	s		xs														2
x	x	xs	x	x		x		s	x	xs		sx	sx	x	sx	xs	x	s												3
x	x		x	x		x		sx	x	xs	x	x	sx	xs	s		x	s	sx											4
x	x		x	xs		x	s	x	x		x	x		xs	sx		x		s	sx										5
c	c		c	sc		c	cn	sc	c		c	c		cn	c		sc		cn	cs	cs	cs	cn							6
x	x		x	sx		x		sx	x		x	x		s	x		s	s		xs	xs	x								7
c	c		c	cn		c		sc	cs		c	c			c	c	sc	cn	cn	sc	cs	cs	cn							8
x	x		x			x			sx	xs	x	xs			xs	sx	sx	s		s	x	x		x						9
x	x		x			x			xs	sx	x	xs			sx	x	sx	s		s	x	x		xs						10
c			c		cs	c		cn	sc	c	c	c			c	cs	sc	cn	cn	sc	c	cs	cn							11
x	x		x		s	x		s	sx	x	x	x			x	xs		s			x	x	s							12
x	x		x		sx	x		sx	xs	x	x	xs			x	sx		s			x	xs	s							13
x	x		x		x	x		xs	s	x	x				x	x	s	s	s		x	sx								14
x	x		x		x	x		xs	sx		x	s			xs	x	s	s	sx		x	x								15
x	x		x	x	x	xs		xs	s	xs	x				sx	x	sx	s			x	sx								16
t	t	ts		t		t	st	t	t	t	tn			tn	st		ts	tn			t	tn	st		ts					17
x	x	x		xs	xs	s		x	x	x	x					sx	sx	s			x	s			x					18
t		t		ts	t	t	tn	ts	ts	t	t	st					t	tn		st		st		tn	t					19
x		x	xs	x		sx	x	sx	x	x	x	x						s		s		sx		xs	xs					20
x		x	x	x	x	xs	s	sx	x	xs	x	x						s		xs		sx			sx					21
x		x	x	x	x	xs	sx	s	xs	x	x	x						s		xs		sx			sx					22
x	x	x	x	xs	x		s	s		x	x	sx				xs				sx		x			sx	xs				23
x	x	sx		x	x	xs	x	x		sx	x	x				sx	s			xs		xs			s					24
x	x	x		xs	x	s	x	xs		x	x	xs				x	s			sx		sx			sx					25
x	x	x		s	x	x	x	sx			sx	sx			s	x	xs			xs		xs			x					26
x	x	x			x	x	x	sx		sx		sx				x	xs			xs		xs		s	x	s				27
x	x	x			x	x	x		sx	xs					sx	x	xs			xs		sx			x	s	s			28
x	x				x	x	x		xs	x					x	x	s			sx		s		sx	x	s	xs			29
x	x				x	x	x		x	xs	s				x	x				sx		sx		xs	x	s	s			30
x	x				x	x	xs	s	x	xs	s				x	x				xs		sx		sx	x	sx				31
x	x	s			x	x		s	x				sx		x	x	x	s				xs			x	xs		sx		32
x	x	s			x	x		sx	x				sx		x	x		s				xs			x	xs		sx	xs	33
x	x	s			xs	x		sx	x	sx					x	x		s				xs			x	x		xs	sx	34
x	x	s			x	x	x	s	x	x					x	x				sx				s	x	xs			s	35
x	x	s			x		x	sx	x	xs					x	x				sx				x	x	s		xs	s	36
x	x	sx		xs	x		x	sx	x	x					x					xs				xs	x	s		sx	s	37
x	x	s			x	x	xs		x	x			sx		x					x				s	xs	sx		sx	xs	38
x	x	s				x	x		x	x					x					x		s		xs	s	x	sx	x	s	39
x	x	s				x	x		xs	x					x					xs		sx		xs	sx	x	sx	x	s	40
x	x	s			sx	x	x	s	xs	x					x							sx		xs	x	sx		x	xs	41
x		x		x	xs	x	x		xs	x	s				x					sx		s		sx		xs		x	sx	42
x		x		x		x	x	s	xs	x	sx				x					s		sx		xs			sx	x	xs	43
x		x		x		x	x	sx	xs	x	sx				x					s		s		xs			sx	x	xs	44
x		x		x		x	x	s	xs	x					x			s		sx		s		x			s	x	x	45
x		x		s		x	x	sx	xs	x					x	sx				x		s		xs			sx	xs	x	46
x	s	x		s		x	x			xs					x	x				xs		sx		x	x	sx	sx		xs	47
x	x	x		s			x	sx	xs	xs					x	xs				sx		sx			x	x	s		x	48
48	37	19	18	13	22	37	21	4	21	25	22	11	0	1	27	18	5	0	0	3	10	6	0	4	17	4	0	7	3	x
0	0	2	2	6	5	4	3	6	14	11	0	5	0	2	2	6	4	0	0	12	3	10	0	10	3	5	1	3	6	xs
0	0	2	0	3	2	1	3	17	5	4	4	6	6	0	6	5	7	0	2	13	0	15	1	3	5	4	6	4	2	sx
0	1	9	0	5	1	2	5	11	2	0	4	1	1	5	3	0	6	22	5	5	0	8	5	4	2	6	4	0	5	s

Abu Ogogo

Angelo Balanta

Charlee Adams

Dean Rance

Elliot Justham

Elliott Johnson

Luke Croll

Mitch Brundle

Myles Weston

Paul McCallum

Scott Wilson

Will Wright

GOALKEEPERS	CS	CCS
Justham	16	2

x/c/t - Played full 90 minutes
xs/cs/ts - Substituted off
sx/sc/st - Substituted on
s/cn/tn - Non-playing sub

DOVER ATHLETIC MATCH RESULTS 2020-21

Date	Comp	H/A	Opponents	Att:	Result	Goalscorers	Pos
Oct 3	NL	H	Notts County		**W** 1 - 0	Ransom 89	8
6	NL	A	Bromley		L 1 - 4	Wood 59	12
10	NL	A	Stockport County		L 0 - 3		16
13	NL	H	Aldershot Town		L 0 - 5		20
17	NL	A	Torquay United		L 0 - 2		22
24	**FAC4Q**	**A**	**Yeovil Town**		**D 3 - 3**	**Collins 40 44 Bramble 63 (Lost 6-7 on pens)**	
27	NL	H	Eastleigh		**W** 3 - 2	Wood 24 Collins 29 Azeez 81	16
31	NL	H	Altrincham		L 0 - 1		20
Nov 17	NL	H	Woking		L 1 - 5	Rigg 3	22
21	NL	A	King's Lynn Town		L 0 - 2		22
Dec 19	**FAT3P**	**A**	**Woking**		**L 1 - 2**	**Azeez 46**	
26	NL	H	Dagenham & Redbridge		L 0 - 1	(RC - Passley 36)	23
Jan 12	NL	H	Boreham Wood		D 1 - 1	Bramble 61	23
16	NL	A	Wrexham		L 1 - 3	Rose 43	23
23	NL	H	Solihull Moors		L 0 - 2		23
26	NL	H	Barnet		**W** 3 - 1	De Havilland 17 20 Rose 35	22
30	NL	A	Yeovil Town		L 1 - 3	Azeez 14	22

Feb 13 - All club personell were furloughed to safeguard the club's long-term future and no further matches were played.

The above results were expunged from the National League's records.

Goalcorers	LGE	FAC	FAT	SG	CSG	HAT	PEN	1Q	2Q	45+	3Q	4Q	90+	T
TOTALS	12	3	1			0	0	4	6	0	4	2	0	16
Azeez	2		1	3	1			1			1	1		3
Collins	1	2		2	2				3					3
Bramble	1	1		2	1						2			2
De Havilland	2			1	1			2						2
Rose	2			2	1				2					2
Wood	2			2	1				1		1			2
Ransom	1			1	1							1		1
Rigg	1			1	1			1						1

	LGE	FAC	FAT	SG	CSG	HAT	PEN	1Q	2Q	45+	3Q	4Q	90+	T

Mersin Y	Passley J	De Havilland W	Ekpiteta M	Gobern O	Munns J	Wood S	Bramble T	Azeez A	Rigg S	Ransom H (L)	Gregory T	Hinchiri B	Rose A	Collins L	Wratten M	Cumberbatch K	Bexon J (Gk)	Moses W	Spencer-Adams B (L)	Smith T (Gk) (L)	Rooney P	Mussa O	Hanson R (L)	Bedford J	Webber O (Gk)	No.
X	XS	X	X	XS	X	X	X	XS	X	X	SX	SX	SX	S	S											1
X		X	X	X	X	X	X	XS	X	XS	X	S	SX	SX	S	S										2
		X	X	X	XS	X	S	X	X		X	XS	SX	SX	S	SX	X	XS								3
S		X	X	X	XS	X	SX	X	XS		X		XS	SX	SX	S	X	X								4
X	XS	X		X	X	X	X		X			SX	XS	SX	SX	XS	S	S	X							5
cn	c		c	sc	c	cn	c	sc	sc			cs	cs	cs	c	c		cn	c	c	cn					6
S	X		X		XS	X	X	X	X				SX	XS	S	XS			X	X	SX	SX				7
S	X		X		X	X	XS	X	XS				SX	XS	S	X			X	X	SX	SX				8
S	X	X	X	X	X	X	XS	XS	X			SX	SX	SX		XS			S	X						9
X	X	X	XS		X	X	SX	SX	X		XS		XS	SX		S			X	S			X			10
t	t	t				t	t	t	tn	ts			ts	st		t			t	tn	ts	st		st		11
X	X	X				X	SX	X	XS	X			XS	SX		S			X	S	XS	SX	X			12
X		X		X	XS	X	X	X		X			XS	SX	S	SX			X	S		SX	XS			13
X		X		X	XS	X	X	X		X			X	SX	S	SX			XS	S		SX	XS			14
S		X		X	XS	SX	X			X	SX		X	SX	X	S			XS			XS	X		X	15
S		X	X	X		X		X	SX	X	X		XS	SX	S	S						XS	X		X	16
S		X	X	X		X		XS	SX	X	XS		X	SX	S	SX						XS	X		X	17
8	7	14	10	10	7	15	9	9	7	7	4	0	3	0	2	3	2	1	8	4	0	0	5	0	3	X
0	2	0	1	1	6	0	2	4	3	2	2	2	8	3	0	3	0	1	2	0	2	3	2	0	0	XS
0	0	0	0	1	0	1	3	2	3	0	2	3	6	13	2	4	0	0	0	0	2	6	0	1	0	SX
8	0	0	0	0	0	1	1	0	1	0	0	1	0	1	9	6	1	2	1	5	1	0	0	0	0	S

GOALKEEPERS	CS	CCS
Mersin	1	1

x/c/t - Played full 90 minutes
xs/cs/ts - Substituted off
sx/sc/st - Substituted on
s/cn/tn - Non-playing sub

EASTLEIGH MATCH RESULTS 2020-21

Date	Comp	H/A	Opponents	Att:	Result	Goalscorers	Pos
Oct 3	NL	A	Barnet		**W** 5 - 1	Barnett 5 Wynter 53 House 56 Miley 64 Baggie 76	1
6	NL	H	Torquay United		**W** 2 - 1	House 73 81	1
10	NL	H	Altrincham		D 1 - 1	Miley 45	3
17	NL	H	Aldershot Town		D 2 - 2	Tomlinson 42 (pen) Wynter 90+1	8
24	**FAC4Q**	**H**	**Weston-s-Mare**		**W 3 - 1**	**Smith 60 (pen) House 70 Bearwish 73**	
27	NL	A	Dover Athletic		L 2 - 3	Barnett 6 Smith 60	10
31	NL	A	Bromley		**W** 2 - 1	House 59 66	5
Nov 8	**FAC1P**	**H**	**Milton Keynes Dons**		**D 0 - 0**	**(Lost 3-4 on pens)**	
17	NL	H	Wealdstone		**W** 2 - 0	Miley 68 Smart 90+3	5
Dec 1	NL	A	Yeovil Town		**W** 3 - 1	Barnett 7 Tomlinson 34 (pen) House 59	5
5	NL	H	Maidenhead United	776	L 0 - 1		7
19	**FAT3P**	**A**	**Wealdstone**		**L 3 - 4**	**Boyce 8 Hill 16 20**	
22	NL	A	FC Halifax Town		L 1 - 3	Barnett 54	15
26	NL	H	Weymouth		D 0 - 0		14
28	NL	A	Woking		D 0 - 0		13
Jan 2	NL	A	Weymouth		D 1 - 1	Green 11	14
19	NL	H	King's Lynn Town		L 0 - 1		16
23	NL	A	Sutton United		L 0 - 3	(RC - Miley 34)	18
26	NL	H	Dagenham & Redbridge		**W** 3 - 0	Hill 9 Tomlinson 51 67 (pens)	15
30	NL	A	Boreham Wood		**W** 2 - 1	Barnett 72 Smith 90+3	11
Feb 2	NL	H	Wrexham		D 1 - 1	Tomlinson 71 (pen)	10
6	NL	H	Solihull Moors		D 1 - 1	Barnett 22 (RC 2xY - Partington 45+1)	10
9	NL	H	Yeovil Town		**W** 1 - 0	Hill 43	8
16	NL	H	Hartlepool United		**W** 2 - 1	House 1 Barnett 27	7
20	NL	H	Stockport County		**W** 1 - 0	Tomlinson 53 (pen)	4
23	NL	A	Wealdstone		D 0 - 0		4
Mar 2	NL	A	Chesterfield		L 0 - 1		7
6	NL	H	Bromley		L 1 - 2	Barnett 57	7
13	NL	A	Hartlepool United		D 0 - 0		8
16	NL	A	Wrexham		D 2 - 2	Tomlinson 11 50 (pen)	9
20	NL	H	FC Halifax Town		**W** 1 - 0	Barnett 59	9
23	NL	A	Stockport County		L 0 - 3		9
29	NL	A	King's Lynn Town		L 1 - 2	Payne 1	9
Apr 2	NL	H	Chesterfield		L 0 - 1		9
5	NL	A	Maidenhead United		**W** 1 - 0	House 87	9
10	NL	H	Woking		D 0 - 0		9
13	NL	A	Dagenham & Redbridge		L 0 - 2		10
17	NL	A	Notts County		**W** 1 - 0	House 45+3	10
24	NL	H	Sutton United		**W** 1 - 0	Marriott 43	10
27	NL	H	Notts County		**W** 2 - 0	Boyce 57 Tomlinson 75	7
May 1	NL	A	Torquay United		L 1 - 3	Barnett 59	8
15	NL	H	Barnet		**W** 3 - 0	Barnett 9 Tomlinson 72 (pen) Smart 82	10
18	NL	A	Aldershot Town		**W** 3 - 1	Wynter 29 Boyce 73 Tomlinson 84	9
22	NL	H	Boreham Wood		**W** 1 - 0	Tomlinson 90+3 (pen)	9
25	NL	A	Altrincham		D 1 - 1	Barnett 53	8
29	NL	A	Solihull Moors		L 0 - 2		9

Goalcorers	LGE	FAC	FAT	SG	CSG	HAT	PEN	1Q	2Q	45+	3Q	4Q	90+	T
TOTALS	51	3	3			0	10	13	6	2	18	14	4	57
Barnett	12			12	2			5	1		5	1		13
Tomlinson	12			10	3		9	1	2		4	4	1	12
House	9	1		8	2			1		1	4	4		10
Hill	2		2	3	1			3	1					4
Boyce	2		1	3	1			1			1	1		3
Miley	3			3	1					1	1	1		3
Smith	2	1		3	2		1				2		1	3
Wynter	3			3	1				1		1		1	3
Smart	2			2	1							1	1	2
Baggie	1			1	1							1		1
Bearwish		1		1	1							1		1
Green	1			1	1			1						1
Marriott	1			1	1				1					1
Payne	1			1	1			1						1

McDonnell J	Boyce A	Wynter A	Tomlinson J	Partington J	Payne J	Miley C	Smart S	Bell-Baggie A	Barnett T	House B	Hollands D	Smith D	Green M	Bird P	Bearwish T	Scorey B	Flitney R (Gk)	Hill R	Blair T	Baughan C	Philpott C (Gk)	Marriott A	No.
x	x	x	x	x	x	x	xs	xs	xs	x	sx	sx	sx	s	s								1
x	x	x	xs	x	x	x	x	xs	xs	x	sx	sx	sx	s	s								2
x	x	x	sx	x	x	x	x	xs	xs	x	s	sx	xs	s	sx								3
x	xs	x	x	x	x	x	x	xs	x	x	sx	sx	s	s	s								4
c	sc	c	c	cs	cn	c	c	sc	sc	cs	c	cs	c	cn	c	cn	cn						5
x	x	x	x		x	x	x	xs	xs		sx	x	x	s	s		s	sx					6
x	x	x	x		x	x	x	s		x	x	x	x	s	s			s	s				7
c	c	c	c		cs	c	cs		sc	c	c	cs	c	sc	sc	cn	cn			cn			8
x	x	x	x		x	xs	x		xs	xs	x	sx	x	s	s			sx	sx				9
x	x	x	x	x	x	x	xs		xs	xs	x	sx		s	s			sx	sx				10
x	x	x	xs	x	x	x	x	s	xs	x	xs	sx		s	sx			sx					11
	ts	st		t	tn	t	tn	st		ts	tn	t	t		t	t	t	t	t		tn		12
x	x	x	xs	x	x	x	xs	s	x	x	xs	sx	sx		s			sx					13
x	x	x	x	xs	x	x	sx	sx	sx	x	s	xs	x					xs	s				14
x	x	x	x		x	x	sx		x	sx	x	s	x		s	s		xs	xs				15
x	x	x	x		x	xs	xs		xs	x	x	sx	x		s	s		sx	sx				16
x	x	x	x		x	x	sx		sx	x	s	x	xs	s	sx			xs	xs				17
x	x	xs	x	sx		x	x	s	x		x	xs	x	sx	s			xs	sx				18
x	x		x	x	x		xs	sx	xs	xs	x	sx	sx	x			s	x	s				19
x	x		x	x	x		xs	sx	xs	x	x	sx	s	x	sx			xs	s				20
x	x		x	x	x		xs	s	xs	x		sx	s	x	x		s	x	sx				21
x	x		x	x	x	sx	xs		xs	x	x	sx	sx	x	s			xs	s				22
x	x		x		x	sx	xs	s	xs	x	x	sx	x	x	s			xs	sx				23
x	x		x		x	sx	xs		xs	xs	x	sx	x	x	s		s	x	sx				24
x	x		x		x	sx	x		xs	xs	x	sx	x	x	s		s	xs	sx				25
x	x		x			x	xs		xs	x	x	sx	x	x	s	s	s	x	sx				26
x	x		x		x	sx	xs	sx	xs	x	x	sx	x	x	s			xs	s				27
x	x		x		x	s	sx	sx	xs	x	x	sx	xs	x	s			xs	x				28
x	x		x	x	x		sx	sx	xs	x	x	sx	s	x	s			xs	xs				29
x	x		x	x	x		sx	xs	x	x	x	sx	sx	xs	s		s		xs				30
x	x		x	x	x		sx	xs	xs	x	x	sx	s	x	sx		s		xs				31
x	x		x	x	x	x	sx	x			s	x	sx	x	xs		s		xs	s			32
x	x		x	xs	x	x	sx	x			x	x	s	x	sx	s	s		xs				33
x	x		x	x	x	sx	xs	x			xs	x	s	x	sx		s	xs	sx				34
x	x		x	x	x	x		xs		sx	s	x	sx	x	sx		s	xs	xs				35
x	x		x	x	x	x	sx	xs		x	s	x	s	xs				xs	sx			sx	36
x	x		xs	x	x	x	xs	xs		x	s	s	sx	x				x	sx			sx	37
x	x			x	x	x	xs	s	sx	x	xs	sx	x	x				sx	s			xs	38
x	x	sx		x	x	x	xs	s	xs	xs		sx	x	x				sx	s			x	39
x	x	s	sx	x	x	x	x	sx	xs			sx	x	x				xs	s			xs	40
x	x	sx	sx	xs	x	x	x	s	x	sx		s	xs	x				xs				x	41
x	x	x	x	s	x	x	sx		x	xs	sx	s	xs	x				sx				xs	42
x	x	xs	x	x	x	x	sx		xs	xs	x	s	sx	x				s				sx	43
x	x		x	x	x	x	sx	s	xs	xs	xs	sx	x	x				s				sx	44
x	x		x	x	x	x	sx	s	xs	x	xs	s	xs	x				sx				sx	45
x	x		x	x	x	x	xs	s	x	x	s	sx	xs	xs				sx				sx	46
45	43	17	36	27	41	31	12	3	8	26	22	9	19	25	3	1	1	6	2	0	0	2	x
0	2	2	4	4	1	2	18	10	25	11	6	4	7	3	1	0	0	16	8	0	0	3	xs
0	1	3	3	1	0	6	14	9	5	3	5	27	10	2	9	0	0	11	12	0	0	6	sx
0	0	1	0	1	2	1	1	12	0	0	9	6	8	11	20	6	14	3	9	2	1	0	s

GOALKEEPERS	CS	CCS
McDonnell	17	3

x/c/t - Played full 90 minutes
xs/cs/ts - Substituted off
sx/sc/st - Substituted on
s/cn/tn - Non-playing sub

Chesterfield 1 - 0 Eastleigh - 02/03/2021

Photos Bill Wheatcroft

FC HALIFAX TOWN MATCH RESULTS 2020-21

Date	Comp	H/A	Opponents	Att:	Result	Goalscorers	Pos
Oct 3	NL	H	Dagenham & Redbridge		**W** 2 - 0	Summerfield 45+2 (pen) Earing 67	3
6	NL	A	Stockport County		L 1 - 2	Earing 12	7
10	NL	A	Boreham Wood		D 0 - 0		10
13	NL	H	Yeovil Town		D 1 - 1	King 6	11
17	NL	A	Woking		D 0 - 0		9
24	**FAC4Q**	**A**	**South Shields**	**300**	**L 0 - 2**		
Nov 10	NL	H	Wealdstone		L 0 - 1		20
17	NL	H	Notts County		D 1 - 1	Allen 90+4	18
21	NL	H	Torquay United		L 1 - 2	Allen 53	18
28	NL	A	Sutton United		L 0 - 1		20
Dec 2	NL	H	Barnet		**W** 5 - 2	King 1 Bell 22 Hyde 44 Earring 48 Woods 57	16
5	NL	A	Weymouth		**W** 5 - 1	Williams 10 Maher 23 Nepomuceno 72 Bradbury 79 Hyde 82	15
8	NL	A	Aldershot Town		**W** 3 - 1	Hyde 63 (pen) 70 Bell 66	13
15	NL	A	Solihull Moors		L 1 - 2	Woods 21	16
19	**FAT3P**	**H**	**Hartlepool United**		**D 3 - 3**	**Summerfield 12 (pen) Nepomuceno 14 Chadwick 75 (Won 4-32 on pens)**	
22	NL	H	Eastleigh		**W** 3 - 1	Allen 33 Green 45+3 Bell 84	11
26	NL	A	Hartlepool United		L 1 - 2	Chadwick 13 (RC 2xY - Bell 70)	12
28	NL	H	Altrincham		**W** 3 - 2	Summerfield 18 (pen) Chadwick 29 Woods 46	7
Jan 9	NL	A	King's Lynn Town		D 1 - 1	Mansell 51	6
19	**FAT4P**	**H**	**Southport**		**L 1 - 2**	**Earing 20**	
23	NL	A	Bromley		**W** 2 - 1	Summerfield 22 (pen) Allen 48	6
26	NL	A	Wrexham		D 0 - 0		6
30	NL	H	Maidenhead United		L 2 - 3	Green 39 Bradbury 77	8
Feb 16	NL	A	Barnet		L 1 - 2	King 45+1	14
20	NL	A	Torquay United		**W** 3 - 2	Sherring 34 (og) Earing 78 King 88	12
Mar 2	NL	H	Hartlepool United		D 1 - 1	Green 77	15
6	NL	A	Wealdstone		**W** 2 - 1	Hyde 57 Earing 82	13
9	NL	A	Notts County		**W** 2 - 1	Hyde 28 Campbell 83	9
13	NL	H	Solihull Moors		**W** 1 - 0	Woods 47 (pen)	7
16	NL	H	Aldershot Town		**W** 1 - 0	Allen 83	6
20	NL	A	Eastleigh		L 0 - 1		8
29	NL	H	Sutton United		D 2 - 2	Chadwick 18 Earing 61	8
Apr 5	NL	H	Weymouth		**W** 3 - 2	Hyde 2 Byrne 31 King 47	7
10	NL	A	Altrincham		**W** 1 - 0	Earing 12	7
13	NL	H	Wrexham		L 0 - 4		8
17	NL	H	King's Lynn Town		**W** 4 - 2	Chadwick 42 Hyde 45 Sumerfield 50 Earing 57	6
20	NL	A	Chesterfield		**W** 2 - 1	King 8 Hyde 29	5
24	NL	H	Bromley		L 1 - 2	Byrne 90+3	5
27	NL	H	Woking		**W** 1 - 0	Hyde 74	5
May 1	NL	H	Stockport County		L 0 - 1		5
3	NL	A	Yeovil Town		**W** 3 - 0	Summerfield 16 (pen) Green 84 Hyde 90+2	5
8	NL	H	Boreham Wood		L 0 - 1		5
15	NL	A	Dagenham & Redbridge		L 0 - 3		9
22	NL	A	Maidenhead United		**W** 2 - 1	Hyde 44 King 58	10
29	NL	H	Chesterfield		L 1 - 2	Stephenson 31	10

Goalcorers	LGE	FAC	FAT	SG	CSG	HAT	PEN	1Q	2Q	45+	3Q	4Q	90+	T
TOTALS	**63**	**0**	**4**			**0**	**7**	**16**	**13**	**4**	**16**	**15**	**3**	**67**
Hyde	12			11	3		1	1	4	1	2	3	1	12
Earing	8		1	9	2			3			4	2		9
King	7			7	2			3		1	2	1		7
Summerfield	5		1	6	1		5	3	1	1	1			6
Allen	5			5	2				1		2	1	1	5
Chadwick	4		1	5	2			2	2			1		5
Green	4			4	1				1	1		2		4
Woods	4			4	1		1	1			3			4
Bell	3			3	1			1			1	1		3

	LGE	FAC	FAT	SG	CSG	HAT	PEN	1Q	2Q	45+	3Q	4Q	90+	T
Bradbury	2			2	1							2		2
Byrne	2			2	1				1				1	2
Nepomuceno	1		1	2	1			1				1		2
Campbell	1			1	1							1		1
Maher	1			1	1				1					1
Mansell	1			1	1						1			1
Opponent	1			1	1				1					1
Stephenson	1			1	1				1					1
Williams	1			1	1			1						1

Johnson S	Clarke N	Byrne N	Bradbury T	Summerfield L	Woods M	Williams D	King J	Earing J	Nepomuceno G	Omotayo G	Allen J	Green K	Benn J	Tear D	Davison-Hale H (Gk)	Senior J	Maher N	Hyde J	Stenson M	Schofield L	Crane N	Danns N	Bell N (L)	Chadwick B (L)	Leroy-Belehouan J (L)	Mansell L (L)	Campbell T (L)	Renshaw C (Gk) (L)	Spence K	Obiero M (L)	Stephenson D (L)	No.
x	x	x	x	x	xs	x	x	xs	xs	x	sx	sx	sx	s	s																	1
x	x	x	x	x	xs	x	x	x	sx	xs	x	sx	s	s	s																	2
x	x	x	x	x	sx	xs	xs	x	s	xs	x	x			s	sx	sx															3
x	x	x	x	x	x	s	x	sx	sx	xs	x	xs			s	x	s															4
x	x	x	s	x	x	xs	x	xs	xs		x	sx			s	sx	x	sx														5
c	c	c	cn	cn	c	cs	c	cs	sc	cs	c	c		cn	cn	sc	c	sc														6
x	x	x	x	x	x	x	x					x	sx	sx	s			xs	xs	s	s											7
x	x	x	x	x	x			sx	sx		x	xs		s	s	x	x	xs				s										8
x	x	x	x	x	x			sx	sx		x	xs		s	s	x	xs	x				s										9
x	xs	x	x	x	xs	x		sx	x		x	sx			s	s	x					xs	sx									10
x		x	x	x	xs	xs	x	x	sx			s			s	sx	x	x				sx	xs									11
x		x	x	x	x	xs	x	sx	sx			xs			s	sx	x	x				s	xs									12
x		x	x	x	xs	x	x	sx	sx			xs			s	s	x	x				sx	xs									13
x		x	xs	x	x	x	x	xs	sx			sx			s	sx	x	xs				s	x									14
t		t	tn	t	ts	st	t	t	ts		st	st		tn	tn	t	t					tn	ts	t								15
x		x	x	x		x		sx	sx		xs	x		s	s	x	x					xs	sx	xs								16
x			x	x	x	x		sx	xs			x		s	s	x	x				s	s	x	x								17
x		x	x	x	x	x	x	x	s			xs		s	s	s	x					sx		x								18
x			x	x	xs	x	x	x			sx	sx			s	sx	x					s		x	xs	xs						19
t		t	ts	t	ts	tn	t	t			st	t	tn	st	tn	ts	t				tn				st	t						20
x		x	x	x		xs	x	x			x	x	s	sx	s	sx	x								s		xs					21
x		x	x	x			x	x			x	x	s	s	s	x	x								s	s	x					22
x		x	x		sx		x	x			sx	x	s	xs	s	x	x								s	xs	x					23
x		x	xs		x	sx		xs			x	x	s	sx		x	x	sx									xs	s				24
x		x	x			xs	x	x			x	x	s	s		x	x	sx									x	s				25
x		x	x		sx	sx	x	x			x	x	s	sx		xs	x	xs									xs	s				26
x		x	x		x		xs	x			sx	x	s	sx		x	x	xs						sx			xs	s				27
x		x	x		x		x	xs			xs	x	s	sx		xs	x	x						sx			sx	s				28
x	s	x	x		x	x	xs	x			sx	x		s			x	xs						x			sx	s				29
x	s	x	x		x		x	x			x	x	s	sx			x							xs			xs	s	sx			30
x	x	x	xs		x		x				x	x	s	s		x	x				s			x				s	sx			31
x	x	x	x			xs	x	xs				x	s	s		x	x	sx						x				s	sx			32
x	x	x	x		s	sx	xs	xs			x	x				xs	x	x										s	sx	sx		33
x	x	x	x	sx	sx	xs	xs	x			x	xs				sx	x	x										s		s		34
x	x	x	xs	x	sx	s	x	xs			x	sx			s	x	x	xs						sx								35
x	s	x	xs	x	x	x	x	xs			sx	sx			s	sx	x	x						x								36
x	x	x	s	x	xs	x	x				sx	x			s	s	x	x						xs					sx			37
x	x	x	s	x	x	xs	x				sx	x			s	sx	x	x						xs					s			38
x	x	x	x	x	x	sx					xs	sx			s	x	s	x						xs			sx		xs			39
x	x	x	s	x	x	x					xs	x		s	s	x	x	x						xs					s			40
x	x	x	xs	x	x	x	x					x			s	s	x	sx						xs					s		sx	41
x	x	x		x	x	x	xs	sx			x	xs			s	s	x	x									sx		sx			42
x	x	x	x	x	x		x					xs	s	sx	s	xs	x										xs		sx		sx	43
x	x	x	s	x	x		xs					xs		sx	s	x	x	x									sx					44
x	x	x	s	x	x		x				sx	x			s	xs	x	x									sx		s		xs	45
45	23	43	29	32	25	16	30	16	1	1	19	24	0	0	0	17	38	15	0	0	0	0	2	8	0	1	3	0	0	0	0	x
0	1	0	7	0	9	10	7	10	4	4	4	10	0	1	0	6	1	7	1	0	0	2	4	7	1	2	6	0	1	0	1	xs
0	0	0	0	1	5	5	0	9	10	0	11	10	2	10	0	11	1	6	0	0	0	3	2	3	1	0	6	0	7	1	2	sx
0	3	0	8	1	1	3	0	0	2	0	0	1	14	15	34	6	2	0	0	1	4	7	0	0	3	1	0	11	4	1	0	s

GOALKEEPERS	CS	CCS
Johnson	9	2

x/c/t - Played full 90 minutes
xs/cs/ts - Substituted off
sx/sc/st - Substituted on
s/cn/tn - Non-playing sub

HARTLEPOOL UNITED MATCH RESULTS 2020-21

Date	Comp	H/A	Opponents	Att:	Result	Goalscorers	Pos
Oct 3	NL	H	Aldershot Town		W 2 - 0	Featherstone 36 (pen) Oates 86	6
6	NL	A	Chesterfield		W 2 - 1	Evans 64 (og) Johnson 70 (goalmouth action to the right)	3
10	NL	A	Maidenhead United		W 4 - 0	Orsi-Dadamo 45+1 (og) Ofosu 47 Johnson 51 Holohan 83	1
13	NL	H	Bromley		D 0 - 0		1
24	**FAC4Q**	**A**	**Ilkeston Town**	**400**	**W 6 - 0**	**Molyneux 5 Grey 7 Crawford 22 Enigbokan-Bloomfield 66 Parkhouse 83 Holohan 89**	
27	NL	H	Altrincham		D 1 - 1	Parkhouse 30	4
31	NL	H	Torquay United		L 0 - 5		6
Nov 7	**FAC1P**	**A**	**Salford City**		**L 0 - 2**	**(aet)**	
17	NL	H	Wrexham		L 0 - 1		11
21	NL	A	Yeovil Town		W 3 - 1	Molyneux 2 Holohan 37 Magloire 43	7
24	NL	A	Barnet		D 0 - 0		8
Dec 1	NL	A	Solihull Moors		L 0 - 2		12
5	NL	H	Boreham Wood		L 1 - 2	Bloomfield 45+1	14
8	NL	H	King's Lynn Town		W 2 - 0	Armstrong 22 51	7
12	NL	A	Woking	799	L 0 - 3		11
19	**FAT3P**	**A**	**FC Halifax Town**		**D 3 - 3**	**Williams 27 (pen) Featherstone 74 (pen) Holohan 78 (Lost 2-4 on pens)**	
22	NL	H	Stockport County		W 4 - 0	Oates 7 Johnson 48 Armstrong 50 90+1	5
26	NL	H	FC Halifax Town		W 2 - 1	Johnson 7 Oates 57	3
28	NL	A	Notts County		W 1 - 0	Armstrong 19	2
Jan 9	NL	H	Wealdstone		W 3 - 1	Armstrong 35 Oates 55 Featherstone 59	2
23	NL	A	Weymouth		L 0 - 1	(RC - Molyneux 69)	3
30	NL	H	Sutton United		W 1 - 0	Oates 53	2
Feb 9	NL	H	Solihull Moors		W 2 - 0	Armstrong 11 Ferguson 57	2
16	NL	A	Eastleigh		L 1 - 2	Grey 90+1	5
20	NL	H	Yeovil Town		W 2 - 1	Armstrong 72 Holohan 90	3
23	NL	A	Wrexham		D 0 - 0		3
27	NL	H	Barnet		W 1 - 0	Armstrong 32	3
Mar 2	NL	A	FC Halifax Town		D 1 - 1	Shelton 13	3
6	NL	A	Torquay United		W 1 - 0	Molyneux 14	3
9	NL	A	Altrincham		D 1 - 1	Oates 33 (RC - Cass 24)	2
13	NL	H	Eastleigh		D 0 - 0	(RC 2xY - Odusina 46)	2
16	NL	A	King's Lynn Town		D 2 - 2	Armstrong 37 Oates 64	2
20	NL	H	Woking		W 1 - 0	Oates 80	2
23	NL	A	Dagenham & Redbridge		W 1 - 0	Armstrong 44	2
29	NL	A	Stockport County		D 1 - 1	Holohan 47	2
Apr 2	NL	H	Dagenham & Redbridge		W 2 - 1	Oates 21 Holohan 61	2
5	NL	A	Boreham Wood		D 2 - 2	Holohan 6 Bennett 78	2
10	NL	H	Notts County		W 2 - 0	Holohan 45 Bennett 86	1
17	NL	A	Wealdstone		W 7 - 2	Oates 25 48 Bennett 39 42 81 (pen) Featherstone 63 (pen) Shelton 76	1
May 1	NL	H	Chesterfield		W 3 - 1	Oates 5 Yarney 39 (og) Armstrong 43	3
3	NL	A	Bromley		L 0 - 1	(RC 2xY - Liddle 86)	4
8	NL	H	Maidenhead United		L 2 - 4	Oates 29 Elliott 85	4
15	NL	A	Aldershot Town		W 3 - 1	Armstrong 59 Oates 77 Featherstone 90+1 (pen)	4
23	NL	A	Sutton United		L 0 - 3		4
29	NL	H	Weymouth		W 4 - 0	Johnson 8 Oates 34 Shelton 64 Holohan 78	4
Jun 6	**NL PO QF**	**H**	**Bromley**		**W 3 - 2**	**Oates 17 24 Armstrong 20**	
13	**NL PO SF**	**A**	**Stockport County**		**W 1 - 0**	**Oates 76**	
20	**NL PO F**	**N**	**Torquay United**	**6606**	**D 1 - 1**	**Armstrong 35 (Won 5-4 on pens)**	

Goalcorers	LGE	FAC	FAT	SG	CSG	HAT	PEN	1Q	2Q	45+	3Q	4Q	90+	T
TOTALS	70	6	3	73	29	1	6	17	20	2	19	17	4	79
Oates	18			16	3			4	5		5	4		18
Armstrong	15			13	2			4	6		3	1	1	15
Holohan	8	1	1	10	4			1	1	1	2	4	1	10
Bennett	5			3	3	1	1		2			3		5
Featherstone	4		1	5	1		4		1		2	1	1	5
Johnson	5			5	2			2			2	1		5
Molyneux	2	1		3	1			3						3
Opponent	3			3	2				1	1	1			3
Shelton	3			3	1			1			1	1		3

Goalcorers	LGE	FAC	FAT	SG	CSG	HAT	PEN	1Q	2Q	45+	3Q	4Q	90+	T
Bloomfield	1	1		2	1				1		1			2
Grey	1	1		2	1			1					1	2
Parkhouse	1	1		2	2				1			1		2
Crawford		1		1	1			1						1
Elliott	1			1	1							1		1
Ferguson	1			1	1						1			1
Magloire	1			1	1				1					1
Ofosu	1			1	1						1			1
Williams			1	1	1		1		1					1

No.	Killip B	Ferguson D	Odusina O	Cass L (L)	Featherstone N	Donaldson R	Liddle G	Holohan G	Shelton M	Parkhouse D (L)	Ofosu C	Oates R	Bloomfield M	Ravas H (Gk) (L)	Johnson R	Crawford T	MacDonald J	Grey J	Molyneux L	Williams L	Magloire T (L)	Bunney J	Armstrong L (L)	Sterry J	White T (L)	Southern-Cooper J (L)	Bennett R (L)	Young B (GK)	Elliott D	Francis-Angol Z	Saunders H (L)	James B (Gk) (L)
1	x	x	x	x	x	x	x	x	x	xs	xs	sx	sx	s	s	s																
2	x	x	x	x	x	x	xs	x	x		xs	sx	xs	s	sx	s	s															
3	x	x	x	x	x	xs		x	xs		xs	sx	x	s	x	sx	s	sx														
4	x	x	x	x	x	x		x	xs		xs	xs	sx	s	x	s		sx	sx													
5	cn	c	sc	c	c	cn	c	c	cn	sc	cn		c	c	cs	c	sc	cs	cs													
6	x	x	x	x	x	x		xs	x	xs	sx		sx	s	x	sx		s	xs													
7	x	x	xs	x	x	x		xs	xs	x			sx	s	x	sx		sx	x	s												
8	cn	c		c	c	c		sc	cn	sc	cs	cs	sc	c	c	cs	cs		sc	cn	c											
9		x	s	x	x	xs		x	s	sx	sx	sx	xs	x	x	xs			x		x											
10		x	s	x	x	x		x	sx	sx	s	xs		x	x	x		s	xs		x											
11		x	s	x	x	xs		x	s	sx	sx	xs		x	x	x		s	x		x											
12			x	x	x	x		x	s	s	sx		xs	x	sx	x		sx	xs		x	xs										
13		x		x	x	xs		x	s		sx	sx	x	x	x	xs		sx	xs		x	s										
14	x	x	x	x	x	s		x	x		s	xs	sx		x			xs	sx			sx	xs									
15	x	x	xs	x	x	sx		x	x		sx	xs	xs		x			sx			s	s	x									
16	tn		tn	t	st	t		st		ts		tn	tn	t	t	t	ts	st		t	t	t	t									
17	x	x	x		x	sx		xs	x			xs	s		x	sx		sx			x	s	x	xs								
18	x	xs	x		x	s		x	x			xs	sx		x	s		s			x	sx	x	x								
19	x		x		x	sx		xs				xs	sx		x	x		sx	s	s	x	x	xs	x								
20	x	x	x		x	s		xs	x			xs	sx		x	s			sx	sx	x		xs	x								
21	x	x	xs	x	x			x	xs			xs	sx		x	s		s	sx	sx			x	x								
22	x	x	x	x	x		s	xs	x			xs	sx		x	sx		s		s			x	x								
23	x	x	x	x		sx	sx		x			xs	s		x	x		sx		s			xs	x	xs							
24	x	x	x	xs		sx	s	x	xs			xs	sx		x	s		sx					x	x	x							
25	x	x	s	x		xs	x	x	x			xs	sx		x	sx		sx		s			x		xs							
26	x	x	s	x		s	x	x	x			sx	s		x	sx		xs					x	x	xs							
27	x	x	s	x			x	x	x			xs	s		x	s		s	sx				x	x	x							
28	x	x	x	x	x		x	xs	x			sx	sx			sx		s	xs				x	xs	s							
29	x	x	s	x	x		x	sx	x			xs	sx		x	s		s	xs				x	x								
30	x	x	sx	x	x		x	sx	x			xs	sx		x	x	s		xs				xs			s						
31	x	x	x		x		x	s	xs			sx	sx			s			x	s			xs	x	x	x						
32	x	x			x	s	x	sx	xs			sx			x	s			xs	sx			x	x	x	xs						
33	x	x			x	sx	x	sx	sx			x	s		x				xs	xs			x	x	xs	s						
34	x	x	sx	x	x		x	xs	xs			xs	s		x				sx	s			x	x	sx							
35	x	x	s	x	x	sx	x	x	x		sx				x				x	s			xs	xs	s							
36	x	x	x	x	x	s	x	x	xs			xs							s	sx			xs	x	sx		sx					
37	xs	x	x	x	x	s	x	x	xs			x							sx	s			x	x	s		sx					
38		x	x	x	x	sx	x	x	x					x					s	s			xs	x	s		x	s				
39		x	x	xs	x	sx	x	xs	x			xs		x						sx			s	x			x	s	sx			
40		x	x	xs	x	sx	x	x	x			xs		x									xs	x	s				s	sx	sx	
41		xs	x		x	x	x	x	xs			sx		x					sx				x	x	s				sx	s	xs	
42		x	xs	sx	x	s		xs	xs			x		x	x				x	sx				x					sx	s	x	
43		xs		x	x	sx	x	x	xs			xs			x				s	s			x	x					sx	sx		x
44		s		xs	x	xs	x	x	s			x			x				sx	sx			x	x					s	x		x
45		x		x	x	sx	xs	x	x			xs		s	x	s			sx					xs					x	sx		x
46		**xs**	**x**		**x**	**sx**	**x**	**xs**	**x**			**xs**		**s**	**x**								**x**	**x**					**sx**	**sx**	**s**	**x**
47	**s**	**x**	**x**		**x**	**sx**	**x**	**xs**	**xs**			**x**			**x**				**sx**				**x**	**x**					**s**	**s**		**x**
48	**s**	**xs**	**xs**		**x**	**sx**	**x**	**xs**	**x**			**xs**			**x**				**sx**				**x**	**x**					**sx**	**sx**		**x**
x	28	39	24	32	42	10	24	27	23	1	0	5	3	13	36	8	0	0	6	1	11	2	22	26	4	1	2	0	1	1	1	6
xs	1	5	5	4	0	6	2	13	14	3	5	26	4	0	1	3	2	3	10	1	0	1	10	4	4	1	0	0	0	0	1	0
sx	0	0	3	1	1	15	1	6	2	5	7	10	17	0	2	8	1	12	13	7	0	2	0	0	2	0	2	0	6	5	1	0
s	5	1	9	0	0	9	2	1	7	1	3	1	7	8	1	12	3	9	4	12	1	3	1	0	6	2	0	2	3	3	1	0

Photo Bill Wheatcroft.

GOALKEEPERS	CS	CCS
Killip	14	2
Ravas	3	1
James	2	1

x/c/t - Played full 90 minutes
xs/cs/ts - Substituted off
sx/sc/st - Substituted on
s/cn/tn - Non-playing sub

KING'S LYNN TOWN MATCH RESULTS 2020-21

Date	Comp	H/A	Opponents	Att:	Result	Goalscorers	Pos
Oct 3	NL	H	Yeovil Town		D 2 - 2	Southwell 77 Marriott 87	9
6	NL	A	Maidenhead United		**W** 3 - 2	Power 40 Southwell 82 Jones 90	5
10	NL	A	Solihull Moors		L 0 - 5		11
13	NL	H	Boreham Wood		L 0 - 3		14
17	NL	A	Weymouth		L 1 - 2	Marriott 52	20
27	NL	H	Wealdstone		L 2 - 3	Mitchell 48 70	21
31	NL	H	Woking		**W** 3 - 2	Marriott 27 Loza 82 88	16
Nov 7	**FAC1P**	**A**	**Port Vale**		**W 1 - 0**	**Carey 82**	
14	NL	A	Sutton United		L 1 - 5	Southwell 78	18
17	NL	A	Barnet		**W** 2 - 0	Loza 6 61	14
21	NL	H	Dover Athletic		**W** 2 - 0	McAuley 43 Marriott 86 (pen)	12
28	**FAC2P**	**A**	**Portsmouth**		**L 1 - 6**	**Southwell 68**	
Dec 1	NL	H	Bromley		L 1 - 4	Power 52	14
8	NL	A	Hartlepool United		L 0 - 2		18
12	NL	H	Torquay United	625	D 0 - 0		18
22	**FAT3P**	**A**	**Alfreton Town**		**W 3 - 1**	**Marriott 3 67 Barrows 85**	
Jan 9	NL	H	FC Halifax Town		D 1 - 1	Kiwomya 39	20
16	**FAT4P**	**A**	**Hornchurch**		**D 1 - 1**	**Mitchell 18 (Lost 0-3 on pens) (RC 2xY - McAuley 86)**	
19	NL	A	Eastleigh		**W** 1 - 0	Marriott 40 (pen)	19
23	NL	A	Dagenham & Redbridge		L 2 - 3	Kiwomya 31 Gash 45+3	19
30	NL	H	Wrexham		L 0 - 2		20
Feb 9	NL	A	Bromley		L 0 - 2		21
16	NL	H	Notts County		L 0 - 1		21
23	NL	H	Barnet		**W** 5 - 1	Gash 8 20 King 63 Southwell 87 Marriott 88	20
27	NL	H	Weymouth		D 2 - 2	Denton 29 King 35	20
Mar 2	NL	A	Notts County		D 2 - 2	Carey 1 Mitchell 90+3	20
6	NL	A	Woking		L 0 - 3		21
9	NL	A	Wealdstone		L 1 - 3	Mitchell 81	21
13	NL	H	Sutton United		L 0 - 1		21
16	NL	H	Hartlepool United		D 2 - 2	Mitchell 17 Gyasi 45	21
20	NL	A	Torquay United		L 0 - 1		21
23	NL	A	Altrincham		L 0 - 3		21
29	NL	H	Eastleigh		**W** 2 - 1	Gyasi 50 Jackson 70 (pen)	21
Apr 5	NL	H	Altrincham		**W** 2 - 0	Mitchell 79 86 (pen)	21
10	NL	H	Chesterfield		L 1 - 2	Carey 39	21
13	NL	A	Stockport County		L 0 - 4		21
17	NL	A	FC Halifax Town		L 2 - 4	Gash 13 Carey 25	21
20	NL	A	Aldershot Town		D 1 - 1	Gash 62	21
24	NL	H	Dagenham & Redbridge		L 0 - 3		21
27	NL	H	Stockport County		L 0 - 4		21
May 1	NL	H	Maidenhead United		D 0 - 0		21
3	NL	A	Boreham Wood		L 1 - 5	Gash 4	21
11	NL	A	Chesterfield		L 1 - 4	Carey 31	21
15	NL	A	Yeovil Town		L 1 - 3	Jackson 23 (pen)	21
22	NL	A	Wrexham		L 3 - 5	Carey 21 Jackson 58 69	21
25	NL	H	Solihull Moors		D 1 - 1	Barrows 30	21
29	NL	H	Aldershot Town		D 4 - 4	Gash 43 Jackson 57 (pen) 65 Fleming 90+3	21

Goalcorers	LGE	FAC	FAT	SG	CSG	HAT	PEN	1Q	2Q	45+	3Q	4Q	90+	T
TOTALS	52	2	4			0	6	10	13	3	12	17	3	58
Marriott	6		2	7	1		2	1	2		2	3		8
Mitchell	7		1	6	1		1	2			1	4	1	8
Gash	7			6	2			4	1	1	1			7
Carey	5	1		6	1			2	3			1		6
Jackson	6			4	1		3			1	3	2		6
Southwell	4	1		5	2						1	4		5
Loza	4			2	1			1			1	2		4
Barrows	1		1	2	1				1			1		2
Gyasi	2			2	1					1	1			2
King	2			2	2				1		1			2
Kiwomya	2			2	1				2					2
Power	2			2	1				1		1			2
Denton	1			1	1				1					1
Fleming	1			1	1								1	1
Jones	1			1	1								1	1
McAuley	1			1	1				1					1

[illegible]	McAuley R	Richards J	Jones A	Brown A	King C	Kelly S	Power S (L)	Smith C	Jarvis R	Southwell D	Marriott A	Carey S	Hawkins R	Mair A (Gk) (L)	Barrows R	Clunan M	Loza J	Barker K	Lupano D	Mitchell K	Fleming T	Callan-McFadden K	Gash M	Kiwomya A	Gyasi M	Denton T	Bastock P (Gk)	Hickman J (L)	Jackson S	Payne A	Richardson T (Gk)	Gascoigne J	Levi-Davis J	Baggott E (L)	Howard R (L)	Coleman E (L)	Tsaguim F	Babos A	No.
x	x	x	x	x	xs	xs	xs	x	x	x	sx	sx	sx	s	s																								1
x	x	x	x	x	xs	sx	xs	x	x	x	xs	sx		s	s	sx																							2
s	x	x	x	x	xs	s		x	xs	x	xs	sx		x	x	sx	sx																						3
	x	x	x	x	s	xs	x	x		xs	sx	sx		x	s	xs	x	sx																					4
	x	x	x	x	xs	s	sx	x	xs	xs	xs	sx		x	sx	x		s																					5
		xs		x		sx	sx	x	x	s	xs	xs		x	x	x	sx	s	x	x																			6
	x	x		xs	xs	s	sx	s		sx	x	x		x	x	x	sx		x	xs																			7
	c	c		c	s	s	cs	sc	c	cs	sc	sc		c	c	c	cs		c		s																		8
	x			x	s	sx	sx	s	xs	x	xs	x		x	x	x	xs		x	sx																			9
	x			x	sx	x		x	x	sx	s	sx		x	x	x	xs		xs	xs	s																		10
	x			x	sx	xs	s	x		s	sx	x		x	x	x	xs		s	x		x																	11
	c	cn		c	sc		cs	c	cn	sc	cs	c		c	c	c	cs				cn	c	sc																12
		x		x	xs		x	x	x	sx	s	sx		x	x	x	s			xs	sx	xs																	13
		x		xs			sx	x	s	s	x	xs		x	x	x	sx			sx	x	x	xs																14
		x	x				x	x	x	xs	sx	s		x	x	s	x			sx	s	x	xs																15
		t	tn	t			tn	t	tn	st	ts	t		t	t	t				t	t	t	tn																16
	s	x		x			xs	x	x	xs	sx	sx		x	x	s				sx		x	x	xs															17
	t	tn		t	st	t		tn	t	ts	st	t		t	tn	ts				ts	t	t	st	tn															18
		x	x		xs			x	x	sx	xs	sx		x	x					sx	s	x	x	xs	s														19
		x	x		xs			x	x	s	xs	sx		x	x					sx		x	x	xs	s	sx													20
	s	x	x		x	s		x	xs	sx	xs			x		xs				sx		x	x		sx	x													21
	x	x	x		x	xs		xs		sx	sx	sx		x	s	s						x	x	xs		x													22
	xs	x			x			x	xs	s	sx	x		x	x	s				xs		x	sx	sx		x													23
	xs				x			sx	sx	sx	x	x		x	x	x				s		xs	x	xs	s	x													24
		sx			x			x	s	sx	xs	x		x		x				s	x	x	x	xs	s	x													25
		x			xs			x	xs			x		x	xs	x				x	x		sx	sx	sx	x	s												26
		xs			xs			x	sx			x		x		sx				x	x	x	x	xs	sx	x	s												27
		xs						x				x		x		x				x	xs	x		x	sx	x	s	xs	sx	sx									28
		x						x				x		x		xs				sx	x	x		x	sx	x	s		x	xs									29
		x						x				x				x				x	x	x	s		xs	x	s		sx	x	x	s							30
		xs						x				x				x				x	x	x	sx		xs	x	s		sx	xs	x		sx						31
		xs						xs				x				x					s	x	x		sx	x	s		xs	sx	x		sx	x	x				32
												x				xs					x	x	x	x	xs	x			sx	sx	x	s	sx		x	xs	s		33
					sx							x								x	s	x	sx		xs	x	s			x	x	xs		x	x	x	s		34
					xs							x									x	xs	x	sx	x	x			sx	sx	x	s			x	x	s	xs	35
												x				xs					s	x	x	sx	xs	x	s		sx	sx	x			x	x	x		xs	36
					xs							x				x					s	x	x	sx	sx	x			xs	s	x			x	x	xs		sx	37
					xs							x				x					xs	x	x	sx	sx	x			s	s	x			x	x	x		s	38
					xs							x				x					xs	xs	x	s	sx	x			sx	s	x			x	x	x		sx	39
												x				x					x	x	x	x	x	x			s	s	x	s			x	x	s	s	40
	x											x				xs					s	x	x	xs	xs	x			sx	sx	x	s			x	x		sx	41
	xs											x				x					s	x	x	xs	xs	x			sx	sx	x	s		x	x			sx	42
	x								xs			x				x					x	x	x	xs	s	x	s		sx	sx	x				x			s	43
												x				x					x	x	x	xs	xs	x	s		x	sx	x				x			sx	44
												x			x	x					x	xs	x	sx	xs	x	s		sx	sx	x				x			xs	45
												x			x	x					x		x	sx	xs	x	s		x	s	x	s			x			x	46
												x			x	x					x		xs	sx	x	x			xs	s	x	sx			x		sx	xs	47
2	15	20	10	15	5	2	3	25	11	4	3	31	0	27	20	28	2	0	4	9	17	29	22	4	3	27	0	0	3	2	18	0	0	7	16	7	0	1	x
0	3	5	0	2	14	4	5	2	7	6	11	2	0	0	1	7	5	0	1	5	3	5	3	11	10	0	0	1	3	2	0	1	0	0	0	2	0	4	xs
0	0	1	0	0	5	3	5	2	2	10	9	12	1	0	1	3	4	1	0	8	1	0	6	9	9	1	0	0	11	10	0	1	3	0	0	0	1	5	sx
1	2	2	1	0	3	5	2	3	4	5	2	1	0	2	5	4	1	2	1	2	11	0	2	2	5	0	13	0	2	6	0	7	0	0	0	0	4	3	s

GOALKEEPERS	CS	CCS
Mair	5	2
Richardson	2	1

x/c/t - Played full 90 minutes
xs/cs/ts - Substituted off
sx/sc/st - Substituted on
s/cn/tn - Non-playing sub

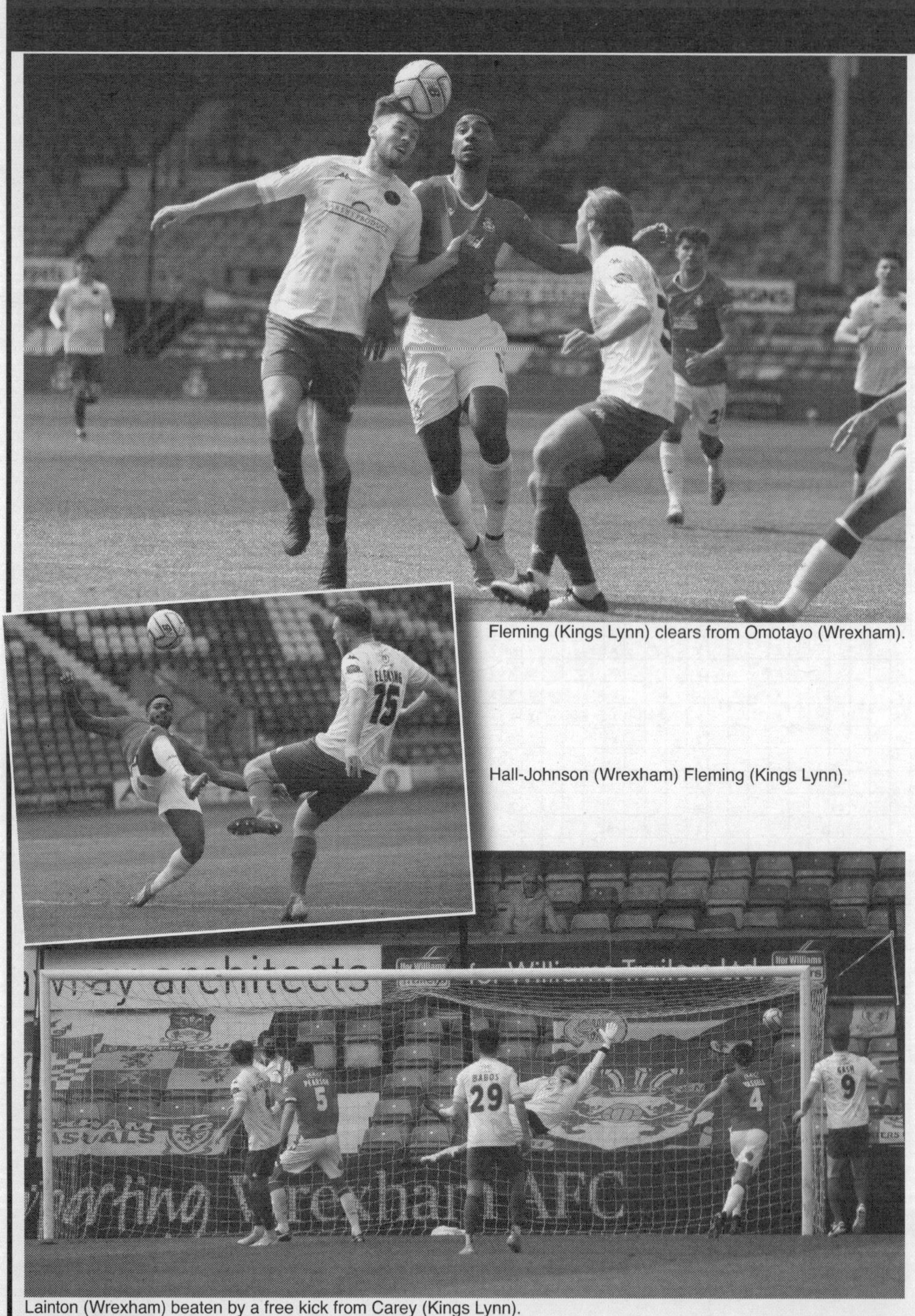

Fleming (Kings Lynn) clears from Omotayo (Wrexham).

Hall-Johnson (Wrexham) Fleming (Kings Lynn).

Lainton (Wrexham) beaten by a free kick from Carey (Kings Lynn).

Wrexham 4 - 1 King's Lynn Town - 22/05/2021

Photos Keith Clayton

Kelleher (Wrexham) sees his header saved by Richardson (Kings Lynn).

Hall-Johnson (Wrexham) heads back into the Kings Lynn box.

MAIDENHEAD UNITED MATCH RESULTS 2020-21

Date	Comp	H/A	Opponents	Att:	Result	Goalscorers	Pos
Oct 3	NL	A	Sutton United		L 0 - 3		23
6	NL	H	King's Lynn Town		L 2 - 3	Barratt 8 55 (pens)	23
10	NL	H	Hartlepool United		L 0 - 4		23
12	NL	A	Wrexham		**W** 1 - 0	Coley 32	19
17	NL	A	Notts County		**W** 3 - 2	Barratt 14 64 Orsi-Dadamo 75	12
24	**FAC4Q**	**H**	**Cray Valley PM**		**L 2 - 3**	**Parry 19 Sparkes 28**	
27	NL	H	Dagenham & Redbridge		**W** 2 - 1	Blissett 56 Coley 76	9
31	NL	H	Solihull Moors		**W** 3 - 1	Barratt 56 83 (pen) 90+3 (pen)	4
Nov 14	NL	A	Chesterfield		**W** 2 - 1	Barratt 55 72	4
17	NL	A	Aldershot Town		D 0 - 0		4
21	NL	H	Bormley		D 2 - 2	Orsi-Dadamo 31 Donnellan 46	5
28	NL	A	Altrincham		L 0 - 2		6
Dec 5	NL	A	Eastleigh	776	**W** 1 - 0	Addai 47	4
8	NL	A	Torquay United	980	L 1 - 2	Donnellan 82	4
19	**FAT3P**	**A**	**Weymouth**	**306**	**L 2 - 3**	**Orsi-Dadamo 42 45+1**	
26	NL	H	Wealdstone		**W** 4 - 0	Upward 5 Coley 38 Blissett 53 Orsi-Dadamo 49 (pen)	6
Jan 23	NL	A	Woking		D 0 - 0		10
27	NL	H	Yeovil Town		**W** 4 - 2	Orsi-Dadamo 31 89 (pen) Parry 49 Sparkes 70	8
30	NL	A	FC Halifax Town		**W** 3 - 2	Orsi-Dadamo 24 45+1 Coley 86	6
Feb 6	NL	H	Boreham Wood		L 0 - 1		8
16	NL	H	Stockport County		D 0 - 0		9
20	NL	A	Bromley		D 2 - 2	Upward 49 Wiltshire 90	10
23	NL	H	Aldershot Town		L 2 - 4	Orsi-Dadamo 43 50	11
Mar 6	NL	A	Solihull Moors		D 1 - 1	Blissett 29	15
9	NL	A	Dagenham & Redbridge		L 1 - 2	Clerima 76	15
13	NL	H	Chesterfield		**W** 2 - 0	Blissett 21 Sparkes 52	15
16	NL	H	Torquay United		**W** 4 - 1	Coley 6 Blissett 43 50 Orsi-Dadomo 54	10
29	NL	H	Altrincham		L 0 - 1		13
Apr 2	NL	A	Weymouth		L 1 - 2	Barratt 49 (RC - Parry 57)	13
5	NL	H	Eastleigh		L 0 - 1	(RC - Coley 67)	14
10	NL	H	Barnet		D 0 - 0		14
17	NL	A	Stockport County		D 2 - 2	Parry 26 Orsi-Dadomo 74	16
20	NL	A	Wealdstone		**W** 6 - 0	Barratt 34 Orsi-Dadomo 64 69 73 Sparkes 81 85	13
24	NL	H	Woking		**W** 2 - 1	Orsi-Dadomo 16 25	12
27	NL	H	Weymouth		L 0 - 1	(RC - Ofori-Twumasi 79)	12
May 1	NL	A	King's Lynn Town		D 0 - 0		12
3	NL	H	Wrexham		D 2 - 2	Barratt 15 Comley 32	12
8	NL	A	Hartlepool United		**W** 4 - 2	Orsi-Dadamo 15 Barratt 38 47 55 (RC - Sheckleford 43)	12
11	NL	H	Notts County		L 0 - 4		13
15	NL	H	Sutton United		L 0 - 3		14
18	NL	A	Yeovil Town	1497	D 0 - 0		14
22	NL	H	FC Halifax Town		L 1 - 2	Orsi-Dadamo 63 (RC 2xY - Upward 38)	14
25	NL	A	Barnet		L 0 - 2		14
29	NL	A	Boreham Wood		**W** 4 - 1	Smith 11 Kelly 45+3 Orsi-Dadomo 54 Lovett 90+3	13

Goalcorers	LGE	FAC	FAT	SG	CSG	HAT	PEN	1Q	2Q	45+	3Q	4Q	90+	T
TOTALS	**62**	**2**	**2**			**2**	**6**	**10**	**15**	**3**	**21**	**14**	**3**	**66**
Orsi-Dadamo	19		2	14	3	1	2	2	6	2	6	5		21
Barratt	15			8	2	1	4	3	2		7	2	1	15
Blissett	6			5	2			1	2		3			6
Coley	5			5	1			1	2			2		5
Sparkes	4	1		4	1				1		1	3		5
Parry	2	1		3	1			1	1		1			3
Donnellan	2			2	1						1	1		2
Upward	2			2	1			1			1			2
Addai	1			1	1						1			1
Clerima	1			1	1							1		1
Comley	1			1	1				1					1
Kelly	1			1	1					1				1
Lovett (Gk)	1			1	1								1	1
Smith	1			1	1			1						1
Wiltshire	1			1	1								1	1

Ashby-Hammond T (L)	Massey A	Parry I	Donnellan S	Sheckleford R	Comley J	Wells G	Upward R	Coley J	Barratt S	Orsi-Dadamo D	Sparkes D	Smile J	Keetch B	Smith R	Ofori-Twumasi S	Blissett N	Wiltshire J	Clerima R	Kelly J	Oluwayemi J (Gk) (L)	Ince R	Addai A (L)	Forster R (Gk) (L)	Egan A (L)	Lovett R (Gk)	Holden J (Gk) (L)	No.
x	x	x	x	x	x	x	xs	x	xs	x	sx	sx	s	s	s												1
x	x	x	x	xs	xs	x	x	sx	xs	s	x	sx			sx	x	s										2
x	x	s	x		s	x	xs	sx	sx	x	x	x			sx	xs	x	xs									3
x	x	x	xs		x	x	x	xs	x	sx	sx	s			sx	xs	s	x									4
x	x	x		s	x	x	x	xs	xs	xs	x	sx			sx			x	sx	s							5
c	c	c	c	c	cn	c	c	cs	c	cs	c	sc	cn		cn	sc			scs	cn							6
x	x	x	x	x	x	x	x	xs	sx	sx	xs	s			s	x				s							7
x	x	x	x		x	x	x	xs	x	sx	xs	sx	s	s		x				s							8
x	x	x	x			xs	x	xs	x	sx	xs	s			sx	x	sx			s	x						9
x	x	x	x	x			x	sx	xs	sx	xs	sx			x	x	s			s	xs						10
x	x	x	x	x			x	xs	x	xs		sx	s		x		s			s	x	sx					11
xs	x	x	x	x			xs	x	x	xs		s			x	sx		s		sx	x	sx					12
x	x	x	sx			x	x	x	xs	sx		s			sx	x		xs		s	x	xs					13
x		x	x	x		x	xs		x	sx		sx	s		s	xs	x			s	x	xs					14
	t	t	t	t		t		ts	ts	t		st	tn		tn	t	tn			t	t	st					15
x	x	x	xs	x	sx	x	x	xs		xs		sx	sx		s	x				s		x					16
x		x		x	s	x	x	sx	xs	xs	x	sx	s		s	x	x				x						17
x	x	x		x	xs	x	xs	sx	x	x	xs	s			sx		sx		s		x						18
x	x	x		x	xs	x	x	sx	x	xs	xs	s			sx		s		sx		x						19
x	x	x		x	x	x		x		x	x	xs	s		s	sx	s		sx		x						20
x	x	x		x	x	x	x	sx		xs	xs		s		s	x	s		sx		x						21
x	x	x		x	xs	x	x	sx		xs	x		s		s	xs	sx		sx		x						22
x	x	x		xs	xs	x	xs	x		x			sx	s	sx	x	s		sx		x						23
x	x	x			x	x	xs	sx		xs	x		s	s	sx	x		x	s		x						24
x	x			x	x	x	x	xs		xs	s		sx	sx		x		x	s		x		s				25
x	x	x		s	xs	x	x	xs	sx	sx	x				sx	x		x	s		x						26
x	x	x		x	xs		x	xs	sx	xs			sx	s	x	x	s		sx		x						27
x	x	x		s		x	x	x	sx	x			s		xs	x		x	sx					xs	s		28
x	x	x		x	xs	x	x	sx	xs	xs	s				sx	x		x						sx	s		29
x	x	x		x		x	x	x	xs	sx	xs				sx	x	s	x						s	s		30
x	x	x		sx		x	x		x	x	xs				s	x	s	xs	sx		x			s			31
x	x	x		s	xs	x	x		x	xs	xs				s		sx	x	sx		x			sx			32
x	x	x		s	x	xs	x		xs	xs	x				sx		s	x	sx		x			sx			33
x	x	x		sx	xs		x		x	xs	xs			s	x		s	x	sx		x			sx			34
x	x	xs		sx	x		x	xs		x	x			s	x		sx	xs	sx		x			s			35
	x	x		x	s		x	sx	x	xs	x	s	s				sx		xs		x			x	x		36
	x	x		x	x		x	xs	x	xs	x		s	s			x		sx		sx			s	x		37
	x	x		x	x	x		sx	xs	xs	xs		s	s			x		sx		x			sx	x		38
	x	x			x	x		x		x	xs		s	sx	x		xs		sx		x			sx	xs		39
	x	x			xs	x	x	xs		x	xs		sx	sx	x		s				x			sx		x	40
	x	x			xs	x	x	xs		xs	sx		sx	xs	x		s				x			sx		x	41
	x	x		x		x	x	xs	xs	x	x		sx	s	s		sx				x					x	42
	x	s		x	x	x		xs		x	x		xs	sx	s		x		sx		x					x	43
	x	x		xs		x	x	x			sx		s	x	sx		xs		xs						sx	x	44
33	42	40	12	24	15	34	32	9	14	13	15	1	0	1	9	19	6	11	0	1	29	1	0	1	3	5	x
1	0	1	2	3	12	2	7	18	12	20	14	1	1	1	1	4	2	4	2	0	1	2	0	1	1	0	xs
0	0	0	1	3	1	0	0	12	5	9	4	11	7	4	15	3	7	0	18	1	1	3	0	8	1	0	sx
0	0	2	0	5	4	0	0	0	0	1	2	8	17	10	14	0	16	1	4	10	0	0	1	4	3	0	s

GOALKEEPERS	CS	CCS
Ashby-Hammond T	9	2
Lovett	1	1
Holden	1	1

x/c/t - Played full 90 minutes
xs/cs/ts - Substituted off
sx/sc/st - Substituted on
s/cn/tn - Non-playing sub

Chesterfield 1 - 2 Maidenhead United - 14/11/2020

Photos Bill Wheatcroft

NOTTS COUNTY MATCH RESULTS 2020-21

Date	Comp	H/A	Opponents	Att:	Result		Goalscorers	Pos
Sept 22	**FAT SF 19/20**	**H**	**Harrogate Town (Lge 2)**		**L**	**0 - 1**		
Oct 3	NL	A	Dover Athletic		L	0 - 1		18
7	NL	H	Altrincham		**W**	3 - 1	Wootton 15 26 Reeves 64	8
10	NL	H	Barnet		**W**	4 - 2	Roberts 14 Wootton 17 Boldewijn 23 Doyle 90+2	5
13	NL	A	Sutton United		**W**	1 - 0	Wootton 90+4	3
17	NL	H	Maidenhead United		L	2 - 3	Knowles 3 Rodrigues 29	7
Nov 7	NL	A	Aldershot Town		L	0 - 1		10
17	NL	A	FC Halifax Town		D	1 - 1	Sam 7	12
21	NL	A	Chesterfield		**W**	3 - 2	Turner 22 Rodrigues 90+1 Wootton 90+3	10
27	NL	H	Wealdstone		**W**	3 - 0	Boldewijn 15 Sam 19 Knowles 89	7
Dec 2	NL	A	Dagenham & Redbridge		D	0 - 0		6
5	NL	H	Woking		**W**	1 - 0	Wootton 80	3
8	NL	H	Boreham Wood		L	0 - 1		3
15	NL	H	Stockport County		**W**	1 - 0	Reeves 35	3
19	**FAT3P**	**A**	**Morpeth Town**		**W**	**3 - 0**	**Sam 5 Graham 58 Knowles 64**	
28	NL	H	Hartlepool United		L	0 - 1	(RC - Turner 82)	
Jan 16	**FAT4P**	**A**	**Stockport County**		**W**	**2 - 1**	**Knowles 32 Wootton 89**	
23	NL	H	Torquay United		D	0 - 0		8
27	NL	H	Solihull Moors		**W**	2 - 0	Wootton 79 87	7
30	NL	A	Weymouth		**W**	1 - 0	Sam 51	5
Feb 6	**FAT5P**	**A**	**Havant & Waterlooville**		**D**	**2 - 2**	**Wolfe 14 Knowles 72 (pen) (Won 4-2 on pens) (RC 2xY - Palmer 86)**	
9	NL	H	Dagenham & Redbridge		**W**	3 - 1	Wootton 10 45+2 Rodrigues 34 (RC - Slocombe 18)	5
16	NL	A	King's Lynn Town		**W**	1 - 0	Reeves 54	3
20	NL	H	Chesterfield		L	0 - 1		5
23	NL	A	Stockport County		D	0 - 0		5
27	**FATQF**	**H**	**Oxford City**		**W**	**3 - 1**	**Sam 49 73 Knowles 90+4**	
Mar 2	NL	H	King's Lynn Town		D	2 - 2	Wootton 38 43	6
9	NL	H	FC Halifax Town		L	1 - 2	Boldewijn 75	6
13	NL	A	Wealdstone		**W**	1 - 0	Ellis 63	6
16	NL	A	Boreham Wood		D	2 - 2	Doyle 75 Effiong 88 (pen)	7
20	NL	H	Yeovil Town		**W**	2 - 0	Reeves 41 Barnett 78	6
23	NL	A	Yeovil Town		D	2 - 2	Boldewijn 79 Rodrigues 86	6
Neil Ardley is sacked as manager - former Viking and Ostersun manager, Ian Burchnall, is named as his replacement.								
29	**FAT SF**	**H**	**Hornchurch**		**D**	**3 - 3**	**Wootton 10 Rodrigues 42 Sam 78 (Lost 4-5 on pens)**	
30	NL	H	Aldershot Town		L	0 - 1		6
Apr 2	NL	H	Wrexham		**W**	1 - 0	Ellis 79	5
5	NL	A	Woking		**W**	4 - 2	Ellis 20 Knowles 60 66 79	5
10	NL	A	Hartlepool United		L	0 - 2		5
13	NL	A	Solihull Moors		L	1 - 2	Knowles 11	6
17	NL	H	Eastleigh		L	0 - 1		8
24	NL	A	Torquay United		D	2 - 2	Kelly-Evans 38 Ellis 49	9
27	NL	A	Eastleigh		L	0 - 2		10
May 1	NL	A	Altrincham		D	1 - 1	Rodrigues 45+2	10
4	NL	H	Sutton United		**W**	3 - 2	Rodrigues 8 90+3 (pen) Wootton 48 (RC 2xY - Kelly-Evans 67)	8
8	NL	A	Barnet		**W**	4 - 1	Ellis 45+2 Rodrigues 47 Richards-Everton 55 (og) Boldewijn 85	7
11	NL	A	Maidenhead United		**W**	4 - 0	O'Brien 10 65 76 (pen) Rodrigues 83	5
15	NL	H	Bromley		D	2 - 2	Wootton 53 Rodrigues 62	6
18	NL	A	Wrexham		**W**	1 - 0	Reeves 27	5
22	NL	H	Weymouth	4000	**W**	3 - 0	Rodrigues 24 (pen) Wootton 28 Boldewijn 64	5
29	NL	A	Bromley		L	0 - 1		5
Jun 5	**NL PO QF**	**H**	**Chesterfield**	**4000**	**W**	**3 - 2**	**Wootton 30 71 Ellis 90**	
12	**NL PO SF**	**A**	**Torquay United**	**1709**	**L**	**2 - 4**	**Rodrigues 39 Chicken 51**	

Goalcorers	LGE	FAC	FAT	SG	CSG	HAT	PEN	1Q	2Q	45+	3Q	4Q	90+	T
TOTALS	**67**	**0**	**13**			**2**	**5**	**15**	**17**	**3**	**18**	**20**	**7**	**80**
Wootton	17		2	14	3			4	5	1	2	5	2	19
Rodrigues	12		1	12	5		2	1	5	1	2	2	2	13
Knowles	6		4	8	1	1	1	2	1		3	3	1	10
Sam	3		4	6	1			3			2	2		7
Boldewijn	6			6	1			1	1		1	3		6
Ellis	6			6	2				1	1	2	1	1	6
Reeves	5			5	1				3		2			5
O'Brien	3			1	1	1	1	1			1	1		3
Doyle	2			2	1							1	1	2
Barnett	1			1	1							1		1
Chicksen	1			1	1						1			1
Effiong	1			1	1		1					1		1
Graham			1	1	1						1			1
Kelly-Evans	1			1	1				1					1
Opponent	1			1	1						1			1
Roberts	1			1	1			1						1
Turner	1			1	1			1						1
Wolfe			1	1	1			1						1

Chicksen A	Rawlinson C	Brindley R	Graham S (L)	Doyle M	Reeves J	Thomas W	Wootton K	Roberts C	Rodrigues R	Boldewijn E	Sam E	Kelly-Evans D	Lacey A	McCrory D	Pilling L (Gk)	O'Brien J	Knowles J (L)	Wolfe M (L)	Turner B	Walker T (L)	Keen J (Gk)	Miller C (L)	Effiong I (L)	Barnett J (L)	Palmer T	Brooks T (Gk)	Golden T (L)	Richardson K (L)	Ellis M (L)	Griffiths R (L)	Knight L	Steele L (Gk)	No.
t	t	t	t	t	t	ts	t	ts	ts	st	st	st	tn	tn	tn																		1
x	x	x	s	x	x	xs	x	x	s	sx		s	x			xs	sx																2
	x	x	s	x	x	xs	xs	xs	sx	sx	sx	x	x			x	s																3
	x	sx	x	x	x	sx	x	xs	xs	xs	s	x	s	x		sx																	4
	x	x	s	x	x		x	sx	xs	xs		x	x	s	s	x	sx																5
x	x		s	x	x		x		xs	xs	sx		xs	x	s		x	sx	sx														6
x		x	xs	x	x	xs	x		xs	sx	sx	s	x			x	s		sx														7
	x	x		x	x		x	sx	s	x	xs	x	xs			x	s	s	sx														8
s	x	x	s	x	x		x	x	sx	xs	sx	x				xs	s		x														9
s	x	x		x	x		x		xs	x	xs	x			s	sx	sx	s	x														10
x	x			x	x		x		xs	xs	xs	x			s	sx	sx	s	x	sx													11
s	x	x		x	x		x		xs	sx	xs	x			s	sx	sx		x	xs													12
	x	x		x	x		x		sx	x	sx	x	s		s	xs	s		x	xs													13
s	x	x		x	x		x		xs	x	s	x	s			x	s		x	sx													14
t	tn	ts	t	tn			tn		ts	st	t	st	t		t	t	t	t		t	tn												15
s	x	x		x	x		x		xs	x	sx	x	s			s	sx		x	xs													16
tn	st	t	t	st	ts		st		t	ts	t	tn	ts		t	tn	t	t				t											17
	x	xs		x	x		x		x	xs	sx	x	x			sx	s	s				sx	xs										18
s	x			x	x		x		sx	x	s	x	x			xs	sx	s				x	xs										19
	x			x	x		x		xs	x	xs	x	x			sx	s	s	s			x	sx										20
	ts		t			tn				st	st	ts	tn	t		t	t	t	t	t			ts		t	st	tn						21
	x	s		x	x		x		x	x	s	x	x			s	xs		s				sx	x									22
	x			x	x		x		xs	xs	s	x	x		x	s	xs		sx			sx	sx	x									23
	x			x	x		x		x	x	xs	x	x		x	s	sx	s	s			xs	sx										24
	x			x			x	sx	xs	x	s	x	x		x	x	sx	x	s			s		xs									25
t	t			st			st			tn	t	st	t		tn	t	t	ts				t		tn	ts		ts						26
	x			x	x		x		xs	xs	s	x	x			sx	xs	sx				s	sx	x									27
	x			x	x		x		x	x	sx	s	x			s	xs					s		x				x	s				28
	x			x			x		s	x	sx	x	x			x	s		s			x	xs	s					x				29
	xs			x	x		x		xs	x	xs	s	x			sx	sx		s			x	sx						x				30
	x			x	x		x		s	x	s	s	xs			x	sx		sx				xs	x					x				31
s	x			x	x		x		sx	x	s	sx				xs	sx		xs				xs	x					x				32
tn	t			t	t		t		ts	ts	st	t			tn	st	st		tn			ts		t			tn		t				33
s	s				x		x		sx	xs	xs	x				x	sx		x			xs	sx	x					x				34
x	x				x		x	sx	s	x		s				xs						s		x					x	x	sx		35
x	x				x				sx	xs	xs	sx				x	x					s		x			s		x	xs	sx		36
x	x				x		x	sx	s	xs		sx	s			x	x							xs					x	xs	sx		37
x	x				x		x		sx	sx	sx	x	x			s	xs							s					xs	x	xs		38
x	x			s	x		x			sx		x	x			sx	x		xs			sx							s	xs	xs		39
x	x			x	x		x			s		x	xs		s	xs	xs					sx							x	sx	sx	x	40
x	x	s		x	x		x		sx	sx		x					sx		x					s					xs	xs	xs	x	41
s	x	x		x	x		x		xs	x		s					sx		x					x					x	s	s	x	42
x	x	sx		x	x		x		xs	s	sx	x					xs		sx			xs							x	s			43
x	x	x		xs	x		xs		xs	sx	x					sx	s		s			x							x	sx			44
x	x	sx		xs	x		x		xs	s	sx	x				x			s			xs							x	sx			45
x		x		x	x		x		x	sx	sx	xs		s		xs			s			x							x	s			46
x		x		x	x		x		xs	s	sx	x		sx		x			s			xs							x	s			47
x	s	x		x	xs		x		xs	sx	sx	xs				x			s			x							x	sx			48
x	x	x		x	xs		x		xs	sx	sx	s				x			s			xs							x	sx			49
x	xs	x		x	xs		x		x	x		sx					sx		s			x		s					x	s			50
xs	sx	x		x	xs		x		x	xs		x					sx		s			xs		sx					x	sx			51
22	40	22	4	39	41	0	44	2	8	18	4	30	20	2	6	18	8	4	11	1	0	10	0	12	0	0	0	1	20	2	0	3	x
2	2	2	1	2	5	4	2	3	24	14	10	2	5	0	0	8	7	1	2	3	0	9	5	2	1	0	1	0	2	4	3	0	xs
0	2	3	0	2	0	1	2	5	10	14	18	7	0	1	0	11	18	2	6	2	0	4	7	1	1	0	0	0	0	6	4	0	sx
11	3	2	5	2	1	0	1	0	6	5	9	10	6	3	10	7	10	7	15	0	1	5	0	5	0	1	2	0	2	5	1	0	s

GOALKEEPERS	CS	CCS
Slocombe	14	3
Pilling	3	1

x/c/t - Played full 90 minutes
xs/cs/ts - Substituted off
sx/sc/st - Substituted on
s/cn/tn - Non-playing sub

Chesterfield celebrate Gavin Gunning's free kick goal.

Notts County 0 - 1 Chesterfield - 20/02/2021

Photos Bill Wheatcroft

George Carline stretches and nicks the ball off Rodrigues.

SOLIHULL MOORS MATCH RESULTS 2020-21

Date	Comp	H/A	Opponents	Att:	Result	Goalscorers	Pos
Oct 3	NL	A	Woking		L 1 - 2	Ward 18 (pen)	18
6	NL	H	Wrexham		**W** 1 - 0	Ball 56	9
10	NL	H	King's Lynn Town		**W** 5 - 0	Sbarra 39 Archer 47 71 Osborne 64 Howe 81	4
17	NL	H	Boreham Wood		**W** 1 - 0	Rooney 75	5
24	**FAC4Q**	**H**	**Wrexham**		**W 4 - 0**	**Sbarra 39 76 Rooney 59 (pen) Archer 62**	
27	NL	A	Stockport County		D 0 - 0		5
31	NL	A	Maidenhead United		L 1 - 3	Gleeson 50 (pen)	7
Nov 8	**FAC1P**	**A**	**Scunthorpe United**		**W 3 - 2**	**Gleeson 4 80 (pens) Pearce 51**	
11	NL	A	Altrincham		**W** 2 - 0	Sbarra 18 Osborne 22	
28	**FAC2P**	**A**	**Morecambe**		**L 2 - 4**	**Hudlin 19 Cranston 69**	
Dec 1	NL	H	Hartlepool United		**W** 2 - 0	Pearce 63 Ball 82	10
5	NL	A	Sutton United	934	L 1 - 4	Ball 47	12
12	NL	H	Bromley		L 0 - 1		16
15	NL	H	FC Halifax Town		**W** 2 - 1	Ball 24 Hudlin 56	11
19	**FAT3P**	**H**	**Farsley Celtic**		**W 4 - 0**	**Hudlin 33 Pearce 67 Archer 73 Hancox 80**	
Jan 2	NL	A	Chesterfield		L 0 - 1		17
5	NL	H	Chesterfield		**W** 2 - 1	Sbarra 61 Hudlin 90+3	10
19	**FAT4P**	**A**	**Aldershot Town**		**L 2 - 3**	**Hudlin 53 Ball 63**	
23	NL	A	Dover Athletic		**W** 2 - 0	Cameron 31 Hudlin 52	7
27	NL	A	Notts County		L 0 - 2		9
Feb 6	NL	A	Eastleigh		D 1 - 1	Sbarra 90+3	14
9	NL	A	Hartlepool United		L 0 - 2		14
16	NL	A	Aldershot Town		**W** 3 - 1	Ward 17 Gudger 45+1 Rooney 62	12
20	NL	A	Weymouth		D 0 - 0		14
23	NL	H	Torquay United		L 1 - 2	Gudger 90+9	15
27	NL	A	Boreham Wood		D 2 - 2	Gudger 2 Rooney 60 (pen) (RC - Hancox 89)	14
Mar 2	NL	H	Dagenham & Redbridge		L 0 - 1		16
6	NL	H	Maidenhead United		D 1 - 1	Ward 83	16
9	NL	H	Stockport County		L 0 - 5	(RC - Williams 17)	17
Jimmy Shan steps down as manager. Mark Yates returns to the club until the end of the season.							
13	NL	A	FC Halifax Town		L 0 - 1		17
20	NL	A	Bromley		L 0 - 1		17
23	NL	A	Torquay United		L 0 - 2		18
27	NL	H	Aldershot Town		**W** 1 - 0	Archer 31 (RC 2xY - Hancox 76, RC - Ball 87)	17
30	NL	H	Wealdstone		**W** 3 - 0	Barnett 29 McNally 47 Sbarra 59	17
Apr 2	NL	A	Barnet		**W** 2 - 0	Williams 44 Hudlin 77	15
5	NL	H	Sutton United		D 0 - 0		15
13	NL	H	Notts County		**W** 2 - 1	Ball 65 Hudlin 79	13
17	NL	A	Dagenham & Redbridge		L 2 - 3	Cranstan 11 Rooney 90+5 (RC - Williams 76)	14
24	NL	H	Yeovil Town		**W** 5 - 1	Donawa 26 58 90+1 Hudlin 62 Ball 83	15
27	NL	A	Yeovil Town		L 0 - 3		15
May 1	NL	A	Wrexham		L 1 - 2	Rooney 80 (pen)	16
3	NL	H	Altrincham		**W** 4 - 0	Thompson 38 Zouma 57 (og) Hudlin 66 Archer 89	14
11	NL	H	Weymouth		**W** 2 - 1	Hudlin 31 Rooney 63	14
15	NL	H	Woking		**W** 2 - 1	Rooney 5 Hudlin 83	12
19	NL	H	Barnet		**W** 1 - 0	Ball 50	12
22	NL	A	Wealdstone		**W** 4 - 1	Williams 21 Addai 31 Ball 58 Donawa 80	11
25	NL	A	King's Lynn Town		D 1 - 1	Rooney 54	11
29	NL	H	Eastleigh		**W** 2 - 0	Ball 29 Sbarra 45+2	11

Goalcorers	LGE	FAC	FAT	SG	CSG	HAT	PEN	1Q	2Q	45+	3Q	4Q	90+	T
TOTALS	60	9	6			1	7	8	14	2	27	16	5	75
Hudlin	9	1	2	12	3			1	2		5	3	1	12
Ball	9		1	10	2				2		6	2		10
Rooney	8	1		9	2		3	1			4	2	1	9
Sbarra	6	2		7	1			1	2	1	2	1	1	8
Archer	4	1	1	5	1				1		2	3		6
Donawa	4			2	1	1			1		1	1	1	4
Gleeson	1	2		2	2		3				1			3
Gudger	3			3	2			1		1			1	3
Pearce	1	1	1	3	1						3			3
Ward	3			3	1		1	2				1		3
Cranston	1	1		2	1				1			1		2
Osborne	2			2	1			1			1			2
Williams	2			2	1			1	1					2
Addai	1			1	1				1					1
Barnett	1			1	1				1					1
Cameron	1			1	1				1					1
Hancox			1	1	1							1		1
Howe	1			1	1							1		1
McNally	1			1	1						1			1
Opponent	1			1	1						1			1
Thompson	1			1	1				1					1

Gudger A	Cranston J	Howe C	Williams T	Ball J	Coxe C	Gleeson S	Storer K	Sbarra J	Ward J	Archer C (L)	Maycock C	Piggott J	Hancox M	Clayton N (Gk)	Carter D	Osborne J	Usher-Shipway B	Rooney A	Shergill J	Miccio L	Hudlin K	Pearce K	Donawa J	McNally R	Clayton-Phillips N (L)	Cameron N	Howkins K (L)	Barnett R (L)	Addai A (L)	Thompson J (L)	No.
x	x	x	x	x	x	x	x	x	xs	sx	s	s	s	s																	1
xs	x	x	x	xs		x	x	xs		x	sx	s	sx	s	x	sx															2
	xs	x	x	xs		x	s	x		xs	x	sx	x	s	x	sx	sx														3
	x	x	x	xs	x	xs	x	xs		sx	sx		sx	s	x	s		x	s												4
	c	cs	c	sc	c		c	c	cn	sc	c	sc	c	cn		cs		cs	cn	cn											5
	x		x	xs	x		x	x		x	x	s	x	s	x	sx				s	s										6
	x		x		x	x	x	sx			x	s	s	s	x	xs					xs	x	sx								7
	cs		c		c	c	c	c	sc		cs	cn	c	cn	sc	sc			cn		cs	c		cn							8
			x			x	x	xs	sx		sx	x	x	s	x	xs					xs	x	sx	s							9
	c		c	sc	c	cs	c	cs	sc	sc	sc	cn	c	cn	cn	cs					cs	c									10
x	x		x	x	xs	x	x		sx	xs	sx		s	s		xs					sx	x									11
	x		x	x		x	sx		x	xs	xs	s	x	s							sx	x	xs		sx						12
	x		x		x	x	x	xs	sx	sx	sx		s	s	xs	x		xs				x									13
	x		x	x	x	x	x	sx	s	s	s		x	s		xs					x	x									14
	ts		t	t	tn	t		ts	t	st	t	t	t	tn		tn	tn				ts	st	st								15
xs	xs		x		sx	x	s	x	x	xs	x	x	sx	s		x					sx										16
	x		x		x	s	x	xs	sx		x	s	s	s	x						x		x			x					17
t	t		t	t	ts	t	ts	ts	st		st	tn	st	tn	tn	tn					t					t					18
	x		x	x	x	sx	xs	sx	xs		x		s	s				sx			xs					x	x				19
	x		x	x	xs	s	x	sx	xs		x		sx	s				sx			xs					x	x				20
xs	x		x			x	xs	sx	xs		x		s	s				sx			x		sx			x	x				21
xs	x		x		xs	sx	x	xs	x		x			s				x			sx		s			x	sx				22
xs	x		x		x	x	xs	sx	xs		x	sx		s				x			sx		s				x				23
s	x		x		xs	x	x	sx			x	s		s				x			xs		sx			x	x				24
x	x				xs	xs	x	x			x	s		s			sx	x			sx		sx			xs	x				25
x			x	xs	sx	x		sx			x	s	x	s			x	x			sx		xs			xs					26
	x		x	xs	sx		x	xs		sx	x	x		s	x		xs	x			sx			s							27
	x		x	x		x	xs		sx	sx	xs	x		s	x		xs	x			sx			s							28
	x		x	x	x	x	x		xs		sx	x		s	sx		sx	xs			xs					s					29
	x			xs	xs	s	x		x	sx	xs	s	x				sx				sx			x		x					30
	x		x	x	x		x	s	x	s	s	s	xs					x					sx	x				x			31
	x		x	sx	x		xs	xs	x		sx	s	s					sx			xs		x	x				x			32
	sx		x	x			x		s	xs	x	s	x				x	xs			sx		sx	x				xs			33
	x		x		sx		x	x	s	xs	x	s					x	xs			sx		sx	x				xs			34
	x		x		s		x	x	sx	xs	x	sx		s			xs				x		sx	x				xs			35
	x		x		s		x	x	x	xs	x	sx	s	s			x				x		sx	xs							36
	x		x	sx	s		x	xs		xs	x	x	s				x	sx			x		sx						xs		37
	x		x	x	s		x	xs		sx	xs	x	sx				x	sx			x		s						xs		38
	x			xs	s		x	xs		sx	x	x	sx					sx			xs		x	x						s	39
	x			x			xs	xs		s	x	x	sx				x	sx			xs		x	x					sx	s	40
	x			xs	xs	xs	x	sx			sx	s	s					x			sx		x			x			x	x	41
	xs			x		s	x	xs		sx	x	x	sx				xs	sx			x		x						s	x	42
	x		x	x		s	x			sx	x	x	s					sx			xs		x			s			xs	x	43
	x		x	x			x	s		sx	x	x	s					xs			sx		x			s			xs	x	44
	x		x	x			x	xs		sx	x	s	s					sx			xs		sx			x			xs	x	45
	x		x	x			x	xs		sx	x	s	sx					xs			s		sx			x			xs	x	46
	x		x	xs			xs	x		sx	x	s	sx					xs			sx		s			x			x	x	47
	x		x	x			x	xs		s	x	s	sx					sx			xs		sx			x			xs	x	48
5	40	4	42	20	15	19	35	11	8	2	30	13	12	0	9	2	7	10	0	0	9	8	8	8	0	13	6	2	2	8	x
5	5	1	0	10	8	4	8	19	6	9	5	0	1	0	1	6	4	8	0	0	15	0	2	1	0	2	0	3	7	0	xs
0	1	0	0	4	4	2	1	9	9	17	10	5	12	0	2	4	4	12	0	0	15	1	15	0	1	0	1	0	1	0	sx
1	0	0	0	0	6	5	2	2	4	4	3	22	14	31	2	3	1	0	3	2	2	0	4	4	0	3	0	0	1	2	s

OALKEEPERS	CS	CCS
oot	17	5

x/c/t - Played full 90 minutes
xs/cs/ts - Substituted off
sx/sc/st - Substituted on
s/cn/tn - Non-playing sub

STOCKPORT COUNTY MATCH RESULTS 2020-21

Date	Comp	H/A	Opponents	Att:	Result	Goalscorers	Pos
Oct 3	NL	A	Torquay United		L 0 - 1		19
6	NL	H	FC Halifax		W 2 - 1	Kitching 23 Thomas 81	10
10	NL	H	Dover Athletic		W 3 - 0	Rooney 54 (pen) 90 Reid 64	6
13	NL	A	Wealdstone		W 5 - 2	Rooney 23 (pen) 84 88 Bennett 77 Maynard 79	2
17	NL	A	Chesterfield		W 2 - 1	Kitching 20 Reid 85	1
24	**FAC4Q**	**H**	**Chesterfield**		**D 1 - 1**	**Hogan 58 (Lost 5-6 on pens)**	
27	NL	H	Solihull Moors		D 0 - 0		2
31	NL	H	Weymouth		L 1 - 2	Palmer 15	2
Nov 4	**FAC4Q**	**H**	**Chesterfield**		**W 4 - 0**	**Bennett 4 Reid 35 Rooney 69 79 (pens)**	
7	**FAC1P**	**A**	**Rochdale**		**W 2 - 1**	**Rooney 7 Reid 14**	
29	**FAC2P**	**H**	**Yeovil Town**		**W 3 - 2**	**Rooney 41 (pen) Palmer 76 Jennings 100**	
Dec 5	NL	A	Bromley		W 2 - 0	Reid 16 Rooney 60	11
8	NL	A	Barnet		W 2 - 1	Reid 43 73	5
15	NL	A	Notts County		L 0 - 1		10
19	**FAT3P**	**H**	**Guiseley**		**W 3 - 1**	**Reid 77 81 Rooney 90+1**	
22	NL	A	Hartlepool United		L 0 - 4	(RC - Palmer 16 & Rooney 55)	13
26	NL	A	Altrincham		D 1 - 1	Jennings C 82	9
28	NL	H	Wrexham		W 2 - 0	Bennett 13 Keane 15	4
Jan 2	NL	H	Altrincham		D 2 - 2	Reid 5 Rooney 56	4
11	**FAC3P**	**H**	**West Ham United**		**L 0 - 1**		
16	**FAT4P**	**H**	**Notts County**		**L 1 - 2**	**Palmer 37**	
19	NL	A	Dagenham & Redbridge		W 2 - 0	Bennett 51 Reid 67	4
Jim Gannon is sacked as manager, assistant Dave Conlon will take interim charge.							
23	NL	H	Boreham Wood		D 1 - 1	Rooney 7	4
Former Brighton & HA U23 coach, Simon Rusk, is named as the new man in charge.							
30	NL	A	Woking		W 4 - 1	Jennings C 2 Rooney 37 Southam-Hales 45+1 Reid 65	3
Feb 2	NL	H	Sutton United		L 0 - 2	(RC - Hogan 58)	5
6	NL	H	Yeovil Town		W 1 - 0	Reid 24	3
13	NL	H	Aldershot Town		D 0 - 0		4
16	NL	A	Maidenhead United		D 0 - 0		4
20	NL	A	Eastleigh		L 0 - 1	(RC - Gilmour 32)	6
23	NL	H	Notts County		D 0 - 0		6
27	NL	H	Chesterfield		W 2 - 0	Jennings J 60 Reid 81	4
Mar 6	NL	A	Weymouth		L 0 - 1		4
9	NL	A	Solihull Moors		W 5 - 0	Rooney 18 (pen) 20 Cardwell 24 Walker 28 Stretton 80	4
16	NL	H	Barnet		W 2 - 1	Hogan 9 Stretton 83	5
20	NL	A	Sutton United		D 1 - 1	Jennings J 90+6	4
23	NL	H	Eastleigh		W 3 - 0	Cardwell 23 Collar 54 Reid 90+1	4
27	NL	H	Hartlepool United		D 1 - 1	Madden 78	4
Apr 2	NL	A	Aldershot Town		W 2 - 1	Stretton 36 Palmer 68	4
5	NL	H	Bromley		D 0 - 0		4
10	NL	A	Wrexham		W 3 - 0	Reid 14 26 Rooney 70 (pen)	4
13	NL	H	King's Lynn Town		W 4 - 0	Reid 14 Rooney 65 Madden 71 84	4
17	NL	H	Maidenhead United		D 2 - 2	Cardwell 38 Madden 78	4
24	NL	A	Boreham Wood		W 3 - 0	Palmer 17 Rooney 32 Reid 71	4
27	NL	A	King's Lynn Town		W 4 - 0	Madden 9 Gash 14 (og) Cardwell 37 43	4
May 1	NL	A	FC Halifax		W 1 - 0	Madden 44	4
3	NL	H	Wealdstone		W 4 - 0	Croasdale 53 Reid 55 86 Rooney 90+1	3
11	NL	H	Dagenham & Redbridge		D 1 - 1	Madden 35	3
16	NL	H	Torquay United		D 2 - 2	Southam-Hales 34 Palmer 63	3
22	NL	H	Woking		D 1 - 1	Gerring 45+2 (og)	3
29	NL	A	Yeovil Town		W 1 - 0	Rooney 23	3
Jun 13	**NL PO SF**	**H**	**Hartlepool United**		**L 0 - 1**		

Goalcorers	LGE	FAC	FAT	SG	CSG	HAT	PEN	1Q	2Q	45+	3Q	4Q	90+	T
TOTALS	72	10	4			0	7	19	21	2	14	24	6	86
Reid	17	2	2	17	2			5	4		4	7	1	21
Rooney	16	4	1	16	4		7	4	5		4	5	3	21
Madden	7			6	2			1	2			4		7
Palmer	4	1	1	6	1			1	2		1	2		6
Cardwell	5			4	1			1	4					5
Bennett	3	1		4	1			2			1	1		4
Jennings C	2	1		3	1			1				1	1	3
Stretton	3			3	2				1			2		3
Hogan	1	1		2	1			1			1			2
Jennings J	2			2	1						1		1	2
Kitching	2			2	1			1	1					2
Opponent	2			2	1			1		1				2
Southam-Hales	2			2	1				1	1				2
Collar	1			1	1						1			1
Croasdale	1			1	1						1			1
Keane	1			1	1			1						1
Maynard	1			1	1							1		1
Thomas	1			1	1							1		1
Walker	1			1	1				1					1

Jennings J	Palmer A	Hogan L	Minihan S	Kitching M	Rooney J	Maynard L	Jennings C	Bennett R	Reid A	Keane J	Bell N	Thomas A	Barnes J (Gk)	Stott J	Southam-Hales M	Croasdale R	Stanyer F	Hopkins J	Owen A	Britton L (L)	Williams J	Gilmour H	Hinchy J	Walker T (L)	Collar W	Dalby S (L)	Cardwell H (L)	Newby E (L)	Stretton J (L)	Madden P	Shaw N (L)	Fitzsimons R (Gk)	Rydel R	No.
x	x	x	x	x	x	x	xs	xs	xs	sx	sx	sx	s	s																				1
sx	x		x	xs	x	x	xs	x	sx	x		sx	s	x	xs	s																		2
sx	x	x	x	xs	x	x	xs	xs	sx	x		sx	s	x		s																		3
xs	x	x	x	sx	xs	x	x	x	xs	x	s	sx	s			sx																		4
sx	x	x	xs	xs	x	x	x	x	sx	x		sx	s	xs		s																		5
	c	c	c		c	c	sc	cs	cs	c	sc	c	cn	cs	cn	sc	cn	cn																6
		x	x		x		xs	xs	x	x	sx	x	s	x	sx	x		s	s															7
	x	x	x	x	x	x	sx	xs	xs	s		sx	s	xs		x				sx														8
	c	c			cs	sc	c	cs	cs	c		c	cn	c	sc	c	cn	sc			**(Tie played again due to Chesterfield playing an ineligible player)**													9
cn	c	c	cn	c	cs	sc	c		cs	c		c	cn	c	cn	cs				sc	sc													10
cn	c	c	sc	cs	c	sc	cs	sc	c	c		cs	cn	c		cs				cn	sc													11
x		x	sx	xs	x	x	x	xs	xs	x		x	s			s				sx	sx													12
x		x	x	sx	x	x	xs	xs	x	x		sx	s			s				sx	xs													13
	x	x	x	xs	x	x	sx	x	x	xs		sxs	s			sx				s	x													14
	t	tn	st	t	st		t	tn	t	t			t	t	ts	t				ts	st	ts	tn											15
	x	x	x	x	x			xs	x	x			s	s	sx	x				s	x	s												16
		x	x	x		x	x	s	x	x		xs	s	s	sx	x					x	s												17
		x	sx	x		x	x	xs	xs	x			s		xs	x				sx	sx	s												18
		x	sx	x	x	x		xs	xs	x		sx	s	x	xs	x					sx	s												19
cn	sc	c	cs	c	cs	c	cs	sc	cs	c		sc	cn	cn	sc	c					cs	cn	sc											20
ts	t	tn	st	st	tn	t	ts	t	st	tn		t	t	t	ts	t					t													21
	s	x	x	x	x	x	sx	xs	xs	x		sx	s	xs		x					sx													22
	x	x	s	xs	x	x	x	x	xs	x			s	s	x	sx					sx													23
	sx	x	x	x	xs	x	x	sx	xs	x			s	s	xs	x					sx													24
	sx	x	x	xs	x	xs	x	sx	xs	x			s	s	x	x					sx													25
sx	x	x	sx		x	s	x	x	xs	s			s	x	x	x					xs													26
x	x	x	sx		x	x		x	xs	s			s	s	x						x			xs	sx									27
s	x	x	sx		x	xs		sx	x	x			s	x	x						sx			xs	xs									28
sx	x	x	x		x	s		xs	x				s	xs	x						sx	x			xs	sx								29
x	x	x	x		x	s		sx	xs	s			s			x						x		xs	sx	x								30
x	x	x	x		xs				x	sx			s			x						x		xs	sx	xs	sx	s						31
x	xs	x	x			s		sx	x	sx			s			x								xs	x	xs	sx	x						32
x		x	x		xs	x		sx	xs	x			s			x								x	s		xs	sx	sx					33
x		x	x			x			x	x			s			x								xs	sx		xs	xs	sx	sx	s			34
x		x	x			xs		sx	x	x			s		sx	x								sx	s			xs	xs	x				35
x	x		x						sx	x			s		sx	x								xs	x		x	xs	s	xs	sx			36
x	x		xs						xs	x			s		sx	x								s	x		sx	x	sx	x	xs			37
x	x	x	x		sx				sx						sx	x								xs	xs		x	s	xs	x		s		38
x	x	x	sx		x				s	s					x	x								xs	xs		x	sx		x		s		39
x	x	x	sx		xs	sx			x						x	x								x	s		xs	sx		xs		s		40
x	x	x	sx		x				xs						xs	x					sx			x	sx		xs	s		x		s		41
x	x	x	sx		x				xs						x	x					s			xs	s		x	sx		x		s		42
x	x	x	s		xs	sx			sx						x	xs								x	x		xs	sx		x		s		43
x	x	xs	x		x	s			sx						sx	x								xs			xs	x		x		s	sx	44
x	x	x	sx		x	sx		sx	s						x	x								xs	xs		xs			x		s		45
xs	x	x	x		x	s		sx	x						s	x								xs			xs	sx		x			sx	46
x	x	x	s		x			sx	sx	s					x	x											x	x		xs		s	xs	47
x	x	x	sx		x	s		sx	xs	sx					x	x								xs			xs	x				s		48
x	x	x	s		x			sx	x	s					x	x					sx			xs				x				s	xs	49
x	x	x	sx		x			sx	xs	x					x	x					s			x			xs	s				s		50
x	**x**	**x**	**s**		**x**			**sx**	**sx**						**x**	**x**								**xs**	**xs**		**xs**	**sx**		**x**		**s**		51
25	37	45	25	11	32	21	12	8	16	28	0	6	2	11	16	35	0	0	0	0	5	3	0	5	4	1	5	6	0	11	0	0	0	x
3	1	1	3	8	9	3	8	13	23	1	0	2	0	5	7	3	0	0	0	1	3	1	0	16	6	2	11	3	2	3	1	0	2	xs
5	3	0	16	3	2	6	4	16	10	4	3	11	0	0	10	4	0	1	0	5	14	0	1	1	5	1	3	7	3	1	1	0	2	sx
4	1	2	6	0	1	7	0	2	2	8	1	0	35	8	3	5	2	2	1	3	2	5	1	1	4	0	0	4	1	0	1	13	0	s

GOALKEEPERS	CS	CCS
Hinchcliffe B	21	3

x/c/t - Played full 90 minutes
xs/cs/ts - Substituted off
sx/sc/st - Substituted on
s/cn/tn - Non-playing sub

SUTTON UNITED MATCH RESULTS 2020-21

Date	Comp	H/A	Opponents	Att:	Result		Goalscorers	Pos
Oct 3	NL	H	Maidenhead United		W	3 - 0	Bugiel 17 Donnellan 35 (og) Kealy 82	2
6	NL	A	Aldershot Town		W	2 - 1	Eastmond 38 Finney 85 (og)	2
10	NL	A	Weymouth		W	1 - 0	Randall 81	2
13	NL	H	Notts County		L	0 - 1		4
24	**FAC4Q**	**H**	**Bromley**		**L**	**0 - 1**		
27	NL	A	Yeovil Town		W	2 - 1	Beautyman 11 50 (pen)	3
Nov 14	NL	H	King's Lynn Town		W	5 - 1	Olaofe 25 53 69 Sho-Silva 68 Beautyman 89	3
17	NL	H	Dagenham & Redbridge		D	1 - 1	Bugiel 14	2
21	NL	A	Wealdstone		D	3 - 3	Olaofe 4 Bugiel 11 Eastmond 90+5	2
24	NL	A	Wrexham		L	0 - 4		2
28	NL	H	FC Halifax Town		W	1 - 0	Beautyman 9 (pen)	2
Dec 1	NL	A	Woking		W	1 - 0	Beautyman 45+5 (pen)	2
5	NL	H	Solihull Moors	934	W	4 - 1	Boot 22 (og) Sho-Silva 42 Ajiboye 73 Simpson 85	2
8	NL	H	Chesterfield		L	0 - 1		2
19	**FAT3P**	**A**	**St Albans City**		**W**	**2 - 0**	**Beautyman 87 Olaofe 90+1**	
Jan 9	NL	H	Altrincham		D	2 - 2	Ajiboye 33 Olaofe 39	3
16	**FAT4P**	**H**	**Dagenham & Redbridge**		**W**	**3 - 1**	**Bugiel 49 Olaofe 61 Randall 90+3**	
23	NL	H	Eastleigh		W	3 - 0	Milsom 37 Ajiboye 42 Eastmond 70	2
26	NL	A	Torquay United		D	0 - 0		2
30	NL	A	Hartlepool United		L	0 - 1		4
Feb 2	NL	A	Stockport County		W	2 - 0	Hinchcliffe 30 (og) Olaofe 69	2
6	**FAT5P**	**H**	**Woking**		**L**	**0 - 1**		
13	NL	H	Boreham Wood		W	2 - 0	John 32 Randall 49	2
20	NL	H	Wealdstone		W	4 - 1	Olaofe 20 Goodliffe 41 John 45 Sho-Silva 82	2
23	NL	A	Dagenham & Redbridge		W	2 - 1	Beautyman 24 90+3 (pens)	2
Mar 2	NL	H	Bromley		W	3 - 2	Eastmond 55 Beautyman 86 Webster 90+3 (og)	2
6	NL	H	Wrexham		D	0 - 0		2
9	NL	H	Yeovil Town		W	2 - 1	Olaofe 33 Beautyman 83	1
13	NL	A	King's Lynn Town		W	1 - 0	Wilson 55	1
16	NL	A	Chesterfield		W	1 - 0	Wilson 35	1
20	NL	H	Stockport County		D	1 - 1	Beautyman 56	1
23	NL	A	Bromley		W	3 - 1	Cousins 6 (og) Beautyman 48 (pen) Olaofe 71	1
29	NL	A	FC Halifax Town		D	2 - 2	Olaofe 75 Eastmond 85	1
Apr 2	NL	A	Boreham Wood		D	0 - 0		1
5	NL	A	Solihull Moors		D	0 - 0		1
13	NL	H	Torquay United		L	0 - 1		2
17	NL	A	Altrincham		W	4 - 0	Milsom 7 Wilson 31 64 Sho-Silva 55	2
24	NL	A	Eastleigh		L	0 - 1		3
27	NL	H	Barnet		W	1 - 0	Bugiel 70	2
May 1	NL	H	Aldershot Town		W	3 - 1	Wilson 8 John 45+1 Olaofe 73	2
4	NL	A	Notts County		L	2 - 3	Olaofe 19 Bugiel 61	2
8	NL	H	Weymouth		W	2 - 0	Eastmond 14 Wilson 51	2
11	NL	H	Woking		W	3 - 2	John 5 Wilson 52 Ajiboye 58	1
15	NL	A	Maidenhead United		W	3 - 0	Ajiboye 65 Olaofe 79 John 90+3	1
23	NL	H	Hartlepool United		W	3 - 0	Milson 35 John 74 Olaofe 80 (National League Champions)	1
29	NL	A	Barnet		L	0 - 2		1

Goalcorers	LGE	FAC	FAT	SG	CSG	HAT	PEN	1Q	2Q	45+	3Q	4Q	90+	T
TOTALS	**72**	**0**	**5**			**1**	**6**	**14**	**16**	**3**	**16**	**22**	**6**	**77**
Olaofe	14		2	14	3	1		3	3		2	7	1	16
Beautyman	11		1	10	2		6	2	1	1	3	4	1	12
Wilson	7			6	2			1	2		4			7
Bugiel	5		1	6	2			3			2	1		6
Eastmond	6			6	1			1	1		1	2	1	6
John	6			6	3			1	1	2		1	1	6
Opponent	6			6	2			2	2			1	1	6
Ajiboye	5			5	1				2		2	1		5
Sho-Silva	4			3	1				1		1	2		4

	LGE	FAC	FAT	SG	CSG	HAT	PEN	1Q	2Q	45+	3Q	4Q	90+	T
Milsom	3			3	1			1	2					3
Randall	2		1	3	1						1	1	1	3
Goodliffe	1			1	1				1					1
Kealy	1			1	1							1		1
Simpson	1			1	1							1		1

Wyatt B	Barden J	Rowe C	Milsom R	Beautyman H	Eastmond C	Randall W	Ajiboye D	Sho-Silva T	Bugiel O	Dundas C	Kealy C	Davis K	Brown W	Simpson A	Olaofe I (L)	Goodliffe B	Brown S (Gk)	John L	Adebayo-Smith J	House B (Gk)	Lovatt A	Chalupniczak F	Browne R	Margetson B (L)	Wilson D (L)	Nembhard	Tiensia J (L)	Mason J		No.
x	x	x	x	x	x	x	x	xs	xs	sx	sx	s	s																	1
x	xs	x	x	x	x	x	x	x	xs	sx	s	s	s	sx																2
x	x	x	s	x	x	x	x	x		s	sx	x		s	xs	s														3
x	x	x	x	x	x	x	x	xs	sx	sx		s		s	xs	s														4
c	c	c	sc	c		c	cs	c	cs	cn	cn	c	cn	cn	sc	c	cn													5
x	xs	x	x	x	x	x	x	sx	xs	sx	s	s			xs	sx														6
	s		x	x	x	x	x	sx	xs	s	sx	x		s	xs	x		x												7
s	sx		x	x	x	xs	x	sx	xs	s	sx	x			xs	x		x												8
s	x		x	x	x		x	sx	xs	s	sx	x		s	xs	x		x												9
xs	x		x	x	x		x	xs	x	s	s	sx		s	sx	x		x												10
sx	sx		x	x	x	xs	xs	xs	sx	s	s	x			x	x		x												11
x	x		xs	x	x			sx	x	s	s	x		sx	xs	x		x												12
x	x		sx	x	x		x	xs		sx	s	xs		sx	x	x		x	s											13
x	x			x	x		x	xs		sx	sx			xs	xs	x		x	sx	s	s									14
t	t			t	t	ts	ts			st	ts	t	tn	st	st	t		t	tn		tn	tn								15
s	x		x	x	x	xs	x	sx	xs		s	x		s	x	x		x					sx							16
tn	t		t	t	t	t	ts	st	ts	st		tn			ts	t		t				tn	st	tn						17
s	x		x	x	xs	x	x	sx	xs	s		sx			xs	x		x					sx							18
s	x		x	x	x	x	x	s	xs	sx		s			xs	x		x					sx							19
s	x		x	x		xs	x	sx	xs	sx		x			xs	x		x					sx	s						20
sx	x		x	x	x		x	sx	xs	s		xs			xs	x		x					sx	s						21
t	t		st	t	t	st	t	ts	st	tn				tn	ts	t		t				tn	t	tn						22
s	x		x	x	x	x	x	sx	xs	sx				s	xs	x		x					s							23
sx	x		xs	x	x	x	x	sx	xs	s		s			xs	x		x					sx							24
s	x		x	x	x	x	x	sx	xs	s		sx			xs	x		x					s							25
	x		x	x	x	x	x		x	s	s	s		s	xs	x		x					sx							26
s	x		x	x	x	x	xs	s	x			s			xs	x		x					sx		sx					27
s	x		x	x	x		x	s	x			x			xs	x		x					s		sx	s				28
s	x		x	xs	x	x		sx	x	s		x		sx		x		x							xs	s				29
s	xs		x	x	x	x		sx	xs			x		sx	sx	x		x							xs	s				30
s			x	x	x	xs	sx	sx	xs			x		x	xs	x		x							sx	s				31
sx			x	xs	x		x	sx	xs			x		x	x	x		x					s		s	s				32
s	x		x	x	x		x	sx	x		sx	xs		s	xs	x		x								s				33
	x		x	x	x	xs	x	sx	xs	s	s			s	x	x		x								sx				34
s	x		x	x	x		x	s	x		s			s	xs	x		x							sx	x				35
	x		x	x	x		x		xs						x	x		x								xs	sx			36
	x	sx	x	x	x		x	xs		sx	sx			s	x	xs		x			s				xs					37
	xs	x	x	x	x		x	xs	sx			s		sx	xs			x			s		sx		x					38
s	x	x	x	x	x		xs	sx	xs			sx		s	x			x					sx		xs					39
	x	x	xs	x	x		x	s	x			sx		sx	x			x		s			s		xs					40
x	x	s		x	x		x	sx	xs			s			xs	x		x		s			sx		x					41
x	x	s		x	x		xs	sx	xs			x		s		x		x		s			sx		x					42
x	x	s	s	x	x		x	sx	xs			x			xs	x		x		s			s		x					43
s	x	s	x		x	sx	x	s	x			x			xs	x		x		s					x					44
s	x		x	sx	x	sx	xs	sx	xs			x			x	x		x		s					xs					45
x		xs			x	x	x	xs		sx	sx	x		x	xs					s	x					sx		s		46
15	36	9	33	41	43	18	34	3	10	0	0	20	0	3	10	36	0	38	0	0	1	0	1	0	5	1	0	0		x
1	4	1	3	2	1	7	8	10	26	0	1	3	0	1	27	1	0	0	0	0	0	0	0	0	6	1	0	0		xs
4	2	1	3	1	0	3	1	24	4	13	9	5	0	8	4	1	0	0	1	0	0	0	13	0	4	2	1	0		sx
19	1	4	2	0	0	0	0	6	0	16	11	11	4	16	0	2	1	0	2	8	4	3	6	4	1	6	0	1		s

OALKEEPERS	CS	CCS
ouzanis	19	2

x/c/t - Played full 90 minutes
xs/cs/ts - Substituted off
sx/sc/st - Substituted on
s/cn/tn - Non-playing sub

TORQUAY UNITED MATCH RESULTS 2020-21

Date	Comp	H/A	Opponents	Att:	Result	Goalscorers	Pos
Oct 3	NL	H	Stockport County		W 1 - 0	Lemonheigh-Evans 90+1	4
6	NL	A	Eastleigh		L 1 - 2	Sherring 25	11
10	NL	A	Bromley		W 2 - 1	Randell 61 Wright 90+3	7
13	NL	H	Chesterfield		W 2 - 1	Britton 9 Hall 90+4	5
17	NL	H	Dover Athletic		W 2 - 0	Cameron 26 44	2
24	**FAC4Q**	**A**	**Sholing**	**400**	**W 2 - 0**	**Hall 44 (pen) Umerah 75**	
27	NL	A	Aldershot Town		W 4 - 1	Wynter 43 Wright 47 90 Whitfield 51	1
31	NL	A	Hartlepool United		W 5 - 0	Wright 12 15 56 Whitfield 37 Warren 87	1
Nov 8	**FAC1P**	**H**	**Crawley Town**		**L 5 - 6**	**Nemane 18 Whitfield 24 Umerah 90+18 Hall 102 107 (pens)**	
14	NL	H	Boreham Wood		D 1 - 1	Sherring 16	1
21	NL	A	FC Halifax Town		W 2 - 1	Hall 17 Lemonheigh-Evans 83	1
Dec 1	NL	A	Wealdstone		W 2 - 1	Waters 60 88	1
5	NL	H	Wrexham	975	W 3 - 1	Whitfield 5 Hall 17 (pen) Lemonheigh-Evans 73	1
8	NL	H	Maidenhead United	980	W 2 - 1	Whitfield 45+3 Wright 59	1
12	NL	A	King's Lynn Town	625	D 0 - 0		1
15	NL	H	Dagenham & Redbridge		L 0 - 1		1
19	**FAT3P**	**A**	**Chesham United**		**W 1 - 0**	**Umerah 48**	
26	NL	H	Yeovil Town	1323	W 6 - 1	Little 5 Wright 9 Lee 21 (og) Nemane 36 Lemonheigh-Evans 53 Cameron 83	1
28	NL	A	Weymouth		W 4 - 3	Hall 15 Umerah 25 Nemane 47 Lemonhaigh-Evans 87	1
Jan 2	NL	A	Yeovil Town		L 1 - 2	Nemane 46	1
19	**FAT4P**	**A**	**Boreham Wood**		**W 4 - 0**	**Hall 51 Waters 82 Randell 84 Lemonheigh-Evans 88**	
23	NL	A	Notts County		D 0 - 0		1
26	NL	H	Sutton United		D 0 - 0	(RC 2xY - Moxey 56)	1
30	NL	A	Barnet		W 2 - 0	Whitfield 8 Andrews 83	1
Feb 2	NL	H	Altrincham		L 1 - 2	Lemonheigh-Evans 21	1
6	**FAT5P**	**A**	**Southport**		**W 2 - 0**	**Umerah 8 Waters 90+2**	
9	NL	H	Wealdstone		D 1 - 1	Waters 90+1	1
20	NL	H	FC Halifax Town		L 2 - 3	Hall 41 71 (pens)	1
23	NL	A	Solihull Moors		W 2 - 1	Hall 18 (pen) Waters 63 (RC 2xY - MacDonald 90+5)	1
27	**FATQF**	**A**	**Woking**		**L 0 - 1**		
Mar 6	NL	H	Hartlepool United		L 0 - 1		1
13	NL	A	Boreham Wood		D 0 - 0		3
16	NL	A	Maidenhead United		L 1 - 4	Boden 90 (pen)	3
20	NL	H	King's Lynn Town		W 1 - 0	Boden 46	3
23	NL	H	Solihull Moors		W 2 - 0	Andrews 9 Randell 40	3
27	NL	A	Dagenham & Redbridge		L 0 - 1		3
Apr 2	NL	H	Woking		W 1 - 0	Wright 83	3
5	NL	A	Wrexham		W 1 - 0	Sherring 90+3	3
10	NL	H	Weymouth		W 2 - 1	Andrews 59 Lemonheigh-Evans 84	3
13	NL	A	Sutton United		W 1 - 0	Hall 81	3
20	NL	A	Woking		W 2 - 0	Boden 14 Lemonheigh-Evans 15	3
24	NL	H	Notts County		D 2 - 2	Lemonheigh-Evans 75 Wynter 90+7 (RC 2xY - Umerah 88	1
27	NL	H	Aldershot Town		W 2 - 1	Hall 12 Boden 90+7	1
May 1	NL	H	Eastleigh		W 3 - 1	Waters 6 Hall 48 Andrews 75	1
3	NL	A	Chesterfield		W 2 - 0	Lemonheigh-Evans 11 Waters 76	1
8	NL	H	Bromley		D 0 - 0		1
16	NL	A	Stockport County		D 2 - 2	Boden 40 (pen) 57	2
22	NL	H	Barnet		D 2 - 2	Andrews 13 Lemonheigh-Evans 23	2
29	NL	A	Altrincham		D 0 - 0		2
Jun 12	**NL PO SF**	**H**	**Notts County**	**1709**	**W 4 - 2**	**Wright 1 48 Hall 101 Moxey 109 (pen)**	
20	**NL PO F**	**N**	**Hartlepool United**	**6606**	**D 1 - 1**	**Lucas 90+5 (Lost 4-5 on pens)**	

Goalcorers	LGE	FAC	FAT	SG	CSG	HAT	PEN	1Q	2Q	45+	3Q	4Q	90+	T
TOTALS	75	7	7			1	10	24	14	1	16	19	15	89
Hall	11	3	1	13	2		7	5	2		2	2	4	15
Lemonheigh-Evans	11		1	12	2			3	1		1	6	1	12
Wright	11			7	2	1		4			4	1	2	11
Waters	6		2	7	2			1			2	3	2	8
Boden	6			5	2		2	1	1		2		2	6
Whitfield	5	1		6	3			2	2	1	1			6
Andrews	5			5	1			2			1	2		5
Umerah	1	2	2	5	1			1	2			2		5
Nemane	3	1		4	3			1	1		2			4
Cameron	3			2	1				2			1		3
Randell	2		1	3	1				1		1	1		3
Sherring	3			3	1			1	1				1	3
Wynter	2			2	1				1				1	2
Britton	1			1	1			1						1
Little	1			1	1			1						1
Lucas (Gk)	1			1	1								1	1
Moxey	1			1	1		1						1	1
Opponent	1			1	1			1						1
Warren	1			1	1							1		1

Cameron K	Sherring S (L)	Whitfield B	Nemane A	Wynter B	Buse M	Andrews J	Wright D	Lemonheigh-Evans C	Umerah J	Hall A	Randell A (L)	Britton L (L)	Koszela O	MacDonald S (Gk)	Warren G	Slough L	Moxey D	Little A	Kerr F	Waters B	Collings A (Gk)	Price O	Evans J	Street R (L)	Sheaf M (L)	Hamon J (Gk) (L)	Lewis J (L)	Boden S (L)	Brzozowski M (Gk) (L)	Law R (L)	Mbunga-Kimpioka B (L)	Tomlinson L (L)	No.
x	x	x	x	x	xs	xs	x	x	xs	sx	sx	sx	s	s																			1
x	x	x	x	x	sx	x	x	xs	xs	xs	sx	sx	s	s																			2
x	x	x	x	x	s	xs	x	x			x	xs	sx	s	sx	s																	3
x	x	x	x	x		sx	xs	x		sx	x	xs	sx	s	s		xs																4
x	x	x	xs	x		sx	x	x		sx	x	xs	s	s	sx		xs																5
c	c	cs	sc	c	cn	c	sc	c	cs	c	cs			c	c			sc	cn														6
x	x	x	x	x		s	x	x	xs	sx	xs			s	sx		xs	sx															7
x	x	xs	x	x		sx	x	x	s	xs	x			s	sx		xs	sx															8
c	c	cs	cs	c		cn	cs	c	sc	c	c			cn	sc		c	sc	cn	sc													9
x	x	x	x	x		s	x	x	s	x	x			x	sx		xs			s	s												10
x	x	x				sx	xs	x	sx	x				x	x				s	xs		s											11
x	x	x	x	x	s	xs	xs	x	sx	x	xs			x					sx	sx													12
x	x	x	x		sx	x	xs	xs	sx	x	x			x	s				xs	sx													13
x	x	xs	x		sx	x	xs	xs	sx	x	x			x	s				x	sx													14
x	xs	x	x		s	x	xs	x	sx	x	xs			x	sx				x	sx													15
x		x	xs		xs	x	x	x	sx		x			x	x			sx	xs	sx		s											16
st		t			t	t	tn	st	t		t			tn	t		ts	ts	t	t		tn	tn										17
x	x	x	x		s	sx	xs	x	sx		x			x	x		xs	xs	sx														18
x	x	xs	x		sx	sx		x	xs	x	x			x	sx		xs		x			s											19
x	x	x	x		s	s		x	x	x	x			s	xs		x		s	sx													20
t	t	t	ts			st		t	ts	ts	t			t	t		t	st		st	tn			tn									21
x	x	x	x			sx		x	sx		x			x	xs		x	sx		xs				s	xs	s							22
x	x	x	x			sx		x	xs		x			x			x	xs		s				sx	s	s	x						23
x	x	x	x			sx		x	s	xs	x			x				xs		sx				xs	sx	s	x						24
x	x	x	xs			sx		x		xs	x			x			x	xs		sx				sx	s	s	x						25
t	st	t				t		st	ts	tn	t			t			ts	ts		t	tn			st	t		t						26
x	x	x				xs				x	x		sx	x		s				x		s		sx	xs	s	x						27
xs	x	x		x		sx		x	xs	x	x		s	x						x				sx	s	s	x						28
	x	xs		x	x	x		x	s	x	x		s	x						xs				s		sx	x	sx					29
	t	t		t	ts	t		t	tn	t	t									t	tn	tn	tn	st	t				t				30
	x	x		x	s	x		x	sx	x	x		s	x				xs		sx							x	xs	s				31
	x	xs		x	sx	s		x	sx	x	x		sx	x				xs		x							x	xs					32
	x			x	s	x		x	sx	xs	x		sx	x				xs		xs							x	x		sx			33
	x			x	sx	x		x	sx	x	x		s	s				xs		s							x	xs		x			34
	x			x	s	x		x	sx	x	x		s	s				xs		sx							x	xs		x			35
	x			x		xs		x	sx	x	x			s			sx	x		s							x	xs		xs	sx		36
	x			x		sx	sx	x		xs	x			s			s	x		sx							x	xs		x	xs		37
	x			x		sx	xs	xs		x	x			s			s	x		sx							x	sx		x	xs		38
	x			x	s	x	xs	x		x	x			s			sx	xs		sx							x	sx		xs			39
sx	x			x		xs	xs	x		x	x			s			xs	x		s							x	sx		sx			40
	x			x	x	xs		x	sx	x	x		s	s	sx		xs			sx							x	xs					41
	x			x	xs	xs		x	sx	x	x			s	s		x			sx							x	xs				sx	42
	x			x	s	x		x		x	x		sx	s	sx		xs			xs							xs	x				sx	43
	x			x	s	x		x	s	x	x			s	x		x	sx		xs								xs			sx		44
	x			x	sx	xs		x	sx	x	x		s	s	xs		x	sx		x											xs		45
	x			x	s	xs		x	sx	x	x			s			x	sx		xs							x	xs			sx		46
sx	x	sx		x		xs		x		x	x			s			x	xs		s							x	xs			sx		47
sx	xs			x		x		x	s	x	x			s			x	xs		sx							x	xs			sx		48
xs	x			x	sx	xs		x	sx	xs	x			s			x	x		sx							x	s					49
xs	x			x	s	sx	xs	x		xs	x			s			x	xs		sx							x				sx		50
xs	x			x	sx	sx	x	x		x	xs			s			xs	x		sx							x				sx		51
26	46	25	17	35	3	18	9	44	2	31	43	0	0	22	7	0	14	6	4	7	0	0	0	0	2	0	25	2	1	4	0	0	x
4	2	7	5	0	4	12	12	4	9	9	5	3	0	0	3	0	13	15	2	7	0	0	0	1	2	0	1	12	0	2	3	0	xs
4	1	1	1	0	9	16	2	2	20	4	2	2	6	0	10	0	2	10	2	21	0	0	0	6	1	1	0	4	0	2	7	2	sx
0	0	0	0	0	14	5	1	0	7	1	0	0	10	28	4	2	2	0	4	6	4	6	2	3	3	6	0	1	1	0	0	0	s

OALKEEPERS	CS	CCS
ucas	13	2
acDonald	8	4

x/c/t - Played full 90 minutes
xs/cs/ts - Substituted off
sx/sc/st - Substituted on
s/cn/tn - Non-playing sub

WEALDSTONE MATCH RESULTS 2020-21

Date	Comp	H/A	Opponents	Att:	Result	Goalscorers	Pos
Oct 6	NL	A	Yeovil Town		D 2 - 2	Emmanuel 25 (pen) Phillips 74	16
10	NL	A	Dagenham & Redbridge		L 0 - 1		19
13	NL	H	Stockport County		L 2 - 5	Slew 17 Lafayette 47	23
17	NL	H	Wrexham		**W** 4 - 3	Wakefield 15 Mendy 22 Dyer 58 Efete 63	18
20	NL	H	Chesterfield		**W** 3 - 2	Emmanuel 13 16 Mendy 82	9
24	FAC4Q	H	Hayes & Yeading United		L 0 - 2		
27	NL	A	King's Lynn Town		**W** 3 - 2	Parish 6 67 73	6
Nov 7	NL	H	Altrincham		**W** 1 - 0	Emmanuel 65	3
10	NL	A	FC Halifax Town		**W** 1 - 0	Parish 86	2
17	NL	A	Eastleigh		L 0 - 2		3
21	NL	H	Sutton United		D 3 - 3	Lafayette 46 65 Mendy 88	4
27	NL	A	Notts County		L 0 - 3		5
Dec 1	NL	H	Torquay United		L 1 - 2	Parish 27	9
5	NL	A	Barnet		D 0 - 0		10
12	NL	H	Weymouth	772	**W** 2 - 1	Lewis 45+2 Cawley 48	5
19	FAT3P	H	Eastleigh		**W** 4 - 3	Wakefield 48 Cawley 59 Lewis 78 Mendy 90+1	
26	NL	A	Maidenhead United		L 0 - 4		8
Jan 9	NL	A	Hartlepool United		L 1 - 3	Mendy 75	14
18	FAT4P	H	Gloucester City		**W** 3 - 1	Dyer 22 Emmanuel 37 Green 81 (pen)	
23	NL	H	Aldershot Town		L 3 - 4	Lewis 19 Dyer 27 Emmanuel 83 (pen)	17
26	NL	A	Altrincham		L 0 - 2		18
Manager Dean Brennan leaves the club. Stuart Maynard takes up interim charge (given the permanent position 11/03/21).							
Feb 6	FAT5P	A	Darlington		L 1 - 4	Emmanuel 43 (pen)	
9	NL	A	Torquay United		D 1 - 1	Mendy 36	18
20	NL	A	Sutton United		L 1 - 4	Parish 55 (RC 2xY - Charles 40)	19
23	NL	H	Eastleigh		D 0 - 0		19
27	NL	A	Wrexham		L 1 - 4	Parish 34	19
Mar 2	NL	H	Boreham Wood		**W** 1 - 0	Smith C 26	19
6	NL	H	FC Halifax Town		L 1 - 2	Lewis 29 (RC - Bowry 90+4)	19
9	NL	H	King's Lynn Town		**W** 3 - 1	Green 9 Lafayette 37 Mendy 66	19
13	NL	H	Notts County		L 0 - 1		19
20	NL	A	Weymouth		L 0 - 4		19
23	NL	H	Woking		L 0 - 1		19
30	NL	A	Solihull Moors		L 0 - 3		19
Apr 2	NL	A	Bromley		D 2 - 2	Gondoh 6 Smith 18 (RC 2xY - Charles 90+1)	20
5	NL	H	Barnet		**W** 5 - 1	Okimo 5 Lewis 30 76 Fasanmade 70 Mendy 72 (pen)	18
10	NL	A	Boreham Wood		L 1 - 3	Mendy 82 (RC - Fasanmade 90)	18
17	NL	H	Hartlepool United		L 2 - 7	Blu-Lo Everton 87 Gondoh 90+4	18
20	NL	H	Maidenhead United		L 0 - 6		18
24	NL	A	Aldershot Town		L 0 - 2		18
May 1	NL	H	Yeovil Town		L 0 - 2		19
3	NL	A	Stockport County		L 0 - 4		19
8	NL	H	Dagenham & Redbridge		L 0 - 5		19
11	NL	H	Bromley		L 0 - 1		19
15	NL	A	Chesterfield		D 0 - 0		19
22	NL	H	Solihull Moors		L 1 - 4	Mendy 88 (pen)	19
29	NL	A	Woking		**W** 4 - 2	Hughes 32 Gondoh 68 (pen) 73 Lo-Everton 76	19

Goalcorers	LGE	FAC	FAT	SG	CSG	HAT	PEN	1Q	2Q	45+	3Q	4Q	90+	T
TOTALS	**49**	**0**	**8**			**1**	**7**	**12**	**13**	**1**	**11**	**18**	**2**	**57**
Mendy	9		1	9	2		2	1	1		1	6	1	10
Emmanual	5		2	6	2		3	2	3		1	1		7
Parish	7			5	2	1		1	2		2	2		7
Lewis	5		1	5	2			1	2	1		2		6
Gondoh	4			3	1		1	1				2	1	4
Lafayette	4			3	1				1		3			4
Dyer	2		1	3	2			1	1		1			3
Cawley	1		1	2	2						2			2
Green	1		1	2	1		1	1				1		2

	LGE	FAC	FAT	SG	CSG	HAT	PEN	1Q	2Q	45+	3Q	4Q	90+	T
Lo-Everton	2			2	1							2		2
Smith C	2			2	1			1	1					2
Wakefield	1		1	2	1			1	1					2
Efete	1			1	1						1			1
Fasanmade	1			1	1							1		1
Hughes	1			1	1				1					1
Okimo	1			1	1			1						1
Phillips	1			1	1							1		1
Slew	1			1	1			1						1

	Okimo J	Efete M	Phillips M	Green D	Smith C	Wakefield C	Benyu K	Emmanual M	Lewis D	Mendy J	Slew J	Parish D	Lafayette R	Charles A	Cawley J	Dyer A	Stevens C	Grafaiti A	Smith G (Gk)	Wishart D	Askew J (Gk) (L)	Parrett D	Moore S (Gk)	Hughes C	Hearn E	Debayo J	Randell J	Lench M	Browne R	Kouogun M	Diallo M	Meekings J	Langston G	Negraru E (Gk)	Dalling D (L)	Olowu J (L)	Bowry D (L)	Harbottle R (L)	Gondoh R	Fasanmade C (L/P)	Tavares N (L)	Shelvey G (Gk) (L)	Lo-Everton S (L)	Shrowder T	No.
	x	x	x	x	x	xs	xs	xs	x	x	sx	sx	sx	s	s																														1
	x	x	x	x	x	xs	xs	xs	x	x	sx	s	sx			sx	s																												2
	x	x	x	s	x	x	xs	s		x	x	sx	xs	sx	sx	xs																													3
	x	x	xs	sx	x	x	xs	sx	x	x	s		xs	s	sx	x																													4
	x	x		sx	x	xs	x	xs	x	x	sx	s	sx		x	xs		s																											5
	c	c		cn	c	c	cs	cs	cs	c	sc	sc	sc	cn	cn	c	c		c	cn																									6
	x	x	x	x			sx	sx	x		s	xs	xs		x	xs			s	sx																									7
	x	x	x	x	sx			xs	x	x		xs	sx		x	xs	s		s	sx																									8
	x	x	x	sx	x			sx	x	x	xs	sx	x		xs	xs			s	s																									9
	x	x	x	xs	x		sx	xs	xs	x	sx	x	sx	s	x						s																								10
	x	x	x	xs	x	sx	sx	xs	x	x		xs	x		s						s	sx																							11
	x	x	xs	xs	x	x	sx		sx	x	s	x	xs		x						s	sx																							12
	x	x	x	x	x	sx	s		x	xs		xs			x	sx					s	xs	x	sx																					13
	x	x	x	xs	x	xs	sx		x		sx			s	x	x					s	xs	x	sx																					14
	x	x	xs	x	x	sx	xs		x	x	sx				sx	x				s	s		x	xs																					15
	t	t		ts	t	st	ts		t	t	st				t	t				st	tn		t	ts	tn	tn	tn																		16
	x	x		x	x	xs	s	xs	x	xs					x	x					s		x			sx		sx	sx																17
	x	x	x	x	x		sx	x	x	x	s									xs	s		x					xs		sx	s														18
	t	t	t	t	t		st	ts	ts	t	st				tn	ts					tn		t	st	tn					tn		t													19
	x	x	x	xs	x			x	x	x					sx	x				s	s		x	s				sx				xs													20
	x	x	xs	x	x			x	x	x					x	xs				sx	s		x	sx				s		s															21
	t	ts	t	t	t			ts	t	t		st			tn	t	tn			tn				st									t	tn	tn										22
	x		s		x			sx	xs	x		s		x	x	x				xs								sx					x		s	x									23
	x		sx	x					xs	x		xs	sx	x	x	x				xs	s											sx			s	x									24
	x		x	x	x				x	x		s	sx		x	x				s	s											xs			s	x									25
	x	xs	x	x	x				xs	x		x	sx	sx	x	xs				s	s														sx										26
	x	x	x	x	xs				sx	xs		sx	xs	x	x	sx				x	s				s																				27
	x		x	x					xs	x		xs	sx	x	x	x				xs	s			sx	s												sx								28
	x	x	x	xs					x	x		sx	xs	x	x	xs				sx	s			sx	s																				29
	x	x	x	xs					xs	x		xs	sx	x	x	x				sx	s			sx	s																				30
	x		x	x	sx				xs	xs		sx	x	xs	x	x					s				s													x	sx						31
	x		x	sx	x				sx	xs		xs	xs	x	x						s																x	x	s	sx					32
	x		xs	sx	x				x	x		sx		x	x						s																sx	x	xs	s	xs				33
	x		xs	x	x				xs	x		s		x	x	sx					s																s	x	x	sx					34
	xs		x	x	xs				x	x		sx			x	x				s	x				sx													x	xs	sx					35
	x		x	x	xs				x	x		sx			x	x					s				s													x	xs	sx		x			36
	x		x	xs	xs				x	x		sx		sx	x	x				s	s															xs			x			x	sx		37
	x		s	sx	s				x	x		x		x	x	x				s	x															x			xs				x	s	38
	x		x	x	x				xs	x		sx		x		xs				xs	x				s											x			sx				sx	s	39
	x		x	x	x				xs	x		s		x		xs				xs	x			sx	s											x			sx				sx		40
	x		xs	x	x				s	x				x		s				xs	x			xs	sx											x			sx				x	sx	41
	x		s	xs	xs				xs	x		sx		x		sx				sx	x			x												x		x	s				x		42
	x		sx						sx	x		x		x		x				xs	x			xs	s											xs		x	sx				x	s	43
	x		s						x	x		xs		x		x					s			x	s											x		x	sx			x	x	s	44
	x								x	x		xs		x	sx	x				s	s			x	s											x		xs	sx			x	x		45
	x								x	x				x	s	x	sx				sx			x	s											xs		x	xs			xs	x	sx	46
4	45	24	27	23	29	4	1	3	27	39	1	5	3	18	26	22	1	0	1	1	7	0	9	4	0	0	0	0	0	0	0	1	2	0	0	10	1	10	2	0	0	4	7	0	x
	1	2	7	10	5	5	7	10	13	5	1	10	7	1	1	11	0	0	0	8	0	2	0	4	0	0	0	1	0	0	0	2	0	0	0	3	0	1	5	0	1	1	0	0	xs
	0	0	2	6	2	4	7	4	4	0	9	14	11	3	5	5	1	0	0	7	1	2	0	9	2	1	0	3	1	1	0	1	0	0	1	0	2	0	7	4	0	0	3	2	sx
	0	0	4	2	1	0	2	1	1	0	4	6	0	5	6	1	3	1	3	11	27	0	0	1	14	1	1	1	0	2	1	0	0	1	4	0	1	0	2	1	0	0	0	4	s

lso Played: Fielding J - 05/04 (s).

GOALKEEPERS	CS	CCS
sted	4	2
Moore	1	1
Shelvey	1	1

x/c/t - Played full 90 minutes
xs/cs/ts - Substituted off
sx/sc/st - Substituted on
s/cn/tn - Non-playing sub

WEYMOUTH MATCH RESULTS 2020-21

Date	Comp	H/A	Opponents	Att:	Result	Goalscorers	Pos
Oct 3	NL	A	Altrincham		D 0 - 0		10
6	NL	H	Woking		L 0 - 1		17
10	NL	H	Sutton United		L 0 - 1		21
13	NL	A	Barnet		L 0 - 1		22
17	NL	H	King's Lynn Town		**W** 2 - 1	Cooke 38 Whelan 86 (pen)	17
24	**FAC4Q**	**H**	**Oxford City**		**L 2 - 3**	**Fernandez 53 (og) Robinson 63**	
27	NL	A	Bromley		L 2 - 3	Wakefield 23 Whelan 87 (pen)	19
31	NL	A	Stockport County		**W** 2 - 1	Brooks 51 Whelan 85	14
Nov 28	NL	H	Chesterfield		L 1 - 2	Shields 40	21
Dec 5	NL	H	FC Halifax Town		L 1 - 5	McQuoid 64	21
8	NL	H	Dagenham & Redbridge		L 2 - 3	McQuoid 14 McCarthy 83	22
12	NL	A	Wealdstone	772	L 1 - 2	Thomson 25	22
15	NL	H	Wrexham		L 2 - 3	McQuoid 3 McCarthy 25	22
19	**FAT3P**	**H**	**Maidenhead United**	**306**	**W 3 - 2**	**Cooke 16 McQuoid 32 (pen) Jordan 53**	
26	NL	A	Eastleigh		D 0 - 0		21
28	NL	H	Torquay United		L 3 - 4	Cooke 31 Murray 50 McQuoid 62 (pen)	22
Jan 2	NL	H	Eastleigh		D 1 - 1	Ngalo 73	21
5	NL	H	Yeovil Town		L 0 - 3	(RC - McCarthy 87)	21
16	**FAT4P**	**H**	**Darlington**		**L 0 - 1**		
23	NL	H	Hartlepool United		**W** 1 - 0	McQuoid 40	21
26	NL	A	Aldershot Town		**W** 2 - 0	Dallas 13 41	21
30	NL	H	Notts County		L 0 - 1		21
Feb 2	NL	A	Boreham Wood		L 0 - 1		21
6	NL	H	Bromley		**W** 2 - 1	Dallas 3 (pen) 7 (RC 2xY - Ngalo 90+1)	20
20	NL	H	Solihull Moors		D 0 - 0		20
23	NL	A	Yeovil Town		L 1 - 3	Mensah 23	21
27	NL	A	King's Lynn Town		D 2 - 2	Dallas 13 Robinson 31	21
Mar 6	NL	H	Stockport County		**W** 1 - 0	Dallas 4	20
13	NL	A	Wrexham		L 0 - 2		20
16	NL	A	Dagenham & Redbridge		D 1 - 1	McCarthy 90+3	20
20	NL	H	Wealdstone		**W** 4 - 0	McQuoid 21 Camp 58 Shields 83 84	20
29	NL	A	Chesterfield		L 0 - 1		20
Apr 2	NL	H	Maidenhead United		**W** 2 - 1	Shields 86 Dallas 90+5 (pen)	19
5	NL	A	FC Halifax Town		L 2 - 3	McCarthy 22 90+3	20
10	NL	A	Torquay United		L 1 - 2	Dallas 41 (pen)	20
13	NL	H	Aldershot Town		L 0 - 3		20
27	NL	A	Maidenhead United		**W** 1 - 0	Brooks 30	18
May 1	NL	A	Woking		**W** 4 - 2	Dallas 44 61 McCarthy 89 Shields 90+5	18
3	NL	H	Barnet		L 0 - 2		18
8	NL	A	Sutton United		L 0 - 2		18
11	NL	A	Solihull Moors		L 1 - 2	McQuoid 9	18
15	NL	H	Altrincham		**W** 2 - 1	Dallas 22 78	18
18	NL	H	Boreham Wood		L 1 - 3	McCarthy 64	18
22	NL	A	Notts County		L 0 - 3		18
29	NL	A	Hartlepool United		L 0 - 4		18

Goalcorers	LGE	FAC	FAT	SG	CSG	HAT	PEN	1Q	2Q	45+	3Q	4Q	90+	T
TOTALS	45	2	3			0	7	12	14	0	10	10	4	50
Dallas	12			8	2		3	6	3		1	1	1	12
McQuoid	7		1	8	2		2	4	2		2			8
McCarthy	7			6	1			1	1		1	2	2	7
Shields	5			4	1				1			3	1	5
Cooke	2		1	3	1			1	2					3
Whelan	3			3	2		2					3		3
Brooks	2			2	1				1		1			2
Robinson	1	1		2	1				1		1			2
Camp	1			1	1						1			1

	LGE	FAC	FAT	SG	CSG	HAT	PEN	1Q	2Q	45+	3Q	4Q	90+	T
Jordan			1	1	1						1			1
Mensah	1			1	1				1					1
Murray	1			1	1						1			1
Ngalo	1			1	1							1		1
Opponent		1		1	1						1			1
Thomson	1			1	1				1					1
Wakefield	1			1	1				1					1

Wakefield J	Jordan C (L)	Harfield O	Camp B (L)	Brooks C	Robinson A	Murray C	McCarthy J	McQuoid J	Cooke C	Hoey J	Thomson B	Benfield G (Gk)	Leslie-Smith J	Whelan T	Ngalo J	Santos A	Burns H	Anderson M	Mullings S	Shields S	Olumuyiwa A	Al Hussaini Z (L)	Dickson J	Lander S	Saydee C (L)	Ross E (Gk) (L)	Revan D (L)	Mensah J	Dallas A (L)	Luque J	Fonkeu P	Morgan B	Worman B (L)	Bruton H (Gk)	No.
x	x	x	x	x	x	xs	x	xs	x	sx	sx	s	s	s																					1
sx		x	x	x	sx		xs	xs	x	s	x	s	x	x	xs	sx																			2
x		x	x	x	x	x	sx		x	sx		s	x	xs		xs	s	s																	3
xs	xs	x	x	x	xs	sx	x		x			s	x	sx				s	x	sx															4
x	x	x	x	x	x		x		x	sx		s	xs	sx		s		s		x															5
cn	**c**	**c**	**c**		**c**		**cs**	**sc**	**c**	**cn**	**sc**	**cn**	**sc**	**c**		**cs**		**cs**		**c**	**cn**														6
xs	x	sx	x	x	x	sx	s	xs		sx	x	s	xs	x						x															7
xs	x	x	xs	x	x	s	sx	x	xs		sx	s	sx	x						x															8
	x	x	x	x	x	sx	x	xs	xs		sx	x	s	xs	s				sx	x															9
s	x	x	x	xs	x	sx	x	xs	sx		sx		x						xs	x		s													10
x	x	x	x	x	xs	xs	sx	xs	s		x		sx						s	x		sx													11
	x		x				x	xs	sx	sx	xs	s	x		x	s		x	sx	x		xs													12
	x	x		x			x	xs	sx	s	xs	s	xs		x			sx	sx	x		x													13
	t	**t**		**t**	**tn**		**t**	**t**	**t**	**t**		**t**			**t**	**t**					**tn**	**ts**	**st**	**tn**											14
sx	xs	x	sx	x		s	x	xs	x	x		s			x	xs				x					sx										15
x		x		x		x	x	x	x	s		s			x	sx					s	s	xs		x										16
sx		x	x	x		xs	x	xs	x	xs		s			x	sx				x		s	sx												17
x		x	x	x	s	xs	x	x	x	s		s			x	sx				x			s			x									18
ts		**t**		**t**	**st**	**ts**		**t**	**ts**	**tn**	**st**	**t**			**t**	**tn**				**t**	**tn**		**st**			**tn**	**t**	**t**							19
		x	s	x	sx	sx	x	xs				s			x					x					s	x	x	x	x	xs					20
		x	s	x	sx	sx	x	xs				s			x					x					sx	x	x	x	xs	xs					21
		x	s	x	s	sx	x	xs				s			x					x						x	x	x	x	xs	sx				22
		x	xs	sx	s	sx	x	xs				s			x					x						x	x	x	x	sx	xs				23
		x	x	x	sx	s	x				sx	s			x					x						x	x	x	xs	xs	s				24
		x	x	x	x	s	x		sx		sx		s							x						x	x	x	xs	xs	s				25
			xs	xs	x	s	x		sx		sx		x		xs					x						x	x	x	x	s	sx				26
		x	x	xs	x		x		sx		xs		s		s					x						x	x	x	x	sx	s				27
		x	x	xs	x		x	xs			sx	s			s					x						x	x	x	x	sx	s				28
sx		x	x		x	sx	x	xs			sx	s	s													x	x	x	x	xs	xs				29
s		x	x		x	s	x	x			sx	s	s													x	x	x	x	xs	x				30
s		x	x	xs	x		x	xs			sx	s			sx					x						x	x	x	xs		sx				31
s		x	x	x		s	x	xs			sx	s			x					x						x	x	xs	x		sx				32
sx		x		x		sx	x				x	s			xs					x						x	x	x	x	s	xs				33
xs		x		x	x	xs	x				sx	s	sx		s					x						x	x	x			s				34
s		x		x	x	s	x				x				s					x						x	x	x	x	s	s	x			35
sx		x	x	x	sx	s	xs				sx				xs					x						x		x	x	s	x	xs			36
		x	x	x	x	sx	x	sx			xs	s			sx					xs						x		x			s	x	xs		37
		x	x	xs	x	sx	x	sx							sx					x			s			x		x	xs		s	x	xs		38
		x	sx	x		x	sx	x					s		xs					sx			xs			x		x	x		s	xs	x		39
		x	x	x	x	s	x	xs			sx		sx							x			s			x		xs	xs		sx		x		40
		x	x	xs	xs	sx	x	x				s	xs		s					x						x		x	x		sx		sx		41
		x	x	xs	x	xs	sx	xs					s		s					x			sx			x		x	x		sx		x		42
		x	x	xs	x	xs	x	x				s	sx		s								sx			x		x	x		sx		xs		43
		x	xs	x	xs	x	x	xs				s	sx		sx											x		x	x		sx		x		44
		x		x	x	x		xs				x	x		sx					s				s		s		x	x		x		x	s	45
6	11	42	28	31	23	5	34	9	11	2	5	4	7	4	14	1	0	1	1	32	0	1	0	0	1	26	17	25	18	0	3	3	5	0	x
5	2	0	4	9	4	8	3	22	3	1	4	0	4	2	5	3	0	1	1	1	0	2	2	0	0	0	0	2	6	7	3	2	3	0	xs
6	0	1	2	1	6	13	5	3	6	5	17	0	7	2	5	4	0	1	3	2	0	1	5	0	2	0	0	0	0	3	9	0	1	0	sx
6	0	0	3	0	4	10	1	0	1	6	0	30	8	1	8	3	1	3	1	1	4	3	3	2	1	2	0	0	0	4	9	0	0	1	s

lso Played: Fielding J - 05/04 (s).

GOALKEEPERS	CS	CCS
Ross	6	2
Bycroft	2	1

x/c/t - Played full 90 minutes
xs/cs/ts - Substituted off
sx/sc/st - Substituted on
s/cn/tn - Non-playing sub

Kia
HOME OF THE
7 YEAR WARRANTY
FONKEU
REVAN
24
WORKWEAR
CAMP
2
TECHNIQUE
22

Chesterfield 1 - 0 Weymouth - 29/03/2021

Photos Bill Wheatcroft

WOKING MATCH RESULTS 2020-21

Date	Comp	H/A	Opponents	Att:	Result	Goalscorers	Pos
Oct 3	NL	H	Solihull Moors		**W** 2 - 1	Kretzschmar 53 Ferdinand 60	5
6	NL	A	Weymouth		**W** 1 - 0	Spasov 45	4
10	NL	A	Chesterfield		L 0 - 4		9
13	NL	H	Dagenham & Redbridge		**W** 2 - 0	Cook 20 Napa 32	6
17	NL	H	FC Halifax		D 0 - 0		4
24	**FAC4Q**	**A**	**Aldershot Town**		**W 2 - 1**	**Davison 44 Kretzschmar 77**	
27	NL	A	Boreham Wood		L 0 - 1		7
31	NL	A	King's Lynn Town		L 1 - 3	Davison 45+4	9
Nov 7	**FAC1P**	**A**	**Gillingham**		**L 2 - 3**	**Kretzschmar 23 Davison 55**	
14	NL	H	Yeovil Town		D 1 - 1	Davison 89	9
17	NL	A	Dover Athletic		**W** 5 - 1	Davison 16 Ferdinand 19 32 Kretzschmar 76 83	6
21	NL	H	Barnet		**W** 4 - 1	Ferdinand 8 Binnom-Williams 17 (og) Kretzschmar 63 Tarpey 82	3
Dec 1	NL	H	Sutton United		L 0 - 1		6
5	NL	A	Notts County		L 0 - 1		8
12	NL	H	Hartlepool United	799	**W** 3 - 0	Jarvis 2 Cook 17 Spasov 59	6
19	**FAT3P**	**H**	**Dover Athletic**		**W 2 - 1**	**Lofthouse 70 (pen) Spasov 73**	
26	NL	A	Aldershot Town		L 0 - 3		10
28	NL	H	Eastleigh		D 0 - 0		10
Jan 2	NL	H	Aldershot Town		L 0 - 1		11
19	**FAT4P**	**A**	**Bromley**		**D 1 - 1**	**Kretzschmar 51 (Won 7-6 on pens)**	
23	NL	H	Maidenhead United		D 0 - 0		15
26	NL	A	Bromley		D 2 - 2	Wareham 72 86	16
30	NL	H	Stockport County		L 1 - 4	Diarra 51	16
Feb 6	**FAT5P**	**A**	**Sutton United**		**W 1 - 0**	**Napa 45+3**	
16	NL	A	Wrexham		L 0 - 2		18
20	NL	A	Barnet		**W** 2 - 0	Loza 28 Diarra 68	16
27	**FAT QF**	**H**	**Torquay United**		**W 1 - 0**	**Loza 37**	
Mar 2	NL	A	Altrincham		L 0 - 1		18
6	NL	H	King's Lynn Town		**W** 3 - 0	Ashford 28 Loza 81 Gerring 90	18
9	NL	H	Boreham Wood		D 0 - 0		18
13	NL	A	Yeovil Town		L 1 - 2	Kretzschmar 65	18
16	NL	H	Altrincham		D 1 - 1	Lofthouse 18	18
20	NL	A	Hartlepool United		L 0 - 1		18
23	NL	A	Wealdstone		**W** 1 - 0	Diarra 86	17
29	**FAT SF**	**A**	**Hereford**		**L 0 - 1**		
Apr 2	NL	A	Torquay United		L 0 - 1		18
5	NL	H	Notts County		L 2 - 4	Kretzschmar 28 (pen) Ashford 33	19
10	NL	A	Eastleigh		D 0 - 0	(RC 2xY - Block 53)	19
13	NL	H	Bromley		L 3 - 4	Diarra 16 Cook 20 Dalby 81	19
17	NL	H	Wrexham		L 0 - 4		19
20	NL	H	Torquay United		L 0 - 2		19
24	NL	A	Maidenhead United		L 1 - 2	Ferdinand 47	19
27	NL	A	FC Halifax		L 0 - 1		20
May 1	NL	H	Weymouth		L 2 - 4	Cooper 31 Ashford 47	20
3	NL	A	Dagenham & Redbridge		L 1 - 3	Ashford 73	20
8	NL	H	Chesterfield		L 1 - 4	Cooper 28 (pen)	20
11	NL	A	Sutton United		L 2 - 3	Cooper 24 (pen) Leslie 87	20
15	NL	A	Solihull Moors		L 1 - 2	Collier 79	20
22	NL	A	Stockport County		D 1 - 1	Kretzschmar 44	20
29	NL	H	Wealdstone		L 2 - 4	Dyer 18 (og) Gerring 50	20

Goalcorers	LGE	FAC	FAT	SG	CSG	HAT	PEN	1Q	2Q	45+	3Q	4Q	90+	T
TOTALS	46	4	5			0	4	11	11	5	11	16	1	55
Kretzschmar	7	2	1	9	2		1		3		4	3		10
Davison	3	2		5	4			1	1	1	1	1		5
Ferdinand	5			4	2			2	1		2			5
Ashford	4			4	2				2		1	1		4
Diarra	4			4	1			1			1	2		4
Cook	3			3	1			3						3
Cooper	3			3	2		2		1	2				3
Loza	2		1	3	2				2			1		3
Spasov	2		1	3	1					1	1	1		3

	LGE	FAC	FAT	SG	CSG	HAT	PEN	1Q	2Q	45+	3Q	4Q	90+	T
Gerring	2			2	1						1		1	2
Lofthouse	1		1	2	1		1	1				1		2
Napa	1		1	2	1				1	1				2
Opponent	2			2	1			2						2
Wareham	2			1	1							2		2
Collier	1			1	1							1		1
Dalby	1			1	1							1		1
Jarvis	1			1	1			1						1
Leslie	1			1	1							1		1
Tarpey	1			1	1							1		1

Casey J	Ferdinand K	Cook J	Collier N	Kretzschmar M	Cooper C	Shotton S (L)	Napa M (L)	Block T	Spasov S (L)	Goddard J	Tarpey D	Wareham J	White H (Gk)	Reid T	Hall C	Jarvis M	Cartwright S (L)	Dempsey B (L)	Davison J (L)	Smith M (Gk)	Lofthouse K (L)	Leslie J	Gerring B	Skinner J	Loza J	Smith J	Diarra M	Muir N (L)	Ashford S (L)	Dalby S (L)	Hodges P	Evans S	Hamblin L	Robinson Z (L)	Freeman J (L)	Saied S	Rumble J	No.
x	x	x	x	xs	x	x	xs	x	xs	sx	sx	sx	s	s																								1
x	x	x	x	s	x	x	x	x	xs	x	s		s	s	sx																							2
x	x	x	xs	sx	x	x	x	xs	x	xs	s				sx	sx	s																					3
x	x	x	x	sx	x	x	xs	s	xs		xs				sx	sx	s	x																				4
x	x	x	x	sx	x	x		s	xs	xs	xs				sx	sx	s	x																				5
c	c	c	cn	sc	c	c	cs	cn	sc	sc	cn			c		cs		c	cs	cn																		6
x	x	x	s	sx	sx	x		xs	sx		s			x		x		xs	x		xs																	7
x	x	x	s	sx	x	x		xs	sx	s	sx			x		xs			xs		x																	8
c	c	c	cn	cs	c	c			c		sc	sc		c				cs	c	cn	cn	cn	cn															9
x	x	x	s	x	x	x			x		sx	s				s		xs	x		x		s															10
x	x	x	s	x	x	x			sx		xs	s				sx		x	xs		x		s															11
x	x	x	s	x	x	x			sx		x	s				s		x	xs		x		s															12
x	x	x	xs	x		x		s	sx		xs	sx		s		sx		xs	x		x																	13
x	xs	x	s	x	x	x		s	xs		sx	sx				sx		xs	x		x																	14
x			s	x	x	x		sx	xs		s	sx				xs		x	xs		x			sx														15
t	tn		t		t	t		st	t	tn	ts	tn		tn		ts		t	t	tn	t				st													16
x	x		x		x	x		s	xs		sx	sx		s		sx		xs	x		x				xs													17
x	sx		x		x	x		x	sx		s			s		xs		xs	x	s	x				x													18
x	x	x	x	x	xs			xs	sx		s			s		sx		sx	x		x				xs													19
t	t	t	tn	t	t			tn	t	t		tn		tn		tn		t		tn	t		t	tn														20
x	x	x	s	xs	x		sx	s	xs	xs						sx		x			x		x			sx												21
	x	x	s	xs	x		sx	s	sx	x		sx						xs			x		x				x											22
	x	x		s	s		sx	x	sx	xs		x		xs		sx					x		x			xs	x											23
	t	t	tn	t	t		ts	tn				ts				tn		t		tn	t		t	tn	st	st	t											24
	x	x	s	x	x		sx	s				xs				xs		xs			x		x		sx	sx	x											25
	x	x	s	x	x		xs	s				s				sx		sx			x		x		xs	x	x											26
tn	t	t	tn	t	ts		ts	st				st				tn		st		tn	t		t		t	ts	t											27
s	x	x		sx	s		xs	xs				xs				sx		x			x		x		x	sx	x											28
s	x	x		x	x		sx					sx				s					x		x		x	s	x	xs	xs									29
s		x		x	x		s	s				sx				sx		x			x		x		x		x	xs	xs									30
sx	s	xs		x	x		sx					sx				s		x			x		x		x		x	xs	xs									31
x	x		s	sx	x		s					sx				xs		x			x		x		x		x	s	xs									32
x	x			sx	s		x	s				sx				x		x		x	x		x	s			x	xs	xs									33
x	s			x	x		xs	x								xs		x			s		x			sx	x	sx		xs	sx							34
t	t	tn		t	t		st	tn								tn				tn	t		t		ts	st	t	st	ts	ts								35
x	x			x	x			x										xs		x	xs		x	sx		sx	x			xs	sx	s	s					36
x	x	x		x	s			x										x		x	s			s	xs	xs	x		x	sx	sx							37
	x	x		x	sx			x										x			x			s	xs	sx	x		xs	x	s		sx					38
x	x	x		x	x													xs			x			sx	s		x			x	s	s	s	x				39
	x	x		xs	x			xs													x		x	s		sx	x			x	sx	sx	s	xs				40
	x	x			x			xs													x	s	x	sx		xs	xs			x	sx	s	sx		x			41
	x	x			x															s	x	sx	x	xs		s	x			x	x	sx	s		xs			42
	x	x			x															s	x	s	x	s			x			x	sx	s	x	x	xs			43
	x				x															s	x	sx	xs				x		xs	sx	xs	s	x	x	x	sx		44
	x				x		sx													s	x	xs					x		x	xs	xs	sx	x	sx	x		s	45
	x	x	x		x		xs													s	x	sx		s					xs	sx	sx		x	x	xs			46
		x	x		x		xs													s	x	sx	x						x	s	xs		x	x	s	sx		47
		x	x		x		xs													x	x	x	x	s					x	sx	sx		x	xs	s			48
		x	x	xs	x		sx													s	x		x	sx					x	s	sx		x	xs	xs			49
		xs	x	x	x															s	x	sx	x	s					x	sx	sx		x	xs	xs			50
28	39	37	13	22	41	18	3	8	5	3	1	1	0	4	0	2	0	18	9	4	39	1	25	0	7	1	23	0	6	6	1	0	8	5	3	0	0	x
0	1	2	2	6	2	0	11	7	8	4	5	3	0	1	0	8	0	11	5	0	2	1	1	1	6	4	1	4	9	4	3	0	0	4	5	0	0	xs
1	1	0	0	9	2	0	9	3	10	2	6	13	0	0	4	13	0	3	0	0	0	5	0	5	3	9	0	2	0	5	10	3	2	1	0	2	0	sx
4	3	1	17	2	4	0	2	15	0	2	7	6	2	8	0	8	3	0	0	16	3	3	4	10	1	2	0	1	0	2	2	5	4	0	2	0	1	s

lso Played: Fielding J - 05/04 (s).

GOALKEEPERS	CS	CCS
Ross	13	2

x/c/t - Played full 90 minutes
xs/cs/ts - Substituted off
sx/sc/st - Substituted on
s/cn/tn - Non-playing sub

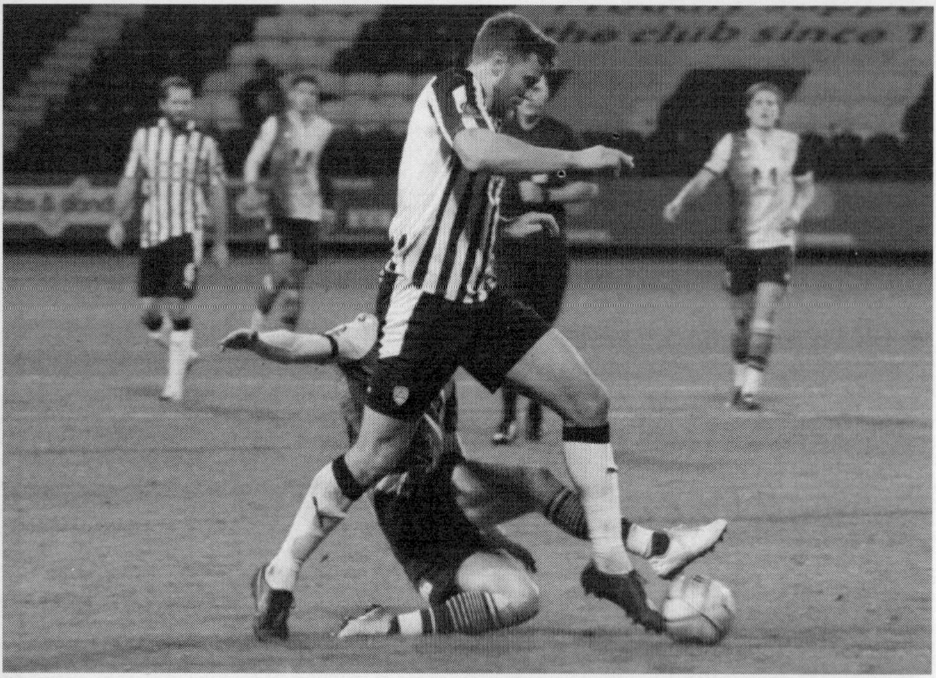
the club since

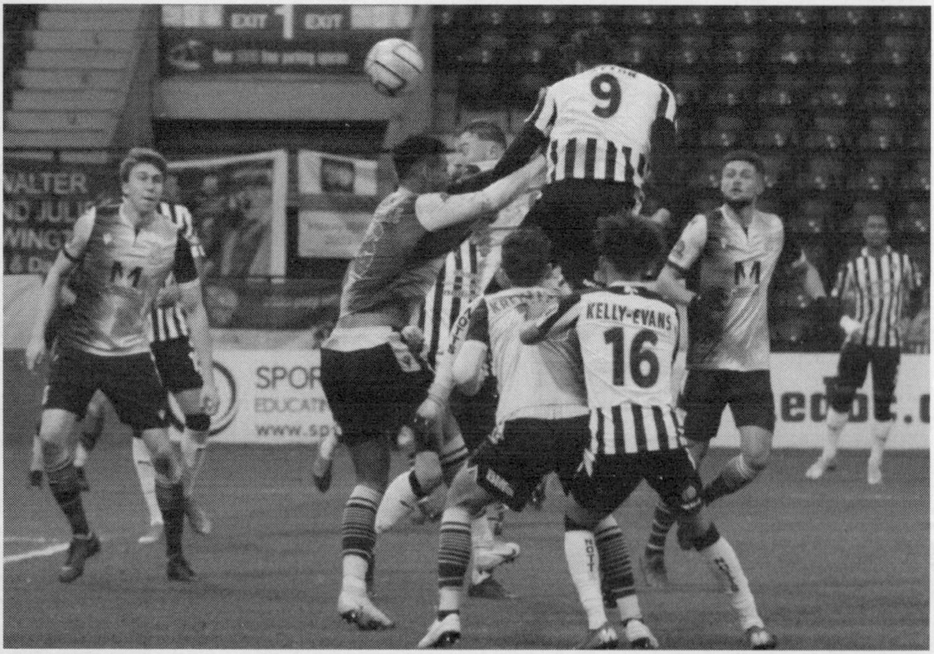
EXIT
EXIT
9
KELLY-EVANS
16

Notts County 1 - 0 Woking - 05/12/2020

Photos Bill Wheatcroft

WREXHAM MATCH RESULTS 2020-21

Date	Comp	H/A	Opponents	Att:	Result	Goalscorers	Pos
Oct 3	NL	H	Boreham Wood		**W** 2 - 1	Hall-Johnson 27 Young 70	6
6	NL	A	Solihull Moors		L 0 - 1		12
10	NL	A	Yeovil Town		**W** 1 - 0	Thomas 11	8
12	NL	H	Maidenhead United		L 0 - 1		9
17	NL	A	Wealdstone		L 3 - 4	Okimo 16 (og) Yussuf 18 90+4	10
24	**FAC4Q**	**A**	**Solihull Moors**		**L 0 - 4**		
27	NL	H	Barnet		D 0 - 0		13
Nov 17	NL	A	Hartlepool United		**W** 1 - 0	Durrell 54	13
21	NL	H	Aldershot Town		**W** 1 - 0	Young 64	11
24	NL	H	Sutton United		**W** 4 - 0	Thomas 28 79 Harris 43 Yussuf 74	6
28	NL	A	Bromley		D 1 - 1	Yussuf 77	4
Dec 1	NL	H	Altrincham		L 0 - 1		7
5	NL	A	Torquay United	975	L 1 - 3	Vassell 19	10
15	NL	A	Weymouth		**W** 3 - 2	Vassell 73 74 Hall-Johnson 90+5	8
19	**FAT3P**	**H**	**Leamington**		**D 0 - 0**	**(Lost 5-6 on pens)**	
28	NL	A	Stockport County		L 0 - 2		12
Jan 16	NL	H	Dover Athletic		**W** 3 - 1	Hall-Johnson 32 Kelleher 61 Young 90+5	8
23	NL	A	Chesterfield		L 1 - 2	Young 20 (pen)	12
26	NL	H	FC Halifax Town		D 0 - 0		10
30	NL	A	King's Lynn Town		**W** 2 - 0	Reckord 8 Yussuf 26	9
Feb 2	NL	A	Eastleigh		D 1 - 1	Thomas 45+1 (RC - French 85)	8
6	NL	H	Dagenham & Redbridge		D 2 - 2	Reckord 30 Hall-Johnson 58	9
9	NL	A	Altrincham		**W** 2 - 1	Thomas 36 68	7
16	NL	H	Woking		**W** 2 - 0	Angus 45 Young 65 (pen)	6
20	NL	A	Aldershot Town		L 0 - 3		7
23	NL	H	Hartlepool United		D 0 - 0		7
27	NL	H	Wealdstone		**W** 4 - 1	Thomas 47 67 Young 53 Angus 75 (RC 2xY - Vassell 72)	5
Mar 6	NL	A	Sutton United		D 0 - 0		5
9	NL	A	Barnet		**W** 2 - 0	Young 42 Durrell 80	5
13	NL	H	Weymouth		**W** 2 - 0	Vassell 67 Ponticelli 78	4
16	NL	H	Eastleigh		D 2 - 2	Hall-Johnson 45+2 Thomas 71 (RC 2xY - Kelleher 49)	4
29	NL	H	Bromley		**W** 3 - 0	Thomas 32 Angus 39 67	5
Apr 2	NL	A	Notts County		L 0 - 1		7
5	NL	H	Torquay United		L 0 - 1		8
10	NL	H	Stockport County		L 0 - 3		8
13	NL	A	FC Halifax Town		**W** 4 - 0	Davies 4 32 36 Angus 22	7
17	NL	A	Woking		**W** 4 - 0	Young 37 (pen) Hall-Johnson 51 Omotayo 90+1 Davies 90+6	5
24	NL	H	Chesterfield		D 0 - 0		7
May 1	NL	H	Solihull Moors		**W** 2 - 1	Young 27 33 (pens)	6
3	NL	A	Maidenhead United		D 2 - 2	Davies 58 Angus 78	6
8	NL	H	Yeovil Town		**W** 3 - 0	Pearson 9 Young 20 Davies 30	6
15	NL	A	Boreham Wood		**W** 3 - 2	Hall-Johnson 60 89 Ponticelli 88	5
18	NL	H	Notts County		L 0 - 1		6
22	NL	H	King's Lynn Town		**W** 5 - 3	Young 18 (pen) Davies 35 Omotayo 43 82 Ponticelli 65	6
29	NL	A	Dagenham & Redbridge		D 1 - 1	Ponticelli 90 (RC - Rutherford 56)	8

Goalcorers	LGE	FAC	FAT	SG	CSG	HAT	PEN	1Q	2Q	45+	3Q	4Q	90+	T
TOTALS	**67**	**0**	**0**			**1**	**6**	**11**	**18**	**3**	**14**	**14**	**6**	**67**
Young	12			11	1		6	3	4		3	1	1	12
Thomas	10			7	2			1	3	1	2	3		10
Hall-Johnson	8			7	1				2	1	3	1	1	8
Davies	7			5	2	1		1	4		1		1	7
Angus	6			5	1			1	1	1	1	2		6
Yussuf	5			4	2			1	1			2	1	5
Ponticelli	4			4	1						1	2	1	4
Vassell	4			3	2			1			1	1		4
Omotayo	3			2	1				1			1	1	3
Durrell	2			2	1						1	1		2
Reckord	2			2	1			1	1					2
Harris	1			1	1				1					1
Kelleher	1			1	1						1			1
Opponent	1			1	1			1						1
Pearson	1			1	1			1						1

Reckord J	Kelleher F	Hall-Johnson R	Vassell T	Durrell E	Harris J	Young L	Jeffrey A	Yussuf A (L)	Thomas K	Rutherford P	Horsfield J	Dibble C (Gk)	Bickerstaff J	Ponticelli J	Davies J	Carrington M	Jarvis D	Redmond D	Cleworth M	Pearson S	French T	Angus D	Austin R	Marsh-Brown K	Omotayo G	Sang C	Green C	No.
x	x	x	x	xs	x	x	xs	x	x	sx	sx	s	s	s														1
x	x	x	x	sx	xs	x	sx		x	xs		s	xs	sx	x	s												2
x	x	x	x	sx	x	x	xs		x	x		s		sx	xs	s	s											3
x	x	x	x	xs	xs	x		sx	xs	sx	s	s		x			sx											4
x	x	x	x	x	x	x		x	x	xs	s	s			s		sx	s										5
c	**c**	**sc**	**c**	**c**	**c**	**c**		**c**	**sc**		**cs**	**cn**			**c**		**cs**		**cn**									6
x	x	xs	xs	x	x	x	x	sx	x		sx	s	xs		sx		s											7
x	x	sx	x	xs	x	x		sx	x		x	s		xs	s				s									8
x	x		x	x	x	x		sx	x	x	x	s		xs	s		s		s									9
x	x	s	x	xs	xs	x	sx	sx	x	x	x	s		xs	sx													10
x	x	s	x	sx	xs	x	xs	x	x	x	x	sx	s		sx													11
x	x	x	x	xs		x	sx	xs	x	xs	s	x	sx		x		sx	s										12
x	x	s	x	x	x	x	sx	sx	xs	x	x	x	xs		s		s											13
xs	x	x	x	xs	x	x		sx	xs		s	s		x	sx		sx			x								14
tn		**tn**		**t**			**st**	**ts**	**t**	**ts**	**t**	**t**	**st**		**t**	**t**	**t**		**t**	**t**								15
	x	x	x	xs	xs	x		sx	xs	sx	s	s		x	x		sx			x								16
	x	x	x	s	x	x		xs	sx	sx	x	s		x	x		xs	s										17
	x	xs	x	sx	x	x		x	s	sx	x	s		xs	x		xs	sx										18
	x	x	x	sx	x	x		x	sx	s	x	s		xs	x		xs	s										19
x	x	xs		s	x	x		xs	x	sx	x	x		sx	x	x	s	s										20
x	x	s		s	x	x			x	s	x	x		sx	x	x	s				x	xs						21
x	x	x		s	x	x			x	sx		x		sx	x	x	xs	s				xs	s					22
x	x	x		s	x	x			x	s	s	x			x	x	s	s			x	x						23
x	x	x		sx		x			x	s	s	x		s	x	x	xs	s			x	x						24
x	x	xs		sx		x			x	s	xs	x		sx	xs	x	sx	s			x	x						25
x	x	xs		sx	s	x			x	s	sx	x		sx	x	x	xs				x	xs						26
x	x		x	xs		x			x	sx	sx	x		sx	xs	x	s				x	xs	s					27
x	x	x		x	s	x			x	s	s	x		s	x	x	s				x	x						28
x	x	s	x	xs	sx	x			x			x		sx	x	x	s				x	xs						29
x	x	x	x	xs	sx	x			x			x		sx	xs	x	sx				s	xs						30
x	x	x	x	xs	x	x			x			x		sx	sx	x	s				s	xs						31
x		xs	x	sx	x	x			x			s		sx	xs	sx	s			x	x	xs						32
x	sx	x	x	sx	xs	x						s		xs	xs	s	sx			x	x	x						33
x	x	x		s	x	x				sx	s	x			xs	x	xs	s		sx	x	x						34
x	x	x				x				sx	s	x			x	x	xs			s	x	x		xs	sx	s		35
x	x	s				x				x		x			x	x	s	sx		x	x	xs		s	xs	sx		36
x	x	xs			sx	x				xs		x			x	x		s		x	sx	xs		s	x	sx		37
x	x	x	x		sx	x				x		s			xs					x	s	xs		sx	x	s		38
	x	x	x		xs	x				sx		s		sx	x		s			x	s	xs			x		x	39
x	x		x		sx	x				xs		s		s	x		s			x	x	sx			x	xs		40
	x	x	x		xs	x				sx		s		sx	xs		sx			x	s	xs			x		x	41
	x	x	x			x				xs		s		sx	x		sx			x	s	x		s	xs		x	42
	xs	x	x			x				s		s		sx	x		xs			x	sx	xs		sx	x		x	43
	x	xs	x		xs	x						s		xs	x		sx			x	sx	s		sx	x		x	44
	xs	x	x			x				sx	xs	s		x	x		sx			x	s	sx			xs		x	45
33	40	25	31	7	19	44	1	6	24	7	11	19	0	5	25	17	1	0	1	15	14	8	0	0	7	0	6	x
1	2	8	1	11	9	0	3	4	4	7	3	0	3	7	9	0	10	0	0	0	0	14	0	1	3	1	0	xs
0	1	2	0	10	5	0	5	8	3	13	4	1	2	16	5	1	12	2	0	1	3	2	0	3	1	2	0	sx
1	0	7	0	6	2	0	0	0	1	8	10	25	2	4	4	3	15	11	3	1	7	1	2	3	0	2	0	s

so Played: Fielding J - 05/04 (s).

OALKEEPERS	CS	CCS
ibble	9	3
ainton	9	4

Dior Angus Elliott Durrell

Fiacre Kelleher Jamie Reckford

Jay Harris Jordan Davies

Jordan Ponticelli Luke Young

Reece Hall Johnson Rob Lainton

Theo Vassell Tyler French

x/c/t - Played full 90 minutes | xs/cs/ts - Substituted off | sx/sc/st - Substituted on | s/cn/tn - Non-playing sub

REEVES
4
JARVIS
12
light source.
gibbs & d
t: 0115 989 4466
sharpesofnottingham.com
13

Notts County 1 - 0 Wrexham - 18/05/2021

Photos Bill Wheatcroft

Notts County celebrate Mark Ellis' winning goal.

YEOVIL TOWN MATCH RESULTS 2020-21

Date	Comp	H/A	Opponents	Att:	Result		Goalscorers	Pos
Oct 3	NL	A	King's Lynn Town		D	2 - 2	Wilkinson 46 Duffus 81	10
6	NL	H	Wealdstone		D	2 - 2	Murphy 46 Lee 60	15
10	NL	H	Wrexham		L	0 - 1		17
13	NL	A	FC Halifax		D	1 - 1	Duffus 53	17
17	NL	A	Dagenham & Redbridge		D	0 - 0		16
24	**FAC4Q**	**H**	**Dover Athletic**		**D**	**3 - 3**	**Murphy 10 30 Quigley 48 (Won 7-6 on pens)**	
27	NL	H	Sutton United		L	1 - 2	Quigley 45+6	18
31	NL	H	Chesterfield		L	0 - 1		22
Nov 7	**FAC1P**	**A**	**Bromley**		**W**	**1 - 0**	**Rogers 120+2**	
14	NL	A	Woking		D	1 - 1	Warburton 44	23
21	NL	H	Hartlepool United		L	1 - 3	Quigley 45+1	23
29	**FAC2P**	**A**	**Stockport County**		**L**	**2 - 3**	**Warburton 2 Wilkinson 70**	
Dec 1	NL	H	Eastleigh		L	1 - 3	Quigley 68	23
8	NL	A	Bromley		**W**	2 - 1	Murphy 8 Quigley 45+1	21
26	NL	A	Torquay United	1328	L	1 - 6	Skendi 48	22
28	NL	H	Aldershot Town		**W**	3 - 0	Duffus 16 78 Skendi 88 (RC 2xY - Quigley 90+3)	20
Jan 2	NL	H	Torquay United		**W**	2 - 1	Neufville 88 Wilkinson 90+1	19
5	NL	A	Weymouth		**W**	3 - 0	Neufville 15 Skendi 19 Quigley 88 (pen)	19
27	NL	A	Maidenhead United		L	2 - 4	Skendi 19 76	20
30	NL	H	Dover Athletic		**W**	3 - 1	Quigley 45 52 Murphy 78	19
Feb 6	NL	A	Stockport County		L	0 - 1	(RC - Collins 90+4)	19
9	NL	A	Eastleigh		L	0 - 1		19
13	NL	H	Altrincham		**W**	2 - 0	Murphy 65 Dagnall 81	17
16	NL	A	Boreham Wood		**W**	3 - 2	Murphy 15 Reid 34 (pen) Neufville 41	15
20	NL	A	Hartlepool United		L	1 - 2	Knowles 54	17
23	NL	H	Weymouth		**W**	3 - 1	Murphy 3 53 82	16
27	NL	H	Dagenham & Redbridge		**W**	1 - 0	Knowles 89	13
Mar 2	NL	A	Barnet		**W**	4 - 1	Smith J 11 Sass-Davies 13 Murphy 59 Neufville 80	10
6	NL	A	Chesterfield		L	0 - 3		12
9	NL	A	Sutton United		L	1 - 2	Reid 56	13
13	NL	H	Woking		**W**	2 - 1	Murphy 32 59	11
16	NL	H	Bromley		L	1 - 2	Murphy 64 (pen)	12
20	NL	A	Notts County		L	0 - 2		14
23	NL	H	Notts County		D	2 - 2	Smith J 30 Reid 38 (pen)	14
29	NL	H	Barnet		**W**	3 - 1	Knowles 10 Lee 25 Neufville 34	14
Apr 17	NL	H	Boreham Wood		**W**	1 - 0	Knowles 28	15
24	NL	A	Solihull Moors		L	1 - 5	Murphy 54	16
27	NL	H	Solihull Moors		**W**	3 - 0	Quigley 27 54 72	16
May 1	NL	A	Wealdstone		**W**	2 - 0	Knowles 14 Quigley 24	13
3	NL	H	FC Halifax		L	0 - 3		16
8	NL	A	Wrexham		L	0 - 3		16
11	NL	A	Aldershot Town		L	0 - 2	(RC - Bradley 55)	16
15	NL	H	King's Lynn Town		**W**	3 - 1	Knowles 8 12 Sonupe 84	16
18	NL	H	Maidenhead United	1497	D	0 - 0	(RC 2xY - Wilkinson 62)	15
22	NL	A	Altrincham		L	3 - 4	Sonupe 56 Quigley 69 Lee 72	15
29	NL	H	Stockport County		L	0 - 1		16

Goalcorers	LGE	FAC	FAT	SG	CSG	HAT	PEN	1Q	2Q	45+	3Q	4Q	90+	T
TOTALS	**61**	**6**	**0**			**2**	**4**	**15**	**12**	**4**	**17**	**18**	**1**	**67**
Murphy	13	2		11	2	1	1	4	2		7	2		15
Quigley	12	1		10	2	1	1		2	4	3	4		13
Knowles	7			6	2			4	1		1	1		7
Neufville	5			5	2			1	2			2		5
Skendi	5			4	2			2			1	2		5
Duffus	4			3	1			1			1	2		4
Lee	3			3	1				1		1	1		3
Reid	3			3	1		2		2		1			3
Wilkinson	2	1		3	1						1	2		3
Smith J	2			2	1			1	1					2
Sonupe	2			2	1						1	1		2
Warburton	1	1		2	1			1	1					2
Dagnall	1			1	1							1		1
Rogers		1		1	1								1	1
Sass-Davies	1			1	1			1						1

Smith A	Lee C	Dickinson C	Collins L	Wilkinson L	Leadbitter D (L)	Staunton J	Worthington M	Clarke J (L)	Murphy R	Duffus C	Smith J	D'Ath L	Rogers G	Palmer H (Gk)	Burke R (L)	Skendi A	Warburton M (L)	Quigley J	Lloyd A	Williams M (L)	Bradley A (L)	Dagnall C	John A	Osho G (L)	Knowles T	Sonupe E	Neufville J (L)	Hunt M (L)	Reid R	Kelly M (L)	Evans M (Gk)	Sass-Davies B (L)	Stephens T	Heaton A	Medrano J	No.
x	x	x	x	x	x	x	xs	xs	x	x	sx	sx	s	s																						1
x	x	x	sx	x	x	x	x	xs	sx	x	xs	xs	sx	s	s																					2
x	x	xs	x	x	x	s	xs		x	sx	xs	s	sx		sx	x	x																			3
x	x	s		x	x	x	s		xs	x	s		sx		xs	x	x	sx																		4
x	x	sx	xs	x	x	x	sx	s	xs		sx		xs		s	x	x	x																		5
c	cs	c			c	c	sc	cn	c		sc	cs	cs	cn	sc	c	c	c	cn																	6
x	xs	sx		x	x	xs		sx	x		sx	x	x	s	s	x	xs	x																		7
x	x	x		x	x		xs		sx		sx	s	sx	s	xs	x	xs	x		x																8
c	c	c		c				cn	c		sc	cs	sc	cn	cn	c	cs	c		c	c															9
x	x	x		x			s		x		s	x	s	s	s	x	x	x		x	x															10
x				x			s		x	sx	xs	xs	sx	s	x	x	x	x	sx	xs	x															11
c	c	c		c	sc	c			sc	cs	sc		sc	cn	cn	c	cs	c			cs	cs	cn													12
x	x	x		x	sx	xs			sx	x			s	s		x	x	sx				xs		x	xs											13
x	x	x		x	x		s		xs	sx						x	xs	x				s		x	sx	xs	sx									14
x	xs	x			x		s			sx		sx		s		x	xs	x				xs		x	sx	x		x								15
x	xs	x		x			xs			xs		x				x	s	x				s		x	sx	sx	sx	x								16
x	xs	x		x			xs			xs		x		s		x	sx				x	s			sx	sx	x	x								17
x		x		x			x					x		s		xs	s	x			x	sx			sx	sx	xs	x	xs							18
x	xs	x	sx				x		sx		x					x		xs			x	s			sx		xs	x	x	s						19
x			x				x		sx		s					x	sx	x			x	sx			xs		xs	x	xs	x	s					20
x		s	x				x		sx		s					x	sx	xs			xs	sx			xs		x	x	x	x						21
x	xs	s					x		x							x	sx	sx			xs	sx			s		x	x	xs	x		x				22
x		x							sx		xs					x	sx	xs			x	sx			x		x	x	xs	s	s	x				23
x		x					s		x		x					x	sx	sx			x	sx			x		xs	x	xs	s		xs				24
x		x					x		xs		xs					x	sx	sx			x	sx			xs		x	x	x	s	s					25
x	s	x					x		xs		x					x		sx			x	sx			sx		xs	x	xs	s		x				26
x	s	xs					xs		xs		x					x		sx			x	s			sx		x	x	x	sx		x				27
x	sx	s					s		x		x					xs		sx			x	sx			x		xs	x	xs	x		x				28
x	sx	s					sx		x		xs					x		sx			x	s			x		xs	x	xs	x		x				29
x	s	s					xs		xs		x					x		sx			x	sx			xs		sx	x	x	x		x				30
x	x	x					sx		xs		s					x		sx			xs	sx			x		x	x	xs	s		x				31
x	xs	x					xs		x		sx					x		xs			x	s			sx		x	x	sx	s		x				32
x		xs					x		xs		x					x		sx				sx			xs		x	x	x	sx	s	x				33
x	x	x					xs				x					x	sx	sx				s			x	s	x	x	xs	x	s					34
x	x	x	s				x				sx					x	s	sx				x			xs	sx	xs	x	xs	x						35
x	sx	x		x			xs		sx		x					xs		sx				s			x		x	s	xs	x		x				36
x	sx	x		xs			x		x		xs					x		s				s			xs		sx	sx	x	x		x				37
x	xs	x					sx		sx		x					x		x				xs			xs	sx	x	s	s	x		x				38
x	x	x									x					x		xs			sx	x			xs	sx	xs	s	sx	x	s	x				39
x		x									xs					xs		x			sx	xs			x	sx	x	sx	x	x	s	x	s			40
x		x					xs		s							xs		x				x			xs	sx	x	sx	x	x	s	x	sx			41
x	x											sx						x			x	xs			x	x	x		x	x	s	x	sx	s	s	42
x	x	x		x								xs						sx				x			x	sx	xs		xs	x	s	x	sx			43
x	x	x		x								x						x				x			x	sx	xs		s	x	s	x	s	s		44
x	x	x										x						x				x			x	sx	xs		xs	x	s	x	sx	s		45
x	x	x									sx	xs						x			x	xs			x	sx			xs	x	s	x	sx	s		46
46	20	32	4	19	10	6	11	0	13	4	11	7	1	0	1	34	7	20	0	3	18	6	0	4	13	2	15	21	10	19	0	21	0	0	0	x
0	9	3	1	1	0	2	11	2	9	3	8	6	2	0	2	5	6	5	0	1	4	7	0	0	11	1	12	0	15	0	0	1	0	0	0	xs
0	4	2	2	0	2	0	5	1	10	4	10	3	7	0	2	0	8	16	1	0	2	12	0	0	9	12	4	3	2	2	0	0	5	0	0	sx
0	3	6	1	0	0	1	7	3	1	0	5	2	3	13	6	0	3	1	1	0	0	10	1	0	1	1	0	3	2	7	13	0	2	4	1	s

Also Played: Fielding J - 05/04 (s).

GOALKEEPERS	CS	CCS
Smith	10	2

x/c/t - Played full 90 minutes
xs/cs/ts - Substituted off
sx/sc/st - Substituted on
s/cn/tn - Non-playing sub

Rob Howard (Kings Lynn) Cameron Green (Wrexham).
jpg

Omotayo (Wrexham) v Richardson (Kings Lynn).

Young (Wrexham) looks to have been thwarted by Richardson (Kings Lynn)...

but the power of the shot is too much. Photos Keith Clayton.

NATIONAL LEAGUE NORTH

As at 17/02/21		P	W	D	L	F	A	GD	Pts
1	Gloucester City	18	10	5	3	36	22	14	35
2	Fylde	15	9	3	3	26	16	10	30
3	Chester	17	8	4	5	32	24	8	28
4	Brackley Town	16	7	6	3	22	19	3	27
5	Kidderminster Harriers	15	7	4	4	24	17	7	25
6	Boston United	13	6	5	2	20	10	10	23
7	Chorley	18	6	5	7	21	25	-4	23
8	York City	13	6	4	3	22	17	5	22
9	Leamington	15	5	7	3	22	20	2	22
10	Gateshead	14	6	3	5	17	15	2	21
11	Farsley Celtic	17	5	6	6	21	26	-5	21
12	Hereford	13	5	5	3	20	16	4	20
13	Spennymoor Town	13	5	5	3	18	14	4	20
14	AFC Telford United	17	5	4	8	17	23	-6	19
15	Bradford (Park Avenue)	16	4	6	6	26	30	-4	18
16	Curzon Ashton	17	4	5	8	18	26	-8	17
17	Southport	14	4	4	6	16	19	-3	16
18	Kettering Town	14	3	6	5	21	23	-2	15
19	Darlington	11	4	1	6	17	11	6	13
20	Guiseley	15	3	3	9	17	22	-5	12
21	Alfreton Town	15	2	6	7	15	27	-12	12
22	Blyth Spartans	14	1	3	10	10	36	-26	6

Alfreton Town v Darlington. Photo Bill Wheatcroft.

AFC FYLDE MATCH RESULTS 2020-21

Date	Comp	H/A	Opponents	Att:	Result	Goalscorers	Pos
Oct 3	**FAC1Q**	**A**	**Hyde United**	**404**	**W 4 - 2**	**Haughton Willoughby Tollitt Burgess 90**	
6	NLN	H	Darlington		W 1 - 0	Haughton 78	9
10	NLN	A	Gateshead		W 1 - 0	Haughton 71	3
13	**FAC3Q**	**A**	**Farsley Celtic**		**W 3 - 1**	**Burgess 21 79 Haughton 29**	
24	**FAC4Q**	**H**	**Altrincham**		**W 2 - 1**	**Hulme 43 Tollitt 54**	
28	NLN	H	Kettering Town		W 3 - 2	Philliskirk 65 Hulme 76 Haughton 88	2
31	NLN	H	Farsley Celtic		W 2 - 0	Shaw 55 Tollitt 85	2
Nov 3	NLN	A	Alfreton Town		D 1 - 1	Burke 38	1
7	**FAC1P**	**A**	**Exeter City**		**L 1 - 2**	**Hulme 11**	
10	NLN	H	Spennymoor Town		W 1 - 0	Haughton 88	2
17	NLN	A	Curzon Ashton		L 0 - 2		2
24	NLN	A	Leamington		D 1 - 1	Philliskirk 47	3
28	NLN	H	Boston United		W 2 - 1	Nolan 54 Shaw 65	3
Dec 1	NLN	H	Bradford (Park Avenue)		D 3 - 3	Tollitt 13 Willoughby 15 Conlan 66	2
12	NLN	A	Hereford	800	L 1 - 2	Perkins 7	3
15	**FAT2P**	**A**	**Curzon Ashton**		**W 4 - 1**	**Mondal 8 73 Sanders 82 Willoughby 86 (pen)**	
19	**FAT3P**	**A**	**Boston United**		**D 1 - 1**	**Mondal 1 (lost 2-4 on pens)**	
26	NLN	A	Chorley		L 1 - 3	Tollitt 19	6
Jan 2	NLN	H	Chorley		W 4 - 0	Tollitt 42 74 87 (pen) Philliskirk 67	4
9	NLN	A	AFC Telford United		W 2 - 0	Hulme 28 Sampson 78	3
Feb 16	NLN	A	York City		W 3 - 1	Whitmore 45+1 Haughton 57 80	2

Goalscorers	LGE	FAC	FAT	SG	CSG	HAT	PEN	1Q	2Q	45+	3Q	4Q	90+	T
TOTALS	26	10	5			0	2	9	8	1	8	14	1	41
Haughton	6	2		7	4			1	1		1	5		8
Tollitt	6	2		6	2		1	2	2		1	3		8
Hulme	2	2		4	2			1	2			1		4
Burgess		3		2	1			1				1	1	3
Mondal			3	2	2			2				1		3
Philliskirk	3			3	1				1		2			3
Willoughby	1	1	1	3	1		1	1	1			1		3
Shaw	2			2	1						2			2
Burke	1			1	1				1					1
Conlon	1			1	1						1			1
Nolan	1			1	1						1			1
Perkins	1			1	1			1						1
Sampson	1			1	1							1		1
Sanders			1	1	1							1		1
Whitmore	1			1	1					1				1

Neal C	Pond N	Conlan L	Burke L	Whitmore A	Perkins D	Philliskirk D	Tollitt B	Burgess L (L)	Hulme J	Willoughby K	Mondal J	Haughton N	Shaw N (L)	Johnstone M (Gk)	Nolan L	Lussey J	Byrne J	Ogle R (L)	Sanders J (L)	Sampson J	Stanley J	Brennan L (L)	Lancaster A (Gk)	Thomas L (Gk) (L)	Osborne S	Obi E	No.
c			c		c		c	c		c	c	c	c														1
x	x	x	x	x	x	x	xs	xs	x	xs	sx	sx	sx	s	s												2
x	x	x	x	x	x	x	x	s	xs	sx	xs	xs	sx	s	sx												3
c	c	c	c	c	cn	cs	cn	c	sc	c	cn	cs	c	cn	c	sc	cn										4
c	cs	c	c	c	c	c	cs	c	c	cn	sc	cs	sc	cn		cn	cn	sc									5
x		x	x	x	x	x	xs		x	sx	xs	xs	sx			s		s	x	sx							6
x		x	x	x	x	x	sx		s	xs	sx	xs	x			s		s	x	x							7
x		x	x	x	x	x	x		xs	sx	sx	xs	xs			s		s	x	sx							8
c		c	c	c	sc	c	c		c	sc	sc	cs	cs			cs	cn	cn	c		cn						9
x	x	x	x	x	x	x	x		xs	sx	sx	xs	xs			s		sx	s								10
x	x	xs	x	xs	x	x	x		sx	xs	s	x	x			s		sx				sx					11
x	xs	x	x	x		x	xs		x	s	s	x	x		x	sx			s			sx					12
x		x	x	x		x	x		xs	sx	s	xs	xs		x	sx	s		x			sx					13
x		x	x	x		x	x		xs	x	s		sx		xs	sx		s	x	sx		xs					14
x	x	x	xs	x	x	x	x			x			x		xs	s		s	s	sx		sx					15
		t		t	ts	st	tn			t	t		tn		tn	t	st	ts	t	t		t	t				16
	t	t	tn	t		t	t			ts	ts		st		tn	t	tn	t	st	ts	tn	st		t			17
x	x	x	x	x		xs	x		sx	s	xs		x		sx	xs			s	x		sx					18
x	x	x	xs	x	x	x	x		x	s	s		x		s			sx	s	x							19
x	x	x	x	x	x	x	x		xs	s		sx	xs		s				s	x					sx		20
x	x	x	x	x	xs	x	x		sx	s	sx	xs			sx					x					xs	s	21
19	11	19	17	19	12	17	14	3	6	5	2	3	8	0	3	2	0	1	7	6	0	1	1	1	0	0	x
0	2	1	2	1	2	2	4	1	6	4	4	10	5	0	2	2	0	1	0	1	0	1	0	0	1	0	xs
0	0	0	0	0	1	1	1	0	4	6	7	2	6	0	3	4	1	4	1	4	0	6	0	0	1	0	sx
0	0	0	1	0	1	0	2	1	1	6	6	0	1	4	5	7	5	6	6	0	2	0	0	0	0	1	s

GOALKEEPERS	CS	CCS
Neal C	6	2

x/c/t - Played full 90 minutes
xs/cs/ts - Substituted off
sx/sc/st - Substituted on
s/cn/tn - Non-playing sub

AFC TELFORD UNITED MATCH RESULTS 2020-21

Date	Comp	H/A	Opponents	Att:	Result	Goalscorers	Pos
Oct 3	**FAC2Q**	**A**	**Chasetown**	**369**	**D 1 - 1**	**Hardy 83**	
6	NLN	H	Brackley Town		**W** 3 - 0	Williams 52 (pen) Oswell 85 Hardy 89	3
10	NLN	A	Blyth Spartans		D 1 - 1	Oswell 13	4
13	**FAC3Q**	**A**	**Leiston**	**334**	**D 0 - 0**	**(Lost 8-9 on pens)**	
17	NLN	H	Gateshead		**W** 3 - 0	Williams 52 (pen) Oswell 85 Hardy 89	2
24	NLN	A	Boston United		L 2 - 3	Williams 18 Oswell 66	3
31	NLN	H	Alfreton Town		L 0 - 1		7
Nov 7	NLN	H	Southport		D 1 - 1	Daniels 68	7
10	NLN	A	Gloucester City		L 1 - 4	McHale 2	9
14	NLN	A	Darlington		**W** 2 - 1	Oswell 6 McHale 51	5
17	NLN	H	Chorley		L 0 - 1		6
21	NLN	A	Bradford (Park Avenue)		**W** 2 - 1	McHale 26 47	4
28	NLN	H	Guiseley		**W** 2 - 0	Lilley 56 Davies 73 (pen)	4
Dec 5	NLN	A	Farsley Celtic		L 0 - 2		5
12	NLN	A	Kettering Town	514	D 0 - 0		6
15	**FAT2P**	**A**	**Coleshill Town**	**30**	**W 10- 1**	**McHale 7 23 45 Williams 18 61 89 Vaughan 19 Hardy 43 Byrne 72 Jones 79**	
19	**FAT3P**	**A**	**Darlington**		**D 2 - 2**	**Williams 45+1 78 (Lost 3-5 on pens)**	
26	NLN	H	Chester	1680	L 1 - 2	Williams 18	9
Jan 2	NLN	A	Chester		L 0 - 3		12
9	NLN	H	AFC Fylde		L 0 - 2		13
16	NLN	H	Curzon Ashton		D 1 - 1	Oswell 69	13

Goalscorers	LGE	FAC	FAT	SG	CSG	HAT	PEN	1Q	2Q	45+	3Q	4Q	90+	T
TOTALS	19	1	12			0	3	8	3	2	7	12	0	32
Williams	4		5	6	3		2	3		1	3	2		9
McHale	4		3	4	2			2	2	1	2			7
Oswell	6			6	2			2			1	3		6
Hardy	2	1	1	4	2				1			3		4
Byrne			1	1	1							1		1
Daniels	1			1	1							1		1
Davies	1			1	1		1					1		1
Jones			1	1	1							1		1
Lilley	1			1	1						1			1

	LGE	FAC	FAT	SG	CSG	HAT	PEN	1Q	2Q	45+	3Q	4Q	90+	T
Vaughan			1	1	1			1						1

No.	Griffiths R	Streete T	Vaughan L	Sutton S	Meppen-Walters C	Walker A	Cowans H	Hardy J	Byrne J	Oswell J	Williams A	McHale D	Barnes-Homer M	Rawlins A (Gk)	Davies J	Lilly Z	Bower H	Scott H (Gk)	White R	Daniels B	Jones E	Bond A	Sweeney J	Hall K (L)	Lenighan S (D)
1	c		c					c		c	c	sc			sc										
2	x	x	x	x	x	x	x	x	x	xs	xs	sx	sx	s	s	s									
3	x	x	x	x	x	x	x	xs	x	x	xs	sx	s	s	sx	s									
4	c	c	c	c	c	c	c	c	c	cs	cs	sc	cn	cn	sc	cn	cn	cn							
5	x	x	x	x	xs	x	x	x	x	xs	xs	sx	s	s	sx				sx						
6	x	x	x	x		x	x	xs	x	xs	xs	sx	sx	s	sx	s			xs						
7	x	x	xs	x		xs	x	x	x	x	xs	sx	s		sx	s			x	sx					
8	x	x	x	x		x		xs	x	x	xs	sx	s	s	sx	s			x	x					
9	x	x	x	x		x		xs	x	x		x	sx	s	sx	x	s		s	xs					
10	x	x	x	xs		x		sx		x	s	xs	s	s	x	x			sx		x	x			
11	x	x	x			x		sx	x	x	sx	x	s	s	xs	x			xs		x	s			
12	x	x	x			x		xs	xs	x	s	x	s		sx	x	s		sx		x	x			
13	x	x	x			x		xs	x	xs	s	x	sx	s	x	x	sx		s		x				
14	x	x	x		s	x		sx	x	x	s	x	sx	s	xs	x					xs	x			
15	x	x	x		x	x		x	x	xs	s		sx	s	x	s				xs	x	sx			
16	t	t	t		ts	ts		t	t		t	ts	st	tn	t	st	tn		tn		t	st			
17	t	t	t		t	ts		t	t		t	t	tn	tn	t	tn	tn		tn		t	st	tn		
18	x	x	x		x	x		x	x	sx	x	x	s	s	xs	s					x	s			
19	x	x	x		x	x		sx	xs	sx	xs	xs			x	s			s	sx	x	x			
20	x	x			x	x		x	xs	s	sx	x		s	sx				x		x	x		xs	s
21	x	x			s	x		xs	xs	sx	sx	x		s	sx	x			x		x	x		xs	
x	21	20	18	8	8	17	6	10	15	9	4	9	0	0	6	7	0	0	4	1	11	6	0	0	0
xs	0	0	1	1	2	3	0	7	4	6	8	3	0	0	3	0	0	0	2	2	1	0	0	2	0
sx	0	0	0	0	0	0	0	4	0	3	3	8	7	0	11	1	1	0	3	2	0	3	0	0	0
s	0	0	0	0	2	0	0	0	0	1	5	0	10	17	1	10	5	1	5	0	0	2	1	0	1

GOALKEEPERS	CS	CCS
Griffiths	5	2

x/c/t - Played full 90 minutes
xs/cs/ts - Substituted off
sx/sc/st - Substituted on
s/cn/tn - Non-playing sub

ALFRETON TOWN MATCH RESULTS 2020-21

Date	Comp	H/A	Opponents	Att:	Result	Goalscorers	Pos
Oct 3	**FAC2Q**	**A**	**Coalville Town**	**437**	**W 2 - 1**	**Smith 2 Day 21**	
5	NLN	A	Curzon Ashton		D 1 - 1	Jones 45+1	
10	NLN	H	Spennymoor Town		D 1 - 1	Reeves 44	12
31	NLN	A	AFC Telford United		**W** 1 - 0	Clarke 71	10
Nov 3	NLN	H	AFC Fylde		D 1 - 1	Reeves 64	9
7	NLN	A	Bradford (Park Avenue)		L 0 - 2		10
10	NLN	H	Brackley Town		L 0 - 2		13
14	NLN	H	Farsley Celtic		**W** 3 - 1	Jones 16 Reeves 23 Day 45	9
17	NLN	A	Leamington		L 3 - 4	Day 1 6 (pen) Reeves 21	10
21	NLN	H	Darlington		L 0 - 2		12
24	NLN	A	Kidderminster Harriers		L 0 - 3		14
Dec 1	NLN	A	Chester		L 0 - 3		16
5	NLN	A	Southport		D 1 - 1	Johnson 31	17
12	NLN	H	Chorley		D 1 - 1	Rawson 24	20
15	**FAT2P**	**H**	**Bedford Town**			**Match postponed - Alfreton progressed to the third round.**	
22	**FAT3P**	**H**	**King's Lynn Town**		**L 1 - 3**	**Johnson 76**	**20**
26	NLN	A	Boston United		L 0 - 2		20
28	NLN	H	Kettering Town		D 3 - 3	Day 6 Bradley 46 Reeves 80	21

Goalscorers	LGE	FAC	FAT	SG	CSG	HAT	PEN	1Q	2Q	45+	3Q	4Q	90+	T
TOTALS	15	2	1			0	1	7	4	2	2	3	0	18
Day	4	1		4	2		1	4		1				5
Reeves	5			5	2			1	2		1	1		5
Johnson	1		1	2	1				1			1		2
Jones	2			2	1			1		1				2
Bradley	1			1	1						1			1
Clarke	1			1	1							1		1
Rawson	1			1	1				1					1
Smith		1		1	1			1						1

	LGE	FAC	FAT	SG	CSG	HAT	PEN	1Q	2Q	45+	3Q	4Q	90+	T

Willis G	Clackstone J	Fox N	Branson C	Jones J	Lees T	Smith D	Bradley D	Day J	Clarke D	Johnson B	Adelekan AJ	Lund A	Grice H	Unwin-Marris T (Gk)	Babos A	Stacey J	Molyneaux R	Reeves E	Sketchley K	Atkinson W	Williams M	Walker N	Tuton S	Rawson L (L)	No.
c	c	cs	c	c	c	c	c	c	c	cs	scs	sc	sc	cn	cn	cn	cn								1
x	x	x	x	xs	x	x	x	sx	x	x		sx	s	s				xs	s						2
x	x	x	x	x	x	x	x	s	xs	x		s	s	s	sx			x							3
x		x	x	x	x	x	x	s	x	xs		s		s				xs		x	sx	sx			4
x	sx	x	x	x	x	x	x	s	xs	x		s		s				x		xs		sx			5
x	sx	xs	x	x	x	xs	x	sx		x		s		s				x		x		xs	sx		6
x	sx	x	x	x	x	x	x	sx		xs		s		s				xs		x	s	x			7
x	x	x	x	x	x	x	xs	x		sx		s		s				xs		x	s	sx			8
x	x	x	x	x	x	x	x	x		sx		sx		s				xs		xs	s	sx			9
x	x	x	x	x	xs	x	x	x	s	sx		s		s				x		xs		sx			10
x	x	x	xs	x	x	x	x	xs	sx	sx		s		s				xs		x		sx			11
x	x	x	x		x	x	x	xs	sx	xs		s		s				sx		x	s	x			12
x	x	sx	x		x	x	x		xs	x		x		s				sx		x	s	xs	s		13
x	x	sx	x	x	s	x	x		sx	xs		x						s		x		xs	sx	xs	14
t	t	st	t	t	tn	t	ts		tn	t		t		tn				st		t		ts	st	ts	15
x	x	s	x	xs	sx	x	x	sx	s	xs		x						x		x		sx		xs	16
x	x	x	x		x	x	x	x	x			x		s			s	x		s			s	s	17
17	13	11	16	12	13	16	15	5	4	6	0	5	0	0	0	0	0	6	0	10	0	2	0	0	x
0	0	2	1	2	1	1	2	2	3	6	0	0	0	0	0	0	0	6	0	3	0	4	0	3	xs
0	3	3	0	0	1	0	0	4	3	4	1	3	1	0	1	0	0	3	0	0	1	7	3	0	sx
0	0	1	0	0	2	0	0	3	3	0	0	9	2	15	1	1	2	1	1	1	5	0	2	1	s

GOALKEEPERS	CS	CCS
Willis	1	1

x/c/t - Played full 90 minutes
xs/cs/ts - Substituted off
sx/sc/st - Substituted on
s/cn/tn - Non-playing sub

Alfreton's Rawson gets a shot in despite Harvey Smith's challenge.

Alfreton's Will Atkinson (red) in a crunching tackle with Chorley's Arlew Birch.

Alfreton Town 1 - 1 Chorley - 12/12/2020

Photos Bill Wheatcroft

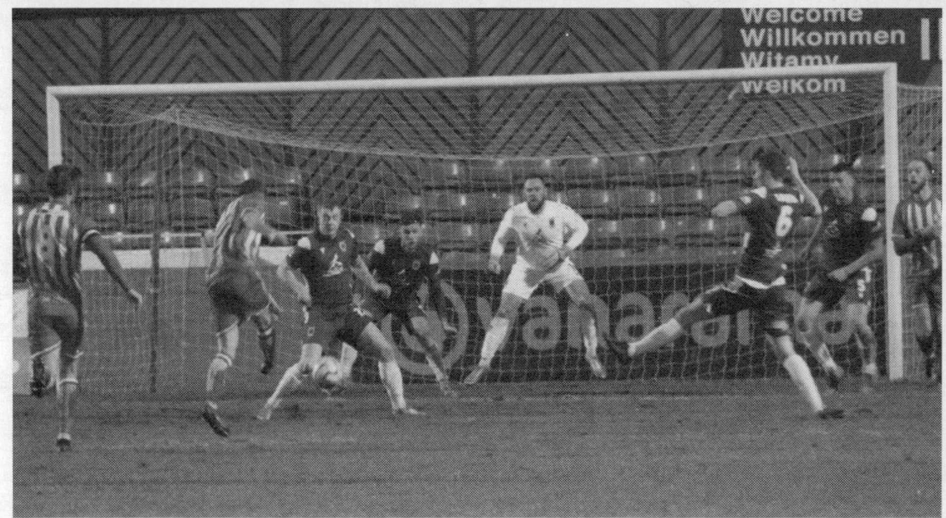

Chorley defenders block this Alfreton shot.

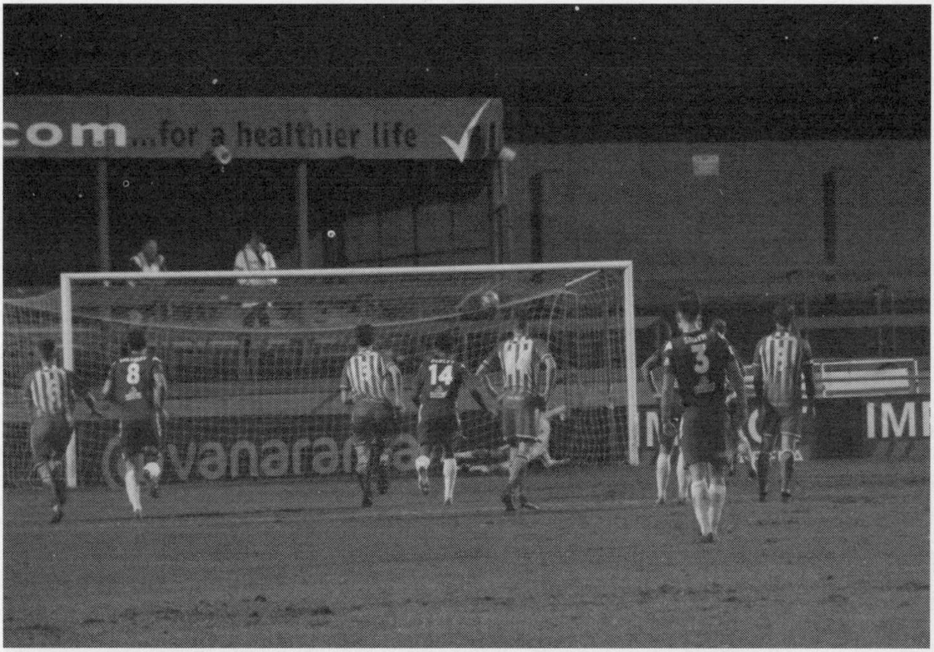

Alfreton v Chorley - Connor Hall's penalty gets Chorley a point at Alfreton. Photo Bill Wheatcroft.jpg

BLYTH SPARTANS MATCH RESULTS 2020-21

Date	Comp	H/A	Opponents	Att:	Result	Goalscorers	Pos
Oct 3	**FAC2Q**	**A**	**Whitley Bay**		**W 4 - 2**	**Heslop (3) Blackett**	
6	NLN	A	Guiseley		L 0 - 4		21
10	NLN	H	AFC Telford United		D 1 - 1	Blackett 90	17
13	**FAC3Q**	**A**	**Marske United**	**400**	**L 0 - 1**		
17	NLN	A	Gloucester City		L 1 - 6	Blackett 3	17
24	NLN	H	Southport		L 0 - 3		18
31	NLN	A	Kidderminster Harriers		L 0 - 2		21
Nov 7	NLN	A	Curzon Ashton		W 3 - 0	Thackray 35 Blackett 44 74	16
10	NLN	H	Farsley Celtic		D 1 - 1	Blackett 90+1	16
14	NLN	H	Hereford		L 0 - 3		17
Dec 2	NLN	H	York City		L 0 - 3		22
5	NLN	A	Kettering Town	637	L 1 - 2	Russell 72	22
8	NLN	H	Boston United		L 0 - 1		22
12	NLN	A	Brackley Town	380	L 1 - 2	O'Donnell 20	22
26	NLN	H	Gateshead		D 2 - 2	Agnew 26 McKeown 63	22
28	NLN	A	Darlington		L 0 - 6		22

Goalscorers	LGE	FAC	FAT	SG	CSG	HAT	PEN	1Q	2Q	45+	3Q	4Q	90+	T
TOTALS	10	4	0			1	0	2	3	0	1	2	2	14
Blackett	5	1		5	2			1	1			1	2	6
Heslop		3		1	1	1								3
Agnew	1			1	1				1					1
McKeown	1			1	1						1			1
O'Donnell	1			1	1			1						1
Russell	1			1	1							1		1
Thackray	1			1	1				1					1

	LGE	FAC	FAT	SG	CSG	HAT	PEN	1Q	2Q	45+	3Q	4Q	90+	T

No.	Pearson B	Sakellaropoulos A	Katsamagkas P	Heslop S	Guy C	McKeown C	Thomson C	Blackett P (L)	Evans R	Elsdon M	Scott O	Griffiths P	Russell K	Charlton K	Nelson M	Dart M	Cunningham A (L)	Taylor E	Young B (Gk) (L)	Thackray K	Agnew L	Gbolohan A	Cain M	Amantchi L	O'Donnell J (L)	Clark J
1	c	c	cs	c	cs	cs	c	c	c	c	c	sc	sc	sc	cn	cn										
2	x		sx	xs	x	xs	x	xs	x	x	x	x	sx	sx		s	x	s								
3	x		s	x	s	sx	x	x	x	x	x	x	x	xs		s	x	s								
4	c		sc	cs	sc	sc	c	c	c		cs	c	cs	c	c		c									
5	s		sx	x	sx		x	xs	x	x	xs	x	s	sx			x		x	x	xs					
6	s	x	xs	x	x	s	x			x		x	sx	s			x		x	x	xs	sx				
7	s	x	sx	x	xs	sx	x			x		xs	sx	s			x		x	x		xs	x			
8	s	x		x	xs	sx	x	xs		x		sx		sx		s	x		x	x		xs	x			
9		x		xs	x	sx	x	x		x		sx	s	xs		sx	x	s	x			xs	x			
10		x		x	xs	sx	xs	x	sx	x		xs	s			s	x		x	x		sx	x			
11	s	x		x	xs	s	xs	xs	x	x	sx	x	sx		x				x				x	sx		
12	s	s		x		sx			x	x	xs	sx	sx		x				x	xs			x	x	x	x
13	x	x		x	sx	s			x	x		x	sx		x	s							x	x	x	x
14	x	x		xs	xs	xs			x	x		x	sx	s					s		sx		sx	x	x	x
15	x	x		x	sx	sx	xs			x		x		x		s	x		s		xs		sx	x		xs
16	x	sx		xs		s	x	x	x	x		x		xs			xs		s		x		sx	sx	x	
x	8	10	0	11	3	0	10	6	10	15	3	10	1	2	4	0	10	0	8	5	1	0	7	4	4	3
xs	0	0	2	5	6	3	3	4	0	0	3	2	1	3	0	0	1	0	0	1	3	3	0	0	0	1
sx	0	1	4	0	4	8	0	0	1	0	1	4	8	4	0	1	0	0	0	0	1	2	3	2	0	0
s	6	1	1	0	1	4	0	0	0	0	0	0	3	3	1	7	0	3	3	0	0	0	0	0	0	0

GOALKEEPERS	CS	CCS
Young	1	1

x/c/t - Played full 90 minutes
xs/cs/ts - Substituted off
sx/sc/st - Substituted on
s/cn/tn - Non-playing sub

BOSTON UNITED MATCH RESULTS 2020-21

Date	Comp	H/A	Opponents	Att:	Result	Goalscorers	Pos
Oct 3	**FAC2Q**	**H**	**AFC Mansfield**		**W 4 - 2**	**Hawkridge 12 Burrow 13 Shiels 43 Preston 74**	
6	NLN	A	Leamington		**W** 4 - 0	Green 39 Shiels 68 Garner 77 Thewlis 85	1
24	NLN	H	AFC Telford United		**W** 3 - 2	Thewlis 21 Burrow 45+2 Garner 47	5
27	NLN	H	Guiseley		D 1 - 1	Hawkridge 55	4
31	NLN	A	Southport		**W** 1 - 0	Thewlis 14	3
Nov 28	NLN	A	AFC Fylde		L 1 - 2	Burrow 20	13
Dec 1	NLN	A	Gloucester City		D 0 - 0		12
5	NLN	H	Chorley		L 0 - 2		14
8	NLN	A	Blyth Spartans		**W** 1 - 0	Garner 52	11
12	NLN	H	Chester		D 0 - 0		12
14	**FAT2P**	**A**	**Evesham United**	**370**	**W 3 - 0**	**Rollins 34 Leesley 57 Burrow 90+2**	
19	**FAT3P**	**H**	**AFC Fylde**		**D 1 - 1**	**Dimaio 83 (Won 4-2 on pens)**	
26	NLN	H	Alfreton Town		**W** 2 - 0	Leesley 45 Platt 52	6
28	NLN	A	Farsley Celtic		**W** 4 - 0	Leesley 25 58 Preston 53 Rollins 83	3
Jan 5	NLN	H	Kettering Town		D 2 - 2	Burrow 59 Shiels 63	6
11	NLN	A	Bradford (Park Avenue)		D 1 - 1	Thewlis 67	6
20	**FAT4P**	**H**	**Chesterfield**		**D 1 - 1**	**Garner 50 (Lost 1-4 on on pens)**	

Goalscorers	LGE	FAC	FAT	SG	CSG	HAT	PEN	1Q	2Q	45+	3Q	4Q	90+	T
TOTALS	20	4	5			0	0	5	4	2	11	6	1	29
Burrow	3	1	1	5	1			2		1	1		1	5
Garner	3		1	4	2						3	1		4
Leesley	3		1	3	2				1	1	2			4
Thewlis	4			4	2			2			1	1		4
Shiels	2	1		3	2				1		1	1		3
Hawkridge	1	1		2	1			1			1			2
Preston	1	1		2	1						1	1		2
Rollins	1		1	2	1				1			1		2
Dimaio			1	1	1							1		1
Green	1			1	1				1					1
Platt	1			1	1						1			1

Fitzsimons R	Warren T	Shiels L	Gibbens L	Askew J	Thanoj A	Platt T	Dimaio C	Thewlis J	Burrow J	Hawkridge T	Preston F	Green P	Archer J	Tootle M	Duxbury S	Garner S	Crook P (Gk)	Rose M	Rollins J	Leesley J (L)	Bird P (L)	Wright J	No.
c	c	c	c	c	cs	c	cs	c	cs	c	sc	sc	sc	cn	cn	cn	cn						1
x	s	x		s	xs	x	sx	sx	xs	xs	x	x	sx	x	x	x							2
x	sx	x		s	xs	x	sx	xs	x	xs		x	sx	x	x	x	s						3
x	sx	x		s	s	x	x	xs	x	xs		x	sx	x	x	x	s						4
x	s	x			x	x	s	xs	x	x	sx	x	s	x	x	x	s						5
x		x			s		x	sx	x	xs	xs	x		x	x	x	s	xs	sx	sx			6
x		x			x		xs	sx	x	xs	sx	sx		x	x	x	s	x	s	xs			7
x		x			x		x	x	x	sx	s	sx		x	x	xs	s	xs	xs	sx			8
x		x		x	x		xs	xs	x	xs	sx	x		x	s	x		s	sx	sx			9
x		x			xs	sx	s	x	x	xs	s	x		x	x	x		xs	sx	sx			10
tn	t	t				st	ts	ts	st	st	t	ts		tn	tn	t	t	t	t	t			11
t	st	t				t	st		t	ts	t	t		ts	ts	st	tn			t	t		12
x	s	xs				x	x		x	xs	x	sx		x	x	sx	s		sx	xs	x		13
x	sx	x				x	x		xs	x	xs	s		xs	x	sx	s		sx	x	x		14
x		x			sx	x	xs	sx	x	xs	xs	s		x	x	s			sx	x	x		15
x		x			x	xs	sx	x	x	s	sx	sx		x	x	s			xs	xs	x		16
t	tn	t			t		t	ts	t	st	tn	t		t	st	t	tn	tn	ts	ts		st	17
16	2	16	1	2	6	9	6	4	13	3	4	9	0	13	12	10	1	2	1	4	5	0	x
0	0	1	0	0	4	1	5	6	3	10	3	1	0	2	1	1	0	3	3	4	0	0	xs
0	4	0	0	0	1	2	4	4	1	3	5	5	4	0	1	3	0	0	6	4	0	1	sx
1	4	0	0	3	2	0	2	0	0	1	3	2	1	2	3	3	11	2	1	0	0	0	s

GOALKEEPERS	CS	CCS
Fitzsimons	7	2
Crook	1	1

x/c/t - Played full 90 minutes
xs/cs/ts - Substituted off
sx/sc/st - Substituted on
s/cn/tn - Non-playing sub

BRACKLEY TOWN MATCH RESULTS 2020-21

Date	Comp	H/A	Opponents	Att:	Result	Goalscorers	Pos
Oct 3	**FAC2Q**	**H**	**Billericay Town**		**D 2 - 2**	**Rolt 79 90 (Won 4-2 on pens)**	
6	NLN	A	AFC Telford United		L 0 - 3		20
10	NLN	H	Curzon Ashton		D 2 - 2	Armson 22 Murombedzi 40	16
17	NLN	A	York City		D 0 - 0		15
24	**FAC4Q**	**H**	**Marske United**		**W 5 - 1**	**Mitford 15 72 Ndlovu 24 32 Armson 81**	
Nov 7	**FAC1P**	**H**	**Bishop's Stortford**		**D 3 - 3**	**Ndlovu 14 Lowe 21 Mitford 69 (Won 3-2 on pens)**	
10	NLN	A	Alfreton Town		W 2 - 0	Mitford 41 Byrne 70	14
14	NLN	A	Gateshead		D 2 - 2	Mitford 86 Ndlovu 90	15
17	NLN	H	Kidderminster Harriers		L 0 - 2		16
21	NLN	H	Chester		D 1 - 1	Lowe 61	17
27	**FAC2P**	**A**	**Tranmere Rovers**		**L 0 - 1**		
Dec 1	NLN	A	Leamington		D 1 - 1	Ndlovu 83	20
5	NLN	A	Guiseley		W 3 - 1	Byrne 71 Coleman 89 York 90+4	16
8	NLN	H	Spennymoor Town		W 1 - 0	Lowe 90	13
12	NLN	H	Blyth Spartans	380	W 2 - 1	Byrne 6 (pen) Ndlovu 44	9
15	**FAT2P**	**H**	**Royston Town**	**159**	**W 3 - 2**	**Chambers 1 52 Byrne 17**	
19	**FAT3P**	**A**	**Chesterfield**		**D 0 - 0**	**(Lost 3-4 on pens)**	
28	NLN	H	Gloucester City		W 3 - 2	Byrne 32 (pen) 88 Ndlovu 44	8
Jan 2	NLN	H	Kettering Town		D 1 - 1	Byrne 88 (pen)	7
5	NLN	H	Darlington		W 2 - 0	York 1 Armson 84	5
Feb 6	NLN	H	Chorley		W 2 - 1	Armson 59 York 62	4
16	NLN	A	Hereford		L 0 - 2		4

Goalcorers	LGE	FAC	FAT	SG	CSG	HAT	PEN	1Q	2Q	45+	3Q	4Q	90+	T
TOTALS	22	10	3			0	3	8	7	0	4	12	4	35
Byrne	6		1	6	2		3	2	1			4		7
Ndlovu	4	3		6	2			1	4			1	1	7
Mitford	2	3		4	4			1	1			3		5
Armson	3	1		4	2			1			1	2		4
Lowe	2	1		3	1			1			1		1	3
York	3			3	1			1			1		1	3
Chambers			2	1	1			1			1			2
Rolt (L)		2		1	1							1	1	2
Coleman	1			1	1							1		1
Murombedzi	1			1	1				1					1

No.	Lewis D	Myles E	Franklin C	Byrne S	Flowers H	Walker G	Lowe M	Murombedzi S	Ndlovu L	York W	Coleman E	Armson J	Mitford T	Rolt B (L)	Phillips A	Noon M	Worby A (Gk)	Chambers A	Dean G	Cullinane-Liburd J	McNally R (L)	Hinds A	Roberts M (L)	Tee C
1	**c**	**c**	**cs**	**c**	**c**	**cs**	**c**	**c**	**c**	**cs**	**c**	**sc**	**sc**	**sc**	**cn**	**cn**								
2	x	x		x	x		x	x	x	xs	x	sx	sx	xs	s	s	s							
3	x	x	x	x	x		x	x	x	xs	x	xs	sx	sx	s		s	s						
4	x	x	x	x	s		x	x	x	xs	x	xs	sx	s		s		sx	x					
5		**c**	**c**	**c**	**c**		**c**	**c**	**cs**	**sc**	**c**	**sc**	**cs**	**sc**		**cn**	**c**	**cs**						
6	**c**	**c**	**cs**	**c**	**sc**	**cs**	**c**	**c**	**c**	**sc**	**c**	**sc**	**cs**	**cn**		**cn**	**cn**	**cs**	**sc**					
7		xs		x	sx	x	xs	x	x	sx	x		x			s	x	s	x	xs				
8	s	xs		x	s	x	x	xs	x	sx	x		x			s	x	sx	x	x				
9	s	xs		x	s	xs	x	x	x	sx	x		x			s	x	sx	x	x				
10	s	sx		x	xs		x	xs	x	sx	x	sx	x			s	x	xs	x	x				
11	**c**	**cn**	**cs**	**c**	**sc**		**c**	**c**	**c**	**sc**	**cs**	**c**	**cs**		**cn**		**cn**	**sc**	**c**		**c**	**cn**		
12	x	sx	x	x			xs	x	x	sx	x	x	xs					sx	x	s	xs	s		
13	x	sx		x			sx	sx	x	x	x	xs	xs		s			s	x	x	xs	x		
14	x	sx		x			x	sx	x	x	x	xs	s		s			s	x	x	x	xs		
15	x	s		x			xs	sx	x	xs	x	x	sx					s	x	x	x	s	x	
16	**t**	**t**		**t**				**t**	**st**	**t**	**t**	**st**	**t**			**tn**	**tn**	**ts**	**t**			**t**	**ts**	
17	**t**	**t**		**t**				**t**	**t**	**t**	**t**	**t**	**st**			**tn**	**tn**	**ts**	**t**			**tn**	**t**	
18	x	xs		x			sx	x	x	x	x	xs	sx				s	xs	x	x	sx	s		
19	x	x	sx	x			sx	xs	xs	x	x	x	sx				s	xs	x	x				s
20	x	x	sx	x			sx	x		x	x	x	xs			s	s	xs	xs	x				sx
21	x	xs	x			sx	x	x	xs	x	x	xs	sx					s	x	x	sx			s
22	x	x	sx			xs	x	x	x	x	x	xs	s					s	x	s	x			sx
X	17	11	5	20	4	2	13	16	17	9	21	6	5	0	0	0	5	0	16	10	4	2	2	0
XS	0	5	3	0	1	4	3	3	3	5	1	7	6	1	0	0	0	8	1	1	2	1	1	0
SX	0	4	3	0	3	1	4	3	1	8	0	6	9	3	0	0	0	5	1	0	2	0	0	2
S	3	2	0	0	3	0	0	0	0	0	0	0	2	2	6	12	9	7	0	2	0	5	0	2

GOALKEEPERS	CS	CCS
Lewis	4	1
Worby	1	1

x/c/t - Played full 90 minutes
xs/cs/ts - Substituted off
sx/sc/st - Substituted on
s/cn/tn - Non-playing sub

BRADFORD (PARK AVENUE) MATCH RESULTS 2020-21

Date	Comp	H/A	Opponents	Att:	Result		Goalscorers	Pos
Oct 3	**FAC2Q**	**H**	**Spennymoor Town**		**L**	**1 - 3**	**Knight 32**	
5	NLN	H	Gateshead		L	1 - 2	Nowakowski 27	
24	NLN	A	Kettering Town		L	1 - 3	Johnson 47	19
27	NLN	A	Hereford		**W**	2 - 0	Johnson 2 38	14
31	NLN	H	Chorley		D	0 - 0		13
Nov 7	NLN	H	Alfreton Town		**W**	2 - 0	Hibbs 70 Clee 77	9
14	NLN	A	Gloucester City		D	4 - 4	Knight 6 Hibbs 32 Boyes 46 Windass 53	11
17	NLN	H	Southport		L	0 - 2		12
21	NLN	H	AFC Telford United		L	1 - 2	Knight 68	16
24	NLN	A	Darlington		**W**	1 - 0	Havern 15	9
28	NLN	A	Spennymoor Town		D	2 - 2	Knight 8 79	9
Dec 1	NLN	A	AFC Fylde		D	3 - 3	Dockerty 4 Knight 30 90+2	9
12	NLN	H	Leamington		L	1 - 3	Dockerty 68	15
15	**FAT2P**	**A**	**Chester**	**552**	**L**	**1 - 3**	**Knight 90**	
26	NLN	H	York City		**W**	4 - 2	Knight 5 57 Booty 20 Boyes 82	14
28	NLN	A	Curzon Ashton		L	0 - 3		16
Jan 11	NLN	H	Boston United		D	1 - 1	Longbottom 65	15
19	NLN	H	Chester		D	3 - 3	Havern 57 Knight 61 Askew 90+2 (og)	14

Goalcorers	LGE	FAC	FAT	SG	CSG	HAT	PEN	1Q	2Q	45+	3Q	4Q	90+	T
TOTALS	26	1	1			0	0	7	5	0	6	7	3	28
Knight	9	1	1	8	2			3	2		2	2	2	11
Johnson	3			2	2			1	1		1			3
Boyes	2			2	1						1	1		2
Dockerty	2			2	2			1				1		2
Havern	2			2	1			1				1		2
Hibbs	2			2	2				1			1		2
Booty	1			1	1			1						1
Clee	1			1	1							1		1
Longbottom	1			1	1						1			1

	LGE	FAC	FAT	SG	CSG	HAT	PEN	1Q	2Q	45+	3Q	4Q	90+	T
Nowakowski	1			1	1				1					1
Opponent	1			1	1								1	1
Windass	1			1	1						1			1

Atkinson D	Ross M	Lund M	Downing M	Havern G	Clee N	Nowakowski A	Hibbs J	Marriott I	Dockerty B	Knight L	Windass J	Johnson O	Bradley L (L)	Hussain T	Fawcett J (Gk)	Lyons J	Henderson E	Boyes H (L)	Toulson R	Sanyang O	Huffer W (Gk)	Lyons L	Ibrian I	Booty R	Longbottom W	Rawson L (L)	No.
c	c	c	c	c	cs	c	c	cs	cs	c	sc	sc	sc	cn	cn	cn	cn										1
x	x	x	xs		xs	x	x	x	x	xs	x	sx	sx	sx	s	s											2
x	x	x	s	x	x	x	xs	x	x		s	xs	sx	sx				x	s								3
x	x	x	sx	x	x	x	x	x	xs		sx	xs			s	s		x	s								4
x	x	x	sx	x	sx	xs	x	x		sx	xs				s	xs		x	x								5
x	x	x	sx	x	x		x	x		xs	s				s	sx		x	x	xs	s						6
x	x	x	s		x	sx	x	x		x	x							x	x	xs	s	s					7
x	x	xs	sx	x	xs	x	x	x		x	sx					s		x	xs	sx	s						8
x	xs	x	s	xs	x	xs	x	x	x	x	s							x	sx	sx			sx				9
x	x		s	x	sx		x	x	x	xs	x							x	x	x	s	s	s				10
x	x		s	x	x		x	x	xs	xs	x			s				x	x	sx	s		sx				11
x	x		s	x	x		x	xs	x	xs	x							x	xs	sx	s	sx	sx				12
x	x		s	x	x		x		x	x	xs			sx				x		xs	s	x		sx			13
sn	t		t	ts	st		t		t	t	ts			st		st		t			t	t		ts			14
x	x		x		xs	x			x	x		s		s	s	s		x		sx		x		x	x		15
x	x		x		sx	xs			xs	xs		sx		sx	s			x	x	s		x		x	x		16
x	x			x	x	x		sx	xs	x	x	sx		s	s				xs	s				x	x		17
x	x			x	x	sx	x	x	x	xs	xs	sx		s						s				x	xs	sx	18
17	17	8	4	12	10	7	14	11	9	8	6	0	0	0	0	0	0	14	6	1	1	4	0	4	3	0	x
0	1	1	1	2	4	3	1	2	5	7	4	2	0	0	0	1	0	0	3	3	0	0	0	1	1	0	xs
0	0	0	4	0	4	2	0	1	0	1	3	5	3	5	0	2	0	0	1	5	0	1	3	1	0	1	sx
0	0	0	7	0	0	0	0	0	0	0	3	1	0	5	8	5	1	0	2	3	7	2	1	0	0	0	s

GOALKEEPERS	CS	CCS
Atkinson	4	3

x/c/t - Played full 90 minutes
xs/cs/ts - Substituted off
sx/sc/st - Substituted on
s/cn/tn - Non-playing sub

CHESTER MATCH RESULTS 2020-21

Date	Comp	H/A	Opponents	Att:	Result	Goalscorers	Pos
Oct 3	**FAC2Q**	**A**	**Worksop Town**		**D 2 - 2**	**Livesey 85 90+3 (Won 5-3 on pens)**	
6	NLN	A	Kidderminster Harriers		W 2 - 1	Elliott 23 Weeks 57	6
10	NLN	H	Leamington		W 3 - 2	Elliott 24 57 (pen) Bauress 36	2
13	**FAC3Q**	**H**	**Spennymoor Town**		**W 3 - 1**	**Morgan 24 Elliott 56 (pen) Waring 81**	
17	NLN	A	Spennymoor Town		L 1 - 2	Livesey 12	5
24	**FAC4Q**	**H**	**Marine**		**L 0 - 1**		
27	NLN	H	Curzon Ashton		W 2 - 1	Elliott 37 Glendon 83	2
31	NLN	A	Gloucester City		L 1 - 2	Dudley 86	5
Nov 21	NLN	A	Brackley Town		D 1 - 1	Cullinane-Liburd 51 (og)	10
24	NLN	A	Farsley Celtic		D 2 - 2	Glendon 5 Lacey 38	8
28	NLN	H	Gateshead		L 1 - 2	Grand 52	5
Dec 1	NLN	H	Alfreton Town		W 3 - 0	Elliott 20 (pen) Morgan 62 Dudley 88	6
5	NLN	A	York City		L 1 - 2	Weeks 58	10
8	NLN	H	Hereford		W 5 - 3	Weeks 44 Elliott 49 White 52 (og) Johnston 62 Livesey 85	5
12	NLN	A	Boston United		D 0 - 0		5
15	**FAT2P**	**H**	**Bradford (Park Avenue)**	**552**	**W 3 - 1**	**Waring 21 Dudley 58 (pen) Goodwin 88**	
19	**FAT3P**	**A**	**Altrincham**		**L 1 - 2**	**Dudley 49**	
26	NLN	A	AFC Telford United	1680	W 2 - 1	Glendon 27 Dudley 67	3
28	NLN	H	Chorley		L 1 - 2	Dudley 35	5
Jan 2	NLN	H	AFC Telford United		W 3 - 0	Askew 8 Weeks 56 Dudley 76	3
5	NLN	H	Guiseley		W 1 - 0	Roberts K 6	2
19	NLN	A	Bradford (Park Avenue)		D 3 - 3	Elliott 19 Johnston 42 Morgan 89	2

Goalcorers	LGE	FAC	FAT	SG	CSG	HAT	PEN	1Q	2Q	45+	3Q	4Q	90+	T
TOTALS	32	5	4			0	4	7	10	0	14	9	1	41
Elliott	7	1		7	3		3	2	3		3			8
Dudley	5		2	7	5		1		1		3	3		7
Livesey	2	2		3	1			1				2	1	4
Weeks	4			4	2				1		3			4
Glendon	3			3	1			1	1			1		3
Morgan	2	1		3	1				1		1	1		3
Johnston	2			2	1				1		1			2
Opponent	2			2	1						2			2
Waring		1	1	2	1			1				1		2
Askew	1			1	1			1						1
Bauress	1			1	1				1					1
Goodwin			1	1	1							1		1
Grand	1			1	1						1			1
Lacey	1			1	1				1					1
Roberts K	1			1	1			1						1

	Roberts K	Livesey D	Grand S	Taylor J	Lacey P	Weeks D	Glendon G	Bauress B	Waring G	Elliott D	Dudley A	Marsh-Hughes L	Roberts G	Morgan J	Clark L	Hughes M	Goodwin W	Johnston J	Jackson B	Burke H	Askew J	Taylor C (L)	No.
c	c	c	c	c	cs	c	c	cs	c	cs	sc	sc	sc	cn	cn	cn	cn						1
x	x	x	x	x	x	x	x	xs	sx	xs	sx	s	sx	s				xs					2
x	x	x	x	x		x	x	xs	xs	xs	sx	sx	sx	s		s		x					3
c	cn	c	c	c		c	c	sc	sc	cs	cs	cn	sc	c	cn	cn		c	cs				4
x	x	x	x	s		x	x	xs	sx	xs	xs		s	x		sx		x	sx				5
c	c	c	c	c		c	c	c	sc	cs	sc	sc	cn	cn	cn	cn		cs	cs				6
x	x	x	x	x		x	x	sx	xs	xs	sx		s	s		sx		xs	x				7
x	x		x	x		x	x	sx	xs	xs	sx	s	s	x		sx		xs	x				8
x	x	x	x	x	x	x	x	xs	sx	xs	xs			s		sx		s	sx				9
x	x	x	x	x	x	x	x	xs	sx	xs	xs			s		s		sx	sx				10
x	x	x	x		xs	x	x	s	sx	x	xs		s	x		sx	sx	xs					11
x	s	x	x	x	sx	x	x	xs	sx	x	sx		s	x			xs	xs					12
x	x	x	x		xs	x	x	s	sx	x	sx		s	x		sx	xs	xs					13
x	x	x	x		sx	x	x	xs	sx	x	sx		s	x		s	xs	xs					14
x	x	x	x		xs	x	x	xs	sx	xs	sx		s	x			s	x	sx				15
t	t	tn	t		t	ts	tn	tn	ts	st	t	st		t	t		t	tn	ts	st			16
t	ts	t	t		tn	t	t	tn	st	ts	t	tn		t	tn		st	ts	t		st		17
x	x	x	x		xs	x	x	xs	sx	sx	x			x			s	sx	xs		s		18
x	s	x	x			x	x	xs	sx	xs	x			xs	s		sx	x			x	sx	19
x	x	xs	xs			x	x	s	sx	sx	x			x	x		s	x			xs	sx	20
x	x		x			x	x	xs	sx	sx	xs	s		x	x		s	xs			sx	x	21
x	x		x			x	x	xs	sx	xs	x	sx		x	s		sx	xs		s	x		22
22	18	17	21	10	4	21	21	1	1	4	6	0	0	14	3	0	1	6	3	0	2	1	x
0	1	1	1	0	5	1	0	13	4	14	6	0	0	1	0	0	3	11	4	0	1	0	xs
0	0	0	0	0	2	0	0	3	17	4	10	5	4	0	0	6	4	2	4	1	2	2	sx
0	3	1	0	1	1	0	1	5	0	0	0	5	9	7	6	6	5	2	0	1	1	0	s

GOALKEEPERS	CS	CCS
Gray	4	2

x/c/t - Played full 90 minutes
xs/cs/ts - Substituted off
sx/sc/st - Substituted on
s/cn/tn - Non-playing sub

CHORLEY MATCH RESULTS 2020-21

Date	Comp	H/A	Opponents	Att:	Result	Goalscorers	Pos
Oct 3	**FAC2Q**	**H**	**Gateshead**		**W 2 - 1**	**Cardwell 19 Reilly 26 (pen)**	
6	NLN	A	York City		L 1 - 3	Reilly 90+4 (pen)	18
10	NLN	H	Gloucester City		L 1 - 2	Newby 52	20
13	**FAC3Q**	**H**	**York City**		**W 1 - 0**	**Reilly 19 (pen) - Received a bye in the FAC4Q**	
17	NLN	A	Southport		L 0 - 1		21
24	NLN	H	Kidderminster Harriers		L 0 - 2		22
31	NLN	A	Bradford (Park Avenue)		D 0 - 0		20
Nov 8	**FAC1P**	**A**	**Wigan Athletic**		**W 3 - 2**	**Newby 48 Cardwell 60 Hall 92 (aet)**	
17	NLN	A	AFC Telford		W 1 - 0	Newby 69	21
21	NLN	A	Hereford		D 2 - 2	Reilly 84 Halls 87	19
28	**FAC2P**	**A**	**Peterborough United**		**W 2 - 1**	**Hall 60 Calveley 62**	
Dec 1	NLN	H	Curzon Ashton		D 1 - 1	Calveley 58	21
5	NLN	A	Boston United		W 2 - 0	Hall 17 (pen) Leather 34	20
8	NLN	H	Guiseley		W 1 - 0	Cardwell 32	15
12	NLN	A	Alfreton Town		D 1 - 1	Hall 90+6	14
15	**FAT2P**	**A**	**Guiseley**		**L 0 - 2**		
26	NLN	H	AFC Fylde		W 3 - 1	Hall 6 Owens 58 Smith 61	13
28	NLN	A	Chester		W 2 - 1	Shenton 24 Hall 45+4	9
Jan 2	NLN	A	AFC Fylde		L 0 - 4		10
9	**FAC3P**	**H**	**Derby County**		**W 2 - 0**	**Hall 10 Calveley 84**	
12	NLN	H	Leamington		L 1 - 2	Shenton 17	11
16	NLN	H	Farsley Celtic		W 3 - 2	Owens 15 Smith 77 Hall 82	9
Feb 6	NLN	A	Brackley Town		L 1 - 2	Newby 12	9
13	NLN	A	Gloucester City		D 1 - 1	Newby 70	7

Goalcorers	LGE	FAC	FAT	SG	CSG	HAT	PEN	1Q	2Q	45+	3Q	4Q	90+	T
TOTALS	**21**	**10**	**0**			**0**	**4**	**8**	**4**	**1**	**8**	**7**	**3**	**31**
Hall	5	3		8	2		1	3		1	1	1	2	8
Newby	4	1		5	2			1			2	2		5
Reilly	2	2		4	2		3	1	1			1	1	4
Calveley	1	2		3	2						2	1		3
Cardwell	1	2		3	1			1	1		1			3
Owens	2			2	1			1			1			2
Shenton	2			2	1			1	1					2
Smith	2			2	1						1	1		2
Halls	1			1	1							1		1

	LGE	FAC	FAT	SG	CSG	HAT	PEN	1Q	2Q	45+	3Q	4Q	90+	T
Leather	1			1	1				1					1

No.		Smith H	Halls A	Leather S	Baines L	Miller S	Calveley M	Cardwell H	Reilly L	Newby E	Shenton O	Baxter J (L)	Rodwell-Grant J (L)	Putnam O	McKenzie M	Awe S	Roberts L	Dutton L (Gk)	Walker S	Birch A	Garratt T	Marah S	Conn-Clarke C (L)	Hall C (L/P)	Tomlinson W	Henley A	Spencer-McDermott C	Baldwin D	Isherwood L	Reeves F	Moran N	Birchall L	Owens A	Jebbison D (L)	UstabasJ (L)
1		c	c	c	c	c	c	cs	c	c	c	cn	sc	cn	cn	cn	cn	cn																	
2		x	x	x	x	xs	x	xs	x	x	xs	s	sx					s	sx	sx															
3		xs	xs	x	x		x	xs	x	x	x	s	sx					s	x	sx	sx														
4		sc	c	c	c		cs	cs	c	c	sc	cn	sc	cn	cn			cn	c	c	cs														
5		xs	x	x	x		x		x	x	x	s	sx	s					xs	xs	sx	sx													
6		s	x	x	xs		x	xs	xs	x	x	s	sx						x	x		sx	sx												
7		s	x	x	x		x	x	sx	xs	xs								x	x	s	s	sx	x											
8		sc	c	c	c		c	cs	sc	cs	cs			sc	cn				c	c	cn	sc	cn	cs											
9		x	x	x	xs		x	xs	sx	x	xs			s						x	sx	sx	s	x											
10		x	x	x	x		x	xs	sx	x	xs									x	s			x	sx	s									
11		c	c	c	c		c	cs	sc	c	cs			cn	cn					c	cn	cn		cs	sc	sc									
12	x	xs	x	x	x		x	sx	xs	x	s									x	s	sx		xs	x	sx									
13	x	sx	xs	x	x		x	x		xs	x			s						x	sx	s		xs	x	sx									
14	x	x		x	x			x		x	x			s	s					x	xs	sx		xs	x	sx	s								
15	x	x		x	xs		x	xs		x	x			s	s					x	s	sx		x	x	sx									
16	t	t			t		ts							t	ts	tn					t	t		t	ts	t	st	st	st	tn	tn	tn			
17	x	x		x	x		xs		xs	x	xs									x	sx	s		x	x	sx							sx	s	
18	x	x		x	sx		s		sx	x	xs			s						x	x			xs	x	xs							x	sx	
19	x	x	s	x	xs		x	sx	sx	x	s									x				xs	x	x							xs	s	
20	c	sc	cs	c	c	cn	c	c	sc	c	cs			cn	cn		cn			c		cn		cs	c	sc									
21	x	xs	s	x	xs	sx	x	s	x	x	xs									sx		sx			x	x							x		
22	x	sx	x	x	s		x	x	sx	x	x									x				sx	xs	x							xs		s
23	x	s	x	x	xs	s	xs	x		x	xs									x	sx			x	x								sx		sx
24	x	xs	x	xs	x	sx	s	x		x	x									x	sx			sx	x								s		xs
x	24	11	14	22	16	1	17	7	6	20	9	0	0	1	0	0	0	0	5	18	2	1	0	7	11	4	0	0	0	0	0	0	2	0	0
xs	0	5	3	1	6	1	4	10	3	3	11	0	0	0	1	0	0	0	1	1	2	0	0	8	2	1	0	0	0	0	0	0	2	0	1
sx	0	5	0	0	1	2	0	2	9	0	1	0	6	1	0	0	0	0	1	3	7	8	2	2	2	7	1	1	1	0	0	0	2	1	1
s	0	3	2	0	1	2	2	1	0	0	2	6	0	10	7	2	2	4	0	0	6	5	2	0	0	1	1	0	0	1	1	1	1	2	1

GOALKEEPERS	CS	CCS
Urwin	6	2

x/c/t - Played full 90 minutes
xs/cs/ts - Substituted off
sx/sc/st - Substituted on
s/cn/tn - Non-playing sub

CURZON ASHTON MATCH RESULTS 2020-21

Date	Comp	H/A	Opponents	Att:	Result	Goalscorers	Pos
Oct 3	**FAC2Q**	**H**	**FC United of Manchester**		**L 1 - 2**	**Waters 14**	
5	NLN	H	Alfreton Town		D 1 - 1	Knowles 39	
10	NLN	A	Brackley Town		D 2 - 2	Knowles 78 86 (pens)	11
17	NLN	H	Farsley Celtic		**W** 2 - 1	Knowles 50 Whitham 57	7
27	NLN	A	Chester		L 1 - 2	Knowles 68	10
31	NLN	H	Darlington		L 0 - 3		11
Nov 7	NLN	H	Blyth Spartans		L 0 - 3		13
10	NLN	A	Gateshead		L 0 - 1		15
14	NLN	A	Kettering Town		**W** 2 - 1	Knowles 26 Stephenson 71	12
17	NLN	H	AFC Fylde		**W** 2 - 0	Waters 36 Stephenson 53	7
21	NLN	H	Leamington		L 0 - 3		7
28	NLN	A	Kidderminster Harriers		L 0 - 1		12
Dec 1	NLN	A	Chorley		D 1 - 1	Mahon 14	11
5	NLN	A	Spennymoor Town		L 1 - 3	Flowers 53	13
12	NLN	H	Gloucester City		L 0 - 1		18
15	**FAT2P**	**H**	**AFC Fylde**		**L 1 - 4**	**Stephenson 45+2**	
26	NLN	A	Southport	706	D 2 - 2	Flowers 72 Cowan 90+2	17
28	NLN	H	Bradford (Park Avenue)		**W** 3 - 0	Waters 30 Evans 71 Cowan 87	17
Jan 16	NLN	A	AFC Telford United		D 1 - 1	Knowles 39	16

Goalcorers	LGE	FAC	FAT	SG	CSG	HAT	PEN	1Q	2Q	45+	3Q	4Q	90+	T
TOTALS	18	1	1			0	2	2	5	1	5	6	1	20
Knowles	7			6	4		2		3		2	2		7
Stephenson	2		1	3	2					1	1	1		3
Waters	2	1		3	1			1	2					3
Cowan	2			2	2							1	1	2
Flowers	2			2	1						1	1		2
Evans	1			1	1							1		1
Mahon	1			1	1			1						1
Whitham	1			1	1						1			1

LGE	FAC	FAT	SG	CSG	HAT	PEN	1Q	2Q	45+	3Q	4Q	90+	T

	Waters M	Turnbull P	Mahon C	Harrop M	Evans R	Poscha M	Whitham D	Curran A (L)	Tharme D	Knowles D	Southern O	Stephenson D	Hughes C	Oyibo J	Adarabioyo F	Stokes N	Mason C (Gk)	McPartlan L (Gk)	Merrill L	Hanson J	Walker S	Flowers H (L)	Cowan D	Da Silva I (L)	Hobson C	No.
	c	c			c		cs			c	sc															1
	X	X	X	XS	X	X		X	X	X	S	XS	SX	SX	S	S										2
		X	X	X	X	X	S	X		X	XS		X	SX		X	X									3
		X	X	XS	X	X	SX	XS	X	X	X	XS	S	SX		SX	X									4
	X	X	X	XS		S	X	XS	X	X	X	X	SX	SX		S	X									5
	X	X	X	S	XS		X	XS	X	XS	X	X	SX	SX		SX	X									6
	X	X	X		XS		X	SX	S	XS	X	X	X	SX		X	X	S	S							7
	X	X	XS		XS		XS	SX	X	X		X	X	SX		X	X		S	SX						8
	X	X	X					XS	X	X	S	X	X	SX		X	X	S	S	S	X					9
	X	X	X	SX				XS	X	X	S	X	XS	SX		X	X		S	S	X					10
	X	XS	X	SX	S			XS	XS	X	SX	X	X	SX		X	X			S	X					11
	X		SX		XS	X	SX	SX	X	X	S		XS	X		XS	X			X	X					12
	X		XS		X	X	X	S	X	X	S	X	S	SX		XS	X			SX	X					13
		X	X			XS	XS	X		X	SX		X	SX		SX	X	S		XS	X	X				14
	X	XS	X		XS			SX	X	X	S	XS	SX			S	X				X	X	X	SX		15
	t	t	t		ts			tn	t	t	st	t	st			tn	t				ts	t	ts	st		16
	X	X	X		X			X	X			X	S			S	X	S			X	X	X	S		17
	X	X	XS		X			X			S	X	XS			S	X	S		SX	X	X	X	SX		18
	X	XS	SX		X	SX		XS	S	XS		X				S	X			X	X	X	X		SX	19
2	16	14	13	1	8	5	4	5	12	14	4	12	6	1	0	6	17	0	0	2	10	6	4	0	0	X
0	0	3	3	3	6	1	3	7	1	3	1	3	3	0	0	2	0	0	0	1	1	0	1	0	0	XS
0	0	0	2	2	0	1	2	4	0	0	4	0	5	12	0	3	0	0	0	3	0	0	0	3	1	SX
2	0	0	0	1	1	1	1	2	2	0	7	0	3	0	1	7	0	5	4	3	0	0	0	1	0	S

GOALKEEPERS	CS	CCS
Mason	2	1

x/c/t - Played full 90 minutes
xs/cs/ts - Substituted off
sx/sc/st - Substituted on
s/cn/tn - Non-playing sub

DARLINGTON MATCH RESULTS 2020-21

Date	Comp	H/A	Opponents	Att:	Result		Goalscorers	Pos
Oct 3	**FAC2Q**	**H**	**Prescot Cables**		**D**	**2 - 2**	**Charman 29 61 (Won 5-4 on pens)**	
6	NLN	A	AFC Fylde		L	0 - 1		17
10	NLN	H	Kidderminster Harriers		L	1 - 3	Penny 11 (og)	21
13	**FAC3Q**	**H**	**Tadcaster Albion**		**W**	**6 - 1**	**Liddle 13 Storey 34 Rivers 36 49 Donawa 47 81**	
24	**FAC4Q**	**H**	**Cambridge City**		**W**	**2 - 0**	**Charman 9 24**	
31	NLN	A	Curzon Ashton		W	3 - 0	Campbell 13 Reid 66 Rivers 73	15
Nov 7	**FAC1P**	**A**	**Swindon Town**		**W**	**2 - 1**	**Campbell 31 60**	
14	NLN	H	AFC Telford United		L	1 - 2	Sousa 22	19
17	NLN	A	Guiseley		W	4 - 1	Campbell 27 (pen) Maguire 43 48 Sousa 74	15
21	NLN	A	Alfreton Town		W	2 - 0	Sousa 11 Campbell 83	11
24	NLN	H	Bradford (Park Avenue)		L	0 - 1		12
29	**FAC2P**	**A**	**Bristol Rovers**		**L**	**0 - 6**		
Dec 15	**FAT2P**	**H**	**City of Liverpool**		**W**	**2 - 0**	**Charman 12 Sousa 75**	
19	**FAT3P**	**H**	**AFC Telford United**		**D**	**2 - 2**	**Rivers 5 Hatfield 84 (Won 5-3 on pens)**	
26	NLN	H	Spennymoor Town		D	0 - 0		21
28	NLN	H	Blyth Spartans		W	6 - 0	Sousa 9 Campbell 15 Rivers 29 O'Neill 70 85 Maguire 84	18
Jan 5	NLN	A	Brackley Town		L	0 - 2		19
12	NLN	A	Farsley Celtic		L	0 - 1		19
16	**FAT4P**	**A**	**Weymouth**		**W**	**1 - 0**	**Hatfield 45**	
Feb 6	**FAT5P**	**H**	**Wealdstone**		**W**	**4 - 1**	**Efete 3 (og) Rivers 13 Charman 63 Sousa 90+3**	
27	**FATQF**	**H**	**Hornchurch**		**L**	**1 - 2**	**Sousa 45+2 (RC 2xY - Hatfield 85)**	

Goalcorers	LGE	FAC	FAT	SG	CSG	HAT	PEN	1Q	2Q	45+	3Q	4Q	90+	T
TOTALS	17	12	10			0	1	12	8	2	7	9	1	39
Sousa	4		3	7	3			3		1		2	1	7
Campbell	4	2		5	2		1	2	2		1	1		6
Charman		4	2	4	1			2	2		2			6
Rivers	2	2	2	5	1			2	2		1	1		6
Maguire	3			2	1				1		1	1		3
Donawa		2		1	1						1	1		2
Hatfield			2	2	1					1		1		2
O'Neill	2			1	1							2		2
Opponent	1		1	2	1			2						2
Liddle		1		1	1			1						1
Reid	1			1	1						1			1
Storey		1		1	1				1					1

	Liddle M	Hunt N	Hatfield W	Campbell A	Rivers J	Donawa J	Storey A	Charman L	McMahon A	Atkinson D	Wheatley J	Reid S	Watson J	Laing L	Hedley B	Armstrong R	Amantchi L	Hudson T	Holness O	Minter M (Gk) (L)	Sousa E	Maguire D	O'Neill T (L)	Brynn S (Gk) (L)	No.
	c	c	c	c	c	c	c	cs	c	cs	sc	sc	cn	cn	cn	cn									1
	x	x	x	xs	x	sx	x	xs	x		xs	x	s	sx	sx	s									2
	x	x	xs		xs	x	x	x	x		xs	x	s	s	sx		sx	sx							3
	c	cs		cn	c	c	c	cs	c		c	cs	cn	sc	c	cn	sc	sc							4
	c	c		cs	c	sc	c	cs	c		c	c	cn	cn	sc		sc	cn	cs	cn					5
	x	x		xs	xs		x	xs			x	x	s		x			sx	sx	s	x	sx			6
	c	c		c	c		c	c		sc	c	c	cn	cn	c		cn	cn	cs	cn		cn			7
	x		x	xs	x		x		s	xs		x		x	x			s	sx	s	x	sx			8
	xs		x	x	sx				x	sx	x		x	x			sx	s	xs	x	x	xs			9
			xs	x	sx				x	x	x	x	x	x	s			sx		x	xs	xs	sx		10
				xs	sx		s	sx		x	xs	x	x	x	x			sx		s	x	xs	x		11
		c	cs	c	c			cs	c	c	c	cs	c	cn	cn			sc	sc	cn		cn	sc		12
		t	t	ts	t			ts	t	tn	t	tn	t	t				st	tn	t	ts	st	st		13
		t	t	st	t		tn		t	tn	ts	st	t	t				tn	st	t	ts	t	ts		14
	x	x	x	x	sx				x	s	x	sx		xs					xs	x	x	xs	sx		15
	sx		x	xs	x		x		s	x	xs	x	x					sx		x	xs	sx	x		16
		x	x	xs	x		s	sx	x		x	x	x					s			x	sx	xs		17
	x	x	x	xs	x		s	x	x	s	x	x	s								xs	sx	sx		18
		t	t	st	t		t	ts	t		t		t		tn				st		ts	ts	st		19
	t	t	t	st	t		t	ts	ts		t	tn	tn		st	tn		tn	st		t	ts			20
	t	t	t	t	t		t		tn	tn	ts	st	tn		t			tn	st		t	t		t	21
4	12	15	13	7	15	3	12	3	14	4	13	11	9	6	6	0	0	0	0	6	8	2	2	1	x
[illegible]	1	1	3	9	2	0	0	9	1	2	6	2	0	1	0	0	0	0	4	0	6	6	2	0	xs
[illegible]	1	0	0	3	4	2	0	2	0	2	1	4	0	2	4	0	4	8	7	0	0	6	6	0	sx
7	0	0	0	1	0	0	4	0	3	5	0	2	10	5	4	4	1	8	1	6	0	2	0	0	s

GOALKEEPERS	CS	CCS
Minter	4	2
Saltmer	3	2

x/c/t - Played full 90 minutes
xs/cs/ts - Substituted off
sx/sc/st - Substituted on
s/cn/tn - Non-playing sub

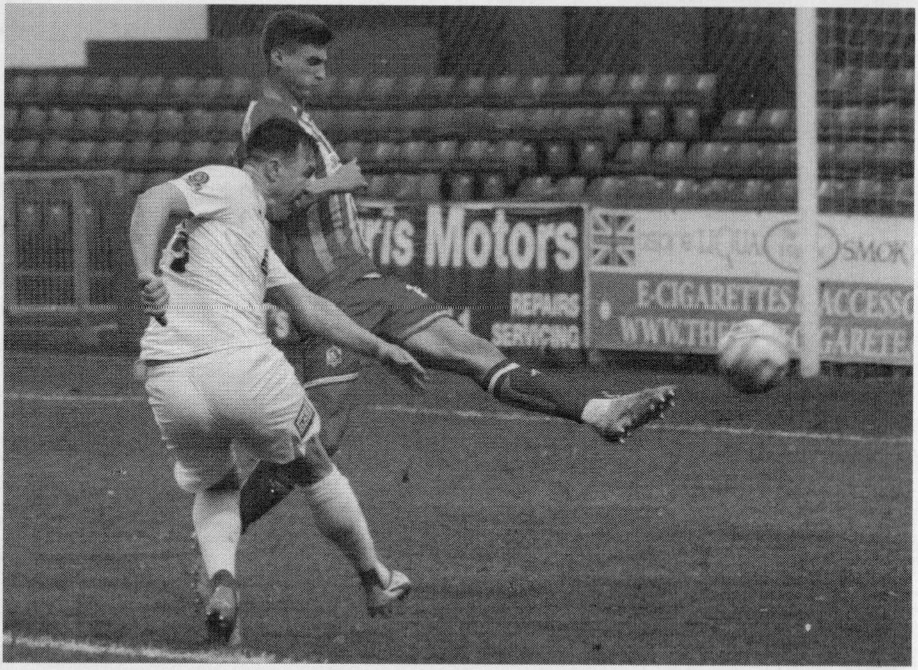
Motors
REPAIRS
SERVICING

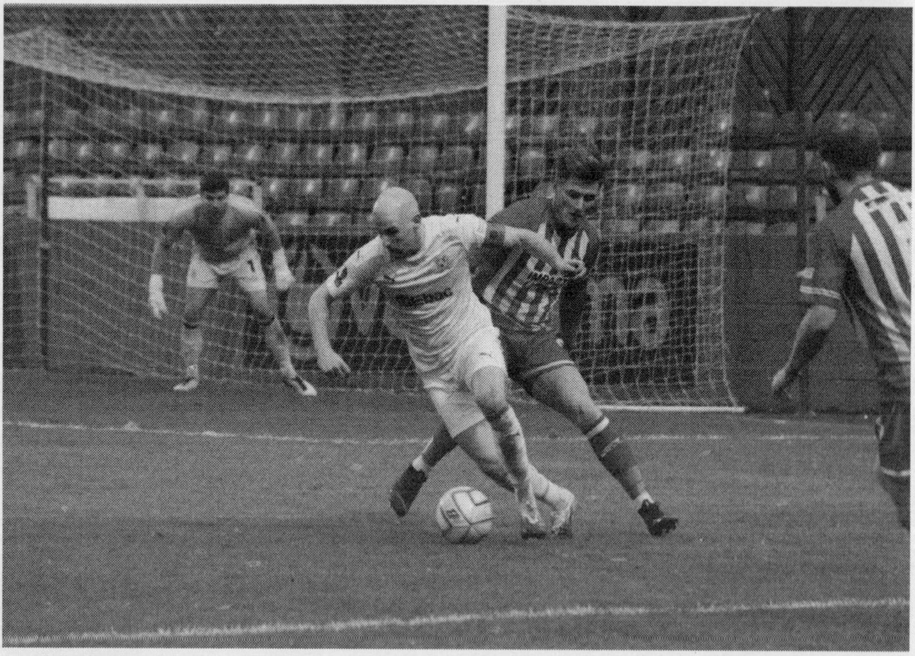

Alfreton Town 0 - 2 Darlington - 21/11/2020

Photos Bill Wheatcroft

FARSLEY CELTIC MATCH RESULTS 2020-21

Date	Comp	H/A	Opponents	Att:	Result	Goalscorers	Pos
Oct 3	**FAC2Q**	**H**	**Radcliffe FC**		**W 2 - 1**	**Spencer 8 43**	
6	NLN	A	Spennymoor Town		L 1 - 2	Charles 83 (RC - Drench 41)	15
10	NLN	H	York City		D 1 - 1	Syers 84	15
13	**FAC3Q**	**H**	**AFC Fylde**		**L 1 - 3**	**Charles 84**	
17	NLN	A	Curzon Ashton		L 1 - 2	Spencer 61	16
31	NLN	A	AFC Fylde		L 0 - 2		19
Nov 3	NLN	H	Leamington		D 1 - 1	Richards 7	19
7	NLN	H	Gateshead		**W** 1 - 0	Richards 90+1	12
10	NLN	A	Blyth Spartans		D 1 - 1	Smith-Brown 28	12
14	NLN	A	Alfreton Town		L 1 - 3	Clayton 18	16
21	NLN	H	Kidderminster Harriers		D 2 - 2	Allan 18 Johnston 47	18
24	NLN	H	Chester		D 2 - 2	Hayhurst 8 Spencer 27	17
28	NLN	A	Gloucester City		**W** 2 - 1	Allan 33 Spencer 75	11
Dec 2	NLN	A	Southport		**W** 1 - 0	Parkin 13	8
5	NLN	H	AFC Telford United		**W** 2 - 0	Spencer 19 Syers 86	6
15	**FAT2P**	**A**	**Gateshead**		**W 3 - 2**	**Allan 8 Parkin 73 Spencer 89**	
19	**FAT3P**	**A**	**Solihull Moors**		**L 0 - 4**		
26	NLN	A	Guiseley		D 2 - 2	Hayhurst 23 (pen) 30	8
28	NLN	H	Boston United		L 0 - 4		13
Jan 12	NLN	H	Darlington		**W** 1 - 0	Clayton 52	9
16	NLN	A	Chorley		L 2 - 3	Spencer 12 44	11

Goalcorers	LGE	FAC	FAT	SG	CSG	HAT	PEN	1Q	2Q	45+	3Q	4Q	90+	T
TOTALS	21	3	3			0	1	8	7	0	3	7	1	27
Spencer	6	2	1	7	2			3	3		1	2		9
Allan	2		1	3	1			2	1					3
Hayhurst	3			2	1		1		2					3
Charles	1	1		2	1							2		2
Clayton	2			2	1			1			1			2
Parkin	1		1	2	1			1				1		2
Richards	2			2	2			1					1	2
Syers	2			2	1							2		2
Johnston	1			1	1						1			1
Smith-brown	1			1	1				1					1

	Richards J	West J	Allan T	Ellis D	Clayton A	Byrom J	Atkinson C	Spencer J	Parkin L	Hayhurst W	Walton T	Atkinson B	Charles J	Kelly S (Gk)	Syers D	Bower M (Gk)	Johnston C (L)	Goldthorp E	Smith-Brown A	Lane P (L)	Heath C (D)	Barton A	Trenerry K (Gk)	No.
	c	c	c	c	c	cs	c	c	cs	cs	sc	sc	sc	cn	cn									1
	x	xs	x	x	x	x	x	x	s	xs	xs	sx	sx	sx	s									2
	x	xs	x	x	x	x	x	x	sx		xs	sx	xs	s	sx									3
	c	sc	c	cs	c	cs	c	c	sc		c	sc	c	c	cs	cn								4
	x	x		x	x		x	x	xs	sx	xs	xs	x	s	sx		sx	s						5
	x	xs	x	x	x		x	x	s		xs	xs	sx		sx		x	sx	s					6
	x	x	x	xs	x		x	x	s	s	sx	x	x		xs		sx		s					7
	x	s	x		x		x	x	s	x	xs	sx	sx		x		x		xs	s				8
	x	s	x		x		x	xs	sx	x	xs	sx	sx		x		x		xs	s				9
x	x		s	x	x		x	x	s	xs	x	sx	sx		xs		xs		x	sx				10
x	x		x		x		x	x	s	sx	xs	sx	s		x		x		xs	xs	sx			11
x	x		x		x		x	x	s	x	xs	sx	sx		x		x		s	xs	s			12
x	x	s	x		x		x	x	xs	x		sx	sx		x		x		s	xs	s			13
x	x		x		x		x	xs	xs	x	sx	sx	sx		x				s	xs	s			14
x	x	s	x		x		x	xs	xs	x	xs	sx	sx	s	x		x		sx					15
t	t	tn	t	tn	t		t	t	ts	t	ts	st	st	tn	t		t	tn	tn					16
t	ts	tn	t		t		t	t	t	ts	ts	st	st	tn	t		t		st					17
x	x		xs		x		x	x	xs	x	sx	s	sx	s	x		x			xs		sx		18
	x				x		x		xs	xs	sx	sx	x	x	xs	s	x	s	sx	x		x		19
x	x		x	s	x		x	xs	xs	x		sx	sx		x		x			xs		sx	s	20
x	x		x	sx	x		x	x	xs	x	sx	s			x		xs			xs		sx	s	21
9	20	3	17	6	21	2	21	16	1	10	2	1	4	2	12	0	12	0	1	1	0	1	0	x
0	1	3	1	2	0	2	0	4	10	5	11	2	1	0	4	0	2	0	3	7	0	0	0	xs
0	0	1	0	1	0	0	0	0	3	2	6	16	14	1	3	0	2	1	3	1	1	3	0	sx
0	0	6	1	2	0	0	0	0	7	1	0	2	1	7	2	2	0	3	6	2	3	0	2	s

GOALKEEPERS	CS	CCS
Drench	4	2

x/c/t - Played full 90 minutes
xs/cs/ts - Substituted off
sx/sc/st - Substituted on
s/cn/tn - Non-playing sub

GATESHEAD MATCH RESULTS 2020-21

Date	Comp	H/A	Opponents	Att:	Result	Goalscorers	Pos
Oct 3	**FAC2Q**	**A**	**Chorley**		**L 1 - 2**	**Smith 50 (og)**	
5	NLN	A	Bradford (Park Avenue)		**W** 2 - 1	Preston 33 Ward 60	
10	NLN	H	AFC Fylde		L 0 - 1		10
17	NLN	A	AFC Telford United		L 0 - 3		13
Nov 7	NLN	A	Farsley Celtic		L 0 - 1		19
10	NLN	H	Curzon Ashton		**W** 1 - 0	Cook 51	11
14	NLN	H	Brackley Town		D 2 - 2	Langstaff 19 Olley 60	14
21	NLN	H	Southport		**W** 4 - 1	Garner 45+1 49 53 Nicholson 59 (pen)	9
24	NLN	H	Gloucester City		**W** 1 - 0	Greenfield 56	6
28	NLN	A	Chester		**W** 2 - 1	Preston 13 Langstaff 86	5
Dec 5	NLN	A	Leamington		D 1 - 1	Olley 28	4
12	NLN	H	Kidderminster Harriers		L 0 - 1		7
15	**FAT2P**	**H**	**Farsley Celtic**		**L 2 - 3**	**Garner 9 Langstaff 62**	
26	NLN	A	Blyth Spartans		D 2 - 2	Olley 20 Preston 34	7
28	NLN	H	Spennymoor Town		L 1 - 3	Olley 90	11
Jan 16	NLN	H	Guiseley		**W** 1 - 0	Langstaff 90+1	10

Goalcorers	LGE	FAC	FAT	SG	CSG	HAT	PEN	1Q	2Q	45+	3Q	4Q	90+	T
TOTALS	17	1	2			1	1	4	3	1	9	1	2	20
Garner	3		1	2	1	1		1		1	2			4
Langstaff	3		1	4	1			1			1	1	1	4
Olley	4			4	2			1	1		1		1	4
Preston	3			3	1			1	2					3
Cook	1			1	1						1			1
Greenfield	1			1	1						1			1
Nicholson	1			1	1		1				1			1
Opponent		1		1	1						1			1
Ward	1			1	1						1			1

	LGE	FAC	FAT	SG	CSG	HAT	PEN	1Q	2Q	45+	3Q	4Q	90+	T

No.	Nicholson A	Smith G	Griffiths K	Deverdics N	Olley G	Hunter J	Langstaff M	Keating R	Southern-Cooper J (L)	Preston J	Ward D	O'Donnell J	Male H (Gk)	Dale N	Forbes E	Vieira R	Greenfield D	Cranston D	Cook J	Garner G (L)	Cameron A (Gk)	Aplin K	Williamson M	Ogbewe N	Bolton R	Battersby O (Gk) (L)	Adams B (L)	Morse D (L)	Hasani L (L)	Blackett P
1	c	c	c	c	c	c	cs	c	c	cs	sc	sc	cn	cn	cn	cn														
2	x	x	x	x	x	x	sx	sx	x	xs	xs	s	s	s			x													
3	x	x	x	x	x	x	sx		x	x	xs	sx	s	s			xs	s												
4	x	x	x	xs	x	x	sx	xs	x	sx	sx	xs	s	s			x													
5	x	x	x	x	xs	x	xs		x	xs	s	sx	s	x					sx	sx										
6	x		x	x	xs	sx	xs	sx	x		xs	x	s	x			x		sx	s										
7	x	x	x	x	x	x	xs		x	sx		s	s	s			x		sx	xs										
8	x	xs	x		x	x	sx		x	x		sx	x	sx			x		xs	xs	s	s								
9	x	x	x	s	x	x	sx		x	x		s	x				x		xs	x	s	s								
10	x	xs	x	sx	x	x	sx		x	x	s		x	sx			xs		xs	x	s									
11	x	x	x	sx	x	x	sx		x	xs	sx		x	s			xs		x	xs	s									
12	x	x	x	s	x	x	sx		x	x	s		x	s			x		x	xs	s									
13	ts	tn		t	t	st	ts		t		t		t	t	st		tn			t	tn	t	ts	st	tn					
14	x	x	x	sx	x	x	sx		x	xs	s		s	s			xs		x	x						x				
15	xs	x	x	xs	x	s	sx			x	sx		s	x	sx		x		x				xs			x				
16	x	s	x	x	x		sx			x	sx		s		sx		xs										x	x	xs	xs
x	14	11	15	8	14	12	0	1	14	7	1	1	6	4	0	0	8	0	4	4	0	1	0	0	0	2	1	1	0	0
xs	2	2	0	2	2	0	5	1	0	5	3	1	0	0	0	0	5	0	3	4	0	0	2	0	0	0	0	0	1	1
sx	0	0	0	3	0	2	11	2	0	2	5	4	0	2	3	0	0	0	3	1	0	0	0	1	0	0	0	0	0	0
s	0	2	0	2	0	1	0	0	0	0	4	3	10	8	1	1	1	1	0	1	6	2	0	0	1	0	0	0	0	0

GOALKEEPERS	CS	CCS
Montgomery	2	1
Male	1	1

x/c/t - Played full 90 minutes
xs/cs/ts - Substituted off
sx/sc/st - Substituted on
s/cn/tn - Non-playing sub

GLOUCESTER CITY MATCH RESULTS 2020-21

Date	Comp	H/A	Opponents	Att:	Result	Goalscorers	Pos
Oct 3	**FAC2Q**	**A**	**Christchurch**	**300**	**D 1 - 1**	**Bailey 93 (Lost 5-6 on pens)**	
6	NLN	H	Kettering Town		**W** 3 - 1	Whittle 1 McClure 33 Bailey 83	4
10	NLN	A	Chorley		**W** 2 - 1	McClure 11 Gunning 66	1
17	NLN	H	Blyth Spartans		**W** 6 - 1	McClure 15 22 25 Mensah 20 Asante 45 O'Sullivan 90	1
31	NLN	H	Chester		**W** 2 - 1	Daly 58 Asante 88	1
Nov 7	NLN	A	Spennymoor Town		D 2 - 2	McClure 66 Asante 82	1
10	NLN	H	AFC Telford United		**W** 4 - 1	Asante 12 (pen) 60 Mensah 66 McClure 77	1
14	NLN	H	Bradford (Park Avenue)		D 4 - 4	Asante 16 23 (pen) McClure 17 Mensah 62	1
17	NLN	A	Hereford		**W** 1 - 0	McClure 13	1
21	NLN	A	Guiseley		**W** 2 - 1	McClure 49 (pen) Asante 51	1
Manager James Rowe leaves the club to take up the vacant job at Chesterfield. Jake Cole takes over as caretaker.							
24	NLN	A	Gateshead		L 0 - 1		1
28	NLN	H	Farsley Celtic		L 1 - 2	Campbell 31	1
Dec 1	NLN	H	Boston United		D 0 - 0		1
Former Maccabi Haifa assistant manager, Paul Groves, is named as the new manager.							
12	NLN	A	Curzon Ashton		**W** 1 - 0	Dawson 51	1
15	**FAT2P**	**H**	**Needham Market**		**W 4 - 2**	**Mensah 3 McClure 12 James 32 72**	
26	NLN	H	Leamington		**W** 1 - 0	Brunt 37	1
28	NLN	A	Brackley Town		L 2 - 3	Dawson 23 McClure 71	1
Jan 2	NLN	A	Leamington		D 1 - 1	Campbell 38	1
9	NLN	H	Kidderminster Harriers		**W** 3 - 2	Marsh-Brown 29 McClure 64 Young 75	1
18	**FAT4P**	**A**	**Wealdstone**		**L 1 - 3**	**Burroughs 75**	
Feb 13	NLN	H	Chorley		D 1 - 1	Omotayo 26	1

Goalcorers	LGE	FAC	FAT	SG	CSG	HAT	PEN	1Q	2Q	45+	3Q	4Q	90+	T
TOTALS	**36**	**1**	**5**			**1**	**3**	**11**	**10**	**1**	**10**	**8**	**2**	**42**
McClure	12		1	11	5	1	1	6	2		3	2		13
Asante	8			6	5		2	2	1	1	2	2		8
Mensah	3		1	4	2			2			2			4
Bailey-Nicholls	1	1		2	2							1	1	2
Campbell	2			2	1				2					2
Dawson	2			2	1				1		1			2
James			2	1	1				1			1		2
Brunt	1			1	1				1					1
Burroughs			1	1	1							1		1
Daly	1			1	1						1			1
Gunning	1			1	1						1			1
Marsh-Brown	1			1	1				1					1
O'Sullivan	1			1	1								1	1
Omotayo	1			1	1				1					1
Whittle	1			1	1			1						1
Young	1			1	1							1		1

	Thomas J	Daly L	Morgan B	Whittle A	Carline G	Gunning G	Dawson K	Asante A	McClure M	Robert F	Mensah B	O'Sullivan T	Bailey-Nicholls K	Cole J (Gk)	James J	Lovett R (Gk)	Jones C	Hainault A	King D	Brunt L (L)	Campbell T (L)	Maher N (Gk)	Bremner J	Marsh-Brown K	Burroughs J (L)	Young J (L)	Harrison T	Webb B (L)	Di Segni R	Leadbitter D (L)	Barnett R (L)	Omotayo G	No.
	c	c	c	cs	c	c	c	cs	c	sc	sc	cs	sc	cn	cn																		1
	xs	x	x	x	x	x	x	xs	xs	x	sx	sx	sx	s	s																		2
	x	x	x	x	x	x	x	xs	xs	sx	xs	sx	sx	s	s	x																	3
	x	x	x	x	x	xs	xs	x	xs	s	x	sx	sx	s	sx	x																	4
	xs	x	x	x	x	x	x	x	xs	sx	xs	sx	s		sx	s																	5
		x	x	x	x		x	x	x	sx	xs	x	s		xs	s	sx	s															6
		x	x	xs	x	x	x	xs	x	s	x	xs	sx		sx	s			sx														7
	x	x	xs	xs	x	x	x	x	x	s	x	sx	s		sx	x			s														8
	x	x	sx	x	x	x	x	x	xs	s	s	xs	sx		x	x			s														9
x	x	x	x	x	x	xs	x	x	xs	s	xs	sx	sx		sx	s																	10
x	x	x	x				x			xs	x	x	sx		x	s	s	x	x														11
x	x	x	x	s		x				sx	x	xs	xs		x	s	s		sx	x	x												12
	x	x	x	x			x			s	x	x	sx		x	x		s	s	x	xs	s											13
s	x	x	x	x			x		xs	sx	xs	x	s		x	x		s		x	sx												14
	t	t	t	t			ts		ts	st	t	t			t	t		tn		t	st	tn	tn										15
	x	x	x	x			x		xs	s	xs	x			xs	x				x	s			sx	sx	sx							16
	x	x	x	xs			x		xs	sx		xs				x		s		x	sx		s	sx	x	x							17
	x	x	x				x			sx		x			x	xs		s		xs	x	sx	s	xs	x	sx							18
	x		x				x		x	sx		x			x	x		s				s	s	xs	x	xs	x	sx					19
	t		ts				t		t	st		t			t	t		tn				tn		t	t	t		ts	st				20
			xs				x		sx	s	sx	x			sx	x						s		x	x	xs	x			x	x	xs	21
8	16	18	17	11	10	8	18	6	6	1	7	10	0	0	9	12	0	1	1	6	2	0	0	2	5	2	2	0	0	1	1	0	X
0	2	0	3	4	0	2	2	4	10	1	6	5	1	0	2	1	0	0	0	1	1	0	0	2	0	2	0	1	0	0	0	1	XS
0	0	0	1	0	0	0	0	0	1	11	3	6	9	0	6	0	1	0	2	0	3	1	0	2	1	2	0	1	1	0	0	0	SX
1	0	0	0	1	0	0	0	0	0	8	1	0	4	4	3	6	2	8	3	0	1	5	4	0	0	0	0	0	0	0	0	0	S

GOALKEEPERS	CS	CCS
Lovett	4	2

x/c/t - Played full 90 minutes
xs/cs/ts - Substituted off
sx/sc/st - Substituted on
s/cn/tn - Non-playing sub

GUISELEY MATCH RESULTS 2020-21

Date	Comp	H/A	Opponents	Att:	Result	Goalscorers	Pos
Oct 3	**FAC2Q**	**H**	**Atherton Collieries**		**W 4 - 0**	**Felix 14 76 Bailey 53 (og) Howarth 89**	
6	NLN	H	Blyth Spartans		W 4 - 0	Mbeka 2 (pen) Bencherif 41 Felix 55 Howarth 67	2
13	**FAC3Q**	**H**	**Matlock Town**		**W 2 - 0**	**Mbeka 24 (pen) Wafula 68**	
17	NLN	H	Hereford		L 0 - 1		11
24	**FAC4Q**	**A**	**FC United of Manchester**	**600**	**L 1 - 2**	**Wafula 34**	
27	NLN	A	Boston United		D 1 - 1	Newall 90+6	11
Nov 17	NLN	H	Darlington		L 1 - 4	Nicholson 83	20
21	NLN	H	Gloucester City		L 1 - 2	Mbeka 88 (pen)	21
24	NLN	A	Kettering Town		D 1 - 1	Haw 70	19
28	NLN	A	AFC Telford United		L 0 - 2		20
Dec 1	NLN	A	Spennymoor Town		W 2 - 0	Kellett 25 Johnson 90+2	19
5	NLN	H	Brackley Town		L 1 - 3	Mbeka 66	21
8	NLN	A	Chorley		L 0 - 1		21
12	NLN	H	Southport		W 4 - 2	Wafula 18 Parsons 49 Felix 80 Mbeka 89 (pen)	19
15	**FAT2P**	**H**	**Chorley**		**W 2 - 0**	**Felix 29 Haw 90+6**	
19	**FAT3P**	**A**	**Stockport County**		**L 1 - 3**	**Wafula 35**	
26	NLN	H	Farsley Celtic		D 2 - 2	Felix 7 Newall 66	18
28	NLN	A	York City		L 0 - 1		20
Jan 5	NLN	A	Chester		L 0 - 1		20
16	NLN	A	Gateshead		L 0 - 1		20

Goalcorers	LGE	FAC	FAT	SG	CSG	HAT	PEN	1Q	2Q	45+	3Q	4Q	90+	T
TOTALS	17	7	3			0	4	4	6	0	6	8	3	27
Felix	3	2	1	5	2			2	1		1	2		6
Mbeka	4	1		4	2		4	1	1		1	2		5
Wafula	1	2	1	4	1			1	2			1		4
Haw	1		1	2	1							1	1	2
Howarth	1	1		2	2						1	1		2
Newall	2			2	1						1		1	2
Bencherif	1			1	1				1					1
Johnson	1			1	1								1	1
Kellett	1			1	1				1					1

	LGE	FAC	FAT	SG	CSG	HAT	PEN	1Q	2Q	45+	3Q	4Q	90+	T
Nicholson	1			1	1							1		1
Opponent		1		1	1						1			1
Parsons	1			1	1						1			1

Wade D (L)	Cantrill G	Nicholson B	Howarth M	Bencherif H	Cowan D	Felix K	Ekpolo P	Mbeka L	Gillam M	Johnson G	Currie I	Wafula J	Ryan J	Hey L	Diamba H (Gk)	Clayton P	Newall N	Haw A	Harratt K (L)	Kellett A	Lufudu J	Jones A	Molokwu C	Lambton D (Gk)	Parsons J	Okafor M	Butterfield M (L)	Kendall R (L)	Tongue L (D)	Thompson B	No.
c	c	c	c	c	c	cs	c	c	cs	cs	sc	sc	sc	cn	cn	cn	cn														1
x	x	xs	x	x	x	xs	x	x	sx	x	s	xs	sx				s	sx													2
c	c	c	c	cs	c	cs	cs	c	sc	c	cn	c	sc	cn	cn		cn	sc													3
x	x	x	x	x	xs	xs	xs	x	sx	x	s	x				sx	sx	s													4
c	c	c	c	c	cs		cs	c	sc	c	cn	cs		cn	cn	sc	sc	cn	c												5
x	x	xs	xs	x	x		x	x	sx	x	s	x		sx			sx	s	xs												6
x	x	x	xs	x	x		x	x	xs	x	s	xs	sx				s		sx	sx											7
x	x	s	xs	x	sx		x	x		x	xs		s	sx			x	sx	x	xs											8
x	x	sx	x	x	s		x	x		xs	xs		sx	s			x	sx	xs	x											9
x	x		sx	x	s	xs	x	x		x	s	sx		xs			x	sx		xs	x										10
x	x	sx	s	x	s		x	x		sx		x		sx			x	xs		xs	x	x									11
x	x	s	x	x		x		x		sx		x					x		s	xs	x	x	s	s							12
x	x	x	s	x		xs		x		xs		x					x	sx	xs			x	s		sx	sx					13
x	x	sx		x		x		xs		sx		xs					x	s			x	x	s		xs	sx	x				14
t	t	t	tn	t		ts	t	t		ts	ts						st	st				t	tn	tn	st	tn	t				15
t	t	t	st	t		t		ts		tn	ts	t					st	tn				t	st	tn	ts	tn	t				16
x	x	sx	s			x		x		sx	xs	x					x	sx			x	x	xs		xs	s					17
x	x	xs	xs	x		x		sx	s	xs	x	x					sx				x	x			sx	s					18
x	x			x		xs		x	sx			xs		sx			x	sx			x	x	s		xs	s	x				19
x	x			x		sx	x	sx	xs								xs	s		sx	x	s			x			x	xs	x	20
20	20	8	7	18	5	5	10	16	0	8	1	9	0	0	0	0	9	0	2	1	8	9	0	0	1	0	4	1	0	1	X
0	0	3	4	1	2	8	3	2	3	5	5	5	0	1	0	0	1	1	3	4	0	0	1	0	4	0	0	0	1	0	XS
0	0	4	2	0	1	1	0	2	6	4	1	2	5	4	0	2	6	9	1	2	0	0	1	0	3	2	0	0	0	0	SX
0	0	2	4	0	3	0	0	0	1	1	7	0	1	4	3	1	4	6	1	0	0	1	5	3	0	5	0	0	0	0	S

GOALKEEPERS	CS	CCS
Wade	5	2

x/c/t - Played full 90 minutes
xs/cs/ts - Substituted off
sx/sc/st - Substituted on
s/cn/tn - Non-playing sub

HEREFORD MATCH RESULTS 2020-21

Date	Comp	H/A	Opponents	Att:	Result	Goalscorers	Pos
Oct 3	**FAC2Q**	**A**	**Gosport Borough**	**501**	**W 3 - 1**	**John-Lewis 27 65 (pen) Owen-Evans 75 (pen)**	
6	NLN	A	Southport		D 0 - 0		12
13	**FAC3Q**	**A**	**Stafford Rangers**	**585**	**L 1 - 3**	**Owen-Evans 15**	
17	NLN	A	Guiseley		W 1 - 0	John-Lewis 30 (pen)	8
27	NLN	H	Bradford (Park Avenue)		L 0 - 2		12
Nov 14	NLN	A	Blyth Spartans		W 3 - 0	Owen-Evans 33 35 John-Lewis 70	13
17	NLN	H	Gloucester City		L 0 - 1		13
21	NLN	H	Chorley		D 2 - 2	Hodgkiss 59 John-Lewis 88	14
28	NLN	H	Kettering Town		D 3 - 3	Mooney 34 Hodgkiss 57 John-Lewis 81 (pen)	15
Dec 8	NLN	A	Chester		L 3 - 5	Owen-Evans 22 38 Digie 74	20
12	NLN	H	AFC Fylde	800	W 2 - 1	John-Lewis 37 59	16
15	**FAT2P**	**H**	**St Neots**	**285**	**W 3 - 0**	**Grimes 17 Finn 25 John-Lewis 66**	
19	**FAT3P**	**A**	**Nantwich Town**	**433**	**W 1 - 0**	**John-Lewis 67**	
26	NLN	H	Kidderminster Harriers	938	W 3 - 1	McQuilkin 16 Camwell 48 John-Lewis 81	16
28	NLN	A	Leamington		D 0 - 0		14
Jan 2	NLN	A	Kidderminster Harriers		D 1 - 1	John-Lewis 66 (pen)	14
19	**FAT4P**	**A**	**Stamford**		**W 2 - 0**	**Owen-Evans 10 75 (RC - Pollock 52 2xY - Haines 75)**	
Feb 6	**FAT5P**	**H**	**Leamington**		**W 1 - 0**	**Camwell 4**	
16	NLN	H	Brackley Town		W 2 - 0	Bakare 49 Camwell 64	12
27	**FAT QF**	**A**	**Aldershot Town**		**D 1 - 1**	**Bakare 6 (Won 5-3 on pens)**	
Mar 29	**FAT SF**	**H**	**Woking**		**W 1 - 0**	**Butlin 21**	
May 22	**FAT F**	**N**	**Hornchurch**	**9000**	**L 1 - 3**	**Owen-Evans 13**	

Goalcorers	LGE	FAC	FAT	SG	CSG	HAT	PEN	1Q	2Q	45+	3Q	4Q	90+	T
TOTALS	21	3	10			0	5	9	8	0	10	7	0	34
John-Lewis	8	2	2	10	4		4		3		5	4		12
Owen-Evans	5	1	3	5	1		1	4	3			2		9
Camwell	2		1	3	2			1			2			3
Bakare	1		1	2	2			1			1			2
Hodgkiss	2			2	2						2			2
Butlin			1	1	1			1						1
Digie	1			1	1							1		1
Finn			1	1	1				1					1
Grimes			1	1	1			1						1
McQuilkin	1			1	1			1						1
Mooney	1			1	1				1					1

Hodgkiss J	Wright J	Grimes J	Camwell C	Lloyd R	Klukowski Y	Haines L	Owen-Evans T	Finn K	John-Lewis	Digie K	Nabi S	Jones A	Vaughan N (Gk)	McQuilkin J	Raison T	Pollock B	Jones Dan	Hall B (Gk)	Mooney K	Coke G	Whittingham R	Brown D	Jones Dylan	Forsyth G	Rowe C (L)	Butlin J	Bakare M	McLean R	Butroid L (L)	Kouhyar M	No.
c	cs	c	c	c	cs	c	c	c	cs	sc	sc	sc	cn	cn	cn	cn															1
xs	x	x	x	x	xs	x	xs	x		s	sx	x		sx			sx	s													2
																															3
x	x	x	s	xs	sx	x	xs	x	x	sx		x		s			x		sx												4
x	x	x		xs	sx	x	xs	x	x	s		x		s					sx	sx											5
x		x	s	x	x		xs	sx	xs	x	sx			sx		xs	x		x	s											6
x		x	s	xs	xs		x	sx	x	x	sx			xs			x		x	sx	s										7
x		x	s	x			xs	sx	x	x	sx			xs			x		xs	x	s	sx									8
x		x	sx	x				xs	x	x	s			xs			x		x	xs	sx	sx									9
x		x	sx	x	sx		x	x	x	x	s			xs			x	s		xs	s										10
x		x	xs	x	sx		x	x	x	xs	s			x			x	x		sx	s										11
t		t	t	ts	ts		t	t	ts		tn			t	st		t	t		st	st		tn								12
		t	t	t	t		ts	t	t		tn			ts	st		ts	t	st	st			t								13
x		x	xs	x	x	x	x	x	xs					xs				x	sx	sx			s	sx							14
x		x	x	x		x	xs	x			s			sx				x	x	x	s		sx	xs							15
x		x	x	x	xs	x	x	x	x					x				x	s	sx			s	s							16
t		t	ts	t	st	t	t	ts			tn			t		t		t			tn		st		t						17
t		t	t	t	st		t	ts		t	st			ts	tn	ts		t			tn		st			t					18
x		x	xs	x	sx	x	xs	x		s				sx		x		x								x	xs	sx			19
t		t	ts	t	tn	t	t	t		tn				tn		st		t					tn		st	ts	t		t		20
t		t	ts	t	st	t	t	ts		tn				tn		st		t							tn	ts	t		t	st	21
t		t	ts	t	st	t	t	ts		tn				st		tn		t					tn			t	ts			st	22
19	3	21	7	17	3	12	12	13	9	6	0	3	0	4	0	2	8	12	4	2	0	0	1	0	1	3	2	0	2	0	x
1	1	0	7	4	5	0	8	5	4	1	0	0	0	7	0	2	1	0	1	2	0	0	0	1	0	2	2	0	0	0	xs
0	0	0	2	0	9	0	0	3	0	2	6	1	0	5	2	2	1	0	4	7	2	2	3	1	1	0	0	1	0	2	sx
0	0	0	4	0	1	0	0	0	0	6	7	0	1	5	2	2	0	2	1	1	7	0	5	1	1	0	0	0	0	0	s

GOALKEEPERS	CS	CCS
Hall	7	3
White P	3	1

x/c/t - Played full 90 minutes
xs/cs/ts - Substituted off
sx/sc/st - Substituted on
s/cn/tn - Non-playing sub

KETTERING TOWN MATCH RESULTS 2020-21

Date	Comp	H/A	Opponents	Att:	Result	Goalscorers	Pos
Oct 3	**FAC2Q**	**H**	**Chelmsford City**		**W 2 - 0**	**Bickley 41 Sheriff 79**	
6	NLN	A	Gloucester City		L 1 - 3	Kennedy 90+3	19
24	NLN	H	Bradford (Park Avenue)		**W** 3 - 1	Stephens 3 Scott 15 35	13
28	NLN	A	AFC Fylde		L 2 - 3	Kennedy 31 Sheriff 73 (pen)	13
Nov 3	NLN	H	Southport		L 0 - 1		
14	NLN	H	Curzon Ashton		L 1 - 2	Kennedy 6	20
24	NLN	H	Guiseley		D 1 - 1	Kennedy 35	22
28	NLN	A	Hereford		D 3 - 3	Powell 46 54 Fryatt 61	19
Dec 1	NLN	A	Kidderminster Harriers		**W** 2 - 0	Graham 57 Kennedy 70	18
5	NLN	H	Blyth Spartans	637	**W** 2 - 1	Fryatt 9 Powell 42	15
8	NLN	A	York City		L 0 - 2		17
12	NLN	H	AFC Telford United	514	D 0 - 0		17
15	**FAT2P**	**H**	**Nuneaton Borough**		**W 5 - 1**	**Perry 42 Sheriff 48 58 65 Fryatt 68**	
19	**FAT3P**	**A**	**Ashton United**		**W 2 - 1**	**Sheriff 68 Kennedy 73**	
28	NLN	A	Alfreton Town		D 3 - 3	Milnes 35 Powell 52 85 (pen)	19
Jan 2	NLN	A	Brackley Town		D 1 - 1	Powell 68 (pen)	18
5	NLN	A	Boston United		D 2 - 2	Kennedy 39 Sheriff 40	18
19	**FAT4P**	**H**	**Leamington**		**L 0 - 3**	**(RC 2xY - McGrath 11 Kennedy 80 Johnson 87)**	

Goalcorers	LGE	FAC	FAT	SG	CSG	HAT	PEN	1Q	2Q	45+	3Q	4Q	90+	T
TOTALS	21	2	7			0	3	4	9	0	8	8	1	30
Kennedy	6		1	7	2			1	3			2	1	7
Sheriff	2	1	4	5	2		1		1		3	3		7
Powell	6			4	2		2		1		3	2		6
Fryatt	2		1	3	1			1			1	1		3
Scott	2			1	1			1	1					2
Bickley		1		1	1				1					1
Graham	1			1	1						1			1
Milnes	1			1	1				1					1
Perry			1	1	1				1					1
Stephens	1			1	1			1						1

No.	Stohrer G	McGrath M	Graham L	Fryatt R	Milnes B	Bickley L	Kennedy C	Scott J (L)	Jones S	Sheriff D	Stephens B	Wilson L	Richens M	Solkhon B	Chisholm J	Turner J	Herbert G	Oyinsan J	Acquaye B	Hunt J	Powell C	Pryce A	Williams J	Sharpe R	Perry K	Anderson J (L)	Johnston E (L)	Johnson C	Wood J	Chapman D	Duggan C	Bailey-Nicholls K	Hughes L (L)
1	c	c	c	c	c	cs	c	c	c	cs	sc	sc	cn	cn	cn	cn	cn																
2	x	x	x	x	x	xs	x	xs	x	xs	sx	sx	s		sx	s																	
3	x	x	x	x	x	s	x	x		xs	xs	s	sx		s			x	sx														
4	x	x	x	x	xs	sx	x	x	sx	x	xs		sx		s			xs	s														
5	x	x	x	xs	x	sx	x	sx	s	xs	x		s					xs	sx	x													
6	x	x	x	xs	x	x	x	sx	x	xs	xs	s	sx					sx	s														
7	x	x	x	x		sx	x	xs	x	xs		s	x						s		x	sx	s										
8	x	x	x	x	sx		x			xs	s		x						s		x	sx	sx	xs	xs								
9	x	x	x	x	x		x	sx		s	s		x								x	s	s	xs	x								
10	x		x	x	x		x	s		sx	s		x								x	sx	s	xs	xs	x							
11	x	sx	x	x	xs		x	s			sx		x								x	sx	s	xs	x	xs							
12	x	x	xs	x	x		x			s	sx		x								x	s	s		x	x	s						
13	t	t		t	t		t			t	ts		t									st			ts	ts		st	tn	tn	tn	st	
14	t	t			ts		t		tn	ts	t		t									tn	st		t	t	st	t			tn		
15	x	x		x	x		x		s	xs	sx		xs								x	s	sx		x	x	s						
16	x	x		x	x		x		s	x	s		x								x	s	s		xs			x				sx	
17	x	x		x	x		x		s	x	s		x								x				xs	s		x				s	sx
18	t	t		t	tn		t		tn	t	st		t									tn			ts	t		t	tn	tn		tn	t
x	18	16	11	15	12	1	18	3	4	5	2	0	11	0	0	0	0	1	0	1	9	0	0	0	5	5	0	4	0	0	0	0	1
xs	0	0	1	2	3	2	0	2	0	9	4	0	1	0	0	0	0	2	0	0	0	0	0	4	6	2	0	0	0	0	0	0	0
sx	0	1	0	0	1	3	0	3	1	1	6	2	3	0	1	0	0	1	2	0	0	5	3	0	0	0	1	1	0	0	0	2	1
s	0	0	0	0	1	1	0	2	6	2	5	3	3	1	3	2	1	0	4	0	0	6	6	0	0	1	2	0	2	2	2	2	0

GOALKEEPERS	CS	CCS
Collin	3	1

x/c/t - Played full 90 minutes
xs/cs/ts - Substituted off
sx/sc/st - Substituted on
s/cn/tn - Non-playing sub

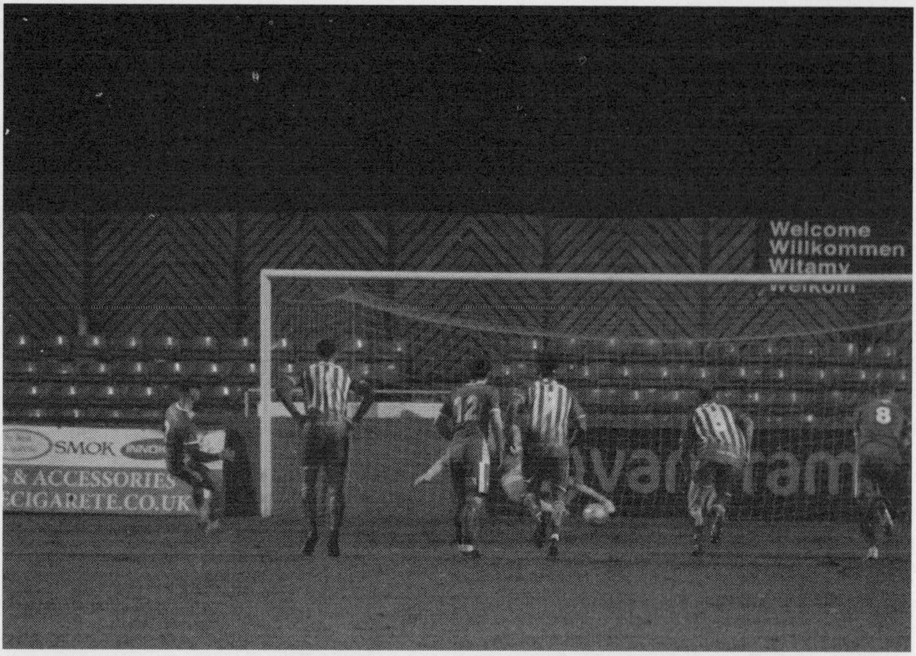
Welcome
Willkommen
Witamy
SMOK

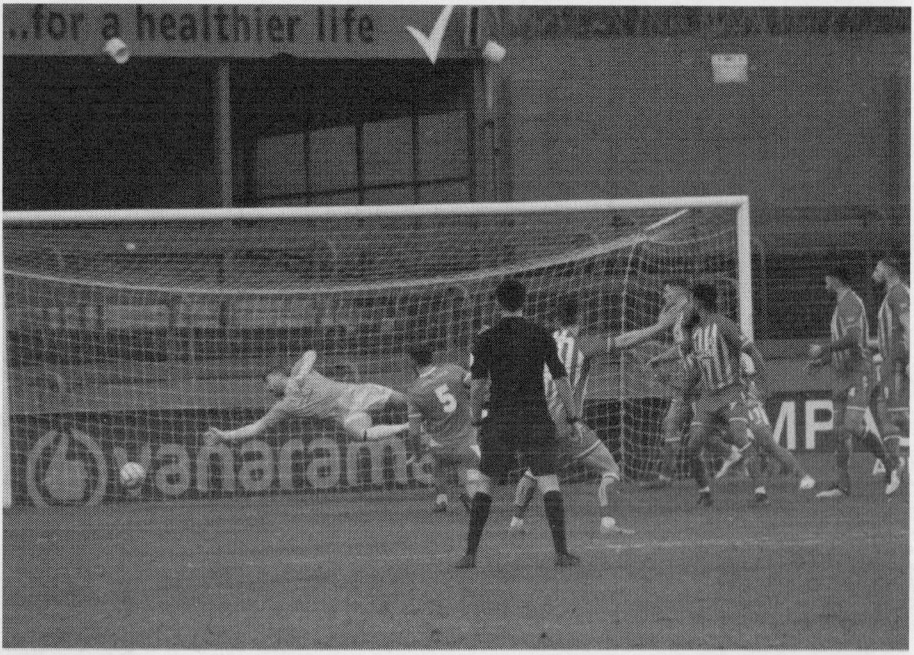
...for a healthier life

Alfreton Town 3 - 3 Kettering Town - 28/12/2020

Photos Bill Wheatcroft

KIDDERMINSTER HARRIERS MATCH RESULTS 2020-21

Date	Comp	H/A	Opponents	Att:	Result	Goalscorers	Pos
Oct 3	**FAC2Q**	**A**	**Alvechurch**	**445**	**D 2 - 2**	**Austin 26 Hemmings 71 (Lost 2-4 on pens)**	
6	NLN	H	Chester		L 1 - 2	Hemmings 29	16
10	NLN	A	Darlington		**W** 3 - 1	Sterling 29 Hemmings 42 Austin 86	9
24	NLN	A	Chorley		**W** 2 - 0	Sterling 39 45+1	6
31	NLN	H	Blyth Spartans		**W** 2 - 0	Hemmings 12 Taylor M 57	4
Nov 7	NLN	H	Leamington		D 1 - 1	Arthur 14	5
17	NLN	A	Brackley Town		**W** 2 - 0	Morgan-Smith 5 Austin 32	4
21	NLN	A	Farsley Celtic		D 2 - 2	Austin 19 Sterling 22	3
24	NLN	H	Alfreton Town		**W** 3 - 0	Moyo 26 Hemmings 70 86	2
28	NLN	H	Curzon Ashton		**W** 1 - 0	Austin 35	2
Dec 1	NLN	H	Kettering Town		L 0 - 2		3
12	NLN	A	Gateshead		**W** 1 - 0	Montrose 83	2
15	**FAT2P**	**A**	**Stamford**		**L 0 - 1**		
26	NLN	A	Hereford	938	L 1 - 3	Maxwell 7	2
Jan 2	NLN	H	Hereford		D 1 - 1	Hemmings 12 (pen)	2
5	NLN	H	York City		D 2 - 2	Lowe 42 Cowley 80	3
9	NLN	A	Gloucester City		L 2 - 3	Freemantle 6 Austin 12	4

Goalcorers	LGE	FAC	FAT	SG	CSG	HAT	PEN	1Q	2Q	45+	3Q	4Q	90+	T
TOTALS	24	2	0			0	1	9	9	1	1	6	0	26
Hemmings	6	1		6	3		1	2	2			3		7
Austin	5	1		6	2			2	3			1		6
Sterling	4			3	2			1	2	1				4
Arthur	1			1	1			1						1
Cowley	1			1	1							1		1
Freemantle	1			1	1			1						1
Lowe	1			1	1				1					1
Maxwell	1			1	1			1						1
Montrose	1			1	1							1		1
Morgan-Smith	1			1	1			1						1
Moyo	1			1	1				1					1
Taylor M	1			1	1						1			1

No.	Penny A	Richards C (L/P)	Lowe K	Montrose L	Austin S	Morgan-Smith A	Hemmings A	Sterling-James O	Taylor M (L)	Prosser A	Martin K	Tolley J	Palmer T (Gk)	Freemantle E	Arthur K	White J	Taylor B	Moyo C	Maxwell L	Kellerman J	Phillips L (Gk)	Cowley J
1	c	c	c	c	cs	c	c	c	c	c	sc	cn	cn	cn	cn	cn	cn					
2	x	x	x	x	xs	x	xs	x	x	x	s		s	sx	s	sx						
3	x	x	x	x	x	xs	xs	x	x	x	s		s	sx		sx		sx				
4	x	x	x	x	x		xs	xs	x	x			s	xs	sx	s		sx	sx			
5	x	x	x	x	x		xs	xs	x	x			s	xs	sx			s	sx	sx		
6	x	x	x	x	x	x	xs		xs	x			s	s	xs			sx	sx	sx		
7	xs	x	x	x	x	xs	x	xs	x	sx			s		sx	s		sx	x			
8	x	x	x	xs	x	x	xs	xs	x	sx			s	sx	sx			s	x			
9	x	x	x	x	xs	x	xs	xs	s	sx			s		sx	sx		x	x			
10		x	x	x	xs	x	xs	xs	x	sx			s		sx	s		x	x	sx		
11		x	x	xs	x	x	x	sx	xs	sx			s		x	s		x	xs	sx		
12	x	x	x	x	xs	x	x	xs	s	sx				sx	sx			x	xs		s	
13	t	t	ts	t	ts	t	t	ts	tn	st	tn			st	st	tn		t	t		tn	
14	x	x	x	x	xs	x	x	xs	s	sx	sx		s		sx			x	xs			
15	x	x	x	x	x		xs	sx		xs	sx		s	xs	s			x	x			sx
16	x	x	x	xs	x		x	sx		xs	s		s	x	s			x	x			sx
17	x	x	x		x		xs	x	s	sx	s		s	xs	sx			x	x			x
x	14	17	16	13	10	10	7	4	8	6	0	0	0	1	1	0	0	9	8	0	0	1
xs	1	0	1	3	7	2	10	9	2	2	0	0	0	4	1	0	0	0	3	0	0	0
sx	0	0	0	0	0	0	0	3	0	9	3	0	0	5	10	3	0	4	3	4	0	2
s	0	0	0	0	0	0	0	0	5	0	5	1	15	2	4	6	1	2	0	0	2	0

OALKEEPERS	CS	CCS
impson	6	2

x/c/t - Played full 90 minutes
xs/cs/ts - Substituted off
sx/sc/st - Substituted on
s/cn/tn - Non-playing sub

LEAMINGTON MATCH RESULTS 2020-21

Date	Comp	H/A	Opponents	Att:	Result	Goalscorers	Pos
Oct 3	**FAC2Q**	**H**	**Banbury United**		**L 0 - 1**		
6	NLN	H	Boston United		L 0 - 4		22
10	NLN	A	Chester		L 2 - 3	English 9 Meredith 76	22
Nov 3	NLN	A	Farsley Celtic		D 1 - 1	Edwards 88	20
7	NLN	A	Kidderminster Harriers		D 1 - 1	Anderson 4	21
17	NLN	H	Alfreton Town		**W** 4 - 3	Osborne 53 68 Smith L 87 Edwards 90+2	18
21	NLN	A	Curzon Ashton		**W** 3 - 0	Osborne 15 Tharme 18 (og) Lane 50	15
24	NLN	H	AFC Fylde		D 1 - 1	Osborne 90+3	13
28	NLN	H	York City		**W** 2 - 1	English 3 Osborne 6	8
Dec 1	NLN	H	Brackley Town		D 1 - 1	Osborne 45	8
5	NLN	H	Gateshead		D 1 - 1	English 90+4	11
12	NLN	A	Bradford (Park Avenue)		**W** 3 - 1	Osborne 9 72 Maye 45+1	8
15	**FAT2P**	**H**	**St Ives Town**		**W 5 - 0**	**Waldron 32 77 Smith 35 63 87**	
19	**FAT3P**	**A**	**Wrexham**		**D 0 - 0**	**(Won 6-5 on pens)**	
26	NLN	A	Gloucester City		L 0 - 1		11
28	NLN	H	Hereford		D 0 - 0		10
Jan 2	NLN	H	Gloucester City		D 1 - 1	English 61	9
12	NLN	A	Chorley		**W** 2 - 1	Allen 6 Turner 80 (pen)	8
19	**FAT4P**	**A**	**Kettering Town**		**W 3 - 0**	**Waldron 1 Edwards 23 Lane 31**	
Feb 6	**FAT5P**	**A**	**Hereford**		**L 0 - 1**		

Goalcorers	LGE	FAC	FAT	SG	CSG	HAT	PEN	1Q	2Q	45+	3Q	4Q	90+	T
TOTALS	22	0	8			0	1	9	4	2	4	8	3	30
Osborne	8			6	5			3		1	1	2	1	8
English	4			4	1			2			1		1	4
Smith L	1		3	2	1				1		1	2		4
Edwards	2		1	3	1				1			1	1	3
Waldron			3	2	1			1	1			1		3
Lane	1		1	2	1				1		1			2
Allen	1			1	1			1						1
Anderson	1			1	1			1						1
Maye	1			1	1					1				1
Meredith	1			1	1							1		1
Opponent	1			1	1			1						1
Turner	1			1	1		1					1		1

No.	Weaver J	English J	Morley S	Meredith D	Morrison K	Lane J	Parker J	Maye S	Waldron D	Edwards J	Osborne S	Gittings C	Taylor C	Smith L	Martin J	Anderson K	Allen J (Gk)	Clarke J	Knott C (Gk)	Newey B (Gk)	Dunbar K	Batchelor R	Allen T (L)	Maxwell B (Gk)	Turner D	Hamilton T (D)	McClean B
1	c	c	c	cs	c	c	cs	c	c	c	cs	sc	sc	sc	cn	cn	cn										
2	x	x	x	s	x	x	xs	x	x		xs	x	sx	s	s	sx		x									
3	x	x	x	sx	x	x		xs	x		xs		xs	sx	x	sx	s	x	s								
4	x	x	x	s	x	x		x	sx	sx	sx	s	xs	xs	xs	x		x									
5	x	x	x	sx	x	x		x	sx	x	x	s	s	xs	s	xs		x									
6	x	x	x	sx	x	x			x	x	xs	x	sx	xs	s			x		s	s						
7	x	sx	x	sx	x	x			x	xs	x	xs	s	xs	x			x		s		sx					
8	x	sx	x	sx	x	x		sx	xs	xs	x	x	s	xs	x			x				s					
9	x	xs	x	sx	x	x		x	s		xs	sx	s	x	x	xs		x					sx				
10	x	sx	x	s	x	x		x	xs	x	xs		s	xs	x	sx		x					sx				
11	x	sx	x	s	x	x		x	xs	xs	x		s	xs	x	sx		x					sx				
12	x	s	x	sx	x	x		xs	sx	x	xs		s	x	x	sx		x					xs				
13	t	st	t	st	t	t		t	t	ts	ts	tn	tn	t	ts	st		t									
14	t	st	t	tn	t	t		ts	ts	t	t	st	tn	ts	t	st		t									
15	x	sx	x	sx	x	x		x	xs	x	x	xs	s		xs	sx							x	s			
16	x	s	x	sx	x	x		xs	xs	x	xs	x	s		x	sx		sx					x				
17	x	sx	x	s	x	x		x	xs	xs	xs	sx	s		x	sx		x					x				
18	x	s	x	sx	x	x		xs	xs	x		sx	s		x	xs		x					x		sx		
19	t	st	t	t	t	t		ts	t	ts		st	st	tn	ts	t		t								tn	
20	t	st	ts	t	t	t		t	t	t		st	st	tn	t	ts		ts									tn
X	20	6	19	2	20	20	0	11	8	10	6	4	0	3	12	2	0	16	0	0	0	0	4	0	0	0	0
XS	0	1	1	1	0	0	2	6	8	6	10	2	2	8	4	4	0	1	0	0	0	0	1	0	0	0	0
SX	0	10	0	11	0	0	0	1	3	1	1	7	5	2	0	10	0	1	0	0	0	1	3	0	1	0	0
S	0	3	0	6	0	0	0	0	1	0	0	3	13	3	4	1	2	0	1	2	1	1	0	1	0	1	1

GOALKEEPERS	CS	CCS
Weaver	5	2

x/c/t - Played full 90 minutes
xs/cs/ts - Substituted off
sx/sc/st - Substituted on
s/cn/tn - Non-playing sub

SOUTHPORT MATCH RESULTS 2020-21

Date	Comp	H/A	Opponents	Att:	Result	Goalscorers	Pos
Oct 3	**FAC2Q**	**H**	**Morpeth Town**		**W 2 - 1**	**Watson 59 Newell 80**	
6	NLN	H	Hereford		D 0 - 0		13
13	**FAC3Q**	**H**	**South Shields**		**D 1 - 1**	**Adams 29 (og) (Lost 2-4 on pens)**	
17	NLN	H	Chorley		**W** 1 - 0	Vassallo 29	9
24	NLN	A	Blyth Spartans		**W** 3 - 0	Newell 37 Vassallo 79 Carver 85	2
31	NLN	H	Boston United		L 0 - 1		6
Nov 3	NLN	A	Kettering Town		**W** 1 - 0	Morgan 33	3
7	NLN	A	AFC Telford United		D 1 - 1	Carver 57	3
10	NLN	H	York City		L 2 - 3	Archer 27 Watson 65	3
14	NLN	H	Spennymoor Town		L 0 - 2		4
17	NLN	A	Bradford (Park Avenue)		**W** 2 - 0	Archer 26 Woods 69	3
21	NLN	A	Gateshead		L 1 - 4	Archer 90	5
Dec 2	NLN	H	Farsley Celtic		L 0 - 1		7
5	NLN	H	Alfreton Town		D 1 - 1	Archer 90+3	8
12	NLN	A	Guiseley		L 2 - 4	Newell 11 Carver 90+2	13
15	**FAT2P**	**A**	**Marine**	**400**	**W 1 - 0**	**Watson 34**	
19	**FAT3P**	**A**	**Spennymoor Town**		**D 2 - 2**	**Ali 14 Newell 80 (Won 5-4 on pens)**	
26	NLN	H	Curzon Ashton	706	D 2 - 2	Carver 18 Woods 74	15
Jan 19	**FAT4P**	**A**	**FC Halifax Town**		**W 2 - 1**	**Newell 10 Anson 68**	
Feb 6	**FAT5P**	**H**	**Torquay United**		**L 0 - 2**		

Goalcorers	LGE	FAC	FAT	SG	CSG	HAT	PEN	1Q	2Q	45+	3Q	4Q	90+	T
TOTALS	16	3	5			0	0	4	7	0	3	7	3	24
Newell	2	1	2	5	1			2	1			2		5
Archer	4			4	2				2				2	4
Carver	4			4	1			1			1	1	1	4
Watson	1	1	1	3	1				1		2			3
Vassallo	2			2	2				1			1		2
Woods	2			2	1							2		2
Ali			1	1	1			1						1
Anson			1	1	1							1		1
Morgan	1			1	1				1					1

	LGE	FAC	FAT	SG	CSG	HAT	PEN	1Q	2Q	45+	3Q	4Q	90+	T
Opponent		1		1	1				1					1

No.	McMillan T	Challoner M	Vassallo D	Anson A	Oliver C	Ali M	Bainbridge J	Woods C	Morgan D	Carver M	Watson N	Benjamin R	Newell G	Hanford D (Gk)	Doyle J	Winnard D	Sampson J	Archer J	Wood M	Antwi C (L)	Fenlon R (L)	Perritt H (L)	Bolton J (L)
1	c	c	c	cs	c	c	c	cs	c	c	c	sc	sc	cn	cn	cn							
2	s	x	sx	s	x	x	x	s	x	xs	sx	x	xs	x	x		x						
3	c	c	sc	sc	c	c	cs	cs	c	sc	cn	c	cs	cn	c		c						
4	s	x	x	x	x	s	s	sx	x	xs	xs	x	sx	x		x	x						
5	s	x	x	x	x	x		xs	x	x	sx	x	xs	x	sx	s	sxs						
6	s	x	sx	sx	xs	x	x	s	x	x	x	x		x	x	xs							
7	s	x	x	x	x	xs	x	s	x	x	x	x	s	x	sx	s							
8	s	x	xs	x	x	x	sx	xs	x	x	sx	x	s	x	x	s							
9	s	x			x	xs	x	sx	x	x	x	sx	s	x	x	s		xs					
10	s	x	sx	x	xs	x	x	sx	x	xs	sx	xs		x	x	s		x					
11	s	x	sx	x	x	sx	x	xs	x	sx	x	xs		x	x	s		xs					
12	s	xs	sx	x	x	xs	x	xs	x	x	x		s	x	x	sx		sx					
13	s		xs	x	x	x	xs		x	x	sx	x	sx	x	x			xs	sx				
14	s	x	sx	x	x	s	xs	x	x	xs		xs	x	x	x			sx		sx			
15		x	s	x	xs	s	x	xs	x	x	sx	x	xs	x	x			sx		sx			
16	t	t	t		tn	t	st	tn	t	st	t	t	ts	tn		t		t		ts			
17	t	t		t	st	t	tn	st	t	ts	t	t	st	tn	ts			t		ts			
18	s	x	x	x	s	x	sx	xs	x	x	s	x	xs	x		x		sx					
19	t	tn	st	t	t	t	t	st	t	tn	t	t	ts	tn	ts			t					
20	t		t	t	t	t	ts	t			t	t		tn	t			t	tn		st	tn	tn
x	6	16	7	14	14	13	10	2	19	10	10	14	1	14	12	3	3	5	0	0	0	0	0
xs	0	1	2	1	3	3	4	8	0	5	1	3	7	0	2	1	0	3	0	2	0	0	0
sx	0	0	8	2	1	1	3	5	0	3	6	2	4	0	2	1	0	4	1	2	1	0	0
s	13	1	1	1	2	3	2	4	0	1	2	0	4	6	1	7	0	0	1	0	0	1	1

GOALKEEPERS	CS	CCS
Hanford	5	3
McMillan	1	1

x/c/t - Played full 90 minutes
xs/cs/ts - Substituted off
sx/sc/st - Substituted on
s/cn/tn - Non-playing sub

SPENNYMOOR TOWN MATCH RESULTS 2020-21

Date	Comp	H/A	Opponents	Att:	Result	Goalscorers	Pos
Oct 3	**FAC2Q**	**A**	**Bradford (Park Avenue)**		**W 3 - 1**	**Taylor 79 90+2 Thompson 80**	
6	NLN	H	Farsley Celtic		**W** 2 - 1	Ramshaw 20 Taylor 57	8
10	NLN	A	Alfreton Town		D 1 - 1	Taylor 30 (pen)	6
13	**FAC3Q**	**A**	**Chester**		**L 1 - 3**	**Hall 6**	
17	NLN	H	Chester		**W** 2 - 1	Taylor 34 Gray 89 (og)	3
Nov 7	NLN	H	Gloucester City		D 2 - 2	Spencer 54 Taylor 86 (pen)	8
10	NLN	A	AFC Fylde		L 0 - 1		8
14	NLN	A	Southport		**W** 2 - 0	Blakeman 3 Taylor 21	3
28	NLN	H	Bradford (Park Avenue)		D 2 - 2	Hall 78 Taylor 85	7
Dec 1	NLN	H	Guiseley		L 0 - 2		10
5	NLN	H	Curzon Ashton		**W** 3 - 1	Ramshaw 18 60 McKenna 89	7
8	NLN	A	Brackley Town		L 0 - 1		9
Jason Ainsley leaves the club after more than 14 years as manager. Assistant Tommy Miller takes temporary charge.							
12	NLN	A	York City	400	D 1 - 1	Taylor 84	11
15	**FAT2P**	**H**	**Marske United**		**W 6 - 2**	**Hornby-Forbes 20 Anderson 36 Tait 44 Taylor 55 Thompson 60 Buddle 77**	
19	**FAT3P**	**H**	**Southport**		**D 2 - 2**	**Taylor 9 Anderson 49 (Lost 4-5 on pens)**	
26	NLN	A	Darlington		D 0 - 0		10
28	NLN	A	Gateshead		**W** 3 - 1	Taylor 6 Ramshaw 51 72	7

Goalcorers	LGE	FAC	FAT	SG	CSG	HAT	PEN	1Q	2Q	45+	3Q	4Q	90+	T
TOTALS	18	4	8			0	2	8	4	0	6	10	1	30
Taylor	8	2	2	11	3		2	3	2		2	4	1	12
Ramshaw	5			3	1			2			1	1		5
Anderson			2	2	2				1		1			2
Hall	1	1		2	1			1				1		2
Thompson		1	1	2	1						1	1		2
Blakeman	1			1	1			1						1
Buddle			1	1	1							1		1
Hornby-Forbes			1	1	1			1						1
McKenna	1			1	1							1		1

	LGE	FAC	FAT	SG	CSG	HAT	PEN	1Q	2Q	45+	3Q	4Q	90+	T
Opponent	1			1	1							1		1
Spencer	1			1	1						1			1
Tait			1	1	1				1					1

Eve D	Hornby-Forbes T	Blakeman A	Kennedy J	Buddle N	Boon J	Thompson S	Anderson M	Taylor G	Ramshaw R	McKenna B	Spencer J	Hall R	Norton J (GK)	Moke A	Curtis J	McLean S	Magnay C	Tait J	Mitchell C	Mulhern F	No.
c	**c**	**cs**	**c**	**c**	**c**	**cs**	**c**	**c**	**c**	**c**	**sc**	**sc**	**cn**	**cn**							1
x	x		xs	x	sx	xs	s	x	x	xs	x	sx	s	sx	x	x					2
x	x		x	x	s		sx	x	x	x	x	xs	s	s	x	x	s				3
c		**cn**	**cs**	**cn**	**c**	**sc**	**sc**	**c**	**c**	**c**	**cn**	**cs**	**cn**	**c**	**c**	**c**	**c**	**cn**			4
x		x	sx	x		xs	xs	x	x	x	x		s	sx	x	x		s	s		5
x	sx	x	xs	x		xs	sx	x	x	sx	x	xs		s	x	x		s			6
x	x	x	sx	x		s	sx	x	x	x	xs	s		xs	x	x		s			7
x	x	x	sx	x		sx	s	x	x	xs	xs			x	x	xs		s		sx	8
x	x	xs		x		sx	s	x	x	xs	x	sx		xs	x	x	s			sx	9
x	x	xs	xs	x		s	sx	x	x	sx	x	sx			x	x	s			xs	10
x		x		s		xs	x	x	x	sx	x	sx		s	x	xs	x	x		s	11
x	sx	xs	x	s		s		x	x	sx	x	xs			x	x	x	x		s	12
x	x			s		sx	x	x	x	xs	x	xs		s	x	s	x	x		sx	13
t	**ts**		**t**	**t**		**t**	**ts**	**ts**	**t**	**tn**	**tn**	**t**	**tn**	**st**	**tn**	**t**	**st**	**t**		**st**	14
t	**st**		**st**	**tn**		**ts**	**t**	**t**	**t**	**st**	**t**	**ts**	**tn**	**tn**	**t**	**t**	**ts**	**t**		**tn**	15
x	x			s		x	x	x	x	s	x	xs	s	s	x	x		x		sx	16
x	s	x	x	x		s	sx	x	xs	x		sx	s	x	x			x		xs	17
17	9	6	5	11	2	2	5	16	16	6	11	1	0	3	15	12	4	7	0	0	X
0	1	4	4	0	0	6	2	1	1	4	2	7	0	2	0	2	1	0	0	2	XS
0	3	0	4	0	1	4	6	0	0	5	1	6	0	3	0	0	1	0	0	5	SX
0	1	1	0	6	1	4	3	0	0	2	2	1	9	7	1	1	3	5	1	3	S

GOALKEEPERS	CS	CCS
Eve	2	1

x/c/t - Played full 90 minutes
xs/cs/ts - Substituted off
sx/sc/st - Substituted on
s/cn/tn - Non-playing sub

YORK CITY MATCH RESULTS 2020-21

Date	Comp	H/A	Opponents	Att:	Result	Goalscorers	Pos
Oct 3	**FAC2Q**	**A**	**Warrington Rylands**	**300**	**W 1 - 0**	**Newton 39 (Fk)**	
6	NLN	H	Chorley		**W** 3 - 1	McLaughlin 12 Barrow 49 Woods 83	5
10	NLN	A	Farsley Celtic		D 1 - 1	Newton 37	5
13	**FAC3Q**	**A**	**Chorley**		**L 0 - 1**		
17	NLN	H	Brackley Town		D 0 - 0		6
Nov 10	NLN	A	Southport		**W** 3 - 2	Newton 54 66 Bunn 77	7
28	NLN	A	Leamington		L 1 - 2	Dyson 11	17
Dec 2	NLN	A	Blyth Spartans		**W** 3 - 0	Woods 9 Bunn 47 Cassidy 64	13
5	NLN	H	Chester		**W** 2 - 1	Bunn 31 Wright 69	9
8	NLN	H	Kettering Town		**W** 2 - 0	Newton 6 (pen) 8	4
12	NLN	H	Spennymoor Town	400	D 1 - 1	Woods 4	4
15	**FAT2P**	**A**	**Ashton United**		**D 3 - 3**	**Dyson 13 Woods 18 Redshaw 24 (Lost 2-4 on pens)**	
26	NLN	A	Bradford (Park Avenue)		L 2 - 4	Redshaw 56 Guilfoyle 70	4
28	NLN	H	Guiseley		**W** 1 - 0	King 27	4
Jan 5	NLN	A	Kidderminster Harriers		D 2 - 2	Woods 4 Newton 51 (pen)	7
Feb 16	NLN	H	AFC Fylde		L 1 - 3	Newton 64 (pen)	8

Goalcorers	LGE	FAC	FAT	SG	CSG	HAT	PEN	1Q	2Q	45+	3Q	4Q	90+	T
TOTALS	22	1	3			0	3	9	5	0	8	4	0	26
Newton	7	1		6	2		3	2	2		4			8
Woods	4		1	5	2			4				1		5
Bunn	3			3	2				1		1	1		3
Dyson	1		1	2	1			2						2
Redshaw	1		1	2	2				1		1			2
Barrow	1			1	1						1			1
Cassidy	1			1	1						1			1
Guilfoyle	1			1	1							1		1
King	1			1	1				1					1
McLaughlin	1			1	1			1						1
Wright	1			1	1							1		1

Jameson P	Kennedy K	Tinkler R	Newton S	Duckworth M	Barrow S	Wright A	Woods M	McLaughlin P	Dyson O	Cassidy J	Brown M	Potts R	Flatters H (Gk)	Spratt H	Wollerton A	Guilfoyle R	Bunn H	Gamble O	King J	Redshaw J	Gilchrist J (L)	McGill G (L)	Whitley R (Gk)	No.
c	**c**	**cs**	**c**	**c**	**c**	**c**	**c**	**c**	**cs**	**c**	**sc**	**sc**	**cn**	**cn**	**cn**	**cn**								1
x	s	x	x	x	x	x	x	x	xs	x	x	s	s	s			sx							2
x	x		x	x	x	x	x	x	xs	x	x	s	s	s			sx	s						3
c	**c**		**c**	**cs**	**c**	**c**	**cs**	**c**	**c**	**c**	**cs**	**sc**	**cn**	**cn**		**cn**	**sc**	**cn**	**sc**					4
x	x	x	x		x		x	x	x	x		sx	s	s		sx	xs	s	xs					5
x	sx	x	x		x	x	sx	xs	xs	xs	x	s	s				x	x		sx				6
x	s	x	x		x	xs	sx	xs	x	x	x	sx	s				x		xs	sx				7
x	sx	xs	x		x	x	x	sx	x	xs	x	sx	s		s		x			xs				8
x	sx	x	x		x	x	xs	sx	xs	x	x	sx	s			s	x			xs				9
x	x	x	x		xs	x	s	x	xs	xs	x	sx	s	sx			x			sx				10
x	x	x	x			x	x	xs	x		x	sx	s	sx		s	xs	s		x				11
t	**tn**	**t**	**t**			**ts**	**t**	**st**	**t**	**t**	**t**	**tn**	**tn**	**t**	**tn**	**st**		**ts**	**tn**	**t**				12
x		xs	x	x	x	sx	x	xs	xs	x	x		s	s		sx	sx			x				13
x	s	x	x		x	x	s	sx	xs	x	x		s			s	xs		x	x				14
x		x	x	s	x	x	x	sx	xs	x	x		s	s		sx			x	xs				15
x	s	xs	x	x	x		x	x	sx	sx	x						x			sx	xs	xs	s	16
16	6	10	16	5	13	11	10	7	6	11	13	0	0	1	0	0	6	1	2	4	0	0	0	X
0	0	4	0	1	1	2	2	4	9	3	1	0	0	0	0	0	3	1	2	3	1	1	0	XS
0	3	0	0	0	0	1	2	5	1	1	1	8	0	2	0	4	4	0	1	4	0	0	0	SX
0	5	0	0	1	0	0	2	0	0	0	0	4	15	7	3	5	0	4	1	0	0	0	1	S

GOALKEEPERS	CS	CCS
Jameson	5	1

x/c/t - Played full 90 minutes
xs/cs/ts - Substituted off
sx/sc/st - Substituted on
s/cn/tn - Non-playing sub

Matt Urwin keeps hold of the ball as Alfreton attack.

Luke Rawson and Chorley's Harvey Smith clash. Photos Bill Wheatcroft.

NATIONAL LEAGUE SOUTH

As at 17/02/21		P	W	D	L	F	A	GD	Pts
1	Dorking Wanderers	18	12	3	3	40	17	23	39
2	Dartford	19	10	4	5	26	17	9	34
3	Eastbourne Borough	19	9	6	4	36	26	10	33
4	Oxford City	17	9	5	3	35	17	18	32
5	St Albans City	15	9	5	1	22	10	12	32
6	Hampton & Richmond Borough	17	9	2	6	24	16	8	29
7	Hungerford Town	19	9	2	8	27	28	-1	29
8	Ebbsfleet United	18	8	4	6	26	24	2	28
9	Havant & Waterlooville	14	6	2	6	25	21	4	20
10	Hemel Hempstead Town	18	6	2	10	28	38	-10	20
11	Maidstone United	13	5	4	4	24	18	6	19
12	Dulwich Hamlet	13	4	4	5	15	17	-2	16
13	Chelmsford City	16	4	4	8	21	25	-4	16
14	Tonbridge Angels	14	5	1	8	16	23	-7	16
15	Billericay Town	17	4	4	9	26	35	-9	16
16	Chippenham Town	14	4	4	6	13	22	-9	16
17	Concord Rangers	14	3	5	6	16	24	-8	14
18	Bath City	13	4	1	8	16	23	-7	13
19	Braintree Town	16	4	1	11	19	34	-15	13
20	Slough Town	12	3	3	6	16	24	-8	12
21	Welling United	14	2	6	6	18	30	-12	12

BATH CITY MATCH RESULTS 2020-21

Date	Comp	H/A	Opponents	Att:	Result	Goalscorers	Pos
Oct 3	**FAC2Q**	**H**	**Winchester City**		**W 3 - 2**	**Conway 2 72 Richards 86**	
6	NLS	A	Oxford City		L 0 - 2		17
10	NLS	H	Billericay Town		W 2 - 0	Conway 24 90+3	9
13	**FAC3Q**	**A**	**Slough Town**		**W 1 - 0**	**Hinds 49**	
17	NLS	A	Dartford		L 0 - 1		12
24	**FAC4Q**	**H**	**Havant & Waterlooville**		**L 0 - 3**		
31	NLS	A	Slough Town		L 1 - 2	Wilson 86	14
Nov 7	NLS	H	Hemel Hempstead Town		L 1 - 2	Wilson 12	15
21	NLS	A	Hampton & Richmond B.		L 0 - 1		20
24	NLS	H	Dulwich Hamlet		L 1 - 4	Wilson 2	21
Dec 5	NLS	A	Dorking Wanderers	680	W 2 - 1	Wilson 35 Smith 71	19
8	NLS	A	Concord Rangers	221	L 2 - 3	Smith 10 Conway 59 (pen)	21
12	NLS	A	Chelmsford City	540	W 4 - 3	Isaac 11 (og) Wilson 25 52 Conway 28	17
15	**FAT2P**	**H**	**Chelmsford City**		**W 3 - 2**	**Conway 8 70 Kpekawa 80 (og)**	
19	**FAT3P**	**H**	**Swindon Supermarine**		**W 4 - 0**	**Smith 60 67 Conway 71 (pen) Richards 84**	
26	NLS	A	Chippenham Town	518	D 1 - 1	Grant 75	15
28	NLS	H	Hungerford Town		L 0 - 2		16
Jan 16	**FAT4P**	**H**	**Peterborough Sports**		**L 0 - 1**	**(RC 2xY - Mehew 62)**	
19	NLS	H	Havant & Waterlooville		W 2 - 1	Mehew 8 Smith 17	17

Goalcorers	LGE	FAC	FAT	SG	CSG	HAT	PEN	1Q	2Q	45+	3Q	4Q	90+	T
TOTALS	16	4	7			0	1	8	4	0	5	9	1	27
Conway	4	2	3	5	3		1	2	2		1	3	1	9
Wilson	6			5	2			2	2		1	1		6
Smith	3		2	4	2			2			2	1		5
Opponent	1		1	2	2			1				1		2
Richards		1	1	2	1							2		2
Grant	1			1	1							1		1
Hinds		1		1	1						1			1
Mehew	1			1	1			1						1

LGE FAC FAT SG CSG HAT PEN 1Q 2Q 45+ 3Q 4Q 90+ T

Clarke R	Grant F	Smith T	Ball D	Artus F	Evans C	Harley R	James L	Conway T (L)	Pope J	Watts C	Richards T	Batten J	Henry W (Gk)	Andrews A	Eglin	Bahadur L	Leak T (L)	Hinds F (L)	Tomlinson (L)	Wilson D	Welsh M (Gk)	Buse M (L)	Horton G (L)	Dean W (L)	Mehew T (L)	Taylor J (L)	Owers J (L)	McCoy O (L)	Fletcher A	No.
c	c	c	c	c	c	c	cs	c	c	cs	sc	sc	cn	cn	cn	cn														1
x	x	x	x	xs	x	x	sx	x	sx	s	x	xs	s			s	x													2
x	xs	x	x		x	x	sx	x	sx	sx	xs	xs	s			s	x	x												3
c	sc	c	c		c	c	cn		c	sc	c	c	cn			cn	c	cs	cs											4
x	sx	xs	x		x	x	sx	x	x	s	sx	xs	s				x	x	xs											5
c	cs	c	sc		c	cs	sc	c	cn	cn	c	c					c	c	cs	sc	cn									6
x	xs	x	x		x	sx	s		x	xs	s	x	s				sx		x	x		x								7
x	x	x		x	x		sx		x	s	sx		s			s	x	x	xs	x		xs								8
x		x	x	x	xs		s	x	s		sx	x	s						s	x			x	x						9
x		x	x	x	s		s	x	sx		sx	xs	s						xs	x			x	x	x					10
x		x	x	s		x	s	x	s		s	x	s							x			x	x	x	x				11
x		x	x	s		x	s	x	s		s	x	s							x			x	x	x	x				12
x		x		x		x	x	x	s	s	s	x	s						sx	xs			x	x		x				13
t	t	t		t		t	tn	t	tn	tn	t	t	tn			tn							t	t		t				14
	ts	t	tn	ts		ts	st	t	st	tn	t	t	t			st					tn		t	t		t				15
	x	x	s	x		x	s	x	s		sx	x	x			s				x			x		x	xs				16
s	x	x	sx	xs		x	s	x	s			x	x							x			x		x	x				17
tn		t	t	ts	st	ts	tn	t	st	tn	t	t	t										ts		t		t	st		18
x	x	x	x		s	s	x	x	x	s	sx	x	s												xs		x		x	19
15	7	18	12	7	8	11	2	16	6	0	6	13	4	0	0	0	6	4	1	8	0	1	9	7	6	6	2	0	1	x
0	4	1	0	4	1	3	1	0	0	2	1	4	0	0	0	0	0	1	5	1	0	1	1	0	1	1	0	0	0	xs
0	2	0	2	0	1	1	6	0	5	2	7	1	0	0	0	1	1	0	1	1	0	0	0	0	0	0	0	1	0	sx
2	0	0	2	2	2	1	10	0	8	9	4	0	14	1	1	7	0	0	1	0	2	0	0	0	0	0	0	0	0	s

GOALKEEPERS	CS	CCS
Clarke	2	2
Henry	1	1

x/c/t - Played full 90 minutes
xs/cs/ts - Substituted off
sx/sc/st - Substituted on
s/cn/tn - Non-playing sub

BILLERICAY TOWN MATCH RESULTS 2020-21

Date	Comp	H/A	Opponents	Att:	Result	Goalscorers	Pos
Oct 3	**FAC2Q**	**A**	**Brackley Town**		**D 2 - 2**	**Reason 45 Robinson 60 (Lost 2-4 on pens)**	
6	NLS	H	Tonbridge Angels		L 0 - 2		18
10	NLS	A	Bath City		L 0 - 2		20
17	NLS	H	Havant & Waterlooville		L 1 - 2	Hutchinson 41	19
31	NLS	H	Ebbsfleet United		L 1 - 2	Robinson 68	20
Nov 3	NLS	A	Hemel Hempstead Town		**W** 4 - 1	Robinson 21 60 (pen) 77 Fenelon 19	16
14	NLS	H	Slough Town		**W** 2 - 0	Robinson 46 Reason 84	13
17	NLS	A	Welling United		D 2 - 2	Reid 5 Robinson 82 (pen)	13
21	NLS	A	Maidstone United		D 1 - 1	Robinson 67 (pen)	15
28	NLS	H	Hampton & Richmond B.		L 2 - 6	Soares-Junior 8 Robinson 55	15
Manager Jamie O'Hara leaves the club. Danny Brown takes interim charge.							
Dec 15	**FAT2P**	**H**	**Braintree Town**	**302**	**D 1 - 1**	**Soares-Junior 66 (Lost 2-4 on pens)**	
28	NLS	H	Braintree Town		**W** 3 - 1	Robinson 22 86 Soares-Junior 47	15
Jan 2	NLS	H	Concord Rangers		L 0 - 1		17
6	NLS	H	Oxford City		L 1 - 3	Wanadio 25	17
Former Ebbsfleet United manager, Kevin Watson, is named as the new manager.							
12	NLS	A	Dartford		L 0 - 3		17
16	NLS	H	Dulwich Hamlet		**W** 2 - 0	Chambers 24 Robinson 90+4	16
19	NLS	H	Chelmsford City		D 3 - 3	Liburd 15 20 Robinson 17	16
Feb 6	NLS	H	St Albans City		D 2 - 2	Liburd 37 Mbambo 87	13
16	NLS	A	Eastbourne Borough		L 2 - 4	Olusanya 16 Liburd 45+4 (pen)	15

Goalcorers	LGE	FAC	FAT	SG	CSG	HAT	PEN	1Q	2Q	45+	3Q	4Q	90+	T
TOTALS	26	2	1			1	3	9	4	2	7	6	1	29
Robinson	12	1		10	6	1	3	3			5	4	1	13
Liburd	4			3	3			2	1	1				4
Soares-Junior	2		1	3	3			1			2			3
Reason	1	1		2	1					1		1		2
CHambers	1			1	1				1					1
Fenelon	1			1	1			1						1
Hutchinson	1			1	1				1					1
Mbambo	1			1	1							1		1
Olusanya	1			1	1			1						1
Reid	1			1	1			1						1
Wanadio	1			1	1				1					1

Henry D	McLean C	Konchesky P	Felix J	Henry R	Chambers M	Wanadio L	Sutherland F	Robinson J	Reason J	Fenelon S	Brzozowski M (Gk) (L)	Hutchinson J	Assal A (L)	Soares-Junior R	Knight L	Loft D	Reid K	Olusanya T	Wilson L	Knott B	Nickless J	Mbambo G	Dunwell L	Ramsay L	Palmer H (Gk)	Liburd R	Foxley D	Lukombo H	Ferguson C	Wind G	Stratford M	Oduntan T	Drake J	Hughes M	Mesuria N	Mciver-Hauser J	No.
c	c	c	c	c	c	c	c	c	c	c																											1
s	xs	x	x	x	x	x	xs	x	x	xs	x	sx	sx	sx	s																						2
x	x	s	xs	x	x		x	sx	xs	xs		x		s	x	x	sx	sx																			3
x		x	x	x	x	xs	x	s	s	sx		xs			s	x	x	sx	x																		4
x		xs	x	x	x	x	xs	x	sx	sx		sx			s	x	xs	s	x																		5
x	x		x	x	sx	x		xs	x	xs		x		s	s	xs	sx	sx	x																		6
x	x		xs	x	x	x		x	sx	xs		xs		s	sx		s	sx	x	x																	7
x	xs		x	x	x	xs		x	sx	sx		x		s	s		x	sx	x	xs																	8
x	s		x	x	xs	x	s	x	x	xs		sx		sx	sx		xs		x	x																	9
x			x	x	x	sx	xs	x	x	s		xs		x	s	sx	sx		x	xs																	10
t	t		st	t	t	t	t	t	ts	tn				ts	tn	ts		st	t		st	tn	tn														11
x			x	x	x	x	xs	x	sx	sx				xs	s	xs	sx	s	x					x													12
x			x	x	x	x		x	xs	sx				x	s	s	sx		x	xs		s		x													13
x			x	x	x	xs	x	x		xs				sx	s	s	sx		x	xs		sx		x													14
s	s		sx	x	xs		x	x	sx					x	sx	xs	x		x	xs				x	x												15
	s		x	x	x		x	x	xs					sx	s		sx		x	s				x	x	xs	x										16
	s		x	x	x		x	x	xs					sx	sx		sx		x	s				xs	x	xs	x										17
														x				xs			x	sx	s		x	x	x	x	x	x	xs	x	sx	s	s		18
														xs				xs			xs	sx	sx		x	x	x	x	x	x	x	x	s		sx	s	19
13	5	3	13	17	14	9	8	14	5	1	1	3	0	4	1	3	3	0	14	2	1	0	0	5	5	2	4	2	2	2	1	2	0	0	0	0	x
0	2	1	2	0	2	3	4	1	5	6	0	3	0	3	0	4	2	2	0	5	1	0	0	1	0	2	0	0	0	0	1	0	0	0	0	0	xs
0	0	0	2	0	1	1	0	1	5	5	0	3	1	5	4	1	8	6	0	0	1	3	1	0	0	0	0	0	0	0	0	0	1	0	1	0	sx
2	4	1	0	0	0	0	1	1	1	2	0	0	0	4	11	2	1	2	0	2	0	2	2	0	0	0	0	0	0	0	0	0	1	1	1	1	s

GOALKEEPERS	CS	CCS
Henry	1	1
Palmer	1	1

x/c/t - Played full 90 minutes
xs/cs/ts - Substituted off
sx/sc/st - Substituted on
s/cn/tn - Non-playing sub

BRAINTREE TOWN MATCH RESULTS 2020-21

Date	Comp	H/A	Opponents	Att:	Result	Goalscorers	Pos
Oct 3	**FAC2Q**	**A**	**Hashtag United**	**300**	**D 1 - 1**	**Olu Olu 90+1 (Won 7-6 on pens)**	
6	NLS	H	Ebbsfleet United		L 0 - 3		19
10	NLS	A	Chippenham Town		L 0 - 1		21
13	**FAC3Q**	**H**	**Maldon & Tiptree**		**L 0 - 1**		
17	NLS	H	Dorking Wanderers		L 0 - 4		21
31	NLS	H	Hemel Hempstead Town		L 3 - 4	Smyth 22 Dunne 37 Clements 77	21
Nov 7	NLS	H	Hungerford Town		L 1 - 2	Chiedozie 89	21
10	NLS	A	St Albans City		L 1 - 2	Dunne 44	21
14	NLS	A	Eastbourne Borough		L 0 - 4		21
George Borg resigns as manager. Ryan Maxwell is named as his successor.							
17	NLS	H	Concord Rangers		**W** 1 - 0	Davidson 8	21
24	NLS	A	Tonbridge Angels		**W** 2 - 0	Renee 51 Derry 70	19
Dec 8	NLS	H	Welling United		D 1 - 1	Derry 80	20
15	**FAT2P**	**A**	**Billericay Town**	**302**	**D 1 - 1**	**Krasniqi 79 (Won 4-2 on pens)**	
19	**FAT3P**	**A**	**Havant & Waterlooville**		**L 0 - 1**		
28	NLS	A	Billericay Town		L 1 - 3	Johnson 51	21
Jan 2	NLS	A	Chelmsford City		L 2 - 4	Olomowewe 18 Derry 40	21
9	NLS	H	Dartford		**W** 2 - 1	Kiangebeni 28 Olomowewe 62	19
12	NLS	H	Oxford City		L 1 - 2	Davidson 11	19
16	NLS	A	Slough Town		L 2 - 3	Krasniqi 41 Yussuff 63 (pen)	20
19	NLS	A	Maidstone United		**W** 2 - 0	Krasniqi 18 Rendell 31 (og)	19

Goalcorers	LGE	FAC	FAT	SG	CSG	HAT	PEN	1Q	2Q	45+	3Q	4Q	90+	T
TOTALS	**19**	**1**	**1**			**0**	**1**	**5**	**6**	**0**	**4**	**5**	**1**	**21**
Derry	3			3	2				1			2		3
Krasniqi	2		1	3	2			1	1			1		3
Davidson	2			2	1			2						2
Dunne	2			2	1				2					2
Olomowewe	2			2	2			1			1			2
Chiedozie	1			1	1							1		1
Clements	1			1	1							1		1
Johnson	1			1	1						1			1
Kiangebeni	1			1	1				1					1

	LGE	FAC	FAT	SG	CSG	HAT	PEN	1Q	2Q	45+	3Q	4Q	90+	T
Olu Olu		1		1	1								1	1
Opponent	1			1	1				1					1
Renee	1			1	1						1			1
Smyth	1			1	1			1						1
Yussuff	1			1	1		1				1			1

Przybek A (L)	Fielding J (L)	O'Keefe C	Ferrell L	Moore-Azille T	Oluwatimilehin O	Forrest G	Dunne R	Yamfam L	Gordon R	Payne A	Okunlola S	Clements K	Schmid R (Gk)	Smyth L (L)	Cameron D	Edwards P (Gk)	Renee-Pringle J	Kensdale O (L)	Johnson M	Krasniqi A	Chiedozie J	Allen G	Rolt B (L)	Holness L	Ofori-Acheampong D	Ohman P (Gk)	Smith N	Johnson-Schuster M	Olomowewe T	Robbins S	Banton J	Davidson C	Derry T	Bassett D	Leslie J	Kiangebeni P	Charles K	Jackson S (Gk)	Henshaw R	Thomas J (L)	Yussuff A	Prestedge R	Amartey F	Giddens J (Gk)	No.
c	c	c	cs	c	cs	cs	c	c	c	sc	sc	sc	cn	cn	cn																														1
	x	x	x	x	x	xs	xs	x	x	xs	sx	s	s	sx		x	sx																												2
	x	x	x	x	xs	x	x	sx	x	xs		s	s	sx		x	s	x																											3
c					c		c	c	c																																				4
s	x	x		x	xs	x	sx	x	x	s		x		x	s	x	s	x																											5
	x	x			sx	xs	x	xs	x			x		x	s	x	sx		x	xs	sx																								6
x	x	sx			sx	s	xs	x	x			x		sx			xs		x	xs	x	x																							7
	x	sx				s	xs	xs	x			x		sx		x	x		x	xs	x	x	sx	s																					8
	x				x		s	sx	xs			x		sx		x	x		x	sx	xs	xs	x		x																				9
	s				x		sx	sx				s					xs		x	sx						x	x	x	x	x	xs	x	xs												10
					xs		s	sx				s					xs		x	sx						x	x	x	x	x	xs	x	x	sx											11
									sx			s					xs		x	x		x				x	x	x	x			xs	x	sx	xs	sx	s								12
									t			t					t		t	t		t		st			tn		t					ts				t							13
									t			t			tn		t		t	t		t		st			t		t					t				t							14
									sx			s					xs		x					sx		x	x	xs	x	x		x	x	x		xs	sx								15
									s			s					xs		x	sx				sx		x	x	x	x	x		xs	x	xs		x	sx								16
																	x		x								x		x	x		x	xs			xs	s	x	x	x	sx	sx	s		17
																	x		x	s							x	sx	x	x		x	xs			xs		x	xs	x	sx	s	sx		18
												x					x		x	x		xs					sx	sx	xs			x	x			s	s			x	x	s		x	19
												s					x		x	xs							x	x				xs	sx				sx		x	x	xs	sx		x	20
3	8	5	2	4	4	2	4	5	10	0	0	8	0	2	0	6	8	2	15	4	2	5	1	0	1	5	9	5	9	6	0	6	5	2	0	1	0	4	2	4	1	0	0	2	x
0	0	0	1	0	4	3	3	2	1	2	0	0	0	0	0	0	6	0	0	4	1	2	0	0	0	0	0	1	1	0	2	3	3	2	1	3	0	0	1	0	1	0	0	0	xs
0	0	2	0	0	2	0	2	4	2	1	2	1	0	5	0	0	2	0	0	4	1	0	1	4	0	0	1	2	0	0	0	0	1	2	0	1	3	0	0	0	2	2	1	0	sx
1	1	0	0	0	0	2	2	0	1	1	0	8	3	1	4	0	2	0	0	1	0	0	0	1	0	0	1	0	0	0	0	0	0	0	0	1	3	0	0	0	0	2	1	0	s

Also Played: Miller N - 03/10 (cn); Greenway J (Gk) - 7/11 (s); Miskin M - 15/12 (ts) 19/12 (tn) 28/12 (s); Piorkowski G - 15/12 19/12 (ts) 19/01 (s); McCulloch D - 15/12 (st); Clowsley J - 15/12 (st); Vukasinovic M - 15/12 19/12 (tn); Scott R - 19/01 (x).

GOALKEEPERS	CS	CCS
Ohman	2	2
Giddens	1	1

x/c/t - Played full 90 minutes
xs/cs/ts - Substituted off
sx/sc/st - Substituted on
s/cn/tn - Non-playing sub

CHELMSFORD CITY MATCH RESULTS 2020-21

Date	Comp	H/A	Opponents	Att:	Result	Goalscorers	Pos
Oct 3	**FAC2Q**	**A**	**Kettering Town**		**L 0 - 2**		
6	NLS	A	Dartford		L 0 - 1		14
10	NLS	H	Oxford City		D 1 - 1	Morgan 28	16
17	NLS	A	Eastbourne Borough		D 1 - 1	Morgan 38	14
24	NLS	H	Maidstone United		**W** 1 - 0	Morgan 49 (pen)	9
31	NLS	A	Dulwich Hamlet		D 0 - 0		10
Nov 7	NLS	A	Welling United		**W** 4 - 0	Teniola 45 (pen) Church 52 70 Liddle 77	8
9	NLS	H	Tonbridge Angels		L 0 - 2		8
14	NLS	H	Hampton & Richmond B.		L 0 - 1		10
21	NLS	H	Chippenham Town		L 0 - 2		14
Dec 5	NLS	A	Havant & Waterlooville	803	L 1 - 3	Sheringham 82	15
12	NLS	H	Bath City	540	L 3 - 4	Sheringham 12 50 Olowu 71	16
15	**FAT2P**	**A**	**Bath City**		**L 2 - 3**	**Morgan 56 Asonganyi 65**	
Jan 2	NLS	H	Braintree Town		**W** 4 - 2	Sheringham 55 Wraight 60 James 64 Morgan 71 (pen)	16
9	NLS	A	St Albans City		**W** 2 - 0	Sheringham 33 Morgan 42	14
19	NLS	A	Billericay Town		D 3 - 3	Cass 41 Wraight 44 Morgan 60	11
Feb 13	NLS	A	Oxford City		L 1 - 4	Jackson 90+2	13
15	NLS	H	Dorking Wanderers		L 0 - 1		13

Goalcorers	LGE	FAC	FAT	SG	CSG	HAT	PEN	1Q	2Q	45+	3Q	4Q	90+	T
TOTALS	**21**	**0**	**2**			**0**	**3**	**1**	**6**	**1**	**9**	**5**	**1**	**23**
Morgan	6		1	7	4		2		3		3	1		7
Sheringham	5			4	2			1	1		2	1		5
Church	2			1	1						1	1		2
Wraight	2			2	1				1		1			2
Asonganyi			1	1	1						1			1
Cass	1			1	1				1					1
Jackson	1			1	1								1	1
James	1			1	1						1			1
Liddle	1			1	1							1		1

	LGE	FAC	FAT	SG	CSG	HAT	PEN	1Q	2Q	45+	3Q	4Q	90+	T
Oluwo	1			1	1							1		1
Teniola	1			1	1		1			1				1

No.	Worgan L	Oluwo A	Spillane M	Ward E	Isaac C	Fraser-Robinson C	Church A	Muldoon O	Harrison C	Teniola A	Liddle A	James C	Imray D	Morgan A	Crook B	Forbes D	Smith K	Kingston S (Gk)	Roberts P	Simpson R	Norton G	Cotter B (L)	Payne E	Wraight T	Kpekawa C	Lewis A	Gregory R	Sheringham C (L)	Asonganyi D (L)	Cass J	Jackson S (L)
1	**c**	**c**	**cs**	**c**	**c**	**cs**	**c**	**cs**	**c**	**c**	**c**	**sc**	**sc**	**sc**	**cn**	**cn**	**cn**	**cn**													
2	x	x		x	xs	s	x	s	sx	sx	x	x	x	xs	xs				x	sx											
3	x	x		x	x		xs	sx	sx	sx	xs	x	x	x	xs				x	s	s										
4	x	x	s	x	x		x	s	sx	x	sx		x	x	xs				xs	s		x									
5	x	x	x	x	x		x		sx	x	sx	x		xs	x			s	xs	s			s								
6	x	x	s	x	x		x		x	sx	xs	x		xs					xs	s		x		sx	sx						
7	x	x	s	x	x		x		x	x	xs	xs	x	sx					xs	s				sx	sx						
8	x	x	s	x			xs		x	x	x	x	xs	sx					sx	sx				xs	x	s					
9	x	x	x	x						xs	xs	x	x	xs					x	sx		sx	s	x	sx		s				
10	x	x	xs	x	sx				sx	x		x	x	s	xs					s		xs		x	x		sx				
11	x	x	s		x				x	s	sx	x	x	sx	xs							xs		sx	xs			x	x		
12	x	x		xs	xs		x		x			x	x	x	sx				sx			s		s	s			x	x		
13	**t**	**t**	**tn**	**ts**	**st**		**t**		**ts**		**st**		**tn**	**t**	**tn**				**st**	**tn**		**t**		**t**	**t**			**t**	**ts**		
14	x		sx		x				x		sx	x	x	xs						s	s	xs		x	x		sx	x	xs		
15	x	x		x	x				x		sx		x	x						s	s		s	x	x		s	x	xs		
16	x	x	s	x	x				x		s		x	x						s	s			x	x		s		x	x	
17	x	x	x		x		x		xs					xs						s	sx			x	xs	sx	s		x	x	sx
18	x	x	xs		x		x		x					x						sx	s			x	sx	s	s		xs	x	x
x	18	17	3	12	12	0	10	0	10	6	3	10	11	7	1	0	0	0	3	0	0	3	0	8	6	0	0	5	4	3	1
xs	0	0	3	2	2	1	2	1	2	1	4	1	1	6	5	0	0	0	4	0	0	3	0	1	2	0	0	0	4	0	0
sx	0	0	1	0	2	0	0	1	5	3	6	1	1	4	1	0	0	0	3	4	1	1	0	3	4	1	2	0	0	0	1
s	0	0	7	0	0	1	0	2	0	1	1	0	1	1	2	1	1	2	0	11	5	1	3	1	1	2	5	0	0	0	0

GOALKEEPERS	CS	CCS
Worgan	4	3

x/c/t - Played full 90 minutes
xs/cs/ts - Substituted off
sx/sc/st - Substituted on
s/cn/tn - Non-playing sub

CHIPPENHAM TOWN MATCH RESULTS 2020-21

Date	Comp	H/A	Opponents	Att:	Result	Goalscorers	Pos
Oct 3	**FAC2Q**	**H**	**Poole Town**		**D 2 - 2**	**Ash 10 Hanks 12 (Won 5-4 on pens)**	
6	NLS	A	Hungerford Town		L 0 - 3		20
10	NLS	H	Braintree Town		**W** 1 - 0	Parselle 85	12
13	**FAC3Q**	**A**	**Ebbsfleet United**		**D 1 - 1**	**Mann 8 (Won 9-8 on pens)**	
17	NLS	A	Dulwich Hamlet		**W** 2 - 0	Zebroski 34 Ash 50	7
24	**FAC4Q**	**A**	**Concord Rangers**		**L 1 - 2**	**Stearn 64**	
27	NLS	H	Dartford		L 1 - 2	Hanks 22	9
31	NLS	A	St Albans City		L 0 - 3		11
Nov 14	NLS	H	Ebbsfleet United		L 1 - 2	Ash 12	14
17	NLS	A	Oxford City		D 1 - 1	Mann 71	16
21	NLS	A	Chelmsford City		**W** 2 - 0	Stearn 26 Ash 90+1	10
28	NLS	H	Concord Rangers		D 1 - 1	Mann 77	10
Dec 1	NLS	H	Hampton & Richmond B.		L 0 - 3		12
5	NLS	H	Slough Town		D 2 - 2	Zebroski 63 Hanks 70	13
12	NLS	A	Welling United	611	**W** 1 - 0	Ash 68	12
15	**FAT2P**	**A**	**Ebbsfleet United**		**D 1 - 1**	**Harrison 90+1 (Lost 2-4 on pens)**	
26	NLS	H	Bath City	518	D 1 - 1	Batten 28 (og)	10
Jan 12	NLS	A	Tonbridge Angels		L 0 - 4		14

Goalcorers	LGE	FAC	FAT	SG	CSG	HAT	PEN	1Q	2Q	45+	3Q	4Q	90+	T
TOTALS	13	4	1			0	0	5	3	0	3	5	2	18
Ash	4	1		5	1			2			1	1	1	5
Hanks	2	1		3	1			2				1		3
Mann	2	1		3	1			1				2		3
Stearn	1	1		2	1				1		1			2
Zebroski	2			2	1				1		1			2
Harrison			1	1	1								1	1
Opponent	1			1	1				1					1
Parselle	1			1	1							1		1

LGE FAC FAT SG CSG HAT PEN 1Q 2Q 45+ 3Q 4Q 90+ T

Puddy W	Jones E	Tyler R	Hamilton S	Parselle K	Russe L	Gunner C	Hanks J	Ash B	Zebroski C	Bray A	Case R	Stearn R	Pratt D	Warre D	Hill E	Snedker J	Golding L	Dyer J (L)	Smerdon N (L)	Mann A	Brunt R	Phillips K (L)	Hughes B (Gk)	Smedley J	Greenslade D	Harrison T (L)	Coppin N	Matthews J (Gk)	Jackson M	Law R (L)	Lolos K (L)	Byrne N	Foulston J	Stevens II J (L)	No.
c	c	c	cs	c	c	c	c	c	c	cs	sc	sc	cn	cn	cn	cn	cn																		1
x		xs		x	x	x	x	x	xs	x	xs	sx	s		sx		sx							s											2
x	x	s		x	x	sx	x	x	sx	s		xs						x	x	xs	xs	sx													3
c	c	cn		c	c	sc	cs	c	sc	cn		c						c	c	cs	cs	sc													4
x	x		s	x	x	x	sx	x	sx	s		xs						x	x	xs	xs	sx													5
c	c		cn	c	c		c	c	c	sc	cn	c						c	c	cs		cn	cn												6
x	x		s	x	x		x	x	xs	sx	sx	x						x	x			xs	s	s											7
x	x		xs	x	x		x	xs	sx	xs	s	x			sx			x			x	sx		s											8
x	x		x	x	x	x	x	x	sx	s	s	xs							x	sx	xs	s													9
x	x		x	x	xs	x	x	x	sx	xs	s	x							xs	sx			s		sx										10
x	x		x	x	sx	x	x	x	sx	xs	sx	xs			s					xs			s		x										11
x	xs		x	x	sx	x	x	x	sx	xs	s	x								x					xs	sx	s								12
x	x		s	x	x	xs	x	x	sx	sx		xs								x			s		xs	x	sx								13
	x		s	x	x	sx	x	xs	sx	sx		x			s					xs					x	x		x	xs						14
x	x			x	x	x	x	sx	x	xs		sx											s	s		x			xs	x	s				15
t	t			t	t	ts	st	t	st	st		ts												tn		t			ts	t	t	tn			16
x	x			x	x	sx	x	xs	sx	sx		xs											s			x			xs	x	x				17
x	x		xs	x	x	x	x	sx	xs	xs		sx					s												x				x	sx	18
17	16	1	4	18	15	9	15	13	3	1	0	7	0	0	0	0	0	6	6	2	1	0	0	0	2	5	0	1	1	3	2	0	1	0	x
0	1	1	3	0	1	2	1	3	3	7	1	7	0	0	0	0	0	0	1	6	4	1	0	0	2	0	0	0	4	0	0	0	0	0	xs
0	0	0	0	0	2	4	2	2	12	6	3	4	0	0	2	0	1	0	0	2	0	4	0	0	1	1	1	0	0	0	0	0	0	1	sx
0	0	2	5	0	0	0	0	0	0	4	5	0	2	1	3	1	2	0	0	0	0	2	7	5	0	0	1	0	0	0	1	1	0	0	s

GOALKEEPERS	CS	CCS
Puddy	4	1

x/c/t - Played full 90 minutes
xs/cs/ts - Substituted off
sx/sc/st - Substituted on
s/cn/tn - Non-playing sub

CONCORD RANGERS MATCH RESULTS 2020-21

Date	Comp	H/A	Opponents	Att:	Result	Goalscorers	Pos
Sep 5	**FAT SF 19/20**	**H**	**Halesowen Town**		**W 2 - 1**	**Evans 37 (og) Wall 79**	
Oct 4	**FAC2Q**	**A**	**Potters Bar**	**148**	**W 2 - 1**	**Wall 55 72**	
10	NLS	H	St Albans City		D 1 - 1	Wall 41 (pen)	14
13	**FAC3Q**	**A**	**Whyteleafe**	**400**	**W 2 - 1**	**Blackman x2**	
17	NLS	A	Hungerford Town		L 0 - 1		16
24	**FAC4Q**	**H**	**Chippenham Town**		**W 2 - 1**	**Babalola 40 Green 90+8**	
31	NLS	A	Maidstone United		L 0 - 6		19
Nov 3	NLS	A	Dulwich Hamlet		W 4 - 1	Raad 18 Wall 30 Babalola 59 Hughes 74	14
7	**FAC1P**	**A**	**Stevenage Borough**		**D 2 - 2**	**Wall 43 Martin 109 (Lost 4-5 on pens)**	
10	NLS	H	Welling United		D 1 - 1	Wall 49 (pen)	16
17	NLS	A	Braintree Town		L 0 - 1		18
21	NLS	H	Dorking Wanderers		L 1 - 3	Wall 48	18
28	NLS	A	Chippenham Town		D 1 - 1	Bridge 36	19
Dec 1	NLS	A	Tonbridge Angels		L 0 - 2		19
8	NLS	H	Bath City	221	W 3 - 2	Wall 14 Pollock 16 Charles R 90+3	16
12	NLS	H	Eastbourne Borough		D 2 - 2	Wall 10 Simper 45+3	15
19	**FAT2P**	**H**	**Truro City**		**L 1 - 2**	**Blackman 90**	
Jan 2	NLS	A	Billericay Town		W 1 - 0	Simper 66	14
12	NLS	A	Ebbsfleet United		L 1 - 2	Wall 1	16
Feb 13	NLS	A	Eastbourne Borough		D 1 - 1	Blanchfield 89	17
May 3	**FAT F 19/20**	**N**	**Harrogate Town (Lge 2)**		**L 0 - 1**		

Goalcorers	LGE	FAC	FAT	SG	CSG	HAT	PEN	1Q	2Q	45+	3Q	4Q	90+	T
TOTALS	**16**	**8**	**3**			**0**	**2**	**5**	**6**	**1**	**5**	**4**	**4**	**27**
Wall	7	3	1	10	3		2	3	3		3	2		11
Blackman		2	1	2	1								1	3
Babalola	1	1		2	1				1		1			2
Simper	2			2	1					1	1			2
Blanchfield	1			1	1							1		1
Bridge	1			1	1				1					1
Charles R	1			1	1								1	1
Green		1		1	1								1	1
Hughes	1			1	1							1		1

	LGE	FAC	FAT	SG	CSG	HAT	PEN	1Q	2Q	45+	3Q	4Q	90+	T
Martin		1		1	1								1	1
Opponent			1	1	1				1					1
Pollock	1			1	1			1						1
Raad	1			1	1			1						1

No.	Haigh C	Carlyle N	Popo T	Roast B	Pollock A	Sterling T	Reynolds L	Blackman S	Wall A	Blanchfield J	Babalola T	Martin O	Alexander G	Green D	Millar C	Hernandez A	McFadden A	Minshull L	Raad J	Remfry S	Hanfrey T	Scott R	Johnson E	Bridge J	Hughes C (L)	Shabani B (L)	Shaw F	Simper L (L)	Przybek A (L)	Charles R	Charles A (L)	Randell J (L)	Kensdale O	Wabo N	McLeod S	Okafor M	Payne J	Cawley J	Search B	Wilks D (Gk)
1	t	t	t	t	t	t	t	t	t	ts	ts	st	st	tn	tn	tn	tn	tn																						
2	c		c	c	c	c	sc	c	c	c	sc	sc		cn					c	c	c	cn	cn																	
3	x		x	x	x	x	x	x	xs	xs	sx	sx		sx					xs	s	x	s																		
4	c		c	c	sc	c	c	c	c	sc		c		cn					c	cn	c	c																		
5	x		x	xs	s	x	x	x	sx	sx	xs	x		sx					xs	s	x	x																		
6	c		c	c	c	c	c	cs	sc	cs	cs			sc					sc	cn	c	c																		
7	x		x	xs	x	x	xs	x			sx	s		s					sx		x	x		xs	x	sx														
8	x		x	sx	x	x	sx	x	xs		x	x		s					xs			x		s	sx	xs														
9	c		c	s	c	cs	sc	c	cs		cs	c		s					cs	s	sc	c		sc	sc	c														
10	x		x	x	x		x	x	x		sx	sx		s					s			x		xs	xs	sx	xs													
11	x		x		s	x	sx	xs	x	sx	x	xs							s			x		xs	sx	x	x													
12	x		xs	s	x	x	sx	xs	x	x	x	s							x			xs			sx	sx	x													
13	x		x	x	x	x	x	x		xs	xs	s		sx								sx	s	xs			x	sx												
14	x		x	xs	x	x	x	x		xs	x			sx						s		sx	s	xs			x	sx												
15			x	x	x	x	sx	xs	x	x	sx			s								s		xs			x	xs	x	sx										
16			x	x	x	x		x	xs		sx	sx		s								s		xs			x	xs	x	sx	x									
17	tn		ts		t	t	tn	t	t		st	tn		tn								t		t			t		t	t	t									
18			sx		x	x		xs	xs	sx	sx	s		s										x			x	x	x	xs		x								
19	s		x	x	x			xs	x	sx	sx	sx											s	xs			x	x	x	xs	x									
20	x			x		x		xs	sx	x		xs					x						s					x		x		s	x	xs	sx	sx				
21	t			ts	t	t	t	t	st	ts	st	st				tn	tn											t		ts							t	t	tn	tn
x	16	1	16	11	17	18	9	14	9	4	4	4	0	0	0	0	1	0	3	1	6	9	0	2	1	2	9	4	5	2	3	1	1	0	0	0	1	1	0	0
xs	0	0	2	4	0	1	1	7	5	6	5	2	0	0	0	0	0	0	4	0	0	1	0	8	1	1	1	2	0	3	0	0	0	1	0	0	0	0	0	0
sx	0	0	1	1	1	0	6	0	4	5	10	7	1	5	0	0	0	0	2	0	1	2	0	1	4	3	0	2	0	2	0	0	0	0	1	1	0	0	0	0
s	2	0	0	2	2	0	1	0	0	0	0	5	0	11	1	2	2	1	2	6	0	4	5	1	0	0	0	0	0	0	0	1	0	0	0	0	0	0	1	1

GOALKEEPERS	CS	CCS
Przybek	1	1

x/c/t - Played full 90 minutes
xs/cs/ts - Substituted off
sx/sc/st - Substituted on
s/cn/tn - Non-playing sub

DARTFORD MATCH RESULTS 2020-21

Date	Comp	H/A	Opponents	Att:	Result	Goalscorers	Pos
Oct 3	**FAC2Q**	**H**	**Slough Town**		**L 0 - 1**		
6	NLS	H	Chelmsford City		**W** 1 - 0	Marsh-Brown 23	7
10	NLS	A	Hampton & Richmond B.		D 0 - 0		7
17	NLS	H	Bath City		**W** 1 - 0	Husin 52	6
27	NLS	A	Chippenham Town		**W** 2 - 1	Bakayoko 8 Bonner 82	1
31	NLS	H	Havant & Waterlooville		**W** 2 - 1	Barham 50 (pen) 72	1
Nov 7	NLS	H	Dorking Wanderers		L 2 - 3	Berkeley-Agyepong 27 Jebb 52	3
10	NLS	A	Hemel Hempstead Town		**W** 3 - 1	Essam 13 Carlyle 17 (og) Romain 41	1
14	NLS	A	Maidstone United		**W** 2 - 0	Bonner 77 Sheringham 82	1
17	NLS	H	St Albans City		L 0 - 1		1
21	NLS	H	Slough Town		**W** 2 - 0	Dickson 46 51	1
28	NLS	A	Hungerford Town		**W** 2 - 1	Berkeley-Agyepong 63 77	1
Dec 5	NLS	A	Eastbourne Borough		L 1 - 3	Berkeley-Agyepong 57	1
15	**FAT2P**	**A**	**Slough Town**		**D 2 - 2**	**Berkeley-Agyepong 73 Bakayoko 76 (Won 6-5 on pens)**	
19	**FAT3P**	**H**	**Haringey Borough**		**L 0 - 1**		
Jan 2	NLS	H	Ebbsfleet United		D 0 - 0		2
5	NLS	H	Tonbridge Angels		**W** 1 - 0	L'Ghoul 81	1
9	NLS	A	Braintree Town		L 1 - 2	Dickson 86 (pen)	2
12	NLS	H	Billericay Town		**W** 3 - 0	Sheringham 57 67 84	1
16	NLS	H	Hungerford Town		D 1 - 1	Hill 58	1
Feb 6	NLS	H	Welling United		D 2 - 2	Allen 58 Berkeley-Agyepong 63	1
9	NLS	H	Eastbourne Borough		L 0 - 1		1

Goalcorers	LGE	FAC	FAT	SG	CSG	HAT	PEN	1Q	2Q	45+	3Q	4Q	90+	T
TOTALS	26	0	2			1	2	3	3	0	12	10	0	28
Berkeley-Agyepong	5		1	5	3				1		3	2		6
Sheringham	4			2	1	1					2	2		4
Dickson	3			2	1		1				2	1		3
Bakayoko	1		1	2	1			1				1		2
Barham	2			1	1		1				1	1		2
Bonner	2			2	1							2		2
Allen	1			1	1						1			1
Essam	1			1	1			1						1
Hill	1			1	1						1			1

	LGE	FAC	FAT	SG	CSG	HAT	PEN	1Q	2Q	45+	3Q	4Q	90+	T
Husin	1			1	1						1			1
Jebb	1			1	1						1			1
L'Ghoul	1			1	1							1		1
Marsh-Brown	1			1	1				1					1
Opponent	1			1	1			1						1
Romain	1			1	1				1					1

No.	[illegible]	Barnum-Bobb J	Braham-Barrett C	Osman A	Vint R	Bonner T	McCallum G	Berkeley-Agyepong J	Romain E	Sheringham C	Husin N	Mitchell K	Wady E (Gk) (L)	Ijaha D	Modeste R	Marsh-Brown K	Wynter J	Hill J	Barham J	Jebb J	Essam C	Bakayoko M	Allen L	Pavey A (L)	Dickson C	Meade J	L'Ghoul N	Akinwande O (L)	Wilks D (Gk)	Carvalho D	Brodie C
1	c	c	cs	c	c	c	cs	c	c	cs	c	sc	cn	cn	cn	sc	cn	sc													
2	x	x	x	sx	x	x	s	x	x	s	x			s	xs	x	x	s													
3	x	x	x	s	x	x	s	x	x	s	x				sx	xs	x	s	x												
4	x	x	x		x	x	s	x	xs	sx	x			sx		sx	x		xs	xs	s										
5	x	x	x		x	x	s	xs	sx		x			sx			x	s	x	xs	sx	xs									
6	x	x	x	sx	x	x	s	xs	sx		x			x				s	x	xs	sx	xs									
7	x	x	x		x	x		x	xs	sx	x			xs		sx	s		x	xs	s		sx								
8	x	sx	x		s	x	sx	xs	xs		x					xs	x	s	x	x	x		sx								
9	x	x	xs			x		x	x	sx	x			sx		sx	x	s	xs	xs	x		s								
10	x	x				x	x	x	xs	xs	xs					s	x	s	sx	x	x		sx	sx							
11		sx				x	x	x	sx	s	xs		x				x	s	xs	x	x		x	sx	xs						
12		xs				x	x	sx			x		x			xs	x	sx	xs	x	x	s	s	sx	x						
13		s				x	x	x	sx		x		x			xs	x	s	sx	x	x		sx	xs	x						
14			t			t		t	t		st		t	ts		tn	st	ts	t	t	t	ts	tn			ts					
15	t	st	t			t	tn	t	t				tn	tn		st	t	tn	st	ts	t	ts	t				ts				
16	x	sx	x			x		x	sx		x			xs		s	x	s	xs		x		s		x		x				
17	x	x	x			x	s	x	sx		x					xs	sx	s		xs	x		sx		xs		x				
18		x	xs			x		x	sx		x		x	s		xs		s		x	x		s		sx		x	x			
19		x				x			s	xs				x		sx		x		x	x		x		sx		xs	xs	x	sx	s
20						x				x				x		sx	xs	x	s	x	x		x		sx		xs	xs	x	s	sx
21		x	x			x		sx	x	xs				x		s		sx	s	xs	xs		x				x	sx	x		
22	x	x	x			x		xs	s	x				x	xs			s	sx	s	x		x				x	sx			
x	14	14	13	1	7	22	4	14	7	2	14	0	5	5	0	1	12	2	6	9	14	0	6	0	3	0	5	1	3	0	0
xs	0	1	3	0	0	0	1	4	4	4	2	0	0	3	2	6	1	1	5	8	1	4	0	1	2	1	3	2	0	0	0
sx	0	4	0	2	0	0	1	2	7	3	1	1	0	3	1	7	2	3	4	0	2	0	5	3	3	0	0	2	0	1	1
s	0	1	0	1	1	0	7	0	2	3	0	0	2	4	1	4	2	14	2	1	2	1	5	0	0	0	0	0	0	1	1

GOALKEEPERS	CS	CCS
King	6	3
Wady	1	1
Wilkes	1	1

x/c/t - Played full 90 minutes
xs/cs/ts - Substituted off
sx/sc/st - Substituted on
s/cn/tn - Non-playing sub

DORKING WANDERERS MATCH RESULTS 2020-21

Date	Comp	H/A	Opponents	Att:	Result	Goalscorers	Pos
Oct 3	**FAC2Q**	**H**	**Eastbourne Borough**		**D 3 - 3**	**Rutherford 37 Prior 45 85 (Lost 3-4 on pens)**	
6	NLS	A	Eastbourne Borough		**W** 3 - 0	Prior 23 39 (pen) Ferry 45+2 (og)	1
10	NLS	H	Slough Town		**W** 3 - 1	Rutherford 25 Harris 42 Prior 80	1
17	NLS	A	Braintree Town		**W** 4 - 0	Fogden 45+2 McShane 49 79 Muitt 84	1
31	NLS	A	Hungerford Town		L 0 - 2		7
Nov 7	NLS	A	Dartford		**W** 3 - 2	Fogden 2 Prior 45+2 Briggs 76	4
14	NLS	H	Tonbridge Angels		**W** 4 - 1	Prior 15 41 43 Fogden 17	2
17	NLS	H	Dulwich Hamlet		D 0 - 0		3
21	NLS	A	Concord Rangers		**W** 3 - 1	Prior 4 81 (pens) Briggs 89	2
24	NLS	H	Oxford City		**W** 3 - 2	Prior 53 58 McShane 73	1
Dec 1	NLS	H	Maidstone United		D 2 - 2	Elokobi 41 (og) Prior 72	2
5	NLS	H	Bath City	680	L 1 - 2	Philpott 84	2
15	**FAT2P**	**H**	**Hungerford Town**		**W 2 - 0**	**McShane 43 48**	
19	**FAT3P**	**H**	**Barnet**		**W 3 - 1**	**McShane 16 Prior 38 Moore 90 (pen)**	
26	NLS	H	Hampton & Richmond B.		L 0 - 1		3
Jan 2	NLS	A	Hampton & Richmond B.		D 0 - 0		4
5	NLS	H	Ebbsfleet United		**W** 2 - 0	Briggs 23 Rowan 45+1 (og)	2
9	NLS	H	Hemel Hempstead Town		**W** 2 - 1	Kennedy 42 (pen) Rutherford 53	1
16	**FAT4P**	**A**	**Maidstone United**		**L 1 - 2**	**McShane 20**	
Feb 6	NLS	A	Hemel Hempstead Town		**W** 3 - 1	Prior 18 51 (pen) Rutherford 23	2
13	NLS	H	Welling United		**W** 5 - 0	Rutherford 17 Wheeler 26 Prior 47 McShane 64 Briggs 80	1
15	NLS	A	Chelmsford City		**W** 1 - 0	Briggs 30	1

Goalcorers	LGE	FAC	FAT	SG	CSG	HAT	PEN	1Q	2Q	45+	3Q	4Q	90+	T
TOTALS	39	3	6			1	6	8	14	5	8	11	1	48
Prior	15	2	1	11	3	1	4	3	5	2	4	4		18
McShane	4		4	6	2			2	1		3	2		8
Briggs	5			5	2				2			3		5
Rutherford	4	1		5	2			1	3		1			5
Fogden	3			3	2			2		1				3
Opponent	3			3	1					2				3
Harris	1			1	1				1					1
Kennedy	1			1	1		1		1					1
Moore			1	1	1		1						1	1
Muitt	1			1	1							1		1
Philpott	1			1	1							1		1
Wheeler	1			1	1				1					1

No.		Philpot I	Harris E	McManus N	Briggs M	Prior J	Rutherford A	McShane J	Wills K	Fuller B	Fogden W	Beard S	Moore L	Gallagher J	Muitt J	Sole G	Howes S (Gk)	Gallagher D	Kennedy C	Wheeler N	Dyett B	El-Abd S	Carey L (Gk) (L)
1		c	c	c	c	c	cs	cs	cs	c	c	sc	sc	sc	cn	cn	cn	cn					
2		x	x	x	s	x	x	xs	xs	x	xs	s	sx	sx	x			sx					
3		x	x	x		x	xs	x	xs		x	sx	sx	s	x			sx	xs	s			
4		x	xs	xs		x	xs	x	x	x	x	sx	s		x			sx		sx	s		
5		x	x	x	sx	x	xs	x	x	xs	x	sx				s		sx		xs		s	
6	x	xs	x	x	sx	x	sx	xs	x	x	x	sx		s		s		xs		x			
7			x	xs	sx	x	x	sx	x	x	x	xs		sx	xs			s		x		s	
8	x		x	x	x	x	xs	x	x	x		xs	sx	s	sx			sx		xs		s	
9			x	x	sx	x	x	xs	xs	x	x	x	sx		xs		x	sx		s		s	
10		x	x	x	x	x	xs	x	sx	x		sx	xs	sx	s		x			xs		s	
11	x	x			x	x		xs	x	x	x	s	x	s	s	s		sx		x		x	
12	x	sx	xs		sx	x		x	x	x	xs	x	x	sx	x	s		s		xs			
13	t	t	t		st	t		t	t	tn	ts	st	t		t	tn		st	ts	ts	tn	tn	
14		t	t	st	st	ts	tn	t	t	t	t	tn	t		ts	tn	t	st		ts		tn	
15		x	x	sx	x	xs	sx	x	x	x	xs	s	x		sx		x	s		xs			
16		xs	x	sx	x		x	sx	xs		x	s	x		xs		x	sx	x	x		s	
17			xs	x	x		xs	x	x	x	x	sx	x		s		x	sx	xs		s	sx	
18			x	xs	x		x	xs	x	x	x	s	xs		sx		x	sx	x		s	sx	
19	tn		t	t	t	st	ts	t	t	t	t	st	ts		st		t	tn	ts	tn		tn	
20			xs	x	sx	x	x	x	x	x	sx	x	s	s	xs					xs		sx	x
21		s		sx	x	xs	x	x	x	x	xs	x	sx	sx	s					xs		x	x
22		s		x	xs	x	xs	x	x	x	xs	x	sx		sx			sx		s		x	x
x	11	10	15	12	10	15	7	14	16	18	13	5	7	0	5	0	8	0	2	4	0	3	3
xs	0	2	4	3	1	3	9	6	5	1	6	2	3	0	5	0	0	1	4	9	0	0	0
sx	0	1	0	4	8	1	2	2	1	0	1	9	7	6	5	0	0	13	0	1	0	3	0
s	1	2	0	0	1	0	1	0	0	1	0	6	2	5	5	7	1	5	0	4	4	9	0

GOALKEEPERS	CS	CCS
Huk	4	1
Carey	2	2
Howes	2	2

x/c/t - Played full 90 minutes
xs/cs/ts - Substituted off
sx/sc/st - Substituted on
s/cn/tn - Non-playing sub

DULWICH HAMLET MATCH RESULTS 2020-21

Date	Comp	H/A	Opponents	Att:	Result	Goalscorers	Pos
Oct 3	**FAC2Q**	**A**	**Corinthian-Casuals**	**417**	**D 2 - 2**	**Henry 71 Moore 88 (Won 3-1 on pens)**	
10	NLS	A	Ebbsfleet United		D 1 - 1	White 33	15
13	**FAC3Q**	**A**	**Christchurch**		**D 1 - 1**	**Moore 88 (Won 3-1 on pens)**	
17	NLS	H	Chippenham Town		L 0 - 2		18
24	**FAC4Q**	**A**	**Eastbourne Borough**		**L 0 - 1**		
31	NLS	H	Chelmsford City		D 0 - 0		17
Nov 3	NLS	H	Concord Rangers		L 1 - 4	Allassani 11	19
11	NLS	A	Havant & Waterlooville		L 1 - 3	Moore 20	20
17	NLS	A	Dorking Wanderers		D 0 - 0		20
21	NLS	A	Hemel Hempstead Town		D 1 - 1	Mills 45	19
24	NLS	A	Bath City		W 4 - 1	Timlin 36 McGregor 47 Moore 58 Mills 79	16
Dec 5	NLS	A	Hungerford Town	393	W 3 - 0	Blackman 40 Ming 47 Hyde 90+6	14
8	NLS	H	Eastbourne Borough	1078	W 2 - 1	Mills 14 Allassani 19	12
12	NLS	A	Oxford City		L 0 - 1		13
15	**FAT2P**	**H**	**Cheshunt**		**W 3 - 1**	**McGregor 25 Taylor 45 Mills 57**	
19	**FAT3P**	**H**	**Hornchurch**		**L 1 - 2**	**Ming 26 (pen)**	
28	NLS	A	Hampton & Richmond B.		W 2 - 1	Mills 41 45	10
Jan 16	NLS	A	Dulwich Hamlet		L 0 - 2		11

Goalcorers	LGE	FAC	FAT	SG	CSG	HAT	PEN	1Q	2Q	45+	3Q	4Q	90+	T
TOTALS	15	3	4			0	1	5	5	3	4	4	1	22
Mills	5		1	5	2			1	1	2	1	1		6
Moore	2	2		4	1			1			1	2		4
Allassani	2			2	1			2						2
McGregor	1		1	2	1				1		1			2
Ming	1		1	2	1		1	1			1			2
Blackman	1			1	1				1					1
Henry		1		1	1							1		1
Hyde	1			1	1								1	1
Taylor			1	1	1					1				1
Timlin	1			1	1				1					1
White	1			1	1				1					1

	Barnes A	Ojo T	Timlin M	Debrah J	Sakho S	White L	Sammut R	Mills D	Hyde T	Moore D	Ming S	Henry K	Higgs J	Taylor Q	Grainger C (Gk)	David K	Allassani R	Barbosa D	Martin M	Clayden C (L)	Masampu R	McGregor G	Splatt J	Aghatise J	Balarabe S	Blackman A	Vint R (L)	Thomas K	Thomas L .	Sekajja I	Harris-Sealy A	No.
	c	cs	c	c	c	cs	cs	c	c	c	sc	sc	sc	cn	cn	cn	cn															1
	x		x	x	x	xs	xs	x	x	xs	x	sx	sx	s		s	sx															2
	cn	c	c	cn	c	sc	cn	cn	sc	c	c	cs	cs	c	c	c	cs	sc														3
	x		xs	x	x	xs	x		x	sx	x	xs	s	sx	x	s	sx	x														4
	sc		c	c	cn	cn	cs	cn	sc	c	c	sc	cs		cn	c	c		cs	c												5
	xs		x	x	x		s		xs	x	x	sx	x				sx			xs	x	sx	sx									6
	s		xs	x	xs		s		x	x	x	sx	x			sx	x			sx	x	xs										7
	s		x	x		s	s		x	x	x			x	x		xs			x	xs	sx		x	sx							8
	x		x	x	xs		s	xs	sx	x	x			x	x		sx	s				x		sx	xs							9
	xs		x	x			s	x	x	xs	x			x	x		sx			x	sx	xs		s	sx							10
	xs		x	x			x	sx	sx	xs	x			x	x		xs	sx				x		s	s	x						11
	x		x	sx			x	xs	sx	sx	x			x	x		x	s				x	s			xs	x					12
	x		x	sx	s		xs	xs	sx	x	x	s		x	x		xs	sx				x					x					13
	x		x	s	xs		s	sx	x	xs	x	sx	xs	x	x		x					sx					x					14
	t		t	st	tn		ts	t	tn	t	t	ts	st	t	t		st	tn				t					ts	tn				15
	t		t	ts	t		tn	ts	st	t	t	st	t	t	t		t	tn				tn							tn			16
	x		x		sx		s	xs	sx	xs	x	s	x	x	x		x	xs				sx					x					17
	xs		x	s			s	xs		sx	x		x	x	x		x	sx								xs	x			x	sx	18
5	10	1	16	10	6	0	3	4	7	10	17	0	5	12	13	2	7	1	0	3	2	5	0	1	0	1	5	0	0	1	0	x
0	4	1	2	1	3	3	5	6	1	5	0	3	3	0	0	0	4	1	1	1	1	2	0	0	1	2	1	0	0	0	0	xs
0	1	0	0	3	1	1	0	2	8	3	1	7	3	1	0	1	6	4	0	1	1	4	1	1	2	0	0	0	0	0	1	sx
0	3	0	0	3	3	2	10	2	1	0	0	2	1	2	2	3	1	4	0	0	0	1	1	2	1	0	0	1	1	0	0	s

GOALKEEPERS	CS	CCS
Grainger	2	1
Pardington	1	1

x/c/t - Played full 90 minutes
xs/cs/ts - Substituted off
sx/sc/st - Substituted on
s/cn/tn - Non-playing sub

EASTBOURNE BOROUGH MATCH RESULTS 2020-21

Date	Comp	H/A	Opponents	Att:	Result	Goalscorers	Pos
Oct 3	**FAC2Q**	**A**	**Dorking Wanderers**		**D 3 - 3**	**Whelpdale 29 35 82**	
6	NLS	H	Dorking Wanderers		L 0 - 3		22
10	NLS	A	Hemel Hempstead Town		W 4 - 1	Walker 1 Whelpdale 7 17 Hammond 61	8
13	**FAC3Q**	**H**	**Sheppey United**		**W 3 - 1**	**Luer 67 75 Whelpdale 69**	
17	NLS	H	Chelmsford City		D 1 - 1	Whelpdale 32	10
24	**FAC4Q**	**H**	**Dulwich Hamlet**		**W 1 - 0**	**Hammond 39 (pen)**	
27	NLS	A	Hampton & Richmond B.		W 2 - 1	Walker 15 55	8
31	NLS	H	Welling United		W 2 - 1	Luer 9 Kendall 69	6
Nov 8	**FAC1P**	**H**	**Blackpool**		**L 0 - 3**		
10	NLS	H	Ebbsfleet United		D 1 - 1	Cox 76	7
14	NLS	H	Braintree Town		W 4 - 0	Cox 35 Walker 78 88 Kendall 90+1	4
17	NLS	A	Tonbridge Angels		D 2 - 2	Cox 69 Kendall 86	5
21	NLS	A	Oxford City		D 1 - 1	Kendall 13	5
28	NLS	H	St Albans City		L 0 - 1		5
Dec 5	NLS	H	Dartford		W 3 - 1	Kendall 10 Whelpdale 76 Rollinson 90+2	4
8	NLS	A	Dulwich Hamlet	1078	L 1 - 2	Hammond 90+4	4
12	NLS	A	Concord Rangers		D 2 - 2	Lambert 64 Whelpdale 66	5
15	**FAT2P**	**A**	**Haringey Borough**		**L 1 - 3**	**Luer 90+2**	
Jan 12	NLS	H	Maidstone United		L 2 - 3	Rollinson 5 Whelpdale 28	8
16	NLS	A	Havant & Waterlooville		W 2 - 1	Whelpdale 35 66	7
Feb 6	NLS	H	Hungerford Town		W 3 - 2	Lambert 20 70 Rollinson 90	7
9	NLS	A	Dartford		W 1 - 0	Whelpdale 42	5
13	NLS	H	Concord Rangers		D 1 - 1	Luer 82	5
16	NLS	H	Billericay Town		W 4 - 2	Walker 12 Whelpdale 77 80 Hammond 87	3

Goalcorers	LGE	FAC	FAT	SG	CSG	HAT	PEN	1Q	2Q	45+	3Q	4Q	90+	T
TOTALS	36	7	1			1	1	10	8	0	6	15	5	44
Whelpdale	11	4		10	3	1		2	6		2	5		15
Walker	6			4	1			3			1	2		6
Kendall	5			5	3			2				2	1	5
Luer	2	2	1	4	1			1			1	2	1	5
Hammond	3	1		4	1		1		1		1	1	1	4
Cox	3			3	3				1			2		3
Lambert	3			2	1			1			1	1		3
Rollinson	3			3	1			1					2	3

	LGE	FAC	FAT	SG	CSG	HAT	PEN	1Q	2Q	45+	3Q	4Q	90+	T

Arnold N	Woollard-Innocent K (L)	Ferry J	Dickenson M	James S	Rollinson J	Hammond J	Luer G	Walker C	Whelpdale C	Folarin E	Cox D	Kendall C (L)	Blackmore D	Lambert C	Gravata L	Glover L (Gk)	Vaughan J	Towning C	Kay J	Basse B	Perez J	Pickering M	No.
cs	c	c	c	c	cs	c	cs	c	c	sc	sc	sc	cn	cn	cn	cn							1
	x	x	x	x	xs	x	x	x	xs		sx	sx	sx	s		s	xs						2
	x	x	x	x	xs	x		x	x		xs	sx	sx	sx	s	s	xs						3
	c	c	c	c	cs	c	scs	c	c		cs	sc	cn	cn	sc	cn	c	cn					4
	x	x	x	x	xs	x		xs	x		xs	sx	s	sx	sx	s	x						5
	c	c	c	c	sc	c	c	c	cs	sc	cs	sc	cn	cn	cn	cn	cs						6
	x	x	x	x	sx	x	xs	x		s	xs	xs	sx		sx	s	x						7
	x	x	x	x	sx	x	x	x		s	xs	xs	sx		s	s	x						8
	c	c	c	c	sc	c	c	cs	cs	cn	cs	sc	cn	cn	sc	cn	c						9
	x	x	x	x	sx	x	x	xs	xs	s	sx	xs	sx			s	x						10
	x	x	x	x	x	xs	xs	x		s	xs	sx	sx	sx		s	x						11
	x	x	x	x	xs	x	x			s	x	x	s	sx	s	s	x						12
	x	x	x	x	sx	x	xs	x		s	xs	x	s	sx		s	x						13
		x	x	x	sx	x	x	xs	sx		x	xs	s	sx		s	x		xs				14
	x	x	x	x	sx	x	x	sx	x		xs	xs	s	s		s	x						15
	x	x	x	x	sx	x	x	sx	xs	s	xs	xs	sx			s	x						16
	x	x	x	x	sx	x	xs	x	x	sx	xs	xs	s	sx		s							17
	t	t	t			ts	t	t	tn	st	tn		t	t	ts	t	tn	st		ts	st		18
	x	x	x	x	x	x	x	sx	xs	s	sx	xs		sx			xs	s					19
	x	x	x	x	x	x	x	xs	x		s	x	s	sx		s		s					20
	x	x	x	x	x	x	x		x		sx		s	xs	s	s	s					x	21
	x	x	x	x	x	x	x		xs		sx		s	xs	sx	s	x	s					22
	x	x	x	x	x		x	sx			x		s	xs	s	s	x	s				x	23
	x	x	x	x	xs	x	x	xs	xs		sx		sx	sx		s	x					s	24
0	23	24	24	23	6	21	16	11	8	0	3	3	1	1	0	1	15	0	0	0	0	2	X
1	0	0	0	0	7	2	5	6	8	0	12	8	0	3	1	0	4	0	1	1	0	0	XS
0	0	0	0	0	10	0	1	4	1	4	7	8	8	10	5	0	0	1	0	0	1	0	SX
0	0	0	0	0	0	0	0	0	1	9	2	0	14	6	7	22	2	5	0	0	0	1	S

GOALKEEPERS	CS	CCS
Ravizzoli	3	1

x/c/t - Played full 90 minutes
xs/cs/ts - Substituted off
sx/sc/st - Substituted on
s/cn/tn - Non-playing sub

EBBSFLEET UNITED MATCH RESULTS 2020-21

Date	Comp	H/A	Opponents	Att:	Result	Goalscorers	Pos
Oct 3	**FAC2Q**	**H**	**Hastings United**		**D 2 - 2**	**Martin 59 (pen) Chapman 90 (Won 4-1 on pens)**	
6	NLS	A	Braintree Town		**W** 3 - 0	Bingham 57 83 Martin 87	2
10	NLS	H	Dulwich Hamlet		D 1 - 1	Bingham 28	3
13	**FAC3Q**	**H**	**Chippenham Town**		**D 1 - 1**	**Rowan 90 (Lost 9-8 on pens)**	
17	NLS	A	St Albans City		L 2 - 3	Bingham 21 (pen) Grant 27	8
24	NLS	H	Hungerford Town		**W** 3 - 2	Grant 8 Martin 66 Taylor 80	4
31	NLS	A	Billericay Town		**W** 2 - 1	Taylor 17 Paxman 33	5
Nov 10	NLS	A	Eastbourne Borough		D 1 - 1	Egan 72	6
14	NLS	A	Chippenham Town		**W** 2 - 1	Goodman 53 82	5
17	NLS	H	Maidstone United		D 0 - 0		6
21	NLS	H	Tonbridge Angels		L 0 - 1		7
Dec 12	NLS	H	Havant & Waterlooville		L 0 - 2		11
15	**FAT2P**	**A**	**Chippenham Town**		**D 1 - 1**	**Bingham 72 (Won 4-2 on pens)**	
19	**FAT3P**	**A**	**Dagenham & Redbridge**		**L 2 - 5**	**Martin 51 Bingham 90+2**	
Jan 2	NLS	A	Dartford		D 0 - 0		10
5	NLS	A	Dorking Wanderers		L 0 - 2		11
12	NLS	H	Concord Rangers		**W** 2 - 1	Bingham 13 Mekki 64	10
16	NLS	A	Hampton & Richmond B.		L 1 - 2	West 83	10
19	NLS	A	Slough Town		**W** 2 - 0	Bingham 29 84	8
Feb 9	NLS	H	Hampton & Richmond B.		**W** 2 - 1	Bingham 18 Egan 36	8
13	NLS	A	Havant & Waterlooville		**W** 2 - 1	Bingham 3 Poleon 79 (RC - Solley 60, 2xY Martin 65)	8
16	NLS	A	Welling United		L 3 - 4	Taylor 25 Poleon 59 Wood 78	8

Goalcorers	LGE	FAC	FAT	SG	CSG	HAT	PEN	1Q	2Q	45+	3Q	4Q	90+	T
TOTALS	**26**	**3**	**3**			**0**	**2**	**6**	**6**	**0**	**7**	**10**	**3**	**32**
Bingham	9		2	9	3		1	4	2		1	3	1	11
Martin	2	1	1	4	2		1				3	1		4
Taylor	3			3	2			1	1			1		3
Egan	2			2	1				1			1		2
Goodman	2			1	1						1	1		2
Grant	2			2	2			1	1					2
Poleon	2			2	2						1	1		2
Chapman		1		1	1								1	1
Mekki	1			1	1						1			1
Paxman	1			1	1				1					1
Rowan		1		1	1								1	1
West	1			1	1							1		1
Wood	1			1	1							1		1

	Adebayo-Rowling T	Goodman J	Mekki A	Payne J	West M	Martin L	Wood W	Grant R	Dobson J (L)	Chapman B	Bingham R	Paxman J	Rowan C	Allen I	Cundle G	Egan A	Holmes J (Gk)	Kahraman S	Taylor B	Frempah B	Eirich A	Solly C	Taylor J (L)	Bellagambi G (Gk)	Poleon D	No.
	c	c	c	c	cs	c	c	cs	cs	c	sc	sc	sc	cn	cn	cn										1
	x	sx	xs	x	sx	x	x			x	x	xs	xs	sx	s		x	x								2
	x	x	xs	xs	sx	x	x		sx	xs	x	x		sx		s	s	x								3
			sc		cs	cs	sc	c	cs	c	sc	c	c	cn	c	cn	c	c	c	cn						4
			xs	x			x	xs		xs	x	x	x	sx	sx	sx	s	x	x	s						5
	x		xs	xs	sx	x	s	xs		sx	x	x	x				x	x	x	sx						6
	x		xs		sx	x	sx	xs	sx	x	x	x				s	x	x	x	xs						7
	x	s	sx		xs	x	xs	sx	sx		x	x				xs	x	x	x	x						8
	x	x			s	x	sx	xs		sx	x	x		s	sx	x		x	xs	xs						9
	x	sx	sx			x	x			sx	xs	x	x	xs		xs	x	x	x	s						10
	x		sx	s		x	xs			sx	x	x	x	xs		xs	x		x	x	sx					11
	x	xs	x	xs		x	xs		s		x	x	sx	sx		sx	x	x	x							12
	t		tn		ts	t	ts		st	t	st	t	t	tn	ts		tn	t	t		st					13
	t	tn	st	st	tn	t	t	ts		t	t	t	t	tn		ts	tn	st	ts							14
	x	xs	sx	x	xs	xs	s	sx	sx	x	x	x					x	x	x							15
	x		x	xs	s		sx	xs	sx	x	x	x	xs			sx	x	x	x							16
	x		x				xs	s	sx	x	x	xs		sx		x	x	x	xs		sx	x				17
	x		x		sx		xs		s	xs	x	x		sx		xs	x	x	x		sx	x				18
	x	sx	xs		sx				xs		x	x	s	sx		x	x	x	x		s	x	xs			19
	x	x	sx	xs	sx	xs	s		xs		x	x		s		x		x	x					x	sx	20
	x	x	sx		sx	x	xs		s		xs	x		s		xs	x	x	x			x			sx	21
	x	x	xs	xs	s	x	sx		s		x	x		sx		xs			x			x		x	sx	22
6	20	6	5	4	0	14	6	1	0	9	17	19	7	0	1	4	14	18	16	2	0	5	0	2	0	X
0	0	2	7	6	5	3	7	7	4	3	2	2	2	2	1	7	0	0	3	2	0	0	1	0	0	XS
0	0	3	8	1	8	0	5	2	7	4	3	1	2	8	2	3	0	1	0	1	4	0	0	0	3	SX
2	0	2	1	1	4	0	3	1	4	0	0	0	1	7	2	4	4	0	0	3	1	0	0	0	0	S

GOALKEEPERS	CS	CCS
Holmes	4	1

x/c/t - Played full 90 minutes
xs/cs/ts - Substituted off
sx/sc/st - Substituted on
s/cn/tn - Non-playing sub

HAMPTON & RICHMOND BOROUGH MATCH RESULTS 2020-21

Date	Comp	H/A	Opponents	Att:	Result	Goalscorers	Pos
Oct 3	**FAC2Q**	**A**	**Corinthian**		**W 1 - 0**	**Donaldson 29**	
6	NLS	A	St Albans City		L 0 - 1		15
10	NLS	H	Dartford		D 0 - 0		17
13	**FAC3Q**	**H**	**Hornchurch**		**D 2 - 2**	**Smith 17 Muir 84 (Won 4-3 on pens)**	
24	**FAC4Q**	**A**	**Hemel Hempstead Town**		**W 1 - 0**	**Muir 7**	
27	NLS	H	Eastbourne Borough		L 1 - 2	Coleman 67	18
31	NLS	A	Oxford City		W 2 - 0	Donaldson 29 Gray 83	13
Nov 8	**FAC1P**	**H**	**Oldham Athletic**		**L 2 - 3**	**Deadfield 30 (pen) 75**	
10	NLS	A	Hungerford Town		W 1 - 0	Muir 52	11
14	NLS	A	Chelsmford City		W 1 - 0	Carvalho 68	9
17	NLS	H	Hemel Hempstead Town		L 0 - 3		9
21	NLS	H	Bath City		W 1 - 0	Deadfield 86 (pen)	8
28	NLS	A	Billericay Town		W 6 - 2	Gondoh 18 69 Muir 27 48 Deadfield 45+1 Minhas 85	6
Dec 1	NLS	A	Chippenham Town		W 3 - 0	Gondoh 49 Donaldson 77 Muir 83	4
5	NLS	H	St Albans City	97	L 0 - 2		5
26	NLS	A	Dorking Wanderers		W 1 - 0	Miller-Rodney 80	5
28	NLS	H	Dulwich Hamlet		L 1 - 2	Gray 60	5
Jan 2	NLS	H	Dorking Wanderers		D 1 - 1	Gondoh 45 (pen)	5
16	NLS	H	Ebbsfleet United		W 2 - 1	Vilhete 68 Fisher 90+3	5
Feb 6	NLS	A	Tonbridge Angels		W 3 - 0	Wassmer 14 Fisher 32 Donaldson 46	4
9	NLS	A	Ebbsfleet United		L 1 - 2	Fisher 44	6

Goalcorers	LGE	FAC	FAT	SG	CSG	HAT	PEN	1Q	2Q	45+	3Q	4Q	90+	T
TOTALS	24	6	0			0	3	4	6	2	6	11	1	30
Muir	4	2		5	2			1	1		2	2		6
Deadfield	2	2		3	2		2		1	1		2		4
Donaldson	3	1		4	1				2		1	1		4
Gondoh	4			3	2		1	1		1	1	1		4
Fisher	3			3	3				2				1	3
Gray	2			2	1						1	1		2
Carvalho	1			1	1							1		1
Coleman	1			1	1						1			1
Miller-Rodney	1			1	1							1		1
Minhas	1			1	1							1		1
Smith		1		1	1			1						1
Vilhete	1			1	1							1		1
Wassmer	1			1	1			1						1

	Uche I	Steer R	Inman D	Wassmer C	Smith C	Donaldson R	Hill R	Deadfield S	Gray J	Muir N	Farrell K	Miller-Rodney T	Minhas N	Bowman M (Gk)	Bassett D	Coleman De-Graft R	Amate D	Wotton J	Ruddick L	Carvalho W	Anderson M (L)	Gondoh R	Fisher D	Cox S	Brown C	Vilhete M	No.
	cs	cs	c	c	c	c	c	c	c	c	sc	sc	cn	cn	cn	cn	cn										1
	s	s	x	x	xs	xs	x	x	x	xs	x	x	sx		sx	sx											2
	s	s	x	x	sx	x	x	xs	x	x	x	x	sx		xs	s											3
	c	sc	c	c	c	cs	c		c	c	c		scs	cn	cs	sc	cn	cn									4
		sc	c	cs	c	c	cs	sc	c	cs	c		c	cn	cn	cn		cn	c	sc							5
		x	x		xs	sx		x	x	x	x		xs	s	sx	x		s	sx	xs							6
	s	x	x			x		x	x	xs	x	xs		s	sx	sx			x	xs	sx						7
c	cn	cs	c		c	cs		c	c	c	c	c	sc	cn	sc	sc	cn	cn		cs							8
x	x	s			x	x		x	x	xs	x	x	s		sx	s				sx	x	xs					9
x	x	s			x	x		xs	x	xs	x	x	sx		sx	s				sx	x	xs					10
x	x	xs			x	s		x	x	x	s		xs		sx	x				xs	x		sx	sx			11
x	s		xs		sx	x		x	x	xs	x		s							sx	x	sx	xs	x	x		12
x			x		s	sx		x	x	xs	x	x	sx							x	x	xs	s	sx	xs		13
x			x		sx	x		xs	sx	x	x	x	s						s	sx	x	xs	xs	x			14
x			x		sx	xs		x	x		x	x	xs	s					s	sx	xs	x	sx	x			15
x	s		x		x	sx		xs	x	xs	x	x	sx						sx	xs		x	s	x			16
x	sx		x		xs	x			x	x	xs	x	sx			s			s	xs		x	sx	x			17
x			x		s	x			x	x	x	x	s	s		sx			xs	sx		x	xs	x			18
x					sx	x		x	x	xs	x	x	sx	s		s			xs	xs			sx	x		x	19
x			x	xs	s	x		x	x	x	x	sx	sx							sx			xs	x	s	xs	20
x			x	xs	s	x		xs	x	x	x	sx	sx							sx			xs	x	s	x	21
21	4	2	16	4	8	13	4	12	20	11	18	12	1	0	0	2	0	0	2	1	6	4	0	9	1	2	X
0	1	3	1	3	3	4	1	5	0	9	1	1	3	0	2	0	0	0	2	7	1	4	5	0	1	1	XS
0	1	2	0	0	5	3	0	1	1	0	1	3	11	0	7	5	0	0	2	9	1	1	4	2	0	0	SX
0	6	4	0	0	4	1	0	0	0	0	1	0	5	9	2	7	3	4	3	0	0	0	2	0	2	0	S

GOALKEEPERS	CS	CCS
Julian	10	2

x/c/t - Played full 90 minutes
xs/cs/ts - Substituted off
sx/sc/st - Substituted on
s/cn/tn - Non-playing sub

HAVANT & WATERLOOVILLE MATCH RESULTS 2020-21

Date	Comp	H/A	Opponents	Att:	Result	Goalscorers	Pos
Oct 4	**FAC2Q**	**H**	**Horsham**		**W 2 - 1**	**Deacon 30 Wright 58**	
10	NLS	H	Maidstone United		D 2 - 2	Iaciofano 29 34	13
13	**FAC3Q**	**H**	**Chatham Town**		**W 4 - 1**	**Iaciofano 16 53 Deacon 39 Wright 63**	
17	NLS	A	Billericay Town		W 2 - 1	Magri 79 Sinclair 90+3	9
24	**FAC4Q**	**A**	**Bath City**		**W 3 - 0**	**Wright 22 Deacon 58 Widdrington 90+3**	
31	NLS	A	Dartford		L 1 - 2	Taylor 78	12
Nov 7	**FAC1P**	**H**	**Cray Valley PM**		**W 1 - 0**	**Gomis 18**	
11	NLS	H	Dulwich Hamlet		W 3 - 1	Magri 27 Aghatise 43 (og) Robson 73	10
14	NLS	H	Oxford City		W 2 - 1	Magri 45 Wright 49	8
29	**FAC2P**	**A**	**Marine**		**L 0 - 1**		
Dec 3	NLS	H	Hemel Hempstead Town		L 2 - 3	Kedwell 14 (pen) Diarra 44	13
5	NLS	H	Chelmsford City	803	W 3 - 1	Wright 19 63 66	10
9	NLS	H	Slough Town		D 0 - 0		10
12	NLS	A	Ebbsfleet United		W 2 - 0	Wright 37 57	7
15	**FAT2P**	**A**	**Bracknell Town**	**324**	**W 3 - 2**	**Iaciofano 10 Taylor 65 Wright 75**	
19	**FAT3P**	**H**	**Braintree Town**		**W 1 - 0**	**Deacon 74 (Qualified for the 5th Round after Altrincham pulled out)**	
Jan 2	NLS	H	Hungerford Town		W 4 - 2	Robson 31 Magri 38 Gomis 67 Wright 90	6
16	NLS	H	Eastbourne Borough		L 1 - 2	Gomis 57	8
19	NLS	A	Bath City		L 1 - 2	Deacon 30	9
Feb 6	**FAT5P**	**H**	**Notts County**		**D 2 - 2**	**Wright 33 Gomis 47 (Lost 2-4 on pens) (RC - Jones 70)**	
9	NLS	A	Hemel Hempstead Town		L 0 - 2		9
13	NLS	H	Ebbsfleet United		L 1 - 2	Robson 48 (RC - Widdrington 60)	9

Goalcorers	LGE	FAC	FAT	SG	CSG	HAT	PEN	1Q	2Q	45+	3Q	4Q	90+	T
TOTALS	24	10	6			1	1	6	12	1	14	4	3	40
Wright	7	3	2	9	2	1		2	2		6	1	1	12
Deacon	1	3	1	5	1				3		1	1		5
Iaciofano	2	2	1	3	2			2	2		1			5
Gomis	2	1	1	4	2			1			3			4
Magri	4			4	2				2	1	1			4
Robson	3			3	1				1		1	1		3
Taylor	1		1	2	1						1	1		2
Diarra	1			1	1				1					1
Kedwell	1			1	1		1	1						1

	LGE	FAC	FAT	SG	CSG	HAT	PEN	1Q	2Q	45+	3Q	4Q	90+	T
Opponent	1			1	1				1					1
Sinclair	1			1	1								1	1
Widdrington		1		1	1								1	1

No.	Read B	Straker A	Magri S	Clifford B	Iaciofano J	Widdrington T	Robson C	Gomis B	Wright T	Deacon R	Tupper J (Gk)	Sinclair L	Ajakaije D	Diarra M	Rowe C	Walton S	Bright L	Taylor J	Luce M	McLennan G	Poku G	Kedwell D	Chambers-Parillon L (L)	Bakayoko M	Lee T	Jones N (L)	Williams A
1	c	c	c	cs	cs	c	c	c	c	c	sc	sc	sc	cn	cn	cn	cn										
2	x	x	x	x	xs	x	s	x	x	xs	s	sx	sx	x	s												
3	c	c	c	c	c	c	c	c	c	c																	
4	x	x	x	xs	xs	sx	xs		x	x		sx	sx	x		s		x	s								
5	c	c	c	cs	cs	sc	c	sc	c	cs	cn	sc	cn	c		cn		c		cn							
6		x	x	x	xs	sx	x	xs	x	xs		sx	sx	x				x		s	s						
7	c	sc	c		cs		sc	c	c	cs	cn	sc	cn	c			cn	c	cn	cs	c						
8	x	sx	x	x	xs		x	xs	sx	s		s		x				x		xs	sx	x					
9	x	s	x	x	xs		x	x	x	sx		sx	s	x				x		xs	s						
10	c	c	c	cs	sc	sc	cs	cs	c	c	cn	sc	cn	c		cn		c		sc							
11	sx	s	x	xs	xs				xs	sx	s	sx		x		x		x		x	x	x					
12	x	sx	x	s	sx		s	x	xs	x			sx	x				x		xs	x	xs					
13	x		x	sx	sx		s	xs	x	x		s	s	x				x		x	x	xs					
14	x	x	x	sx	s		sx	x	x	xs			sx	xs				x			xs	s	x				
15		t	t	t	t		t		st		t	ts	t		tn	tn		t		t	st	ts					
16	t	t	t		ts		t	ts	t	st	tn	tn	t		st	tn		t			ts	st					
17	s		x	sx	sx		x	x	x	x	s	s		x	xs			x			x			xs			
18		x		s	sx		x	x	x	x			sx	x	xs			xs			x	sx	xs		s		
19	xs	x	x	xs				xs	x	x				x	s			x			sx	x	sx	sx	s		
20		tn	t	t	tn	tn	t	t	t	t	t		tn		tn			t		t	ts	tn				t	st
21		s	x	x	sx		x	xs	x	x	x				sx			x		x		sx	xs			xs	s
22		x	x	x	sx	x	x	sx	x	sx	x				s			x				xs	s		xs		xs
x	13	13	21	9	2	4	13	10	18	11	4	0	2	14	0	1	0	18	0	5	6	3	1	0	0	1	0
xs	1	0	0	6	10	0	2	7	2	5	0	1	0	1	2	0	0	1	0	4	3	4	2	1	1	1	1
sx	1	3	0	3	7	4	2	2	2	4	1	9	7	0	2	0	0	0	0	1	3	3	1	1	0	0	1
s	1	4	0	2	2	1	3	0	0	1	7	4	6	1	6	6	2	0	2	2	2	2	1	0	2	0	1

GOALKEEPERS	CS	CCS
Worner	5	2

x/c/t - Played full 90 minutes
xs/cs/ts - Substituted off
sx/sc/st - Substituted on
s/cn/tn - Non-playing sub

HEMEL HEMPSTEAD TOWN MATCH RESULTS 2020-21

Date	Comp	H/A	Opponents	Att:	Result	Goalscorers	Pos
Oct 3	**FAC2Q**	**A**	**AFC Dunstable**	**214**	**W 2 - 1**		
6	NLS	A	Slough Town		L 0 - 1		16
10	NLS	H	Eastbourne Borough		L 1 - 4	Balarabe 80	19
17	NLS	A	Maidstone United		L 1 - 4	Balarabe 80	20
24	**FAC4Q**	**H**	**Hampton & Richmond B.**		**L 0 - 1**	**NB: got a bye in the 3Q when Boston United pulled out.**	
31	NLS	A	Braintree Town		**W** 4 - 3	Olomowewe 20 Bateman 42 (pen) Forrest 45 (og) Evans 45+1	16
Nov 3	NLS	H	Billericay Town		L 1 - 4	Cole 45+2	18
7	NLS	A	Bath City		**W** 2 - 1	Bateman 20 (pen) Young 80	12
10	NLS	H	Dartford		L 1 - 3	Christie 81	15
14	NLS	H	Welling United		L 1 - 2	Olagunju 51 (og)	16
17	NLS	A	Hampton & Richmond B.		**W** 3 - 0	Cooper 16 Anderson 47 (og) Evans 86	11
21	NLS	H	Dulwich Hamlet		D 1 - 1	Cooper 45+3	12
28	NLS	A	Tonbridge Angels		**W** 2 - 1	Lacey 22 (pen) Rowe 82	9
Dec 2	NLS	A	Havant & Waterlooville		**W** 3 - 2	Ajayi 2 Rowe 11 Lacey 31	8
12	NLS	H	Hungerford Town	400	L 0 - 1		10
19	**FAT2P**	**A**	**Corinthian-Casuals**		**D 0 - 0**	**(Won 4-2 on pens)**	
22	**FAT3P**	**A**	**Bromley**		**L 0 - 2**		
Jan 9	NLS	A	Dorking Wanderers		L 1 - 2	Lacey 41	13
19	NLS	H	Oxford City		L 3 - 5	Lacey 1 Sellers 36 Christie 46	15
Feb 6	NLS	H	Dorking Wanderers		L 1 - 3	Lacey 75	16
9	NLS	H	Havant & Waterlooville		**W** 2 - 0	Christie 13 Young 52	11
16	NLS	A	St Albans City		D 1 - 1	Lacey 71 (pen)	10

Goalcorers	LGE	FAC	FAT	SG	CSG	HAT	PEN	1Q	2Q	45+	3Q	4Q	90+	T
TOTALS	28	0	0			0	4	8	4	4	4	8	0	28
Lacey	6			6	3		2	2	2			2		6
Christie	3			3	1			1			1	1		3
Opponent	3			3	2					1	2			3
Balalarabe	2			2	2							2		2
Bateman	2			2	1		2	1	1					2
Cooper	2			2	2			1		1				2
Evans	2			2	1					1		1		2
Rowe	2			2	2			1				1		2
Young	2			2	1						1	1		2
Ajayi	1			1	1			1						1
Cole	1			1	1					1				1
Olomowewe	1			1	1			1						1
Sellers	1			1	1				1					1

	Howells J	Kinnane R	Howell L	Evans J	Kpohomouh J	Cook J	Owen T	Young R	Bateman M	Lacey J	Cole A	Webb D	Ajayi K	Snedker D (Gk)	Perkins T (L)	Pennell L	Balarabe S	Vine R	Sellers R	Glover R (L)	Olomowewe T	Carlyle N (L)	Duke-McKenna S (L)	Paul C	Scott-Morris G (D)	Christie B (D)	McDevitt L (L)	Cooper N (D)	Rowe O (L)	Mantom S	Carruthers S	Craig P	Oyinsan J	Saunders D (Gk)	Bircham L	Balogun J	Muleba J (D)	Goather-Braithwaite D	Hayes N (Gk)	Steer R	Blackman R (D)	No.
																																										1
x	x	x	xs	x	x	x	xs	x	x	xs	sx	sx	sx	s	s																											2
x	x	x		x	x	xs	xs	x	x		x	xs	sx	s		sx	sx	s																								3
s	xs	x		sx	xs	sx			x		xs	s	x	x	sx	x	x		x	x																						4
n	c			cn	cn	cs		c	c	sc	sc		c	c		c	cs			cs	c	c	sc																			5
s	sx	x		x				xs	x	sx	xs		x	x			s			sx	x	x	xs	x																		6
s		x	s	x				x	x	sx	xs		s	x		xs	sx				x	x	x	x																		7
x	sx	x		x	s			x	xs	xs			x	s		x					s	x	x		x	sx																8
x	sx	x		xs				x	x	sx			xs	s		x					s	xs	x	sx	x	x																9
x	x	s		sx				x	xs	xs				s		x							xs	x	x	sx	x	x	sx													10
s	x	s		sx	sx			x		xs				x		x							xs	x	xs	x	x	x	sx													11
s	x			sx	s			xs		xs			s	x		x							x	x	x	x	x	x	sx													12
s	x	s		xs				xs		xs			sx	x		x								x	x	x	x	x	sx	sx												13
s	x	sx		s				sx		xs		sx	x	x										x	x	xs	x	x	xs	x												14
s	xs	x						x	sx	x		sx	s	x										x	x	xs	x		xs	x	sx											15
n	t	t						ts	st	t		t	st	t					t											t	t	t	ts	tn	tn							16
tn	ts	t						t	st	t		ts	st	t					t											t	t	t	st		tn	ts						17
s		x						sx	sx	xs			s	x					x					x	x	xs	x	xs		x	x		sx									18
x	xs	x						s	x	x			sx						xs					sx		x	x			x	xs			s			x	sx				19
	s	xs						sx	xs	x			sx											xs	x	x		x		x	x			s					x	x	s	20
		s						x	s	x		sx	x											xs	x	xs		x		x	x			s					x	x	s	21
		s						x	sx	xs		sx	x											x	x	xs		x		x	xs			s					x	x	sx	22
6	9	12	0	5	2	1	0	12	8	6	1	1	7	12	0	8	1	0	4	1	3	4	4	10	11	6	8	8	0	9	5	2	0	0	0	0	1	0	3	3	0	x
0	4	1	1	2	1	2	2	4	3	9	3	2	1	0	0	1	1	0	1	1	0	1	3	2	1	5	0	1	2	0	2	0	1	0	0	1	0	0	0	0	0	xs
0	3	1	0	4	1	1	0	3	5	4	2	5	7	0	1	1	2	0	0	1	0	0	1	2	0	2	0	0	4	1	1	0	2	0	0	0	0	1	0	0	1	sx
12	1	5	1	2	3	0	0	1	1	0	0	1	4	5	1	0	1	1	0	0	2	0	0	0	0	0	0	0	0	0	0	0	0	5	2	0	0	0	0	0	2	s

GOALKEEPERS	CS	CCS
Snedker	2	1
Hayes	1	1

x/c/t - Played full 90 minutes
xs/cs/ts - Substituted off
sx/sc/st - Substituted on
s/cn/tn - Non-playing sub

HUNGERFORD TOWN MATCH RESULTS 2020-21

Date	Comp	H/A	Opponents	Att:	Result	Goalscorers	Pos
Oct 3	**FAC2Q**	**A**	**Truro City**	**257**	**L 0 - 4**		
6	NLS	H	Chippenham Town		W 3 - 0	Seager 10 Rusby 40 Fasanmade 59	3
10	NLS	A	Tonbridge Angels		W 2 - 0	Seager 68 Harding 90+4	2
17	NLS	H	Concord Rangers		W 1 - 0	Seager 30	2
24	NLS	A	Ebbsfleet United		L 2 - 3	Jones 3 Hopper 38	2
31	NLS	H	Dorking Wanderers		W 2 - 0	Seager 50 85 (pen)	2
Nov 7	NLS	A	Braintree Town		W 2 - 1	Hopper 45 70 (pen)	1
10	NLS	H	Hampton & Richmond B.		L 0 - 1		2
17	NLS	A	Slough Town		W 3 - 1	Seager 6 43 Fasanmade 54	2
21	NLS	A	St Albans City		D 0 - 0		3
28	NLS	H	Dartford		L 1 - 2	Seager 32 (pen)	4
Dec 1	NLS	H	Oxford City		L 1 - 4	Partridge 25	5
5	NLS	H	Dulwich Hamlet	393	L 0 - 3		6
12	NLS	A	Hemel Hempstead Town	400	W 1 - 0	Seager 53	4
15	**FAT2Q**	**A**	**Dorking Wanderers**		**L 0 - 2**		
28	NLS	A	Bath City		W 2 - 0	Seager 12 Fasanmade 20	3
Jan 2	NLS	A	Havant & Waterlooville		L 2 - 4	Seager 46 62	3
9	NLS	H	Maidstone United		W 2 - 1	Lewington 15 (og) Evans 57	3
16	NLS	A	Dartford		D 1 - 1	Fasanmade 42	4
Feb 6	NLS	A	Eastbourne Borough		L 2 - 3	Seager 45 90+4 (pen)	5
9	NLS	A	Oxford City		L 0 - 4		7

Goalcorers	LGE	FAC	FAT	SG	CSG	HAT	PEN	1Q	2Q	45+	3Q	4Q	90+	T
TOTALS	27	0	0			0	4	6	7	2	7	2	3	27
Seager	14			10	3		3	3	3	1	4	2	1	14
Fasanmade	4			4	1			1	1		2			4
Hopper	3			2	1		1		1	1			1	3
Evans Jack	1			1	1						1			1
Harding	1			1	1								1	1
Jones	1			1	1			1						1
Opponent	1			1	1			1						1
Partridge	1			1	1				1					1
Rusby	1			1	1				1					1

Cairney L	Bayley H	Partridge M	Rusby J	Angell C	Emmerson K	Willmoth C	Fasanmade C	Jones Mike	McGory L	Seager R	Giamattei M (L)	Harding J	Edwards J	Graham R	Berry-Hargreaves M	Tooze K	Hopper L	Tyler R	Smith S	Alderson S	Burley A (L)	Evans Jack	Evans Jake	Crowther M (Gk)	Diaz A (L)	Atkinson M	No.
																											1
x	x	x	x	x	x	x	xs	x	xs	xs	sx	sx	sx	s	s												2
x	x	x	x	x	x	xs	xs	x	x	x	s	sx	s		s	sx											3
x	x	x	x	x		x		x	x	xs	s	s	s	s	x	x	sx										4
x	x	x	x	x	x	xs		x	xs	x		sx	sx	s	s		xs	sx									5
x	x	x	x	x	x	xs	sx	x	sx	x		s	s		s		xs	x									6
x	x		x	x	x	x	s	x	s	x		s	s		x	s	x	x									7
x	x		x	x	x	x	sx	xs	x	x		sx	sx		xs	s	xs		s								8
x	x		x	x	x	x	xs	x	x	xs		s	sx		x	s	sx			s							9
x	x	sx	x	xs	x	x	xs	x	x	xs		s	s		x	sx	sx										10
x	xs	sx	xs	x	x	x	xs		x	x		sx	s		x	sx	s	x									11
x	xs	x		x	x	x	x	xs	sx	x		s	sx		xs	s	sx	x									12
x	xs	x		x	x	x	sx	sx	s	x		xs	sx		xs		x	x		s							13
x	x	x	x	xs	x	x	xs	x	x	xs		s	sx				sx	sx			s						14
t	t	tn	t	tn	t	tn	tn	t	t	t		tn	t				t				t	t	tn				15
x	x	x	x	x	x	xs	xs		sx	xs		sx	s				sx	x			x			s			16
x	x	x	x	x	x	x	x	s		x		s	s					x			x				s		17
x	sx	x	x	x	x	xs	xs		sx	x		s	s					x			x	xs			sx		18
x	sx	x	x	x	x	xs	xs		sx	x		s	s					x			x		xs		sx		19
x	sx	x	x	xs	x	xs	x	s	sx	x		sx					s	x			x		xs				20
x	x	x	xs		x	x	sx	xs	x	x		sx	s				sx	xs							x	s	21
20	14	14	16	15	19	12	3	10	9	14	0	0	1	0	5	1	3	10	0	0	6	1	0	0	1	0	x
0	3	0	2	3	0	7	9	3	2	6	0	1	0	0	3	0	3	1	0	0	0	1	2	0	0	0	xs
0	3	2	0	0	0	0	4	1	6	0	1	8	7	0	0	3	7	2	0	0	0	0	0	0	2	0	sx
0	0	1	0	1	0	1	2	2	2	0	2	11	11	3	4	4	2	0	1	2	1	0	1	1	1	1	s

GOALKEEPERS	CS	CCS
Cairney	7	3

x/c/t - Played full 90 minutes
xs/cs/ts - Substituted off
sx/sc/st - Substituted on
s/cn/tn - Non-playing sub

MAIDSTONE UNITED MATCH RESULTS 2020-21

Date	Comp	H/A	Opponents	Att:	Result	Goalscorers	Pos
Oct 3	**FAC2Q**	**A**	**Hendon**	**310**	**W 1 - 0**	**Olutade 76**	
6	NLS	H	Welling United		W 2 - 1	Rendell 62 Seaman 85	6
10	NLS	A	Havant & Waterlooville		D 2 - 2	Porter 90+2 Ellul 90+5	5
13	**FAC3Q**	**A**	**Wimborne Town**	**323**	**D 2 - 2**	**Seaman 29 52 (Lost 1-3 on pens)**	
17	NLS	H	Hemel Hempstead Town		W 4 - 1	Corne 23 Brown 24 Luque 28 Chesmain 86	4
24	NLS	A	Chelmsford City		L 0 - 1		5
31	NLS	H	Concord Rangers		W 6 - 0	Luque 11 Amaluzor 45 68 Porter 47 Rendell 76 Seaman 85	3
Nov 7	NLS	A	Slough Town		W 3 - 2	Rendell 7 Porter 42 87	2
14	NLS	H	Dartford		L 0 - 2		6
17	NLS	A	Ebbsfleet United		D 0 - 0		7
21	NLS	H	Billericay Town		D 1 - 1	Olutade 7	6
Dec 1	NLS	A	Dorking Wanderers		D 2 - 2	Krasniqi 76 Luque 90	6
19	**FAT2P**	**H**	**Poole Town**		**W 2 - 0**	**Hoyte 61 Olutade 79**	
23	**FAT3P**	**H**	**Frome Town**		**Walkover**		
Jan 9	NLS	A	Hungerford Town		L 1 - 2	Rendell 74	9
12	NLS	A	Eastbourne Borough		W 3 - 2	Seaman 11 Luque 14 Rendell 47	9
16	**FAT4P**	**H**	**Dorking Wanderers**		**W 2 - 1**	**Khan 7 Luque 29**	
19	NLS	H	Braintree Town		L 0 - 2		10
Feb 6	**FAT5P**	**A**	**Hornchurch**		**L 4 - 5**	**Christou 16 (og) Porter 29 59 Rendell 71 (RC 2xY - Ellul 85)**	

Goalcorers	LGE	FAC	FAT	SG	CSG	HAT	PEN	1Q	2Q	45+	3Q	4Q	90+	T
TOTALS	**24**	**3**	**8**			**0**	**0**	**7**	**7**	**1**	**6**	**11**	**3**	**35**
Porter	4		2	4	2				2		2	1	1	6
Rendell	5		1	6	2			1			2	3		6
Luque	4		1	5	2			2	2				1	5
Seaman	3	2		4	1			1	1		1	2		5
Olutade	1	1	1	2	1			1				2		3
Amaluzor	2			1	1					1		1		2
Brown	1			1	1				1					1
Chesmain	1			1	1							1		1
Corne	1			1	1				1					1
Ellul	1			1	1								1	1
Hoyte			1	1	1						1			1
Khan			1	1	1			1						1
Krasniqi	1			1	1							1		1
Opponent			1	1	1			1						1

	Elokobi G	Hoyte G	Khan S	Ellul J	Seaman C (L)	Brown R	Porter G	Corne S	Krasniqi K	Rendell S	Olutade I	Constable R (Gk)	Agboola D	Odusanya D	De Niro P	Amaluzor J	Pattison C	Randell J	Chesmain N	Akanbi I	Luque J	Richefond R	Temelci Z	Johnson B (Gk)	Gench N	Mundle-Smith J (L)	No.
	c	c	c	c		c	sc	c	cs	c	sc	cn	cn	sc	cn	cs	cs	cn									1
	x	x	x	x	x	x	x	x	x	x	s	s	s	s	s												2
	x	x	xs	x	xs	x	x		x	x	sx	s	s	sx	sx	xs											3
n	c	c		c	cs	c	c	c	cs	c	sc	c		sc	sc		cs	cn	cn	cn							4
	x	x		x		x	x	x		x	sx	s	s	xs		xs			sx		xs	sx					5
	x	x		x	xs	x	x	x		x	sx	s		xs		sx			s		xs		sx				6
	x	x	xs	x	sx	xs	xs	x		x	s	x		sx		x			sx		x			s			7
	x	x		x	sx		x	x	s	xs	sxs	x		x		x			x	sx	xs						8
	x	x		x	sx		x	x	s	x	s	x		xs		x			x		xs		sx				9
	x	x		x	xs		x	x	x	xs	sx	x		sx		x			x		s		s				10
	x	x		x	x	s		x	x		xs	x		s		x			x	sx	xs		sx				11
	x	x		x	x	s	x	xs	x	x	s	s				xs			x		sx		sx				12
	t	t		t			ts	t	t		st	tn	tn	tn		ts	st		t	ts	t		st		tn		13
	x	x		x	x		xs	x	x	x	sx	s				xs	sx		xs		sx		s				14
	x	x	s	x	x		xs	x	sx	x	s	s				sx			xs		x		x				15
n	t	t	ts		ts		ts	st		t	tn	t		t		tn	st		t	tn	t		st			t	16
	x	x	xs		x		x	x	s	x	sx	x				xs	sx		s				x	s		x	17
n		t	t	t	t		t	ts	st	t	tn	t		tn		st	ts		ts	st			tn			t	18
9	17	18	3	16	7	6	11	14	7	14	0	9	0	2	0	5	0	0	7	0	4	0	2	0	0	3	x
0	0	0	4	0	5	1	5	2	2	2	1	0	0	3	0	7	3	0	3	1	5	0	0	0	0	0	xs
0	0	0	0	0	3	0	1	1	2	0	9	0	0	5	2	3	4	0	2	3	2	1	6	0	0	0	sx
7	0	0	1	0	0	2	0	0	3	0	7	9	5	4	2	1	0	2	3	2	1	0	3	2	1	0	s

GOALKEEPERS	CS	CCS
Constable	2	1
Lewington	2	1

x/c/t - Played full 90 minutes
xs/cs/ts - Substituted off
sx/sc/st - Substituted on
s/cn/tn - Non-playing sub

OXFORD CITY MATCH RESULTS 2020-21

Date	Comp	H/A	Opponents	Att:	Result	Goalscorers	Pos
Oct 3	**FAC2Q**	**A**	**Royal Wootton Bassett**		**W 2 - 1**	**Matsuzaka 67 Bancroft 87**	
6	NLS	H	Bath City		W 2 - 0	Ashby 38 90+5	4
10	NLS	A	Chelmsford City		D 1 - 1	Roberts 22	4
13	**FAC3Q**	**H**	**Tamworth**		**W 6 - 1**	**Coyle 32 Roberts 42 56 (pen) Bradbury 62 71 Ashby 84**	
17	NLS	H	Tonbridge Angels		W 4 - 0	Bradbury 10 Roberts 18 28 Benyon 85	3
24	**FAC4Q**	**A**	**Weymouth**		**W 3 - 2**	**Roberts 13 (pen) Ashby 15 Hall 88**	
31	NLS	H	Hampton & Richmond B.		L 0 - 2		8
Nov 9	**FAC1P**	**H**	**Northampton Town**		**W 2 - 1**	**Roberts 12 Ashby 68 (pen)**	
14	NLS	A	Havant & Waterlooville		L 1 - 2	Bradbury 10	11
17	NLS	H	Chippenham Town		D 1 - 1	Drewe 30	12
21	NLS	H	Eastbourne Borough		D 1 - 1	Ashby 57 (pen)	13
24	NLS	A	Dorking Wanderers		L 2 - 3	Hall 15 Roberts 77	13
29	**FAC2P**	**A**	**Shrewsbury Town**		**L 0 - 1**	**(aet)**	
Dec 1	NLS	A	Hungerford Town		W 4 - 1	Roberts 9 39 Ashby 57 (pen) Benyon 85	11
8	NLS	H	St Albans City		D 0 - 0		10
12	NLS	H	Dulwich Hamlet		W 1 - 0	Drewe 60	9
15	**FAT2P**	**A**	**Welling United**		**W 2 - 0**	**Owusu 39 58 (Received a walkover in the Third Round v Truro City)**	
Jan 6	NLS	A	Billericay Town		W 3 - 1	McEachran 54 Roberts 72 81	8
9	NLS	H	Welling United		D 0 - 0		7
12	NLS	A	Braintree Town		W 2 - 1	Roberts 33 Colye 42	5
16	**FAT4P**	**H**	**Haringey Borough**		**W 4 - 2**	**Oastler 44 Bancroft 68 72 Benyon 76**	
19	NLS	A	Hemel Hempstead Town		W 5 - 3	Martinez 45+1 Fleet 58 Bradbury 73 75 Bancroft 89	5
Feb 6	**FAT5P**	**H**	**Peterborough Sports**		**W 2 - 0**	**Roberts 18 Fleet 51**	
9	NLS	H	Hungerford Town		W 4 - 0	Bradbury 35 48 Potter 63 Roberts 89	4
13	NLS	H	Chelmsford City		W 4 - 1	Roberts 13 32 Bradbury 28 54	3
27	**FATQF**	**A**	**Notts County**		**L 1 - 3**	**Golden 26 (og)**	

Goalcorers	LGE	FAC	FAT	SG	CSG	HAT	PEN	1Q	2Q	45+	3Q	4Q	90+	T
TOTALS	35	13	9			0	5	11	14	1	13	17	1	57
Roberts	12	4	1	12	4		2	7	5		1	4		17
Bradbury	8	2		6	2			2	2		3	3		10
Ashby	4	3		6	1		3	1	1		2	2	1	7
Bancroft	1	1	2	3	2							4		4
Benyon	2		1	3	1							3		3
Coyle	1	1		2	1				2					2
Drewe	2			2	1				1		1			2
Fleet	1		1	2	2						2			2
Hall	1	1		2	1			1				1		2
Owusu			2	1	1				1		1			2
Martinez	1			1	1					1				1
Matsuzaka		1		1	1						1			1
McEachran	1			1	1						1			1
Oastler			1	1	1				1					1
Opponent			1	1	1				1					1
Potter	1			1	1						1			1

No.	Hall L	Matsuzaka D	Oastler J	Drewe A (L)	Fleet R	Ashby J	Coyle L	Roberts J	Bradbury H	Benyon E	Bancroft J	McEachran Z	Owusu N	Gough E (Gk)	Wright J	Naylor D	Gubbins J	George A	Fernandez L (L)	Martinez P (L)	Grantham A (Gk)	Gerring B (L)	Potter A	Cartwright S (L)	Elechi M (L)
1	c	c	c	c	c	c	c	c	c	cs	sc	cn	cn	cn	cn	cn									
2	x	x	x	x	x	x	x	xs	sx	xs	sx				s	s	x	s							
3	xs	x	xs	x	x	x	xs	x	x		s	sx	sx		s		x		sx						
4	c	c	c	c	c	c	cs	cs	c	cn	sc	cs	sc	cn	cn			cn	sc						
5	x	xs	x	x	x	x	x	xs	xs	sx	s	sx	s				x		sx						
6	c		c	c	c	c	cs	c	cs	sc	sc	cs	sc	cn		cn		cn	c	cn					
7	x		x	x	xs	x	x	x	xs	sx	s	sx	s				xs		x	sx					
8	c		c	c	c	c	cs	c	cs	sc	cn	cs	sc						c	sc	cn				
9	xs		x	x	x	x	xs	x	xs	sx	sx	x	sx				s		x	s					
10	x		x	x	x	x	xs	sx	sx	xs	s	x	sx				x		s	xs					
11	xs		x	x	x	x	xs	x	xs	sx	s	x	sx				sx		x	s					
12	xs		x	x	x	x	sx	x	sx		sx	x	xs				xs	s	s	x					
13	c	sc		c	c	c	cs	c	sc	sc	sc	cs	cs					cn	c	cn	cn	cs			
14	x		x	x	x	xs	sx	xs	s	x	s	xs	sx						x	sx		x			
15	x	s	x	x	x	x	xs		sx	xs	sx	x	sx						xs	s		x			
16	x	sx	x	x	x	x	sx		xs	x	s	xs	s						x		s	x			
17	t	t	t	t	t	ts	st		tn	t	ts	st	ts						tn	t	tn		st		
18	x	x	x	x	x		sx	xs	s	x	sx	xs	xs					s		x			sx		
19	x	xs	x	x	x	s	x	x	sx	x		x						s		xs	s		sx		
20	x		x	x	x	x	xs	x	x	sx	s	sx	xs							s	s			x	
21	t		t	t	t	t	t	t	ts	st	st	ts						s		st	s			ts	
22			x	x	x	x	xs	x	x		sx	x			s					xs	s		sx	x	
23		t	t	t	t	t	st	t	ts	st			tn					tn	t	tn	tn		ts	tn	t
24		xs	x	x	x	xs	sx	x	x	s			s						x	sx			xs	sx	x
25	s	x	x	x	x	xs	s	x	xs	sx			sx						x	sx			xs		x
26	tn	t	t	t	ts	t	tn	t	ts	st		st	st						ts	tn			t	tn	t
x	17	9	24	26	24	20	6	17	6	5	0	7	0	0	0	0	4	0	11	3	0	3	1	2	4
xs	4	3	1	0	2	4	11	5	11	4	1	8	5	0	0	0	2	0	2	3	0	1	3	1	0
sx	0	2	0	0	0	0	7	1	6	12	11	6	11	0	0	0	1	0	3	6	0	0	4	1	0
s	2	1	0	0	0	1	2	0	3	2	9	1	6	3	5	3	1	9	3	8	9	0	0	2	0

GOALKEEPERS	CS	CCS
Dudzinski	8	3

x/c/t - Played full 90 minutes
xs/cs/ts - Substituted off
sx/sc/st - Substituted on
s/cn/tn - Non-playing sub

SLOUGH TOWN MATCH RESULTS 2020-21

Date	Comp	H/A	Opponents	Att:	Result	Goalscorers	Pos
Oct 3	**FAC2Q**	**A**	**Dartford**		**W 1 - 0**	**McKnight 90+2 (pen)**	
6	NLS	H	Hemel Hempstead Town		**W** 1 - 0	Hodges 45+1	8
10	NLS	A	Dorking Wanderers		L 1 - 3	Harris 23 (og)	11
13	**FAC3Q**	**H**	**Bath City**		**L 0 - 1**		
17	NLS	H	Welling United		D 4 - 4	Bird 22 Lench 70 Harris 90+1 Worsfold 90+4	11
31	NLS	H	Bath City		**W** 2 - 1	McGlip 84 Worsfold 90+1	9
Nov 7	NLS	H	Maidstone United		L 2 - 3	Hodges 3 55	10
14	NLS	A	Billericay Town		L 0 - 2		12
17	NLS	H	Hungerford Town		L 1 - 3	Roberts 32	14
21	NLS	A	Dartford		L 0 - 2		16
Dec 5	NLS	A	Chippenham Town		D 2 - 2	Harris B 76 Togwell L 90+1	17
9	NLS	A	Havant & Waterlooville		D 0 - 0		16
15	**FAT2P**	**H**	**Dartford**		**D 2 - 2**	**Jackman 39 Harris W 49 (Lost 5-6 on pens)**	
Jan 16	NLS	H	Braintree Town		**W** 3 - 2	Harris W 39 Harris B 57 Bird 90+3	18
19	NLS	H	Ebbsfleet United		L 0 - 2		20

Goalcorers	LGE	FAC	FAT	SG	CSG	HAT	PEN	1Q	2Q	45+	3Q	4Q	90+	T
TOTALS	**16**	**1**	**2**			**0**	**0**	**2**	**4**	**1**	**2**	**4**	**6**	**19**
Harris W	2		1	3	2				1		1		1	3
Hodges	3			2	1			1		1		1		3
Bird	2			2	1			1					1	2
Harris B	2			2	1						1	1		2
Worsfold	2			2	2								2	2
Jackman			1	1	1				1					1
Lench	1			1	1							1		1
McGlip	1			1	1							1		1
McKnight		1		1	1								1	1

	LGE	FAC	FAT	SG	CSG	HAT	PEN	1Q	2Q	45+	3Q	4Q	90+	T
Opponents	1			1	1				1					1
Roberts	1			1	1				1					1
Togwell L	1			1	1								1	1

No.	Jackman J	Lomas L (L)	Togwell S	Worsfold M	Lench M	Harris B	Kuhl A	Bird R	McKnight J	Hodges P	Togwell L	Harris W	Edegbe M	Okorogheye A	Fraser S	Gouth E	McGlip C	Roberts D	Davies F (Gk)	Hollis G	Linton M (L)	Nisbet M	Flood C	Moore S	Davies S
1	c	c	c	cs	c	cs	c	cs	c	c	sc	sc	cn	sc	cn										
2	x	x	x	s	x	xs	sx	sx	x	x	x	xs	s		x	s									
3	s	x	x	xs	x		x	x	sx	sx	xs	xs			x		x	sx	s						
4	c	c	c	c			c	cs	c	cs		sc	cn		sc	cn	cs	c		cn					
5	x	x	xs	sx	sx		x	x	sx	xs	s	x	s		x		xs	x							
6	x	x	x	x	x		xs	s	xs	sx	x	s			sx		x	xs			sx				
7	x	x	x	x	x		x	sx	s	xs	xs	sx			s		x	xs			sx				
8	xs	x	x	x	sx		x	x	s	xs	sx	x			s		xs	sx			x				
9	s	x	x	xs	x		xs	s		sx	x	x			sx		xs	x			x	sx			
10	x	s	x	sx	sx		x			x	x	sx	s		xs			x		xs	xs	x			
11	x	x	x	x	x	sxs	s	x	sx	xs	x	xs			s			sx		x					
12	x	x	x	s	x		x	x	sx	x	x	xs			sx					xs			s	s	
13	t	t	t		ts		t	t	st	ts	t	ts	tn		st			st		t					
14	x	x	x	xs		xs	x	x	s	s	x	x					sx	sx				x			s
15	x	x	x			x	x	xs	sx	sx	xs	x			s		xs	sx				x			s
X	12	14	14	5	8	1	11	7	3	4	8	5	0	0	3	0	3	4	0	2	2	3	0	0	0
XS	1	0	1	4	1	3	2	3	1	6	3	5	0	0	1	0	5	2	0	2	1	0	0	0	0
SX	0	0	0	2	3	1	1	2	6	4	2	4	0	1	5	0	1	6	0	0	2	1	0	0	0
S	2	1	0	2	0	0	1	2	3	1	1	1	6	0	5	2	0	0	1	1	0	0	1	1	2

GOALKEEPERS	CS	CCS
Turner	3	2

x/c/t - Played full 90 minutes
xs/cs/ts - Substituted off
sx/sc/st - Substituted on
s/cn/tn - Non-playing sub

ST ALBANS CITY MATCH RESULTS 2020-21

Date	Comp	H/A	Opponents	Att:	Result	Goalscorers	Pos
Oct 3	**FAC2Q**	**H**	**Hitchin Town**		**W 5 - 0**	**Jeffers 12 19 19 (pen) Banton 87 Chidyausiku 90+4**	
6	NLS	H	Hampton & Richmond B.		W 1 - 0	Nwabuokei 75	9
10	NLS	A	Concord Rangers		D 1 - 1	Diedhiou 78	6
13	**FAC3Q**	**H**	**Mickleover**		**D 1 - 1**	**Kaloczi 22**	
17	NLS	H	Ebbsfleet United		W 3 - 2	Weiss 38 Jeffers 40 58	5
24	**FAC4Q**	**A**	**Bishop's Stortford**	**600**	**L 0 - 2**		
31	NLS	H	Chippenham Town		W 3 - 0	Banton 15 Weiss 44 Jeffers 90+4	4
Nov 10	NLS	H	Braintree Town		W 2 - 1	Banton 64 Weiss 73	4
17	NLS	A	Dartford		W 1 - 0	Banton 90 (pen)	4
21	NLS	H	Hungerford Town		D 0 - 0		4
28	NLS	A	Eastbourne Town		W 1 - 0	Jeffers 22	3
Dec 5	NLS	A	Hampton & Richmond B.	97	W 2 - 0	Weiss 45 Nwabuokei 90+7	3
8	NLS	A	Oxford City		D 0 - 0		2
12	NLS	H	Tonbridge Angels	700	W 3 - 1	Weiss 17 Miles 70 (og) Jeffers 77 (pen)	1
15	**FAT2P**	**H**	**Cray Wanderers**	**174**	**W 3 - 0**	**Wiltshire 49 Banton 61 Weiss 86**	
19	**FAT3P**	**H**	**Sutton United**		**L 0 - 2**		
Jan 9	NLS	H	Chelmsford City		L 0 - 2		4
12	NLS	A	Welling United		W 2 - 0	Jeffers 30 45 (pen)	3
Feb 6	NLS	A	Billericay Town		D 2 - 2	Jeffers 58 Nwabuokei 67	3
16	NLS	H	Hemel Hempstead Town		D 1 - 1	Nwabuokei 58	5

Goalcorers	LGE	FAC	FAT	SG	CSG	HAT	PEN	1Q	2Q	45+	3Q	4Q	90+	T
TOTALS	22	6	3			1	4	6	5	2	6	7	4	31
Jeffers	8	3		7	2	1	3	3	3	1	2	1	1	11
Weiss	5		1	6	2			1	2	1		2		6
Banton	3	1	1	5	3		1	1			1	1	1	5
Nwabuokei	4			4	2						2	1	1	4
Chidyausiku		1		1	1								1	1
Diedhiou	1			1	1							1		1
Kaloczi		1		1	1			1						1
Opponent	1			1	1							1		1
Wiltshire			1	1	1						1			1

No.	Stanley D	Bender T	Mukena J	Warner-Eley L	Nwabuokei S	Noble D	Sundrie M	Jeffers S	Banton Z	Weiss M	Wiltshire K	Diedhiou D	Chidyausiku J	Jackson D (Gk)	Kaloczi J	Clark M	Oluwadara M	de Groot J (Gk)	Onokwai C	Matrevics R (Gk)	Akinola R	Lankshear A	Shakes R	Kinoshi J (D)
1	c	c	c	c	c	cs	c	c	c	cs	sc	sc	sc	cn	cn	cn								
2	x	x	s	x	x		x	xs	x	x	xs	sx	sx		x	s	s							
3	s	x	x	sx	x	sx	x	xs	xs	xs	x	x	sx		x	s								
4	c	c	cn	c	cs	c	cs	c	c	sc	c	cn	sc		c	cn		cn						
5	x	x	x	sx	x		x	xs	xs	xs	x	x	sx			s	s		sx					
6	c	c	c	cn	c		c	cs	cs	cs	c	c	sc	cn	cn	cn			sc	c	sc			
7	s	x	s	x	x		x	x	x	xs	x	sx	s		x	x				x	s			
8		x	sx		x		x	xs	x	xs	x	xs	sx		x	x	s		s		sx			
9	s	x	x			sx	x	xs	x	xs	x	x	sx		x	x			s		s			
10	s	x	x	sx		sx	x	x		xs	x	xs	sx		x	x			s		xs			
11	sx	x	x	sx	x		x	x	x	xs	xs	sx	s		x	xs			s					
12	sx	x	x	sx	x	sx	xs	x	xs	xs	x	s	s		x	x								
13	sx	x		x	x	sx	x	xs	xs	xs	x	s	sx		x	x			s					
14	s	xs		x	xs	sx	x	xs	x	x	x	sx			x	x			sx	s				
15	t		ts	t	t	st	ts	t	t	t	ts	tn			t	st	st		tn	tn		tn		
16	tn		t	ts	t	tn	t	t	t	ts	t	tn			t	t	tn		st	tn	st			
17	x		x	xs		sx	xs	x		xs	x	x	s		x	s					sx		x	sx
18	s		x	x		xs	x	xs		xs	x	sx	sx		x	x					sx		x	s
19		xs	x	sx	x	s	x	x	xs	s	x	s			x	x					sx		x	
20		x	x	s	x		x	x	x	xs	x	s			x	s					sx	s	x	
x	7	14	13	8	14	1	16	11	11	3	16	5	0	0	17	10	0	0	0	2	0	0	4	0
xs	0	2	1	2	2	2	4	9	6	15	3	2	0	0	0	1	0	0	0	0	1	0	0	0
sx	3	0	1	6	0	8	0	0	0	1	1	6	11	0	0	1	1	0	4	0	7	0	0	1
s	7	0	3	2	0	2	0	0	0	1	0	7	4	2	2	8	4	1	6	3	2	2	0	1

OALKEEPERS	CS	CCS
ohnson	9	5
latrevics	1	1

x/c/t - Played full 90 minutes
xs/cs/ts - Substituted off
sx/sc/st - Substituted on
s/cn/tn - Non-playing sub

TONBRIDGE ANGELS MATCH RESULTS 2020-21

Date	Comp	H/A	Opponents	Att:	Result	Goalscorers	Pos
Oct 3	**FAC2Q**	**A**	**Farnborough**	**382**	**W 1 - 0**	**Derry 66**	
6	NLS	A	Billericay Town		**W** 2 - 0	Da Costa 5 Beere 84	5
10	NLS	H	Hungerford Town		L 0 - 2		10
13	**FAC3Q**	**A**	**Chichester City**	**400**	**W 2 - 1**	**Turner 23 65**	
17	NLS	A	Oxford City		L 0 - 4		13
24	**FAC4Q**	**H**	**Taunton Town**		**W 5 - 0**	**Greenhalgh 28 51 Akrofi 42 Splatt 75 Turner 90+3**	
Nov 7	**FAC1P**	**H**	**Bradford City**		**L 0 - 7**		
9	NLS	A	Chelmsford City		**W** 2 - 0	Parkinson 10 Beere 55	13
14	NLS	A	Dorking Wanderers		L 1 - 4	Akrofi 32	15
17	NLS	H	Eastbourne Borough		D 2 - 2	Beere 1 Wood 59	15
21	NLS	A	Ebbsfleet United		**W** 1 - 0	Wood 45+2	11
24	NLS	H	Braintree Town		L 0 - 2		11
28	NLS	H	Hemel Hempstead Town		L 1 - 2	Parkinson 17	12
Dec 1	NLS	H	Concord Rangers		**W** 2 - 0	Parkinson 59 Greenhalgh 90+2	9
12	NLS	A	St Albans City	700	L 1 - 3	Turner 6	14
15	**FAT2P**	**H**	**Hornchuch**		**L 0 - 1**		
Jan 5	NLS	A	Dartford		L 0 - 1		15
12	NLS	H	Chippenham Town		**W** 4 - 0	Turner 8 Da Costa 38 Wood 52 Rush 73	12
Feb 6	NLS	H	Hampton & Richmond B.		L 0 - 3		14

Goalcorers	LGE	FAC	FAT	SG	CSG	HAT	PEN	1Q	2Q	45+	3Q	4Q	90+	T
TOTALS	16	8	0			0	0	6	5	1	7	3	2	24
Turner	2	3		4	1			2	1		1		1	5
Beere	3			3	1			1			1	1		3
Greenhalgh	1	2		2	1				1		1		1	3
Parkinson	3			3	2			2			1			3
Wood	3			3	2					1	2			3
Akrofi	1	1		2	1				2					2
Da Costa	2			2	1			1	1					2
Derry		1		1	1						1			1
Rush	1			1	1							1		1
Splatt		1		1	1							1		1

No.	Shaw J	Folkes J	Campbell K	Parkinson T	Miles S	Bray R	Da Costa K	Beere T	Derry T	Splatt J	Turner J	Greenhalgh B	Parter J	Lee A	McDonald T (Gk)	Theobalds D	Woodhouse L	Lewis N	Williams J	Henly J (Gk)	Akrofi A	Wood T	Phipp T	Kaiser E	Guerfi Z	Crugas-Cowin J	Botley R (Gk)	Twist B	Wootton C	Hanfrey T	Lovatt A (L)	Rush M (L)
1	c	cs	c	cs	c	c	c	c	c	cs	c	sc	sc	sc	cn																	
2	x		x		x	x	xs	xs	x	sx	x	sx	x	x	s	x	s	s														
3	x		x		x	x	xs	x	xs	x	x	sx	x	sx	s	x	s		s													
4	c		c				c			cs	c																					
5	s		x		x	x	sx	xs		s	x	sx	xs	x		x			sx	x	xs	x										
6			c	cs	c	cn	cn	sc		sc	c	c	c	c	cn	c			sc	c	cs	cs										
7	cn	cn	c	cs	c	cn	sc	sc		sc	c	cs	c	c		c		cn		c	c	cs										
8		x	x	x	s	x	xs	xs		s	x	sx	sx	xs		x				x	sx	x										
9	s	x	x	x		x	x	x		sx	sx	s	x			xs			sx	x	xs	xs										
10	s	x	x			x	sx	xs		sx	x	x	x			x			s	x	x	xs										
11	s	x	s		x	x	x			s	x	x	x			x			sx	x	sx	xs	xs									
12	s	x	x	s	x	x	x	x		sx	xs	sx				x			sx	x	xs	xs										
13	s	x	x	x	x	x	x	x		x	sx	xs				sx				x	s	xs		s								
14	s	x	x	x	x	x	xs	sx		s	x	x				x				x	sx	xs		s								
15		x	x	x	x	x				sx	x	x	s			x				x		x			xs	s	s					
16			t	t	t	t				ts	t	t	t							t	st	t			t		tn	tn	tn			
17		s			x	x	sx			s	x	x	x			sx				x	xs	x			xs					x	xs	sx
18		s		sx	x	x	x	xs			x	s	x			sx				x	x	xs								x	xs	sx
19		s		xs	x	x	x	xs		sx	x	s	x			sx				x	x	xs			sx					x		
x	4	8	15	6	15	16	8	5	2	2	16	7	11	4	0	11	0	0	0	15	4	5	0	0	1	0	0	0	0	3	0	0
xs	0	1	0	4	0	0	4	6	1	3	1	2	1	1	0	1	0	0	0	0	5	10	1	0	2	0	0	0	0	0	2	0
sx	0	0	0	1	0	0	4	3	0	8	2	6	2	2	0	4	0	0	5	0	4	0	0	0	1	0	0	0	0	0	0	2
s	8	4	1	1	1	2	1	0	0	5	0	3	1	0	4	0	2	2	2	0	1	0	0	2	0	1	2	1	1	0	0	0

GOALKEEPERS	CS	CCS
Henly	5	1
Shaw	2	2

x/c/t - Played full 90 minutes
xs/cs/ts - Substituted off
sx/sc/st - Substituted on
s/cn/tn - Non-playing sub

WELLING UNITED MATCH RESULTS 2020-21

Date	Comp	H/A	Opponents	Att:	Result	Goalscorers	Pos
Oct 3	**FAC2Q**	**A**	**Sheppey United**	**300**	**L 0 - 2**		
6	NLS	A	Maidstone United		L 1 - 2	Ilic 6	13
17	NLS	A	Slough Town		D 4 - 4	Ilic 3 Akinyemi 25 38 Cook 50	15
31	NLS	A	Eastbourne Borough		L 1 - 2	Ainsworth 19	18
Nov 7	NLS	H	Cheslmford City		L 0 - 4		20
10	NLS	A	Concord Rangers		D 1 - 1	Della Verde 51	19
14	NLS	A	Hemel Hempstead Town		**W** 2 - 1	Shokunbi 36 Della Verde 56	18
17	NLS	H	Billericay Town		D 2 - 2	Cook 37 (pen) Liburd 48	17
Dec 8	NLS	A	Braintree Town		D 1 - 1	Akinyemi 89	19
12	NLS	H	Chippenham Town	611	L 0 - 1		20
15	**FAT2P**	**H**	**Oxford City**		**L 0 - 2**		
Jan 9	NLS	A	Oxford City		D 0 - 0		21
12	NLS	H	St Albans City		L 0 - 2		21
Manager Bradley Quinton is sacked. Steve Lovell is named as his replacement.							
Feb 6	NLS	A	Dartford		D 2 - 2	Della Verde 18 Akinyemi 47 (pen)	21
13	NLS	A	Dorking Wanderers		L 0 - 5		21
16	NLS	H	Ebbsfleet United		**W** 4 - 3	Durojaiye 9 Akinyemi 37 49 (pen) Campbell 86	21

Goalcorers	LGE	FAC	FAT	SG	CSG	HAT	PEN	1Q	2Q	45+	3Q	4Q	90+	T
TOTALS	**18**	**0**	**0**			**0**	**3**	**5**	**5**	**0**	**6**	**2**	**0**	**18**
Akinyemi	6			4	1		2		3		2	1		6
Della Verde	3			3	2			1			2			3
Cook	2			2	1		1		1		1			2
Ilic	2			2	2			2						2
Ainsworth	1			1	1			1						1
Campbell	1			1	1							1		1
Durojaiye	1			1	1			1						1
Liburd	1			1	1						1			1
Shokunbi	1			1	1				1					1

	LGE	FAC	FAT	SG	CSG	HAT	PEN	1Q	2Q	45+	3Q	4Q	90+	T

Charles-Cook R	Green N	Boateng D	McLean R	Beeden L	Danquah R	Ainsworth L	Cook A	Ilic S	Simon K	Liburd R	Azeez L	Akinyemi D	Barrington M	Ryan B	Maja E	Johnson C	Duncan R	Isiaka K	Olagunju M (L)	Hobbs L (L)	Tanimowo A (L)	Headley J (L)	Shokunbi A	Agyemang M	Blackman R (D)	Ward-Cochrane B (L)	Della Verde L (D)	Everitt M (L)	Harness N (Gk) (L)	O'Mara F (L)	Strachan R (L)	Murrell-Williamson R (L)	Taylor J (D)	Mvemba S	Bennett B	Campbell K	Durojaiye O	Oldaker D	Vose D	Hughes D (GK) (L)	Doe S	Gordon Q	No.
				c						c																																	1
x	x	xs	xs	x	x	x	x	x	x	xs	sx	sx	sx	s	s																												2
x	x	x	sx		x	x	x	x	xs	s		x	sx	sx		xs	x	s																									3
x	x				s	xs	xs	x		x		sx	sx				x		x	x	x	xs	sx	s																			4
x	x	x				xs	x	sx		x		xs		s			xs		x	x		sx	s		x	sx																	5
x	x			x		sx	sx	s		xs		sx							x	x	x	s	x		x	xs	xs																6
x	x			x		sx	x	sx		xs		sx							x	x	xs	s	x		x	s	xs																7
x	x			x			x	s		xs	sx	s							x	x		s	x		x	sx	xs	x															8
	x			x		s	x	s		xs		x		s		x		sx	x	x		s	x				x		x														9
				x		s	x	xs		sx	s	x				x		sx	xs	x			x		x		xs	sx	x														10
t	t			t		t	tn	st		tn	st	t	ts	ts		t		st	tn	t			t					ts															11
x	x					sx		s	xs			sx		s		x				s			x		x		x			x	x	xs	x										12
x						xs		s	sx			sx				x				s			x		x		xs			x	x	xs	x	x	sx								13
x						sx	xs					xs				x				x			x				x				x	sx				x	xs	x	sx	s	s		14
x	s					sx	x					xs				x				x			x				x				xs	sx				x	xs	x		s	sx		15
x	x						x					x	s			x							sx				sx				sx	xs				x	x	x	s		x	xs	16
13	11	2	0	8	2	3	9	3	1	3	0	5	0	0	0	8	2	0	6	10	2	0	10	0	7	0	4	1	2	2	3	0	2	1	0	3	1	3	0	0	1	0	x
0	0	1	1	0	0	3	2	1	2	5	0	3	1	1	0	1	1	0	1	0	1	1	0	0	0	1	5	1	0	0	1	3	0	0	0	0	2	0	0	0	0	1	xs
0	0	0	1	0	0	5	1	3	1	1	3	6	3	1	0	0	0	3	0	0	0	1	2	0	0	2	1	1	0	0	1	2	0	0	1	0	0	0	1	0	1	0	sx
0	1	0	0	0	1	2	1	5	0	2	1	1	1	4	1	0	0	1	1	2	0	4	1	1	0	1	0	0	0	0	0	0	0	0	0	0	0	0	1	2	1	0	s

GOALKEEPERS	CS	CCS
Charles-Cook	1	1

x/c/t - Played full 90 minutes
xs/cs/ts - Substituted off
sx/sc/st - Substituted on
s/cn/tn - Non-playing sub

Chesterfield v Weymouth. Photo Bill Wheatcroft.

Chesterfield v Maidenhead United. Photo Bill Wheatcroft.

NATIONAL LEAGUE, NORTH AND SOUTH PLAYERS 2020-21

If a player featured on a team sheet during the 2020-21 season, in the starting 11 or as an unused substitute, then they should be contained within the following pages. 1,882 players were named on team sheets across what was again a shortened season for most clubs.

Eastleigh used the least amount of players during their completed National League season, with only 23 players named over 48 games. Not surprisingly, as the table below shows, nine of the players that lined up in the opening game of the season, also took to the field in their last match.
Meanwhile, Wealdstone named 46 different players over their 46 game season to record the most used. Braintree Town used 53 players in their shortened National South season of 20 matches, the highest by some margin across Step 2.

Appearance details for National League (Step 1 & 2) games, FA Cup and FA Trophy are all included in the players' totals as well as any goals scored or clean sheets registered.
The key for appearances is as follows:
x / c / t = starting 11 (an s after these letters denotes subbed off)
sx / sc / st = sub on
s / cn / tn = unused sub.
Note, there are a few missing line-ups, mainly in the early rounds of the FA Trophy so some players/ clubs totals will be out by one or two.

Also included is the position of the player, their age and club history. Within this section (L) denotes 'On Loan', (Lx2) denotes two loan periods within the same season, (L/P) is a loan move that turned into a permanent one and (D) is signed on a duel registration.

League (Inc P-Offs), FA Cup & FA Trophy	Unbeaten Run	Wins	Consecutive Draws	Loses	No. Managers*	Starters 1st - Last	In the squad 1st - Last	Top Goalscorer
Aldershot Town	4	3	0	3	1	7	10	J Rees - 13
Altrincham	5 (x2)	4	2 (x2)	5	1	7	8	J Hancock - 12
Barnet	4	2 (x2)	0	8	3	3	4	M Petrasso (L) - 10
Boreham Wood	9	5	**7**	2 (x2)	1	7	11	K Tshimanga - 22
Bromley	6 (x3)	4	2 (x3)	2 (x3)	3	7	11	**M Cheek - 25**
Chesterfield	6 (x3)	5	2	4	3	4	4	A Asante - 10
Dagenham & Redbridge	8	**6**	2	3	1	6	9	P McCallum - 18
Dover Athletic (17 games)	2	0	0	5	1	6	12	A Azeez & L Collins - 3
Eastleigh	8	3 (x3)	3	3 (x2)	1	**9**	**14**	T Barnett - 13
FC Halifax Town	6	4	3	2 (x2)	1	6	10	J Hyde - 12
Hartlepool United	16	4	3	3	1	6	10	R Oates - 18
King's Lynn Town	5	2 (x3)	2 (x2)	4 (x3)	1	0	2	A Marriott & K Mitchell - 8
Maidenhead United	5	3	2 (x4)	3 (x2)	1	6	10	D Orsi-Dadamo - 21
Notts County	7	3 (x2)	2	3	2	9	10	K Wootton - 19
Solihull Moors	7	5	0	4	2	6	10	K Hudlin - 12
Stockport County	**18**	5	3	2	2	5	8	A Reid & J Rooney - 21
Sutton United	13	4 (x2)	3	2	1	7	11	I Olaofe (L) - 16
Torquay United	15	**6**	4	2	1	6	11	A Hall - 15
Wealdstone	3 (x2)	3	1	8	2	3	5	J Mendy - 10
Weymouth	2 (x6)	2 (x2)	1	5	1	5	7	A Dallas (L) - 12
Woking	3 (x3)	2 (x4)	3	**10**	1	5	5	M Kretzschmar - 10
Wrexham	7 (x2)	3	2	3 (x2)	1	5	9	L Young - 12
Yeovil Town	3 (x4)	3 (x2)	3	3 (x2)	1	3	5	R Murphy - 15

*Includes caretaker managers.

2020-21 NATIONAL. NORTH & SOUTH PLAYERS

SURNAME	FIRSTNAME	AGE	POSITION	CLUB PLAYED FOR	X	SX	S	Ap	G/Cs
					APPEARANCES				
Acquaye	Ben		Midfielder	Kettering Town		2	4	2	
Kempston R, Kettering									
Adams	Blair	29	Defender	Gateshead (L)	1			1	
Sunderland, Brentford (L), Northampton (L), Coventry (L), Coventry, Notts Co, Mansfield (L), Cambridge U, Hamilton, Hartlepool, South Shields, Gateshead (L)									
Adams	Charlee	26	Midfielder	Dagenham & Redbridge	9	7	6	16	
Birmingham, Lincoln (L), Lincoln (L),Kilmarnock (L), Dagenham & R, Barnet, Dagenham & R									
Adarabioyo	Fisayo	26	Forward	Curzon Ashton			1		
				Altrincham	8	1	1	9	2
Macclesfield, AFC Fylde, NAC (NL), TOP Oss (L), U Craiova (Rom), Curzon A, Altrincham									
Addai	Alex	27	Forward	Maidenhead United (L)	3	3		6	1
				Solihull Moors (L)	9	1	1	10	1
Blackpool (Y), Whitehawk, Grays, Wingate & F (L), Merstham, Cheltenham, Maidenhead (L), Solihull (L)									
Addai	Cory	23	Goalkeeper	Chesterfield (L)	2		1	2	
Coventry (Y), Hendon (L), Telford (L), Barnsley, Chesterfield (L)									
Adebayo-Rowling	Tobi	24	Defender	Ebbsfleet United	20			20	
Brighton, Eastbourne B, Peterborough, Sligo Rovers, Cork City, Bromley, Eastbourne B (L), Eastbourne B, Ebbsfleet									
Adebayo-Smith	Jordan	20	Forward	Sutton United		1	2	1	
Lincoln C, Grantham (L), Boston U (L), Gainsborough T (L), Sutton U									
Adelekan	AJ		Defender	Alfreton Town		1		1	
Redbridge, Walthamstow, Rushall O, Grantham, Alfreton, Stamford (L)									
Adeloye	Tomi	25	Forward	Barnet	11	6	1	17	3
Stoke, Macclesfield (L), Chelmsford, Dover, Welling, Altrincham, FC Utd, Hartlepool, Whitehawk, Dagenham & R, Ebbsfleet, Barnet									
Agboola	David		Defender	Maidstone United			5		
Maidstone									
Aghatise	Jordan		Defender	Dulwich Hamlet	1	1	2	2	
Barnstaple, Kettering, Dulwich H									
Agnew	Liam	26	Midfielder	Blyth Spartans	4	1		5	1
Sunderland (Y), Boston (L), Boston, Harrogate, Boston (L), York (L), Spennymoor (L), Gateshead (L), Blyth S									
Agyemang	Montel	24	Midfielder	Welling United			1		
Leyton O, Grays (L), Malden & T, East Thurrock, Wealdstone, Welling									
Ainsworth	Lionel	33	Midfielder	Welling United	6	5	2	11	1
Watford (Y), Huddersfield, Brentford (L), Shrewsbury, Burton (L), Rotherham, Aldershot (L), Motherwell (L), Motherwell, Plymouth, Bradford (L), Weymouth, Dulwich H, Welling									
Ajakaiye	Daniel	24	Midfielder	Havant & Waterlooville	2	7	6	9	
West Ham (Y), Bromley (Y), Grays (L), Hastings, Havant & W									
Ajayi	Kyle		Forward	Hemel Hempstead Town	8	7	4	15	1
AFC Dunstable, Hemel H									
Ajiboye	David	22	Forward	Sutton United	42	1		43	5
Brighton (Y), Worthing, Sutton U									
Akanbi	Ibrahim	23	Forward	Maidstone United	1	3	2	4	
Crystal P (Y), Guildford, Whyteleafe, Whitehawk, Maidstone									
Akinola	Romeo	22	Midfielder	St Albans City	1	7	2	8	
Mora (Swe), Haringey B, St Albans									
Akinwande	Olufemi	25	Midfielder	Dartford (L)	3	2		5	
Dartford, Colchester, Bishop's S (L), East Thurrock (L), East Thurrock, Concord, Braintree, Billericay T, Stevenage, Dartford (L)									
Akinyemi	Dipo	24	Forward	Welling United	8	6	1	14	6
Stevenage (Y), Aldershot (L), St Albans (L), Dulwich H (L), Dulwich H, Braintree, Welling									
Akrofi	Alex	26	Forward	Tonbridge Angels	9	4	1	13	2
Maidstone, Concord R (L), Hastings, Tonbridge A, Aveley, Tonbridge A									
Al Hussaini	Zaid	21	Midfielder	Weymouth (L)	3	1	3	4	
Derby, Gloucester (L), Hampton & R, Staines, Crawley, Weymouth (L)									
Alabi	James	26	Forward	Bromley	9	31	7	40	8
Stoke, Scunthorpe (L), Mansfield (L), Forest Green (L), Scunthorpe (L), Accrington (L), Ipwsich, Grimsby (L), Chester, Tranmere, Dover (L)Leyton Orient, Eastleigh (L), Bromley									
Alderson	Sam		Midfielder	Hungerford Town			2		
Leyton O, Hungerford,									
Alexander	George		Forward	Concord Rangers		1		1	
Concord R									

Key: X - Started; SX - Sub on; S - Non-playing Sub; Ap - Total Appearances; G/Cs - Total goals/clean sheets.

SURNAME	FIRSTNAME	AGE	POSITION	CLUB	X	SX	S	Ap	G/Cs
Ali	Mahamud	26	Midfielder	Southport	16	1	3	17	1
Northwich V, Curzon A, Southport									
Allan	Tom	26	Defender	Farsley Celtic	18		1	18	3
York (Y), Hucknall (L), Harrogate T (L), Tadcaster A (L), Gateshead, Alfreton, York, Alfreton (L), Farsley C (Lx2), Farsley C									
Allassani	Reise	25	Forward	Dulwich Hamlet	11	6	1	17	2
Crystal Pal (Y), Bromley (L), Dulwich H, Coventry, Ebbsfleet (L), Woking (L), Dulwich H (L), Dulwich H									
Allen	George	26	Defender	Braintree Town	7			7	
Stevenage (Y), Bishop's S (L), Bishop's S, Welling, Bishop's S (L), Canvey I, East Thurrock, Aveley, Braintree									
Allen	Ifeanyi (Iffy)	27	Midfielder	Ebbsfleet United	2	8	7	10	
Barnet, Yeovil, Torquay (L), Aldershot, Wrexham, Bromley, Wealdstone (L), Dulwich H, Braintree, Maidstone, Ebbsfleet									
Allen	Jamie	26	Forward	FC Halifax	23	11		34	5
Fleetwood, AFC Fylde (L), Stalybridge (L), Southport, Dover, Halifax									
Allen	Josh		Goalkeeper	Leamington			2		
Leamington (Y)									
Allen	Luke	28	Midfielder	Dartford	6	5	5	11	1
Tottenham (Y), Cambridge U (Y), Cambridge C (L), Hemel (L), Hemel, St Albans, Tonbridge A, Braintree, Dartford									
Allen	Taylor	21	Forward	Leamington (L)	5	3		8	1
Leicester (Y), Nuneaton (L), Forest GR, Hereford (L), Gloucester (L), Leamington (L)									
Amaluzor (Formerly Nwogu)	Justin	24	Forward	Maidstone United	12	3	1	15	2
Dartford (Y), Barnet, Hayes & Y (L), Hemel (L), Hemel (L), Hampton & R (L), Bognor (L), Braintree, Maidstone									
Amantchi	Levi	20	Forward	Darlington		4	1	4	
				Blyth Spartans		4	2		6
Chesterfield (Y), Blyth S (L), Middlesbrough (U23), Darlington, Blyth S									
Amartey	Francis	22	Forward	Braintree Town		1	1	1	
Slough (Y), Hayes & Y, Braintree									
Amate	David		Midfielder	Hampton & Richmond Borough			3		
Wimbledon (Y), Hampton & R (Y), Westfield (L)									
Anderson	Jermaine	25	Midfielder	Aldershot Town	31	3		34	4
Peterborough (Y), Doncaster (L), Bradford C, Aldershot									
Anderson	Jevan	21	Defender	Kettering Town (L)	7		1	7	
Formartine Utd, Burton, Hereford (L), Kettering (L)									
Anderson	Kaiman	24	Forward	Leamington	6	10	1	16	1
Shrewsbury (Y), Telford (L), Halesowen (L), Oxford C (L), Southport, Stourbridge, Leamington									
Anderson	Mark	32	Midfielder	Spennymoor Town	7	6	3	13	2
Fort Lauderdale, North Carolina, Spennymoor									
Anderson	Myles	31	Defender	Weymouth	2	1	3	3	
				Hampton & Richmond Borough (L)	7	1		8	
Leyton Orient, Aberdeen, Blackburn R, Aldershot (L), Exeter, Monza, Chievo, Barrow, Torquay, Chester (L), Chester, Hartlepool, Aldershot (L), Weymouth, Hampton & RB (L)									
Andrews	Alfie			Bath City			1		
Bath (Y)									
Andrews	Jake	23	Midfielder	Torquay United	30	16	5	46	5
Bristol C (Y), Chippenham (L), Cheltenham (L), Torquay (L), Torquay									
Angell	Curtis		Defender	Hungerford Town	18		1	18	
Thatcham, Hungerford									
Angus	Dior	27	Forward	Wrexham	22	2	1	24	6
Solihull, Kidderminster, Worcester (L), Solihull, Stratford, Redditch U, Port Vale, Tamworth (L), Nuneaton (L), Barrow (L), Barrow, Wrexham									
Anson	Adam	24	Defender	Southport	15	2	1	17	1
Wigan Athletic, Macclesfield Town, Wigan Athletic, Chorley, Witton, Southport, Witton (L)									
Antwi	Cameron	19	Midfielder	Southport (L)	2	2		4	
Fulham (Y), Blackpool, Southport (L)									
Aplin	Kieren	21	Midfielder	Gateshead	1		2	1	
Newcastle U (Y), North Shields, Gateshead									
Archer	Cameron	19	Forward	Solihull Moors (L)	11	17	4	28	6
Villa (Y), Solihull M (L)									
Archer	Jordan	27	Forward	Boston United		4	1	4	
				Southport	8	4		12	4
Bedworth United, Stourbridge, Chester, Bury, Maidenhead (L), Southport (L), Port Vale, Stockport (L), Boston U, Southport									
Armson	James	31	Midfielder	Brackley Town	13	6		19	4
Nuneaton, Solihull, Brackley									

Anderson Jevan - Kettering Town.

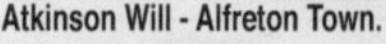
Atkinson Will - Alfreton Town.

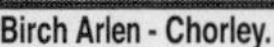
Birch Arlen - Chorley.

Bradley Dan - Alfreton Town.

Key: X - Started; SX - Sub on; S - Non-playing Sub; Ap - Total Appearances; G/Cs - Total goals/clean sheets.

SURNAME	FIRSTNAME	AGE	POSITION	CLUB	APPEARANCES X	SX	S	Ap	G/Cs
Armstrong	Luke	24	Forward	Hartlepool United (L)	32		1	32	15
Middlesbrough (Y), Birmingham, Cowdenbeath, Blyth Sp, Middlesbrough, Gateshead (L), Accrington (L), Salford, Hartlepool (L)									
Armstrong	Rhys	19	Forward	Darlington			4		
Blyth S (Y), Darlington									
Arnold	Nick	30	Defender	Eastbourne Borough	1			1	
Reading, Wycombe (L), Woking, Whitehawk, Aldershot, Wealdstone, Dartford, Eastbourne B									
Arthur	Koby	25	Midfielder	Kidderminster Harriers	2	10	4	12	1
Birmingham, Lincoln (L), Cheltenham (L), Cheltenham (L), Macclesfield, Kidderminster									
Arthurs	Jude	19	Midfielder	Bromley	13	3	3	16	2
Gillingham (U18), Bromley, Ramsgate (L),									
Artus	Frankie	32	Midfielder	Bath City	11		2	11	
Exeter, Brentford, Kettering, Cheltenham, Grimsby, Hereford, Bath									
Asante	Akwasi	28	Forward	Gloucester City	10			10	8
				Chesterfield	22	2		24	10
Birmingham, Northampton (L), Shrewsbury (L), Shrewsbury (L), Kidderminster, Solihull M, Grimsby, Solihull M (L), Tamworth, Chester (L), Chester, Gloucester, Chesterfield									
Ash	Bradley	25	Forward	Chippenham Town	16	2		18	5
Weston-s-Mare, Barnsley, Weston-s-Mare (L), Boreham W (L), Boreham W, Weston-s-Mare (L), Hereford, Chippenham									
Ashby	Josh	25	Midfielder	Oxford City	24		1	24	7
Oxford U (Y), Telford (L), Brackley (L), Oxford C (L), Oxford C									
Ashby-Hammond	Taye	22	Goalkeeper	Maidenhead United (L)	34			34	9
Fulham (Y), Maidenhead (L), Maidenhead (L)									
Ashford	Sam	25	Forward	Woking (L)	15			15	4
Witham, East Thurrock, Concord R, Hemel H, Crawley, Woking (L)									
Ashmore	Nathan	31	Goalkeeper	Boreham Wood	48			48	16
Havant & W, Gosport B, Ebbsfleet, Boreham W (L), Boreham W									
Askew	Jake	19	Goalkeeper	Wealdstone (L)	7	1	27	8	
Chelsea (Y), Wealdstone (L)									
Askew	Josh	23	Defender	Boston United	2		3	2	
				Chester	3	2	1	5	1
Blackburn (Y), Ramsbottom (L), Salford, Stockport (L), Ashton U (L), Curzon A (L), Boston U, Chester									
Asonganyi	Dylan	20	Forward	Chelmsford City (L)	8			8	1
MK Dons (Y), Maidenhead (L), Oxford U, Chelmsford (L)									
Assal	Ayoub	19	Midfielder	Billericay Town (L)		1		1	
Wimbledon (Y), Billericay T (L)									
Atkinson	Ben	25	Midfielder	Farsley Celtic	3	16	2	19	
Huddersfield (Y), Curzon A, Brighouse (L), Farsley C									
Atkinson	Chris	29	Midfielder	Farsley Celtic	21			21	
Huddersfield (Y), Darlington (L), Chesterfield (L), Tranmere (L), Bradford (L), Crewe, Crawley (L), Salford, Farsley C (L), Farsley C									
Atkinson	Dan	25	Goalkeeper	Bradford (Park Avenue)	17			17	4
Leeds (Y), Guiseley, Bradford (PA)									
Atkinson	David	28	Defender	Darlington	6	2	5	8	
Middlesbrough (Y), Hartlepool (L), Carlisle (L), Carlisle, Blyth S, ÍBV (Icel), Blyth S, ÍBV, Blyth S (L), Darlington									
Atkinson	Mike	26	Midfielder	Hungerford Town			1		
York, Farsley, Northallerton, Scarborough, Oxford C, Bracknell, Hungerford									
Atkinson	Will	32	Midfielder	Alfreton Town	13		1	13	
Hull (Y), Port Vale (L), Rochdale (L), Rotherham (L), Plymouth (L), Bradford, Southend, Mansfield, Port Vale, Alfreton									
Austin	Ryan	18	Midfielder	Wrexham			2		
Wrexham (Y)									
Austin	Sam	24	Midfielder	Kidderminster Harriers	17			17	6
Burton, Telford (L), Leamington (L), Kidderminster									
Awe	Sope		Forward	Chorley			2		
Chorley (Y)									
Azaze	Aymen	19	Goalkeeper	Barnet	12	1	25	13	3
Barnet (Y)									
Azeez	Ade	27	Forward	Dover Athletic	13	2		15	3
Charlton, Wycombe (L), Leyton O (L), Torquay (L), Dagenham & R (L), AFC Wimbledon, Partick, Cambridge U, Dover (L)Newport C, Torquay (L), Dover									

2020-21 NATIONAL. NORTH & SOUTH PLAYERS

SURNAME	FIRSTNAME	AGE	POSITION	CLUB PLAYED FOR	X	SX	S	Ap	G/Cs
					APPEARANCES				
Azeez	Lanre	28	Midfielder	Welling United		3	1	3	
Ebbsfleet, Margate, Thamesmead, Maidenhead, VCD, Havant & W, Welling									
Babalola	Temi	20	Forward	Concord Rangers	9	10		19	2
Woodford T, Romford, Brentwood T, Concord R (D)									
Babos	Alex	22	Midfielder	Alfreton Town		1	1	1	
				King's Lynn Town	5	5	3	10	
Derby (Y), Real Union (Spa) (L), FC United (L), Alfreton, King's Lynn									
Baggie	Abdulai	29	Forward	Eastleigh	13	9	12	22	1
Rotherham, Port V, Yeovil, Hayes & Y, Salisbury, Tranmere, Bristol R, Stockport, Poole, Weymouth, Eastleigh									
Baggott	Elkan	18	Defender	King's Lynn Town (L)	7			7	
Ipswich (Y), King's Lynn (L)									
Bahadur	Lewis		Midfielder	Bath City		1	7	1	
Bath (Y)									
Bailey-Nicholls	Khaellem	23	Forward	Gloucester City	1	9	4	10	2
				Kettering Town		2	2	2	
Birmingham (Y), Wrexham, Nantwich, Gloucester, Kettering									
Bainbridge	Jack	23	Defender	Southport	14	3	2	17	
Everton (Y), Derby (U23), Stoke (U23), Swansea, Sunderland (U23), Southport									
Baines	Lewis	22	Defender	Chorley	22	1	1	23	
Fleetwood (Y), Bamber B (L), Ashton U (L), Ashton U (L), Chorley (L), Stockport (L), Chorley									
Bakare	Michael	34	Forward	Hereford FC	4			4	2
Thurrock, Bishop's S, Chelmsford, Macclesfield, Southport, Droylsden (L), Chelmsford, Dover, Tonbridge, Braintree, Welling, Wrexham, Billericay T, Connah's Q, Hereford FC									
Bakayoko	Moussa	24	Midfielder	Dartford	4		1	4	2
				Havant & Waterlooville	1	1		2	
Shirak (Armenia), Derry, Dartford, Havant & W									
Baker-Richardson	Courtney	25	Forward	Barnet (L)	14	3		17	3
Coventry (Y), Tamworth (L), Nuneaton (L), Redditch U, Kettering, Leamington, Swansea (U23), Accrington (L), Barrow, Barnet (L)									
Balanta	Angelo	31	Midfielder	Dagenham & Redbridge	35	5	2	40	13
QPR, Wycombe (L), MK Dons (L), MK Dons (L), MK Dons (L), Yeovil (L), Bristol R, Carlisle, Boreham W, Dagenham & R									
Balarabe	Sadik	29	Forward	Hemel Hempstead Town	2	2	1	4	2
				Dulwich Hamlet	1	2	1	3	
Iraklis P (Gre), Torbalispor (Tur), Salihli BS, Urraca (Spa), Ibiza P, Hemel H, Dulwich H									
Baldwin	Declan		Midfielder	Chorley		1		1	
Chorley (Y)									
Ball	Danny	29	Defender	Bath City	12	2	2	14	
Bristol C (Y), Bath									
Ball	Jimmy	25	Defender	Solihull Moors	30	4		34	10
Bolton (Y), Hyde U (L), Northwich V, Stalybridge, Stockport, Stevenage, Ebbsfleet, Solihull M									
Balogun	Jamal	21	Midfielder	Hemel Hempstead Town	1			1	
Reading (Y), Brighton (YL), Watford (U23), Hemel H									
Bancroft	Jacob	20	Midfielder	Oxford City	1	11	9	12	4
Swindon (Y), Oxford C, Stevenage									
Banton	Jason	28	Midfielder	Braintree Town	2			2	
Arsenal, Blackburn, Liverpool, Leicester, Burton (L), Crystal Palace, Plymouth (L), MK Dons (L), Plymouth, Wycombe, Hartlepool (L), Notts Co (L), Crawley, Partick (L), Woking, Torquay, St Albans (L), Dulwich H (L), Truro (L), Braintree									
Banton	Zane	25	Forward	St Albans City	17			17	5
Luton (Y), Concord R (L), Hemel H (L), Boreham W (L), Hemel H (L), St Albans (L), St Albans									
Barbosa	Diogo	25	Midfielder	Dulwich Hamlet	2	4	4	6	
Torrense (Por), Vilafranquense, Dulwich H									
Barden	Jonathan	28	Defender	Sutton United	40	2	1	42	
ÍBV, Ottawa Fury, St Louis, Sutton U									
Barham	Jack	25	Forward	Dartford	11	4	2	15	2
Heybridge Swifts, Tilbury, Thurrock, Greenwich, Barnet, Bromley (L), Welling (L), Dorking W (LP), Dartford, Maidstone									
Barker	Kyle	20	Midfielder	King's Lynn Town (L)		1		1	
Peterborough (Y), Wrexham (L), King's Lynn (L)									
Barnes	Aaron	24	Defender	Dulwich Hamlet	14	1	3	15	
Charlton, Torquay (L), Colchester, Torquay (L), Dulwich H									

Key: X - Started; SX - Sub on; S - Non-playing Sub; Ap - Total Appearances; G/Cs - Total goals/clean sheets.

SURNAME	FIRSTNAME	AGE	POSITION	CLUB	X	SX	S	Ap	G/Cs
Barnes	Joshua	23	Goalkeeper	Stockport County	2		35	2	
Derby (Y), Mickleover S (L), Eastleigh (L), Bedworth U (L), Farsley C (L), Stockport									
Barnes-Homer	Matthew	35	Forward	AFC Telford United		7	10	7	
Aldershot (Y), Hednesford, Bromsgrove, Willenhall, Wycombe, Kidderminster, Luton (L), Luton, Rochdale (L), Nuneaton, Ostersund (Swe), Macclesfield, Forest GR, Cambridge U, Tamworth (L), Whitehawk, Macclesfield (L), Aldershot, Wilmington (US), Brackley, Telford, Halesowen (D)									
Barnett	Jordan	21	Defender	Notts County (L)	14	1	5	15	1
Oldham (Y), Notts Co (L)									
Barnett	Ryan	21	Midfielder	Gloucester City (L)	1			1	
				Solihull Moors (L)	5			5	1
Shrewsbury (Y), Telford (L), Telford (L), Gloucester (L), Solihull M (L)									
Barnett	Tyrone	35	Forward	Eastleigh	33	5		38	12
Macclesfield, Crawley, Peterborough, Ipswich (L), Bristol C (L), Oxford U (L), Shrewsbury, Southend (L), Wimbledon, Port Vale, Cheltenham (L), Cheltenham, Eastleigh									
Barnum-Bobb	Jazzi	25	Defender	Dartford	15	4	1	19	
Cardiff, Newport Co (L), Newport Co, Torquay (L), Chelmsford, Wrexham, Dartford									
Barratt	Sam	25	Midfielder	Maidenhead United	26	5		31	15
Maidenhead, Southend, Maidenhead									
Barrington	Marcel	25	Forward	Welling United	1	3	1	4	
Stoke (Y), Harrow B (L), Leicester, Nuneaton (L), Bishop's S (L), Walton C, Tooting & M, Margate, Grays, Tooting & M, Hendon, Braintree, Hampton & R, Concord R, Dartford, Welling									
Barrow	Scott	32	Defender	York City	14			14	1
Tamworth, Macclesfield, Newport, Gateshead, York									
Barrows	Ross		Defender	King's Lynn Town	21	1	5	22	2
Halifax (Y), North Ferriby (L), King's Lynn									
Barton	Adam	30	Midfielder	Farsley Celtic	1	3		4	
Preston (Y), Crawley (L), Coventry, Fleetwood (L), Portsmouth, Partick, Dundee U, Connah's Q (L), Wrexham, Farsley C									
Basse	Benjamin	29	Defender	Eastbourne Borough	1			1	
Rennes II, Mantes 78, Fleury 91, Viry, St Maur Lusita, St Genevieve, Eastbourne B									
Bassett	Danny	25	Forward	Hampton & Richmond Borough	2	7	2	9	
				Braintree Town	4	2		6	
Staines, Egham, Hampton RB, Braintree									
Bastock	Paul	51	Goalkeeper	King's Lynn Town			13		
Cambridge U, Bath (L), Cheltenham, Fisher A, Kettering, Aylesbury U (L), Boston U, Scarborough, Dagenham & R, St Albans, Rushden & D, St Albans, Boston U, Worksop, St Albans, Royston T, St Neots, Dunstable, Stamford, Corby, Wisbech (D), Wisbech, Kettering (D), Grantham, Pinchbeck, King's Lynn (Asst Man)									
Batchelor	Richard	33	Midfielder	Leamington		1	1	1	
Romulus, Chasetown, Leamington, Hednesford, Brackley, Worcester, Stafford R, Stourbridge, Highgate, Redditch, Mickleover, Rushall O, Leamington									
Bateman	Matt		Forward	Hemel Hempstead Town	11	5	1	16	2
Berkhamsted, Royston, Hemel H									
Batten	Jack	25	Defender	Bath City	17	1		18	
Bath									
Battersby	Oliver	19	Goalkeeper	Gateshead (L)	2			2	
Sheff Utd (Y), Grimsby (Y), Lincoln U (L), Mickleover S (L), Gateshead (L)									
Baughan	Callum		Defender	Eastleigh			2		
Eastleigh (Y)									
Bauress	Bradley	25	Midfielder	Chester	14	3	5	17	1
Blackburn, Colwyn Bay, Witton, Barrow, Southport, Chester									
Baxter	Jack	20	Midfielder	Chorley (L)			6		
PNE (Y), Chorley (L), Cork (L)									
Bayley	Andre	21	Midfielder	Hungerford Town (L)	6		1	6	
Reading (Y), Waterford, Wycombe, Hungerford (L)									
Bayley	Harrison	31	Midfielder	Hungerford Town	17	3		20	
Reading (Y), Glen Hoddle Acad, Cyprus, Hayes & Y, Didcot, Thatcham, Hungerford									
Beard	Sam		Midfielder	Dorking Wanderers	7	9	6	16	
				Barnet (L)	11			11	
Loxwood, Dorking W, Barnet (L)									

2020-21 NATIONAL. NORTH & SOUTH PLAYERS

SURNAME	FIRSTNAME	AGE	POSITION	CLUB PLAYED FOR	X	SX	S	Ap	G/Cs
Bearwish	Tom	21	Forward	Eastleigh	4	9	20	13	1
Eastleigh (Y)									
Beautyman	Harry	29	Midfielder	Sutton United	43	1		44	12
Leyton O, Sutton U, Welling, Peterborough, Northampton, Stevenage, Sutton U									
Bedford	Joe	23	Midfielder	Dover Athletic		1		1	
Southend, East Thurrock (L), Dover, Dulwich H (L)									
Beeden	Lexus		Defender	Welling United	8			8	
Reading, Welling,									
Beere	Tom	26	Midfielder	Tonbridge Angels	11	3		14	3
Wimbledon (Y), Bishop's S (L), Gateshead (L), Hampton RB, Leatherhead, Tonbridge A									
Bell	Nyal	24	Forward	Stockport County		3	1	3	
				FC Halifax (L)	6	2		8	3
				Altrincham (L)	3	6	1	9	
Rochdale (Y), Chester (L), Gateshead, Chester (L), Alfreton (L), Stockport, FC Halifax (L), Altrincham (L)									
Bellagambi	Giosue	19	Goalkeeper	Ebbsfleet United	2			2	
Ebbsfleet (Y)									
Bencherif	Hamza	33	Midfielder	Guiseley	19			19	1
Lincoln C, Macclesfield, Notts Co, Plymouth, JS Kabylie (Alg), Lincoln C, Halifax, Wrexham, York, Guiseley									
Bender	Thomas	28	Defender	St Albans City	16			16	
Colchester, Accrington (L), Chelmsford (L), Millwall, Welling (L), Dartford, Forest GR, St Albans (L), St Albans									
Benfield	Gerard	23	Goalkeeper	Weymouth	4		30	4	
Wimborne, Salisbury, Weymouth									
Benjamin	Russell	29	Midfielder	Southport	17	2		19	
Southport, Colwyn B (L), Telford, Stockport, Warrington, Southport									
Benn	Jay	19	Defender	FC Halifax		2	14	2	
FC Halifax (Y)									
Bennett	Billy		Midfielder	Welling United		1		1	
Ilkeston T, Welling									
Bennett	Richie	30	Forward	Stockport County	21	16	2	37	4
				Hartlepool United (L)	2	2		4	5
Northwich V, Barrow, Carlisle, Morecambe (L), Port Vale, Stockport, Hartlepool (L)									
Benyon	Elliot	33	Forward	Oxford City	9	12	2	21	3
Torquay (Y), Swindon, Wycombe (L), Southend, Torquay (L), Torquay, Hayes & Y (L), Hayes & Y, Wealdstone, Whitehawk, Leatherhead, Oxford C									
Benyu	Kundai	23	Midfielder	Wealdstone	8	7	2	15	
Ipswich (Y), Aldershot (L), Celtic, Oldham (L), Helsingborg (L), Wealdstone									
Berkeley-Agyepong	Jacob Kwame	24	Midfielder	Dartford	18	2		20	6
Cystal Palace (Yth), Aldershot, Dartford (L), Dartford									
Berry-Hargreaves	Matt		Defender	Hungerford Town	8		4	8	
Wickham W, Hungerford (Y), Oxford U, AFC Rushden & D (L), Banbury (L), Hungerford									
Bettamer	Mohamed	28	Forward	Aldershot Town	28	16		44	12
Watford (Y), London Tigers, Hayes & Y, Hampton & R, Al-Ahli Ben (Libya), Staines, Braintree, Barnet, Welling (L), Hemel H (L), Aldershot									
Bexon	Josh	23	Goalkeeper	Dover Athletic	2		1	2	
Southend (Y), FC Kitzbuhel (Aus) (L), Harlow (L), Harlow, Dover									
Bickerstaff	Jake		Defender	Wrexham	3	2	2	5	
Wrexham (Y)									
Bickley	Lorne		Forward	Kettering Town	3	3	1	6	1
Hartlepool, Kettering									
Bingham	Billy	30	Midfielder	Bromley	29	2		31	
Dagenham & R, Grays (L), Crewe, Gillingham, Bromley									
Bingham	Rakish	27	Forward	Ebbsfleet United	19	3		22	11
Falkirk, Wigan, Mansfield, Hartlepool (L), Hartlepool, Hamilton, Cheltenham, Doncaster, Dundee U, Ebbsfleet									
Binnom-Williams	Jerome	26	Defender	Barnet	23		2	23	
Crystal P (Y), Forest Green (L), Southend (L), Burton (L), Leyton O (L), Peterborough, Chesterfield, Halifax, Barnet									
Birch	Arlen	24	Defender	Chorley	19	3		22	
Everton (Yth), Burnley (Yth), AFC Fylde, Telford, Chorley									
Birchall	Liam		Midfielder	Chorley			1		
Chorley (Y)									

Key: X - Started; SX - Sub on; S - Non-playing Sub; Ap - Total Appearances; G/Cs - Total goals/clean sheets.

SURNAME	FIRSTNAME	AGE	POSITION	CLUB	X	SX	S	Ap	G/Cs
Bircham	Lee	44	Midfielder	Hemel Hempstead Town			2		
Beaconsfield, Wakehurst (L), Ruislip M, Beaconsfield, Fisher A, Greenwich, VCD Ath, Kings Langley, Leverstock, Aylesbury U, Bovingdon (L), Bovingdon (P/Man), Berkhamsted (P/Man), Hemel H (Man)									
Bird	Pierce	22	Defender	Eastleigh	28	2	11	30	
				Boston United (L)	5			5	
Notts Co (Y), Alfreton (L), Boston U (L), Eastleigh, Boston U (L)									
Bird	Ryan	33	Forward	Slough Town	10	2	2	12	2
Burnham, Portsmouth, Cambridge U (L), Cambridge U, Hartlepool (L), Yeovil, Eastleigh, Newport Co, Dover, Maidenhead, Slough									
Blackett	Paul	23	Forward	Blyth Spartans (L)	10			10	6
				Gateshead	1			1	
Newcastle (Y), Sheffield U (Y), Heaton S, Newcastle B, Gateshead, Blyth S (L)									
Blackman	Andre	30	Defender	Dulwich Hamlet	3			3	1
Wimbledon, Celtic, Inverness (L), Plymouth, Dover, Maidenhead, Blackpool, Crawley, Barnet, Southend, Ebbsfleet, Dulwich H									
Blackman	Ryan	26	Midfielder	Welling United (D)	7			7	
				Hemel Hempstead Town (D)		1	2	1	
Tilbury, Witham, Biggleswade, Canvey I, Enfield T, Welling (D), Hemel H (D)									
Blackman	Sam		Midfielder	Concord Rangers	21			21	3
Leatherhead, Margate, Concord R, Dartford, Concord R									
Blackmore	Daniel	19	Defender	Eastbourne Borough	1	8	14	9	
Eastbourne B (Y), Langney W (D)									
Blair	Tom		Midfielder	Eastleigh	10	12	9	22	
Dorchester, Eastleigh									
Blakeman	Adam	29	Midfielder	Spennymoor Town	10		1	10	1
Bolton Wanderers, Hyde United, Ayr United, Southport, Chorley, Spennymoor									
Blanchfield	James	23	Midfielder	Concord Rangers	10	5		15	1
Arsenal (Y), Ipswich (Y),Aldershot (L), Dagenham & R, Concord R									
Blissett	Nathan	30	Forward	Maidenhead United	23	3		26	6
Romulus, Kidderminster, Cambridge U (L), Hednesford (L), Bristol R (L), Bristol R, Tranmere (L), Lincoln (L), Torquay, Plymouth, Macclesfield (L), Macclesfield, Solihull, Maidenhead									
Block	Tommy	21	Midfielder	Woking	15	3	15	18	
Bognor Regis, Hibs, QPR (L), Woking									
Bloomfield	Mason	24	Forward	Hartlepool United	7	17	7	24	2
Dagenham & R (Y), Chatham (L), Erith & Bel (L), Maldon & Tiptree (L), Chelmsford, Billericay, Grays, Witham, Brentwood, Aveley, Dagenham & R, Norwich, Hamilton Ac (L), AFC Fylde (L), Hartlepool									
Blyth	Jacob	28	Forward	Altrincham	1	2		3	
Nuneaton Griff, Bedworth U, Leamington, Leicester, Burton (L), Notts Co (L), Northampton (L), Burton (L), Cambridge U (L), Blackpool (L), Motherwell, Barrow, Macclesfield, Altrincham, Gateshead									
Boateng	Daniel	28	Defender	Welling United	3			3	
Arsenal (Y), Swindon (L), Oxford U (L), Hibernian (L), Sodertaije (Swe), Airdrieonians, Rakow (Pol), Grudziadz, Aerostar (Rom), Welling									
Boden	Scott	31	Forward	Chesterfield	6	5	2	11	3
				Torquay United (L)	14	4	1	18	6
Chesterfield, Macclesfield (L), Macclesfield, Halifax, Newport Co, Inverness CT, Wrexham, Gateshead, Chesterfield, Torquay (L)									
Boldewijn	Enzio	28	Forward	Notts County	32	14	5	46	6
Utrecht, Den Bosch (L), Almere, Crawley, Notts Co									
Bolton	Jack	19	Defender	Southport (L)			1		
Accrington (Y), Southport (L)									
Bolton	Ryan		Defender	Gateshead			1		
Gateshead (Y)									
Bond	Andy	35	Midfielder	AFC Telford United	6	3	2	9	
Crewe, Barrow, Colchester, Crewe (L), Bristol R (L), Chester, Stevenage, Chorley, Crawley, AFC Fylde, York, Telford									
Boness	Danny	23	Goalkeeper	Hemel Hempstead Town	6		12	6	
Hemel H									
Bonner	Thomas	33	Defender	Dartford	22			22	2
Hinckley U, Ilkeston, Dartford, Cambridge U, Dover (L), Ebbsfleet, Dartford									
Boon	Jordan	20	Defender	Spennymoor Town	2	1	1	3	
Bolton (Y), Spennymoor,									
Boot	Ryan	26	Goalkeeper	Solihull Moors	48			48	17
Port Vale (Y), Worcester (L), Norton U (L), Newcastle T (L), Worcester (L), Worcester (L), Macclesfield (L), Solihull M									

Branson Conor - Alfreton Town.

Brindley Richard - Notts Co.

Calveley Mike - Chorley.

Cardwell Harry - Chorley.

Key: X - Started; SX - Sub on; S - Non-playing Sub; Ap - Total Appearances; G/Cs - Total goals/clean sheets.

SURNAME	FIRSTNAME	AGE	POSITION	CLUB	X	SX	S	Ap	G/Cs
Booty	Regan	23	Midfielder	Bradford (Park Avenue)	5	1		6	1
Huddersfield (Y), Aldershot (L), Notts Co, Bradford (PA), Chorley									
Botley	Ryan		Goalkeeper	Tonbridge Angels			1		
Tonbridge A									
Bouzanis	Dean	30	Goalkeeper	Sutton United	46			46	19
Accrington, Oldham, Aris (EL), Carlisle, Western Sydney, Melbourne C, Zwolle (NL), Sutton U									
Bower	Harry		Midfielder	AFC Telford United		1	5	1	
New Saints (Y), Oswestry (L), Telford									
Bower	Mark	41	Goalkeeper	Farsley Celtic			2		
Notts F (Y), Thackley, Yorkshire Am, Eccleshill U, Farsley C									
Bowman	Myles	21	Goalkeeper	Hampton & Richmond Borough			9		
Aldershot, Cove, QPR (Y), Beaconsfield T, Hampton & R, Alresford (D)									
Bowry	Daniel	23	Defender	Wealdstone (L)	1	2	1	3	
Charlton (Y), Hampton & R (L), Cheltenham, Bath (L), Wealdstone (L)									
Boyce	Andrew	31	Defender	Eastleigh	45	1		46	3
Gainsborough, Lincoln, Scunthorpe (L), Scunthorpe, Grimsby (L), Grimsby (L), Hartlepool (L), Notts Co (L), Grimsby, Eastleigh									
Boyes	Harry		Midfielder	Bradford (Park Avenue) (L)	14			14	2
Sheff Utd (Y), Bradford (PA) (L)									
Bradbury	Harvey	22	Forward	Oxford City	17	6	3	23	10
Watford, St Albans (L), Hungerford (L), Oxford U, Hungerford (L), Woking (Lx2), Morecambe, Oxford C									
Bradbury	Thomas	23	Defender	FC Halifax	36		8	36	2
Dundee, York (L), Yeovil, FC Halifax									
Bradley	Alex	22	Midfielder	Yeovil Town (L)	22	2		24	
WBA (Y), Havant & W (L), Burton (L), Lincoln C, Harrogate (L), Yeovil (L)									
Bradley	Daniel	30	Midfielder	Alfreton Town	17			17	1
Aston Villa (Y), Tamworth, Kidderminster, Alfreton, Barnet, Alfreton, AFC Fylde, Kidderminster, AFC Fylde, Alfreton									
Bradley	Lewis	20	Midfielder	Bradford (Park Avenue) (L)		3		3	
Rochdale (Y), Bradford (PA) (L)									
Braham-Barrett	Craig	32	Defender	Dartford	16			16	-
Welling, Grays, Farnborough, Havant & W, Sutton U, Macclesfield, Cheltenham (L), Cheltenham, Ebbsfleet, Woking (L), Whitehawk (L), Dover, Braintree, Welling (L), Chelmsford, Welling, Hemel H, Dartford									
Bramble	TJ	20	Midfielder	Dover Athletic	11	3	1	14	2
Gillingham (Y), Deal (L), East Grinstead (L), Dover									
Branson	Conor	29	Defender	Alfreton Town	17			17	
Barnlsey (Y), Guiseley, Golden Eagles (US), Pittsburgh, Bradford PA, Altrincham, Alfreton									
Bray	Alexander	25	Midfielder	Chippenham Town	8	6	4	14	
Swansea (Y), Plymouth (L), Rotherham (L), Rotherham, Forest GR (L), York (L), Weston-s-Mare (L), Hereford, Chippenham									
Bray	Rian	22	Defender	Tonbridge Angels	16		2	16	
Millwall (Y), Welling (L), Bishop's S (L), Hendon, Hampton & R, Tonbridge A									
Bremner	Jamie		Defender	Gloucester City			4		
Bristol R (Y), Gloucester									
Brennan	Luke	19	Forward	AFC Fylde (L)	2	6		8	
Blackburn (Y), AFC Fylde (L)									
Brennan	Martin	38	Goalkeeper	Boreham Wood			1		
Cambridge U, Welling, Stevenage, Dagenham & R, GK Coach at Spurs, Wycombe, Fulham, Leyton O, Boreham W (Gk Coach)									
Bridge	Jack	25	Midfielder	Concord Rangers	10	1	1	11	1
				Bromley	29			29	3
Southend (Y), Chelmsford (L), Chelmsford (L), Northampton, Carlisle, Concord R, Bromley									
Briggs	Matt		Midfielder	Dorking Wanderers	11	8	1	19	5
Blackburn (Y), Dorking W									
Bright	Lawson		Midfielder	Havant & Waterlooville			2		
Havant & W (Y)									
Brindley	Richard	28	Defender	Notts County	24	3	2	27	
Norwich (Y), Chelmsford, Chesterfield, Rotherham, Scunthorpe (L), Oxford U (L), Colchester (L), Colchester, Barnet, Bromley, Notts Co									
Britton	Louis	20	Forward	Torquay United (L)	3	2		5	1
				Stockport County (L)	1	5	3	6	
Bristol C (Y), Yate (L), Bath (L), Torquay (L)Stockport (L)									
Brodie	Cameron		Midfielder	Dartford		1	1	1	
Dartford (Y)									

2020-21 NATIONAL. NORTH & SOUTH PLAYERS — APPEARANCES

SURNAME	FIRSTNAME	AGE	POSITION	CLUB PLAYED FOR	X	SX	S	Ap	G/Cs
Brooks	Calvin	27	Midfielder	Weymouth	40	1		41	2
Dorchester, Yeovil, Weymouth (L), Weymouth									
Brooks	Tiernan	18	Goalkeeper	Notts County			1		
Notts Co (Y)									
Brown	Alex	22	Defender	King's Lynn Town	17			17	
Buxton, King's Lynn									
Brown	Cole	23	Forward	Hampton & Richmond Borough	2		2	2	
Hayes & Y, Hendon, Walton C, Hampton & R									
Brown	Demetri		Forward	Hereford FC		2		2	
Sutton Coldfield, AFC Wulfruniuns, Tividale, Hednesford, Worcester, Hereford FC									
Brown	Kai	20	Forward	Dagenham & Redbridge (L)	3		5	3	
Ipswich (Y), Dagenham & R (L)									
Brown	Matt	31	Defender	York City	14	1		15	
Manchester C, Chesterfield, Southport (L), Chester (L), Chester, Halifax, York									
Brown	Raphe		Defender	Maidstone United	7		2	7	1
Herne Bay, VCD Ath, Herne Bay, Maidstone									
Brown	Sebastian	31	Goalkeeper	Sutton United			1		
AFC Wimbledon, Woking (L), Bromley, Whitehawk (L), Hampton & R, Whitehawk, Hampton & R, Sutton U									
Brown	Wayne	32	Midfielder	Sutton United			4		
Fulham (Y), Brentford (L), TPS (Fin) (L), Bristol R (L), Bristol R, TPS, SLK Seinajoki, Newcastle (Aus), Sutton U									
Browne	Rhys	25	Midfielder	Wealdstone		1		1	
				Sutton United	1	13	6	14	
Aldershot, Grimsby, Macclesfield (L), Yeovil, Port Vale, Wealdstone, Sutton U									
Brundle	Mitch	26	Midfielder	Dagenham & Redbridge	20			20	5
Yeovil, Bristol C, Cheltenham, Braintree, Hemel H (L), Gateshead, Dover, Dagenham & R									
Brunt	Lewis	20	Midfielder	Gloucester City (L)	7			7	1
Aston Villa (Y), Gloucester (L), Gloucester (L)									
Brunt	Ryan	28	Forward	Chippenham Town	5			5	
Stoke (Y), Nantwich (L), Luton (L), Tranmere (L), Leyton O (L), Bristol R (L), Bristol R, York (L), Stevenage (L), Plymouth (L), Plymouth, Exeter, Bath, Chippenham									
Bruton	Harrison	18	Goalkeeper	Weymouth			1		
Weymouth (Y), Portland (D)									
Brynn	Solomon	20	Goalkeeper	Darlington (L)	1			1	
Middlesbrough (Y), Darlington (L)									
Brzozowski	Marcin	22	Goalkeeper	Billericay Town (L)	1			1	
				Torquay United (L)	1		1	1	
QPR, Yeovil (L), Braintree (L), Billericay T (L), Torquay (L)									
Buchanan	David	38	Defender	Chesterfield	12		1	12	
Bury, Hamilton, Tranmere, PNE, Northampton, Chesterfield									
Buddle	Nathan	27	Defender	Spennymoor Town	11		6	11	1
Hartlepool (Y), Blyth S, Carlisle, Gateshead, Blyth S, Spennymoor									
Bugiel	Omar	26	Forward	Sutton United	36	4		40	6
Forest Green Rovers, Bromley (L), Bromley, Sutton U									
Bunn	Harry	28	Forward	York City	9	4		13	3
Man City (Y), Rochdale (L), Preston (L), Oldham (L), Crewe (L), Sheff Utd (L), Huddersfield (L/P), Bury, Southend (L), Kilmarnock, York									
Bunney	Joe	27	Defender	Hartlepool United	3	2	3	5	
Stockport, Rochdale, Northampton, Blackpool (L), Rochdale (L), Bolton, Matlock, Hartlepool									
Burgess	Luke	22	Midfielder	AFC Fylde	4		1	4	3
Wigan (Y), Chorley (L), Barrow (L), Salford, AFC Fylde (L)									
Burke	Harrison	18	Defender	Chester		1	1	1	
Chester (Y)									
Burke	Luke	23	Defender	AFC Fylde	19		1	19	1
Wigan Athletic, Barrow, AFC Fylde (L), AFC Fylde									
Burke	Ryan	20	Defender	Yeovil Town (L)	3	2	6	5	
Birmingham (Y), Yeovil (L)									
Burns	Harry		Midfielder	Weymouth			1		
Weymouth (Y)									
Burroughs	Jack	20	Midfielder	Gloucester City (L)	5	1		6	1
Coventry (Y), Gloucester (L)									

Key: X - Started; SX - Sub on; S - Non-playing Sub; Ap - Total Appearances; G/Cs - Total goals/clean sheets.

SURNAME	FIRSTNAME	AGE	POSITION	CLUB	X	SX	S	Ap	G/Cs
Burrow	Jordan	28	Forward	Boston United	16	1		17	5
Chesterfield, Morecambe, Stevenage, Lincoln, Halifax, Gateshead, York, Boston U									
Buse	Matt	23	Midfielder	Torquay United	7	9	14	16	
				Bath City (L)	2			2	
Yeovil (Y), Weymouth, Taunton, Gosport (L), Torquay, Bath (L)									
Bush	Chris	29	Defender	Bromley	41			41	1
Brentford, Wimbledon (L), Wimbledon, Gateshead, Hereford, Welling, Lincoln, Chelmsford, Ebbsfleet, Bromley									
Butlin	Joey	28	Forward	Hereford FC	5			5	1
Walsall, Solihull (L), Hednesford, Chasetown, Hereford									
Butroid	Lewis	22	Defender	Hereford FC (L)	2			2	
Scunthorpe (Y), Spennymoor (L), Hereford (L)									
Butterfield	Milan	23	Midfielder	Chesterfield	7	2	1	9	1
				Guiseley (L)	4			4	
Walsall (Y), Leamington (L), Kidderminster, Chesterfield, Guiseley (L)									
Bycroft	Jack	19	Goalkeeper	Weymouth (L)	15		1	15	
Southampton (Y), Weymouth (L)									
Byrne	Jack		Defender	AFC Fylde		1	5	1	
AFC Fylde (Y)									
Byrne	Jack	31	Forward	AFC Telford United	19			19	1
Redditch, Kidderminster, Solihull, Brackley, Nuneaton, Telford U									
Byrne	Nathan			Chippenham Town			1		
Taunton (Y), Chippenham (Y)									
Byrne	Neill	28	Defender	FC Halifax	43			43	2
Nottingham Forest, Rochdale, Barrow (L), Southport (L), Telford, Macclesfield, Gateshead, AFC Fylde, FC Halifax									
Byrne	Shane	28	Midfielder	Brackley Town	20			20	7
Leicester (Y), Bury (L), Bury, Bray W, Corby, Nuneaton, Brackley									
Byrom	Joel	34	Midfielder	Farsley Celtic	4			4	
Northwich V, Stevenage, Preston, Oldham (L), Northampton (L/P), Mansfield, Stevenage, Farsley C									
Cain	Michael	27	Defender	Blyth Spartans	7	3		10	
Luton (Y), Leicester, Mansfield (L), Walsall (L), Blackpool (L), Whitehawk, Hemel H, Hitchin, Blyth S									
Cairney	Luke	29	Goalkeeper	Hungerford Town	20			20	7
Army, Poole, Hungerford									
Callan	James		Goalkeeper	Barnet		1	20	1	
Barnet (Y)									
Callan-McFadden	Kyle	26	Defender	King's Lynn Town	34			34	
Norwich (Y), Orlando City B, Sligo Rovers, King's Lynn									
Calveley	Mike	22	Midfielder	Chorley	21		2	21	3
Port Vale (Y), Nuneaton (L), Curzon A, Chorley									
Cameron	Adam		Goalkeeper	Gateshead			6		
Newcastle (Y), Sunderland (U18/U23), Gateshead (Y)									
Cameron	Declan		Midfielder	Braintree Town			4		
Braintree									
Cameron	Kyle	24	Defender	Torquay United	30	4		34	3
Newcastle (Y), York (L), Newport Co (L), Queen OTS (L), Torquay									
Cameron	Nathan	29	Defender	Solihull Moors	15		3	15	1
Coventry (Y), Northampton (L), Bury, Macclesfield, Wigan, Solihull M									
Camp	Brennan	20	Defender	Weymouth (L)	32	2	3	34	1
Bournemouth (Y), Weymouth (L), Weymouth (L)									
Campbell	Adam	26	Forward	Darlington	16	3	1	19	6
Newcastle (Y), Carlisle (L), St Mirren (L), Fleetwood (L), Hartlepool (L), Gateshead (L), Notts Co, Morecambe, Carlisle (L), Darlington									
Campbell	Kristian		Defender	Tonbridge Angels	15		1	15	
				Welling United	3			3	1
Merstham, Bromley, Bognor R (Lx2), Eastbourne B, Tonbridge A, Welling									
Campbell	Tahvon	24	Forward	Gloucester City (L)	3	3	1	6	2
				FC Halifax (L)	9	6		15	1
West Brom, Kidderminster (L), Yeovil (L), Yeovil (L), Notts Co (L), Solihull M (L), Forest GR (L), Forest GR, Gillingham (L), Cheltenham, Gloucester (L), Halifax (L)									
Campbell	Tate	18	Midfielder	Bromley (L)		5	5	5	1
Birmingham (Y), Bromley (L)									

2020-21 NATIONAL. NORTH & SOUTH PLAYERS

SURNAME	FIRSTNAME	AGE	POSITION	CLUB PLAYED FOR	X	SX	S	Ap	G/Cs
					APPEARANCES				
Camwell	Chris	22	Defender	Hereford FC	14	2	4	16	3
Coventry (Y), Solihull M (L), Nuneaton, Hereford									
Cantrill	George	21	Defender	Guiseley	20			20	
Sheff Utd (Y), Guiseley (L), Guiseley									
Cardwell	Harry	24	Forward	Chorley	17	2	1	19	3
				Stockport County (L)	16	3		19	5
Reading (Y), Woking (L), Braintree (L), Brighton (L), Grimsby, Chorley (L), Chorley, Stockport (L)									
Carey	Lewis	28	Goalkeeper	Dorking Wanderers (L)	3			3	2
Bristol C (Y), Gloucester (L), Weston (L), Bromley, Tonbridge A, Eastbourne B, Cray W, Dorking W (L)									
Carey	Sonny	20	Midfielder	King's Lynn Town	33	12	1	45	6
Norwich (Y), Wroxham, King's Lynn									
Carline	George	28	Midfielder	Gloucester City	10			10	
				Chesterfield	32			32	3
Solihull M, Leamington (Lx2), Gloucester, Chesterfield									
Carlyle	Nathan	20	Defender	Concord Rangers (L)	1			1	
				Hemel Hempstead Town (L)	5			5	
QPR (Y), Concord R (L), Concord R (L), Hemel H (L)									
Carrington	Mark	34	Defender	Wrexham	17	1	3	18	
Crewe, MK Dons, Hamilton, Bury, Wrexham									
Carruthers	Samir	28	Midfielder	Hemel Hempstead Town	7	1		8	
Aston Villa (Y), MK Dons (L), Sheff Utd, Oxford U (L), Cambridge U, Hemel H									
Carter	Darren	37	Midfielder	Solihull Moors	10	2	2	12	
Birmingham, Sunderland (L), West Brom, Preston, Millwall (L), Cheltenham, Northampton, Forest Green, Solihull M									
Cartwright	Samuel	20	Defender	Woking (L)			3		
				Oxford City (L)	3	1	2	4	
Peterborough (Y), Kettering (L), Woking (L), Oxford C (L)									
Carvalho	Denilson	22	Midfielder	Dartford		1	1	1	
Huddersfield, Dartford									
Carvalho	Wilson	27	Midfielder	Hampton & Richmond Borough	8	9		17	1
Fulham (Y), Stevenage (Y), Nike Academy, Port Vale, Hemel H (L), Corby T, Kettering, Oxford C, Stratford, Accrington, Macclesfield, Hampton & R									
Carver	Marcus	27	Forward	Southport	15	3	1	18	4
Accrington Stanley, Marine, FC Halifax Town, Barrow, AFC Fylde, Chorley (L), Chorley, Southport									
Case	Ryan	27	Defender	Chippenham Town	1	3	5	4	
Havant & W, Dorchester, Braintree, Basingstoke, Wealdstone, Basingstoke, Poole, Eastbourne B, Bath, Gosport B, Oxford C, Dulwich, Chippenham									
Casey	Josh	29	Defender	Woking	28	1	4	29	
Salisbury, Hampton & R, Woking									
Cass	Jake	27	Forward	Chelmsford City	3			3	1
Egham T, Chalfont S.P, Bishop's S, Braintree, Chelmsford									
Cass	Lewis	21	Defender	Hartlepool United (L)	36	1		37	
Newcastle U (Y), Hartlepool (L)									
Cassidy	Jake	28	Forward	York City	14	1		15	1
Ilandudno J, Airbus, Wolves, Tranmere (Lx3), Notts Co (L), Southend (L), Oldham, Guiseley, Hartlepool, Maidstone (Lx2), Maidenhead, Stevenage, York									
Cawley	Jack	28	Defender	Wealdstone	27	5	6	32	2
				Concord Rangers (L)	1			1	
Ann Arbor (US), Heybridge S, Malden/Tiptree, Concord R, Wealdstone, Concord R (L)									
Ceesay	Yusifu	26	Midfielder	Altrincham	25	9	2	34	3
Alvechurch, Blackpool, Boston (L), Telford (L), Nuneaton (L), Alvechurch (L), Altrincham (L), Altrincham (L), Altrincham									
Chadwick	Billy	21	Midfielder	FC Halifax (L)	15	3		18	5
Hull (Y), FC Halifax (Lx2)									
Challoner	Matt	27	Defender	Southport	17		1	17	
Blackpool, Northwich Victoria, Southport, Chorley, Boston U, Southport									
Chalupniczak	Filip		Goalkeeper	Sutton United			3		
Oxhey Jets, Hanwell T, Sutton U									
Chambers	Ashley	31	Forward	Brackley Town	8	5	7	13	2
Leicester (Y), Wycombe (L), Grimsby (L), York (L), York, Cambridge U, Dagenham & R (L), Dagenham & R, Grimsby, Nuneaton (L), Nuneaton, Kidderminster, Brackley									
Chambers	Michael	27	Defender	Billericay Town	16	1		17	1
Crystal P (Y), Welling (L), Welling, Dulwich H, Wrexham, Chelmsford (L), Bromley, Billericay T									

Key: X - Started; SX - Sub on; S - Non-playing Sub; Ap - Total Appearances; G/Cs - Total goals/clean sheets.

SURNAME	FIRSTNAME	AGE	POSITION	CLUB	X	SX	S	Ap	G/Cs
Chambers-Parillon	Leon	19	Midfielder	Havant & Waterlooville (L)	3	1	1	4	
Oxford U (Y), Biggleswade (L), Havant & W (L)									
Champion	Tom	35	Midfielder	Boreham Wood	27	2	2	29	1
Dartford, Cambridge U, Barnet, Lincoln (L), Boreham W, Woking									
Chapman	Ben	22	Midfielder	Ebbsfleet United	12	4		16	1
Crystal P (Y)Bearsted, Gillingham, Dulwich H, Ebbsfleet									
Chapman	David		Midfielder	Kettering Town			2		
Kettering									
Charles	Ashley	22	Midfielder	Wealdstone	19	3	5	22	
				Concord Rangers (L)	3			3	
Watford (Y), Barnet (L), Wealdstone, Concord R (L)									
Charles	Jake	25	Forward	Farsley Celtic	5	14	1	19	2
Huddersfield (Y), Guiseley (L), Barnsley (L), York (L), Stafford R, Farsley C									
Charles	Ken		Forward	Braintree Town		3	3	3	
Enfield T, Braintree									
Charles	Ryan		Midfielder	Concord Rangers	5	2		7	1
Needham M, Witham T, Canvey I, Bishop's S, Maldon & T, Concord R, Canvey I (D)									
Charles-Cook	Reice	27	Goalkeeper	Welling United	13			13	1
Arsenal (Y), Chelmsford (L), Bury, Coventry, Nuneaton (L), Swindon, Sonderjyske (Den), Shrewsbury, Macclesfield, Boreham W, Welling									
Charlton	Kieran	20	Midfielder	Blyth Spartans	5	4	3	9	
Middlesbrough (Y), South Shields, Blyth S									
Charman	Luke	23	Forward	Darlington	12	2		14	6
Newcastle U (Y), Accrington (L), Darlington									
Cheek	Michael	33	Forward	Bromley	47			47	25
Heybridge S, Stanway R, Chelmsford, Braintree, Dagenham & R, Ebbsfleet, Bromley									
Chesmain	Noah	23	Defender	Maidstone United	10	2	3	12	1
Millwall,Welling (L), Boreham W (L), Colchester, Hitchin (L), Hungerford (L), Maidstone									
Chicksen	Adam	29	Defender	Notts County	33		11	33	1
MK Dons (Y), Leyton O (L), Brighton, Gillingham (L), Fleetwood (L), Leyton O (L), Gillingham (L), Charlton, Bradford, Bolton, Notts Co									
Chidyausiku	Joseph	23	Forward	St Albans City		11	4	11	1
Havant & W, Bradford PA, Chelmsford, St Albans									
Chiedozie	Jordan	31	Forward	Braintree Town	3	1		4	1
Bournemouth, Dorchester (L), Poole (Lx2), Concord R, Cambridge U, Dartford (L), Braintree (L), Boreham W, Concord R, Margate, Chelmsford, Braintree									
Chisholm	Jamie	20	Defender	Kettering Town		1	3	1	
Mansfield, Kettering									
Christie	Bernard (BJ)		Forward	Hemel Hempstead Town (D)	11	2		13	3
AFC Dunstable, Hemel H (D)									
Church	Anthony	34	Midfielder	Chelmsford City	12			12	2
Boston U, Grimsby, Alfreton (L), Chelmsford, Bishop's S, Chelmsford									
Clackstone	Josh	24	Midfielder	Alfreton Town	13	3		16	
Hull, Notts Co (L), Halifax (L), Alfreton									
Clark	Jamie		Forward	Blyth Spartans	4			4	
Blyth S (Y)									
Clark	Kenny	32	Defender	Dagenham & Redbridge	37		1	37	
Dagenham & R, Thurrock, Chelmsford, Dartford,Ebbsfleet, Dagenham & R									
Clark	Luke	27	Defender	Chester	3		6	3	
Everton (Y), PNE, Accrington, Witton, Salford, Curzon A, Chester									
Clark	Michael	23	Defender	St Albans City	11	1	8	12	
Leyton Orient, East Thurrock (L), Braintree, Concord R, St Albans, Braintree, St Albans									
Clarke	Danny	36	Midfielder	Alfreton Town	7	3	3	10	1
Hull United, Frickley, Hall Road R, Winterton R, North Ferriby, Halifax, Alfreton									
Clarke	Jack	22	Midfielder	Yeovil Town (L)	2	1	3	3	
				Chesterfield (L)	13	8	6	21	2
Aston Villa (Y), Yeovil (L), Chesterfield (L)									
Clarke	Joe	32	Midfielder	Leamington	17	1		18	
Redditch, Darlington, Solihull, Wrexham, Kidderminster, Brackley (L), Brackley, Tamworth, Leamington									
Clarke	Nathan	37	Defender	FC Halifax	24		3	24	
Huddersfield, Colchester (L), Oldham (L), Bury (L), Leyton O, Bradford, Coventry, Grimsby, FC Halifax									

Clackstone Josh - Alfreton Town.

Collin Adam - Kettering Town.

Day Jake - Alfreton Town.

Doyle Michael - Notts Co.

Key: X - Started; SX - Sub on; S - Non-playing Sub; Ap - Total Appearances; G/Cs - Total goals/clean sheets.

SURNAME	FIRSTNAME	AGE	POSITION	CLUB	X	SX	S	Ap	G/Cs
Clarke	Ryan	39	Goalkeeper	Bath City	15		2	15	
Bristol R, Southend (L), Kidderminster (L), Forest Green (L), Salisbury, Northwich, Oxford U, Northampton, AFC Wimbledon, Eastleigh, Torquay, Bath									
Clayden	Charles		Forward	Dulwich Hamlet (L)	4	1		5	
Leyton Orient (Y), Charlton, Dulwich H (L)									
Clayton	Adam	34	Defender	Farsley Celtic	21			21	2
Bradford (PA), Farsley C									
Clayton	Max	26	Forward	Altrincham		1		1	
Crewe (Y), Bolton, Blackpool, Altrincham									
Clayton	Niall	22	Goalkeeper	Solihull Moors			31		
Wolves (Y), Birmingham (Y), Oxford U (Y), Thame (L), Solihull M									
Clayton	Paul	36	Forward	Guiseley		2	1	2	
Gainsborough, Alfreton, Harrogate (L), Harrogate, Alfreton, Shaw Lane, Guiseley									
Clayton-Phillips	Nick	21	Forward	Solihull Moors (L)		1		1	
WBA (Y), Braintree (L), Kidderminster (L), Solihull M (L), Solihull M (L)									
Clee	Nicky	37	Midfielder	Bradford (Park Avenue)	14	4		18	1
Hyde U, Altrincham, Guiseley, Harrogate, Altrincham, Bradford PA									
Clements	Bailey	20	Defender	Dagenham & Redbridge (L)		1	5	1	
Ipswich (Y), Hemel H (L), Dagenham & R (L)									
Clements	Kyran	24	Defender	Braintree Town	8	1	8	9	1
AFC Sudbury, Bury T, Braintree, Leiston (L)									
Clerima	Remy	31	Defender	Maidenhead United	15		1	15	1
Histon, Braintree, Maidenhead									
Cleworth	Max		Midfielder	Wrexham	1		3	1	
Wrexham (Y)									
Clifford	Billy	28	Midfielder	Havant & Waterlooville	15	3	2	18	
Chelsea (Y), Colchester (L), Yeovil (L), Royal Antwerp (L), Walsall, Boreham W, Crawley, Boreham W, Hemel H, Billericay, Slough (L), Wealdstone, Havant & W									
Clifton	Adrian	32	Midfielder	Dagenham & Redbridge		6	1	6	
Maidenhead, Havant & W, Maidenhead, Bromley, Dagenham & R									
Clowsley	Jake		Forward	Braintree Town		1		1	
Braintree									
Clunan	Michael	27	Midfielder	King's Lynn Town	35	3	4	38	
Norwich (Y), Boston U, Histon, Lowestoft, Dereham, King's Lynn									
Coke	Giles	35	Midfielder	Hereford FC	4	7	1	11	
Northampton, Motherwell, Sheff Wed, Bury (L), Swindon (L), Bolton (L), Ipswich, Chesterfield, Oldham, Hereford, Grimsby									
Colclough	Ryan	26	Forward	Altrincham	23	5		28	8
Wigan (Y), MK Dons (L), Scunthorpe, Altrincham									
Cole	Adeyinka	26	Midfielder	Hemel Hempstead Town	4	2		6	1
Blackpool (Y), Enfield T, Romford, Grays, Braintree, Billericay T, Hemel H									
Cole	Jake	35	Goalkeeper	Gloucester City			4		
QPR, Hayes (L), Farnborough, Plymouth, Woking, Aldershot, Maidstone, Gloucester									
Coleman	Ethan	21	Midfielder	Brackley Town	22			22	1
				King's Lynn Town (L)	9			9	
Reading (Y), Brackley, King's Lynn (L/P)									
Coleman De-Graft	Razzaq		Forward	Hampton & Richmond Borough	2	5	7	7	1
Charlton (Y), Crystal P (Y), Tooting & M, Erith T (L), Hampton & R									
Coley	Josh	22	Midfielder	Maidenhead United	27	12		39	5
Hitchin, Norwich, Dunfermline (L), Maidenhead, Exeter									
Collar	William	24	Midfielder	Stockport County	10	5	4	15	1
Brighton (Y), Hamilton, Stockport									
Collier	Nathan	35	Midfielder	Woking	15		17	15	1
Hampton & R, Dartford, Eastbourne B, Hampton & R, Dartford, Woking									
Collin	Adam	36	Goalkeeper	Kettering Town	18			18	2
Carlisle, Rotherham, Aberdeen (L), Notts Co, Carlisle, Kettering									
Collings	Andy		Goalkeeper	Torquay United			4		
Torquay (Y)									
Collins	Lee	32	Defender	Yeovil Town	5	2	1	7	
Port Vale, Barnsley (L), Barnsley, Shrewsbury (L), Northampton, Mansfield, Forest GR, Yeovil									

2020-21 NATIONAL. NORTH & SOUTH PLAYERS — APPEARANCES

SURNAME	FIRSTNAME	AGE	POSITION	CLUB PLAYED FOR	X	SX	S	Ap	G/Cs
Collins	Louis	19	Forward	Dover Athletic	3	13	1	16	3
Scunthorpe (Y), Sevenoaks, Dover									
Colombie	Killian	25	Defender	Aldershot Town	9	4	10	13	
Sporting KC II (US), Aldershot									
Comley	James	30	Midfielder	Maidenhead United	27	1	4	28	1
Crystal Palace, St Albans, Maidenhead									
Conlon	Luke	26	Defender	AFC Fylde	20			20	1
Burnley (Y), St Mirren (L), Morecambe (L), Morecambe, AFC Fylde									
Conn-Clarke	Christopher	19	Midfielder	Chorley (L)		2	2	2	
Glentoran, Burnley (U23), Chorley (L)									
Connors	Jack	26	Defender	Barnet	8		7	8	
Fulham, Dagenham & R, Hendon (L), Boreham W (L), Ebbsfleet, Dover, Hampton & R (Lx2), Dulwich H, Barnet									
Constable	Ravan	21	Goalkeeper	Maidstone United	9		9	9	2
Barnet (Y), Potters B (L), Wealdstone, Beaconsfield, Potters B, Maidstone									
Conway	Tommy		Forward	Bath City (L)	16			16	9
Bristol C (Y), Yate (L), Bath (L)									
Cook	Anthony	31	Midfielder	Welling United	11	1	1	12	2
Dagenham & R, Chelmsford, Bromley, Ebbsfleet, Woking (L), Dulwich H, Welling									
Cook	Jack	27	Defender	Woking	39		1	39	3
Worthing, Hampton & R, Woking									
Cook	Jacob		Midfielder	Hemel Hempstead Town	3	1		4	
Kings Langley, Wealdstone, Hayes & Y (L), Billericay T, Hemel H									
Cook	Jordan	31	Midfielder	Gateshead	7	3		10	1
Sunderland (Y), Darlington (L), Walsall (L), Carlisle (L), Charlton, Yeovil (L), Walsall, Luton, Grimsby, Gateshead									
Cooke	Cody	28	Forward	Weymouth	14	6	1	20	3
Truro, St Mirren, Weymouth									
Cooper	Charlie	24	Midfielder	Woking	43	2	4	45	3
Birmingham (Y), Forest GR (L), York (L), Forest GR (L), Forest GR, Newport Co (L), Boreham W (L), FC Halifax, Woking									
Cooper	Nathan		Defender	Hemel Hempstead Town (D)	9			9	2
Romford, Hornchurch, Hemel H (D)									
Coppin	Noah		Midfielder	Chippenham Town		1	1	1	
Taunton (Y), Chippenham (Y)									
Corne	Sam	24	Midfielder	Maidstone United	16	1		17	1
Welling, Braintree, Greenwich B, Ashford U, Maidstone									
Cotter	Barry	22	Defender	Chelmsford City (L)	6	1	1	7	
Limerick, Ipswich, Chelmsford (L), Chelmsford (L)									
Coulson	Luke	27	Midfielder	Bromley	21	6	1	27	1
Cardiff, Oxford C, Eastleigh, Barnet, Ebbsfleet, Bromley									
Coulthirst	Shaq	26	Forward	Boreham Wood	4	16	12	20	1
Tottneham (Yth), Leyton O (L), Torquay (L), Southend (L), York (L), Wigan (L), Peterborough, Mansfield (L), Barnet, Boreham W									
Cousins	Mark	34	Goalkeeper	Bromley	48			48	14
Fulham, Colchester U, Dagenham & R, Barnet, Bromley									
Covolan Cavagnari	Lucas	30	Goalkeeper	Torquay United	28		11	28	14*
Esportivo (Bra), Rio Branco, Whitehawk, Worthing, Torquay				**Includes a goal scored in the Play-off Final.*					
Cowan	Dan	29	Defender	Guiseley	7	1	3	8	
				Curzon Ashton	5			5	2
Macclesfield, Chorley (L), Stockport, Guiseley, Curzon A									
Cowans	Henry	25	Midfielder	AFC Telford United	6			6	
Aston Villa (Y), Stevenage (L), Telford									
Cowley	Jason	25	Forward	Kidderminster Harriers	1	2		3	1
Stevenage, Solihull M (L), Kidderminster									
Cox	Dean	33	Midfielder	Eastbourne Borough	15	7	2	22	3
Brighton, Leyton O, Crawley, Eastbourne B									
Cox	Sam	30	Midfielder	Hampton & Richmond Borough	9	2		11	
Tottenham (Y), Cheltenham (L), Histon (L), Torquay (L), Barnet, Boreham W (L), Hayes & Y, Boreham W, Wealdstone, Hampton & R (L), Hampton & R									
Coxe	Cameron	22	Defender	Solihull Moors	23	4	6	27	
Cardiff (Y), Solihull M									
Coyle	Lewis		Forward	Oxford City	17	7	2	24	2
Old Woodstock T, North Leigh, Kidlington, Thatcham, Oxford C									

Key: X - Started; SX - Sub on; S - Non-playing Sub; Ap - Total Appearances; G/Cs - Total goals/clean sheets.

SURNAME	FIRSTNAME	AGE	POSITION	CLUB	X	SX	S	Ap	G/Cs
					APPEARANCES				
Craig	Paco	28	Defender	Hemel Hempstead Town	2			2	
Bishop's S, Louisville City (US), Hemel H									
Crane	Nick			FC Halifax			4		
FC Halifax									
Cranston	Dan		Midfielder	Gateshead			1		
Gateshead (Y)									
Cranston	Jordan	27	Defender	Solihull Moors	45	1		46	2
Wolves (Y), Nuneaton (L), Hednesford, Nuneaton, Notts Co, Lincoln C (L), Gateshead, Cheltenham, Morecambe, Solihull M									
Crawford	Tom	22	Midfielder	Hartlepool United	11	8	12	19	1
Stoke City, Chester, Notts Co, AFC Fylde (L), Hartlepool									
Croasdale	Ryan	26	Midfielder	Stockport County	38	4	5	42	1
PNE, Tamworth (L), Sheffield Wed, Kidderminster, AFC Fylde, Stockport									
Croll	Luke	26	Defender	Dagenham & Redbridge	22	4	4	26	
Crystal P (Y), Plymouth (L), Exeter (L), Exeter, Dagenham & R									
Crook	Billy	30	Midfielder	Chelmsford City	6	1	2	7	
Peterborough (Y), Weymouth (L), Histon (L), Tooting & M, Carshalton, Met Police, Enfield T, Braintree, Dartford, Chelmsford									
Crook	Peter	27	Goalkeeper	Boston United	1		11	1	1
Harrogate T, Hyde U, Boston U									
Cropper	Jordan	21	Forward	Chesterfield	11	2	1	13	2
Chesterfield (Y)									
Crowther	Matthew		Goalkeeper	Hungerford Town			1		
Hungerford									
Crugas-Cowin	Jordan		Midfielder	Tonbridge Angels			1		
Tonbridge A									
Cullinane-Liburd	Jordan	26	Defender	Brackley Town	11		2	11	
Redditch, Solihull M, Rushall, Hereford, Brackley									
Cumberbatch	Kurtis	25	Forward	Dover Athletic	6	4	6	10	
Tottenham (Y), Watford (Y), Charlton (Y), Hadley Town, Welling, Harrow B, Farnborough, Dover									
Cundle	Greg	24	Forward	Ebbsfleet United	2	2	2	4	
Gillingham (Y), Margate (L), Billericay T (L), Bishop's S (L), Kingstonian, Ebbsfleet									
Cunningham	Aaron	23	Defender	Blyth Spartans (L)	11			11	
Hartlepool (Y), Blyth S (L), Blyth S (L), Blyth S (L)									
Curran	Alex	22	Midfielder	Curzon Ashton (L)	12	4	2	16	
Blackburn (Y), Colne, Stockport, Curzon A (L),									
Currie	Isaac		Defender	Guiseley	6	1	7	7	
Burton (Y), Ilkeston T, Philadelphia Fury, Grantham T, Guiseley									
Curtis	James	39	Defender	Spennymoor Town	15		1	15	
Gateshead, Spennymoor									
D'Ath	Lawson	28	Midfielder	Yeovil Town	13	3	2	16	
Reading, Yeovil (L), Cheltenham (L), Exeter (L), Dagenham & R, Northampton, Luton, MK Dons, Yeovil									
Da Costa	Khale	27	Midfielder	Tonbridge Angels	12	4	1	16	2
Harlow, Concord R, St Albans, Tonbridge A									
Da Silva	Ivanilson	18	Forward	Curzon Ashton (L)		3	1	3	
Oldham (Y), Curzon A (L)									
Dagnall	Chris	35	Forward	Yeovil Town	13	12	10	25	1
Rochdale, Scunthorpe, Barnsley, Bradford (L), Coventry (L), Leyton O, Kerala Blasters (Ind), Hibernian, Crewe, Bury, Tranmere, Yeovil									
Dalby	Sam	21	Forward	Stockport County (L)	3	1		4	
				Woking (L)	10	5	2	15	1
Leyton O (Y), Leeds, Morecambe (L), Watford, Stockport (L), Woking (L)									
Dale	Nathan	21	Midfielder	Gateshead	4	2	8	6	
Middlesbrough (Y), Gateshead									
Dales	Andy	26	Midfielder	Altrincham (L)	3			3	
Derby (Y), Mickleover, Scunthorpe, Dundee (L), Hamilton (L), Altrincham (L)									
Dallas	Andrew	21	Forward	Weymouth (L)	24			24	12
Rangers (Y), Stenhousemuir (L), Cambridge U, Weymouth (L)									
Dalling	Deshane	22	Midfielder	Wealdstone (L)		1	4	1	
QPR (Y), Cork (L), Wealdstone (L)									

2020-21 NATIONAL. NORTH & SOUTH PLAYERS

SURNAME	FIRSTNAME	AGE	POSITION	CLUB PLAYED FOR	X	SX	S	Ap	G/Cs
					APPEARANCES				
Daly	Liam	33	Defender	Gloucester City	18			18	1
				Barnet	19		1	19	
Evesham, Corby, Redditch, Solihull M, Halesowen, Leamington, Barwell, Leamington, Solihull M, Kidderminster, Solihull M, Gloucester, Barnet									
Daniels	Brendon	27	Forward	AFC Telford United	3	2		5	1
Crewe (Y), Leicester, Blackburn, Chester, Tamworth, Harrogate, AFC Fylde, Alfreton, Port Vale, Altrincham (L), Telford (L), Telford									
Danns	Neil	38	Midfielder	FC Halifax	2	3	7	5	
Blackburn, Blackpool (L), Hartlepool (L), Colchester (L), Colchester, Birmingham, Crystal P, Leicester, Bristol C (L), Huddersfield (L), Bolton (L), Bolton, Bury, Blackpool (L), Tranmere, FC Halifax									
Danquah	Richie	25	Defender	Welling United	2		1	2	
Aveley, Welling									
Dart	Morgan	20	Forward	Blyth Spartans		1	7	1	
TyneMet College, Blyth S									
David	Kuagica	30	Defender	Dulwich Hamlet	2	1	3	3	
Minangkabau (Ind), Rochdale, CD 1 de Agosto (Angola), FC Stumbras (Lith), Ermis Aradippou (Cyp), Barnstaple, Dulwich H									
Davidson	Correy	28	Midfielder	Braintree Town	9			9	2
Bohemians, Carrick, Ards, AFC Sudbury, Walthamstow, Bishop's S, Concord R, Kidderminster, Bishop's S, Braintree									
Davies	Felix		Goalkeeper	Slough Town			1		
Slough (Y)									
Davies	Jordan	22	Midfielder	Wrexham	34	5	4	39	7
Wrexham (Y), Bangor (L), Brighton, Wrexham									
Davies	Jordan	30	Forward	AFC Telford United	9	11	1	20	1
West End, Llanelli, Prestatyn, Nantwich, Market D, Telford U									
Davies	Scott	33	Midfielder	Slough Town			2		
Reading (Y), Wycombe (L), Yeovil (L), Wycombe (L), Bristol R (L), Crawley, Aldershot (L), Oxford U, Wealdstone, Oxford C, Chelmsford, Slough									
Davis	Kenny	33	Midfielder	Sutton United	23	5	11	28	
Grays, Braintree, Boreham W, Sutton U									
Davison	Josh	21	Forward	Woking (L)	14			14	5
Charlton (Y), Woking (L)									
Davison-Hale	Harrison	20	Goalkeeper	FC Halifax			34		
Huddersfield (Y), Liversedge (L), FC Halifax									
Dawson	Kevin	30	Midfielder	Gloucester City	20			20	2
Sporting Fingal, Shelbourne, Yeovil, Cheltenham, Forest GR, Gloucester									
Day	Jake		Forward	Alfreton Town	7	4	3	11	5
Scarborough, Bridlington T (D), Tadcaster A, Alfreton									
De Groot	Jack	17	Goalkeeper	St Albans City			1		
St Albans (Y)									
De Havilland	Will	26	Defender	Dover Athletic	14			14	2
Millwall, Sheffield W, Wycombe, Aldershot (L), Maidstone (L), Maidstone, Dover									
Deacon	Roarie	29	Midfielder	Havant & Waterlooville	16	4	1	20	5
Arsenal (Y), Sunderland, Stevenage, Crawley, Sutton U, Dundee, Sutton U, Havant & W									
Deadfield	Sam	24	Midfielder	Hampton & Richmond Borough	17	1		18	4
Reading (Y), Birmingham (Y), Basingstoke, Beaconsfield, Hungerford, Basingstoke, Hampton & R									
Dean	Gareth	31	Defender	Brackley Town	17	1		18	
Nuneaton, Solihull, Brackley									
Dean	Will	20	Defender	Bath City (L)	7			7	
Exeter (Y), Truro (L), Bath (L)									
Debayo	Josh	24	Defender	Wealdstone		1	1	1	
Chelsea (Y), Southampton (Y), Leicester, Cheltenham, Dover (L), Wealdstone									
Debrah	Jesse	20	Defender	Dulwich Hamlet (L)	11	3	3	14	
Millwall (Y), Billericay (L), Eastbourne B (L), Dulwich H (L), Dulwich H (L)									
Deering	Sam	30	Midfielder	Dagenham & Redbridge	16	6	1	22	2
Newport, Oxford U, Barnet (L), Whitehawk, Ebbsfleet, Billericay, Dagenham & R									
Della-Verde	Lyle	26	Midfielder	Welling United (D)	9	1		10	3
Southend (Y), Fulham (Y), Bristol R (L), Fleetwood, Crawley, Welling, Concord R, Dartford, Braintree, Enfield T, Welling (D)									
Dempsey	Ben	21	Defender	Woking (L)	29	3		32	
Charlton (Y), Dulwich H (L), Woking (L), Woking (L)									
Densmore	Shaun	32	Defender	Altrincham	7	8	13	15	
Everton (Y), Altrincham									

Key: X - Started; SX - Sub on; S - Non-playing Sub; Ap - Total Appearances; G/Cs - Total goals/clean sheets.

SURNAME	FIRSTNAME	AGE	POSITION	CLUB	X	SX	S	Ap	G/Cs
Denton	Tom	31	Forward	Chesterfield	17	1		18	9
Wakefield, Huddersfield, Woking (L), Cheltenham (L), Wakefield (L), Alfreton, North Ferriby, Halifax, Alfreton, Chesterfield									
Denton	Tyler	25	Defender	Chesterfield	2	5	3	7	
				King's Lynn Town	27	1		28	1
Leeds (Y), Port Vale (L), Peterborough (L), Stevenage, Chesterfield, King's Lynn									
Derry	Tom	26	Forward	Tonbridge Angels	3			3	1
				Braintree Town	8	1		9	3
Gillingham (Y), Chelmsford (L), Eastbourne B (L), Eastbourne B, Aldershot, Hayes & Y, East Thurrock, Tonbridge A, Braintree									
Deverdics	Nicky	33	Midfielder	Gateshead	10	3	2	13	
Gretna, Barnet, Alfreton, Dover, Hartlepool, Dover (L), Wrexham, Gateshead									
Di Niro	Pinto		Forward	Maidstone United		2	2	2	
Maidstone									
Di Segni	Roberto		Midfielder	Gloucester City		1		1	
Gloucester									
Diallo	Mohammed	21	Midfielder	Wealdstone			1		
Arsenal (Y), Stoke (U18), Lewes, Newhaven, Bognor R, Worthing, Wealdstone, Worthing									
Diamba	Hagie	18	Goalkeeper	Guiseley			3		
Guiseley (Y)									
Diarra	Moussa	31	Defender	Havant & Waterlooville	15		1	15	1
				Woking	24			24	4
St Albans, Hemel H, Hampton & R (L), Hampton & R, Barrow, Dover, Woking (L), Woking, Havant & W, Woking									
Diaz	Antonio	21	Midfielder	Hungerford Town (L)	1	2	1	3	
Bournemouth (Y), Dorchester (L), Weymouth, Dorchester, Wimborne, Salisbury, Hungerford (L)									
Dibble	Christian	27	Goalkeeper	Wrexham	19	1	25	20	9
Bury, Barnsley, Nuneaton (L), Chelmsford (L), Boston Utd, Nuneaton, Chorley (L), Wrexham									
Dickinson	Carl	34	Defender	Yeovil Town	35	2	6	37	
Stoke (Y), Blackpool (L), Leeds (L), Barnsley (L), Portsmouth (L), Watford, Portsmouth (L), Coventry (L), Port Vale, Notts Co, Yeovil									
Dickinson	Mitchell	24	Defender	Eastbourne Borough	24			24	
Gillingham (Y), Hythe, Hemel H, Hornchurch (L), Eastbourne B									
Dickson	Christopher	36	Forward	Dartford	5	3		8	3
Charlton (Y), Bristol R (L), Gillingham (L), Nea Salamis (Cyp), AEL, Shanghai SIPG, Dag & Red, Paphos (Cyp), Enosis, Ermis, Sutton U, Chelmsford, Hampton & R, Hornchurch, Dartford (D)									
Dickson	Jack	25	Defender	Weymouth	2	5	3	7	
Bournemouth (Y), Poole, New Hants Wildcats (US), Poole, Weymouth									
Diedhiou	Dave	32	Defender	St Albans City	7	6	7	13	1
Hendon, St Albans									
Digie	Kennedy	24	Forward	Hereford FC	7	2	6	9	1
Kidderminster, Hednesford (L), Worcester (L), Nuneaton (L), York (L), Guiseley, Hereford									
Dimaio	Connor	25	Midfielder	Boston United	11	4	2	15	1
Sheff Utd (Y), Chesterfield, Stockport, Ashton U (L), Curzon A (L), Boston U									
Dinanga	Marcus	23	Forward	Chesterfield (L)	6	7	7	13	1
Burton (Y), Mickleover (L), Matlock (L), Telford (L), Hartlepool (L), Telford, Stevenage, Chesterfield (L)									
Dobson	James	29	Midfielder	Ebbsfleet United (L)	4	7	4	11	
Oxford U (Y), North Leigh, Slough, Sutton U, Dagenham & R, Hemel H (L), Ebbsfleet (L)									
Dockerty	Brad		Midfielder	Bradford (Park Avenue)	14			14	2
Hemsworth MW, Bradford PA									
Doe	Scott	32	Defender	Welling United	1	1	1	2	
Weymouth, Dagenham & Redbridge, Boreham Wood, Dagenham & Redbridge, Whitehawk (L), Boreham W, Billericay, Dover, Romford, Hornchurch, Welling									
Donaldson	Ruaridh	27	Defender	Hampton & Richmond Borough	17	3	1	20	3
Bonnyrigg, Stenhousemuir, Hampton & R									
Donaldson	Ryan	30	Midfielder	Hartlepool United	16	15	9	31	
Newcastle, Hartlepool (L), Tranmere (L), Gateshead, Cambridge U, Plymouth, Hartlepool									
Donawa	Justin	24	Forward	Darlington	3	2		5	2
				Solihull Moors	10	15	4	25	4
Somerset Trojans (Y) (Ber), Black Rock, Darlington, Solihull M									
Donnellan	Shaun	24	Defender	Maidenhead United	14	1		15	2
WBA (Y), Worcester (L), Stevenage (L), Dagenham & R (L), Walsall (L), Yeovil, Maidstone, Woking, Maidenhead									

2020-21 NATIONAL. NORTH & SOUTH PLAYERS

SURNAME	FIRSTNAME	AGE	POSITION	CLUB PLAYED FOR	X	SX	S	Ap	G/Cs
Downing	Matthew	21	Defender	Bradford (Park Avenue)	5	4	7	9	
Leeds (Y), Bradford (PA)									
Doyle	Jack	24	Defender	Southport	14	2	1	16	
Blackburn (Y), Derry (L), Maidstone (L), Southport									
Doyle	Michael	39	Midfielder	Notts County	41	2	2	43	2
Coventry, Leeds (L), Sheff Utd, Portsmouth, Coventry, Notts Co									
Drake	Jamie		Midfielder	Billericay Town		1	1	1	
Billericay T (U23)									
Drench	Steven	35	Goalkeeper	Farsley Celtic	19			19	4
Blackburn (Y), Morecambe, Southport, Cambridge U (L), Leigh Genesis, Guiseley, Halifax, Bradford PA, Altrincham, Farsley C									
Drewe	Aaron	20	Defender	Oxford City (L)	26			26	2
QPR (Y), Chelmsford (L), Oxford C (L)									
Duckworth	Michael	29	Defender	York City	6		1	6	
York, Harrogate Railway, Bradford PA, Hartlepool, Fleetwood, Morecambe (L), Halifax, York									
Dudley	Anthony	25	Forward	Chester	12	10		22	7
Bury (Y), Guiseley (Lx2), Macclesfield (L), Salford, Chester (L), Chester									
Dudzinski	Ben	25	Goalkeeper	Oxford City	26			26	8
Durham City, Hartlepool, Darlington (L), Lowestoft, Havant & W, Sutton U, Oxford C									
Duffus	Courtney	25	Forward	Yeovil Town	7	4		11	4
				Bromley	15	4	1	19	5
Everton (Y), Bury (L), Oldham, Waterford (L), Yeovil, Bromley									
Duffus	Tyrone	24	Midfielder	Barnet	2	2	1	4	
Everton (Y), Cardiff (U23), Hereford (L), Warrington, Barnet									
Duggan	Connor		Forward	Kettering Town			2		
Kettering									
Duke-Mckenna	Stephen	20	Defender	Hemel Hempstead Town (L)	7	1		8	
Everton (Y), QPR, Hemel H (L)									
Dunbar	Kieran	24	Midfielder	Leamington			1		
Fleetwood, Stalybridge, Telford, Leamington (L), Leamington									
Duncan	Reuben		Midfielder	Welling United	3			3	
Millwall (Y), Welling									
Dundas	Craig	40	Forward	Sutton United		13	16	13	
Sutton U, Hampton & R (L), Hampton & R, Sutton U									
Dunne	James	31	Midfielder	Barnet	24			24	
Exeter (Y), Stevenage, St Johnstone (L), Portsmouth, Dagenham & R, Cambridge U, Swindon, Barnet									
Dunne	Romario		Forward	Braintree Town	7	2	2	9	2
Braintree, Cheshunt (L)									
Dunwell	Louie			Billericay Town		1	2	1	
Billericay T									
Durojaiye	Scott Olumide	28	Defender	Welling United	3			3	1
Tottenham (Y), Norwich, Falkirk, Brechin (L), Enfield T, Hayes & Y, Hungerford, Hayes & Y, Haringey, Welling, Braintree, Maidstone, Woking, Haringey B, Welling									
Durrell	Elliott	31	Midfielder	Wrexham	18	10	6	28	2
Hednesford, Wrexham, Tamworth, Chester, Macclesfield, York, Altrincham, Wrexham									
Dutton	Lewis	20	Goalkeeper	Chorley			4		
TNS (Y), Chorley									
Duxbury	Scott	26	Defender	Boston United	13	1	3	14	
Blackburn (Y), Burnley (Y), PNE (Y), Stockport, Northwich V, Stockport, AFC Fylde, Chorley (L), Boston U									
Dyer	Alex	31	Midfielder	Wealdstone	33	5	1	38	3
Northampton (Y), Wealdstone, Welling, Ostersunds FK, Elfsborg, Lillestrom (L), Al Tadhamon (Kuwait), Wealdstone									
Dyer	Jordan	21	Defender	Chippenham Town (L)	6			6	
Exeter (Y), Chippenham (L)									
Dyett	Ben	31	Midfielder	Dorking Wanderers			4		
KaPa (Fin), Hayes, Chipstead, Dorking W									
Dyson	Olly	21	Midfielder	York City	15	1		16	2
Barrow (Y), York									
Earing	Jack	22	Midfielder	FC Halifax	26	9		35	9
Bolton (Y), Curzon A (L), FC Halifax, Spennymoor (L), Farsley C (L)									

Key: X - Started; SX - Sub on; S - Non-playing Sub; Ap - Total Appearances; G/Cs - Total goals/clean sheets.

SURNAME	FIRSTNAME	AGE	POSITION	CLUB	X	SX	S	Ap	G/Cs
Eastmond	Craig	30	Midfielder	Sutton United	44			44	6
Arsenal, Millwall (L), Wycombe (L), Colchester (L), Colchester, Yeovil, Sutton U									
Edegbe	Michael		Goalkeeper	Slough Town			6		
Slough (Y)									
Edser	Toby	22	Midfielder	Aldershot Town	39	8		47	4
Nottm Forest, Woking (L), Port Vale (L), Woking (L), Aldershot									
Edwards	Jack	29	Midfielder	Leamington	16	1		17	3
Leamington, Solihull M, Leamington									
Edwards	Jordan	21	Midfielder	Hungerford Town	1	7	11	8	
Norwich, Swindon, Chippenham (L), Marlow (L), Hungerford									
Edwards	Kameron		Goalkeeper	Bromley			1		
Bromley (Y)									
Edwards	Preston	34	Goalkeeper	Braintree Town	6			6	
Liverpool (Y), Millwall, Dover (L), Grays, Ebbsfleet, Boreham W (L), Dulwich H, Dartford, Braintree									
Efete	Michee	24	Defender	Wealdstone	26			26	1
Norwich, Torquay (L), Maidstone, Bath (L), Billericay (L), Wealdstone									
Effiong	Inih	30	Forward	Barnet (L)	6			6	1
				Notts County (L)	5	7		12	1
Boreham W, Barrow, Woking, Ross Co, Dover, Stevenage, Barnet (L), Notts Co (L)									
Egan	Alfie	23	Midfielder	Ebbsfleet United	11	3	4	14	2
				Maidenhead United (L)	2	8	4	10	
AFC Wimbledon, Sutton U (L), East Thurrock (L), Ebbsfleet, Maidenhead (L)									
Eglin	Leo		Midfielder	Bath City			1		
Bath (Y)									
Eirich	Alexander	27	Forward	Ebbsfleet United		4	1	4	
Luckenwalde (Ger), Furstenwalde, Ebbsfleet									
Ekpiteta	Marvel	25	Defender	Dover Athletic	11			11	
Chelmsford, Bishop's S, East Thurrock, Hungerford, Newport Co, Ebbsfleet (L), Macclesfield, Dover									
Ekpolo	Prince	27	Midfielder	Guiseley	13			13	
Glossop NE, Guiseley									
El-Abd	Sami	34	Defender	Dorking Wanderers	3	3	9	6	
Team Bath, Hayes & Y, Chelmsford, Whitehawk, Bognor R, Dorking W									
Elechi	Michael	19	Defender	Oxford City (L)	4			4	
Oxford U (Y), Oxford C (L)									
Eleftheriou	Andrew	23	Defender	Dagenham & Redbridge	19	3	5	22	1
Watford (Y), Sandefjord (Nor) (L), Braintree (L), Dagenham & R									
Elliott	Daniel	25	Forward	Chester	18	4		22	8
				Hartlepool United	1	6	3	7	1
NC Fusion (US), San Cristobel (L), Port Vale, Chester, Alfreton (L), Hartlepool									
Ellis	Daniel	32	Defender	Farsley Celtic	8	1	2	9	
Guiseley, Harrogate T, Farsley									
Ellis	Mark	32	Defender	Notts County (L)	22		2	22	6
Exeter, Bolton, Torquay (L), Torquay, Forest Green (L), Crewe, Shrewsbury, Carlisle (L), Carlisle, Forest Green (L), Leyton Orient (L), Tranmere, Notts Co (L)									
Ellul	Joe	32	Defender	Maidstone United	16			16	1
East Thurrock, Billericay, Braintree, Tasman Utd (NZ), Maidenhead, Maidstone									
Elokobi	George	35	Defender	Maidstone United	17			17	
Dulwich H, Colchester, Chester (L), Wolves, Nottingham F (L), Bristol C, Oldham, Colchester, Braintree (L), Leyton Orient, Aldershot, Maidstone									
Elsdon	Matty	24	Defender	Blyth Spartans	15			15	
Sunderland (Y), Middlesbrough (Y), Inverness C (L), Whitby (L), FC United (L), Barrow, Blyth S									
Emmanuel	Moses	31	Forward	Wealdstone	13	4	1	17	7
Brentford, Woking (L), Woking, Bromley, Dover, Sutton, Maidenhead (L), Billericay, Welling, Wealdstone									
Emmerson	Keith		Defender	Hungerford Town	19			19	
Farnborough, Taunton, Poole, Winchester, Hungerford									
English	Junior	35	Midfielder	Leamington	7	10	3	17	4
Solihull, Brackley (L), Worcester, Leamington									

Fox Nathan - Alfreton Town.

Fryatt Ryan - Kettering Town.

Hall Connor - Chorley.

Henley Adam - Chorley.

Key: X - Started; SX - Sub on; S - Non-playing Sub; Ap - Total Appearances; G/Cs - Total goals/clean sheets.

SURNAME	FIRSTNAME	AGE	POSITION	CLUB	X	SX	S	Ap	G/Cs
Essam	Connor	28	Defender	Dartford	15	2	2	17	1
Gillingham, Luton (L), Crawley, Dartford (L), Dover, Leyton O, Dover (L), Eastleigh, Woking (L), Dover (L), Dover, Concord R (L), Hemel H, Dartford									
Evans	Callum	25	Defender	Bath City	9	1	2	10	
Barnsley, Macclesfield (L), Forest Green, Torquay (L), Macclesfield (L), Macclesfield, Port Vale, Bath									
Evans	Jack	20	Midfielder	Hungerford Town (L)	2			2	1
Blackburn (Y), Forest GR, Hungerford (L)									
Evans	Jacob		Midfielder	Torquay United			2		
Torquay U (Y)									
Evans	Jake	23	Midfielder	Hemel Hempstead Town	7	4	2	11	2
				Hungerford Town	2		1	2	
Swindon (Y), Farnborough (L), Waterford (L), Cardiff, Hemel H (L), Hemel H, Hungerford									
Evans	Max		Goalkeeper	Yeovil Town			13		
Yeovil (Y), Frome (L)									
Evans	Rhys	24	Defender	Blyth Spartans	10	1		11	
South Shields, Blyth S									
Evans	Rob	25	Midfielder	Curzon Ashton	14		1	14	1
Wrexham (Y), Billericay, Warrington, Curzon A									
Evans	Sam	18	Forward	Woking		3	5	3	
Woking (Y)									
Evans	Will	29	Defender	Chesterfield	29	1	2	30	1
Swindon, Hereford (L), Hereford, Newport Co (L), Eastleigh, Aldershot, Chesterfield									
Eve	Dale	26	Goalkeeper	Spennymoor Town	17			17	2
Derby (Y), Stoke, Nuneaton (L), Newcastle T (L), Congleton (L), Forest GR (L), Forest GR, Spennymoor									
Everitt	Matthew	18	Forward	Welling United (L)	2	1		3	
Brighton (Y), Welling (L)									
Faal	Muhammadu	23	Forward	Barnet (L)	6	16	5	22	1
L'Aquila (It), Enfield T, Bolton, Barnet (L)									
Farrell	Kyron	25	Midfielder	Hampton & Richmond Borough	19	1	1	20	
Millwall (Y), Braintree (L), Concord R, Cray W, Hampton & R									
Fasanmade	Craig	21	Midfielder	Hungerford Town	12	4	2	16	4
				Wealdstone (L/P)		4	1	4	1
Reading (Y), Oxford C, Thame U (L), Banbury (L), Hungerford, Wealdstone (L/P)									
Fawcett	Jacob		Goalkeeper	Bradford (Park Avenue)			8		
Bradford (PA)									
Featherstone	Nicky	32	Midfielder	Hartlepool United	42	1		43	5
Hull, Grimsby (L), Hereford, Walsall, Scunthorpe, Hartlepool									
Felix	Joe	21	Defender	Billericay Town	15	2		17	
Fulham (Y), QPR (U23), Burgess H (L), Woking, Farnborough (L), Hampton & RB, Hendon, Maidstone, Billericay T									
Felix	Kaine	25	Forward	Guiseley	13	1		14	6
St Neots, Boston U, York, Stockport (L), Leamington, Brackley, Guiseley									
Fenelon	Shamir	26	Forward	Billericay Town	7	5	2	12	1
Brighton, Torquay (L), Rochdale (L), Tranmere (L), Dagenham & R (L), Crawley, Whitehawk (L), Aldershot, Maidenhead, Billericay T									
Fenlon	Rhys	19	Midfielder	Southport (L)		1		1	
Accrington (Y), Southport (L)									
Ferdinand	Kane	28	Midfielder	Woking	40	1	3	41	5
Southend, Peterborough, Northampton (L), Luton (L), Cheltenham (L), Dagenham & R, East Thurrock, Woking									
Ferguson	Craig		Midfielder	Billericay Town	2			2	
Billericay T (U23)									
Ferguson	David	27	Defender	Hartlepool United	44		1	44	1
Darlington, Sunderland, Boston U (L), Blackpool, Shildon, Darlington, York, Hartlepool									
Fernandez	Luis	19	Defender	Oxford City (L)	13	3	3	16	
Stevenage (Y), Oxford C (2xL)									
Ferrell	Lewis	30	Defender	Braintree Town	3			3	
Hayes & Y, Hampton & RB, Staines, Farnborough, Hayes & Y, Hitchin, Biggleswade T, Braintree, Biggleswade T									
Ferry	James	24	Midfielder	Eastbourne Borough	24			24	
Brentford (Y), Wycombe (L), Welling (L), Stevenage, Nuneaton (L), FC Halifax (L), Woking, Eastbourne B									

2020-21 NATIONAL. NORTH & SOUTH PLAYERS

SURNAME	FIRSTNAME	AGE	POSITION	CLUB PLAYED FOR	X	SX	S	Ap	G/Cs
Fielding	Jamie	21	Defender	Braintree Town (L)	8		1	8	
				Wealdstone			1		
Hastings U, Little Common (L), Stevenage, St Albans (L), Braintree (L), Wealdstone									
Finn	Kyle	22	Midfielder	Hereford FC	18	3		21	1
Coventry (Y), Hereford (L), Hereford, Rushall O (L)									
Finney	Alex	25	Defender	Aldershot Town	12	1	2	13	1
Leyton Orient, Bolton, QPR, Maidstone (L), Maidstone, Aldershot									
Fisher	David	19	Forward	Hampton & Richmond Borough	5	4	2	9	3
Wimbledon (Y), Carshalton (L), Hampton & R									
Fitzsimons	Ross	27	Goalkeeper	Boston United	16		1	16	7
				Stockport County			13		
Crystal P (Y), Havant & W (L), Farnborough (L), Bolton, Bishop's S (L), Braintree, Chelmsford, Notts Co, Chesterfield (L), Boston U, Stockport									
Flatters	Harry	19	Goalkeeper	York City			15		
Middlesbrough (Y), York									
Fleet	Reece	29	Midfielder	Oxford City	26			26	2
Oxford C, Solihull, Oxford C									
Fleming	Tai		Defender	King's Lynn Town	20	1	11	21	1
Norwich (Y), Yeovil (Y), King's Lynn									
Fletcher	Alex	22	Forward	Bath City	1			1	
Plymouth, Torquay (L), Aldershot (L), Tiverton (L/P), Bath									
Flintney	Ross	37	Goalkeeper	Eastleigh	1		14	1	
Fulham, Brighton (L), Brighton (L), Doncaster (L), Barnet, Grays, Dover, Gillingham, Eastleigh, Whitehawk, Bromley, Eastleigh									
Flood	Chris	31	Midfielder	Slough Town			1		
Salisbury, Crawley, Forest GR (L), Dorchester, Eastleigh, Maidenhead (L), Winchester, Basingstoke, Gosport B, Slough									
Flowers	Harry	25	Defender	Brackley Town	5	3	3	8	
				Curzon Ashton (L)	6			6	2
Brocton, Burnley (Y), Guiseley, Solihull, Kidderminster (L), Brackley, Curzon A (L)									
Fogden	Wes	33	Midfielder	Dorking Wanderers	19	1		20	3
Brighton (Y), Bognor (L), Dorchester (L), Dorchester, Havant & W, Bournemouth, Portsmouth, Yeovil, Havant & W, Dorking W									
Folarin	Emmanuel	29	Defender	Eastbourne Borough		4	9	4	
Coggeshall T, Braintree, Eastbourne B									
Folkes	James	31	Midfielder	Tonbridge Angels	9		4	9	
Hayes & Y, Ebbsfleet, Sutton U, Tonbridge A									
Fondop-Talom	Mike	27	Forward	Aldershot Town	3	2		5	1
Whitehawk, Billericay, Oxford C, Guiseley, Halifax (L), Wrexham, Maidenhead (L), Chesterfield, Aldershot									
Fonguck	Wesley	23	Midfielder	Barnet	12	1	1	13	3
Barnet (Y), Hendon (L), Hampton & R (L), Barnet									
Fonkeu	Pierre	23	Forward	Weymouth	6	9	9	15	
Norwich (Y), Lens, Beroe, Grimsby, Weymouth									
Forbes	Dominic		Defender	Chelmsford City			1		
Chelmsford (Y)									
Forbes	Elliot	22	Midfielder	Gateshead		3	1	3	
Gateshead (Y), N Benfield (L)									
Forrest	George		Defender	Braintree Town	5		2	5	
Crawley, Braintree									
Forster	Harry	21	Defender	Bromley (L)	11	9	2	20	2
Watford (Y), St Albans (L), Bromley (L)									
Forster	Rhys		Goalkeeper	Maidenhead United (L)			1		
Met Police, Maidenhead (L)									
Forsyth	George		Midfielder	Hereford FC	1	1	1	2	
Kidderminster, Gloucester, Halesowen, Hereford									
Foulston	Jay	20	Defender	Chippenham Town	1			1	
Newport Co (Y), Norwich U18, Brighton U18, Chippenham (L/P), Taunton, Chippenham (L)									
Fowler	George	23	Defender	Aldershot Town	31	1	1	32	
Ipswich, Aldershot (L), Aldershot									
Fox	Ben	23	Midfielder	Barnet (L)	1			1	1
Burton, Tamworth (L), Solihull (L), Gateshead (L), Barnet (L)									

Key: X - Started; SX - Sub on; S - Non-playing Sub; Ap - Total Appearances; G/Cs - Total goals/clean sheets.

SURNAME	FIRSTNAME	AGE	POSITION	CLUB	APPEARANCES X	SX	S	Ap	G/Cs
Fox	Charlie	22	Defender	Bromley	13			13	
QPR (Y), Wycombe (L), Basingstoke (L), Hampton & R, Bromley									
Fox	Nathan	28	Defender	Alfreton Town	13	3	1	16	
Notts Co (Y), Corby, Kettering (L), Rugby T (L), Rugby T, Stamford, Slough, Mickleover, Rushall O, Rugby T, Coalville, Sutton C, Redditch U, Hednesford, King's Lynn, Alfreton									
Foxley	Darren	24	Forward	Billericay Town	4			4	
Hungerford, St Albans, Bishop's S, Billericay T									
Francis-Angol	Zaine	27	Defender	Boreham Wood	12	6	11	18	
				Hartlepool United	1	5	3	6	
Tottenham, Motherwell, Kidderminster, AFC Fylde, Accrington, Boreham W, Hartlepool									
Franklin	Connor	33	Defender	Brackley Town	8	3		11	
Leicester (Y), Nuneaton, Hinckley U, Alfreton, Nuneaton, Solihull, Brackley									
Fraser	Sean	40	Defender	Slough Town	4	5	5	9	
Slough									
Fraser-Robinson	Cadell		Midfielder	Chelmsford City	1		1	1	
Chelsea (Y), Stevenage, Chelmsford									
Freeman	John	19	Midfielder	Woking (L)	8		2	8	
MK Dons (Y), Woking (L)									
Freemantle	Ethan		Forward	Kidderminster Harriers	5	5	2	10	1
Walsall (Y), Kidderminster									
Frempah	Ben	26	Midfielder	Ebbsfleet United	4	1	3	5	
Cray Wanderers, Leicester, Ross County, Hendon, Solihull M, Guiseley, Wycombe, Ebbsfleet									
French	Tyler	22	Defender	Wrexham	14	3	7	17	
AFC Sudbury, Bradford C, AFC Fylde (L), Wrexham									
Fryatt	Ryan	27	Defender	Kettering Town	17			17	3
Norwich (Y), Cambridge U (Y), Dereham, King's Lynn, Dereham (D), Wisbech (D), Dereham (D), Kettering									
Fuller	Barry	36	Defender	Dorking Wanderers	19		1	19	
Charlton (Y), Gillingham, Barnet, Wimbledon, Gillingham, Dorking W									
Fyfield	Jamal	32	Defender	Boreham Wood	47		1	47	4
York, Grimsby, Welling, Wrexham, Gateshead, Boreham W									
Gallagher	Daniel	24	Midfielder	Dorking Wanderers	1	13	5	14	
Wimbledon, Leatherhead, Dorking W									
Gallagher	Jake	28	Midfielder	Dorking Wanderers		6	5	6	
Millwall, Welling, Aldershot, Dorking W									
Gamble	Owen	22	Defender	York City	2		4	2	
Sunderland (Y), York									
Garner	Gerard	22	Forward	Gateshead (L)	8	1	1	9	4
Fleetwood (Y), Southport (L), FC United (L), Gateshead (L)									
Garner	Scott	31	Defender	Boston United	11	3	3	14	4
Leicester, Mansfield, Grimsby, Cambridge U, Lincoln (L), Boston, Halifax, Guiseley, Boston U									
Garratt	Tyler	24	Defender	Chorley	4	7	6	11	
Bolton (Y), Doncaster, Eastleigh (L), Wimbledon (L), Stockport, Wrexham (L),Chorley									
Gascoigne	Joe		Midfielder	King's Lynn Town	1	1	7	2	
King's Lynn (Y)									
Gash	Michael	34	Forward	King's Lynn Town	25	6	2	31	7
Peterborough (Y), Cambridge U (Y), Cambridge C (Y), Cambridge U, Cambridge C, Ebbsfleet, York, Rushden & D (L), Cambridge U, Braintree (L), Kidderminster (L), Kidderminster, Nuneaton (L), Barnet, King's Lynn, Peterborough S									
Gbolahan	Ade		Forward	Blyth Spartans	3	2		5	
Eastbourne B, Blyth S,									
Gench	Necati		Defender	Maidstone United			1		
Yeni Bogazici, Maidstone									
George	Adriel	24	Midfielder	Oxford City			9		
Oxford U (Y), Banbury (L), Mansfield, Mickleover (L), Hednesford (L), North Ferriby (L), Chippenham, Oxford C									
Gerring	Ben	30	Defender	Woking	26		4	26	2
				Oxford City (L)	4			4	
Cambridge U, Taunton, Truro, Bideford, Hayes & Y, Gosport, Hayes & Y, Truro, Margate, Hayes & Y, Bideford, Torquay, Weston-s-Mare (L), Truro (L), Truro, Billericay, Truro (L), Woking, Oxford C (L)									
Giamattei	Massimo		Midfielder	Hungerford Town (L)		1	2	1	
Swindon (Y), Hungerford (L)									

2020-21 NATIONAL. NORTH & SOUTH PLAYERS — APPEARANCES

SURNAME	FIRSTNAME	AGE	POSITION	CLUB PLAYED FOR	X	SX	S	Ap	G/Cs
Gibbens	Lewis	20	Defender	Boston United	1			1	
Mansfield (Y), Boston U (L), Boston U (L), Boston U, Worksop (L)									
Gibson	Montel	23	Forward	Altrincham (L)	2			2	
Highgate U, Notts Co, Romulus (L), Barwell (L), Hednesford (L), Sutton C (L), Ilkeston T, Redditch, Bedworth U, Halesowen, Grimsby, Altrincham (L)									
Giddens	Jack	29	Goalkeeper	Braintree Town	2			2	
Leyton O (Y), Grindavik (Ice), Tooting & M, Tilbury, Billericay, East Thurrock, Bishop's S, Braintree									
Gilchrist	Jason	26	Forward	York City (L)	1			1	
Burnley (Y), Droylsden (L), Accrington (L), Chester (L), FC United, Southport, Stockport C (L), South Shields, York (L)									
Gillam	Matty	23	Forward	Guiseley	3	6	1	9	
Rochdale (Y), Stalybridge (L), Cork (L), Guiseley									
Gillela	Dinesh	21	Defender	Aldershot Town (L)	3		2	3	
Watford (Y), Bournemouth (Y), Billericay (L), Aldershot (L)									
Gilmour	Harvey	22	Midfielder	Stockport County	4		5	4	
Sheff Utd (Y), Tranmere (L/P), Stockport									
Gittings	Callum	35	Midfielder	Leamington	6	7	3	13	
Kidderminster, Solihull, Telford, Leamington									
Gleeson	Stephen	32	Midfielder	Solihull Moors	23	2	5	25	3
Wolves (Y), Stockport (L), MK Dons, Birmingham, Ipswich, Aberdeen, Solihull M									
Glendon	George	26	Midfielder	Chester	21		1	21	3
Man City (Y), Fleetwood (L), Fleetwood, Carlisle, Chester									
Glover	Luke		Goalkeeper	Eastbourne Borough	1		22	1	
Haywards H, Eastbourne B									
Glover	Ryan	20	Midfielder	Hemel Hempstead Town (L)	2	1		3	
Southampton (Y),Bournemouth (Y), Weymouth (L), Hemel H (L)									
Goather-Braithwaite	Darnell		Forward	Hemel Hempstead Town		1		1	
QPR (Y), Haringey B, Romford, Westfield, Hemel H									
Gobern	Oscar	30	Midfielder	Dover Athletic	11	1		12	
Southampton (Y), MK Dons (L), Huddersfield, Chesterfield (L), QPR, Doncaster (L), Mansfield, Ross Co, Yeovil, Eastleigh, Dover									
Goddard	John	28	Forward	Woking	7	2	2	9	
Reading (Y), Hayes & Y, Woking, Swindon, Stevenage, Bromley (L), Aldershot, Ebbsfleet, Woking									
Golden	Tylor	21	Defender	Notts County (L)	1		2	1	
Wigan (Y), Salford, Notts Co (L)									
Golding	Landon		Defender	Chippenham Town		1	2	1	
Chippenham (Y)									
Goldthrope	Eliot		Midfielder	Farsley Celtic		1	3	1	
Bradford (Y), Mossley (L), Radcliffe (L), Matlock (L), Sunderland (U18), Farsley C									
Gomis	Bedsente	33	Midfielder	Havant & Waterlooville	17	2		19	4
FC Lens, Puertollano, Almeria, Southend, Sutton, Barrow, Dover, Havant & W									
Gondoh	Ryan	24	Midfielder	Hampton & Richmond Borough	8	1		9	4
				Wealdstone	7	7	2	14	4
Barnet, Hendon (L), Met Police, Kingstonian, Carshalton, Maldon & T, Colchester, FC Halifax (L), Concord R, Whyteleafe, Hampton & R, Wealdstone, Hampton & R									
Goodliffe	Ben	22	Defender	Sutton United	37	1	2	38	1
Boreham Wood (Y), Wolves, Dagenham & R (L), Sutton U									
Goodman	Jake	27	Defender	Ebbsfleet United	8	3	2	11	2
Millwall, Luton (L), Aldershot (L), AFC Wimbledon (L), Margate, Braintree, Maidenhead, Bromley, Ebbsfleet									
Goodwin	Will		Forward	Chester	4	4	5	8	1
Chester (Y), Sandbach U (L)									
Gordon	Liam	22	Defender	Dagenham & Redbridge	20	5	2	25	4
Dagenham & R, Whitehawk (L), Dartford (L)									
Gordon	Quba	23	Defender	Welling United	1			1	
QPR (Y), Boreham W (Y), Haringey B (L), Maldon & T, Welling									
Gordon	Rohdell	25	Midfielder	Braintree Town	11	2	1	13	
Arlesey, Bishop's S, Stevenage, Chelmsford (L), Bromley (L), Braintree, Bishop's S, Walton C, St Albans, Braintree									
Goueth	Eitel		Midfielder	Slough Town			2		
Slough (Y)									
Gough	Ethan		Goalkeeper	Oxford City			3		
Oxford C (Y)									

Key: X - Started; SX - Sub on; S - Non-playing Sub; Ap - Total Appearances; G/Cs - Total goals/clean sheets.

SURNAME	FIRSTNAME	AGE	POSITION	CLUB	X	SX	S	Ap	G/Cs
Gould	Matt	27	Goalkeeper	Altrincham	1		6	1	
Hawkes Bay (NZ), Cheltenham, Livingston, Stenhousemuir (L), Stourbridge, Spennymoor, Altrincham									
Grafaiti	Adel	26	Defender	Wealdstone			1		
Nancy (Y), Rangers (Y), Norwich (Y), Oldham (L), Algerian clubs, Yeovil, Mousehole (L), Truro, Wealdstone, Hayes & Y									
Graham	Luke	35	Defender	Kettering Town	12			12	1
Northampton (Y), Billericay (L), Aylesbury U (L), Kettering (L), Forest GR (L), Kettering, King's Lynn (L), Mansfield, York (L), York, Kettering, Luton (L), Forest GR, Hereford U, Alfreton, Brackley, Kettering									
Graham	Ralph		Midfielder	Hungerford Town			3		
Swindon (Y), Highworth T (L), Hungerford (L), Hungerford									
Graham	Sam	20	Defender	Notts County (L)	5		5	5	1
Sheffield U, Halifax (L), C Coast (Aus) (L), Notts Co (L), Notts Co (L)									
Grainger	Charlie	24	Goalkeeper	Dulwich Hamlet	13		2	13	2
Leyton Orient, Farnborough (L), Hampton & R (L), Dulwich H									
Grand	Simon	37	Defender	Chester	22			22	1
Rochdale, Carlisle, Grimsby, Morecambe, Northwich, Fleetwood, Mansfield (L), Aldershot (L), Southport, AFC Telford, Barrow, Salford, AFC Fylde, Chester									
Grant	Freddie	24	Defender	Bath City	11	2		13	1
Oxford U (Y), Farnborough (L), Oxford C, Wealdstone, Maidenhead, Hemel H (L), Bath									
Grant	Reece	26	Forward	Ebbsfleet United	8	2	1	10	2
Wealdstone, Northwood (L), Heybridge, Braintree, Kingstonian (L), Aldershot, Dagenham & R, Aldershot (L), Ebbsfleet U									
Grantham	Alex		Goalkeeper	Oxford City			9		
Oxford C									
Granville	Sam		Midfielder	Barnet			1		
Barnet (Y)									
Gravata	Leone	20	Midfielder	Eastbourne Borough	1	5	7	6	
Brighton (Y), Eastbourne B									
Gray	Jake	25	Midfielder	Hampton & Richmond Borough	20	1		21	2
Crystal P (Y), Cheltenham (L), Hartlepool (L), Luton, Yeovil, Woking, Hampton & R, Woking, Hampton & R (L), Hampton & R									
Gray	Louis	25	Goalkeeper	Chester	22			22	4
Wrexham (Y), Rhyl (L), Cefn Druids (L), Everton, Carlisle (L), Nuneaton, Carlisle, Chester (L), Chester									
Green	Cameron	22	Defender	Wrexham	6			6	
Met Police, Reading (Y), Watford U23, Braintree (L), Wrexham									
Green	Danny	32	Midfielder	Concord Rangers		5	11	5	1
Dag & Red, Charlton, MK Dons (L), MK Dons, Luton, Chelmsford, Concord R									
Green	Danny	30	Midfielder	Wealdstone	33	6	2	39	2
Bishop's S, St Albans, Braintree, Boreham W, Dag & Red, Bishop's S, Maidenhead, Margate, Wealdstone									
Green	Donnabhan		Goalkeeper	Boreham Wood		1	10	1	
Boreham W (Y)									
Green	Kieran	23	Midfielder	FC Halifax	34	10	1	44	4
Hartlepool, Gateshead (L), Gateshead, Blyth S (Lx2), Blyth S, York, FC Halifax									
Green	Mike	32	Defender	Eastleigh	26	10	8	36	1
Bristol R, Port Vale, Eastleigh									
Green	Nathan	29	Defender	Welling United	11		1	11	
Lewes, Billericay, Tonbridge A, Dag & Red, St Albans (L), Dartford, Margate, Dulwich H, Welling									
Green	Paul	38	Midfielder	Boston United	10	5	2	15	1
Doncaster (Y), Derby, Leeds, Ipswich (L), Rotherham, Oldham, Crewe (L/P), Boston U									
Greenfield	Danny	20	Midfielder	Gateshead	13		1	13	1
Gateshead, West Auckland (L)									
Greenhalgh	Ben	29	Midfielder	Tonbridge Angels	9	6	3	15	3
Welling, Ebbsfleet, Inverness, Maidstone, Concord R, Maidstone, Hemel H (L), Concord R, Dartford, Tonbridge A (L), Tonbridge A									
Greenslade	Danny	27	Defender	Chippenham Town	4	1		5	
Bristol R (Y), Bath (L), Gloucester (L), Weston (L), Weston, Hereford, Chippenham									
Greenway	Jamie		Goalkeeper	Braintree Town			1		
Braintree									
Gregory	Reggie		Forward	Chelmsford City		2	5	2	
Chelmsford									
Gregory	Travis		Forward	Dover Athletic	6	2		8	
Chelsea (Y), Rangers (Y), Leatherhead, Dover									
Grey	Joe		Forward	Hartlepool United	3	12	9	15	2
Hartlepool (Y)									

Key: X - Started; SX - Sub on; S - Non-playing Sub; Ap - Total Appearances; Gls - Total goals.

SURNAME	FIRSTNAME	AGE	POSITION	CLUB PLAYED FOR	X	SX	S	Ap	G/Cs
Grice	Harvey		Midfielder	Alfreton Town		1	2	1	
Alfreton (Y)									
Griffiths	Kallum	31	Defender	Gateshead	15			15	
Spennymoor, York, Gateshead									
Griffiths	Priestley	25	Midfielder	Blyth Spartans	12	4		16	
Bishop A, IBV (Ice), Blyth S									
Griffiths	Regan	21	Midfielder	Notts County (L)	6	6	5	12	
Crewe (Y), Notts Co (L)									
Griffiths	Russell	25	Goalkeeper	AFC Telford United	21			21	4
Everton (Yth), Northwich Vic (L), Colwyn (L), Halifax (L), Cheltenham (L), Motherwell (L), Motherwell, AFC Fylde, Chester, Telford (L), Telford									
Grimes	Jamie	30	Defender	Hereford FC	21			21	1
Haverfordwest, Forest GR, Brackley, Kidderminster, Worcester (L), Dover, Cheltenham, Macclesfield, Ebbsfleet, Hereford									
Gubbins	Joseph	19	Defender	Oxford City (L)	6	1	1	7	
Southampton (Y), QPR, Oxford C (L)									
Gudger	Alex	29	Defender	Solihull Moors	10		1	10	3
Brackley, Solihull M									
Guerfi	Zak	22	Midfielder	Tonbridge Angels	3	1		4	
Stevenage (Y), Boden (Swe), Monastir (Tunisa), Braintree, Tonbridge A									
Guilfoyle	Rob	18	Forward	York City		4	5	4	1
York (Y), Hull (U18/23), York									
Gunner	Callum	22	Midfielder	Chippenham Town	11	4		15	
Swindon (Y), Bradford, Chippenham (L), Chippenham									
Gunning	Gavin	30	Defender	Gloucester City	10			10	1
				Chesterfield	18	1	2	19	2
Blackburn (Y), Tranmere (L), Rotherham (L), Bury (L), Motherwell (L), Dundee U, Birmingham, Oldham, Dundee U, Morton, Grimsby, Port Vale, Forest GR, Billericay, Solihull M, Gloucester, Chesterfield									
Guy	Callum	21	Midfielder	Blyth Spartans	9	4	1	13	
South Shields, Blyth S									
Gyasi	Michael	21	Forward	King's Lynn Town	13	9	5	22	2
Chelsea (Y), Leicester (Y), Stoke (U18), Nuneaton (Y), St Ives, King's Lynn									
Hackett-Fairchild	Recco	22	Forward	Bromley (L)	10	3		13	2
Dagenham & R (Y), Dulwich (L), Charlton (Y), Boreham W (L), Bromley (L), Bromley, Portsmouth, Bromley (L), Southend (L)									
Hadler	Tom	24	Goalkeeper	Ebbsfleet United	6		12	6	
Gillingham (Y), Gloucester (L), Gloucester (L), Eastbourne B, Ebbsfleet									
Haigh	Chris	24	Goalkeeper	Concord Rangers	16		2	16	
Northwood, Braintree, Merstham, East Grinstead (L), Maldon/Tiptree (L), Heybridge S, Concord R									
Hainault	Alex		Defender	Gloucester City	1		8	1	
St Francis Uni (US), Ytterhogdal IK (Swe), Gimo IF FK, Westfields, Gloucester, Lydney T (D)									
Haines	Luke	20	Midfielder	Hereford FC (L)	12			12	
Swindon (Y), Chippenham (L), Hereford (L)									
Hall	Asa	34	Midfielder	Torquay United	40	4	1	44	15
Birmingham , Boston (L), Shrewsbury (L), Luton, Oxford U, Shrewsbury, Aldershot (L), Oxford U (L), Cheltenham, York (L), Barrow, Torquay									
Hall	Brandon	27	Goalkeeper	Hereford FC	12		2	12	6
Charlton (Y), Nike Acad, St Mirren, Hayes & Y, Ebbsfleet, Lewes (L), Woking, Kidderminster, Hereford									
Hall	Connor	23	Forward	Woking		4		4	
				Chorley (L/P)	15	2		17	8
Sheff Utd (Y), Woking (L), Bolton, Accrington (L), Chorley (L), Woking, Chorley (L/P)									
Hall	Kole		Forward	AFC Telford United (L)	2			2	
Radcliffe, Telford (L)									
Hall	Louis	22	Midfielder	Oxford City	21		2	21	2
Aston Villa (Y), Stourbridge, Oxford C									
Hall	Ryan	27	Forward	Spennymoor Town	8	6	1	14	2
Workington, Curzon Ashton, Spennymoor, Bradford PA (L)									
Hall	Ryan		Goalkeeper	Aldershot Town	4		10	4	
Aldershot (Y)									
Hall	Will		Defender	Altrincham			3		
Salford, Altrincham, Whitchurch A (D)									
Hall-Johnson	Reece	26	Defender	Wrexham	33	2	7	35	8
Norwich, Maidstone, Bishop's St, Braintree, Grimsby, Chester (L), Northampton, Wrexham									

Key: X - Started; SX - Sub on; S - Non-playing Sub; Ap - Total Appearances; G/Cs - Total goals/clean sheets.

SURNAME	FIRSTNAME	AGE	POSITION	CLUB	X	SX	S	Ap	G/Cs
Halls	Andy	29	Defender	Chorley	17		2	17	1
Stockport, Macclesfield, Chester, Guiseley, Curzon A, Chorley									
Hamblin	Leo	18	Defender	Woking	8	2	4	10	
Woking (Y),									
Hamilton	Spencer		Defender	Chippenham Town	7		5	7	
Gloucester, Chippenham									
Hamilton	Tyrell	21	Forward	Leamington (D)			1		
Bournemouth (Y), Salisbury (L), Gosport (L), Alvechurch, Leamington (D)									
Hammond	James	24	Midfielder	Eastbourne Borough	23			23	4
Peacehaven & T, Lewes, Eastbourne B									
Hamon	James	25	Goalkeeper	Torquay United (L)		1	6	1	
Exeter (Y), Hayes & Y (L), Gloucester (L), Truro, Torquay (L)									
Hampson	Connor	28	Midfielder	Altrincham	19	2	6	21	1
Curzon Ashton, Stockport, Altrincham									
Hancock	Josh	30	Midfielder	Altrincham	35	3	1	38	12
Witton, Telford, Witton (L), Witton, Salford, Nantwich, Altrincham									
Hancox	Mitch	27	Defender	Solihull Moors	13	12	14	25	1
Birmingham, Crawley (L), Macclesfield, MK Dons, Solihull M, Harrogate T (L)									
Hanford	Dan	30	Goalkeeper	Southport	14		6	14	5
Hereford, Floriana, Carlisle, Gateshead, Southport									
Hanfry	Tom	20	Defender	Concord Rangers	6	1		7	
				Tonbridge Angels	3			3	
Bournemouth (Y), Concord, Carshalton, Tonbridge A									
Hanks	Joe	26	Midfielder	Chippenham Town	16	2		18	3
Cheltenham, Gloucester (L), Gloucester (L), Gloucester, Chippenham									
Hannigan	Tom	32	Midfielder	Altrincham	34		5	34	
Vauxhall M (Y), AFC Fylde, Altrincham									
Hanson	Jacob	23	Defender	Curzon Ashton	3	3	3	6	
Huddersfield, Bradford, Halifax (L), Halifax (L), Halifax, Curzon A									
Hanson	Ryan	20	Midfielder	Dover Athletic (L)	7			7	
Dover Rangers, Dover (Y), Crystal P (Y), Hull, Dover (L)									
Harbottle	Riley	20	Defender	Wealdstone (L)	11			11	
Notts F (Y), Wealdstone (L)									
Harding	James		Forward	Hungerford Town	1	8	11	9	1
Gloucester, Cinderford, Hungerford									
Hardy	James	25	Midfielder	AFC Telford United	17	4		21	4
				Altrincham	5	6	6	11	1
Man City (Y), AFC Fylde, FC Halifax (L), Walsall, Telford U, Altrincham									
Harfield	Ollie	23	Defender	Weymouth	42	1		43	
Bournemouth, Poole (L), Boreham W (L), Dagenham & R, Weymouth									
Harley	Ryan	36	Midfielder	Bath City	14	1	1	15	
Exeter (Y), Swansea, Exeter (L), Brighton, MK Dons (L), Swindon, Exeter (L), Exeter, MK Dons, Bath									
Harness	Nathan	21	Goalkeeper	Welling United (L)	2			2	
West Ham (Y), Charlton, Billericay (L), Welling (L)									
Harratt	Kian	19	Forward	Guiseley (L)	5	1	1	6	
Huddersfield (Y), Harrogate T (L), Guiseley (L)									
Harris	Ben	30	Forward	Slough Town	4	1		5	2
Team Wellington (NZ), Slough									
Harris	Ed	30	Defender	Dorking Wanderers	19			19	1
QPR (Y), Hayes & Y (L), AFC Wimbledon, Dover, Havant & W, Dorking W									
Harris	Jay	34	Midfielder	Wrexham	28	5	2	33	1
Everton, Accrington, Chester, Wrexham, Tranmere, Macclesfield, Wrexham									
Harris	Warren	30	Midfielder	Slough Town	10	4	1	14	3
Staines, Slough									
Harris-Sealey	Andrew	22	Forward	Dulwich Hamlet		1		1	
Wolves (Y), Farnborough, Dulwich									
Harrison	Byron	34	Forward	Altrincham	7	1	3	8	
Havant & W, Worthing, Boreham Wd, Harrow B, Ashford (Mx), Carshalton, Stevenage, AFC Wimbledon, Cheltenham, Chesterfield, Stevenage (L), Barrow, Sutton U (L), Barnet, Barrow, Altrincham									

2020-21 NATIONAL. NORTH & SOUTH PLAYERS

SURNAME	FIRSTNAME	AGE	POSITION	CLUB PLAYED FOR	X	SX	S	Ap	G/Cs
					APPEARANCES				
Harrison	Callum	24	Midfielder	Chelmsford City	12	5		17	
Colchester (Y), Chelmsford									
Harrison	Tom		Defender	Chippenham Town (L)	5	1		6	1
				Gloucester City	2			2	
Yate (Y), Paulton, Bristol C, Hereford (L), Weston (L), Gloucester (L), Chippenham (L), Gloucester									
Harrop	Max	27	Midfielder	Curzon Ashton	4	2	1	6	
Bury (Y), Blyth S (L), Hinckley U (L), Tamworth (L), Nantwich, Altrincham, Curzon A									
Hasani	Lirak	19	Midfielder	Gateshead (L)	1			1	
Doncaster (Y), Gateshead (L)									
Hatfield	Will	29	Midfielder	Darlington	16			16	2
Leeds, York (L), Accrington (L), Accrington, Halifax (L), Guiseley, Darlington									
Haughton	Nick	26	Midfielder	AFC Fylde	13	2		15	8
Bolton (Y), Runcorn Town, Fleetwood, Nantwich (L), Salford (L), Chorley (L), Salford, AFC Fylde									
Havern	Gianluca	32	Defender	Bradford (Park Avenue)	14			14	2
Stockport (Y), Mansfield, Stockport, Mossley, Ashton U, Hyde, Altrincham, Telford, Bradford PA									
Haw	Adam	19	Forward	Guiseley	1	9	6	10	2
Burnley (Y), Leeds (Y), Bradford C (Y), Guiseley									
Hawkins	Ryan	26	Forward	King's Lynn Town		1		1	
Norwich (Y), Dereham, St Neots, King's Lynn, Dereham (L)									
Hawkridge	Terry	31	Midfielder	Boston United	13	3	1	16	2
Tranmere (Y), Carlton, Hucknall, Carlton, Gainsborough, Scunthorpe, Mansfield (L), Lincoln C (L), Lincoln C, Notts Co, Solihull, Boston U									
Hayes	Nicholas	22	Goalkeeper	Hemel Hempstead Town	3			3	1
Norwich (Y), Woking (L), Salford, Hemel H									
Hayhurst	Will	27	Midfielder	Farsley Celtic	15	2	1	17	3
PNE (Y), York (L), Notts Co, Warrington, Farsley C									
Headley	Jaheim	19	Midfielder	Welling United (L)	1	1	4	2	
Huddersfield (Y), Bradford PA (L), Welling (L)									
Hearn	Eli		Defender	Wealdstone		2	14	2	
Wealdstone									
Heath	Connor	20	Midfielder	Farsley Celtic (D)		1	3	1	
Crewe (Y), Nantwich, Farsley C (D)									
Heaton	ADAM	18	Midfielder	Yeovil Town			4		
Yeovil (Y)									
Hedley	Ben	22	Midfielder	Darlington	6	4	4	10	
Morecambe (Y), Bradford PA, Darlington									
Hemmings	Ashley	30	Midfielder	Kidderminster Harriers	17			17	7
Wolves (Yth), Cheltenham (L), Torquay (L), Plymouth (L), Walsall, Burton (L), Dagenham & R, Mansfield, Boston U, Salford, AFC Fylde, Altrincham (L), Altrincham (L), Kidderminster									
Henderson	Ethan	19	Forward	Bradford (Park Avenue)			1		
Hartlepool (Y), Carlisle (Y), Tennessee FC (Y), York (Y), Bradford (PA),									
Henley	Adam	27	Defender	Chorley	5	7	1	12	
Blackburn (Y), Salt Lake, Bradford C, Chorley									
Henly	Jonathan	27	Goalkeeper	Tonbridge Angels	15			15	5
Reading (Y), Bromley (L), Aldershot (L), Oxford U (L), Welling (L), Ipswich, Hemel H, Margate (L), Tonbridge A (L), Tonbridge A									
Henry	Dion	23	Goalkeeper	Billericay Town	13		2	13	1
Peterborough (Y), Soham R (L), Boston U (L), Crystal P, Maidstone (L), Hampton & RB (L), Billericay T									
Henry	Korrey	21	Forward	Dulwich Hamlet	3	7	2	10	1
West Ham (Y), Yeovil, Braintree, Bromley, Welling (L/P), Dulwich H									
Henry	Ronnie	37	Defender	Billericay Town	17			17	
Tottenham (Y), Southend (L), Dublin City, Stevenage, Luton, Stevenage, Billericay T									
Henry	Will	22	Goalkeeper	Bath City	4		14	4	1
Bristol C (Y), Swindon (Y), Shrivenham (L), Dunstable (L), Hampton & R (L), Chippenham (L), Swindon S (L), Gloucester (L), Chippenham (L), Gloucester (L), Hereford (L), Hungerford (L), Bath City									
Henshaw	Ryan	27	Defender	Braintree Town	3			3	
Chertsey, Sudbury, Heybridge, Bishop's S, Braintree									
Herbert	George	17	Forward	Kettering Town			1		
Kettering (Y)									
Hernandez	Alex	18	Forward	Concord Rangers			2		
Concord R (Y)									

Key: X - Started; SX - Sub on; S - Non-playing Sub; Ap - Total Appearances; G/Cs - Total goals/clean sheets.

SURNAME	FIRSTNAME	AGE	POSITION	CLUB	X	SX	S	Ap	G/Cs
Hernandez	Loic	21	Defender	Barnet	1	1	3	2	
Barnet (Y), Wingate & F (L)									
Heslop	Simon	34	Midfielder	Blyth Spartans	16			16	3
Barnsley, Kidderminster (L), Tamworth (L), Northwich (L), Halifax (L), Grimsby (L), Kettering (L), Luton (L), Oxford U, Stevenage, Mansfield, Torquay, Wrexham, York, Eastleigh (L), Boston U, Blyth S									
Hey	Lewis	18	Midfielder	Guiseley	1	4	4	5	
Guiseley (Y)									
Hibbs	Jake	25	Midfielder	Bradford (Park Avenue)	15			15	2
Halifax, Droylsden (L), Hyde (L), Telford (L), Bradford PA (L), Spennymoor, Bradford PA (L/P),									
Hickman	Jak	22	Forward	King's Lynn Town (L)	1			1	
Coventry (Y), Ashton U (L), Hereford (L), Bolton, King's Lynn (L)									
Higgs	Jordan	24	Midfielder	Dulwich Hamlet	8	3	1	11	
Bromley, Carshalton, Bromley, Dulwich H									
Hill	Ethan	19	Defender	Chippenham Town		2	3	2	
Southampton (Y), Forest GR (Y), Chippenham (Y)									
Hill	Josh	29	Defender	Dartford	3	3	14	6	1
Ilkeston T, Coalville T, Worksop, Dartford, Boreham W, Hemel (L), Havant & W (L), St Albans, Wealdstone, Braintree, Welling, Dartford									
Hill	Ryan	23	Midfielder	Hampton & Richmond Borough	5			5	
				Eastleigh	22	11	3	33	4
Stoke (Y), Hampton & R, Eastleigh									
Hinchiri	Bilel	25	Midfielder	Dover Athletic	2	3	1	5	
Charitoise (Fra), Dover, Tonbridge A (L)									
Hinchliffe	Ben	32	Goalkeeper	Stockport County	49		2	49	21
PNE (Y), Kendal (L), Tranmere (L), Derby, Oxford U, Worcester, Kendal, Bamber B, Northwich V, AFC Fylde, Stockport									
Hinchy	Jack		Midfielder	Stockport County		1	1	1	
Stockport (Y)									
Hinds	Akeem	22	Defender	Brackley Town	3		5	3	
Rotherham (Y), Frickley (L), Bradford PA (L), Lincoln, Brackley									
Hinds	Freddie	22	Forward	Bath City (L)	5			5	1
Luton (Y), Bristol C, Cheltenham (L), Wrexham (L), Colchester (L), Bath (L), Bath (L)									
Hinds	Kaylen	23	Forward	Aldershot Town	1	6	5	7	
Leyton O (Y), Arsenal (Y), Stevenage (L), VfL Wolfsburg, SpVgg Greuther Furth (L), Watford, Aldershot									
Hobbs	Lewis	21	Defender	Welling United (L)	10		2	10	
Crystal P (U23), Welling (L)									
Hobson	Craig	33	Forward	Curzon Ashton		1		1	
Kendal Town, Stalybridge, Stockport, Lincoln (L), Guiseley, Chester, Altrincham, Aberystwyth, Ashton U, Alfreton, Ashton U, Curzon A									
Hodges	Paul	28	Forward	Slough Town	10	4	1	14	3
				Woking	4	10	2	14	
Hartley, Woking, Slough, Woking									
Hodgkiss	Jared	34	Defender	Hereford FC	20			20	2
West Brom, Aberdeen (L), Northampton (L), Forest Green, Kidderminster, Torquay (L), Macclesfield, Hereford									
Hoey	Jack		Midfielder	Weymouth	3	5	6	8	
Bournemouth (Y), AFC Totton, Greenville (US), Gardner Webb Uni, Weymouth									
Hogan	Liam	32	Defender	Stockport County	46		2	46	2
Stockport Sports, Halifax, Fleetwood, Macclesfield (L), Tranmere, Gateshead, Salford, Stockport									
Holden	James		Goalkeeper	Maidenhead United (L)	5			5	1
Reading (Y), Maidenhead (L)									
Holgate	Harrison	20	Defender	Altrincham (L)	3			3	
Fleetwood (Y), Ashton U (L), Altrincham (L)									
Holland	Jack	29	Defender	Bromley	15	11	12	26	2
Bromley, Crystal Palace, Eastbourne (L), Bromley									
Hollands	Danny	35	Midfielder	Eastleigh	28	5	9	33	
Chelsea, Torquay (L), Bournemouth, Charlton, Swindon (L), Gillingham (L), Portsmouth (L), Portsmouth, Crewe, Eastleigh									
Hollis	Guy	30	Defender	Slough Town	4		1	4	
Carshalton, Godalming, Slough									
Hollis	Haydon	28	Defender	Chesterfield	19	1	6	20	3
Notts Co (Y), Barrow (L), Darlington (L), Forest Green, Chesterfield (L), Chesterfield									
Holmes	Jordan	24	Goalkeeper	Ebbsfleet United	14		4	14	4
Bournemouth (Y), Eastbourne B (L), St Mirren (L), Ebbsfleet									

2020-21 NATIONAL. NORTH & SOUTH PLAYERS

SURNAME	FIRSTNAME	AGE	POSITION	CLUB PLAYED FOR	X	SX	S	Ap	G/Cs
Holness	Luke		Defender	Braintree Town		4	1	4	
Braintree									
Holness	Omar	27	Defender	Darlington	4	7	1	11	
Real Salt Lake, Real Monarchs (L), Bethlehem Steel, Darlington									
Holohan	Gavan	29	Midfielder	Hartlepool United	40	6	1	46	10
Hull, Alfreton, Drogheda, Cork, Galway Utd, Waterford, Hartlepool									
Hooper	Jonathan	27	Forward	Barnet	26	2	1	28	8
Newcastle (Y), Workington (L), Northampton, Alfreton (L), Farnborough (L), Havant & W, Port Vale, Northampton (L), Grimsby, Bromley (L), Wrexham, Barnet									
Hopkins	Jack		Midfielder	Stockport County		1	2	1	
Stockport (Y)									
Hopper	Luke	32	Forward	Hungerford Town	6	7	2	13	3
Swindon Sup, Gloucester, Hungerford, Salisbury, Chippenham, Hungerford									
Hornby-Forbes	Tyler	25	Midfielder	Spennymoor Town	10	3	1	13	1
Fleetwood (Y), Brighton U23, Accrington (L), Newport, AFC Fylde, Spennymoor									
Horsfield	James	25	Defender	Wrexham	14	4	10	18	
Man City (Y), Doncaster (L), NAC Breda (Hol), NAC Breda, Scunthorpe, Dundee (L), Wrexham (L), Wrexham									
Horton	Grant		Defender	Bath City (L)	10			10	
Cheltenham (Y), Worcester (L), Bromsgrove S (L), Yate (L), Chippenham (L), Bath (L)									
House	Ben	21	Forward	Eastleigh	37	3		40	10
Reading (Y), Swindon (L), Dagenham & R (L), Eastleigh									
House	Bradley	22	Goalkeeper	Sutton United			8		
Arsenal (Y), WBA (Y), Chippenham (Lx2), Sutton U, Horsham (D)									
Howard	Rob	22	Midfielder	King's Lynn Town (L)	16			16	
Southend (Y), Dartford (L), Braintree (L), King's Lynn (L)									
Howarth	George	19	Forward	Altrincham			1		
Altrincham (Y)									
Howarth	Mark	22	Midfielder	Guiseley	11	2	4	13	2
Burnley (Y), Salford, Marine (L), Buxton (L), Droylsden (L), Guiseley,									
Howe	Callum	27	Defender	Solihull Moors	5			5	1
Scunthorpe, Gateshead (L), Alfreton (L), Lincoln, Southport (L), Eastleigh (L),Port Vale, Harrogate, Solihull M									
Howell	Luke	34	Midfielder	Hemel Hempstead Town	1		1	1	
Gillingham, MK Dons, Lincoln (L), Lincoln, Dagenham & R, Boreham W, Dagenham & R, Aldershot, Hemel H									
Howells	Jake	30	Midfielder	Hemel Hempstead Town	13	3	1	16	
Luton, Yeovil (L), Eastleigh, Dagenham & R, Ebbsfleet (L), Billericay, Hemel H									
Howes	Sam	23	Goalkeeper	Dorking Wanderers	8		1	8	2
West Ham (Y), Wealdstone (L), Hampton & R (L), Watford, Hampton & R (L), Eastbourne B (L), Woking, Chelmsford (L), Dorking W (L), Dorking W									
Howkins	Kyle	25	Defender	Solihull Moors (L)	6	1		7	
Kidderminster, WBA, Mansfield (L), Port Vale (L), Port Vale (L), Newport, Solihull M (L)									
Hoyte	Gavin	31	Defender	Maidstone United	18			18	1
Arsenal, Watford (L), Brighton (L), Lincoln (L), AFC Wimbledon (L), Dagenham & R, Gillingham, Barnet, Eastleigh, Dagenham & R, Maidstone									
Huddart	Ryan	24	Goalkeeper	Boreham Wood			29		
Charlton (Y), Arsenal (Y), Eastleigh (L), Boreham W, Bromley, Boreham W									
Hudlin	Kyle		Forward	Solihull Moors	24	15	2	39	12
Boldmere S & S F, Solihull U, Solihull M									
Hudson	Theo	20	Midfielder	Darlington		8	8	8	
Leeds (Y), Darlington									
Huffer	William	22	Goalkeeper	Bradford (Park Avenue)	1		7	1	
Leeds (Y), Barnet (L), Bradford (PA), Bradford C									
Hughes	Ben		Goalkeeper	Chippenham Town			7		
Chippenham (Y)									
Hughes	Charlee	25	Forward	Concord Rangers (L)	2	4		6	
				Wealdstone	8	9	1	17	1
Brentwood, Maldon, Wealdstone, Concord R (L)									
Hughes	Connor	28	Midfielder	Curzon Ashton	9	5	3	14	
Oldham (Y), Hyde, Halifax, Bradford PA (L), Worcester, Warrington, Stalybridge, Curzon A, Atherton Col (L)									
Hughes	David	28	Goalkeeper	Welling United (L)			2		
Thurrock, East Thurrock, Enfield T, Harlow, Aveley, Welling (L)									

Key: X - Started; SX - Sub on; S - Non-playing Sub; Ap - Total Appearances; G/Cs - Total goals/clean sheets.

SURNAME	FIRSTNAME	AGE	POSITION	CLUB	X	SX	S	Ap	G/Cs
Hughes	Liam	28	Midfielder	Kettering Town (L)	1	1		2	
Cambridge U, Inverness CT, Barrow, Guiseley, Billericay, Darlington, Gainsborough, Bradford PA, Frickley (D), Matlock, Kettering (L)									
Hughes	Mark	37	Midfielder	Billericay Town			1		
Chester, Barnet, Eastleigh, Chelmsford, Eastbourne B, Bishop's S, Cheshunt, Billericay T (Asst Manager)									
Hughes	Matty	28	Forward	Chester		6	6	6	
Skelmersdale, Fleetwood, Chester (L), AFC Fylde, Chorley, Chester									
Huk	Slavomir	28	Goalkeeper	Dorking Wanderers	11		1	11	4
Kosice (Slovakia), Dorking W									
Hulme	Jordan	30	Midfielder	AFC Fylde	12	4	1	16	4
Padiham, Ramsbottom, Salford, Altrincham, AFC Fylde									
Hungbo	Joseph	21	Midfielder	Aldershot Town (L)	2	4		6	
Watford (Y), Aldershot (L)									
Hunt	Johnny	30	Defender	Kettering Town	1			1	
Wrexham (Y), Droylsden (L), Cambridge U, Wrexham (L), Chester, Mansfield, Stevenage, Hamilton, KetteringConnah's Q									
Hunt	Max	22	Defender	Yeovil Town (L)	21	3	3	24	
WBA (Y), Matlock, Derby (U23), Aldershot (L), Carlisle, Yeovil (L)									
Hunt	Nicky	37	Defender	Darlington	16			16	
Bolton (Y), Birmingham (L), Derby (L), Bristol C, Preston, Rotherham, Accrington (L), Accrington, Mansfield, Leyton O, Notts Co, Crewe, Darlington									
Hunter	Jack	23	Midfielder	Gateshead	12	2	1	14	
Newcastle (Y), Gateshead, Blyth S, Gateshead									
Husin	Noor	24	Midfielder	Dartford	16	1		17	1
Reading (Y), Hemel H (L), Crystal P, Accrington (L), Notts Co, Stevenage, Dartford									
Hussain	Tabish	20	Forward	Bradford (Park Avenue)		5	5	5	
Guiseley (Y), Bradford (PA)									
Hutchinson	Josh		Midfielder	Billericay Town	6	3		9	1
Billericay T, Potters B, Wealdstone, Potters B, Billericay T									
Hutchinson	Regan	19	Defender	Chesterfield			2		
Rothernham (Y), Chesterfield (Y), Sheffield FC (L)									
Hyde	Jake	30	Forward	FC Halifax	22	6		28	12
Swindon, Weymouth (L), Weymouth (L), Barnet, Hayes & Yeading, Dundee, Dunfermline, Dundee, Barnet, York, Stevenage, Maidenhead (L), Maidenhead, Woking, FC Halifax									
Hyde	Tyrique	22	Midfielder	Dulwich Hamlet	8	8	1	16	1
Dagenham & Redbridge, Whitehawk (L), Ware (L), Colchester, Maldon/T (L), Dartford (L), Dulwich H									
Iaciofano	Joe	22	Forward	Havant & Waterlooville	12	7	2	19	5
Northampton (Y), Chesham (L), Brackley (L), St Albans, Havant & W									
Ibrain	Ion	23	Forward	Bradford (Park Avenue)		3	1	3	
Zimbru (Moldova), Nisporeni, Milsami, Codru, Bradford (PA)									
Ijaha	David	31	Midfielder	Dartford	8	3	4	11	
Harrow, Tonbridge A, Hayes & Y, Whitehawk, Plymouth, Wealdstone, Whitehawk, Welling, Dulwich H, Dartford									
Ilesanmi	Femi	30	Defender	Boreham Wood	44	1	3	45	1
AFC Wimbledon, QPR, Ashford T (Kent), Dagenham & R, Histon (L), York, Boreham W, Dover, Boreham W,									
Ilic	Stefan	29	Midfielder	Welling United	4	3	5	7	2
Rosengard (Swe), Lunds BK, Ostersund, Syrianska, Brage, GAIS, Syrianska, Welling									
Imray	Danny		Midfielder	Chelmsford City	12	1	1	13	
Chelmsford (Y)									
Ince	Rohan	28	Midfielder	Maidenhead United	30	1		31	
Chelsea (Y), Yeovil (L), Brighton, Fulham (L), Swindon (L), Bury (L), Cheltenham, Maidenhead									
Inman	Dean	30	Defender	Hampton & Richmond Borough	17			17	
Hampton & R, Hayes & Yeading, Maidenhead, Billericay, Hampton & R									
Isaac	Chez	28	Midfielder	Chelmsford City	14	2		16	
Watford, Tamworth (L), Boreham W, Braintree, Woking, Dartford, Chelmsford									
Isherwood	Louis		Defender	Chorley		1		1	
Chorley (Y)									
Isiaka	Kareem		Forward	Welling United		3	1	3	
Charlton (Y), Welling, Vikingur O (Ice)									
Isted	Harvey	24	Goalkeeper	Wealdstone (L)	24			24	4
Stoke (Y), Luton, Oxford C (L), Wealdstone (L), Wealdstone (L)									
Jackman	Josh		Defender	Slough Town	13		2	13	1
Slough									

Johnson Bobby - Alfreton Town.

Jones James - Alfreton Town.

Kelly-Evans Dion - Notts Co.

Kennedy Connor - Kettering Town.

Key: X - Started; SX - Sub on; S - Non-playing Sub; Ap - Total Appearances; G/Cs - Total goals/clean sheets.

SURNAME	FIRSTNAME	AGE	POSITION	CLUB	X	SX	S	Ap	G/Cs
Jackson	Bradley	24	Forward	Chester	7	4		11	
Burnley (Y), Bangor (L), Southport (L), Ashton U, Chester									
Jackson	Declan	18	Goalkeeper	St Albans City			2		
St Albans (Y)									
Jackson	Marlon	30	Forward	Chippenham Town	5			5	
Bristol C (Y), Hereford (L), Aldershot (L), Aldershot (L), Northampton (L), Cheltenham (L), Telford (L), Hereford, Bury, Lincoln (L), Halifax, Oxford C, Tranmere, Oxford C, Newport Co, Hereford, Weston, Gloucester, Chippenham									
Jackson	Samuel	21	Goalkeeper	Braintree Town	4			4	
Millwall (Y), Dundee (U20), Aberdeen, Braintree									
Jackson	Simeon	34	Forward	Chelmsford City	1	1		2	1
				King's Lynn Town	6	11	2	17	6
Gillingham (Y), Norwich, Braunschweig (Ger), Millwall, Coventry, Barnsley, Blackburn, Walsall, Grimsby (L), St Mirren, Kilmarnock, Stevenage, Chelmsford, King's Lynn									
Jallow	Momodou		Forward	Boreham Wood	1	2	7	3	
Boreham W (U19)									
James	Bradley	21	Goalkeeper	Aldershot Town (L)	11	1	4	12	3
				Hartlepool United (L)	6			6	2
Middlesbrough (Y), Gateshead (L), Aldershot (L), Hartlepool (L)									
James	Cameron	23	Defender	Chelmsford City	11	1		12	1
Colchester (Y), Chelmsford (L), Braintree (L), Maidstone (L), Welling (L), Chelmsford									
James	Jack	21	Defender	Gloucester City	11	6	3	17	2
Luton (Y), Hitchin (L), Havant & W (L), Braintree, Gloucester									
James	Lloyd	33	Midfielder	Bath City	3	6	10	9	
Southampton (Y), Colchester, Leyton O, Exeter, Forest GR, Torquay (L), Bath									
James	Steven		Defender	Eastbourne Borough	23			23	
Lewes (Y), US Colleges, Eastbourne B									
Jameson	Pete	28	Goalkeeper	York City	16			16	5
South Shields, Darlington, Blyth S, York									
Jarvis	Daniel	23	Midfielder	Wrexham	11	12	15	23	
Stoke (Y), Wrexham									
Jarvis	Matt	35	Midfielder	Woking	10	13	8	23	1
Gillingham (Y), Wolves, West Ham, Norwich (L), Norwich, Woking									
Jarvis	Ryan	34	Midfielder	King's Lynn Town	18	2	4	20	
Norwich (Y), Colchester (L), Leyton O (L), Kilmarnock (L), Notts Co (L), Leyton O, Northampton (L), Walsall, Torquay (L), Torquay, York, Aldershot (L), Lowestoft, King's Lynn									
Jebb	Jack	25	Midfielder	Dartford	17		1	17	1
Arsenal (Y), Stevenage (L), Newport Co, Sutton U, Welling, Wealdstone, Dartford									
Jebbison	Daniel	17	Forward	Chorley (L)		1	2	1	
Sheff Utd (Y), Chorley (L)									
Jeffers	Shaun	29	Forward	St Albans City	20			20	11
Coventry, Cheltenham (L), Cambridge U (L), Tamworth (L), Peterborough, Newport Co, Yeovil, Woking (L), Chelmsford, Boreham W, Hampton & R (L), Brackley, Chelmsford, St Albans									
Jeffrey	Anthony	26	Midfielder	Wrexham	4	5		9	
Arsenal, Stevenage (L), Boreham W (L), Wycombe (L), Boreham W, Welling, Concord R, Boreham W (L), Boreham W, Forest Green, Boreham W (L), Boreham W (L),Sutton, Dover (L), Dover, Wrexham									
Jennings	Connor	29	Forward	Stockport County	20	4		24	3
Scunthorpe, Stockport (L), Macclesfield (L), Grismby (L), Wrexham, Tranmere, Macclesfield (L), Stockport									
Jennings	James	33	Defender	Stockport County	28	5	4	33	2
Macclesfield, Altrincham (L), Kettering, Cambridge U, Mansfield (L), Mansfield, Forest Green, Cheltenham (L), Morecambe (L), Wrexham (L), Wrexham, Stockport									
John	Alex	20	Midfielder	Yeovil Town			1		
Yeovil (Y)									
John	Louis	27	Defender	Sutton United	38			38	6
Sutton U (Y), Crawley, Sutton U (L), Sutton U, Hemel H (L), Hampton & R (L), Ebbsfleet (L), Cambridge U, Sutton U (L), Sutton U									
John-Lewis	Lenell	32	Forward	Hereford FC	13			13	12
Lincoln C, Bury, Grimsby, Newport, Shrewsbury, Hereford									
Johnson	Billy		Goalkeeper	Maidstone United			2		
Maidstone									

2020-21 NATIONAL. NORTH & SOUTH PLAYERS

SURNAME	FIRSTNAME	AGE	POSITION	CLUB PLAYED FOR	APPEARANCES				
					X	SX	S	Ap	G/Cs
Johnson	Bobby		Midfielder	Alfreton Town	12	4		16	2
AFC Goole, North Ferriby, Alfreton									
Johnson	Chiori	23	Defender	Welling United	9			9	
Arsenal (Y), Blackburn (L), Bolton, Welling									
Johnson	Connor	23	Defender	Kettering Town	4	1		5	
Wolves (Y), Boreham W (L), Telford (L), Walsall (L), Kilmarnock (L), Sunderland (U23), Kettering									
Johnson	Elliott	26	Midfielder	Dagenham & Redbridge	41	1	2	42	
Barnet (Y), Dagenham & R									
Johnson	Elliott	24	Defender	Concord Rangers			5		
Lone Star (US), Concord R									
Johnson	Gabriel	24	Forward	Guiseley	13	4	1	17	1
Brighouse, Guiseley									
Johnson	Matt	31	Midfielder	Braintree Town	15			15	1
Rushden & D, Dover, Braintree, Bishop's S, Ebbsfleet, Bishop's S (L), Margate (L), Margate, Billericay T, Chelmsford, Hornchurch, Braintree									
Johnson	Michael	27	Goalkeeper	St Albans City	18			18	9
Hitchin, Braintree, St Albans									
Johnson	Oli	33	Forward	Bradford (Park Avenue)	2	5	1	7	3
Nostell Miners, Stockport, Norwich, Yeovil (L), Yeovil (L), Oxford U, York, Guiseley, Bradford PA (L), Bradford PA									
Johnson	Ryan	24	Defender	Hartlepool United	37	2	1	39	5
Stevenage Borough, St Albans City (L), Boreham Wood (L), Nuneaton Town (L), Kidderminster (L), Kidderminster, Hartlepool									
Johnson	Sam	28	Goalkeeper	FC Halifax	45			45	9
Stoke, Port Vale, Stafford (L), Alfreton (L), Halifax (L), Gateshead (L), Halifax (L), Halifax									
Johnson-Schuster	Marcus		Defender	Braintree Town	6	2		8	
Basingstoke, Wealdstone, Hungerford, Hayes & Y, Braintree									
Johnston	Carl	19	Midfielder	Farsley Celtic (L)	14	2		16	1
Fleetwood (Y), Farsley C (L)									
Johnston	Ethan	19	Forward	Kettering Town (L)		1	2	1	
Northampton (Y), Kettering (L)									
Johnston	John	26	Midfielder	Chester	17	2	2	19	2
Kidsgrove, Leek, Crewe, Leek (L), Alfreton (L), Alfreton, Salford (L), Salford, Nantwich (L), Altrincham, Chester									
Johnstone	Max	22	Goalkeeper	AFC Fylde			4		
Man Utd (Y), Sunderland (U23), St Johnstone, AFC Fylde									
Jones	Andrai Ricardo	29	Defender	Hereford FC	3	1		4	
				Guiseley	9		1	9	
Bury (Y), Altrincham (L), Barnsley, Tranmere (L), Alfreton (L), Gateshead, Southport, Bala, Guiseley, Hereford, Guiseley									
Jones	Aron	27	Defender	King's Lynn Town	10		1	10	1
Ipswich (Y), College Football (US), Philadelphia Union, Bethlehem Steel (L), Harlow, King's Lynn									
Jones	Ciaren	21	Defender	Gloucester City		1	2	1	
Luton (Y), Norwich (U23), Gloucester, South Shields									
Jones	Daniel	34	Defender	Hereford FC	9	1		10	
Wolves (Y), Northampton (L), Oldham (L), Notts Co (L), Bristol R (L), Sheff Wed, Port Vale, Chesterfield, Notts Co, Cambridge U, Hereford									
Jones	Dylan		Defender	Hereford FC	1	3	5	4	
Bangor, Hereford									
Jones	Eddie	30	Midfielder	Chippenham Town	17			17	
Solihull, Telford, Oxford C, Chippenham									
Jones	Emem		Defender	AFC Telford United	12			12	1
Telford (Y)									
Jones	James	22	Defender	Alfreton Town	14			14	2
Chester, Salford, Boston U (L), Ashton U (L), Chester (L), Alfreton									
Jones	Joey	27	Defender	Dagenham & Redbridge	14	3	4	17	
Arsenal (Y), Leicester (Y), Yeovil (Y), Woking (L), Woking, Eastleigh, Salford, Dagenham & R									
Jones	Mike	26	Midfielder	Hungerford Town	13	1	2	14	1
Fisher FC, Greenwich, Bromley, Canvey Isle, Hungerford, Chippenham, Hungerford									
Jones	Nico	19	Defender	Havant & Waterlooville (L)	2			2	
Oxford U (Y), Oxford C (L), Havant & W (L)									
Jones	Sam	29	Midfielder	Kettering Town	4	1	6	5	
Heanor, Alfreton, Gateshead, Grimsby, Shrewsbury, Cheltenham (L), Harrogate, Solihull M (L), York (L), Kettering									
Jordan	Corey	22	Defender	Weymouth (L)	13			13	1
Bournemouth (Y), Eastbourne B (L), Weymouth (L)									

Key: X - Started; SX - Sub on; S - Non-playing Sub; Ap - Total Appearances; G/Cs - Total goals/clean sheets.

SURNAME	FIRSTNAME	AGE	POSITION	CLUB	X	SX	S	Ap	G/Cs
					APPEARANCES				
Judd	Myles	21	Midfielder	Barnet (L)	8			8	
Leyton O, Barnet (L)									
Julian	Alan	38	Goalkeeper	Hampton & Richmond Borough	21			21	10
Gillingham, Stevenage, Newport, Dartford, Sutton U, Bromley, Billericay T, Hampton & R									
Justham	Elliot	30	Goalkeeper	Dagenham & Redbridge	48			48	16
Waltham F, Leyton, Redbridge, Brentwood, East Thurrock, Luton, Dagenham & R									
Kahraman	Sefa	24	Midfielder	Ebbsfleet United	18	1		19	
Werder Bremen (Y), BAK'07, Ebbsfleet									
Kaiser	Ethan		Midfielder	Tonbridge Angels			2		
Tonbridge A									
Kaloczi	James	26	Defender	St Albans City	17		2	17	1
St Albans, Hemel H, St Albans									
Kandi	Chike	25	Forward	Aldershot Town	22	17	1	39	7
Birmingham, Chelsea, West Brom, Brighton, Bognor Regis (Lx2), Woking, Leatherhead, Dagenham & R, Aldershot									
Katsamagkas	Panos		Forward	Blyth Spartans	2	4	1	6	
Harrogate T, Ossett U (L), Blyth S									
Kay	Joseph		Defender	Eastbourne Borough	1			1	
Eastbourne B (Y)									
Kealy	Callum	22	Forward	Sutton United (D)	1	9	11	10	1
Worthing, Sutton U (D)									
Kean	Jake	30	Goalkeeper	Notts County			1		
Blackburn (Y), Hartlepool (L), Rochdale (L), Yeovil (L), Oldham (L), Norwich, Colchester (L), Swindon (L), Sheff Wed, Mansfield (L), Grimsby (L), Mansfield, Notts Co									
Keane	Jordan	27	Midfielder	Stockport County	29	4	8	33	1
Stoke (Y), Tamworth (L), Alfreton, Lincoln (L), Nuneaton, Worcester, Boston U, Stockport									
Keating	Ruairi	25	Forward	Gateshead	2	2		4	
Sligo Rovers, Galway, Finn Harps, Torquay, Gateshead									
Kedwell	Danny	37	Forward	Havant & Waterlooville	7	3	2	10	1
Herne Bay, Welling, Grays, Wimbledon, Gillingham, Ebbsfleet, Havant & W									
Keetch	Bradley	20	Midfielder	Maidenhead United	1	7	17	8	
Maidenhead (Y)									
Kefalas	Themis	21	Defender	Barnet (L)	20	2	5	22	2
QPR, Billericay (L), Barnet (L)									
Kelleher	Fiacre	25	Defender	Wrexham	42	1		43	1
Celtic (Y), Peterhead (L), Oxford U, Solihull M (L), Macclesfield, Wrexham									
Kellerman	Jim	25	Midfielder	Kidderminster Harriers		4		4	
Wolves (Yth), Aldershot, St Mirren, AFC Fylde (L), Kidderminster									
Kellett	Andy	27	Defender	Guiseley	5	2		7	1
Bolton (Y), Plymouth (L), Man U (L), Wigan, Chesterfield (L), Notts Co, AFC Fylde, Alfreton, Guiseley									
Kelly	Josh	22	Forward	Maidenhead United	2	18	4	20	1
Maidenhead (Y), Walton C (L)									
Kelly	Michael	23	Defender	Yeovil Town (L)	19	2	7	21	
Stoke (U23), Bristol R, Bath (L), Yeovil (L)									
Kelly	Sam	27	Midfielder	King's Lynn Town	6	3	5	9	
Norwich (Y), Everton, Cambridge C, Norwich, Port Vale, Grimsby, Hamilton, Braintree, Billericay, King's Lynn									
Kelly	Sam		Goalkeeper	Farsley Celtic	2	1	7	3	
Sheff Utd (Y), Farsley C									
Kelly-Evans	Dion	24	Midfielder	Notts County	32	7	10	39	1
Coventry (Y), Kettering, Notts Co									
Kendall	Charley	20	Forward	Eastbourne Borough (L)	11	8		19	5
Eastbourne B (Y), Ratton Rangers (Y), Eastbourne T, QPR (Y), Eastbourne B (L)									
Kendall	Reece	21	Defender	Guiseley (L)	1			1	
Brighouse, Matlock, Guiseley (L)									
Kennedy	Callum	32	Defender	Dorking Wanderers	6			6	1
Swindon (Y), Gillingham (L), Rotherham (L), Scunthorpe, Wimbledon, Leyton O, Wimbledon, Billericay T, Dorking W									
Kennedy	Connor	24	Defender	Kettering Town	18			18	7
Corby, Kettering									
Kennedy	Jason	34	Midfielder	Spennymoor Town	9	4		13	
Middlesbrough (Y), Darlington, Rochdale, Bradford, Rochdale (L), Carlisle (L), Carlisle, Hartlepool, Spennymoor (L), Spennymoor									

2020-21 NATIONAL. NORTH & SOUTH PLAYERS — APPEARANCES

SURNAME	FIRSTNAME	AGE	POSITION	CLUB PLAYED FOR	X	SX	S	Ap	G/Cs
Kennedy	Kieran	27	Defender	York City	6	3	5	9	
Man City (Y), Leicester, Motherwell, AFC Fylde, Macclesfield, Shrewsbury, Wrexham, Port Vale, Wrexham (L), York City									
Kensdale	Ollie	21	Defender	Braintree Town (L)	2			2	
				Concord Rangers	1			1	
Colchester (Y), Bath (L), Braintree (L), Concord R									
Kerr	Fraser	28	Defender	Torquay United	6	2	4	8	
				Chesterfield	16		1	16	1
Birmingham, Motherwell, Cowdenbeath, Stenhousemuir, Gateshead, Hartlepool, Torquay, Chesterfield									
Khan	Saidou	25	Defender	Maidstone United	7		1	7	1
				Dagenham & Redbridge (L)	9	2	5	11	
Tooting & M, Maidstone, Dagenham & R (L)									
Kiangebeni	Percy	24	Defender	Braintree Town	4	1	1	5	1
St Albans, Concord R (L), Braintree									
Killip	Ben	25	Goalkeeper	Hartlepool United	29		5	29	13
Chelsea (Y), Norwich, Lowestoft (L), Grimsby, Braintree, Hartlepool									
King	Cameron	25	Midfielder	King's Lynn Town	19	5	3	24	2
Norwich (Y), Thetford, Shamrock, King's Lynn, FC Halifax, King's Lynn									
King	Craig	24	Goalkeeper	Dartford	14			14	6
Luton (Y), Bishop's S (L), Southport (L), Oxford C, Dartford									
King	Dan		Midfielder	Gloucester City	1	2	3	3	
Gloucester									
King	Jeff	25	Midfielder	FC Halifax	37			37	7
Altrincham, Prescot C (L), Nantwich, Kendal, Trafford, Witton, Droylsden, Bolton, FC United (L), St Mirren, FC Halifax									
King	Josh		Defender	York City	4	1	1	5	1
Chester-le-Street, Carlisle U Acad, York, Morpeth (L)									
Kingston	Sam		Goalkeeper	Chelmsford City			2		
Chelmsford (Y)									
Kinnane	Ryan	26	Defender	Hemel Hempstead Town	13	1	5	14	
Harefield T, Hanwell T, Aylesbury U, Hayes & Y, Berkhamsted, Hemel H									
Kinoshi	Jordan	25	Forward	St Albans City (D)		1	1	1	
Tottenham (Y), Norwich (Y), Luton (Y), California State Uni, Welwyn GC, St Albans (D)									
Kinsella	Lewis	26	Defender	Aldershot Town	9	4	1	13	
Arsenal, Aston Villa, Luton (L), Kidderminster (L), Colchester, Aldershot									
Kirby	Connor	22	Midfielder	Altrincham (L)	5	2		7	1
Sheff Wed (Y), Macclesfield (L), Harrogate, Altrincham (L)									
Kitching	Mark	25	Defender	Stockport County	19	3		22	2
Middlesbrough (Y), York (L), Rochdale, Hartlepool, Stockport									
Kiwomya	Alex	25	Forward	Chesterfield	5	2		7	1
				King's Lynn Town	15	9	2	24	2
Chelsea (Y), Barnsley (L), Fleetwood (L), Crewe (L), Doncaster, Chesterfield (L), Chorley (L), Chesterfield, King's Lynn									
Kizzi	Joseph	28	Defender	Bromley	42		1	42	7
Billericay, Bromley									
Klukowski	Yan	34	Midfielder	Hereford FC	8	9	1	17	
Forest Green, Newport Co, York, Torquay, Kidderminster (L), Chippenham, Hungerford, Hereford									
Knight	Lewis	22	Forward	Bradford Park Avenue	15	1		16	11
Leeds (Y), Bradford PA, Notts Co				Notts County	3	4	1	7	
Knight	Lewis	28	Defender	Billericay Town	1	4	11	5	
Concord R, East Thurrock, St Albans, Maidstone, St Albans (L), Billericay T									
Knott	Billy	28	Midfielder	Billericay Town	7		2	7	
Sunderland (Y), Wimbledon (L), Wycombe (L), Bradford, Gillingham, Lincoln C (L), Lincoln, Rochdale (L), Concord R, Chelmsford, Billericay T									
Knott	Chris		Goalkeeper	Leamington			1		
Knowle (Y), Lowestoft (Staff), Heather St Johns (Coach), Leamington (Coach)									
Knowles	Dominic	29	Forward	Curzon Ashton	17			17	7
Burnley (Y), Gainsborough, Harrogate, Burton, Kidderminster (L), Harrogate, Boston U, Curzon A									
Knowles	Jimmy	20	Forward	Notts County (L)	15	18	10	33	10
Mansfield (Y), Notts Co (L)									
Knowles	Tom	22	Forward	Yeovil Town	24	9	1	33	7
Cambridge U (Y), Dartford (L), Hemel H (L), Chelmsford (L), Yeovil									
Konchesky	Paul	40	Defender	Billericay Town	4		1	4	
Charlton (Y), Tottenham (L), West Ham, Fulham, Liverpool, Nottingham F (L), Leicester, QPR (L), Gillingham, Billericay, East Thurrock, Billericay T									

Key: X - Started; SX - Sub on; S - Non-playing Sub; Ap - Total Appearances; G/Cs - Total goals/clean sheets.

SURNAME	FIRSTNAME	AGE	POSITION	CLUB	X	SX	S	Ap	G/Cs
					APPEARANCES				
Kosylo	Matt	28	Midfielder	Altrincham	31	3		34	3
Stockport, Ashton, Hyde, Nantwich, Halifax, AFC Fylde, Altrincham									
Koszela	Olaf		Forward	Torquay United		6	10	6	
Torquay (Y)									
Kouhyar	Maziar	23	Midfielder	Hereford FC		2		2	
Coventry (Y), Walsall, Hereford									
Kouogun	Maxim	24	Defender	Wealdstone		1	2	1	
Uni College Dublin, Warrenpoint, Waterford, Harrogate T, Wealdstone, Shelbourne									
Kpekawa	Cole	25	Defender	Chelmsford City	8	4	1	12	
QPR (Y), Colchester (L), Portsmouth (L), Leyton O (L), Barnsley, Colchester, St Mirren, Billericay T, Trencin (Slov), Chelmsford									
Kpohomouh	Jacques	24	Midfielder	Hemel Hempstead Town	3	1	3	4	
Bangor, Radcliffe B, Southport, Droylsden, Hemel H,									
Krasniqi	Arjanit	21	Midfielder	Braintree Town	8	4	1	12	3
Waltham Forest, Colchester, Billericay T, SJK (Fin), Braintree									
Krasniqi	Kreshnic	26	Midfielder	Maidstone United	9	2	3	11	1
Ethnikos Achna (Cyp), Concord R, Wealdstone, Maidstone									
Kretzschmar	Max	27	Midfielder	Woking	28	9	2	37	10
Wycombe, Woking, Hampton & R, Woking									
Kuhl	Aaron	25	Midfielder	Slough Town	13	1	1	14	
Reading (Y), Dundee U (L), Boreham W (L), Slough									
Kyprianou	Harry	24	Midfielder	Bromley (L)	4	1	2	5	
Southend (Y), Lowestoft (L), Bromley (L)									
L'Ghoul	Nassim	23	Midfielder	Bromley	4	2	7	6	1
				Dartford	8			8	1
St Neots, Whitehawk (L), Welling, Dover, Bromley, Dartford									
Lacey	Alex	28	Defender	Notts County	25		6	25	
Luton, Cambridge C (L), Thurrock (L), Eastbourne B (L), Eastleigh (L), Yeovil, Gillingham, Notts Co									
Lacey	Jonathan		Forward	Hemel Hempstead Town (D)	15	4		19	6
Berkhamsted, Hemel H (D)									
Lacey	Patrick	28	Midfielder	Chester	9	2	1	11	1
Bradford (Y), Vauxhall M (L), Droylsden (L), Altrincham, Barrow, Accrington, Southport, Chester									
Lafayette	Ross	35	Forward	Wealdstone	10	11		21	4
Wealdstone, Welling, Luton, Woking (L), Welling (L), Eastleigh, Aldershot (L), Dover, Sutton U, Maidstone (L), Billericay, Wealdstone									
Laing	Louis	28	Defender	Darlington	7	2	5	9	
Sunderland, Wycombe (L), Nottingham F, Notts Co (L), Motherwell (L), Motherwell, Notts Co (L), Inverness CT, Hartlepool, Blyth S, Darlington									
Lainton	Rob	31	Goalkeeper	Wrexham	26		4	26	9
Bolton (Y), Bury, Burton (L), Cheltenham (L), Port Vale, Wrexham (L), Wrexham									
Lambert	Charlie		Forward	Eastbourne Borough	4	10	6	14	3
Peacehaven & T, Eastbourne B									
Lambton	Declan	20	Goalkeeper	Guiseley			3		
Bradford C (Y), Campion, Guiseley, Campion (D), Albion S (L)									
Lancaster	Aaron		Goalkeeper	AFC Fylde	1			1	
AFC Fylde (Y)									
Lander	Sammy		Midfielder	Weymouth			2		
Weymouth (Y)									
Lane	Jack	28	Defender	Leamington	20			20	2
Macclesfield (Y), Newcastle T (L), Stockport S (L), Hinckley U, Ventura County (US), Sacramento, Ilkeston, Nuneaton, Tamworth, Alfreton, Leamington									
Lane	Paddy	20	Forward	Farsley Celtic (L)	8	1	2	9	
Hyde U (Y), Farsley C (L)									
Langstaff	Macaulay	24	Forward	Gateshead	5	11		16	4
Gateshead, Blyth (L), York, Bradford PA (L), Blyth S (L), Gateshead									
Langston	George	18	Defender	Wealdstone	2			2	
Wealdstone (Y)									
Lankshear	Alex	18	Midfielder	St Albans City			2		
St Albans (Y)									
Law	Ryan	21	Defender	Chippenham Town (L)	3			3	
				Torquay United (L)	6	2		8	
Plymouth (Y), Gloucester (L), Chippenham (L), Torquay (L)									

Leather Scott - Chorley.

Lees Toby - Alfreton Town.

Marah Sewa - Chorley.

McGrath Michael - Kettering Town.

Key: X - Started; SX - Sub on; S - Non-playing Sub; Ap - Total Appearances; G/Cs - Total goals/clean sheets.

SURNAME	FIRSTNAME	AGE	POSITION	CLUB	X	SX	S	Ap	G/Cs
Leadbitter	Daniel	30	Defender	Yeovil Town (L)	10	2		12	
				Gloucester City (L)	1			1	
Torquay (Y), Hereford, Bristol R, Newport, Yeovil (L), Gloucester (L)									
Leak	Tom	20	Defender	Bath City (L)	6	1		7	
Walsall (Y), Salisbury (L), Bath (L)									
Leather	Scott	28	Defender	Chorley	23			23	1
PNE (Y), Altrincham, Chorley									
Lee	Arthur	29	Defender	Tonbridge Angels	5	2		7	
Peterborough (Y), Hinckley U (L), Concord R, St Neots, Hemel H, Concord R, Hendon, Hornchurch, Tonbridge A									
Lee	Charlie	34	Midfielder	Yeovil Town	29	4	3	33	3
Tottenham, Millwall (L), Peterborough, Gillingham (L), Gillingham, Stevenage, Leyton Orient, Yeovil									
Lee	Tony		Forward	Havant & Waterlooville (D)	1		2	1	
Wimborne, Poole, Havant & W (D)									
Lees	Toby	24	Defender	Alfreton Town	14	1	2	15	
Harrogate Harrogate RW (L), Boston (L), Whitby (L), Gateshead (L), Alfreton									
Leesley	Joe	27	Midfielder	Boston United (L)	8	4		12	4
Matlock, Alfreton, Harrogate, Stockport (L), Stevenage (L), Boston U (L)									
Lemonheigh-Evans	Connor	24	Midfielder	Torquay United	48	2		50	12
Bristol C, Bath (L), Torquay (L), Torquay (L), Torquay (L), Torquay									
Lench	Matt		Midfielder	Slough Town	9	3		12	1
				Wealdstone	1	3	1	4	
Hitchin, Slough, Wealdstone, Slough, Wealdstone									
Lenighan	Simon	27	Midfielder	AFC Telford United (D)			1		
Leeds, Bradford PA (L), Halifax (L), Harrogate T, Alfreton (L), Frickley A, Rotherham, Warrington T, Altrincham, Shaw Lane, Glossop NE, Guiseley, FC Halifax, Buxton, Radcliffe, Telford (D)									
Leroy-Belehouan	Jean	20	Midfielder	FC Halifax (L)	1	1	3	2	
Man Utd (Y), Sheff U (U23), FC Halifax (L)									
Leslie	Joe	20	Forward	Woking	2	5	3	7	1
				Braintree Town (L)	1			1	
Colney H, Stevenage (U18), Biggleswade T (L), Woking, Leatherhead (L), Braintree (L)									
Leslie-Smith	Josh	21	Defender	Weymouth	11	7	8	18	
Poole (Y), Weymouth									
Letheren	Kyle	33	Goalkeeper	Chesterfield	16			16	7
Kilmarnock, Dundee, Blackpool, York, Plymouth, Salford, Chesterfield									
Levi-Davis	Jordan		Forward	King's Lynn Town		3		3	
King's Lynn									
Lewington	Chris	32	Goalkeeper	Maidstone United	9		7	9	1
Charlton, Dulwich, Fisher Ath, Sittingbourne, Leatherhead, Dagenham & R, Colchester, Margate, Welling, Dover, Maidstone									
Lewis	Annisuis		Midfielder	Chelmsford City		1	2	1	
Chelmsford									
Lewis	Danny	39	Goalkeeper	Brackley Town	17		3	17	4
Alvechurch, Studley, Kidderminster, Moor Green, Redditch, Kidderminster, Solihull, Brackley									
Lewis	Dennon	24	Forward	Wealdstone	40	4	1	44	6
Watford (Y), Woking (L), Crawley (L), Falkirk, Bromley, Weladstone									
Lewis	Joe	21	Defender	Torquay United (L)	26			26	
Swansea (Y), Torquay (L), Torquay (L)									
Lewis	Ned		Midfielder	Tonbridge Angels			2		
Tonbridge A									
Liburd	Rowan	28	Forward	Welling United	8	1	1	9	1
				Billericay Town	4			4	
Billericay, Reading, Wycombe (L), Stevenage, Leyton Orient (L), Hemel H (L), Guiseley (L), Guiseley, Hereford, Dartford (L), Welling, Billericay T									
Liddle	Adam	21	Midfielder	Chelmsford City	7	6	1	13	1
Reading (Y), Eastbourne B (L), Derry, Chelmsford									
Liddle	Gary	35	Midfielder	Hartlepool United	26	1	2	27	
Hartlepool, Notts Co, Bradford C, Chesterfield, Carlisle, Walsall, Hartlepool (L), Hartlepool									
Liddle	Michael	31	Defender	Darlington	13	1		14	1
Sunderland (Y), Carlisle (L), Leyton O (L), Gateshead (L), Accrington (L), Accrington, Dunston UTS, Blyth S, Darlington									

2020-21 NATIONAL. NORTH & SOUTH PLAYERS — APPEARANCES

SURNAME	FIRSTNAME	AGE	POSITION	CLUB PLAYED FOR	X	SX	S	Ap	G/Cs
Lilley	Zak		Defender	AFC Telford United	7	1	10	8	1
Telford (Y), Tamworth (L)									
Linton	Malachi	20	Forward	Slough Town (L)	3	2		5	
Ipswich (Y), Crewe (U23), Lowestoft (L), Wycombe, Slough (L)									
Little	Armani	24	Midfielder	Torquay United	21	10		31	1
Southampton (Y), Oxford U, Woking (Lx3), Torquay									
Livesey	Danny	36	Defender	Chester	18			18	4
Carlisle, Wrexham (L), Barrow, Salford, Chester (L), Chester									
Lloyd	Alfie	18	Forward	Yeovil Town		1	1	1	
Yeovil (Y)									
Lloyd	Ryan	27	Midfielder	Hereford FC	21			21	
Port Vale, Tamworth (L), Chester (Lx2), Macclesfield, Port Vale, Hereford									
Lo-Everton	Sonny	18	Midfielder	Wealdstone (L)	7	3		10	2
Watford (Y), Wealdstone (L)									
Loach	Scott	33	Goalkeeper	Barnet	27			27	3
Ipswich, Lincoln C, Watford, Stafford (L), Morecambe (L), Bradford (L), Ipswich, Rotherham, Bury (L), Peterborough (L), Yeovil (L), Notts Co, York (L), Hartlepool, Barnet									
Loft	Doug	34	Midfielder	Billericay Town	7	1	2	8	
Brighton, Dag & Red (L), Port Vale, Gillingham, Colchester, Shrewsbury, Dag & Red (L), Billericay T									
Lofthouse	Kyran	20	Forward	Woking (L)	41		3	41	2
Oxford U (Y), Oxford C (L), Woking (L)									
Lolos	Klaidi	19	Forward	Chippenham Town (L)	2		1	2	
Plymouth (Y), Chippenham (L)									
Lomas	Louis	20	Defender	Slough Town (L)	14		1	14	
Norwich (Y), Tampa Bay Rowdies (L), Slough (L)									
Longbottom	William	22	Forward	Bradford (Park Avenue)	4			4	1
Doncaster (Y), Halesowen (L), Kidderminster (L), Waterford, Bradford (PA)									
Lovatt	Adam		Midfielder	Sutton United	1		4	1	
				Tonbridge Angels (L)	2			2	
Eastbourne B, Hastings U, Sutton U, Tonbridge A (L)									
Lovett	Rhys	24	Goalkeeper	Gloucester City	13		6	13	4
				Maidenhead United **Includes League goal.*	4	1	3	5	2*
Walsall (Y), Rochdale (Y), Cheltenham, Tiverton (L), Shepton M (L), Shortwood (L), Gloucester, Maidenhead									
Lowe	Keith	35	Defender	Kidderminster Harriers	17			17	1
Wolves, Burnley (L), QPR (L), Swansea (L), Brighton (L), Cheltenham (Lx2)Port Vale (L), Kidderminster, Hereford, Cheltenham, York (L), York, Kidderminster, Macclesfield, Bradford PA, Kidderminster									
Lowe	Matt	25	Midfielder	Brackley Town	16	4		20	3
Cambridge U (Y), Wealdstone (Lx2), Brackley (L), Brackley									
Loza	Jamar	27	Forward	King's Lynn Town	7	4	1	11	4
				Woking	13	3	1	16	3
Norwich, Coventry (L), Leyton Orient (L), Southend (L), Yeovil (L), Stevenage (L), Southend (L), Maidstone, Woking (L), Billericay, Chelmsford, Woking (L), King's Lynn, Woking									
Luce	Mathieu	20	Defender	Havant & Waterlooville			2		
Clermont (Y), Havant & W									
Luer	Greg	26	Forward	Eastbourne Borough	21	1		22	5
Hull, Port Vale (L), Scunthorpe (L), Stevenage (L), Maidstone (L), Woking, Eastbourne B									
Lufudu	John	26	Defender	Guiseley	8			8	
Tadcaster A, Carlton T, Sheffield FC, Guiseley									
Lukombo	Henry		Defender	Billericay Town	2			2	
Uxbridge (Y), Billericay T (U23)									
Lund	Adam	22	Defender	Alfreton Town	5	3	9	8	
Barnsley (Y), Norwich (U23), Goole, Pickering, Staveley MW, Alfreton									
Lund	Mitchell	24	Defender	Bradford (Park Avenue)	9			9	
Doncaster (Y), Wrexham (L), Morecambe (L), Bradford PA									
Lupano	Danny	20	Defender	King's Lynn Town	5		1	5	
Derry City, King's Lynn									
Luque	Joan	29	Forward	Maidstone United	9	2	1	11	5
				Weymouth	7	3	4	10	
Cornella (Y), Gramenet B, Montanesa, Vilassar de Mar, FC Santboia, CE Sabadell B, San Rafael, CD Llosetense, Heybridge S, Lincoln C, Bromley (L), Concord R, Dagenham & R, Maidstone, Weymouth									

Key: X - Started; SX - Sub on; S - Non-playing Sub; Ap - Total Appearances; G/Cs - Total goals/clean sheets.

SURNAME	FIRSTNAME	AGE	POSITION	CLUB	X	SX	S	Ap	G/Cs
Lussey	Jordan	26	Midfielder	AFC Fylde	4	4	7	8	
Liverpool (Y), Bolton (L), Bolton, York (L), Southport, Telford, Chorley, Witton (D), Nuneaton, AFC Fylde									
Lyons	Jamie		Forward	Bradford (Park Avenue)	1	2	5	3	
Bradford PA (Y)									
Lyons	Luke	20	Defender	Bradford (Park Avenue)	4	1	2	5	
Leeds (Y), Bradford (PA)									
Lyons-Foster	Kodi	24	Defender	Aldershot Town	38	5	3	43	3
Aldershot, Whitehawk (L), Whitehawk, Braintree, Aldershot									
MacDonald	Josh	26	Midfielder	Hartlepool United	2	1	3	3	
Middlesbrough (Y), Marske Utd, Halifax, Hartlepool									
MacDonald	Shaun	24	Goalkeeper	Torquay United	22		28	22	8
Gateshead, Blyth, Torquay									
Madden	Paddy	31	Forward	Stockport County	14	1		15	7
Bohemians, Shelbourne (L), Carlisle, Yeovil (L/P), Scunthorpe, Fleetwood, Stockport									
Mafuta	Gus	26	Midfielder	Boreham Wood	44	1	2	45	6
Colchester (Y), Bristol C (Y), Weston (L), Nuneaton (L), Gateshead, Salford, Hartlepool, Boreham W									
Magloire	Tyler	22	Defender	Hartlepool United (L)	11		1	11	1
Blackburn (Y), Rochdale (L), Hartlepool (L)									
Magnay	Carl	32	Defender	Spennymoor Town	5	1	3	6	
Leeds, Chelsea, MK Dons (L), Northampton (L), Gateshead, Grimsby, Hartlepool, Spennymoor									
Magri	Sam	27	Defender	Havant & Waterlooville	21			21	4
Portsmouth, QPR, Nuneaton (L), Dover (L), Dover, Ebbsfleet, Havant & W									
Maguire	Dan	28	Forward	Darlington	8	6	2	14	3
Blyth S, Halifax, Blyth S, York, Darlington									
Maguire	Laurence	24	Defender	Chesterfield	45			45	1
Chesterfield (Y), AFC Fylde (L)									
Maher	Niall	25	Defender	FC Halifax	39	1	2	40	1
Bolton, Blackpool (L), Bury, Galway, Telford, Halifax									
Maher	Niall	22	Goalkeeper	Gloucester City		1	5	1	
Wolves (Y), MorecambeHalesowen (L), Stourbridge, Weston SM, Gloucester									
Mahon	Craig	32	Midfielder	Curzon Ashton	16	2		18	1
Wigan, Accrington (L), Salford, Vauxhall M, Chester, Altrincham, Curzon A									
Mair	Archie	20	Goalkeeper	King's Lynn Town (L)	27		2	27	5
Norwich (Y), King's Lynn (L)									
Maja	Emmanuel		Midfielder	Welling United			1		
Man City (Y), Welling									
Male	Harrison	20	Goalkeeper	Gateshead	6		10	6	1
Leeds (Y), Gateshead									
Maloney	Taylor	22	Midfielder	Bromley	16	2	4	18	
Charlton (Y), Concord R (L), Newport Co (L), Concord R (L), Bromley									
Mandeville	Liam	24	Forward	Chesterfield	17	21	5	38	3
Doncaster, Colchester (L), Morecambe (L), Chesterfield									
Mann	Adam	29	Forward	Chippenham Town	8	2		10	3
Gloucester, Shortwood, Gloucester, Evesham, Bath, Chippenham									
Mansell	Lewis	23	Forward	FC Halifax (L)	3		1	3	1
Blackburn (Y), FC United (L), Partick (L/P), Accrington, FC Halifax (L)									
Mantom	Sam	29	Midfielder	Hemel Hempstead Town	9	1		10	
WBA (Y), Haukar (Ice) (L), Tranmere (L), Oldham (L), Walsall (L), Walsall (L/P), Scunthorpe, Southend (L/P), Hemel H									
Marah	Sewa	21	Forward	Chorley	1	8	5	9	
Southend (Y), East Thurrock, Grays, Chorley									
Margetson	Ben	20	Defender	Sutton United (L)			4		
Cardiff (Y), Sutton U (L)									
Marriott	Adam	30	Forward	King's Lynn Town	14	9	2	23	8
				Eastleigh	5	6		11	1
Cambridge U (Y), Cambridge C (L), Bishop's S (L), Cambridge C (L), Stevenage, Lincoln C, Royston T, Boston U, King's Lynn, Eastleigh									
Marriott	Isaac	21	Midfielder	Bradford (Park Avenue)	13	1		14	
Huddersfield (Y), Larne (L), Bradford PA (L), Bradford (PA)									
Marsh	Tyrone	27	Forward	Boreham Wood	23		2	23	6
Oxford U, Welling (L), Torquay, Dover, Macclesfield, Boreham W, Stevenage, Boreham W									

SURNAME	FIRSTNAME	AGE	POSITION	CLUB PLAYED FOR	X	SX	S	Ap	G/Cs
Marsh-Brown	Keanu	28	Midfielder	Gloucester City	4	2		6	1
				Wrexham	1	3	3	4	
Fulham, MK Dons (L), Dundee U (L), Oldham, Yeovil, Barnet (L), Barnet, Forest Green, Dover (L), Newport Co, Memphis 901, Gloucester, Wrexham									
Marsh-Brown	Kyjoun	24	Midfielder	Dartford	7	7	4	14	1
Whitehawk, Welling, Dartford									
Marsh-Hughes	Lloyd	20	Forward	Chester		5	5	5	
Chester									
Martin	Josh	22	Defender	Leamington	16		4	16	
Hungerford, Leamington									
Martin	Keziah		Midfielder	Kidderminster Harriers	2	5	1	7	
Solihull M (Y), Barnsley, Kidderminster									
Martin	Lee	34	Midfielder	Ebbsfleet United	17			17	4
Man Utd (Y), Rangers (L), Ipswich, Charlton (L), Millwall, Northampton (L), Gillingham, Exeter, Ebbsfleet									
Martin	Mahlondo	24	Midfielder	Dulwich Hamlet	1			1	
Kings Langley, Salisbury, Hayes & Y, Northwood, Chalfont St P, Dulwich Hamlet									
Martin	Odei		Midfielder	Concord Rangers	6	7	5	13	1
Youth Lges (Spain), Heybridge S, Concord R									
Martinez	Pablo	20	Defender	Oxford City (L)	6	6	8	12	1
WBA (Y), Bristol R, Oxford C (L)									
Masampu	Renedi	21	Defender	Dulwich Hamlet	3	1		4	
Met Police (Y), Chelsea (Y), Whyteleafe, Dulwich H									
Mason	Cameron	25	Goalkeeper	Curzon Ashton	17			17	2
Chesterfield (Y), Southport (L), Curzon A									
Mason	Jude	20	Defender	Sutton United			1		
Sutton U (Y), Hamptn & R (L), Walton C (L), Merstham (L)									
Mason-Clarke	Ephron	21	Forward	Barnet	37	7		44	3
Barnet (Yth), Met Police (L),									
Massey	Alan	32	Defender	Maidenhead United	42			42	
Wealdstone, Braintree (L), Braintree, Maidenhead									
Matrevics	Rihards	22	Goalkeeper	St Albans City	2		3	2	1
West Ham (Yth), Barnet, St Albans									
Matsuzaka	Daniel	22	Defender	Oxford City	12	2	1	14	1
Southend (Y), Harlow (L), Kataller Toyama (Jap), Braintree, Sutton U, Braintree, Oxford C									
Matthews	Jason	46	Goalkeeper	Chippenham Town	1			1	
Bristol R (Y), Welton R, Salisbury, Nuneaton, Exeter, Aberystwyth, Clevedon, Weymouth, Eastleigh, Bath, Dorchester, Weymouth, Chippenham (Coach), Bath (Coach), Bracknell (Coach), Chippenham (Coach), Bracknell (Coach)									
Maxwell	Ben		Goalkeeper	Leamington			1		
Solihull M (Y), Leamington									
Maxwell	Luke	23	Midfielder	Kidderminster Harriers	11	3		14	1
Kidderminster, Birmingham, Kidderminster (L), Grimsby (L), Gateshead (L), Solihull (L), Solihull, Gloucester (L), Kidderminster									
Maycock	Callum	23	Defender	Solihull Moors	35	10	3	45	
Coventry (Y), Macclesfield (L), Leamington (L), Solihull M									
Maye	Simeon	26	Midfielder	Leamington	17	1		18	1
Redditch, Hednesford, Solihull, Rushall O, Hereford, Brackley, Leamington									
Maynard	Lois	32	Midfielder	Stockport County	24	6	7	30	1
Winsford, Halifax, Tranmere, Salford, Stockport									
Mbambo	Gabriel			Billericay Town		3	2	3	1
Billericay T									
Mbeka	Lebrun		Midfielder	Guiseley	18	2		20	5
Sheffield FC, Ossett A, Ossett U, Tadcaster A, Guiseley									
Mbunga-Kimpioka	Benjamin	21	Midfielder	Torquay United (L)	3	7		10	
Sunderland (Y), Torquay (L)									
McAuley	Rory	31	Defender	King's Lynn Town	18		2	18	1
Norwich (Y), Cambridge C (Y), Cambridge U (Y), Chelmsford (L), Dartford (L), Dartford, Chelmsford, Lowestoft, King's Lynn									
McBurnie	Alexander	23	Forward	Barnet	6	13	13	19	
Ytterhogdal (Swe), Barnet									
McCallum	Gavin	33	Defender	Dartford	5	1	7	6	
Hereford, Lincoln C, Barnet (L), Woking, Sutton U, Tonbridge A (L), Eastbourne B, Welling, Dartford									

Key: X - Started; SX - Sub on; S - Non-playing Sub; Ap - Total Appearances; G/Cs - Total goals/clean sheets.

SURNAME	FIRSTNAME	AGE	POSITION	CLUB	APPEARANCES X	SX	S	Ap	G/Cs
McCallum	Paul	27	Forward	Dagenham & Redbridge	36	4		40	18
Dulwich H, West Ham, Rochdale (L), AFC Wimbledon (L), Aldershot (L), Torquay (L), Hearts (L), Portsmouth (L), Leyton Orient, Eastleigh, Solihull M, Barnet (L), Dagenham & R									
McCarthy	Jake	25	Midfielder	Weymouth	37	5	1	42	7
Bournemouth (Y), Dorchester (L), Havant & W (L), Maidstone, Weymouth, Havant & W									
McClean	Ryan		Midfielder	Hereford FC (L)		1		1	
Lancaster, Newcastle T, Hereford (L)									
McClure	Matt	29	Forward	Gloucester City	16	1		17	13
Wycombe, Hayes & Y Utd (L), Dagenham & R, Aldershot, Maidstone, Gloucester									
McCormack	Ross	34	Forward	Aldershot Town	1	2		3	
Rangers (Y), Doncaster (L), Motherwell, Cardiff, Leeds, Fulham, Aston Villa, Nottm Forest (L), Melborne City (L), Central Coast (L), Aldershot									
McCourt	Jak	25	Midfielder	Chesterfield	15	6	1	21	2
Leicester (Y), Torquay (L), Port Vale (L), Barnsley, Northampton, Chesterfield, Swindon, Macclesfield, Chesterfield									
McCoy	Ollie	23	Forward	Bath City (L)		1		1	
Beaconsfield SYCOB, Birmingham (Y), Yeovil (L), Wealdstone (L), Bath (L)									
McCrory	Damien	31	Defender	Notts County	2	1	3	3	
Plymouth, Port Vale (L), Grimsby (L), Dagenham & R, Burton, Portsmouth (L), Notts Co									
McCulloch	Danny			Braintree Town		1		1	
Braintree									
McDevitt	Liam	31	Midfielder	Hemel Hempstead Town (L)	8			8	
Hayes & Y, Hemel H (L)									
McDonald	Edward (Ted)		Goalkeeper	Tonbridge Angels			4		
Tonbridge A									
McDonald	Jamie	28	Forward	Altrincham		3	2	3	1
City of Liverpool, Warrington, City of Liverpool, Altrincham									
McDonnell	Adam	24	Midfielder	Boreham Wood	4	6	10	10	
Ipswich, Aldershot (L), Aldershot, Boreham W									
McDonnell	Joe	27	Goalkeeper	Eastleigh	45			45	17
Basingstoke, Wimbledon, Notts Co, Eastleigh									
McEachran	Zac		Forward	Oxford City	15	6	1	21	1
Oxford C, Banbury, Oxford C									
McFadden	Archie		Defender	Concord Rangers	1		2	1	
Concord R (Y)									
McGill	Gabriel	20	Forward	York City (L)	1			1	
York (Y), Middlesbrough (Y), Dunfermline, Edinburgh City (L), York (L)									
McGlip	Cameron	23	Midfielder	Slough Town	8	1		9	1
Swindon (Y), Hungerford (2xL), Slough									
McGory	Louis	24	Forward	Hungerford Town	11	6	2	17	
Forest GR (Y), Aldershot (L), Hungerford (L), Gloucester (L), Telford, Weston, Hungerford									
McGrath	Michael	35	Midfielder	Kettering Town	16	1		17	
Redditch, Kidderminster, Worcester (L), Galway Utd, Sligo R, Rushall, Stratford T, Hednesford, Hereford, Bromsgrove Sp, Redditch, Kettering									
McGregor	Giovanni		Midfielder	Dulwich Hamlet	7	4	1	11	2
Crystal P (Y), Dartford (L), Dulwich H									
McHale	Dom	25	Midfielder	AFC Telford United	12	8		20	7
Man City (Y), Barnsley, Northwich V (D), Ramsbottom, Northwich V, Northwich MV, Achyronas L (Cyp), Salford, Trafford (L), Hyde (L), Ashton U, Southport, FC United, Oldham, Romford, Ashton U, Telford U									
McIver-Hauser	Jack		Midfielder	Billericay Town			1		
Billericay T (U23)									
McKay	John	24	Forward	Chesterfield		1	1	1	
Doncaster (Y), Ilkeston (L), Leeds, Airdrieonians (L), Cardiff, Chesterfield (L), Chesterfield									
McKenna	Ben	28	Midfielder	Spennymoor Town	10	5	2	15	1
Burnley (Y), Carlisle (Y), Annan Ath (L), Workington, Stalybridge, Bradford PA, Southport, Stockport, Curzon A, Bradford PA, Chester, Spennymoor									
McKenzie	Malakai		Midfielder	Chorley	1		7	1	
Bury (Y), Chorley (Y)									
McKeown	Corey	18	Forward	Blyth Spartans	3	8	4	11	1
Gateshead (Y), Blyth S									
McKnight	Jack	25	Midfielder	Slough Town	4	6	3	10	1
Beaconsfield, Eastleigh, Slough									

2020-21 NATIONAL. NORTH & SOUTH PLAYERS

SURNAME	FIRSTNAME	AGE	POSITION	CLUB PLAYED FOR	X	SX	S	Ap	G/Cs
McLaughlin	Patrick	30	Midfielder	York City	11	5		16	1
Newcastle, York, Grimsby, Harrogate T (L), Gateshead, Hartlepool, York (L), York									
McLean	Ben	20	Midfielder	Leamington			1		
Birmingham, Leamington									
McLean	Chevron	25	Defender	Billericay Town	7		4	7	
Maldon, Billericay T									
McLean	Rian	22	Defender	Welling United	1	1		2	
Leyton O, Doncaster, Welling									
McLean	Scott	23	Midfielder	Spennymoor Town	14		1	14	
Kilmarnock, Albion Rovers, Queen's Park, Annan, Spennymoor									
McLennan	George	25	Defender	Havant & Waterlooville	9	1	2	10	
Reading (Y), Hayes & Y (L), Cheltenham, Sutton U, Ashford U, Maidstone, Billericay, Wealdstone, Havant & W									
McLeod	Sammie	21	Midfielder	Concord Rangers		1		1	
Maidstone (Y), Leicester (U18), Maldon & T, Colchester (U23), Concord R									
McMahon	Antony	35	Defender	Darlington	15		3	15	
Middlesbrough (Y), Blackpool (L), Sheff Wed (L), Sheff Utd, Blackpool (L/P), Bradford (L/P), Oxford U, Scunthorpe, Darlington									
McManus	Niall	26	Midfielder	Dorking Wanderers	15	4		19	
Millwall (Y), Hayes & Y (L), Leatherhead, Dorking W									
McMillan	Anthony	39	Goalkeeper	Southport	6		13	6	1
Burscough, Southport, Altrincham, Barrow, Stalybridge, Warrington, Chorley (D), Southport									
McNally	Reiss	20	Defender	Solihull Moors	9		4	9	1
				Brackley Town (L)	6	2		8	
Solihull M (Y), Guiseley, Solihull M, Brackley (L)									
McPartlan	Lewis		Goalkeeper	Curzon Ashton			5		
AFC Fylde (Y), St Helens (L), Pennington (L), Darwen (L), Curzon A									
McQueen	Alex	26	Defender	Barnet	33	4	2	37	1
Tottenham (Y), Carlisle, VPS, Dagenham & R, Barnet									
McQueen	Darren	26	Forward	Dagenham & Redbridge	10	17	11	27	2
Tottenham, Ipswich, Maldon & Tiptree, Ebbsfleet, Sutton U, Dartford (L), Dartford, Dagenham & R									
McQuilkin	James	32	Midfielder	Hereford FC	11	5	5	16	1
FC Zlin (Czech), Tescoma Zlin, Hereford, Walsall, Hednesford, Torquay, Kidderminster, Telford, Hereford									
McQuoid	Josh	31	Midfielder	Weymouth	31	3		34	8
Bournemouth, Millwall (L), Millwall, Burnley (L), Bournemouth, Peterborough (L), Coventry (L), Luton, Stevenage (L), Torquay (L), Aldershot, Weymouth									
McShane	James		Forward	Dorking Wanderers	20	2		22	8
Dorking W									
Meade	Jernade	28	Defender	Dartford	1			1	
Arsenal (Y), Swansea, Luton (L), Hadley, St Albans, AFC Eskilstuna (Swe), Aalesund (Den), Dartford									
Medrano	JIAH	18	Defender	Yeovil Town			1		
Yeovil (Y)									
Meekings	Josh	28	Defender	Wealdstone	3	1		4	
Inverness CT, Dundee, Wealdstone									
Mehew	Tom	20	Midfielder	Bath City (L)	7			7	1
Bristol R (Y), Yate (L), Frome (L), Stratford (L), Bath (L)									
Mekki	Adam	29	Midfielder	Ebbsfleet United	12	8	1	20	1
Aldershot Town, Barnet, Dover Athletic, Tranmere Rovers, Bromley, Ebbsfleet (L), Ebbsfleet									
Mendy	Jacob	24	Forward	Wealdstone	44			44	10
Carshalton, Wealdstone									
Mensah	Bernard	26	Forward	Gloucester City	13	3	1	16	4
Watford, Braintree (L), V Guimaraes (L), V Guimaraes (L), Barnet (L), Braintree (L), Aldershot, Bristol R, Lincoln C (L), Aldershot (L), Maidenhead (L), Gloucester									
Mensah	Jacob	20	Defender	Weymouth	27			27	1
Crystal P (Y), Weymouth									
Meppen-Walters	Courtney	26	Defender	AFC Telford United	10		2	10	
Man City (Y), Carlisle, Ashton U, Chorley, Stockport, Glossop, Chorley, AFC Telford									
Meredith	Dan	21	Defender	Leamington	3	11	6	14	1
WBA (Y), Maidstone (L), Leamington (L), Leamington									
Merrill	Luke	20	Midfielder	Curzon Ashton			4		
Blackburn (Y), Curzon A									

Key: X - Started; SX - Sub on; S - Non-playing Sub; Ap - Total Appearances; G/Cs - Total goals/clean sheets.

SURNAME	FIRSTNAME	AGE	POSITION	CLUB	X	SX	S	Ap	G/Cs
Mersin	Yusuf	26	Goalkeeper	Dover Athletic	8		8	8	1
Kasimpasa (Tur), Crawley, Dover									
Miccio	Lewis	22	Defender	Solihull Moors			2		
Central Coast Mariners (Aus), Manly United, Kidderminster, Solihull M, Stourbridge (L)									
Miles	Sonny	31	Defender	Tonbridge Angels	15		1	15	
Tonbridge A (Y), Maidstone, Tonbridge A									
Miley	Cavanagh	26	Midfielder	Eastleigh	33	6	1	39	3
Jersey, Eastleigh									
Miller	Calvin	23	Defender	Notts County (L)	19	4	5	23	
Celtic (Y), Dundee (L), Ayr (L), Harrogate, Notts Co (L)									
Miller	Curtis		Forward	Altrincham		7	6	7	
Altrincham (Y)									
Miller	Nathan		Midfielder	Braintree Town			1		
Braintree									
Miller	Reece	20	Forward	Aldershot Town	15	9	1	24	4
Watford (U18), Aldershot (Y)									
Miller	Sean	26	Forward	Chorley	2	2	2	4	
Chester (Y), Connah's Q, Altrincham, Chester, Droylsden (D), Curzon A, Chorley									
Miller-Rodney	Tyrell	27	Midfielder	Hampton & Richmond Borough	13	3		16	1
Brentford (Y), Maidenhead (L), Boreham W (L), Maidenhead (L), Hayes & Y, Hampton & R									
Mills	Danny	29	Forward	Dulwich Hamlet	10	2	2	12	6
Crawley, Peterborough, Torquay (L), Rushden (L), Histon (L), Kettering (L), Tamworth (L), Kettering (L), Carshalton, Whitehawk, Ebbsfleet, Dartford (L), Welling (L), Dulwich H									
Milnes	Ben	29	Midfielder	Kettering Town	15	1	1	16	1
Boston U, Corby, Kettering									
Milsom	Robert	34	Midfielder	Sutton United	36	3	2	39	3
Brentford, Fulham, Southend (L), TPS (Fin) (L), Aberdeen, Rotherham, Bury (L), Notts Co, Crawley, Notts Co (L), Notts Co, Sutton U									
Ming	Sanchez	31	Forward	Dulwich Hamlet	17	1		18	2
Fisher, Welling, Bishop's S, Bromley, Staines, Dulwich H, Welling, Dartford, Dulwich H									
Mingoia	Piero	29	Midfielder	Boreham Wood	7	4	11	11	
Watford (Y), Hayes & Y (L), Accrington, Boreham W (L), Cambridge U, Accrington, Morecambe (L), Boreham W									
Minhas	Nathan	23	Forward	Hampton & Richmond Borough	4	11	5	15	1
Beaconsfield, Billericay T, Hampton & R									
Minihan	Sam	27	Defender	Stockport County	28	16	6	44	
Rochdale, Droylsden (L), Loughborough U, Worcester, Stockport									
Minshull	Lee	35	Midfielder	Concord Rangers			1		
Wimbledon, Newport Co (L), Newport Co, Bromley, Leatherhead, Concord R									
Minter	Melvin	26	Goalkeeper	Darlington (L)	6		6	6	4
Canvey I, Kings Langley, Harrogate, Darlington (L)									
Miskin	Mack		Defender	Braintree Town	1		2	1	
Braintree									
Mitchell	Alex		Defender	Bromley (L)	10			10	
Millwall (Y), Bromley (L)									
Mitchell	Corbyn	18	Midfielder	Spennymoor Town			1		
Spennymoor (Y)									
Mitchell	Kairo	23	Forward	Dartford		1		1	
				King's Lynn Town	14	8	2	22	8
				Chesterfield	6	2	1	8	1
Leicester (Y), Nuneaton (L), Nuneaton, Dartford, King's Lynn, Chesterfield									
Mitford	Tre	26	Forward	Brackley Town	11	9	2	20	5
Leatherhead, Kettering, Brackley									
Modeste	Ricky	33	Forward	Dartford	2	1	1	3	
Chelmsford, Dover, Billericay, Dover, Dartford									
Mohsni	Bilel	33	Defender	Barnet	3		3	3	
Southend, Ipswich (L), Rangers, Angers SCO, Paris FC, ES Sahel, Dundee U, Panachaiki, Grimsby, Barnet									
Moke	Adriano	31	Midfielder	Spennymoor Town	5	3	7	8	
York (Y), Cambridge U, Tamworth (L), Halifax, Stockport, Macclesfield, Wrexham, Boreham, York, Spennymoor									
Molokwu	Chukwudalu		Defender	Guiseley	1	1	5	2	
Guiseley									

2020-21 NATIONAL. NORTH & SOUTH PLAYERS — APPEARANCES

SURNAME	FIRSTNAME	AGE	POSITION	CLUB PLAYED FOR	X	SX	S	Ap	G/Cs
Molyneaux	Rio		Midfielder	Alfreton Town			2		
Mansfield (Y), Alfreton									
Molyneux	Luke	23	Midfielder	Hartlepool United	16	13	4	29	3
Sunderland (Y), Gateshead (L), Hartlepool (L), Hartlepool									
Mondal	Junior	24	Forward	AFC Fylde	6	7	6	13	3
Middlesbrough (Y), Spennymoor, Whitby, Forest GR, AFC Fylde									
Montgomery	James	27	Goalkeeper	Gateshead	8			8	2
				Chesterfield	7			7	1
Telford, Gateshead, Forest GR, AFC Fylde, Gateshead, Southend (L), Chesterfield									
Montrose	Lewis	32	Midfielder	Kidderminster Harriers	16			16	1
Man City, Wigan, Rochdale (L), Cheltenham (L), Cheltenham (L), Chesterfield (L), Wycombe, Gillingham, Oxford U (L), York , Stockport, AFC Fylde, Kidderminster									
Mooney	Daniel	21	Forward	Altrincham	12	9		21	3
Fleetwood (Y), Chorley (L), Chester (L), Altrincham									
Mooney	Kelsey	22	Forward	Hereford FC	5	4	1	9	1
Aston Villa (Y), Cheltenham (L), Hereford									
Moore	Deon	22	Defender	Dulwich Hamlet	15	3		18	4
Peterborough (Y), Bristol R, Bath (L), Billericay (L), Hemel H, Dulwich H									
Moore	Luke	33	Forward	Dorking Wanderers	10	7	2	17	1
Ebbsfleet, Wimbledon, Margate, Dorking W									
Moore	Sean		Forward	Slough Town			1		
Slough (Y)									
Moore	Stuart	26	Goalkeeper	Wealdstone	9			9	1
Reading (Y), Basingstoke (L), Peterborough (L), Luton (L), Barrow, Swindon, MK Dons, Wealdstone									
Moore-Azille	Tarik	25	Defender	Braintree Town	4			4	
Bishop's S, Margate, St Albans, Hungerford, Oxford C, Braintree									
Moran	Niall		Midfielder	Chorley			1		
Chorley (Y)									
Morgan	Adam	27	Forward	Chelmsford City	13	4	1	17	7
Liverpool, Rotherham (L), Yeovil (L), Yeovil, St Johnstone (L), Accrington, Hemel H, Curzon A, Halifax, Sligo Rovers, Curzon A, Chelmsford									
Morgan	Ben	22	Defender	Gloucester City	20	1		21	
				Weymouth	5			5	
Swansea (Y), Bristol R, Brackley (L), Gloucester, Weymouth									
Morgan	David	26	Midfielder	Southport	19			19	1
Nottm Forest (Y), Lincoln C (L), Dundee (L), Tamworth (L), Ilkeston, Nuneaton, AFC Fylde, Harrogate, Southport									
Morgan	Jamie	23	Defender	Chester	15		7	15	3
Nantwich, Chester									
Morgan-Smith	Amari	32	Forward	Kidderminster Harriers	12			12	1
Crewe (Y), Stockport, Ilkeston T, Luton, Macclesfield, Kidderminster (L), Kidderminster, Oldham, Cheltenham, York (L), York, Telford, Alfreton, Kidderminster									
Morias	Junior	25	Forward	Boreham Wood (L)	13	2	2	15	1
Wycombe, Boreham W (L), Boreham W, Whitehawk (L), St Albans, Peterborough, Northampton, St Mirren, Boreham W (L),									
Morley	Stephan	34	Defender	Leamington	20			20	
Hinckley U, Leamington, Corby, Brackley, Tamworth, Telford, Leamington									
Morrison	Kyle		Defender	Leamington	20			20	
Alvechurch, Halesowen, Alvechurch, Leamington									
Morse	Dillon	26	Defender	Gateshead (L)	1			1	
Carlisle (Y), Newcastle Benfield, Gateshead, Blyth S, South Shields, Gateshead (L)									
Moses	Will		Defender	Dover Athletic	2		2	2	
Dover (Y)									
Moulden	Louie	19	Goalkeeper	Gloucester City (L)	8		1	8	
Man City (Y), Gloucester (L), Villa (U23), Derby (U23), Wolves (U23)									
Moult	Jake	32	Midfielder	Altrincham	40	1		41	2
Plymouth (Y), Kidderminster, Leek, Stafford R, Alfreton, Altrincham									
Moxey	Dean	35	Defender	Torquay United	27	2	2	29	1
Exeter (Y), Derby, Crystal P, Bolton, Exeter, Torquay									
Moyo	Cliff	28	Defender	Kidderminster Harriers	9	4	2	13	1
Alfreton, Barrow, Northwich, Drolsden, Trafford, Halifax, Guiseley, Kidderminster									

Key: X - Started; SX - Sub on; S - Non-playing Sub; Ap - Total Appearances; G/Cs - Total goals/clean sheets.

SURNAME	FIRSTNAME	AGE	POSITION	CLUB	X	SX	S	Ap	G/Cs
Muir	Niko	28	Forward	Hampton & Richmond Borough	20			20	6
				Woking (L)	4	2	1	6	
Grays, Northwood, Hendon, Northwood, Wingate, Northwood, VCD Ath, Northwood, Hendon, Leiston, Hendon, Hartlepool, Hemel H (L), Hampton & R (L), Hampton & R, Woking (L)									
Muitt	Jimmy		Forward	Dorking Wanderers	10	5	5	15	1
Brighton & HA (Y), Bognor R, Dorking W									
Mukena	Joy	21	Defender	St Albans City	14	1	3	15	
Tottenham (Y), Watford, Bracknell, St Albans									
Muldoon	Oliver	26	Midfielder	Chelmsford City	1	1	2	2	
Charlton, Gillingham (L), Dagenham & R (L), Braintree (L), Gillingham, Maidstone, Chelmsford									
Muleba	Jonathan	25	Defender	Hemel Hempstead Town (D)	1			1	
Chelsea (Y), Bournemouth, Poole (L), Gosport (L), Bishop's S (L), Folkstone Inv, Enfield T, Braintree, Enfield T, Hemel H (D)									
Mulhern	Euan (Frank)	24	Forward	Spennymoor Town	2	5	3	7	
Leeds, Southport (L), Huddersfield, Guiseley, Stockport, Boston U (L), Spennymoor									
Mullarkey	Toby	25	Defender	Altrincham	28	4		32	1
Crewe (Y), Nantwich, Altrincham									
Mullings	Shamir	27	Forward	Weymouth	2	3	1	5	
Southend (Y), Thurrock (L), Tilbury (L), Harlow (L), Bromley, Thamesmead (L), Havant & W, Chelmsford, Forest Green, Macclesfield (L), Maidstone, Dagenham & R (L), Macclesfield, Aldershot, Dulwich H (L/P), Weymouth									
Mundle-Smith	Jayden	21	Defender	Maidstone United (L)	3			3	
Fulham (Y), Maidenhead (L), Maidstone (L)									
Munns	Jack	27	Midfielder	Dover Athletic	13			13	
Leyton O, Tottenham, Aldershot, Charlton, Cheltenham, Hartlepool, Dagenham & R, Dover									
Murombedzi	Shepherd	26	Midfielder	Brackley Town	19	3		22	1
Reading, Torquay, Nuneaton, Hayes & Y, Solihull M, Chester, Brackley									
Murphy	Rhys	30	Forward	Yeovil Town	22	10	1	32	15
Arsenal, Brentford (L), Preston (L), Dagenham & R, Oldham, Crawley (L), AFC Wimbledon (L), Forest Green, York (L), Crawley (L), Torquay (L), Gillingham, Chelmsford, Yeovil									
Murray	Cameron	26	Midfielder	Weymouth	13	13	10	26	1
York (Y), Scarborough, FC United, Stalybridge, Dorchester, Weymouth									
Murrell-Williamson	Rhys	27	Midfielder	Welling United (L)	3	2		5	
Sutton U, Harrow, Hayes & Y, Dulwich, Boreham W, Dulwich, Welling (L), St Albans, Hampton & R, Billericay, Woking, St Albans, Braintree, Cray W, Welling (L)									
Murtagh	Keiran	32	Midfielder	Boreham Wood	36	3	2	39	1
Charlton, Fisher, Yeovil, Wycombe, Cambridge U, Macclesfield, Mansfield, Woking (L), Woking, Boreham W									
Mussa	Omar	20	Midfielder	Dover Athletic	3	6		9	
Mechelen (Bel) (Y), Walsall, Dover									
Mvemba	Sam		Defender	Welling United	1			1	
Aveley, Bishop's S, Welling									
Myles	Ellis	28	Defender	Brackley Town	16	4	2	20	
Brackley, Rugby T, Stamford, Corby, Brackley									
Nabi	Samir	24	Midfielder	Hereford FC		6	7	6	
WBA (Y), Delhi Dynamos, Carlisle, Torquay, Halesowen (L), Kidderminster, Hereford									
Najia	Tarek	19	Goalkeeper	Bromley			6		
Dagenham & R (Y), Bromley (L), Bromley									
Napa	Malachi	22	Midfielder	Woking (L)	14	9	2	23	2
Oxford U (Y), Hampton RB (L), Macclesfield (L), Woking (L)									
Naylor	Daniel		Midfielder	Oxford City			3		
Oxford C (U23)									
Ndlovu	Lee		Forward	Brackley Town	20	1		21	7
Holbeach U, Grantham, Ilkeston, Brackley									
Neal	Chris	35	Goalkeeper	AFC Fylde	19			19	6
PNE (Y), Tamworth (L), Shrewsbury (L), Shrewsbury, Port Vale, Doncaster (L), Bury (L), Fleetwood, Salford, AFC Fylde									
Negraru	Eric		Goalkeeper	Wealdstone			1		
Wealdstone									
Nelson	Michael	41	Defender	Blyth Spartans	4		1	4	
Leek, Spennymoor, Bishop A, Bury, Hartlepool, Norwich, Scunthorpe, Kilmarnock, Bradford, Hibernian, Cambridge U, Barnet, Chesterfield, Gateshead, Blyth S (PM)									
Nemane	Aaron	24	Midfielder	Torquay United	22	1		23	4
Man City (Y), Rangers (L), Go Ahead Eagles (Hol), Tubize (Ger), Torquay									

Milnes Ben - Kettering Town.

Newby Elliot - Chorley / Stockport (L).

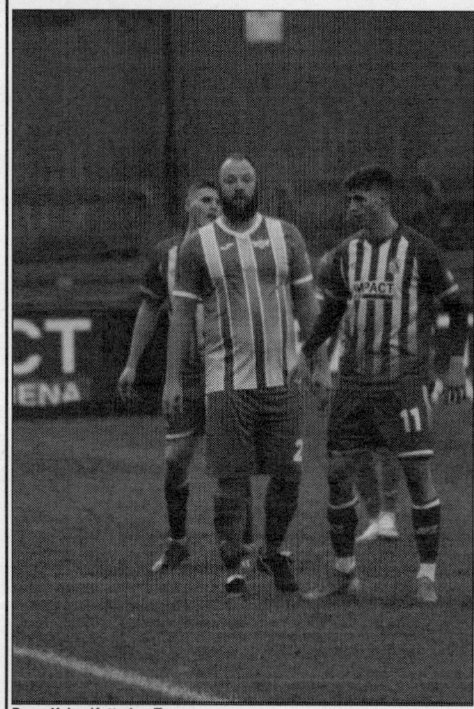

Perry Kyle - Kettering Town.

Powell Callum - Kettering Town.

Key: X - Started; SX - Sub on; S - Non-playing Sub; Ap - Total Appearances; G/Cs - Total goals/clean sheets.

SURNAME	FIRSTNAME	AGE	POSITION	CLUB	X	SX	S	Ap	G/Cs
Nembhard	Joash	23	Defender	Sutton United	2	2	6	4	
The New Saints, Cefn (L), Sutton U									
Nepomuceno	Gevaro	28	Forward	FC Halifax	5	10	2	15	1
Den Bosch (Hol), Fortuna, Petrolul (Rom), Maritimo (Por), Famalicao (L), Oldham, Chesterfield, FC Halifax									
Neufville	Josh	21	Midfielder	Yeovil Town (L)	27	4		31	5
Luton (Y), Solihull M (L), Woking (L), Yeovil (L)									
Newall	Nathan	19	Defender	Guiseley	10	6	4	16	2
Guiseley (Y)									
Newby	Elliot	25	Midfielder	Chorley	23			23	5
				Stockport County (L)	9	7	4	16	
Bolton (Y), Barrow, Burscough (L), Altrincham (L), Telford, Chorley, Stockport (L)									
Newell	George	24	Forward	Southport	8	4	4	12	5
Bolton (Y), AFC Fylde (L), Motherwell, Albion R (L), Southport									
Newey	Ben		Goalkeeper	Leamington			2		
Leamington (Y)									
Newton	Sean	32	Defender	York City	16			16	8
Droylsden, Barrow, Telford, Stockport (L), Stockport, Lincoln C, Notts Co (L), Wrexham, York (L), York									
Ngalo	Jordan	22	Midfielder	Weymouth	19	5	8	24	1
Poole, Blackfield & L, Weymouth, Blackfield & L (L)									
Nicholson	Alex	27	Defender	Gateshead	16			16	1
PNE (Y), Chorley (L), Blyth S, South Shields, Blyth S, Gateshead									
Nicholson	Brad	22	Defender	Guiseley	11	4	2	15	1
Guiseley									
Nickless	Jake		Midfielder	Billericay Town	2	1		3	
North Greenford, Billericay T, Harlow (L)									
Nisbet	Mark	34	Defender	Slough Town	3	1		4	
Maidenhead, Slough									
Noble	David	39	Midfielder	St Albans City	3	8	2	11	
Bristol C, Yeovil (L), Exeter, Rotherham, Cheltenham (L), Oldham, Exeter (L), Exeter, St Albans									
Nolan	Liam	26	Midfielder	AFC Fylde	5	3	5	8	1
Crewe (Y), Southport, Accrington, Salford (L), FC Halifax, AFC Fylde									
Noon	Mark	37	Midfielder	Brackley Town			12		
Coventry (Y), Tamworth, Nuneaton, Brackley									
Norton	Guy		Defender	Chelmsford City		1	5	1	
Chelmsford									
Norton	Jack	34	Goalkeeper	Spennymoor Town			9		
Darlington (Y), Gateshead, Blyth S, Whitby T, Consett, Bedlington Te, Newcastle BS, Guisborough, Hampton & RB, Dagenham, Cray W, Witham, Brentwood, UMF Sindri (Ice), Dunston UTS, South Shields, Spennymoor									
Nouble	Joel	25	Forward	Aldershot Town	30	5	9	35	5
Chelsea (Y), Millwall (Y), Dagenham & R (Y), Thurrock (L), Grays (L), Welling (L), St Albans (L), Bishop's S, Haringey B, Concord R, Aldershot									
Nowakowski	Adam	33	Midfielder	Bradford (Park Avenue)	10	2		12	1
Harrogate T, Darlington, Bradford PA (L), Bradford PA									
Nugent	Ben	28	Defender	Barnet	21	2	5	23	
Cardiff (Y), Brentford (L), Peterborough (L), Yeovil (L), Crewe, Gillingham, Stevenage, Barnet									
Nwabuokei	Solomon	25	Midfielder	St Albans City	16			16	4
Biggleswade, St Albans									
O'Brien	Jim	33	Midfielder	Notts County	26	11	7	37	3
Motherwell, Barnsley, Coventry, Scunthorpe (L), Shrewsbury, Ross Co (L), Ross Co, Bradford C, Notts Co									
O'Donnell	Jonathan	29	Midfielder	Gateshead	2	4	3	6	
				Blyth Spartans (L)	4			4	1
Luton, Hyde (L), Gateshead (L), Gateshead, Blyth S (L)									
O'Keefe	Charley	21	Defender	Braintree Town	5	2		7	
Stevenage, Wingate & F, Braintree									
O'Mara	Finn	22	Defender	Welling United (L)	2			2	
Gillingham (Y), Folkstone I (L), Folkstone I, Welling (L)									
O'Neill	Tyrone	21	Forward	Darlington (L)	4	6		10	2
Middlesbrough (Y), Hartlepool (L), Darlington (L), Darlington (L)									

2020-21 NATIONAL. NORTH & SOUTH PLAYERS

SURNAME	FIRSTNAME	AGE	POSITION	CLUB PLAYED FOR	X	SX	S	Ap	G/Cs
					APPEARANCES				
O'Sullivan	Tommy	26	Midfielder	Gloucester City	15	6		21	1
Cardiff, Port Vale (L), Newport Co (Lx2), Colchester,Torquay (L), Hereford, Gloucester									
Oastler	Joe	30	Defender	Oxford City	25			25	1
QPR (Y), Torquay (L), Torquay, Aldershot, Gosport B, Oxford C									
Oates	Rhys	26	Forward	Hartlepool United	31	10	1	41	18
Barnsley, Grimsby (L), Chester (L), Hartlepool, Morecambe, Hartlepool									
Obi	Emeka	20	Defender	AFC Fylde			1		
Bury (Y), Liverpool, Wigan, AFC Fylde									
Obiero	Micah	20	Forward	FC Halifax (L)		1	1	1	
Huddersfield (Y), Carlisle (L), FC Halifax (L)									
Oduntan	Timi		Midfielder	Billericay Town	2			2	
Billericay T (U23)									
Odusanya	Dominic		Midfielder	Maidstone United	5	5	4	10	
Maidstone									
Odusina	Oluwarotimi Mark	21	Defender	Hartlepool United	29	3	9	32	
Norwich (Y), AFC Fylde (L), Hartlepool (L), Hartlepool									
Ofori-Acheampong	Duane	28	Forward	Braintree Town	1			1	
Southend (Y), Grays, Braintree, Harrow B, Torquay, Dover, Dartford, Woking, Whitehawk (L), WhitehawkBraintree									
Ofori-Twumasi	Nathan	31	Defender	Maidenhead United	10	15	14	25	
Chelsea, Dagenham & R (L), Peterborough, Northampton (L), Northampton, Yeovil, Newport Co, Maidstone, Maidenhead									
Ofosu	Claudio	22	Forward	Hartlepool United	5	7	3	12	1
St Neots, Stevenage (Y), Biggleswade U (L), Kings Langley (L), Mildenhall T (L), Royston, Hartlepool									
Ogbewe	Nelson		Forward	Gateshead		1		1	
Gateshead (Y), West Allotment C (L)									
Ogie	Shadrach	19	Defender	Aldershot Town (L)	31	2	12	33	2
Leyton Orient (Y), Dover (L), Aldershot (L)									
Ogle	Reagan	22	Defender	AFC Fylde (L)	3	4	5	7	
				Altrincham (L)	11	1	4	12	
Accrington (Y), Stoke U23 (L), Wealdstone (L), Southport (L), Southport (L), AFC Fylde (L), Altrincham (L)									
Ogogo	Abumere	31	Midfielder	Dagenham & Redbridge (L)	13			13	
Arsenal (Y), Barnet (L), Dagenham & R, Shrewsbury, Coventry, Bristol R, Dagenham & R (L)									
Ohman	Patrik		Goalkeeper	Braintree Town	5			5	2
Upsala (Swe), Egham, Chelmsford, Carshalton, Hendon, Walton C, Hungerford, Braintree									
Ojo	Taiwo Daniel	20	Defender	Dulwich Hamlet	2			2	
Charlton (Y), Yeovil (Y), Dulwich H, Cheshunt									
Okafor	Miracle/Michael		Forward	Guiseley		2	5	2	
				Concord Rangers		1		1	
Scunthorpe (Y), Frickley A (L), Alvechurch, Bradford C, Solihull U, Guiseley, Concord R									
Okimo	Jerome	33	Defender	Wealdstone	46			46	1
Stevenage, Braintree, Wealdstone									
Okorogheye	Ada		Forward	Slough Town		1		1	
Slough (Y)									
Okunlola	Seye		Midfielder	Braintree Town		2		2	
Marlow, Braintree									
Olagunju	Mustapha	19	Defender	Welling United (L)	7		1	7	
Huddersfield (Y), Welling (L), Port Vale									
Olaofe	Isaac		Midfielder	Sutton United (L)	37	4		41	16
Millwall (Y), Sutton U (L), St Johnstone (L), Sutton U (L)									
Oldaker	Darren	22	Midfielder	Welling United	3			3	
QPR (Y), Gillingham, Billericay T, Welling									
Oliver	Charlie	23	Defender	Southport	17	1	2	18	
Man City (Y), Fleetwood (L), Brentford B (L), Southport									
Olley	Greg	25	Midfielder	Gateshead	16			16	4
Newcastle (Y), Hull (Y), Gateshead									
Olomowewe	Taofiq	24	Defender	Hemel Hempstead Town	3		2	3	1
				Braintree Town	10			10	2
Wealdstone, Hungerford, Chelmsford, Hemel H, Braintree									
Olowu	Joseph	21	Defender	Wealdstone (L)	13			13	
Arsenal (Y), Cork (L), Wealdstone (L)									

Key: X - Started; SX - Sub on; S - Non-playing Sub; Ap - Total Appearances; G/Cs - Total goals/clean sheets.

SURNAME	FIRSTNAME	AGE	POSITION	CLUB	X	SX	S	Ap	G/Cs
					APPEARANCES				
Olumuyiwa	Adeoye		Defender	Weymouth			4		
New Orleans Jesters, Team Solent, Blackfield & L, Weymouth									
Olusanya	Toyosi	23	Forward	Billericay Town	2	6	2	8	1
Wimbledon (Y), Kingstonian (L), Reading (U23), Gosport, Bishop's S, Cheshunt, Billericay T									
Olutade	Ibrahim	22	Forward	Maidstone United	1	10	7	11	3
Hanwell, Leatherhead, Maidstone, Leatherhead (L)									
Oluwadara	Michael (Dara)	22	Midfielder	St Albans City		1	4	1	
Chalfont St P, Hertford T, Berkhamsted, Staines, Barking, St Albans									
Oluwatimilehin	Olumide		Midfielder	Braintree Town	8	2		10	1
Hoddesdon T, Whitehawk, Hornchurch, Wingate & F, Braintree									
Oluwayemi	Josh	20	Goalkeeper	Maidenhead United (L)	1	1	10	2	
Tottenham (Y), Maidenhead (L)									
Oluwo	Adebola		Defender	Chelmsford City	17			17	1
Bromley (Y), Tower H, Fisher, Chelmsford									
Omotayo	Gold	27	Forward	FC Halifax	5			5	
				Gloucester City	1			1	1
				Wrexham	10	1		11	3
FC Zurich (Y), FC Schlieren, FC Wettswil, Whitehawk, Bury, Maidstone (L), Yeovil, FC Halifax, Gloucester, Wrexham									
Onokwai	Chid	26	Forward	St Albans City		4	6	4	
FC Romania, Kempston R, Aylesbury, Aylesbury U, Bowers & P, Eton Manor, Haringey B, St Albans, Hendon (D)									
Orsi-Dadamo	Danilo	25	Forward	Maidenhead United	33	9	1	42	21
East Thurrock, Hungerford, Hampton & R, Maidenhead									
Osborne	Jamey	29	Midfielder	Solihull Moors	8	4	3	12	2
Hednesford, Ringmer (L), Redditch, Solihull M, Grimsby, Solihull M (L), Solihull M									
Osborne	Samuel	21	Midfielder	Leamington	16	1		17	8
				AFC Fylde	1	1		2	
Notts Co (Y), Basford (L), Shaw Lane (L), Leamington, AFC Fylde									
Osho	Gabriel	22	Defender	Yeovil Town (L)	4			4	
Reading (Y), Maidenhead (L), Aldershot (L), Yeovil (L), Luton, Yeovil (L)									
Osman	Abdul	34	Midfielder	Dartford	1	2	1	3	
Gretna, Northampton, Kerkyra (Greece), Crewe, Partick, Lamia (Greece), Falkirk, Queen otS, Dartford									
Oswell	Jason	28	Forward	AFC Telford United	15	3	1	18	6
Crewe (Y), Rhyl (L), Inverness, Nantwich, APIA Leichhardt (Aus), Rhyl, Airbus, Newtown, Stockport, Morecambe, Wrexham, Telford									
Owen	Adam		Forward	Stockport County			1		
Stockport (Y)									
Owen	Tyrese	21	Defender	Hemel Hempstead Town	2			2	
Potters B, Carshalton, Ytterhogdals IK (Swe), Hemel H									
Owen-Evans	Tom	24	Midfielder	Hereford FC	20			20	9
Newport Co (Y), Gloucester (L), Truro (L), Falkirk, Hereford, Chippenham (L)									
Owens	Andrew	31	Forward	Chorley	4	2	1	6	2
Accrington, Southport, Mansfield (L), Telford, Barrow (L), Stockport, Telford, Marine, Stalybridge, Altrincham, Connah's Q, Airbus, Chorley									
Owers	Josh		Midfielder	Bath City (L)	2			2	
Bristol C (Y), Bath (L)									
Owusu	Nana	25	Defender	Oxford City	5	11	6	16	2
Tranmere, Maidenhead, Oxford C									
Oyeleke	Emmanuel	28	Midfielder	Chesterfield (L)	13			13	
Brentford, Northampton (L), Aldershot (L), Aldershot (L), Woking (L), Exeter, Aldershot, Canvey I (L), Port Vale, Chesterfield (L)									
Oyibo	Jude		Forward	Curzon Ashton	1	12		13	
Glossop NE, Buxton, Alfreton, Curzon A									
Oyinsan	Josh	26	Forward	Kettering Town	3	1		4	
				Hemel Hempstead Town	1	2		3	
Bromley, Cambridge C, Welling, St Albans, Braintree, Royston, Kettering, Hemel H									
Palmer	Ashley	28	Defender	Stockport County	38	3	1	41	6
Scunthorpe, Southport (L), Droylsden, Buxton, North Ferriby, Guiseley, Stockport									
Palmer	Harry	26	Goalkeeper	Yeovil Town			13		
				Billericay Town	5			5	1
Braintree, Lewes, Haringey B, Dorking W, Brightlingsea R, AFC Hornchurch, Canvey I, Ebbsfleet, Yeovil, Billericay T									
Palmer	Tom	21	Goalkeeper	Kidderminster Harriers			15		
Kidderminster (Y)									

2020-21 NATIONAL. NORTH & SOUTH PLAYERS

SURNAME	FIRSTNAME	AGE	POSITION	CLUB PLAYED FOR	X	SX	S	Ap	G/Cs
Palmer	Tyreace	18	Forward	Notts County	1	1		2	
Notts Co (Y)									
Panayiotou	Harrison (Harry)	26	Forward	Aldershot Town	31	6	4	37	12
Leicester, Port Vale (L), Raith (L), Barrow, Salford City (L), Nuneaton, Aittitos (Gre), Aldershot									
Pardington	James	20	Goalkeeper	Dulwich Hamlet (L)	5			5	1
Rushall, Wolves (Y), Bath (L), Stratford T (L), Dulwich H (L)									
Parish	Danny	22	Forward	Wealdstone	15	14	6	29	7
Concord R, Maldon, Wealdstone									
Parker	Joe	26	Forward	Leamington	2			2	
Gloucester, Newport Co, Gloucester (L), Gloucester (Lx2), Gloucester, Leamington									
Parkes	Adam	21	Goalkeeper	Barnet (L)	8			8	3
Southampton (Y), Watford, Havant & W (L), Barnet (L)									
Parkhouse	David	21	Forward	Hartlepool United (L)	4	5	1	9	2
Maiden City (NI), Sheff Utd (Y), Boston U (L), Derry City (L), Hartlepool (L)									
Parkin	Luke	25	Forward	Farsley Celtic	11	3	7	14	2
Leeds (Y), Guiseley (L), Gainsborough, Brighouse, Farsley C									
Parkinson	Tom	30	Midfielder	Tonbridge Angels	10	1	1	11	3
Ramsgate, Maidstone, Leatherhead, Tonbridge A									
Parrett	Dean	29	Midfielder	Wealdstone	2	2		4	
				Barnet	1	1	1	2	
Tottenham (Y), Aldershot (L), Plymouth (L), Charlton (L), Yeovil (L), Swindon (L), Stevenage, Wimbledon, Gillingham, Stevenage, Wealdstone, Barnet									
Parry	Immanuel (Manny)	27	Defender	Maidenhead United	41		2	41	3
Millwall, Stoke, Maidenhead (L), Nuneaton T (L), Weston-S-M (L), Worcester (L), Grays Ath, Maidstone, Margate, Braintree, Dover, Boreham W, Woking, Maidenhead									
Parselle	Kieran	24	Defender	Chippenham Town	18			18	1
Newport Co, Salisbury (L), Gloucester, Chippenham									
Parsons	Joshua		Midfielder	Guiseley	5	3		8	1
Solihull U, Guiseley									
Parter	Jack	27	Defender	Tonbridge Angels	12	2	1	14	
Gillingham (Y), Ramsgate (L), Whitstable, Tonbridge A, Kingstonian (L),									
Partington	Joe	31	Midfielder	Eastleigh	31	1	1	32	
Bournemouth (Y), Aldershot (L), Eastleigh (L), Eastleigh, Bristol R, Eastleigh									
Partridge	Matthew	36	Defender	Hungerford Town	14	2	1	16	1
Reading (Y), Basingstoke (L), Dagenham & R, Basingstoke, Newport, Basingstoke, Hungerford, Salisbury, Hungerford									
Pascal	Dwight	20	Defender	Barnet	4	2	10	6	
Barnet (Y), Potters Bar, Barnet									
Passley	Josh	26	Defender	Dover Athletic	9			9	
Fulham, Shrewsbury (L), Portsmouth (L), Dagenham & R, Whitehawk, Dover									
Pattison	Christie	24	Midfielder	Maidstone United	3	4		7	
Welling, Carshalton, Braintree, Carshalton, Maidstone									
Paul	Christopher	23	Midfielder	Hemel Hempstead Town	12	2		14	
Tottenham (Y), QPR (Y), Havant & W, Hampton & R (L), Hemel H									
Pavey	Alfie	25	Forward	Barnet	4	7		11	
				Dartford (L)	1	3		4	
Maidstone, Millwall (Y), Barnet (L), Aldershot (L), Bromley (L), Hampton & R (L), Dartford (L), Welling, Dartford, Havant & W, Dover, Barnet, Dartford (L)									
Paxman	Jack	27	Midfielder	Ebbsfleet United	21	1		22	1
Maidstone, East Thurrock (L), Billericay T, Ebbsfleet									
Payne	Alfie	21	Midfielder	Braintree Town	2	1	1	3	
				King's Lynn Town	4	10	6	14	
Norwich (Y), King's Lynn (L), Braintree, Lowestoft, King's Lynn									
Payne	Evan		Defender	Chelmsford City			3		
Chelmsford (Y)									
Payne	Jack	29	Midfielder	Eastleigh	42		2	42	1
Gillingham, Peterborough (L), Peterborough, Leyton Orient (L), Blackpool, Ebbsfleet, Eastleigh (L), Eastleigh									
Payne	Joe	22	Defender	Concord Rangers	1			1	
Barnet, Grays (L), Solihull M (L), Wealdstone (L), Enfield T (L), Enfield T, Concord R									

Key: X - Started; SX - Sub on; S - Non-playing Sub; Ap - Total Appearances; G/Cs - Total goals/clean sheets.

SURNAME	FIRSTNAME	AGE	POSITION	CLUB	X	SX	S	Ap	G/Cs
Payne	Josh	30	Midfielder	Ebbsfleet United	10	1	1	11	
Portsmouth (Y),Southampton (Y), West Ham (Y), Cheltenham (L), Colchester (L), Wycombe (L), Doncaster, Oxford U (L), Oxford U, Aldershot (L), Aldershot, Woking, Eastleigh, Crawley, Ebbsfleet (L), Ebbsfleet									
Pearce	Krystain	31	Defender	Solihull Moors	8	1		9	3
				Boreham Wood	20	1	6	21	
Birmingham (Y), Notts Co (L), Port Vale (L), Scunthorpe (L), Peterborough (L), Huddersfield, Notts Co, Barnet (L), Torquay, Mansfield, Solihull M, Boreham W									
Pearson	Brendan	24	Goalkeeper	Blyth Spartans	8		6	8	
Newcastle U (Y),Gateshead (Lx2), South Shields, Morton, Blyth S									
Pearson	Shaun	32	Defender	Wrexham	15	1	1	16	1
Grimsby, Wrexham									
Peers	Tom	25	Forward	Altrincham	14	21	6	35	7
Chester (Y), Salford (L), Hednesford (L), Hednesford, Telford, Nantwich, Altrincham, FC United, Altrincham									
Pennell	Luke	25	Defender	Hemel Hempstead Town	9	1		10	
MK Dons, Rushden, Banbury United, Wolverton, Dunstable, Dagenham & R, Maidstone, Gloucester, Hemel H									
Penny	Alex	24	Defender	Kidderminster Harriers	15			15	
Stourbridge, Hinckley, Nuneaton, Peterborough, Hamilton, Boston U, Kidderminster									
Perez	Jaden		Midfielder	Eastbourne Borough		1		1	
Eastbourne B (Y)									
Perkins	David	39	Midfielder	AFC Fylde	14	1	1	15	1
Colchester (Y), Chesterfield (L), Stockport (L), Barnsley, Blackpool, Wigan, Rochdale, Tranmere, AFC Fylde									
Perkins	Teddy	21	Defender	Hemel Hempstead Town (L)		1	1	1	
Leyton O (Y), Burnley (U23), Ramsbottom (L), Watford (U23), Hemel H (L)									
Perritt	Harrison	21	Defender	Southport (L)			1		
Accrington (Y), Southport (L)									
Perry	Kyle	35	Forward	Kettering Town	11			11	1
Tamworth, Lincoln C, Telford (L), Nuneaton, Hereford (L), Tamworth (L), Altrincham, Hednesford, Worcester, Stourbridge, Kettering									
Petrasso	Michael	25	Forward	Barnet (L)	20	10	1	30	10
QPR (Y), Oldham (L), Coventry (L), Leyton O (L), Notts Co (L), Montreal (Can), Valour, York9, Barnet (L)									
Phillips	Aaron	27	Midfielder	Brackley Town			6		
Coventry (Y), Nuneaton (L), Northampton, Kidderminster, Brackley									
Phillips	Giles	24	Defender	Aldershot Town (L)	19		1	19	
QPR, Wycombe (L), Wycombe, Aldershot (L)									
Phillips	Kiran	18	Forward	Chippenham Town (L)	1	4	2	5	
Bristol R (Y), Wolves (U23) (L), Chippenham (L)									
Phillips	Leon		Goalkeeper	Kidderminster Harriers			2		
Kidderminster (Y)									
Phillips	Michael	23	Midfielder	Wealdstone	34	2	4	36	1
Crystal Palace, Maidstone, Wealdstone									
Philliskirk	Danny	30	Midfielder	AFC Fylde	19	1		20	3
Chelsea, Oxford U (L), Sheffield U (L), Sheffield U, Oxford U (L), Coventry, Oldham, Blackpool, AFC Fylde									
Philpott	Charlie		Goalkeeper	Eastleigh			1		
Eastleigh (Y)									
Philpott	Isaac	26	Defender	Dorking Wanderers	12	1	2	13	1
Sutton U, Cardiff M Uni, Dorking W									
Phipp	Tom	28	Midfielder	Tonbridge Angels	1			1	
Ebbsfleet (Y), Maidstone (L), Margate, Tonbridge A, Cray W (L/P),									
Pickering	Matthew		Defender	Eastbourne Borough	2		1	2	
Eastbourne B (Y)									
Piggott	Joe	22	Forward	Altrincham	8	3	1	11	
Rochdale (Y), Dundee Utd, Warrington, Wigan, Morecambe (L), Altrincham (L), Stockport (L), Altrincham									
Piggott	Jordan	22	Defender	Solihull Moors	13	5	22	18	
WBA (Y), Dundee, East Fife (L), Bangor, Halesowen, Solihull M									
Pilling	Luke	23	Goalkeeper	Notts County	6		10	6	3
Tranmere (Y), Glossop NE (L), Trafford (L), Ashton U (L), Notts Co									
Piorkowski	Gabriel		Midfielder	Braintree Town	2		1	2	
Hayes & Y, Braintree									
Platt	Tom	27	Midfielder	Boston United	10	2		12	1
York (Y), Halifax (L), Harrogate, Alfreton, Boston U									

2020-21 NATIONAL. NORTH & SOUTH PLAYERS — APPEARANCES

SURNAME	FIRSTNAME	AGE	POSITION	CLUB PLAYED FOR	X	SX	S	Ap	G/Cs
Poku	Godfrey	30	Midfielder	Havant & Waterlooville	9	3	2	12	
Luton (Y), St Albans (L), Southport (L), Mansfield, Southport (L), Alfreton (L), Telford, Woking, Havant & W (L), Oxford C, Wealdstone, Woking, Havant & W									
Poleon	Dominic	27	Forward	Ebbsfleet United		3		3	2
Leeds (Y), Bury (L), Sheff Utd (L), Oldham, Wimbledon, Bradford C, Crawley, Newport C, Dover, Ebbsfleet									
Pollock	Aron	23	Defender	Concord Rangers	17	1	2	18	1
Leyton Orient, Wingate (L), Wealdstone (L), Leatherhead (L), Leatherhead, Concord R									
Pollock	Ben	23	Midfielder	Hereford FC	4	2	2	6	
Middlesbrough (Y), Leeds (Y), Newcastle U (Y), Hartlepool, Dunston, Billingham S, Hereford									
Pond	Nathan	36	Defender	AFC Fylde	13			13	
Lancaster, Fleetwood, Kendal (L), Grimsby (L), Salford, AFC Fylde									
Ponticelli	Jordan	22	Forward	Wrexham	12	16	4	28	4
Coventry (Y), Macclesfield (L), Tranmere (L), Wrexham (L), Wrexham									
Pope	Jason	25	Midfielder	Bath City	6	5	8	11	
Exeter (Y), Weston (L), Weston, Hereford, Bath									
Popo Ebigbeyi	Tosan	28	Forward	Concord Rangers	18	1		19	
Charlton, Chelmsford (L), San Roque Lepe (Sp), San Roque Lepe, Concord R, Hemel H, Concord R									
Porter	George	28	Forward	Maidstone United	16	1		17	6
Cray W, Leyton O, Burnley, Colchester (L), AFC Wimbledon (L), Rochdale, Dagenham & R, Welling, Bromley, Maidstone, Dartford									
Poscha	Marcus	25	Midfielder	Curzon Ashton	6	1	1	7	
Bury (Y), Stockport (L), Colne, Curzon A									
Potter	Alfie	32	Forward	Oxford City	4	4		8	1
Peterborough, Kettering (L), Oxford U, Wimbledon, Northampton, Mansfield, Billericay T, Oxford C									
Potter	Darren	36	Midfielder	Altrincham	1			1	
Liverpool (Y), Southampton (L), Wolves, Sheff Wed (L), MK Dons, Rotherham, Tranmere, Altrincham									
Potts	Reon	20	Forward	York City		8	4	8	
Sheff Utd (Y), Tamworth (L), Sheffield FC (L), Lincoln U (L), Scunthorpe, York									
Powell	Callum	25	Midfielder	Kettering Town	9			9	6
Rugby, Wrexham, Tamworth (L), Tamworth, Stratford, Stourbridge, Kettering									
Power	Simon	23	Midfielder	King's Lynn Town (L)	8	5	2	13	2
Cabinteely, Uni College Dublin, Norwich, Dordrecht (L), Ross Co (L), King's Lynn (L), King's Lynn (L)									
Pratt	David	33	Forward	Chippenham Town			2		
Basingstoke, Maidenhead, Bath, Chippenham, Wealdstone, Chippenham									
Prestedge	Reece	35	Midfielder	Braintree Town		2	2	2	
Bishop's St, Bromley, Chelmsford (L), Maidstone, Hemel H, East Thurrock, Welling, Margate, Braintree									
Preston	Fraser	22	Forward	Boston United	7	5	3	12	2
Sheff Wed (Y), Boston U									
Preston	Jordan	25	Forward	Gateshead	12	2		14	3
Blackburn, Ayr (L), Ayr, Guiseley, Gateshead, FC Halifax, Gateshead									
Preston	Matt	26	Defender	Barnet	16		3	16	
Walsall (Y), IBV (IS) (L), Barwell (L), Swindon, Mansfield, Barnet									
Price	Owen		Defender	Torquay United			6		
Torquay (Y)									
Prior	Jason	32	Forward	Dorking Wanderers	18	1		19	18
Wimbledon, Dartford (L), Dartford, Gosport (L), Margate, Bognor R, Havant & W, Dorking W									
Prosser	Alexander	22	Midfielder	Kidderminster Harriers	8	9		17	
Aston Villa (Y), Brackley (L), Kidderminster									
Pryce	Ashanti	21	Forward	Kettering Town		5	6	5	
Aston Villa (Y), Birmingham (Y), Mansfield, Kettering									
Przybek	Adam	21	Goalkeeper	Braintree Town (L)	3		1	3	
				Concord Rangers (L)	5			5	1
				Chesterfield (L)	3			3	1
WBA (Y), Gloucester (L), Ipswich, Braintree (L), Concord C (L), Chesterfield (L)									
Puddy	Willem	33	Goalkeeper	Chippenham Town	17			17	4
Swindon Sup, Chippenham, Salisbury, Bristol R, Braintree (L), Sutton U (L), Hereford, Chippenham									
Purrington	Tom	20	Midfielder	Bromley	1	1	27	2	
Plymouth (Y), Bromley									
Putnam	Oliver		Forward	Chorley	1	1	10	2	
Newcastle T, Eccleshall, Hanley T, Chorley									

Key: X - Started; SX - Sub on; S - Non-playing Sub; Ap - Total Appearances; G/Cs - Total goals/clean sheets.

2020-21 NATIONAL. NORTH & SOUTH PLAYERS — APPEARANCES

SURNAME	FIRSTNAME	AGE	POSITION	CLUB	X	SX	S	Ap	G/Cs
Quigley	Joe	24	Forward	Yeovil Town	25	16	1	41	13
Bournemouth, Torquay (L), Wrexham (L), Woking (L), Woking (L), Gillingham (L), Gillingham (L), Newport Co (L), Boreham W (L), Maidstone, Bromley, Eastbourne B (L)Havant & W (L), Dagenham & R, Billericay T (L), Yeovil									
Raad	Jason		Midfielder	Concord Rangers	7	2	2	9	1
Aveley, Concord R									
Rabbetts	Joe		Defender	Aldershot Town		1	2	1	
Aldershot (Y)									
Raison	Toby		Defender	Hereford FC		2	2	2	
Hereford (Y)									
Ramsay	Louis	23	Defender	Billericay Town	6			6	
Tottenham (Y), Norwich U23, Woking (L), Leicester U23, Billericay T									
Ramshaw	Rob	27	Midfielder	Spennymoor Town	17			17	5
Darlington, Gateshead, Spennymoor									
Rance	Dean	30	Midfielder	Dagenham & Redbridge	27	2	1	29	2
Gillingham, Maidstone (L), Bishop's S (L), Dover (L), Dover, Ebbsfleet, Aldershot, Dagenham & R									
Randall	Will	24	Midfielder	Sutton United	25	3		28	3
Swindon (Y), Wolves, Walsall (L), Forest GR (L), FC Jumilla (Spa) (L), Newport Co, Sutton U									
Randell	Adam	20	Midfielder	Torquay United (L)	48	2		50	3
Plymouth (Y), Torquay (L)									
Randell	Jayden		Defender	Maidstone United			2		
				Wealdstone			1		
				Concord Rangers (L)	1		1	1	
Heybridge S, Maidstone, Wealdstone, Concord R (L)									
Ransom	Harry	21	Defender	Dover Athletic (L)	9			9	1
Brighton & HA (Y), Eastbourne B (Y), Millwall, Dover (L)									
Ravas	Henrich	23	Goalkeeper	Hartlepool United (L)	13		8	13	3
Spartak Myjava (Slov), Peterborough, Boston U, Derby, Gainsborough T (L), Hartlepool (L)									
Ravizzoli	Franco	23	Goalkeeper	Eastbourne Borough	23		1	23	3
Merlo (Arg), Moron, Eastbourne B									
Rawlins	Ashley	25	Goalkeeper	AFC Telford United			17		
Telford U, Market D, Telford U									
Rawlinson	Connell	29	Defender	Notts County	42	2	3	44	
Chester, TNS, Newtown (L), Port Vale, Notts Co									
Rawson	Luke	20	Forward	Chesterfield	2	8	1	10	2
				Alfreton Town (L)	2	1	1	3	1
				Bradford Park Avenue (L)		1		1	
Chesterfield (Y), Matlock (L), Brighouse (L), Alfreton (L), Bradford PA (L)									
Raymond	Frankie	28	Midfielder	Bromley	27	12	9	39	
Reading, Dagenham & R, Bromley									
Read	Benny		Defender	Havant & Waterlooville	14	1	1	15	
Horndean, Havant & W									
Reason	Jai	31	Midfielder	Billericay Town	10	5	1	15	2
Ipswich, Cambridge U (L), Cambridge U, Crawley, Braintree, Eastleigh, Boreham W, Maidstone, Chelmsford, Dover, Billericay T									
Reckord	Jamie	29	Defender	Wrexham	34		1	34	2
Wolves, Northampton (L), Scunthorpe (L), Coventry (L), Plymouth (L), Swindon (L), Ross Co, Oldham, Solihull M, Wrexham									
Redmond	Devonte	24	Midfielder	Wrexham		2	11	2	
Man United (Y), Scunthorpe (L), Salford, Wrexham									
Redshaw	Jack	30	Forward	York City	7	4		11	2
Rochdale (Y), Altrincham, Morecambe, Altrincham (L), Blackpool, Rochdale, Salford, Halifax, York									
Rees	Josh	21	Midfielder	Aldershot Town	43			43	13
Nottingham F, Nuneaton (L), Torquay (L), Torquay, Chelmsford, Bromley, Gillingham, Bromley, Aldershot									
Reeves	Elliott		Forward	Alfreton Town	12	3	1	15	5
Margate, Alfreton									
Reeves	Fenton		Midfielder	Chorley			1		
Chorley (Y)									
Reeves	Jake	28	Midfielder	Notts County	46		1	46	5
St Albans, Brentford, Wimbledon (L), Swindon, Wimbledon, Bradford, Notts Co									
Reid	Alex	25	Forward	Stockport County	39	10	2	49	21
Fleetwood, Wrexham (L), Solihull M (L), Stevenage, AFC Fylde (L), Ebbsfleet (L), Dagenham & R (L), Stockport									

Reeves Elliott - Alfreton Town.

Reeves Jake - Notts Co.

Richens Michael - Kettering Town.

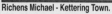

Rodrigues Ruben - Notts Co.

Key: X - Started; SX - Sub on; S - Non-playing Sub; Ap - Total Appearances; G/Cs - Total goals/clean sheets.

SURNAME	FIRSTNAME	AGE	POSITION	CLUB	X	SX	S	Ap	G/Cs
Reid	Kyel	33	Midfielder	Billericay Town	5	8	1	13	1
West Ham (Y), Barnsley (L), Crystal P (L), Blackpool (L), Wolves (L), Sheffield U, Charlton, Bradford, PNE, Bradford (L), Coventry, Colchester (L), Chesterfield, Sutton U, Billericay T									
Reid	Reuben	32	Forward	Yeovil Town	25	2	2	27	3
Plymouth (Y), Kidderminster (L), Rochdale (L), Torquay (L), Wycombe (L), Brentford (L), Rotherham, WBA, Peterborough (L), Walsall (L), Oldham, Yeovil, Plymouth (L), Plymouth, Exeter, Forest GR, Cheltenham, Yeovil									
Reid	Sean	29	Midfielder	Darlington	13	4	2	17	1
Ryton & Crawcrook A, West Allotment C, Ryton, Newcastle Benfield, Blyth S, Morpeth, Darlington									
Reid	Tyler	23	Defender	Woking	5		8	5	
Arsenal (Y), Man U (Y), Swansea (Y), Newport Co (L), Swindon, Wrexham (L), Woking									
Reilly	Lewis	21	Forward	Chorley	9	9		18	4
Crewe (Y), Curzon A (L), Telford (L), Chorley									
Remfry	Sam		Midfielder	Concord Rangers	1		6	1	
Concord R									
Rendell	Scott	34	Forward	Maidstone United	16			16	6
Aldershot, Forest Green, Crawley, Cambridge U, Peterborough (L), Peterborough, Yeovil (L), Cambridge U (L), Torquay (L), Wycombe, Bristol R (L), Oxford U (L), Luton, Woking, Aldershot, Eastleigh, Maidstone									
Renee-Pringle	Johnville	24	Defender	Braintree Town	14	2	2	16	1
Stoke (U23), Wimbledon, Maldon & T, Bishop's S, Wingate (L), Braintree									
Renshaw	Chris	23	Goalkeeper	FC Halifax (L)			11		
Everton (Y), Oldham (L), Witton, FC Halifax (L)									
Revan	Dominic	20	Defender	Weymouth (L)	17			17	
Aston Villa (Y), Weymouth (L)									
Reynolds	Callum	31	Defender	Dagenham & Redbridge	21	2	9	23	2
Rushden, Portsmouth, Luton (L), Tamworth, Corby (L), Boreham W, Aldershot, Barnet, Dagenham & R									
Reynolds	Lamar	25	Midfielder	Concord Rangers	10	6	1	16	
Newport Co, Leyton Orient (L), Dag & Red, Chelmsford (L), Concord R									
Rhead	Matthew	37	Forward	Boreham Wood	18	14	4	32	2
Eastwood, Corby, Mansfield, Lincoln C, Billericay T, Boreham W									
Richards	Caleb	22	Defender	Kidderminster Harriers (L/P)	17			17	
Marine, Blackpool, Southport (L), Norwich, FC United (L), Tampa Bay (L), Yeovil (L), Kidderminster (L/P)									
Richards	Eliot	29	Forward	Barnet	5			5	1
Bristol R (Y), Exeter (L), Tranmere, Cheltenham, Bath (L), Weston, Merthyr, Hereford, Barnet									
Richards	Jordan	28	Defender	Farsley Celtic	21			21	2
Hartlepool, Alfreton (L), Darlington, AFC Fylde, Southport, Farsley C									
Richards	Jordan	23	Defender	King's Lynn Town	25	1	2	26	
Notts Co (Y), Boston U (L), Sligo Rovers, Gainsborough, King's Lynn									
Richards	Tom	22	Midfielder	Bath City	7	7	4	14	2
Bristol C, Truro (L), Bath									
Richards-Everton	Ben	29	Defender	Barnet	20	3		23	1
Hinckley U, Rushall (L), Tamworth, Partick, Airdrie (L), Dunfermline, Accrington, Bradford C, Barnet									
Richardson	Kenton	22	Defender	Notts County (L)	1			1	
Hartlepool, Sunderland, Notts Co (L)									
Richardson	Theo	22	Goalkeeper	King's Lynn Town (L/P)	18			18	2
Man Utd (Y), Cleethorpes T, King's Lynn (L/P)									
Richefond	Ryan	25	Midfielder	Maidstone United	1		1		
Crawley (Y), Grays, Margate, Bishop's S, Maidstone									
Richens	Michael	26	Defender	Kettering Town	12	3	3	15	
Peterborough (Y), Histon (L), Nuneaton (L), Whitehawk (L), Bishop's S (L), Stevenage (L), Farnborough (L), Stevenage, Farnborough (L), Hemel H, Bishop's S, Kettering									
Richman	Simon	31	Midfielder	Altrincham	4	9	11	13	
Port Vale (Y), Worcester, Altrincham									
Ricketts	Mark	36	Midfielder	Boreham Wood	29		1	29	1
Charlton, MK Dons (L), Ebbsfleet, Woking, Boreham W									
Rigg	Steven	28	Forward	Dover Athletic	10	3	1	13	1
Penrith (Y), Carlisle, Queen OTS, Carlisle, Chorley, Workington (L), Gateshead, Dover									
Rivers	Jarrett	27	Midfielder	Darlington	17	4		21	6
Middlesbrough (Y), Sunderland RCA (L), Whitley B, Blyth S, Blackpool, Blyth S, Darlington									

2020-21 NATIONAL. NORTH & SOUTH PLAYERS — APPEARANCES

SURNAME	FIRSTNAME	AGE	POSITION	CLUB PLAYED FOR	X	SX	S	Ap	G/Cs
Roache	Rowan	21	Midfielder	Altrincham			2		
Blackpool (Y), Southport (L), FC United (L), Derby U23 (L), Lancaster C (L), Bamber B (L/P), Altrincham									
Roast	Billy	26	Defender	Concord Rangers	15	1	2	16	
Colchester, Maldon, Concord R, Dartford, Concord R									
Robbins	Joe	19	Midfielder	Altrincham (L)	4	1	3	5	
Crewe (Y), Altrincham (L)									
Robbins	Sam		Midfielder	Braintree Town	6			6	
Bishop's S, Braintree									
Robert	Fabien	32	Midfielder	Gloucester City	2	11	8	13	
Lorient, Boulogne (L), Doncaster (L), Swindon, Forest Green, Aldershot (L), Gloucester (Lx2), Gloucester									
Roberts	Callum	24	Forward	Notts County	5	5		10	1
Newcastle U (Y), Gateshead (L), Kilmarnock (L), Colchester (L), Middlesbrough U23, Blyth S, Notts Co									
Roberts	Dan		Forward	Slough Town	6	6		12	1
Slough									
Roberts	Gary	34	Midfielder	Chester		4	9	4	
Crewe, Yeovil, Rotherham, Port Vale, Mansfield, Connah's Q, Bangor, Southport, Chester									
Roberts	James	25	Forward	Oxford City	22	1		23	17
Wycombe (Y), Oxford U (Y), Chester (L), Oxford C (L), Barnet (L), Oxford C (L), Chelmsford (L), Guiseley (L), Hereford, Spennymoor, Oxford C									
Roberts	Kevin	31	Defender	Chester	19		3	19	1
Chester, Cambridge U, Halifax, Wrexham, Chester									
Roberts	Kory	23	Defender	Bromley	23	3	8	26	1
Walsall (Y), Leamington (L), Bromley									
Roberts	Leo		Defender	Chorley			2		
AFC Fylde (Y), Witton (D), Chorley									
Roberts	Morgan	20	Midfielder	Brackley Town (L)	3			3	
Northampton (Y), Brackley (L)									
Roberts	Phil	27	Forward	Chelmsford City	7	3		10	
Arsenal (Y), Inverness (L), Falkirk, Dundee, Alloa (L), Sligo, Chelmsford, Braintree, Chelmsford, Hemel H, Dartford, Wealdstone, Hayes & Y, Welling, Chelmsford									
Roberts	Theo	22	Goalkeeper	Curzon Ashton	2		2	2	
Wigan (Y), Chester, Mossley (L), Curzon A, City of Liverpool									
Robinson	Andy	28	Midfielder	Weymouth	27	6	4	33	2
Southampton (Y), Bolton (L), Bolton, Dorchester, Gosport, Havant & W, Weymouth									
Robinson	Jake	34	Forward	Billericay Town	15	1	1	16	13
Brighton, Aldershot, Shrewsbury (L), Northampton, Luton (L), Whitehawk, Hempstead, Billericay T, Maidstone, Billericay T									
Robinson	Matt	27	Midfielder	Dagenham & Redbridge	24	3	5	27	8
Leicester, Luton, Kidderminster (L), Grimsby (L), Woking (L), Dagenham & R									
Robinson	Zach	19	Forward	Woking (L)	9	1		10	
Wimbledon (Y), Woking (L)									
Robson	Craig	29	Defender	Havant & Waterlooville	15	2	3	17	3
Havant & W, Sorrento FC (W.Aus), Bognor Regis, Dagenham & R, Barnet, Billericay, Havant & W									
Rodrigues	Ruben da Rocha	25	Forward	Notts County	32	10	6	42	13
Gemert (NL), Den Bosch, Treffers (L), Notts Co									
Rodwell-Grant	Joe	18	Forward	Chorley (L)		6		6	
PNE (Y), Chorley (L)									
Rogers	Gabriel	21	Midfielder	Yeovil Town	3	7	3	10	1
Yeovil (Y)									
Rollins	Jay		Midfielder	Boston United	4	6	1	10	2
Armthorpe, Boston U									
Rollinson	Joel	22	Midfielder	Eastbourne Borough	13	10		23	3
Reading (Y), Eastbourne B (L), Stevenage, Eastbourne B									
Rolt	Bradley		Forward	Brackley Town (L)	1	3	2	4	2
				Braintree Town (L)	1	1		2	
Peterborough (Y), Welling (L), Brackley (L), Braintree (L)									
Romain	Elliott	29	Forward	Dartford	11	7	2	18	1
Brighton, Millwall, Three Bridges, Lewes, Horsham YMCA (L), Eastbourne B, Dagenham & R, Welling (L), Torquay (L), Maidstone, Eastbourne B, Dartford, Ebbsfleet									

Key: X - Started; SX - Sub on; S - Non-playing Sub; Ap - Total Appearances; G/Cs - Total goals/clean sheets.

SURNAME	FIRSTNAME	AGE	POSITION	CLUB	X	SX	S	Ap	G/Cs
Rooney	Adam	33	Forward	Solihull Moors	18	12		30	9
Crumlin Utd (Eire), Stoke (Y), Yeovil (L), Chesterfield (L), Bury (L), Inverness, Birmingham, Swindon (L), Oldham, Aberdeen, Salford, Solihull M									
Rooney	John	30	Midfielder	Stockport County	41	2	1	43	21
Macclesfield, Barnsley, Bury, Chester, Wrexham, Guiseley, Barrow, Stockport									
Rooney	Paul	24	Defender	Dover Athletic	2	2	1	4	
St Pats, Bohemians, Millwall, Torquay (L), Colchester, Bromley (L), Billericay (L), Dover									
Rose	Ahkeem	22	Forward	Dover Athletic	11	6		17	2
Heather St John, Grimsby, Boston U (L), Dover									
Rose	Mitchell	26	Midfielder	Boston United	5		2	5	
Rotherham (Y), Crawley (L), Ilkeston (L), Mansfield, Newport, Grimsby, Notts Co, Boston U									
Ross	Craig	31	Goalkeeper	Woking	46		1	46	13
Hampton & R, Cambridge U, Eastbourne B (L), Eastbourne B, Farnborough, Whitehawk, Macclesfield, Barnet, Boreham W, Woking									
Ross	Ethan	24	Goalkeeper	Weymouth (L)	26		2	26	6
Arsenal (Y), WBA (Y), Worcester (L), Worcester (L), Redditch (L), Colchester, Maidstone (L), Lincoln C, Weymouth (L)									
Ross	Mark	31	Defender	Bradford (Park Avenue)	18			18	
Leigh Gen, Chorley, Stockport, Bradford PA, Chorley, Bradford (PA)									
Rowan	Charlie	23	Defender	Ebbsfleet United	9	2	1	11	1
Watford (Y), Accrington (L), QPR, Barnet (L), Ebbsfleet									
Rowe	Callum		Defender	Hereford FC (L)	1	1	1	2	
Aston Villa (Y), Hereford (L)									
Rowe	Christian		Midfielder	Havant & Waterlooville	2	2	6	4	
Andover T (Y), Havant & W									
Rowe	Coby	25	Defender	Sutton United	10	1	4	11	
Haringey B, Sutton U									
Rowe	Danny M	31	Forward	Chesterfield	9			9	4
Man Utd (Y), Fleetwood, Droylsden (L), Stockport, Barrow, Macclesfield, AFC Fylde, Oldham, Bradford, Chesterfield									
Rowe	James	29	Midfielder	Aldershot Town	11	7	15	18	
Forest Green, Tranmere, Cheltenham, Aldershot									
Rowe	Omar	26	Midfielder	Hemel Hempstead Town (L)	2	4		6	2
West Ham (Y), Southampton (Y), Tower H, Woodford T, Bishop's S, Ayia Napa, Enosis NP, Ayia Napa, Hayes & Y, Hemel H (L)									
Rowley	Joe	22	Midfielder	Chesterfield	5	7	7	12	
Chesterfield (Y)									
Ruddick	Luke	31	Defender	Hampton & Richmond Borough	4	2	3	6	
Salisbury, Bath, Salisbury, Sutton U, Oxford C, Hampton & R									
Rumble	Jake	17	Defender	Woking			1		
Woking (Y), Westfield (L)									
Rusby	James		Defender	Hungerford Town	18			18	1
Hungerford									
Rush	Matt	20	Forward	Tonbridge Angels (L)	2		2	1	
Southend (Y), Tonbridge A (L)									
Russe	Luke	21	Midfielder	Chippenham Town	16	2		18	
Bristol R, Gloucester (L), Gloucester (L), Chippenham (L), Chippenham									
Russell	Kurtis	21	Forward	Blyth Spartans	2	8	3	10	1
Newcastle U (Y), NK Novigrad (Croa), Newcastle B, Blyth S									
Rutherford	Alfie		Forward	Dorking Wanderers	16	2	1	18	5
Moneyfields, Bognor, Havant & W, Eastbourne B (L), Dorking W									
Rutherford	Paul	33	Midfielder	Wrexham	14	13	8	27	
Chester, Barrow, Southport, Wrexham									
Ryan	Bradley		Midfielder	Welling United	1	1	4	2	
Welling (Y)									
Ryan	Jack	25	Midfielder	Guiseley		5	1	5	
PNE (Y), Stalybridge (L), Stockport (Lx2), Morecambe (L), Southport (L), Bradford PA, Workington, Olympia FC W (Aus), Guiseley									
Rydel	Ryan	20	Defender	Stockport County	2	2		4	
Fleetwood (Y), Stockport									
Sagaf	Mohammed	23	Midfielder	Dagenham & Redbridge	9	4	6	13	
North Greenford, Ternana (Y), Leatherhead, Waltham F, Ipswich T, Barking, Braintree, Carlisle, Dagenham & R									
Saied	Selim	18	Forward	Woking		2		2	
Woking (Y), Westfield (L)									

2020-21 NATIONAL. NORTH & SOUTH PLAYERS — APPEARANCES

SURNAME	FIRSTNAME	AGE	POSITION	CLUB PLAYED FOR	X	SX	S	Ap	G/Cs
Sakellaropoulos	Alexandros	21	Defender	Blyth Spartans	10	1	1	11	
Panegialios (Gre), Carlisle, Gateshead, Blyth S									
Sakho (Embalo)	Sandro	25	Defender	Dulwich Hamlet	9	1	3	10	
Sporting (Por) (Y), Braga (Y), Leiria (Y), Athletico M (Spa) (Y), Genoa (It) (Y), Kalev (Estonia), Ermis Aradippou (Cyp), Vitoria (Por) (U23), CD Fatima, Dulwich H									
Salmon	Lewis	19	Forward	Altrincham			3		
Altrincham (Y), Trafford (L),									
Saltmer	Jonathan	22	Goalkeeper	Darlington	14		7	14	3
Barrow (Y), Darlington									
Sam	Elisha	24	Forward	Notts County	14	18	9	32	7
Hapoel A (Isr), Hapoel Nof HG, Eindhoven, Arda (Bul), Notts Co									
Sammut	Ruben	23	Midfielder	Dulwich Hamlet	8		10	8	
Chelsea (Y), Falkirk (L), Sunderland (U23), Dulwich H									
Sampson	Jack	28	Forward	Southport	3	1		4	
				AFC Fylde	7	4		11	1
Bolton (Y), Southend (L), Accrington (L), Morecambe, Macclesfield (L), Macclesfield, Chorley (L), Southport, AFC Fylde									
Sanders	Jack		Defender	AFC Fylde (L)	7	1	6	8	1
Wigan (Y), Blyth S (L), Southport (L), AFC Fylde (L)									
Sang	Chris	22	Forward	Wrexham	1	2	2	3	
Wigan (Y), Bury, Southport (L), Marine (L), Altrincham (L), Barnsley, Guiseley (L), Wrexham									
Santos	Alefe	26	Midfielder	Weymouth	4	4	3	8	
Bristol R, Derby, Notts Co (L), Eastleigh (L), Yeovil, Aldershot, Weymouth									
Sanyang	Omar		Forward	Bradford (Park Avenue)	4	5	3	9	
Scunthorpe (U23), Bradford (PA)									
Sass-Davies	Billy	21	Defender	Altrincham (L)	5	2		7	
				Yeovil Town (L)	22			22	1
Crewe (Y), Colwyn B (L), Leek (L), FC United (L), Altrincham (L), Telford (L), Altrincham (L), Yeovil (L)									
Saunders	David		Goalkeeper	Hemel Hempstead Town			5		
Hemel H (Y)									
Saunders	George		Midfielder	Dagenham & Redbridge	15	13	5	28	1
Hornchurch, Dagenham & R									
Saunders	Harvey	23	Forward	Hartlepool United (L)	2	1	1	3	
Durham City, Darlington, Fleetwood, Darlington (L), Hartlepool (L)									
Saydee	Christian	19	Forward	Weymouth (L)	1	2	1	3	
Bournemouth (Y), Poole (L), Weymouth (L)									
Sbarra	Joe	22	Midfielder	Solihull Moors	30	9	2	39	8
Burton, Solihull M (L), Solihull M									
Schmid	Ryan	22	Goalkeeper	Braintree Town			3		
Stevenage (Y), Kings L, Leverstock, Welwyn GC, Bedford T, Potton U, Braintree, Harrow B									
Schofield	Lucas		Midfielder	FC Halifax			1		
FC Halifax									
Scorey	Ben	20	Midfielder	Eastleigh	1		6	1	
Eastleigh (Y)									
Scott	George		Goalkeeper	AFC Telford United			1		
New Saints, Telford (Y), Bridgnorth (L)									
Scott	Josh	19	Forward	Kettering Town (L)	5	3	2	8	2
Hartlepool (Y), Mansfield, Kettering (L)									
Scott	Oliver	20	Midfielder	Blyth Spartans	6	1		7	
Blyth S (Y)									
Scott	Ryan	27	Defender	Concord Rangers	10	2	4	12	
				Braintree Town	1			1	
East Thurrock, Concord R, Braintree									
Scott-Morris	Gus		Defender	Hemel Hempstead Town (D)	12			12	
Royston T, Hemel H (D)									
Seager	Ryan	25	Forward	Hungerford Town	20			20	14
Southampton (Y), Crewe (L), MK Dons (L), Yeovil (L), Yeovil, Havant & W (L), Frome (L), Hungerford									
Seaman	Charlie	21	Defender	Maidstone United (L)	12	3		15	5
Bournemouth (Y), Dundee U (L), Eastleigh (L), Maidstone (L), Maidstone (L)									

Key: X - Started; SX - Sub on; S - Non-playing Sub; Ap - Total Appearances; G/Cs - Total goals/clean sheets.

SURNAME	FIRSTNAME	AGE	POSITION	CLUB	X	SX	S	Ap	G/Cs
Search	Ben		Forward	Concord Rangers			1		
Concord R (Y)									
Sekajja	Ibra	28	Forward	Dulwich Hamlet	1			1	
Crystal P (Y), Kettering (L), MK Dons (L), Barnet (L), Inverness C, Livingston, Braintree, Hemel, Dulwich, Bognor, Havant & W, Maidenhead, Dulwich									
Sellers	Ryan	26	Defender	Hemel Hempstead Town	5			5	1
Bolton, Wycombe, Wingate, Wealdstone, FC Halifax, Wealdstone, Hemel H									
Sendles-White	Jamie	27	Defender	Aldershot Town	28	3	9	31	1
QPR, Colchester (L), Mansfield (L), Hamilton, Swindon, Leyton Orient, St Albans, Torquay, Crawley, Aldershot									
Senior	Jack	24	Defender	FC Halifax	23	11	6	34	
Huddersfield (Y), Luton, Harrogate (L), Gloucester, FC Halifax									
Senior	Joel	22	Defender	Altrincham	40	1	2	41	1
Oldham (Y), Maine Rd, FC United, Curzon A, Burnley (U23), Altrincham									
Shabani	Brendan	19	Defender	Concord Rangers (L)	3	3		6	
Leyton O, Concord R (L)									
Shakes	Ricky	36	Midfielder	St Albans City	4			4	
Bolton, Bristol R (L), Bury (L), Swindon, Brentford, Ebbsfleet, Kidderminster, Boreham W, St Albans									
Sharman	Jamie		Defender	Chesterfield	7		2	7	
Chesterfield (Y), Kidderminster (L)									
Sharpe	Rhys	26	Defender	Kettering Town	4			4	
Derby (Y), Shrewsbury (L), Notts Co, Swindon, Matlock, Tamworth, Nuneaton, Kettering									
Shaw	Frazer	26	Defender	Concord Rangers	10			10	
Dulwich H, Leyton Orient, Accrington, Woking, Eastleigh, Leatherhead, Concord R, Chelmsford, Concord R									
Shaw	James		Goalkeeper	Tonbridge Angels	4		8	4	2
Eastbourne B, Burgess H, Tonbridge A									
Shaw	Nathan	20	Midfielder	AFC Fylde (L)	13	6	1	19	2
				Stockport County (L)	1	1	1	2	
Blackpool (Y), AFC Fylde (L), Stockport (L)									
Sheaf	Mac	21	Midfielder	Torquay United (L)	4	1	3	5	
Hull (Y), Cheltenham (L), Torquay (L)									
Sheckleford	Ryheem	24	Defender	Maidenhead United	27	3	5	30	
Fulham (Y), Wealdstone (L), Maidenhead									
Shelton	Mark	24	Midfielder	Hartlepool United	37	2	7	39	3
Burton (Y), Ilkeston, Alfreton, Salford, Woking (L), Hartlepool (L), Hartlepool									
Shelvey	George	20	Goalkeeper	Wealdstone (L)	5			5	1
Notts F (Y), Truro (L), Wealdstone (L)									
Shenton	Oliver	23	Midfielder	Chorley	20	1	2	21	2
Stoke (Y), Wrexham (L), Kidderminster (L), Chorley									
Shergill	Joshveer	19	Defender	Solihull Moors			3		
WBA (Y), Walsall (Y), Leeds (Y), Solihull M									
Sheriff	Decarrey	23	Midfielder	Kettering Town	14	1	2	15	7
Dulwich H, Concord R, Kettering									
Sheringham	Charlie	33	Forward	Dartford	6	3	3	9	4
				Chelmsford City (L)	5			5	5
Bishop's S, Histon, Dartford, Bournemouth, Dartford (L), Wimbledon, Salisbury (L), Ebbsfleet, Bishop's S (L), Hemel H (L), Hemel H, Saif (Bangl), Hemel H, Dartford, Chelmsford (L)									
Sherring	Sam	21	Defender	Torquay United (L)	48	1		49	3
Bournemouth (Y), Weymouth (L), Weymouth (L), Torquay (L)									
Shields	Sean	29	Midfielder	Weymouth	33	2	1	35	5
Tottenham, Potters Bar, St Albans, Dagenham & R, St Albans (L), Ebbsfleet (L), Ebbsfleet, Chelmsford (L), Margate (L), Hemel (L), Maidstone (L), Boreham W (L), Notts Co (L), Weymouth									
Shiels	Luke	31	Defender	Boston United	17			17	3
Worksop, Harrogate, Alfreton, Boston U									
Sho-Silva	Tobi	26	Forward	Sutton United	13	24	6	37	4
CharltonWelling (L), Welling (L), Inverness CT (L), Bromley, Dover, Chelmsford (L), Halifax, Sutton U									
Shokunbi	Ademola	22	Defender	Welling United	10	2	1	12	1
Reading (Y), Billericay (L), Welling									
Shotton	Saul	20	Midfielder	Woking (L)	18			18	
Stoke (Y), Bury, WBA, Woking (L)									

Shenton Oliver - Chorley.

Sheriff Decarrey - Kettering Town.

Slocombe Sam - Notts Co.

Smith Dominic - Alfreton Town.

Key: X - Started; SX - Sub on; S - Non-playing Sub; Ap - Total Appearances; G/Cs - Total goals/clean sheets.

SURNAME	FIRSTNAME	AGE	POSITION	CLUB	X	SX	S	Ap	G/Cs
					APPEARANCES				
Shroll	Ben	20	Defender	Aldershot Town	1		2	1	
Aldershot (Y), Met Police (L)									
Shrowder	Tecane			Wealdstone		2	4	2	
Wealdstone (Y)									
Simon	Kaleem	24	Forward	Welling United	3	1		4	
UCD (Eire), Longford, Bohemians, Longford, Cabinteely, Athlone, Warrenpoint (NI), Wexford (Eire), Welling									
Simper	Lewis	20	Defender	Concord Rangers (L)	6	2		8	2
Cambridge U (Y), Concord R (L)									
Simpson	Aaron	24	Defender	Sutton United	4	8	16	12	1
Wolves (Y), AFC Telford (L), Kilmarnock (L), FC Jumilla (L) (Spa), Waterford, Dover, Sutton U									
Simpson	Luke	26	Goalkeeper	Kidderminster Harriers	17			17	6
Oldham (Y), Workington (L), Leicester (L), Accrington, Watford, York, Macclesfield, Tamworth, Wrexham, Barrow, Kidderminster									
Simpson	Robbie	36	Forward	Chelmsford City		4	11	4	
Cambridge C, Coventry, Huddersfield, Brentford (L), Oldham (L), Oldham, Leyton O, Cambridge U, Exeter, MK Dons, Chelmsford									
Sinclair	Lucas		Midfielder	Havant & Waterlooville	1	9	4	10	1
Havant & W									
Skeffington	Sam	20	Midfielder	Barnet (L)	12			12	
Millwall (Y), Barnet (L)									
Skendi	Albi	27	Midfielder	Yeovil Town	39			39	5
Oxford C, Stratford, Yeovil									
Sketchley	Kian		Defender	Alfreton Town			1		
Mansfield (Y), Alfreton									
Skinner	Jack	21	Midfielder	Woking	1	5	10	6	
Woking (Y), Hampton & R (L), Eastbourne B (L)									
Slew	Jerome	23	Forward	Wealdstone	2	9	4	11	1
Sheff Utd (Y), Goole, Chester, North Ferriby, Wealdstone, Ashton U, Ramsbottom, Maldon, Wealdstone									
Slocombe	Sam	33	Goalkeeper	Notts County	42		1	42	14
Scunthorpe, Oxford U, Blackpool, Bristol R, Lincoln C (L), Notts Co									
Slough	Louie		Defender	Torquay United			2		
Torquay (Y)									
Smart	Sam	22	Midfielder	Eastleigh	30	14	1	44	2
Basingstoke (Y), Eastleigh									
Smedley	Joel		Midfielder	Chippenham Town			5		
Chippenham (Y)									
Smerdon	Noah	20	Midfielder	Chippenham Town (L)	7			7	
WBA (Y), Gloucester (Y), Exeter, Chippenham (L)									
Smile	Josh	24	Midfielder	Maidenhead United	2	11	8	13	
Fulham (Y), Chippenham, Maidenhead									
Smith	Adam	28	Goalkeeper	Yeovil Town	46			46	10
Leicester (Y), Chesterfield (L), Lincoln (L), Nuneaton (L), Stevenage (L), Cambridge U (L), Mansfield (L), Northampton, Bristol R, Forest GR, Yeovil (L), Yeovil									
Smith	Alistair	22	Midfielder	Altrincham (L/P)	30	1	1	31	3
Mansfield (Y), Kettering (L), Altrincham (L/P)									
Smith	Chris	23	Defender	King's Lynn Town	27	2	3	29	
Ipswich (Y), Chelmsford (L), Aldershot (L), King's Lynn									
Smith	Christian	33	Midfielder	Hampton & Richmond Borough	11	5	4	16	1
Port Vale, Cambridge U (L), Northwich (L), Clyde, Wrexham, York, Wrexham, Newport Co (L), Barrow (L), Tamworth (L), Telford, Chelmsford, Hayes & Yeading, Bishop's St, Maidenhead, Wealdstone, Dulwich H, Hampton & R									
Smith	Connor	28	Midfielder	Wealdstone	34	2	1	36	2
Watford (Y), Wealdstone (L), Gillingham (L), Stevenage (L), AFC Wimbledon, Plymouth, Yeovil, Boreham W, Billericay, Wealdstone									
Smith	Dan	21	Forward	Eastleigh	13	27	6	40	3
Portsmouth (Y), Cork (L), Eastleigh									
Smith	Dominic	25	Defender	Alfreton Town	17			17	1
Shrewsbury (Y), Tamworth (L), Barrow (L), Southport (L), Telford, Alfreton (L), Alfreton									
Smith	George	24	Defender	Gateshead	13		2	13	
Barnsley (Y), Crawley (L), Gateshead, Northampton, Chesterfield, Dover (L)Boston U (L), Harrogate, Gateshead									
Smith	Grant	27	Goalkeeper	Wealdstone	1		3	1	
				Chesterfield	18			18	10
Fulham, Brighton, Hayes & Y (L), Bognor (L), Bognor, Boreham W, Lincoln C, Maidstone (L), Boreham W (L), Wealdstone, Chesterfield									

2020-21 NATIONAL. NORTH & SOUTH PLAYERS — APPEARANCES

SURNAME	FIRSTNAME	AGE	POSITION	CLUB PLAYED FOR	X	SX	S	Ap	G/Cs
Smith	Harvey	22	Defender	Chorley	16	5	3	21	2
Bristol C (Y), Weston (L), Hereford (L), Bath (L), Gloucester (L), Chorley									
Smith	Jimmy	34	Midfielder	Yeovil Town	19	10	5	29	2
Chelsea (Y), Sheff Wed (L), Leyton O (L), Leyton O, Stevenage, Crawley, Yeovil (L), Yeovil									
Smith	Jonathan	34	Midfielder	Chesterfield	11	2	5	13	1
Morecambe (Y), Fleetwood (L), Forest Green, York, Swindon, York, Luton (L), Luton, Stevenage, Chesterfield (L), Chesterfield									
Smith	Jonte	26	Forward	Woking	5	9	2	14	
Crawley, Eastbourne B (L), Havant & W (L), Gosport (L), PS Kemi (Fin), Gloucester, Lewes, Welling, Oxford U, Cheltenham, Woking									
Smith	Kane	25	Defender	Boreham Wood	48			48	5
Hitchin, Boreham W									
Smith	Kieran		Forward	Chelmsford City			1		
Chelmsford (Y)									
Smith	Lance	29	Forward	Leamington	11	2	3	13	4
Littleton, Badsey Rangers, Evesham, Hereford, Leamington									
Smith	Mark	25	Goalkeeper	Woking	4		7	4	
Brentford (Y), Lowestoft (L), Aldershot, Eastbourne B (L), Eastbourne B, Billericay, Eastbourne B (L), Dartford, Woking									
Smith	Martin	25	Midfielder	Chesterfield	9	3	7	12	
Sunderland (Y), Gateshead (L), Carlisle (L), Kilmarnock, Coleraine, Swindon, Salford, Chorley (L), Chesterfield									
Smith	Nathan	34	Defender	Braintree Town	9	1	1	10	
Enfield T, Waltham F, Potters Bar, Yeovil, Chesterfield, Yeovil, Dagenham & R, Dulwich H, Braintree									
Smith	Reece		Midfielder	Maidenhead United	2	4	10	6	1
Maidenhead (Y)									
Smith	Soloman	22	Forward	Hungerford Town			1		
Southampton (Y), Salisbury, Hungerford									
Smith	Tom	23	Midfielder	Bath City	19			19	5
				Dagenham & Redbridge (L)	1	6	4	7	
Swindon (Y), Waterford (L), Bath (Lx3), Cheltenham, Bath (L), Bath, Dagenham & R (L)									
Smith	Tom	19	Goalkeeper	Dover Athletic (L)	4		5	4	
Arsenal (Y), Dover (L)									
Smith-Brown	Ashley	25	Defender	Farsley Celtic	4	3	6	7	1
Man City (Y), NAC Breda (L), Hearts (L), Oxford U (L), Plymouth, Oldham (L), South Shields, Farsley C									
Smyth	Liam	19	Forward	Braintree Town (L)	2	5	1	7	1
Stevenage (Y), Braintree (L), Braintree (L)									
Snedker	Dean	26	Goalkeeper	Hemel Hempstead Town	12		5	12	2
Northampton, Brackley (Lx2), Brackley, Kidderminster, Nuneaton, Hempstead, Kettering, Cambridge C, St Albans,Hemel H									
Snedker	Joel			Chippenham Town			1		
Chippenham									
Soares-Junior	Ruben		Forward	Billericay Town	7	5	4	12	3
Biggleswade, Billericay T									
Sole	Giuseppe	33	Forward	Dorking Wanderers			7		
Havant & W, Woking, Basingstoke (L), Basingstoke (L), Hampton & R, Dorking W									
Solkhon	Brett	38	Midfielder	Kettering Town			1		
Kettering, Rushden & D, Corby, Brackley, Kettering									
Solly	Chris	30	Defender	Ebbsfleet United	5			5	
Charlton (Y), Ebbsfleet									
Sonupe	Emmanuel	25	Midfielder	Yeovil Town	3	12	1	15	2
Tottenham (Y), St Mirren (L), Northampton, Kidderminster (L), Kidderminster, Stevenage, Yeovil									
Sousa	Erico	26	Forward	Darlington	14			14	7
Vinhense (Y), Fabril Barreiro (Y), Barnsley (Y), Hyde (L), NK Celje, Tadcaster, Accrington, Tranmere, Accrington, Barrow (L), Darlington									
Southam-Hales	Macauley	25	Defender	Stockport County	23	10	3	33	2
Barry Town, Fleetwood, Hartlepool (L), Stockport									
Southern	Oliver		Defender	Curzon Ashton	5	4	7	9	
Man Utd (Y), Preston, Blackburn, Rochdale, Crewe, Curzon A, Norwich (U23)									
Southern-Cooper	Jake	21	Midfielder	Gateshead (L)	14			14	
				Hartlepool United (L)	2		2	2	
Rotherham (Y), Gateshead (L), Gateshead (L), Hartlepool (L)									
Southwell	Dayle	27	Forward	King's Lynn Town	10	10	5	20	5
Grimsby, Harrogate (L), Boston U, Wycombe, Guiseley, FC Halifax, Boston U (L), King's Lynn									

Key: X - Started; SX - Sub on; S - Non-playing Sub; Ap - Total Appearances; G/Cs - Total goals/clean sheets.

SURNAME	FIRSTNAME	AGE	POSITION	CLUB	X	SX	S	Ap	G/Cs
Sparkes	Daniel	29	Midfielder	Maidenhead United	29	4	2	33	5
Histon, Braintree, Torquay, Dagenham & R, Barnet, Maidenhead									
Spasov	Slavi	19	Forward	Woking (L)	13	10		23	3
Oxford U (Y), Woking (L)									
Spence	Kian	20	Midfielder	FC Halifax	1	7	4	8	
Middlesbrough (Y), Scarborough A, FC Halifax, Scarborough A (L)									
Spencer	James (Jimmy)	29	Forward	Farsley Celtic	20			20	9
Huddersfield (Y), Northwich V (L), Morecambe (L), Cheltenham (L), Brentford (L), Crawley (L), Scunthorpe (L), Notts Co, Plymouth, Mansfield, Farsley C									
Spencer	Jamie	23	Midfielder	Spennymoor Town	13	1	2	14	1
Bradford PA, Guiseley, Spennymoor									
Spencer-Adams	Bayli	20	Defender	Dover Athletic (L)	10		1	10	
West Ham (Y), Tottenham (Y), Arsenal (Y), Watford, Dover (L)									
Spencer-McDermott	Cian		Midfielder	Chorley		1	1	1	
Chorley (Y)									
Spillane	Michael	32	Defender	Chelmsford City	6	1	7	7	
Norwich, Luton (L), Brentford, Dag & Red (L), Dag & Red, Southend, Cambridge U, Sutton U, Lowestoft, Chelmsford									
Splatt	Jamie		Defender	Dulwich Hamlet		1	1	1	
Dulwich H									
Splatt	Javaun	20	Forward	Tonbridge Angels	5	8	5	13	1
Derby (Y), Carshalton (L), Mickleover S (L), Barnsley U23 (L), Tonbridge A									
Spratt	Harry	21	Defender	York City	1	2	7	3	
Man Utd (Y), Huddersfield U23, York									
Stacey	Joe		Midfielder	Alfreton Town			1		
Bluefield College (US), Dalton RW, Alfreton									
Stanley	Devante	24	Defender	St Albans City	7	3	7	10	
St Neots, Biggleswade T, St Albans									
Stanley	James		Midfielder	AFC Fylde			2		
AFC Fylde (Y)									
Stanyer	Finley		Defender	Stockport County			2		
Stockport (Y)									
Staunton	Joshua	25	Defender	Yeovil Town	8		1	8	
Gillingham, St Albans (L), Dagenham & R, Woking, FC Halifax, Yeovil									
Stearn	Ross	30	Midfielder	Chippenham Town	14	4		18	2
Forest Green, Sutton U, Eastleigh, Sutton U, Bath (L), Bath, Chippenham									
Steele	Luke	36	Goalkeeper	Notts County	3			3	
Peterborough, Man Utd, WBA, Coventry (L), Barnsley (L), Barnsley, Panathinaikos, Bristol C, Notts F, Millwall (L), Stamford, Notts Co									
Steer	Rene	31	Defender	Hampton & Richmond Borough	5	2	4	7	
				Hemel Hempstead Town	3			3	
Arsenal, Gillingham (L), Oldham, Boston Utd, Maidenhead, Hampton & R, Hemel H									
Stenson	Matty	27	Forward	FC Halifax	1			1	
Barwell, Leamington, Solihull, Telford (L), FC Halifax									
Stephens	Ben	23	Midfielder	Kettering Town	6	6	5	12	1
Stratford T, Macclesfield, Kettering									
Stephens	Dave	29	Defender	Boreham Wood	8	8	27	16	
Norwich , Lincoln (L), Hibernian, Barnet, Boreham W									
Stephens	Toby		Midfielder	Yeovil Town		5	2	5	
Yeovil (Y)									
Stephenson	Darren	28	Forward	Curzon Ashton	15			15	3
				FC Halifax (L)	1	2		3	1
Bradford (Y), Hinckley U (L), Woodley Sp (L), Stocksbridge (L), Southport (L), Southport, Chorley, Tranmere, AFC Fylde (L), Stockport, Curzon A, Halifax (L)									
Sterling	Tyrone	33	Defender	Concord Rangers	19			19	
Cray W, Dartford, Dover, Bromley, Concord R, Hemel H, Concord R									
Sterling-James	Omari	27	Forward	Kidderminster Harriers	13	3		16	4
Birmingham (Y), Cheltenham, Oxford C (L), Gloucester (L), Solihull M, Mansfield, Solihull M (L), Brackley (L), Kettering (L), Kidderminster									
Sterry	Jamie	25	Defender	Hartlepool United	30			30	
Newcastle U (Y), Coventry (L), Crewe (L), Crewe (L), South Shields, Hartlepool									

Smith Harvey - Chorley.

Stohrer Gary - Kettering Town.

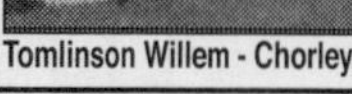

Tomlinson Willem - Chorley.

Turner Ben - Notts Co.

Key: X - Started; SX - Sub on; S - Non-playing Sub; Ap - Total Appearances; G/Cs - Total goals/clean sheets.

SURNAME	FIRSTNAME	AGE	POSITION	CLUB	X	SX	S	Ap	G/Cs
Stevens	Connor	23	Defender	Wealdstone	1	1	3	2	
Watford (Y), Oxford C (L), Wealdstone									
Stevens	Jack	20	Forward	Chippenham Town (L)	1		1		
Oxford U (Y), Chippenham (L)									
Stohrer	Gary	28	Defender	Kettering Town	18			18	
Irchester, Long Buckby, Garforth, Ossett T, Shaw Lane, Frickley, Kettering									
Stokes	Noah	19	Defender	Curzon Ashton	8	3	7	11	
Bangalow Bluedogs (Y) (Aus), Mansfield (Y), Curzon A									
Storer	Kyle	34	Midfielder	Solihull Moors	43	1	2	44	
Leicester (Y), Bedworth U, Tamworth, Hinckley U, Atherstone, Nuneaton, Kidderminster, Wrexham, Cheltenham, Solihull M									
Storey	Alex	22	Defender	Darlington (D)	12		4	12	1
Sunderland (Y), Sunderland RCA, Darlington (D)									
Stott	Jamie	23	Defender	Stockport County	16		8	16	
Oldham, Curzon A (L), AFC Fylde (L), Curzon A (L), Stockport (L), Stockport (Lx2), Stockport									
Strachan	Rob	20	Defender	Welling United (L)	4	1		5	
Millwall (Y), Welling (L)									
Straker	Anthony	32	Midfielder	Havant & Waterlooville	13	3	4	16	
Aldershot (Y), Southend, York, Motherwell (L), Grimsby, Aldershot, Bath, Havant & W									
Stratford	Marlon		Defender	Billericay Town	2			2	
Billericay T (U23)									
Street	Alex	29	Goalkeeper	King's Lynn Town	2		1	2	
Wisbech, King's Lynn, Wisbech (D), Deeping R (D), Spalding (D), Leiston (L)									
Street	Robert	19	Forward	Torquay United (L)	1	6	3	7	
Crystal P (Y), Torquay (L)									
Streete	Theo	33	Defender	AFC Telford United	20			20	
Derby (Y), Doncaster (L), Rotherham, Solihull, Alfreton, Nuneaton, Solihull, Brackley, Telford									
Stretton	Jack	19	Forward	Stockport County (L)	2	3	1	5	3
Derby (Y), Stockport (L)									
Strizovic	Josh	21	Goalkeeper	Dagenham & Redbridge			22		
Braintree (Y), Waltham F (L), Burnham R, Billericay, Maidstone, Dagenham & R									
Summerfield	Luke	33	Midfielder	FC Halifax	32	1	1	33	6
Plymouth (Y), Bournemouth (L), Leyton O (L), Cheltenham, Shrewsbury, York, Grimsby, Macclesfield (L), Wrexham, FC Halifax									
Sundrie	Munashe	24	Defender	St Albans City	20			20	
Kettering, Hemel H, St Albans									
Sutherland	Frankie	27	Forward	Billericay Town	12		1	12	
QPR, Portsmouth (L), Leyton O (L), AFC Wimbledon (L), Dagenham & R (L), Crawley Town (L), Woking, Whitehawk, Bromley, Ebbsfleet, Billericay T									
Sutton	Richard	35	Defender	Altrincham	16	2	8	18	1
Stafford, Northwich, Port Vale, Mansfield, Tranmere, Barrow (L), Morecambe, Altrincham									
Sutton	Shane	32	Defender	AFC Telford United	9			9	
Newtown, Telford									
Sweeney	Jack		Midfielder	AFC Telford United			1		
Telford (Y), Walsall (Y), Telford, Shawbury (L)									
Syers	David	33	Midfielder	Farsley Celtic	16	3	2	19	2
Farsley C, Harrogate T, Guiseley, Bradford, Doncaster, Scunthorpe (L), Scunthorpe, Rochdale, Guiseley, Darlington, Farsley C									
Tait	Joe	31	Defender	Spennymoor Town	7		5	7	1
Dayton Dutch Lions (US), Philadelphia Union, Gateshead, Spennymoor, York, Spennymoor									
Tanimowo	Ayo	19	Defender	Welling United (L)	3			3	
Norwich (Y), Brighton (U18), Welling (L)									
Tanner	Craig	26	Forward	Aldershot Town	12	5	1	17	3
Plymouth (Y), Reading, Wimbledon (L), Plymouth (L), Plymouth (L), Motherwell, Aldershot									
Tarpey	Dave	32	Forward	Woking	6	6	7	12	1
Henley Town, Basingstoke, Hampton & R, Walton & H (L), Chertsey (L), Farnborough, Hampton & R, Maidenhead, Barnet, Maidenhead (L), Woking (L), Woking									
Tavares	Nikola	22	Defender	Wealdstone (L)	1			1	
Wolves (U18), Middlesbrough (U18), Brighton (U18), Crystal P, Wealdstone (L)									
Taylor	Bobby-Joe	26	Midfielder	Ebbsfleet United	19			19	3
Chelsea (Y), Cambridge U, Bishop's St (L), Maidstone, Aldershot, Bromley, Dover (L/P), Ebbsfleet									

2020-21 NATIONAL. NORTH & SOUTH PLAYERS — APPEARANCES

SURNAME	FIRSTNAME	AGE	POSITION	CLUB PLAYED FOR	X	SX	S	Ap	G/Cs
Taylor	Brett		Defender	Kidderminster Harriers			1		
Kidderminster (Y)									
Taylor	Connor	28	Forward	Leamington	2	5	13	7	
Aston Villa (Y), Tamworth (L), Walsall, Nuneaton (L), Nuneaton, Tamworth, Leamington									
Taylor	Eithne		Midfielder	Blyth Spartans			3		
TyneMet College, Blyth S									
Taylor	Glen	31	Forward	Spennymoor Town	17			17	12
Blyth Spartans, Spennymoor									
Taylor	Harry	24	Defender	Barnet	44	1		45	1
Chelsea (Y), Barnet (Y), Woking (L)									
Taylor	James	19	Defender	Bath City (L)	7			7	
Bristol C (Y), Yate (L), Bath (L)									
Taylor	Joe	30	Forward	Welling United (D)	2			2	
				Ebbsfleet United (L)	1			1	
Ramsgate, Sittingbourne, Farnborough, Folkstone, Margate, Cray W, Welling (D), Ebbsfleet (L)									
Taylor	Joel	25	Defender	Chester	10		1	10	
				Chesterfield	12	6	2	18	
Stoke (Y), Rochdale (L), Kidderminster, Chester, Chesterfield									
Taylor	Josh	26	Forward	Havant & Waterlooville	19			19	2
Halifax, Sutton U, Hampton & R (L), Maidstone (L), Havant & W									
Taylor	Max	21	Defender	Kidderminster Harriers (L)	10		5	10	1
Man Utd (Y), Kidderminster (L)									
Taylor	Quade	27	Defender	Dulwich Hamlet	12	1	2	13	1
Dulwich H, Crystal P (U23), Welling (L), Bolton, Dag & Red (L), Braintree, Dulwich H									
Taylor	Richard	20	Defender	Barnet	3	1	2	4	
Southend (Y), Barnet									
Tear	Dominic	21	Midfielder	FC Halifax	1	10	15	11	
Huddersfield (Y), Larne (NI) (L), Gateshead (L), FC Halifax									
Tee	Conor	20	Midfielder	Brackley Town		2	2	2	
Leicester (Y), Brackley									
Temelci	Zihni	22	Midfielder	Maidstone United	2	6	3	8	
Goztepe (Y) (Tur), Maidstone									
Teniola	Alex		Forward	Chelmsford City	7	3	1	10	1
Tonbridge A, Concord C, Chelmsford									
Thackray	Kris	33	Defender	Blyth Spartans	6			6	1
Reggina, Monopoli (L), Ancona (L), Andria, Cosenza, QFC (Malta), Alem Aachen (Ger), KFC Uerduingen, Gzira Utd (Malta), Spennymoor, Blyth S									
Thanoj	Andi	28	Midfielder	Boston United	10	1	2	11	
Grimsby (Y), Alfreton, Harrogate, Redditch, Boston U									
Tharme	Douglas		Defender	Curzon Ashton	13		2	13	
Wrexham (Y), Telford (L), Curzon A									
Theobalds	D'Sean		Midfielder	Tonbridge Angels	12	4		16	
Leatherhead, Concord R, Leatherhead, Tonbridge A									
Thewlis	Jordan	28	Forward	Boston United	10	4		14	4
Scunthorpe (Y), Gainsborough, Harrogate, Boston U (L), Boston U									
Thomas	Adam	27	Midfielder	Stockport County	8	11		19	1
Stoke (Y), Macclesfield (L), Hednesford (L), Hednesford, Stockport									
Thomas	Jack		Midfielder	Braintree Town (L)	4			4	
Bishop's S, Braintree (L)									
Thomas	Josh	22	Midfielder	Gloucester City	18			18	
Cheltenham (Y), Gloucester									
Thomas	Kwame	25	Forward	Wrexham	28	3	1	31	10
Derby, Notts Co (L), Blackpool (L), Coventry, Sutton U (L), Solihull (L), Solihull, Kidderminster (L), Doncaster, Burton, Wrexham									
Thomas	Kymani		Midfielder	Dulwich Hamlet			1		
Dulwich H (Y)									
Thomas	Leon		Forward	Dulwich Hamlet			1		
Dulwich H (Y)									
Thomas	Lewis	19	Goalkeeper	AFC Fylde (L)	1			1	
Leicester (Y), Man City (Y), Burnley (Y), AFC Fylde (L)									

Key: X - Started; SX - Sub on; S - Non-playing Sub; Ap - Total Appearances; G/Cs - Total goals/clean sheets.

SURNAME	FIRSTNAME	AGE	POSITION	CLUB	X	SX	S	Ap	G/Cs
Thomas	Sorba	21	Midfielder	Boreham Wood	13	1		14	3
Boreham W (Y), Huddersfield									
Thomas	Wes	34	Forward	Notts County	4	1		5	
Fisher, Dagenham & R, Grays (L), Cheltenham, Crawley, Bournemouth, Portsmouth (L), Blackpool (L), Birmingham (L), Rotherham, Birmingham, Swindon (L), Bradford (L), Oxford U, Grimsby, Notts Co									
Thompson	Bailey	20	Forward	Guiseley	1			1	
Man Utd (Y), Accrington (Y), Bury (Y), Blackburn (Y), Everton (Y), Tranmere (Y), Tadcaster A, Guiseley									
Thompson	Jordan	22	Defender	Solihull Moors (L)	8		2	8	1
Coventry, Barrow (L), Boreham W (L), Wrexham (L), Solihull M (L)									
Thompson	Stephen	32	Forward	Spennymoor Town	8	4	4	12	2
Middlesbrough (Y), Port Vale, Stafford R (L), Telford, Durham C, Darlington, Spennymoor									
Thompson	Tony	26	Goalkeeper	Altrincham	44			44	11
Rotherham (Y), Southport (L), Morecambe, Chester, AFC Fylde, Altrincham									
Thompson-Brissett	Jaden	20	Midfielder	Dagenham & Redbridge		2	5	2	
Norwich (Y), Brentford, Maidenhead (L), Dagenham & R									
Thomson	Ben	32	Midfielder	Weymouth	9	17		26	1
Team Bath, Weymouth									
Thomson	Connor	25	Defender	Blyth Spartans	13			13	
Carlisle (Y), Blackburn (Y), Barrow (L), FC Halifax, Gateshead, Scarborough (L), Blyth S									
Tiensia	Junior	20	Defender	Sutton United (L)		1		1	
Millwall (Y), Havant & W (L), Sutton U (L)									
Timlin	Michael	36	Midfielder	Dulwich Hamlet	18			18	1
Swindon (Y), Southend (L), Southend (L), Southend, Stevenage, Ebbsfleet, Dulwich H									
Tinkler	Robbie	24	Defender	York City	14			14	
Middlesbrough (Y), North Ferriby (L), Gateshead (L), Gateshead, Aldershot, York									
Togwell	Lee		Midfielder	Slough Town	11	2	1	13	1
Slough									
Togwell	Sam	36	Midfielder	Slough Town	15			15	
Crystal Palace, Oxford U (L), Northampton (L), Port Vale (L), Barnsley, Scunthorpe, Chesterfield, Wycombe (L), Barnet, Eastleigh, Slough									
Tolley	Jack	17	Midfielder	Kidderminster Harriers			1		
Kidderminster (Y)									
Tollitt	Ben	26	Midfielder	AFC Fylde	18	1	2	19	8
Skelmersdale, Portsmouth, Tranmere, Wrexham (L), Blackpool, Wrexham (L), Macclesfield, AFC Fylde									
Tomlinson	Joe	21	Defender	Eastleigh	40	3		43	12
Yeovil (Y), Brighton (U23), Bognor R (L), Hungerford, Eastleigh									
Tomlinson	Lucas	20	Midfielder	Bath City (L)	6	1	1	7	
				Torquay United (L)		2		2	
Bristol R (Y), Bath (L), Torquay (L)									
Tomlinson	Willem	23	Midfielder	Chorley	13	2		15	
Blackburn (Y), Mansfield, Chorley									
Tompkins	Jack	19	Midfielder	Barnet			3		
Barnet (Y)									
Tongue	Liam	23	Midfielder	Guiseley (D)	1			1	
Stockport Georgians, Cheadle, Mossley, Marine, Stalybridge, Hyde U, Guiseley (D)									
Tootle	Matt	30	Defender	Boston United	15		2	15	
Crewe (Y), Shrewsbury, Notts Co, Chesterfield (L), Boston U									
Tooze	Kyle		Forward	Hungerford Town	1	3	4	4	
Thatcham, Hungerford									
Toulson	Ryan	35	Defender	Bradford (Park Avenue)	9	1	2	10	
Halifax, Harrogate T, Guiseley, Halifax, Guiseley, Bradford PA									
Towning	Charlie		Midfielder	Eastbourne Borough		1	5	1	
Eastbourne B (Y)									
Trennery	Kyle	21	Goalkeeper	Farsley Celtic			2		
Halifax (Y), Albion Sports (L), Farsley C, Clitheroe (L)									
Trotter	Liam	32	Midfielder	Bromley	31	6	4	37	2
Ipswich (Y), Millwall (L), Millwall, Bolton (L), Bolton, Nottm Forest (L), Wimbledon, Orange County, Bromley									
Tsaguim	Florian		Forward	King's Lynn Town		1	4	1	
King's Lynn (Y)									

2020-21 NATIONAL. NORTH & SOUTH PLAYERS

SURNAME	FIRSTNAME	AGE	POSITION	CLUB PLAYED FOR	X	SX	S	Ap	G/Cs
					APPEARANCES				
Tshimanga	Kabongo	25	Forward	Boreham Wood	47		1	47	22
MK Dons, Aldershot (L), Chelmsford (L), Corby (L), Nuneaton (L), Throttur Reykjavik, MK Dons, Yeovil (L), Boston U, Oxford C, Boreham W									
Tupper	Joe	23	Goalkeeper	Havant & Waterlooville	4	1	7	5	
Reading (Y), Margate (L), Crystal P U23, Margate, Havant & W									
Turnbull	Paul	32	Midfielder	Curzon Ashton	17			17	
Stockport, Altrincham (L), Northampton, Stockport (L), Stockport (L), Lincoln (L), Macclesfield, Barrow, Chester, Stockport, Curzon A									
Turner	Ben	32	Defender	Notts County	13	6	15	19	1
Coventry, Peterborough (L), Oldham (L), Cardiff, Coventry (L), Burton, Mansfield, Notts Co									
Turner	Dan	23	Forward	Leamington		1		1	1
Port Vale (Y), Worcester (L), Tamworth (L), Falkirk (L), Hyde U, Matlock, Hednesford, Leamington									
Turner	Jack	28	Goalkeeper	Slough Town	15			15	3
Wimbledon, Staines, Slough									
Turner	Jack	21	Defender	Kettering Town			2		
Bristol C (U18), Kettering									
Turner	Joe	27	Forward	Tonbridge Angels	17	2		19	5
Hampton & R, Wealdstone, Tonbridge A									
Tuton	Shaun	29	Forward	Alfreton Town		3	2	3	
Halifax, Barnsley, Grimsby (L), Barrow (L), Halifax (L), Chester (NC), Spennymoor, Chorley (L), Boston U, Alfreton									
Twist	Ben		Midfielder	Tonbridge Angels			1		
Tonbridge A									
Tyler	Rhys	29	Defender	Chippenham Town	2		2	2	
				Hungerford Town	11	2		13	
Rot-Weib Erfurt (Ger), Hungerford, Wealdstone, Chippenham, Hungerford									
Tyson	Nathan	39	Forward	Chesterfield	6	15	3	21	2
Wycombe, Notts F, Derby, Millwall (L), Blackpool, Fleetwood (L), Notts Co (L), Doncaster, Kilmarnock, Wycombe, Notts Co, Chesterfield (L), Chesterfield									
Uche	Imran		Defender	Hampton & Richmond Borough	5	1	6	6	
Hampton & R									
Umerah	Josh	23	Forward	Torquay United	11	20	7	31	5
Charlton (Y), Kilmarnock (L), Wycombe (L), Boreham W (L), Ebbsfleet, Torquay									
Unwin-Marris	Teddy	20	Goalkeeper	Alfreton Town			15		
Chesterfield (Y), Alfreton									
Upward	Ryan	29	Midfielder	Maidenhead United	39			39	2
Maidenhead									
Urwin	Matthew	27	Goalkeeper	Chorley	24			24	5
Blackburn (Y), Stalybridge (L), Bradford, AFC Fylde, Fleetwood, Telford (L), Chorley (L), Chorley (L), Chorley									
Usher-Shipway	Ben	22	Forward	Solihull Moors	11	4	1	15	
Solihull M (Y), Alvechurch (L), Sutton C (L), Rushall O (L)									
Ustabasi	Jonathan	27	Forward	Chorley (L)	1	1	1	2	
Denizlispor (Tur), Fethiye, Yesil Bursa, Bursaspor, Yesil Bursa (L), Bandirma, Shkupi (Mac), Stalybridge, Chorley (L), Chorley									
Vasiliou	Antonis	20	Midfielder	Barnet	2	12	16	14	
Barnet (Y), St Albans (L)									
Vassallo	Dylan	24	Midfielder	Southport	9	8	1	17	2
Southport (Y), Warrington, Southport									
Vassell	Theo	24	Defender	Wrexham	32			32	4
Oldham, Chorley (L), Walsall, Chester (L), Gateshead, Port Vale, Macclesfield, Wrexham									
Vaughan	James	26	Midfielder	Eastbourne Borough	19		2	19	
Eastbourne B, Flint City (US), AFC Ann Arbor, Eastbourne B									
Vaughan	Lee	34	Defender	AFC Telford United	19			19	1
				Barnet	20			20	
Walsall (Y), Telford U, Kidderminster, Cheltenham, Tranmere, Kidderminster, Solihull, Telford U, Barnet									
Vaughan	Nathan	40	Goalkeeper	Hereford FC			1		
Kidderminster, Worcester (L), Worcester, Solihull M, Worcester (L), Chester, Kidderminster, Gloucester, Newport Co, Hereford (GK Coach)									
Vieira	Romario		Midfielder	Gateshead			1		
Leeds (Y), Tadcaster A, Gateshead, Tadcaster A									
Vijay	Nyan	18	Midfielder	Billericay Town (L)		1	1	1	
Ipswich (Y), Sunderland (U18), Billericay T (L), Derby (U18)									

Key: X - Started; SX - Sub on; S - Non-playing Sub; Ap - Total Appearances; G/Cs - Total goals/clean sheets.

SURNAME	FIRSTNAME	AGE	POSITION	CLUB	X	SX	S	Ap	G/Cs
Vilhete	Mauro	28	Midfielder	Hampton & Richmond Borough (D)	3			3	1
				Dagenham & Redbridge	10	4		14	1
Barnet, Hendon (L), Boreham W (L), Boreham W (L), Boreham W (L), Wingate & F, Hampton & RB (D), Dagenham & R									
Vincent	Liam	24	Midfielder	Bromley	4	4	13	8	
Bromley (Y)									
Vine	Rowan	38	Forward	Hemel Hempstead Town			1		
Portsmouth (Y), Brentford (L), Colchester (L), Luton (L/P), Birmingham, QPR (L/P), Hull (L), Brentford (L), MK Dons (L), Exeter (L), Gillingham (L), St Johnstone, Hibs, Morton, Welling, Gosport B, Basingstoke (L), Hemel H									
Vint	Ronnie	24	Defender	Dartford	7		1	7	
				Dulwich Hamlet (L)	6			6	
Dartford, Dulwich H (L)									
Vose	Dominic	27	Midfielder	Welling United		1	1	1	
Braintree, Barnet, Colchester, Welling, Wrexham, Scunthorpe, Grimsby (L), Whitehawk, Bromley, Chester, Dulwich H, Welling									
Vukasinovic	Milos		Defender	Braintree Town			2		
Braintree									
Wabo	Norman	23	Forward	Concord Rangers	1			1	
Southend, Cambridge C (L), Ebbsfleet (L), Maidstone (L), Braintree (L), Dartford, Concord R									
Wade	Bradley	20	Goalkeeper	Guiseley (L)	20			20	5
Rochdale (Y), Barrow (L), Guiseley (L), Guiseley (L)									
Wady	Ethan	19	Goalkeeper	Dartford (L)	5		2	5	1
Chelsea (Y), Dartford (L)									
Wafula	Jonathan	27	Midfielder	Guiseley	14	2		16	4
Chesterfield, Worksop, Gainsborough, Boston U, Guiseley									
Wakefield	Charlie	23	Midfielder	Wealdstone	9	4		13	2
				Bromley	4	7	5	11	1
Chelsea (Y), Stevenage (L), Coventry, Wealdstone, Bromley									
Wakefield	Josh	27	Defender	Weymouth	11	6	6	17	1
Bournemouth (Y), Dagenham & R (L), Dorchester (L), Welling (L), Torquay (L), Bristol R (L), Yeovil (L), Walsall (L), Aldershot, Poole, Weymouth									
Waldron	Danny		Forward	Leamington	16	3	1	19	3
Rushall O (Y), Leamington									
Walker	Adam	30	Midfielder	AFC Telford United	20			20	
Coventry (Y), Nuneaton (L), Nuneaton, Solihull, Brackley, Telford									
Walker	Charlie	31	Forward	Eastbourne Borough	17	4		21	6
Luton, Boreham W (L), Aldershot, St Albans, Eastbourne B									
Walker	Glenn	34	Midfielder	Brackley Town	6	1		7	
Banbury, Corby, Brackley, Hednesford, Brackley									
Walker	Josh	23	Forward	Barnet	3	5		8	1
Tottenham (Yth), Fulham (Yth), Hendon, Barnet									
Walker	Mitch	29	Goalkeeper	Aldershot Town	32		10	32	10
Brighton, Eastbourne B (L), Dover, Aldershot									
Walker	Nicky	26	Midfielder	Alfreton Town	6	7		13	
Rotherham (Y), Barrow (L), Wycombe (L), Boston U, Bradford PA, Boston U, Clipstone (L), Buxton, Shaw Lane, Gainsborough, Boston U, Alfreton									
Walker	Sam	34	Midfielder	Chorley	6	1		7	
				Curzon Ashton	11			11	
Curzon Ashton, Halifax, Salford, Stockport, Curzon Ashton (L), Chorley, Curzon Ashton									
Walker	Tom	25	Midfielder	Notts County (L)	3			3	
				Stockport County (L)	21	1	1	22	1
Bolton (Y), Bury (L), FC United, Salford City, Stockport (L), AFC Fylde, Harrogate T, Notts Co (L), Stockport (L)									
Wall	Alex	30	Forward	Concord Rangers	14	4		18	11
Maidenhead, Luton (L), Luton, Dartford (L), Bristol R (L), Bromley, Hungerford, Concord R, Hemel H, Woking, Concord R									
Walton	Simon	33	Midfielder	Havant & Waterlooville	1		6	1	
Leeds, Charlton, Ipswich (L), Cardiff (L), QPR, Hull (L), Plymouth, Blackpool (L), Crewe (L), Sheff U (L), Hartlepool, Stevenage, Crawley, Guiseley, Sutton U, Billericay, Maidstone (L), Maidstone, Havant & W									
Walton	Tyler	22	Midfielder	Farsley Celtic	13	6		19	
Man City (Y), Leeds (Y), Barnsley, York, Frickley, Farsley C									
Wanadio	Luke	28	Midfielder	Billericay Town	12	1		13	1
Staines, Welling, Dartford, Bromley, Aldershot, Dulwich H (L), Dartford, Billericay T									

Urwin Matt - Chorley.

Walker Nicky - Alfreton Town.

Walker Tom - Notts Co.

Willis George - Alfreton Town.

Key: X - Started; SX - Sub on; S - Non-playing Sub; Ap - Total Appearances; G/Cs - Total goals/clean sheets.

SURNAME	FIRSTNAME	AGE	POSITION	CLUB	X	SX	S	Ap	G/Cs
Warburton	Matthew	29	Forward	Yeovil Town (L)	13	8	3	21	2
Curzon Ashton, Salford, Curzon Ashton, Stockport Co, Northampton, Yeovil (L)									
Ward	Dan	23	Midfielder	Gateshead	4	5	4	9	1
Newcastle (Y), Middlesbrough U23, Spennymoor, St Patrick's, Gateshead									
Ward	Elliott	36	Defender	Chelmsford City	14			14	
West Ham (Y), Peterborough (L), Bristol R (L), Plymouth (L), Coventry, Doncaster (L), PNE (L), Norwich, Notts F (L), Bournemouth, Huddersfield (L), Blackburn, MK Dons (L), Notts Co, Cambridge U, Chelmsford									
Ward	Jamie	35	Forward	Solihull Moors	14	9	4	23	3
Villa (Y), Stockport (L), Torquay, Chesterfield, Sheff Utd, Derby (L), Derby, Nottm F, Burton (L), Cardiff (L), Charlton (L), Scunthorpe, Solihull M									
Ward-Cochrane	Ben		Forward	Welling United (L)	1	2	1	3	
Hatfield, Enfield T, Kingstonian, Chalfont St. P, Hertford, Potter B, Welling (L)									
Wareham	Jayden		Forward	Woking	4	13	6	17	2
Woking (Y)									
Waring	George	26	Forward	Chester	5	17		22	2
Stoke (Y), Barnsley (L), Oxford U (L), Shrewsbury (L), Carlisle (L), Tranmere, Halifax (L), Kidderminster (L), Kidderminster (L), Chester									
Warner-Eley	Luke	24	Defender	St Albans City	10	6	2	16	
Uxbridge, St Ives, Barton R, Chesham, Dartford, Harrow B, Royston, St Albans									
Warre	Dan		Forward	Chippenham Town			1		
Chippenham (Y)									
Warren	Gary	36	Defender	Torquay United	10	10	4	20	1
Team Bath, Newport Co, Inverness, Yeovil, Exeter, Torquay (L), Torquay									
Warren	Tyrell	22	Defender	Boston United	2	4	4	6	
Man Utd (Y), Salford, Radcliffe B (L), Boston U (L), Boston U									
Wassmer	Charlie	30	Defender	Hampton & Richmond Borough	7			7	1
Hayes (Y), Harrow B (L), Crawley, Fleetwood (L), Dagenham & R (L), Cambridge U, Hayes & Y, Margate, Maidenhead, Hampton & R, Woking, Met Police (L), Leatherhead (L), Maidstone (L), Billericay, Hampton & R (L), Hampton & R									
Waters	Billy	26	Forward	Torquay United	14	21	6	35	8
Crewe (Y), Cheltenham, Northampton, Cambridge U (L), Cheltenham (L), Newport Co, Torquay									
Waters	Matty	23	Midfielder	Curzon Ashton	16			16	3
Chester (Y), Curzon A									
Watson	Jordan	28	Defender	Darlington	9		10	9	
Sunderland (Y), Blyth S, Darlington, Blyth S, Darlington									
Watson	Niall	21	Midfielder	Southport	11	6	2	17	3
Accrington, Marine (L), Sligo (L), Airbus (L), Southport									
Watts	Callum	19	Midfielder	Bath City	2	2	9	4	
Southampton (Y), Bath									
Weaver	Jake	24	Goalkeeper	Leamington	20			20	5
Birmingham (Y), Hungerford (L), Kidderminster (L), Leamington (L), Leamington									
Webb	Bradley	20	Midfielder	Gloucester City (L)		2		2	
Fulham (Y), Bristol C, Yate (L), Taunton (L), Hungerford (L), Newport Co (L), Gloucester (L)									
Webb	Dan		Forward	Hemel Hempstead Town	3	5	1	8	
Potton U, Leighton T, Hemel H									
Webber	Oliver	21	Goalkeeper	Dover Athletic (L)	3			3	
Crystal P (Y), Dover (L)									
Webster	Byron	34	Defender	Bromley	30	1		31	3
York (Y), Banik Most (Cz), Doncaster, Northampton, Yeovil, Millwall, Yeovil (L), Scunthorpe, Carlisle, Bromley									
Weeks	Declan	25	Midfielder	Chester	22			22	4
Southport, Kidderminster, Chester									
Weiss	Mitchell	27	Forward	St Albans City	18	1	1	19	6
Hayes & Y, Hemel H, King's L, St Albans									
Wells	George	25	Midfielder	Maidenhead United	36			36	
Slough, Maidenhead									
Welsh	Mackenzie		Goalkeeper	Bath City			2		
Bath (Y)									
West	Joe	21	Defender	Farsley Celtic	6	1	6	7	
Sheff Wed (Y), Farsley C									
West	Michael	30	Midfielder	Ebbsfleet United	5	8	4	13	1
Ebbsfleet, Crewe, Hereford (L), Ebbsfleet, Whitehawk (L), Whitehawk, Chelmsford, Eastbourne B, Ebbsfleet									

(X, SX, S, Ap, G/Cs under the heading APPEARANCES)

2020-21 NATIONAL. NORTH & SOUTH PLAYERS — APPEARANCES

SURNAME	FIRSTNAME	AGE	POSITION	CLUB PLAYED FOR	X	SX	S	Ap	G/Cs
Weston	Curtis	34	Midfielder	Chesterfield	41	1		42	
Millwall (Y), Swindon, Leeds, Scunthorpe (L), Gillingham, Barnet, Chesterfield									
Weston	Myles	33	Midfielder	Dagenham & Redbridge	24	5		29	1
Charlton, Notts Co (L), Notts Co, Brentford, Gillingham, Southend, Wycombe, Ebbsfleet, Dagenham & R									
Wharton	Dylan		Goalkeeper	Chesterfield	1		11	1	
Chesterfield (Y)									
Wheatley	Josef	24	Midfielder	Darlington	19	1		20	
Middlesbrough (Y), Darlington									
Wheeler	Nick	30	Midfielder	Dorking Wanderers	13	1	3	14	1
Charlton, Lewis, Burgess Hill, Lewes, Tonbridge A, Dagenham & R, Billericay, Woking, Eastbourne B, Dorking W									
Whelan	Tom	25	Midfielder	Weymouth	6	2	1	8	3
				Chesterfield	17	11	3	28	5
Bury, Salisbury, Yeovil, Chippenham (L), Weymouth (L), Weymouth, Chesterfield									
Whelpdale	Chris	32	Midfielder	Eastbourne Borough	16	1	1	17	15
Peterborough, Gillingham (L), Gillingham, Stevenage, Wimbledon, Stevenage, Chelmsford, Eastbourne B									
White	Andy	28	Defender	Altrincham	11	3	4	14	
Crewe (Y), Nantwich, Southport, Altrincham									
White	Harvey	20	Goalkeeper	Woking			2		
QPR (Y), Watford (U23), Stratford T (L), Hendon (L), Woking									
White	Jaiden		Forward	Kidderminster Harriers		3	6	3	
Kidderminster (Y), Stafford R (L)									
White	Lewis	22	Midfielder	Dulwich Hamlet	3	1	2	4	1
Millwall (Y), Concord R (L), Dulwich H									
White	Nicholas (Ross)	25	Defender	AFC Telford United	6	3	5	9	
Wrexham (Y), Southport, Telford									
White	Paul	26	Goalkeeper	Hereford FC	9		12	9	3
Cork, Forest GR, Gloucester (Lx2), Boreham W, Accrington, Kettering, Hereford									
White	Tom	24	Midfielder	Hartlepool United (L)	8	2	6	10	
Gateshead (Y), Spennymoor (L), West Auckland (L), Ashington (L), Scarborough (L), Blackburn, Barrow (L), Bolton (L), Hartlepool (L)									
Whitely	Corey	29	Forward	Boreham Wood (L)	31	5	2	36	5
Tottenham, Waltham F, Cheshunt, Enfield T, Dagenham & R, Ebbsfleet, Newport, Bromley (L), Boreham W (L)									
Whitfield	Ben	25	Midfielder	Torquay United	32	1		33	6
Guiseley, Bournemouth, Kidderminster (L), Yeovil (L), Port Vale (L), Port Vale, Torquay									
Whitham	Dale	29	Midfielder	Curzon Ashton	7	2	1	9	1
Maine Road, Leigh Gen, Chorley, FC United (L), Alfreton, Curzon A									
Whitley	Ryan	21	Goalkeeper	York City			1		
York, Whitby T (L), Scarborough A (L)									
Whitmore	Alex	25	Defender	AFC Fylde	20			20	1
Burnley (Y), Chester (L), Gateshead (L), Morecambe (L), Bury (L), Chesterfield, Grimsby, AFC Fylde									
Whittingham	Alfy		Midfielder	Aldershot Town	20	8	8	28	1
Havant & W (Y), Hungerford, Aldershot									
Whittingham	Richard	30	Midfielder	Hereford FC		2	7	2	
Gosport B, Whitehawk, Hungerford (L), Hungerford, Hemel H, Hereford									
Whittle	Alex	28	Midfielder	Gloucester City	15		1	15	1
				Chesterfield	18	2	3	20	1
Dunfermline, AFC Fylde, Southport, York, Forest GR, Southport (L), Warrington, Boston U, Gloucester, Chesterfield									
Widdrington	Theo	22	Midfielder	Havant & Waterlooville	4	4	1	8	1
Portsmouth (Y), Havant & W (L), Bristol R, Welling (L), Hemel H (L), Havant & W									
Wilkinson	Luke	29	Defender	Yeovil Town	20			20	3
Eastleigh, Dagenham & R, Boreham W (L), Dartford (L), Luton, Stevenage, Yeovil									
Wilks	Daniel	25	Goalkeeper	Dartford	3			3	1
				Concord Rangers			1		
Watford (Y), St Mirren, Maldon, Whitehawk (L), Whitehawk, Welling, Biggleswade T, Dartford, Concord R									
Williams	Aaron	27	Forward	AFC Telford United	12	3	5	15	9
Walsall (Y), Redditch (L), Romulus (L), Telford (L), Worcester, Rushall, Nuneaton, Peterborough, Nuneaton (L), Newport C, Brackley (L), Brackley, Harrogate, AFC Telford									
Williams	Aryn	27	Midfielder	Havant & Waterlooville	1	1	1	2	
Perth Glory, NEROCA (India), Persebaya (Indonesia), Havant & W, Oakleigh C (Aus)									
Williams	Danny	33	Midfielder	FC Halifax	26	5	3	31	1
Daisy Hill, FC United, Clitheroe, Kendal, Chester (L), Inverness, Dundee, Unattached, Accrington, AFC Fylde (L), FC Halifax									

Key: X - Started; SX - Sub on; S - Non-playing Sub; Ap - Total Appearances; G/Cs - Total goals/clean sheets.

SURNAME	FIRSTNAME	AGE	POSITION	CLUB	X	SX	S	Ap	G/Cs
Williams	Jason	25	Forward	Tonbridge Angels		5	2	5	
Southend, Chelmsford (L), Welling (L), Chelmsford (L), Boreham W (L), Concord R, Hemel H, Tonbridge A									
Williams	Jay	20	Defender	Kettering Town		3	6	3	
Northampton (Y), Kettering (L), Wealdstone, Kettering, Harrogate									
Williams	Jordan	28	Midfielder	Stockport County	8	14	2	22	
Northwich Victoria, Barrow, Rochdale, Lincoln C (L), AFC Fylde, Stockport									
Williams	Luke	28	Forward	Hartlepool United	2	7	12	9	1
Middlesbrough (Y), Hartlepool (L), Scunthorpe (L), Coventry (L), Peterborough (L), Scunthorpe, Northampton (L), Hartlepool									
Williams	Michael	27	Midfielder	Alfreton Town		1	5	1	
Ilkeston, Matlock, Sheffield, Alfreton									
Williams	Morgan	21	Defender	Yeovil Town (L)	4			4	
Coventry (Y), Yeovil (L), Yeovil (L)									
Williams	Sean	29	Midfielder	Altrincham	10	4	5	14	
Stockport, Vauxhall M, Hyde, Vauxhall M, Colwyn, Halifax, Colwyn, Altrincham, Hinckley U, Hednesford, Telford, Warrington, Altrincham									
Williams	Tyrone	26	Defender	Solihull Moors	42			42	2
Kidderminster, Hednesford (L), Solihull M									
Williamson	Ben	32	Forward	Bromley	30	10	5	40	3
Worthing, Jerez Ind., Bournemouth, Hyde, Port Vale (L), Port Vale, Gillingham, Cambridge U (L), Cambridge U, Eastleigh, Bromley									
Williamson	Mike	37	Defender	Gateshead	2			2	
Torquay (Y), Southampton, Torquay (L), Doncaster (L), Wycombe, Watford, Portsmouth, Newcastle, Wolves (L), Wolves, Oxford U, Gateshead									
Willis	George	25	Goalkeeper	Alfreton Town	17			17	1
Sheff Utd (Y), Bradford PA (L), Alfreton (L), Matlock (L), Stalybridge, Gainsborough, Boston U, Alfreton									
Willmoth	Callum	30	Midfielder	Hungerford Town	19		1	19	
Hungerford									
Willoughby	Kurt	23	Forward	AFC Fylde	9	6	6	15	3
Fleetwood (Y), Clitheroe, FC United, AFC Fylde, York (L)									
Wills	Kane	31	Midfielder	Dorking Wanderers	21	1		22	
Ebbsfleet, Eastbourne B (L), Lewes (L), Margate, Worthing, Eastbourne B, Dorking W									
Wilson	Donovan	24	Forward	Bath City	9	1		10	6
				Sutton United (L)	11	4	1	15	7
Bristol R (Y), Wolves (L/P), Port Vale (L), Jumila (L) (Spain), Exeter (L), Burgos (Spain), Macclesfield, Bath, Sutton U (L)									
Wilson	Lawrie	33	Defender	Billericay Town	14			14	
Charlton, Colchester, Stevenage, Charlton, Rotherham (L), Bolton, Peterborough (L), Port Vale, Ebbsfleet, Maidstone (L), Billericay T									
Wilson	Lewis	28	Forward	Kettering Town		2	3	2	
Newport P, Northampton, Bishop's S (L), Kettering, Whitehawk, Oxford C, Stratford, Kettering									
Wilson	Scott	28	Forward	Dagenham & Redbridge	16	15	8	31	3
Bristol C (Y), Gloucester, Bath, Gloucester, Paulton, Weston SM, Eastleigh, Macclesfield, Oldham, Notts Co (L), Dagenham & R									
Wiltshire	Jerry	25	Defender	Maidenhead United	8	7	16	15	1
QPR (Y), Bethal Wildcats (US), Memphis City, Chattanooga, Peach Tree City, W Florida Argonauts, Des Moines Mence, Maidenhead									
Wiltshire	Kyran	24	Midfielder	St Albans City	19	1		20	1
Maidenhead, Bishop's S (L), Oxford C, St Albans									
Wind	George	18	Defender	Billericay Town	2			2	
Bowers & P, Billericay T									
Windass	Jordan		Defender	Bradford (Park Avenue)	10	3	3	13	1
North Ferriby, Gainsborough, Bradford (PA)									
Winnard	Dean	31	Defender	Southport	4	1	7	5	
Accrington (Y), Morecambe, Southport									
Wishart	Dan	29	Defender	Wealdstone	9	7	11	16	
Hayes & Y, Alfreton, Hayes & Y (L), Margate (L), Eastleigh (L), Hayes & Y, Sutton U, Forest GR, Sutton U, Maidstone, Wealdstone									
Wolfe	Matthew		Midfielder	Notts County (L)	5	2	7	7	1
Barnsley (Y), Notts Co (L)									
Wollerton	Alex	21	Forward	York City			3		
Leeds (Y), Darlington (L), Barnsley, York, Bradford PA (L)									
Wood	Jacob		Goalkeeper	Kettering Town			2		
Kettering									
Wood	Marcus	23	Midfielder	Southport		1	1	1	
Man City (Y), Bolton, Southport (L), Bradford PA, Southport									

2020-21 NATIONAL. NORTH & SOUTH PLAYERS

SURNAME	FIRSTNAME	AGE	POSITION	CLUB PLAYED FOR	X	SX	S	Ap	G/Cs
Wood	Sam	34	Midfielder	Dover Athletic	15	1	1	16	2
Brentford, Rotherham (L), Wycombe, Eastleigh, Bromley, Dover									
Wood	Tommy	22	Forward	Tonbridge Angels	15			15	3
Wimbledon, Slough (L), Tonbridge A (L), Tonbridge A									
Wood	William	24	Defender	Ebbsfleet United	13	5	3	18	1
Southampton (Y), Accrington, Havant & W (L), Dagenham & R, Ebbsfleet									
Woodards	Danny	37	Defender	Boreham Wood	1	3	22	4	
Exeter, Crewe, MK Dons, Bristol R, Tranmere, Boreham W									
Woodhouse	Luca		Midfielder	Tonbridge Angels			2		
Tonbridge A									
Woods	Connor		Midfielder	Southport	10	5	4	15	2
St Helens T, Southport									
Woods	Martin	35	Midfielder	FC Halifax	34	5	1	39	4
Sunderland (Y), Rotherham, Doncaster, Yeovil (L), Barnsley, Ross Co, Shrewsbury, Ross Co, Partick, Dundee, FC Halifax									
Woods	Michael	31	Midfielder	York City	12	2	2	14	5
Leeds, Chelsea, Notts Co (L), Yeovil, Doncaster, Harrogate T, Hartlepool, Harrogate, Dover, York									
Woollard-Innocent	Kai	20	Defender	Eastbourne Borough (L)	23			23	
QPR (Y), Stratford T (L), Eastbourne B (L)									
Wootton	Cameron		Midfielder	Tonbridge Angels			1		
Tonbridge A									
Wootton	Kyle	24	Forward	Notts County	46	2	1	48	19
Scunthorpe (Y), North Ferriby (L), Cheltenham (L), Stevenage (L), FC Halifax (L), Notts Co									
Worby	Alastair	28	Goalkeeper	Brackley Town	5		9	5	1
Reading (Y), Coventry, St Johnstone, Nike Academy, Loughborough Uni, Brackley									
Wordsworth	Anthoy	32	Midfielder	Barnet	19		1	19	2
Colchester (Y), Ipswich, Rotherham (L), Crawley (L), Southend, Wimbledon, Barnet									
Worgan	Lee	37	Goalkeeper	Chelmsford City	18			18	4
MK Dons, Wycombe (L), Rushden, Cardiff, Merthyr T (L), Eastbourne, Hastings, Tonbridge A, Maidstone, Dover, Chelmsford									
Worman	Ben	19	Midfielder	Weymouth (L)	8	1		9	
Cambridge U (Y), Chelmsford (L), Weymouth (L)									
Worner	Ross	31	Goalkeeper	Havant & Waterlooville	18		1	18	5
Woking (Y), Charlton, Aldershot, Eastbourne B (L), AFC Wimbledon, Woking (L), Sutton U, Chelmsford (L), Maidstone (L), Havant & W									
Worsfold	Max	28	Midfielder	Slough Town	9	2	2	11	2
Aldershot (Y), Maidenhead (L), Dorchester (L), Staines, Hayes & Y, Staines, Maidenhead, Slough									
Worthington	Matt	23	Midfielder	Yeovil Town	22	5	7	27	
Bournemouth, Eastbourne B (L), Yeovil (L), Forest GR (L), Yeovil									
Wotton	Joe		Midfielder	Hampton & Richmond Borough			4		
Hampton & R (Y)									
Wraight	Tom	26	Forward	Chelmsford City	9	3	1	12	2
East Thurrock, Maidstone, Chelmsford									
Wratten	Marshall		Forward	Dover Athletic	2	2	9	4	
Dover (Y)									
Wright	Akil	25	Defender	York City	13	1		14	1
Fleetwood, AFC Fylde (L), Barrow (L), Wrexham, York									
Wright	Danny	36	Forward	Torquay United	21	2	1	23	11
Dereham, Histon, Cambridge U, Wrexham, Forest GR, Gateshead, Kidderminster, Cheltenham, Solihull, Torquay									
Wright	Jake	24	Forward	Boston United		1		1	
Sheff Utd (Y), York (L), Southport (L), Gateshead (L), Harrogate (L), Harrogate, York, Boston U (L), Boston U (L), Boston U									
Wright	Jake	35	Defender	Hereford FC	4			4	
Brighton, Oxford U, Sheff Utd, Bolton (L), Hereford, Mansfield									
Wright	Jenson	20	Midfielder	Oxford City			5		
MK Dons (Y), Oxford C, Banbury U (D)									
Wright	Tommy	24	Forward	Havant & Waterlooville	20	2		22	12
Sutton U, Salisbury (L), Havant & W									
Wright	Will	24	Defender	Dagenham & Redbridge	29	6	3	35	1
Hitchen, Colchester, Dagenham & R (L), Dagenham & R									
Wyatt	Ben	25	Defender	Sutton United	16	4	19	20	
Ipswich (Y), Colchester, Concord R (L), Braintree, St Albans, Sutton U									

Key: X - Started; SX - Sub on; S - Non-playing Sub; Ap - Total Appearances; G/Cs - Total goals/clean sheets.

SURNAME	FIRSTNAME	AGE	POSITION	CLUB	X	SX	S	Ap	G/Cs
					APPEARANCES				
Wylie	Reece		Midfielder	Aldershot Town		2	6	2	
Aldershot (Y)									
Wynter	Alex	27	Defender	Eastleigh	19	3	1	22	3
Crystal Palace, Colchester (L), Portsmouth (L), Colchester, Maidstone, Eastleigh									
Wynter	Ben	23	Defender	Torquay United	35			35	2
Crystal Palace, BromleyHampton & R (L), Hampton & R, Torquay									
Wynter	Jordan	27	Midfielder	Dartford	13	2	2	15	
Arsenal, Bristol C, Cheltenham (L), Cheltenham, Telford (Lx2), Bromley, Woking, Maidstone, Dartford (L), Dartford									
Yamfam	Louis-Michel	23	Midfielder	Braintree Town	7	4		11	
Stevenage (Y), Charlton (U23), Dulwich H (L), Royston, Watford (U23), Braintree									
Yarney	Josef	23	Defender	Chesterfield	13	6	11	19	1
Everton (Y), Newcastle (Y), Morecambe (L), Chesterfield (L), Chesterfield									
York	Wesley	28	Forward	Brackley Town	14	8		22	3
Nuneaton, Wrexham, Gateshead, York, Brackley (L), Brackley									
Young	Brad	19	Goalkeeper	Blyth Spartans (L)	8		3	8	1
				Hartlepool United			2		
Hartlepool (Y), Blyth S (L)									
Young	Jordan	21	Midfielder	Gloucester City (L)	4	2		6	1
Swindon (Y), Coventry, Gloucester (L)									
Young	Luke	28	Midfielder	Wrexham	44			44	12
Plymouth, Torquay, Wrexham									
Young	Reggie	22	Midfielder	Hemel Hempstead Town	16	3	1	19	2
Woking (Y), Farnborough (L/P), Hemel H									
Yussuf	Adi	29	Forward	Wrexham (L)	10	8		18	5
				Chesterfield (L)	6	5	7	11	2
Tamworth, Burton Albion, Lincoln City, Oxford City, Mansfield Town, Crawley Town (L), Grimsby Town (L), Barrow, Solihull Moors, Blackpool, Solihull Moors (L), Boreham W (L), Wrexham (L), Chesterfield (L)									
Yussuff	Ade	27	Forward	Braintree Town	2	2		4	1
Chatham, Dagenham & R, St Albans (L), East Thurrock (L), Welling (L), Chatham, Heybridge S, Folkestone I, Dulwich H, Tonbridge A (L), Dover, Cray V, Braintree									
Zebroski	Chris	34	Forward	Chippenham Town	6	12		18	2
Cirencester, Plymouth, Millwall, Oxford U (L), Torquay (L), Wycombe, Torquay (L), Torquay, Bristol R, Cheltenham, Eastleigh, Newport Co, Eastleigh, Chippenham									
Zouma	Lindsay	23	Defender	Altrincham (L)	5		1	5	
Angers SCOII (Fra), Bolton, Barrow, Altrincham (L)									

All player photos taken by Bill Wheatcroft.

Wootton Kyle - Notts Co.

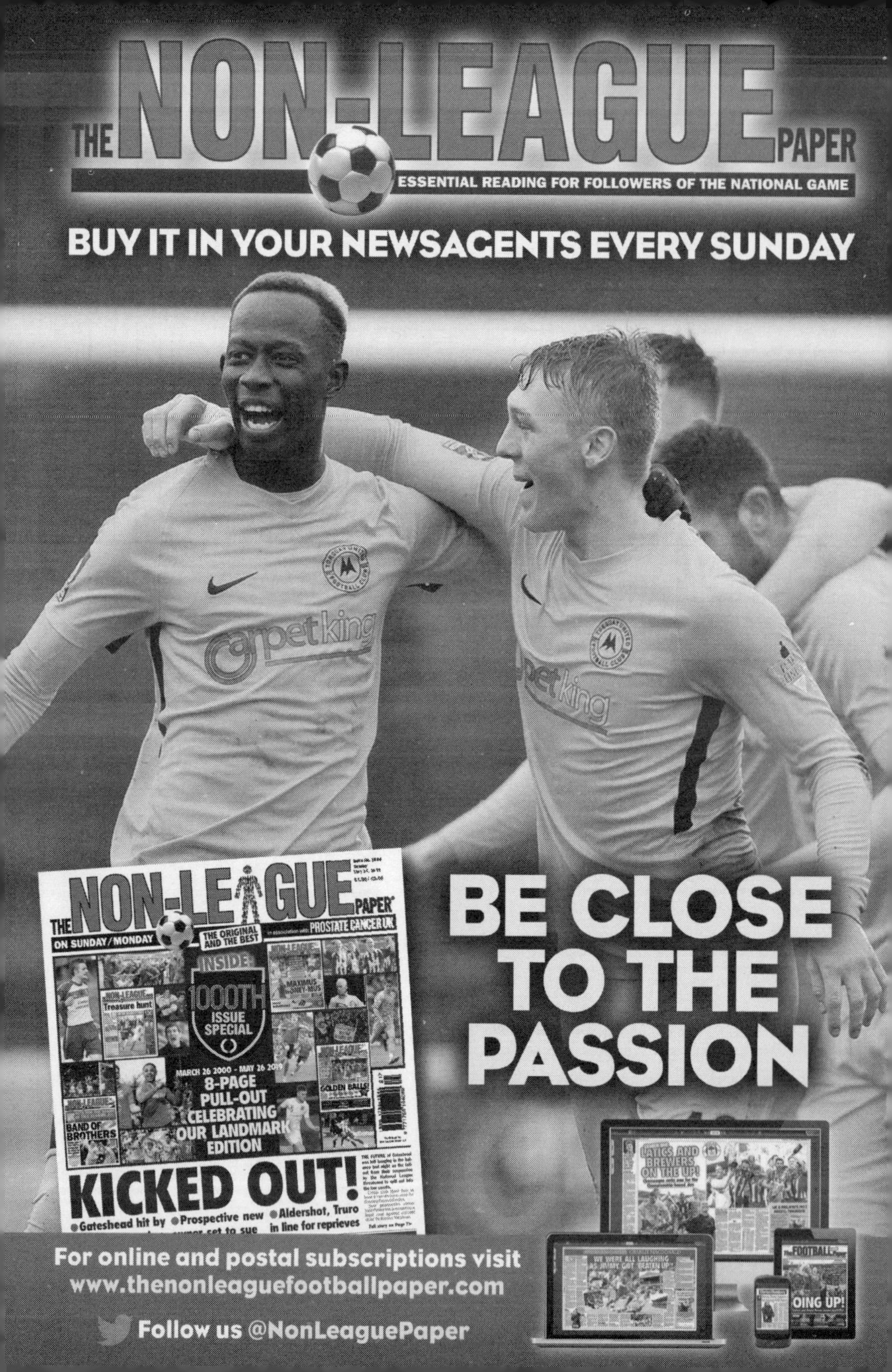
THE NON-LEAGUE PAPER
ESSENTIAL READING FOR FOLLOWERS OF THE NATIONAL GAME
BUY IT IN YOUR NEWSAGENTS EVERY SUNDAY
THE NON-LEAGUE PAPER
ON SUNDAY/MONDAY
THE ORIGINAL AND THE BEST
PROSTATE CANCER UK
INSIDE
1000TH ISSUE SPECIAL
Treasure hunt
MARCH 26 2000 - MAY 26 2019
8-PAGE PULL-OUT CELEBRATING OUR LANDMARK EDITION
GOLDEN BALLS!
BAND OF BROTHERS
KICKED OUT!
Gateshead hit by
Prospective new
Aldershot, Truro in line for reprieves
BE CLOSE TO THE PASSION
LATICS AND BREWERS ON THE UP!
WE WERE ALL LAUGHING AS JIMMY GOT BEATEN UP
OING UP!
For online and postal subscriptions visit
www.thenonleaguefootballpaper.com
Follow us @NonLeaguePaper

ISTHMIAN LEAGUE 2020-21

	PREMIER	P	W	D	L	F	A	GD	Pts
1	Worthing	8	7	0	1	22	10	12	21
2	Cheshunt	10	6	1	3	13	14	-1	19
3	Enfield Town	10	6	0	4	15	17	-2	18
4	Kingstonian	10	6	0	4	15	18	-3	18
5	Carshalton Athletic	8	5	1	2	14	10	4	16
6	Folkestone Invicta	10	5	1	4	13	13	0	16
7	Cray Wanderers	7	5	0	2	21	10	11	15
8	Bishop's Stortford	6	4	2	0	13	5	8	14
9	Hornchurch	10	4	2	4	17	12	5	14
10	Horsham	10	4	2	4	19	15	4	14
11	Haringey Borough	8	4	0	4	13	13	0	12
12	Leatherhead	9	3	3	3	8	15	-7	12
13	Bowers & Pitsea	7	3	1	3	13	5	8	10
14	Bognor Regis Town	7	4	1	2	12	6	6	10*
15	Potters Bar Town	9	3	1	5	13	11	2	10
16	Wingate & Finchley	8	3	1	4	18	17	1	10
17	Corinthian-Casuals	9	3	1	5	9	13	-4	10
18	Lewes	8	2	2	4	8	15	-7	8
19	Brightlingsea Regent	10	2	1	7	11	20	-9	7
20	Margate	9	1	3	5	6	13	-7	6
21	East Thurrock United	9	1	2	6	10	21	-11	5
22	Merstham	8	1	1	6	8	18	-10	4

	NORTH	P	W	D	L	F	A	GD	Pts
1	Tilbury	8	5	1	2	14	9	5	16
2	AFC Sudbury	8	3	3	2	15	14	1	12
3	Maldon & Tiptree	5	3	2	0	9	3	6	11
4	Bury Town	4	3	1	0	9	2	7	10
5	Heybridge Swifts	8	3	1	4	10	9	1	10
6	Histon	6	3	1	2	10	9	1	10
7	Soham Town Rangers	7	3	1	3	7	7	0	10
8	Grays Athletic	6	3	1	2	5	6	-1	10
9	Aveley	6	3	0	3	8	9	-1	9
10	Romford	8	2	3	3	7	10	-3	9
11	Coggeshall Town	6	2	2	2	7	6	1	8
12	Dereham Town	7	2	2	3	7	7	0	8
13	Felixstowe & Walton U	5	2	2	1	7	7	0	8
14	Great Wakering Rovers	7	2	2	3	11	14	-3	8
15	Canvey Island	5	1	3	1	8	5	3	6
16	Hullbridge Sports	5	2	0	3	11	9	2	6
17	Cambridge City	4	2	0	2	3	3	0	6
18	Brentwood Town	5	1	3	1	5	6	-1	6
19	Basildon United	6	1	2	3	11	9	2	5
20	Witham Town	8	1	0	7	7	27	-20	3

	SOUTH EAST	P	W	D	L	F	A	GD	Pts
1	Hastings United	7	5	2	0	13	3	10	17
2	VCD Athletic	8	5	1	2	18	7	11	16
3	East Grinstead Town	6	4	2	0	16	6	10	14
4	Whyteleafe	6	4	1	1	15	7	8	13
5	Sevenoaks Town	8	3	4	1	14	10	4	13
6	Faversham Town	6	3	3	0	8	3	5	12
7	Whitstable Town	9	3	2	4	12	20	-8	11
8	Hythe Town	6	3	1	2	14	12	2	10
9	Ramsgate	6	2	1	3	10	10	0	7
10	Herne Bay	6	2	1	3	9	9	0	7
11	Ashford United	6	2	1	3	9	11	-2	7
12	Cray Valley PM	5	1	3	1	6	6	0	6
13	Three Bridges	6	2	0	4	11	15	-4	6
14	Chichester City	5	2	0	3	7	11	-4	6
15	Phoenix Sports	7	2	0	5	7	16	-9	6
16	Whitehawk	6	1	2	3	7	9	-2	5
17	Haywards Heath Town	7	1	2	4	11	19	-8	5
18	Sittingbourne	5	1	1	3	8	12	-4	4
19	Burgess Hill Town	7	1	1	5	5	14	-9	4

	SOUTH CENTRAL	P	W	D	L	F	A	GD	Pts
1	Waltham Abbey	8	5	1	2	13	9	4	16
2	Staines Town	8	5	1	2	17	17	0	16
3	Ware	7	5	0	2	20	10	10	15
4	Tooting & Mitcham United	7	5	0	2	12	3	9	15
5	Bracknell Town	5	4	1	0	14	5	9	13
6	Chertsey Town	7	4	1	2	14	9	5	13
7	Hanwell Town	8	4	1	3	15	12	3	13
8	Ashford Town (Middx)	8	4	1	3	8	8	0	13
9	Hertford Town	7	4	0	3	10	10	0	12
10	Marlow	7	3	2	2	16	8	8	11
11	Westfield	7	3	1	3	15	11	4	10
12	Barking	7	3	1	3	9	9	0	10
13	Chipstead	8	3	1	4	12	19	-7	10
14	Bedfont Sports	6	3	0	3	10	8	2	9
15	Chalfont St Peter	8	3	0	5	6	10	-4	9
16	FC Romania	7	2	0	5	8	14	-6	6
17	Uxbridge	6	1	2	3	5	11	-6	5
18	South Park	7	1	2	4	12	20	-8	5
19	Northwood	8	1	1	6	7	19	-12	4
20	Harlow Town	8	1	0	7	6	17	-11	3

BISHOP'S STORTFORD MATCH RESULTS 2020-21

Date	Comp	H/A	Opponents	Att:	Result		Goalscorers	Pos	No.
Sept 19	IsthP	H	Bognor Regis Town	322	D	2 - 2	Richardson 79 84 (pens)	10	1
22	**FAC1Q**	**A**	**Welwyn Garden City**	**210**	**D**	**1 - 1**	**Foxley 58 (Won 4-3 on pens)**		2
26	IsthP	H	Hornchurch	314	W	1 - 0	Henshaw 72	9	3
29	IsthP	H	Enfield Town	289	W	4 - 1	Merrifield 18 (pen) 26 52 Richardson 68	4	4
Oct 3	**FAC2Q**	**H**	**Brentwood Town**	**314**	**W**	**1 - 0**	**Henshaw 62**		5
6	IsthP	H	Folkestone Invicta	254	D	1 - 1	Greene 13	6	6
11	IsthP	A	Cray Wanderers	338	W	3 - 1	Greene 57 Merrifield 68 (pen) 74	4	7
13	**FAC3Q**	**H**	**Royston Town**	**600**	**W**	**3 - 0**	**Merrifield 28 75 Davidson 87**		8
17	IsthP	H	Cheshunt	421	W	2 - 0	Richardson 19 89	3	9
26	**FAC4Q**	**H**	**St Albans City**	**600**	**W**	**2 - 0**	**Foxley 3 Greene 16**		10
Nov 4	**FAT3Q**	**H**	**Brentwood Town**	**406**	**W**	**3 - 2**	**Richardson 38 Jones 63 Merrifield 86**		11
7	**FAC1P**	**A**	**Brackley Town**	**0**	**D**	**3 - 3**	**Foxley 65 87 Richardson 72**		12
Dec 8	**FAT1P**	**A**	**Haringey Borough**	**192**	**L**	**1 - 2**	**Jones 44**		13

Goalscorers	LGE	FAC	FAT	SG	HAT	PEN	1Q	2Q	45+	3Q	4Q	90+	T
TOTALS	13	10	4		1	4	5	4	0	6	12	0	27
Merrifield	5	2	1	4	1	2	1	2		1	4		8
Richardson	5	1	1	5		2	1	1			5		7
Foxley		4		3			1			2	1		4
Greene	2	1		3			2			1			3
Henshaw	1	1		2						1	1		2
Jones			2	2				1		1			2
Davidson		1		1							1		1

BOGNOR REGIS TOWN MATCH RESULTS 2020-21

Date	Comp	H/A	Opponents	Att:	Result		Goalscorers	Pos	No.
Sept 19	IsthP	A	Bishop's Stortford	322	D	2 - 2	Leigh T 24 Mongoy 49	11	1
22	**FAC1Q**	**A**	**South Park**	**202**	**D**	**2 - 2**	**Mongoy 59 Wood 80 (Won 4-2 on pens)**		2
26	IsthP	A	Haringey Borough	390	L	1 - 2	Mongoy 25	14	3
29	IsthP	A	Horsham	595	W	1 - 0	Leigh A 53	10	4
Oct 3	**FAC2Q**	**A**	**Hayes & Yeading United**	**301**	**L**	**0 - 5**			5
6	IsthP	H	Carshalton Athletic	431	W	2 - 1	Cook 22 Dowridge 35	9	6
10	IsthP	A	Cheshunt	266	L	0 - 1		13	7
17	IsthP	H	East Thurrock United	518	W	4 - 0	Leigh A 28 34 55 (pen) Leigh T 42 (pen)	11	8
24	IsthP	H	Margate	597	W	2 - 0	Lethbridge 16 43	5	9
31	**FAT3Q**	**H**	**Tooting & Mitcham United**	**486**	**W**	**2 - 0**	**Lethbridge 70 Lis 81**		10
Dec 8	**FAT1P**	**A**	**Thame United**	**161**	**W**	**5 - 2**	**Lethbridge 22 82 Leigh A 38 Mongoy 44 Cook 78**		11
15	**FAT2P**	**A**	**Maldon & Tiptree**	**184**	**L**	**1 - 2**	**Whyte 47**		12

Goalscorers	LGE	FAC	FAT	SG	HAT	PEN	1Q	2Q	45+	3Q	4Q	90+	T
TOTALS	12	2	8		1	2	3	9	0	5	5	0	22
Leigh A	4		1	3	1	1		3		2			5
Lethbridge	2		3	3			2	1			2		5
Mongoy	2	1	1	4				2		2			4
Cook	1		1	2			1				1		2
Leigh T	2			2		1		2					2
Dowridge	1			1				1					1
Lis			1	1							1		1
Whyte			1	1						1			1
Wood		1		1							1		1

BOWERS & PITSEA MATCH RESULTS 2020-21

Date	Comp	H/A	Opponents	Att:	Result	Goalscorers	Pos	No.
Sept 12	**FACP**	**H**	**Barton Rovers**	**155**	**W 5 - 1**	**Trendall 20 Monville 42 Knott 55 68 (pens) De Bourg 86**		1
20	IsthP	A	Wingate & Finchley	302	W 2 - 1	Monville 21 Trendall 85	4	2
22	**FAC1Q**	**H**	**Hornchurch**	**242**	**L 0 - 3**			3
26	IsthP	H	Leatherhead	155	W 7 - 0	Knott 10 56 Trendall 38 50 Cornhill 52 Monville 68 Balde 771		4
29	IsthP	H	Brightlingsea Regent	142	W 2 - 1	Thomas 32 Knott 70 (pen)	1	5
Oct 6	IsthP	H	Lewes	132	D 1 - 1	Knott 75 (pen)	1	6
10	IsthP	A	Worthing	600	L 1 - 2	Knott 19 (pen)	4	7
17	IsthP	H	Kingstonian	-	L	Awarded to Kingstonin		8
20	IsthP	A	Folkestone Invicta	-	L	Awarded to Folkestone Invicta		9
31	**FAT3Q**	**H**	**Hornchurch**	**260**	**L 1 - 3**	**Albon 15 (pen)**		10

Goalscorers	LGE	FAC	FAT	SG	HAT	PEN	1Q	2Q	45+	3Q	4Q	90+	T
TOTALS	13	5	1		0	6	5	3	0	4	7	0	19
Knott	5	2		5		5	2			2	3		7
Trendall	3	1		3			1	1		1	1		4
Monville	2	1		3			1	1			1		3
Albon			1	1		1	1						1
Balde	1			1							1		1
Cornhill	1			1						1			1
De Bourg		1		1							1		1
Thomas	1			1				1					1

BRIGHTLINGSEA REGENT MATCH RESULTS 2020-21

Date	Comp	H/A	Opponents	Att:	Result	Goalscorers	Pos	No.
Sept 19	IsthP	H	Margate	202	L 1 - 2	Rocha 68	14	1
22	**FAC1Q**	**A**	**Bury Town**	**400**	**L 1 - 2**	**Oti 45**		2
26	IsthP	A	Lewes	359	W 2 - 1	Kamanzi 43 Rocha 71	11	3
29	IsthP	A	Bowers & Pitsea	142	L 1 - 2	Bennett 85	15	4
Oct 3	IsthP	H	East Thurrock United	174	D 1 - 1	Oti 84 (pen)	13	5
6	IsthP	A	Corinthian-Casuals	178	L 0 - 2		19	6
10	IsthP	H	Haringey Borough	192	L 0 - 3		20	7
17	IsthP	A	Horsham	600	L 0 - 4		21	8
20	IsthP	H	Leatherhead	182	W 3 - 0	Birse 19 Clowsley 21 44	19	9
24	IsthP	H	Folkestone Invicta	186	L 1 - 2	Clowsley 66	19	10
31	**FAT3Q**	**A**	**Kings Langley**		**L 1 - 4**	**Byrne-Hewitt 78**		11
Nov 3	IsthP	A	Enfield Town	331	L 2 - 3	Byrne-Hewitt 15 Durling 55	19	12

Goalscorers	LGE	FAC	FAT	SG	HAT	PEN	1Q	2Q	45+	3Q	4Q	90+	T
TOTALS	11	1	1	11	0	1	3	2	1	2	5	0	13
Clowsley	3			2			1	1		1			3
Byrne-Hewitt	1		1	1			1				1		2
Oti	1	1		2		1			1		1		2
Rocha	2			2							2		2
Bennett	1			1							1		1
Birse	1			1			1						1
Durling	1			1						1			1
Kamanzi	1			1				1					1

CARSHALTON ATHLETIC MATCH RESULTS 2020-21

Date	Comp	H/A	Opponents	Att:	Result		Goalscorers	Pos	No.
Sept 12	**FACP**	**H**	**Whitstable Town**	**326**	**W**	**5 - 1**	**Fisher 37 Haxhiu 44 Cheadle 69 Bradford 72 Koroma 76**		1
19	IsthP	H	Potters Bar Town	452	W	3 - 0	Koroma 62 Quarrington-Carter 71 (og) Cheadle 90	3	2
21	**FAC1Q**	**H**	**Faversham Town**	**334**	**W**	**5 - 0**	**Fisher 6 49 62 Bradford 11 Read 14**		3
26	IsthP	A	Margate	254	D	2 - 2	Fisher 5 Sogbanmu 34	7	4
29	IsthP	A	East Thurrock United	304	W	2 - 1	Clunis 14 Koroma 65	5	5
Oct 3	**FAC2Q**	**A**	**Bedfont Sports**	**174**	**L**	**0 - 2**			6
6	IsthP	A	Bognor Regis Town	431	L	1 - 2	Ottaway 84	8	7
10	IsthP	H	Corinthian-Casuals	600	W	1 - 0	Hamilton-Downes 83	6	8
12	IsthP	H	Horsham	453	W	3 - 1	Cheadle 11 O'Toole 25 (og) Koroma 55		9
17	IsthP	A	Hornchurch	444	L	0 - 4		4	10
24	IsthP	H	Enfield Town	600	W	2 - 0	Bradford 54 85	3	11
Nov 4	**FAT3Q**	**A**	**Merstham**	**166**	**W**	**3 - 1**	**Fisher 19 Ottaway 28 69**		12
Dec 8	**FAT1P**	**H**	**Barking**	**396**	**W**	**3 - 0**	**Ottaway 27 Price 53 White 90**		13
12	**FAT2P**	**A**	**Swindon Supermarine**	**281**	**D**	**0 - 0**	**(Lost 4-5 on pens)**		14

Goalscorers	LGE	FAC	FAT	SG	HAT	PEN	1Q	2Q	45+	3Q	4Q	90+	T
TOTALS	14	10	6		1	0	7	6	0	7	8	2	30
Fisher	1	4	1	4	1		3	1		1	1		6
Bradford	2	2		3			1			1	2		4
Koroma	3	1		4						3	1		4
Ottaway	1		3	3				2			2		4
Cheadle	2	1		3			1			1		1	3
Opponent	2			2				1			1		2
Clunis	1			1			1						1
Hamilton-Downes	1			1							1		1
Haxhiu		1		1				1					1
Price			1	1						1			1
Read		1		1			1						1
Sogbanmu	1			1				1					1
White			1	1								1	1

CHESHUNT MATCH RESULTS 2020-21

Date	Comp	H/A	Opponents	Att:	Result		Goalscorers	Pos	No.
Sept 19	IsthP	H	East Thurrock United	245	W	1 - 0	Adarkwa 28	9	1
22	**FAC1Q**	**A**	**Long Melford**	**286**	**W**	**3 - 1**	**Cunnington 9 47 Newton 70**		2
26	IsthP	A	Horsham	489	W	2 - 1	Reynolds 32 Re 76	6	3
29	IsthP	A	Cheshunt	248	L	0 - 3		8	4
Oct 3	**FAC2Q**	**H**	**Cambridge City**	**356**	**L**	**1 - 2**	**Miles 90**		5
6	IsthP	A	Margate	216	W	2 - 0	Camara 46 Knight 58	5	6
10	IsthP	H	Bognor Regis Town	266	W	1 - 0	Beckles-Richards 78	3	7
13	IsthP	H	Folkstone Invicta	205	W	2 - 1	Camara 7 Cunnington 78	1	8
17	IsthP	A	Bishop's Stortford	421	L	0 - 2		2	9
20	IsthP	H	Hornchurch	276	L	0 - 3		3	10
24	IsthP	H	Kingstonian	313	W	3 - 2	Miles 4 Beckles-Richards 14 (pen) Nogueira 79	2	11
31	**FAT3Q**	**A**	**East Thurrock United**	**132**	**W**	**4 - 3**	**Reynolds 34 McKenzie 44 Beckles-Richards 50 Asamoah 84**		12
Nov 3	IsthP	A	Wingate & Finchley	262	D	2 - 2	Reynolds 58 Pinto 84	2	13
Dec 8	**FAT1P**	**A**	**Lowestoft Town**	**200**	**W**	**3 - 0**	**Pinto 15 55 Camara 60**		14
15	**FAT2P**	**A**	**Dulwich Hamlet**		**L**	**1 - 3**	**Pinto 85**		15

Goalscorers	LGE	FAC	FAT	SG	HAT	PEN	1Q	2Q	45+	3Q	4Q	90+	T
TOTALS	13	4	8		0	1	5	4	0	7	8	1	25
Pinto	1		3	3			1			1	2		4
Beckles-Richards	2		1	3		1	1			1	1		3
Camara	2		1	3			1			2			3
Cunnington	1	2		2			1			1	1		3
Reynolds	2		1	3				2		1			3
Miles	1	1		2			1					1	2
Adarkwa	1			1				1					1
Asamoah			1	1							1		1
Knight	1			1						1			1
McKenzie			1	1				1					1
Newton		1		1							1		1
Nogueira	1			1							1		1
Re	1			1							1		1

CORINTHIAN-CASUALS MATCH RESULTS 2020-21

Date	Comp	H/A	Opponents	Att:	Result		Goalscorers	Pos	No.
Sept 19	IsthP	H	Haringey Borough	365	L	1 - 2	Wilson 88	15	1
22	**FAC1Q**	**A**	**Little Common**		**W**	**3 - 0**	**Checklist 48 Pinney 54 (pen) Parsons 85 (og)**		2
26	IsthP	A	Potters Bar Town	213	W	2 - 1	Wilson 66 72	12	3
29	IsthP	A	Merstham	252	L	0 - 3		17	4
Oct 3	**FAC2Q**	**H**	**Dulwich Hamlet**	**417**	**D**	**2 - 2**	**Cadogan 45 Checklit 84 (Lost 1-3 on pens)**		5
6	IsthP	H	Brightlingsea Regent	178	W	2 - 0	Pinney 76 Cadogan 86	12	6
10	IsthP	A	Carshalton Athletic	600	L	0 - 1		16	7
17	IsthP	H	Enfield Town	402	W	2 - 0	Dos Santos 58 77	12	8
20	IsthP	A	Wingate & Finchley	182	L	1 - 4	Strange 49	14	9
24	IsthP	H	Leatherhead	600	D	0 - 0		16	10
31	**FAT3Q**	**H**	**Hendon**	**407**	**W**	**5 - 4**	**Dos Santos 23 27 Cadogan 57 Strange 72 Checklit 82**		11
Nov 3	IsthP	A	Horsham	600	L	1 - 2	Jamison 56	17	12
Dec 19	**FAT2P**	**H**	**Hemel Hempstead Town**	**0**	**D**	**0 - 0**	**(Lost 2-4 on pens) Received a walkover in Round One.**		13

Goalscorers	LGE	FAC	FAT	SG	HAT	PEN	1Q	2Q	45+	3Q	4Q	90+	T
TOTALS	9	5	5		0	1	0	2	1	7	9	0	19
Dos Santos	2		2	2				2		1	1		4
Cadogan	1	1	1	3					1	1	1		3
Checklist		2	1	3						1	2		3
Wilson	3			2						1	2		3
Pinney	1	1		2		1				1	1		2
Strange	1		1	2						1	1		2
Jamison	1			1						1			1
Opponent		1		1							1		1

CRAY WANDERERS MATCH RESULTS 2020-21

Date	Comp	H/A	Opponents	Att:	Result		Goalscorers	Pos	No.
Sept 19	IsthP	H	Kingstonian	290	W	5 - 1	Taylor 8 81 Banton 39 Murrell-Williamson 51 Parker 59	1	1
23	**FAC1Q**	**H**	**Fisher**	**302**	**W**	**3 - 1**	**Banton 14 63 Parker 45**		2
26	IsthP	A	East Thurrock United	319	W	3 - 1	Taylor 26 37 Parker 55	2	3
29	IsthP	A	Folkestone Invicta	574	W	3 - 1	Taylor 24 Allen 62 Murrell-Williamson 67	2	4
Oct 3	**FAC2Q**	**A**	**Moneyfields**	**194**	**W**	**6 - 2**	**Taylor 8 13 90 Parker 32 Leader 35 Allen 56**		5
6	IsthP	A	Potters Bar Town (16)	186	L	0 - 3		3	6
11	IsthP	H	Bishop's Stortford	338	L	1 - 3	Parker 16	7	7
13	**FAC3Q**	**A**	**Bristol Manor Farm**	**392**	**D**	**3 - 3**	**Mundele 6 Parker 11 45 (Won 4-2 on pens)**		8
17	IsthP	A	Haringey Borough	415	W	3 - 1	Pritchard 27 Mundele 69 Murrell-Williamson 76	5	9
24	**FAC4Q**	**A**	**Canvey Island**	**400**	**L**	**2 - 3**	**Taylor 60 (pen) Lewis 67**		10
28	IsthP	H	Merstham	376	W	6 - 0	Mundele 5 Pritchard 9 Leader 30 Murrell-Williamson 48 Taylor 63 82	4	11
31	**FAT3Q**	**A**	**Whitehawk**	**390**	**W**	**3 - 0**	**Murrell-Williamson 20 Allen 45 Parker 86**		12
Dec 8	**FAT1P**	**A**	**Uxbridge**	**102**	**W**	**3 - 1**	**Taylor 15 64 Banton 27**		13
15	**FAT2P**	**A**	**St Albans City**	**174**	**L**	**0 - 3**			14

Goalscorers	LGE	FAC	FAT	SG	HAT	PEN	1Q	2Q	45+	3Q	4Q	90+	T
TOTALS	21	14	6		1	1	11	9	3	12	5	1	41
Taylor	7	4	2	7	1	1	4	3		3	2	1	13
Parker	3	4	1	7			2	1	2	2	1		8
Murrell-Williamson	4		1	5			1			3	1		5
Banton	1	2	1	3			1	2		1			4
Allen	1	1	1	3					1	2			3
Mundele	2	1		3			2				1		3
Leader	1	1		2				2					2
Pritchard	2			2			1	1					2
Lewis		1		1						1			1

EAST THURROCK UNITED MATCH RESULTS 2020-21

Date	Comp	H/A	Opponents	Att:	Result		Goalscorers	Pos	No.
Sept 19	IsthP	A	Cheshunt	245	L	0 - 1		19	1
22	**FAC1Q**	**A**	**Potters Bar Town**	**206**	**L**	**0 - 1**			**2**
26	IsthP	H	Cray Wanderers	319	L	1 - 3	Nzengo 86	18	3
29	IsthP	H	Carshalton Athletic	304	L	1 - 2	Aileru 78	19	4
Oct 3	IsthP	A	Brightlingsea Regent	174	D	1 - 1	Brown-Bahpoe 90	21	5
5	IsthP	A	Haringey Borough	266	L	1 - 3	Aileru 79	21	6
10	IsthP	H	Merstham	207	D	2 - 2	Aileru 33 Illsley 56	22	7
17	IsthP	A	Bognor Regis Town	518	L	0 - 4		22	8
20	IsthP	H	Horsham	266	W	3 - 2	Illsley 12 Stylianides 42 53	21	9
24	IsthP	H	Worthing	301	L	1 - 3	Bademosi 90	21	10
31	**FAT3Q**	**H**	**Cheshunt**	**132**	**L**	**3 - 4**	**Taylor 52 Illsley 90 Bademosi 90**		**11**

Goalscorers	LGE	FAC	FAT	SG	HAT	PEN	1Q	2Q	45+	3Q	4Q	90+	T
TOTALS	10	0	3		0	0	1	2	0	3	3	4	13
Aileru	3			3				1			2		3
Illsley	2		1	3			1			1		1	3
Bademosi	1		1	2								2	2
Stylianides	2			1				1		1			2
Brown-Bahpoe	1			1								1	1
Nzengo	1			1							1		1
Taylor			1	1						1			1

ENFIELD TOWN MATCH RESULTS 2020-21

Date	Comp	H/A	Opponents	Att:	Result		Goalscorers	Pos	No.
Sept 19	IsthP	H	Lewes	250	W	4 - 1	Okojie 24 Walsh 42 (og) Blackman 50 Della-Verde 79	2	1
22	**FAC1Q**	**A**	**Peterborough Sports**	**233**	**D**	**2 - 2**	**Gyebi 4 Okojie 84 (Lost 4-5 on pens)**		**2**
26	IsthP	A	Merstham	235	W	1 - 0	Bricknell 87	4	3
29	IsthP	A	Bishop's Stortford	289	L	1 - 4	Della-Verde 32	6	4
Oct 6	IsthP	A	Horsham	462	L	2 - 5	Bricknell 45 Youngs 45	14	5
10	IsthP	H	Leatherhead	350	W	1 - 0	Bricknell 22	7	6
13	IsthP	H	Kingstonian	323	W	2 - 1	Bricknell 50 Urquhart 88	5	7
17	IsthP	A	Corinthian-Casuals	402	L	0 - 2		7	8
20	IsthP	H	Margate	350	W	1 - 0	Urquhart 61	2	9
24	IsthP	A	Carshalton Athletic	600	L	0 - 2		4	10
31	**FAT3Q**	**H**	**Ramsgate**	**415**	**W**	**8 - 1**	**Della-Verde 5 46 Nzembela 12 Bricknell 32 44 88 (pen) McLeod-Urquhart 83 Taaffe 85**		**11**
Nov 3	IsthP	H	Brightlingsea Regent	331	W	3 - 2	Nzembela 22 Kiangebeni 28 Della-Verde 65	3	12
Dec 9	**FAT1P**	**H**	**Maldon & Tiptree**	**335**	**D**	**2 - 2**	**Gyebi 55 Youngs 65 (Lost 3-4 on pens)**		**13**

Goalscorers	LGE	FAC	FAT	SG	HAT	PEN	1Q	2Q	45+	3Q	4Q	90+	T
TOTALS	15	2	10		1	1	5	6	2	7	7	0	27
Bricknell	4		3	5	1	1	1	2	1	1	2		7
Della-Verde	3		2	4			1	1		2	1		5
Gyebi		1	1	2			1			1			2
Nzembela	1		1	2			2						2
Okojie	1	1		2				1			1		2
Urquhart	2			2						1	1		2
Youngs	1		1	2					1	1			2
Blackman	1			1						1			1
Kiangebeni	1			1				1					1
McLeod-Urquhart			1	1							1		1
Opponent	1			1				1					1
Taaffe			1	1							1		1

FOLKSTONE INVICTA MATCH RESULTS 2020-21

Date	Comp	H/A	Opponents	Att:	Result	Goalscorers	Pos	No.
Sept 19	IsthP	H	Worthing	518	L 1 - 2	Smith D 67	16	1
23	**FAC1Q**	**A**	**Wingate & Finchley**	**158**	**W 4 - 1**	**Draycott 24 85 (pen) Smith D 31 Heard 55**		2
26	IsthP	H	Wingate & Finchley	408	W 4 - 1	Rifat 57 (og) Draycott 61 Simpson 75 Heard 90	10	3
29	IsthP	H	Cray Wanderers	574	L 1 - 3	Smith D 15	14	4
Oct 3	**FAC2Q**	**H**	**Chatham Town**	**594**	**L 0 - 2**			5
6	IsthP	A	Bishop'S Stortford	254	D 1 - 1	Wright 77	17	6
10	IsthP	H	Potters Bar Town	511	W 1 - 0	Smith D 54	12	7
13	IsthP	A	Cheshunt	205	L 1 - 2	Smith D 46	12	8
17	IsthP	A	Leatherhead	489	L 0 - 2		16	9
20	IsthP	A	Bowers & Pitsea	-	W	Awarded to Folkestone		10
24	IsthP	A	Brightlingsea Regent	186	W 2 - 1	Paxman 44 Smith D 60	15	11
31	**FAT3Q**	**H**	**Walton Casuals**	**203**	**L 1 - 2**	**Vincent 16**		12
Nov 3	IsthP	H	Hornchurch	508	W 2 - 1	Vincent 15 Draycott 90	11	13

Goalscorers	LGE	FAC	FAT	SG	HAT	PEN	1Q	2Q	45+	3Q	4Q	90+	T
TOTALS	13	4	1		0	1	3	3	0	7	3	2	18
Smith D	5	1		6			1	1		4			6
Draycott	2	2		3		1		1		1	1	1	4
Heard	1	1		2						1		1	2
Vincent	1		1	2			2						2
Opponent	1			1						1			1
Paxman	1			1				1					1
Simpson	1			1							1		1
Wright	1			1							1		1

HARINGEY BOROUGH MATCH RESULTS 2020-21

Date	Comp	H/A	Opponents	Att:	Result	Goalscorers	Pos	No.
Sept 19	IsthP	A	Corinthian-Casuals	365	W 2 - 1	Akindayini 50 Dombaxe 55	5	1
22	**FAC1Q**	**H**	**Tunbridge Wells**	**176**	**W 5 - 1**	**McDonald 22 Dombaxe 42 Akindayini 48 Aresti 65 Ajani-Salau 82**		2
26	IsthP	H	Bognor Regis Town	390	W 2 - 1	Michael-Percil 55 (pen) Dombaxe 74	5	3
28	IsthP	H	Leatherhead	288	L 0 - 1		7	4
Oct 3	**FAC2Q**	**H**	**Chertsey Town**	**266**	**W 2 - 0**	**Bawling 9 86**		5
5	IsthP	H	East Thurrock United	266	W 3 - 1	Michael-Percil 3 35 (pens) O'Donoghue 75	4	6
10	IsthP	A	Brightlingsea Regent (19)	192	W 3 - 0	O'Donoghue 43 Bawling 60 Michael-Percil 82	2	7
13	**FAC3Q**	**H**	**Bracknell Town**	**347**	**W 5 - 1**	**Richards 16 Bawling 41 Aresti 76 Djassi-Sambu 83 Akindayini 87**		8
17	IsthP	H	Cray Wanaderers	415	L 1 - 3	Bawling 12	6	9
24	**FAC4Q**	**A**	**Maldon & Tiptree**	**382**	**L 0 - 1**			10
27	IsthP	A	Hornchurch	328	L 1 - 3	Bawling 79	9	11
31	**FAT3Q**	**A**	**Faversham Town**	**228**	**W 2 - 1**	**Vilcu 33 Miles 50**		12
Nov 4	IsthP	A	Kingstonian	346	L 1 - 3	Dombaxe 44	12	13
Dec 8	**FAT1P**	**H**	**Bishop's Stortford**	**192**	**W 2 - 1**	**O'Donoghue 61 McDonald 90+1**		14
15	**FAT2P**	**H**	**Eastbourne Borough**	**0**	**W 3 - 1**	**Richards 21 Michael-Percil 45+2 (pen) 50**		15
19	**FAT3P**	**A**	**Dartford**	**0**	**W 1 - 0**	**Bawling 90**		16
Jan 16	**FAT4P**	**A**	**Oxford City**	**0**	**L 2 - 4**	**Vilcu 11 Bawling 19**		17

Goalscorers	LGE	FAC	FAT	SG	HAT	PEN	1Q	2Q	45+	3Q	4Q	90+	T
TOTALS	13	12	10		0	4	8	6	1	9	9	2	35
Bawling	3	3	2	7			3	1		1	2	1	8
Michael-Percil	4		2	4		4	1	1	1	2	1		6
Dombaxe	3	1		4				2		1	1		4
Akindayini	1	2		3						2	1		3
O'Donoghue	2		1	3				1		1	1		3
Aresti		2		2						1	1		2
McDonald		1	1	2			1					1	2
Richards		1	1	2			2						2
Vilcu			2	2			1	1					2
Ajani-Salau		1		1							1		1
Djassi-Sambu		1		1							1		1
Miles			1	1						1			1

HORNCHURCH MATCH RESULTS 2020-21

Date	Comp	H/A	Opponents	Att:	Result		Goalscorers	Pos	No.
Sept 19	IsthP	H	Merstham	366	W	2 - 1	Clark 67 Spence 89	6	1
22	**FAC1Q**	**A**	**Bowers & Pitsea**	**242**	**W**	**3 - 0**	**Brown 15 87 Stimson 54**		2
26	IsthP	A	Bishop's Stortford	314	L	0 - 1		13	3
29	IsthP	A	Margate	225	D	1 - 1	Christou 53	11	4
Oct 3	**FAC2Q**	**A**	**Walthamstow**		**W**	**2 - 0**	**Spence 2 Brown 13**		5
6	IsthP	H	Wingate & Finchley	242	L	2 - 3	Brown 15 Dickson 27	18	6
10	IsthP	A	Kingstonian	366	L	0 - 2		19	7
13	**FAC3Q**	**A**	**Hampton & Richmond B.**		**D**	**2 - 2**	**Dickson 43 Brown 55 (Lost 3-4 on pens)**		8
17	IsthP	H	Carshalton Athletic		W	4 - 0	Ruff 39 Dickson 67 75 Dudley 79 (og)	14	9
20	IsthP	A	Cheshunt	276	W	3 - 0	Purcell 14 Brown 44 Ruff 64	10	10
24	IsthP	H	Horsham	404	D	1 - 1	Dickson 70	11	11
27	IsthP	H	Haringey Borough	328	W	3 - 1	Dickson 15 53 Ruff 89	7	12
31	**FAT3Q**	**A**	**Bowers & Pitsea**	**260**	**W**	**3 - 1**	**Osborn 66 Brown 68 Ruff 90+3**		13
Nov 3	IsthP	A	Folkestone Invicta	508	L	1 - 2	Wright 80 (og)	8	14
Dec 8	**FAT1P**	**H**	**Wingate & Finchley**	**208**	**W**	**4 - 1**	**Muldoon 13 Ruff 37 Higgins 56 Nash 88**		15
15	**FAT2P**	**A**	**Tonbridge Angels**		**W**	**1 - 0**	**Christou 90+4 (RC - Parcell 49)**		16
19	**FAT3P**	**A**	**Dulwich Hamlet**		**W**	**2 - 1**	**Higgins 26 (pen) Ruff 86**		17
Jan 16	**FAT4P**	**H**	**King's Lynn Town**		**D**	**1 - 1**	**Nash 52 (Won 3-0 on pens)**		18
Feb 6	**FAT5P**	**H**	**Maidstone United**		**W**	**5 - 4**	**Higgins 13 58 Winn 41 Ellul 65 (og) Nash 90+7**		19
27	**FATQF**	**A**	**Darlington**		**W**	**2 - 1**	**Nash 26 Higgins 54 (pen)**		20
Mar 29	**FATSF**	**A**	**Notts County**		**D**	**3 - 3**	**Spence 38 Nash 45+3 90+1 (Won 5-4 on pens)**		21
May 22	**FAT F**	**N**	**Hereford**	**9000**	**W**	**3 - 1**	**Ruff 75 Nash 86 Brown 90+5**		22

Goalscorers	LGE	FAC	FAT	SG	HAT	PEN	1Q	2Q	45+	3Q	4Q	90+	T
TOTALS	17	7	21		0	2	8	9	1	13	11	6	48
Brown	2	4	2	7			3	1		1	2	1	8
Dickson	6	1		5			1	2		2	2		7
Nash			7	6				1	1	1	2	2	7
Ruff	3		4	7				2		1	2	2	7
Higgins			5	4		2	1	1		3			5
Opponent	2		1	3						1	2		3
Spence	1	1	1	3			1	1			1		3
Christou	1		1	2						1		1	2
Clark	1			1						1			1
Muldoon			1	1			1						1
Osborn			1	1						1			1
Purcell	1			1			1						1
Stimson		1		1						1			1
Winn			1	1				1					1

HORSHAM MATCH RESULTS 2020-21

Date	Comp	H/A	Opponents	Att:	Result		Goalscorers	Pos	No.
Sept 19	IsthP	A	Leatherhead	540	D	1 - 1	Brivio 81	12	1
22	**FAC1Q**	**H**	**Kingstonian**	**509**	**W**	**2 - 1**	**D'Sane 13 22 (pen)**		2
26	IsthP	H	Cheshunt	489	L	1 - 2	O'Toole 25	15	3
29	IsthP	H	Bognor Regis Town	595	L	0 - 1		18	4
Oct 3	**FAC2Q**	**A**	**Havant & Waterlooville**	**0**	**L**	**1 - 2**	**Miles 90**		5
6	IsthP	H	Enfield Town	462	W	5 - 2	Smith 9 Sparks 54 Harris 69 86 90	16	6
10	IsthP	A	Wingate & Finchley	255	W	2 - 1	O'Toole 33 51	11	7
12	IsthP	A	Carshalton Athletic	453	L	1 - 3	Harris 90 (pen)		8
17	IsthP	H	Brightlingsea Regent	600	W	4 - 0	Day 18 Miles 32 Smith 49 O'Toole 52	10	9
20	IsthP	A	East Thurrock United	266	L	2 - 3	Harris 29 64	12	10
24	IsthP	A	Hornchurch	404	D	1 - 1	O'Toole 27	12	11
31	**FAT3Q**	**H**	**Welwyn Garden City**	**473**	**D**	**1 - 1**	**Smith 19 (Lost 3-5 on pens)**		12
Nov 3	IsthP	H	Corinthian-Casuals	600	W	2 - 1	Harris 11 O'Toole 21	9	13

Goalscorers	LGE	FAC	FAT	SG	HAT	PEN	1Q	2Q	45+	3Q	4Q	90+	T
TOTALS	19	3	1		1	2	7	5	0	5	3	3	23
Harris	7			4	1	1	1	1		1	2	2	7
O'Toole	6			5			1	3		2			6
Smith	2		1	3			2			1			3
D'Sane		2		1		1	2						2
Miles	1	1		2				1				1	2
Brivio	1			1							1		1
Day	1			1			1						1
Sparks	1			1						1			1

KINGSTONIAN MATCH RESULTS 2020-21

Date	Comp	H/A	Opponents	Att:	Result		Goalscorers	Pos	No.
Sept 12	**FACP**	**H**	**Horley Town**	**355**	**W**	**4 - 1**	**Andrews 12 Cooper 41 68 Pearch 78**		1
19	IsthP	A	Cray Wanderers	290	L	1 - 5	Andrews 75	22	2
22	**FAC1Q**	**A**	**Horsham**	**509**	**L**	**1 - 2**	**Sow 87**		3
26	IsthP	H	Worthing	417	L	0 - 4		22	4
30	IsthP	H	Wingate & Finchley	229	W	3 - 2	Cook 5 Buchanan 25 Andrews 90	18	5
Oct 6	IsthP	A	Merstham	307	W	2 - 1	Osborne 2 Buchanan 39	15	6
10	IsthP	H	Hornchurch	366	W	2 - 0	Kavanagh 70 Daniel 79	8	7
17	IsthP	A	Bowers & Pitsea	-	W		Awarded to Kingstonian		8
13	IsthP	A	Enfield Town	323	L	1 - 2	Andrews 39	9	9
21	IsthP	H	Potters Bar Town	269	W	1 - 0	Coker 49	8	10
24	IsthP	A	Cheshunt	313	L	2 - 3	Buchanan 16 Kavanagh 20	9	11
31	**FAT3Q**	**A**	**Maldon & Tiptree**	**256**	**L**	**2 - 3**	**Andrews 60 87**		12
Nov 4	IsthP	H	Haringey Borough	346	W	3 - 1	Andrews 33 59 73	6	13

Goalscorers	LGE	FAC	FAT	SG	HAT	PEN	1Q	2Q	45+	3Q	4Q	90+	T
TOTALS	15	5	2		1	0	5	5	0	3	8	1	22
Andrews	6	1	2	6	1		1	2		2	3	1	9
Buchanan	3			3			1	2					3
Cooper		2		1				1			1		2
Kavanagh	2			2			1				1		2
Coker	1			1						1			1
Cook	1			1			1						1
Daniel	1			1							1		1
Osborne	1			1			1						1
Pearch		1		1							1		1
Sow		1		1							1		1

LEATHERHEAD MATCH RESULTS 2020-21

Date	Comp	H/A	Opponents	Att:	Result		Goalscorers	Pos
Sept 19	IsthP	H	Horsham	540	D	1 - 1	Djemaili 2	13
22	**FAC1Q**	**A**	**Chertsey Town**	**400**	**D**	**0 - 0**	**(Lost 4-5 on pens)**	
26	IsthP	A	Bowers & Pitsea	155	L	0 - 7		16
28	IsthP	A	Haringey Borough	288	W	1 - 0	Rowe 47	12
Oct 3	IsthP	H	Margate	407	D	0 - 0		10
6	IsthP	H	Worthing	401	W	4 - 3	Rowe 4 Leslie 63 Brown 78 Lema 85	7
10	IsthP	A	Enfield Town	350	L	0 - 1		10
17	IsthP	H	Folkestone Invicta	489	W	2 - 0	Lema 1 Briggs 56	8
20	IsthP	A	Brightlingsea Regent	182	L	0 - 3		8
24	IsthP	A	Corinthian-Casuals	600	D	0 - 0		10
31	**FAT3Q**	**H**	**Potters Bar Town**	**258**	**W**	**3 - 1**		
Dec 8	**FAT1P**	**H**	**Felixstowe & Walton United**	**223**	**L**	**0 - 1**		

No. 1 2 3 4 5 6 7 8 9 10 11 12 13 14 15 16 17

Goalscorers	LGE	FAC	FAT	SG	HAT	PEN	1Q	2Q	45+	3Q	4Q	90+	T
TOTALS	8	0	0		0	0	3	0	0	3	2	0	8
Lema	2			2			1				1		2
Rowe	2			2			1			1			2
Briggs	1			1						1			1
Brown	1			1							1		1
Djemaili	1			1			1						1
Leslie	1			1						1			1

LEWES MATCH RESULTS 2020-21

Date	Comp	H/A	Opponents	Att:	Result	Goalscorers	Pos	No.
Sept 19	IsthP	A	Enfield Town	250	L 1 - 4	Cosgrove 43	20	1
22	**FAC1Q**	**A**	**Bedfont Sports**	**113**	**L 1 - 3**	**Cosgrove 64**		2
26	IsthP	H	Brightlingsea Regent	359	L 1 - 2	Cosgrove 17	19	3
29	IsthP	H	Worthing	450	L 1 - 3	Arthurs 36	21	4
Oct 3	IsthP	A	Wingate & Finchley	208	L 1 - 4	Bolarinwa 4	22	5
6	IsthP	A	Bowers & Pitsea	132	D 1 - 1	Cosgrave 29 (pen)	22	6
10	IsthP	H	Margate	450	W 1 - 0	Swift 73 (og)	21	7
17	IsthP	A	Potters Bar Town	213	D 1 - 1	Bosma 7	19	8
20	IsthP	H	Merstham	457	W 1 - 0	Cosgrave 63	16	9
31	**FAT3Q**	**A**	**Lowestoft Town**	**236**	**L 1 - 3**	**Noel 82**		10

Goalscorers	LGE	FAC	FAT	SG	HAT	PEN	1Q	2Q	45+	3Q	4Q	90+	T
TOTALS	8	1	1		0	1	3	3	0	2	2	0	10
Cosgrove	4	1		5		1	1	2		2			5
Arthurs	1			1				1					1
Bolarinwa	1			1			1						1
Bosma	1			1			1						1
Noel			1	1							1		1
Opponent	1			1							1		1

MARGATE MATCH RESULTS 2020-21

Date	Comp	H/A	Opponents	Att:	Result	Goalscorers	Pos	No.
Sept 19	IsthP	A	Brightlingsea Regent	202	W 2 - 1	Carey 10 Bancroft 66	7	1
22	**FAC1Q**	**H**	**Hayes & Yeading United**	**205**	**L 1 - 2**	**Ufuah 83 (pen)**		2
26	IsthP	A	Carshalton Athletic	254	D 2 - 2	Procter 62 (og) Ufuah 90 (pen)	8	3
29	IsthP	H	Hornchurch	225	D 1 - 1	Swift 69	9	4
Oct 3	IsthP	A	Leatherhead	407	D 0 - 0		7	5
6	IsthP	H	Cheshunt	216	L 0 - 2		13	6
10	IsthP	A	Lewes	450	L 0 - 1		17	7
17	IsthP	H	Worthing	435	L 1 - 3	Afrane-Kesey 29	18	8
20	IsthP	A	Enfield Town	350	L 0 - 1		20	9
24	IsthP	A	Bognor Regis Town	597	L 0 - 2		20	10
Nov 1	**FAT3Q**	**A**	**Aylesbury United**	**243**	**W 4 - 2**	**Wabo 21 47 Leighton 76 78 (Withdrawn from 1st Round)**		11

Goalscorers	LGE	FAC	FAT	SG	HAT	PEN	1Q	2Q	45+	3Q	4Q	90+	T
TOTALS	6	1	4		0	2	2	1	0	3	4	1	11
Leighton			2	1							2		2
Ufuah	1	1		2		2					1	1	2
Wabo			2	1			1			1			2
Afrane-Kesey	1			1				1					1
Bancroft	1			1						1			1
Carey	1			1			1						1
Opponent	1			1						1			1
Swift	1			1							1		1

MERSTHAM MATCH RESULTS 2020-21

Date	Comp	H/A	Opponents	Att:	Result		Goalscorers	Pos	No.
Sept 19	IsthP	A	Hornchurch	366	L	1 - 2	Ekpiteta 81	17	1
22	**FAC1Q**	**H**	**AFC Dunstable**	**177**	**D**	**2 - 2**	**Gugas-Cowin Patterson-Bohner (Lost 6-7 on pens)**		2
26	IsthP	A	Enfield Town	235	L	0 - 1		17	3
29	IsthP	H	Corinthian-Casuals	252	W	3 - 0	Mensah 33 Bolton 52 Calucane 59	13	4
Oct 6	IsthP	H	Kingstonian	307	L	1 - 2	Ekpiteta 66	20	5
10	IsthP	A	East Thurrock United (21)	207	D	2 - 2	Ekpiteta 30 Leahy 84	18	6
20	IsthP	A	Merstham	457	L	0 - 1		22	7
24	IsthP	H	Potters Bar Town	223	L	1 - 4	Ebwa 50	22	8
28	IsthP	A	Cray Wanderers	376	L	0 - 6		22	9
Nov 4	**FAT3Q**	**H**	**Carshalton Athletic**	**166**	**L**	**1 - 3**	**Folkes 90**		10

Goalscorers	LGE	FAC	FAT	SG	HAT	PEN	1Q	2Q	45+	3Q	4Q	90+	T
TOTALS	8	2	1		0	0	0	2	0	4	2	1	11
Ekpiteta	3			3				1		1	1		3
Bolton	1			1						1			1
Calucane	1			1						1			1
Ebwa	1			1						1			1
Folkes			1	1								1	1
Gugas-Cowin		1		1									1
Leahy	1			1							1		1
Mensah	1			1				1					1
Patterson-Bohner		1		1									1

POTTERS BAR TOWN MATCH RESULTS 2020-21

Date	Comp	H/A	Opponents	Att:	Result		Goalscorers	Pos	No.
Sept 19	IsthP	A	Carshalton Athletic	452	L	0 - 3		21	1
22	**FAC1Q**	**H**	**East Thurrock United**	**206**	**W**	**1 - 0**	**Cochrane 66**		2
26	IsthP	H	Corinthian-Casuals	213	L	1 - 2	Esan 75	21	3
29	IsthP	H	Cheshunt	248	W	3 - 0	Cochrane 30 Kyei 33 60	16	4
Oct 4	**FAC2Q**	**A**	**Concord Rangers**	**148**	**L**	**1 - 2**	**Esan 21**		5
6	IsthP	H	Cray Wanderers	186	W	3 - 0	Cochrane 8 38 Gogo 17	10	6
10	IsthP	A	Folkestone Invicta	511	L	0 - 1		14	7
17	IsthP	H	Lewes	213	D	1 - 1	Charles 80	15	8
21	IsthP	A	Kingstonian	269	L	0 - 1		17	9
24	IsthP	A	Merstham	223	W	4 - 1	Charles 18 (pen) 82 Payne 41 Kyei 45 (pen)	14	10
27	IsthP	H	Worthing	313	L	1 - 2	Charles 27	14	11
31	**FAT3Q**	**A**	**Leatherhead**	**258**	**L**	**1 - 3**	**Cochrane 70**		12

Goalscorers	LGE	FAC	FAT	SG	HAT	PEN	1Q	2Q	45+	3Q	4Q	90+	T
TOTALS	13	2	1	13	0	2	4	5	1	2	4	0	16
Cochrane	3	1	1	4			1	2		1	1		5
Charles	4			3		1	1	1			2		4
Kyei	3			2		1		1	1	1			3
Esan	1	1		2			1				1		2
Gogo	1			1			1						1
Payne	1			1				1					1

WINGATE & FINCHLEY MATCH RESULTS 2020-21

Date	Comp	H/A	Opponents	Att:	Result	Goalscorers	Pos	No.
Sept 20	IsthP	H	Bowers & Pitsea	302	L 1 - 2	Sayoud 42	18	1
23	**FAC1Q**	**H**	**Folkestone Invicta**	**158**	**L 1 - 4**	**Doyle 90**		2
26	IsthP	A	Folkestone Invicta	408	L 1 - 4	Bakalandwa 86 (pen)	20	3
30	IsthP	A	Kingstonian	229	L 2 - 3	Cotter 51 Bakalandwa 56	21	4
Oct 3	IsthP	H	Lewes	208	W 4 - 1	Sayoud 11 Cotter 14 Healey 28 77	17	5
6	IsthP	A	Hornchurch	242	W 3 - 2	Vihete 30 Edwards 45 Healey 55	11	6
10	IsthP	H	Horsham	255	L 1 - 2	Tejan-Sie 28	15	7
20	IsthP	H	Corinthian-Casuals	182	W 4 - 1	Rifat 39 (pen) 77 83 Ofori-Acheampong 90	13	8
31	**FAT3Q**	**A**	**Coggeshall Town**	**104**	**D 1 - 1**	**Ofori-Acheampong 30 (Won 3-0 on pens)**		9
Nov 3	IsthP	H	Cheshunt	262	D 2 - 2	Edwards 73 Capela 89	16	10
Dec 8	**FAT1P**	**A**	**Hornchurch**	**208**	**L 1 - 4**	**Tejan-Sie 13**		11

Goalscorers	LGE	FAC	FAT	SG	HAT	PEN	1Q	2Q	45+	3Q	4Q	90+	T
TOTALS	18	1	2		1	2	3	6	1	3	6	2	21
Healey	3			2				1		1	1		3
Rifat	3			1	1	1		1			2		3
Bakalandwa	2			2		1				1	1		2
Cotter	2			2			1			1			2
Edwards	2			2					1		1		2
Ofori-Acheampong	1		1	2				1				1	2
Sayoud	2			2			1	1					2
Tejan-Sie	1		1	2			1	1					2
Capela	1			1							1		1
Doyle		1		1								1	1
Vihete	1			1				1					1

WORTHING MATCH RESULTS 2020-21

Date	Comp	H/A	Opponents	Att:	Result	Goalscorers	Pos	No.
Sept 19	IsthP	A	Folkestone Invicta	518	W 2 - 1	Aguiar 42 Pearce 52	8	1
22	**FAC1Q**	**A**	**East Grinstead Town**	**273**	**D 3 - 3**	**Starkey 25 Diallo 44 Golding 74 (Lost 3-4 on pens)**		2
26	IsthP	A	Kingstonian	417	W 4 - 0	Colbran 22 Pearce 60 70 Pattenden 75	3	3
29	IsthP	A	Lewes	450	W 3 - 1	Golding 30 53 69	3	4
Oct 6	IsthP	A	Leatherhead	401	L 3 - 4	Pearce 15 74 (pen) Diallo 69	2	5
10	IsthP	H	Bowers & Pitsea	600	W 2 - 1	Diallo 51 85	1	6
17	IsthP	H	Margate	435	W 3 - 1	Diallo 40 Aguiar 45 Golding 54	1	7
24	IsthP	A	East Thurrock United	301	W 3 - 1	Colbran 36 Diallo 41 Koroma 85	1	8
27	IsthP	A	Potters Bar Town	313	W 2 - 1	Koroma 71 86	1	9
31	**FAT3Q**	**A**	**Leiston**		**D 4 - 4**	**Pearce 45 Koroma 70 Diallo 75 Barker 88 (Lost 2-4 on pens)**		10

Goalscorers	LGE	FAC	FAT	SG	HAT	PEN	1Q	2Q	45+	3Q	4Q	90+	T
TOTALS	22	3	4		1	1	2	7	2	6	12	0	29
Diallo	5	1	1	6				3		2	2		7
Pearce	5		1	4		1	1		1	2	2		6
Golding	4	1		3	1			1		2	2		5
Koroma	3		1	3							4		4
Aguiar	2			2				1	1				2
Colbran	2			2			1	1					2
Barker			1	1							1		1
Pattenden	1			1							1		1
Starkey		1		1				1					1

AFC SUDBURY MATCH RESULTS 2020-21

Date	Comp	H/A	Opponents	Att:	Result		Goalscorers	Pos	No.
Sept 1	**FACEP**	**A**	**Burton Park Rangers**			**P - P**			1
12	**FACP**	**H**	**Harborough Town**	**179**	**W**	**4 - 2**	**Temple 33 37 50 55**		2
19	IsthN	H	Coggeshall Town	342	**W**	2 - 1	Munday 8 Grimwood 46	4	3
22	**FAC1Q**	**A**	**Stamford**	**309**	**L**	**0 - 4**			4
26	**FAT1Q**	**H**	**Barking**	**178**	**L**	**1 - 2**	**Grimwood 60**		5
29	IsthN	A	Felixstowe & Walton United	332	L	2 - 3	Temple 7 Marks 34	9	6
Oct 3	IsthN	H	Hullbridge Sports	247	L	0 - 3		14	7
10	IsthN	A	Basildon United	145	D	2 - 2	Collinge 51 Andrews 63	18	8
24	IsthN	H	Brentwood Town	282	D	2 - 2	Swaine 25 (og) Holland 34	17	9
27	IsthN	A	Soham Town Rangers	191	**W**	1 - 0	Hunter 62	12	10
31	IsthN	H	Witham Town	226	**W**	5 - 2	Hunter 15 Machaya 33 53 Whight 47 King 90	3	11
Nov 4	IsthN	H	Heybridge Swifts	252	D	1 - 1	Hunter 71	2	12

Goalscorers	LGE	FAC	FAT	SG	HAT	PEN	1Q	2Q	45+	3Q	4Q	90+	T
TOTALS	15	4	1		0	0	3	7	0	8	1	1	20
Temple	1	4		2			1	2		2			5
Hunter	3			3			1			1	1		3
Grimwood	1		1	2				1		1			2
Machaya	2			1				1		1			2
Andrews	1			1						1			1
Collinge	1			1						1			1
Holland	1			1				1					1
King	1			1								1	1
Marks	1			1				1					1
Munday	1			1			1						1
Opponent	1			1				1					1
Whight	1			1						1			1

AVELEY MATCH RESULTS 2020-21

Date	Comp	H/A	Opponents	Att:	Result		Goalscorers	Pos	No.
Sept 12	**FACP**	**A**	**Harpenden Town**	**300**	**W**	**3 - 0**	**Sach 7 Sykes 27 Allen 58**		1
19	IsthN	H	Dereham Town	303	**W**	3 - 2	Sach 45 Reid 63 Ogunrinde 75	3	2
22	**FAC1Q**	**A**	**Lowestoft Town**	**275**	**W**	**3 - 2**	**Sach 4 Sykes 18 64**		3
26	IsthN	A	Romford	202	**W**	1 - 0	Gibbs 80	2	4
Oct 3	**FAC2Q**	**A**	**Brantham Athletic**	**300**	**W**	**3 - 0**	**Gibbs 27 Sheehan 60 Reid 89**		5
5	IsthN	H	Brentwood Town	367	L	0 - 1		5	6
13	**FAC3Q**	**A**	**Cray Valley PM**	**301**	**L**	**0 - 2**			7
17	**FAT2Q**	**A**	**Hanwell Town**	**201**	**D**	**1 - 1**	**Sykes 65 (Won 8-7 on pens)**		8
19	IsthN	H	Tilbury	397	L	0 - 3		11	9
24	IsthN	H	Witham Town	318	**W**	4 - 2	Sykes 11 (pen) 54 Clark 22 Knight 57	4	10
27	IsthN	A	Coggeshall Town	126	L	0 - 1		8	11
31	**FAT3Q**	**H**	**Beaconsfield Town**	**164**	**W**	**3 - 0**	**Donovan 29 Clark 46 Sykes 74**		12
Dec 8	**FAT1P**	**H**	**Hastings United**	**139**	**W**	**1 - 0**	**Gilbey 57**		13
15	**FAT2P**	**H**	**Chesham United**		**L**	**1 - 3**	**Gard 82 (pen)**		14

Goalscorers	LGE	FAC	FAT	SG	HAT	PEN	1Q	2Q	45+	3Q	4Q	90+	T
TOTALS	8	9	6		0	2	5	4	0	9	5	0	23
Sykes	2	3	2	5		1	2	1		3	1		7
Sach	1	2		3			2	1					3
Clark	1		1	2			1			1			2
Gibbs	1	1		2				1			1		2
Reid	1	1		2						1	1		2
Allen		1		1						1			1
Donovan			1	1				1					1
Gard			1	1		1					1		1
Gilbey			1	1						1			1
Knight	1			1						1			1
Ogunrinde	1			1							1		1
Sheehan		1		1						1			1

BASILDON UNITED MATCH RESULTS 2020-21

Date	Comp	H/A	Opponents	Att:	Result	Goalscorers	Pos	No.
Sept 12	**FACP**	**A**	**Stansted**	**171**	**L 0 - 2**			1
19	IsthN	H	Bury Town	92	L 0 - 1		17	2
26	**FAT1Q**	**A**	**Northwood**	**111**	**D 1 - 1**	**Carvalho 30 (Lost 3-4 on pens)**		3
30	IsthN	A	Romford	183	L 0 - 1		17	4
Oct 6	IsthN	A	Great Wakering Rovers	119	W 6 - 0	Jeremiah 2 38 Greene 6 Dutton 16 (pen) Baker 44 Rusoke 70	15	5
10	IsthN	H	AFC Sudbury	145	D 2 - 2	Baker 12 Dutton 44 (pen)	16	6
24	IsthN	A	Heybridge Swifts	278	L 0 - 2		19	7
27	IsthN	H	Canvey Island	197	D 3 - 3	O'Connor 2 (pen) Jeremiah 23 Boylan 76	19	8

Goalscorers	LGE	FAC	FAT	SG	HAT	PEN	1Q	2Q	45+	3Q	4Q	90+	T
TOTALS	11	0	1		0	3	5	5	0	0	2	0	12
Jeremiah	3			2			1	2					3
Baker	2			2			1	1					2
Dutton	2			2		2	1	1					2
Boylan	1			1							1		1
Carvalho			1	1				1					1
Greene	1			1			1						1
O'Connor	1			1		1	1						1
Rusoke	1			1							1		1

BRENTWOOD TOWN MATCH RESULTS 2020-21

Date	Comp	H/A	Opponents	Att:	Result	Goalscorers	Pos	No.
Sept 12	**FACP**	**A**	**FC Romania**	**78**	**W 1 - 0**	**Bantick**		1
19	IsthN	H	Grays Athletic	302	L 0 - 2		19	2
21	**FAC1Q**	**A**	**New Salamis**	**300**	**W 2 - 1**	**Oyenuga 20 Bantick 79**		3
26	IsthN	A	Maldon & Tiptree	173	D 1 - 1	Harvey 24	15	4
Oct 3	**FAC2Q**	**A**	**Bishop's Stortford**	**314**	**L 0 - 1**			5
5	IsthN	A	Aveley	367	W 1 - 0	Freeman 63	11	6
10	IsthN	H	Canvey Island	393	D 1 - 1	Ocran 62	13	7
17	**FAT2Q**	**H**	**Chichester City**	**301**	**W 3 - 2**	**Freeman 43 61 Harvey 90**		8
24	IsthN	A	AFC Sudbury	282	D 2 - 2	Freeman 24 36	14	9
Nov 4	**FAT3Q**	**A**	**Bishop's Stortford**	**406**	**L 2 - 3**	**Freeman 4 Rees 29**		10

Goalscorers	LGE	FAC	FAT	SG	HAT	PEN	1Q	2Q	45+	3Q	4Q	90+	T
TOTALS	5	3	5		0	0	2	5	0	4	1	1	13
Freeman	3		3	4			1	3		2			6
Bantick		2		2						1	1		2
Harvey	1		1	2				1				1	2
Ocran	1			1						1			1
Oyenuga		1		1			1						1
Rees			1	1				1					1

BURY TOWN MATCH RESULTS 2020-21

Date	Comp	H/A	Opponents	Att:	Result	Goalscorers	Pos	No.
Sept 12	**FACP**	**A**	**Cogenhoe United**		**W 1 - 0**	**Ramadan 60**		1
19	IsthN	A	Basildon United	92	W 1 - 0	Nyadzayo 26	6	2
22	**FAC1Q**	**H**	**Brightlingsea Regent**	**400**	**W 2 - 1**	**Ramadan 29 (pen) Gardner 68**		3
26	**FAT1Q**	**A**	**Market Drayton Town**		**W 1 - 0**	**Altintop 52**		4
29	IsthN	H	Witham Town	400	W 5 - 0	Shaw 14 54 67 Ramadan 31 Hughes 33		5
Oct 3	**FAC2Q**	**H**	**Waltham Abbey**	**400**	**W 4 - 1**	**Ramadan 1 53 (pen) Shaw 77 Nyadzayo 89**		6
10	IsthN	H	Dereham Town	400	W 1 - 0	Ramadan 55	9	7
13	**FAC3Q**	**H**	**Nuneaton Borough**	**400**	**W 2 - 0**	**Ramadan 33 Hughes 37**		8
17	**FAT2Q**	**A**	**Loughborough Dynamo**	**120**	**L 0 - 1**			9
24	**FAC4Q**	**A**	**Banbury United**		**L 1 - 2**	**Hughes 23**		10
31	IsthN	H	Romford	400	D 2 - 2	Ramadan 21 Jolland 90	3	11

Goalscorers	LGE	FAC	FAT	SG	HAT	PEN	1Q	2Q	45+	3Q	4Q	90+	T
TOTALS	9	10	1		0	2	3	7	0	6	3	1	20
Ramadan	3	4		7		2	2	3		3			7
Shaw	3	1		2			1			2	1		4
Hughes	1	2		3				3					3
Altintop		1	1	1						1			2
Nyadzayo	1	1		2				1			1		2
Gardner		1		1							1		1
Jolland	1			1								1	1

CAMBRIDGE CITY MATCH RESULTS 2020-21

Date	Comp	H/A	Opponents	Att:	Result	Goalscorers	Pos	No.
Sept 12	**FACP**	**H**	**Biggleswade United**	**293**	**W 4 - 0**	**Sharman x2 Olukanmi Ingrey**		1
19	IsthN	H	Tilbury	250	L 0 - 1		18	2
22	**FAC1Q**	**H**	**Stowmarket Town**	**315**	**D 1 - 1**	**Robson (Won 4-2 on pens)**		3
26	**FAT1Q**	**H**	**Kidsgrove Athletic**	**212**	**L 2 - 3**	**Robson 34 Gent 43**		4
29	IsthN	A	Dereham Town	195	L 0 - 1		18	5
Oct 3	**FAC2Q**	**A**	**Cheshunt**	**356**	**W 2 - 1**	**Sharman Crowther (og)**		6
7	IsthN	H	Soham Town Rangers	306	W 2 - 1	Hitchcock 29 Ingrey 86	18	7
10	IsthN	A	Coggeshall Town	110	W 1 - 0	Sharman 38	11	8
13	**FAC3Q**	**H**	**Halesowen Town**	**400**	**W 2 - 0**	**Davis Robson**		9
24	**FAC4Q**	**A**	**Darlington**		**L 0 - 2**			10

Goalscorers	LGE	FAC	FAT	SG	HAT	PEN	1Q	2Q	45+	3Q	4Q	90+	T
TOTALS	3	9	2		0	0	0	4	0	0	1	0	14
Sharman	1	3		3				1					4
Robson		2	1	3				1					3
Ingrey	1	1		2							1		2
Davis		1		1									1
Gent			1	1				1					1
Hitchcock	1			1				1					1
Olukanmi		1		1									1
Opponent		1		1									1

CANVEY ISLAND MATCH RESULTS 2020-21

Date	Comp	H/A	Opponents	Att:	Result	Goalscorers	Pos	No.
Sept 12	**FACP**	**H**	**Ware**	**216**	**W 2 - 0**	**Madden 22 (og) Joseph 70**		1
19	IsthN	H	Romford	336	D 0 - 0		10	2
22	**FAC1Q**	**A**	**Dereham Town**	**234**	**W 2 - 0**	**Hubble 30 Ronto 43**		3
26	IsthN	A	Grays Athletic	336	W 4 - 0	Kouassi 7 Joseph 40 Ronto 66 Chatting 71	3	4
Oct 3	**FAC2Q**	**H**	**Biggleswade**	**289**	**D 2 - 2**	**Hubble 2 Ronto 17 (Won 4-3 on pens)**		5
6	IsthN	H	Maldon & Tiptree	313	L 0 - 1		9	6
10	IsthN	A	Brentwood Town	393	D 1 - 1	Humphreys 44	12	7
13	**FAC3Q**	**A**	**Bedfont Sports**	**237**	**W 2 - 0**	**Chatting 28 Finneran 45**		8
24	**FAC4Q**	**H**	**Cray Wanderers**	**400**	**W 3 - 2**	**Kouassi 2 20 Hubble 22**		9
27	IsthN	A	Basildon United	197	D 3 - 3	Joseph 23 Hubble 62 73 (pens)	15	10
Nov 7	**FAC1P**	**A**	**Banbury United**		**W 2 - 1**	**Hubble 23 Ronto 71**		11
30	**FAC2P**	**H**	**Boreham Wood**		**L 0 - 3**			12

Goalscorers	LGE	FAC	FAT	SG	HAT	PEN	1Q	2Q	45+	3Q	4Q	90+	T
TOTALS	8	13	0		0	2	7	7	1	2	4	0	21
Hubble	2	4		5		2	2	2		1	1		6
Ronto	1	3		4			1	1		1	1		4
Joseph	2	1		3				2			1		3
Kouassi	1	2		2			3						3
Chatting	1	1		2				1			1		2
Finneran		1		1					1				1
Humphreys	1			1				1					1
Opponent		1		1			1						1

COGGESHALL TOWN MATCH RESULTS 2020-21

Date	Comp	H/A	Opponents	Att:	Result	Goalscorers	Pos	No.
Sept 12	**FACP**	**H**	**Tilbury**	**171**	**W 2 - 0**	**Nwachuku 39 Simmons 81**		1
19	IsthN	A	AFC Sudbury	342	L 1 - 2	Nwachuku 69	15	2
22	**FAC1Q**	**H**	**Stansted**	**170**	**L 0 - 1**			3
26	IsthN	H	Heybridge Swifts	151	W 2 - 0	Baker 36 Price 86	5	4
Oct 3	IsthN	A	Felixstowe & Walton United	391	D 2 - 2	Coley 25 Price 45	9	5
10	IsthN	H	Cambridge City	110	L 0 - 1		17	6
17	**FAT2Q**	**A**	**Bedfont Sports**	**92**	**D 0 - 0**	**(Won 6-5 on pens)**		7
24	IsthN	A	Dereham Town	280	D 1 - 1	Price 23	16	8
27	IsthN	H	Aveley	126	W 1 - 0	Claridge 36	9	9

Goalscorers	LGE	FAC	FAT	SG	HAT	PEN	1Q	2Q	45+	3Q	4Q	90+	T
TOTALS	7	2	0		0	0	0	5	1	0	3	0	9
Price	3			3				1	1		1		3
Nwachuku	1	1		1				1			1		2
Baker	1			1				1					1
Claridge	1			1				1					1
Coley	1			1				1					1
Simmons		1		1							1		1

DEREHAM TOWN MATCH RESULTS 2020-21

Date	Comp	H/A	Opponents	Att:	Result	Goalscorers	Pos	No.
Sept 12	**FACP**	**H**	**Whitton United**	**171**	**W 3 - 2**	**Hillard 19 80 Crisp 37**		1
19	IsthN	A	Aveley	303	L 2 - 3	Hilliard 26 Crisp 83	14	2
22	**FAC1Q**	**H**	**Canvey Island**	**234**	**L 0 - 2**			3
26	IsthN	A	Tilbury	205	L 0 - 2		18	4
29	IsthN	H	Cambridge City	195	W 1 - 0	Johnson 32	11	5
Oct 3	IsthN	A	Heybridge Swifts	201	W 3 - 0	Norman 24 (og) Nkosi 26 (og) Hipperson 81	4	6
6	IsthN	H	Histon	202	D 0 - 0		1	7
10	IsthN	A	Bury Town	400	L 0 - 1		5	8
17	**FAT2Q**	**A**	**Sutton Coldfield Town**	**283**	**W 3 - 2**	**Hillard 25 Lay 49 Logan 90 (pen)**		9
24	IsthN	H	Coggeshall Town	280	D 1 - 1	Logan 53 (pen)	6	10
31	**FAT3Q**	**A**	**Mickleover**	**203**	**L 0 - 5**			11

Goalscorers	LGE	FAC	FAT	SG	HAT	PEN	1Q	2Q	45+	3Q	4Q	90+	T
TOTALS	7	3	3		0	2	1	6	0	2	3	1	13
Hilliard	1	2	1	3			1	2			1		4
Crisp	1	1		2				1			1		2
Logan	1		1	2		2				1		1	2
Opponent	2			1				2					2
Hipperson	1			1							1		1
Johnson	1			1				1					1
Lay			1	1						1			1

FELIXSTOWE & WALTON UNITED MATCH RESULTS 2020-21

Date	Comp	H/A	Opponents	Att:	Result	Goalscorers	Pos	No.
Sept 13	**FACP**	**A**	**Hashtag United**	**300**	**D 1 - 1**	**Barley 82 (Lost 12-13 on pens)**		1
19	IsthN	A	Great Wakering Rovers	132	D 0 - 0		11	2
26	**FAT1Q**	**H**	**Great Wakering Rovers**	**202**	**W 2 - 1**	**Canfer 58 69**		3
29	IsthN	H	AFC Sudbury	332	W 3 - 2	Canfer 28 Ottely-Gooch 65 Kerridge 90	4	4
Oct 3	IsthN	H	Coggeshall Town	391	D 2 - 2	Howell 27 Bennett 90 (pen)	6	5
10	IsthN	A	Maldon & Tiptree	224	L 0 - 3		14	6
17	**FAT2Q**	**H**	**Westfield**	**266**	**W 5 - 0**	**Nunn 47 78 Ainsley 56 Canfer 62 Bennett 88**		7
24	IsthN	H	Hullbridge Sports	393	W 2 - 0	Powell 82 Canfer 90	7	8
31	**FAT3Q**	**H**	**Metropolitan Police**	**322**	**W 3 - 1**	**Nunn 14 74 Barley 80**		9
Dec 8	**FAT1P**	**A**	**Leatherhead**	**223**	**W 1 - 0**	**Nunn 55**		10
12	**FAT2P**	**A**	**Basford United**	**247**	**L 0 - 3**			11

Goalscorers	LGE	FAC	FAT	SG	HAT	PEN	1Q	2Q	45+	3Q	4Q	90+	T
TOTALS	7	1	11		0	1	1	2	0	6	7	3	19
Canfer	2		3	4				1		2	1	1	5
Nunn			5	3			1			2	2		5
Barley		1	1	2							2		2
Bennett	1		1	2		1					1	1	2
Ainsley			1	1						1			1
Howell	1			1				1					1
Kerridge	1			1								1	1
Ottely-Gooch	1			1						1			1
Powell	1			1							1		1

GRAYS ATHLETIC MATCH RESULTS 2020-21

Date	Comp	H/A	Opponents	Att:	Result	Goalscorers	Pos	No.
Sept 12	**FACP**	**H**	**Witham Town**	**223**	**W 1 - 0**	**Okay 90+2 (og)**		1
19	IsthN	A	Brentwood Town	302	W 2 - 0	Stokes 78 Omolabi 90	2	2
23	**FAC1Q**	**H**	**Potton United**	**271**	**W 3 - 1**	**Melaugh Stokes 54 Omolabi 81**		3
26	IsthN	H	Canvey Island	336	L 0 - 4		9	4
Oct 3	**FAC2Q**	**A**	**Maldon & Tiptree**	**251**	**D 2 - 2**	**Hahn 57 Paxman 90+1 (Lost 4-5 on pens)**		5
6	IsthN	A	Tilbury	367	W 1 - 0	Agunbiade 21	6	6
10	IsthN	H	Romford	368	D 1 - 1	Agunbiade 45	7	7
17	**FAT2Q**	**A**	**Maldon & Tiptree**	**319**	**L 1 - 4**	**Hahn 90**		8
24	IsthN	H	Soham Town Rangers	168	W 1 - 0	Watson 37	9	9
28	IsthN	H	Great Wakering Rovers	286	W 1 - 0	Chukwu 44	5	10

Goalscorers	LGE	FAC	FAT	SG	HAT	PEN	1Q	2Q	45+	3Q	4Q	90+	T
TOTALS	6	6	1		0	0	1	3	1	2	3	3	13
Agunbiade	2			2			1		1				2
Hahn		1	1	2						1		1	2
Omolabi	1	1		2							2		2
Stokes	1	1		2						1	1		2
Chukwu	1			1				1					1
Melaugh		1		1				1					1
Opponent		1		1								1	1
Paxman		1		1								1	1
Watson	1			1				1					1

GREAT WAKERING ROVERS MATCH RESULTS 2020-21

Date	Comp	H/A	Opponents	Att:	Result	Goalscorers	Pos	No.
Sept 12	**FACP**	**H**	**Brantham Athletic**	**125**	**L 0 - 1**			1
19	IsthN	H	Felixstowe & Walton United	132	D 0 - 0		12	2
26	**FAT1Q**	**A**	**Felixstowe & Walton United**	**202**	**L 1 - 2**	**Tuohy 82**		3
Oct 3	IsthN	H	Romford	171	W 3 - 0	Pitty 45 Hernandez 56 Sotoyinbo 82	8	4
6	IsthN	H	Basildon United	119	L 0 - 6		13	5
10	IsthN	A	Witham Town	110	W 2 - 0	Hernandez 75 Tuohy 87	6	6
13	IsthN	A	Tilbury	161	D 3 - 3	Harris 44 Odukoya 68 Barton 74 (og)	3	7
24	IsthN	H	Histon	159	L 3 - 4	Apenteng 6 77 Brown 49 (og)	8	8
28	IsthN	A	Grays Athletic	286	L 0 - 1		13	9

Goalscorers	LGE	FAC	FAT	SG	HAT	PEN	1Q	2Q	45+	3Q	4Q	90+	T
TOTALS	11	0	1		0	0	1	1	1	2	7	0	12
Apenteng	2			1			1				1		2
Hernandez	2			2						1	1		2
Opponent	2			2						1	1		2
Tuohy	1		1	2							2		2
Harris	1			1				1					1
Odukoya	1			1							1		1
Pitty	1			1					1				1
Sotoyinbo	1			1							1		1

HEYBRIDGE SWIFTS MATCH RESULTS 2020-21

Date	Comp	H/A	Opponents	Att:	Result	Goalscorers	Pos	No.
Sept 12	**FACP**	**A**	**Barking**	**129**	**L 0 - 2**			1
19	IsthN	H	Histon	247	L 1 - 2	Gregan 58	16	2
26	IsthN	A	Coggeshall Town	151	L 0 - 2		19	3
Oct 3	IsthN	H	Dereham Town	201	L 0 - 3		19	4
6	IsthN	H	Hullbridge Sports	175	W 5 - 0	Humphrey 6 Craddock 6 Adlington-Pile 45 Okoh 49 Fennell 68	17	5
10	IsthN	A	Soham Town Rangers	136	L 0 - 1		19	6
17	**FAT2Q**	**A**	**Northwood**	**151**	**D 3 - 3**	**Osei-Owusu 26 Fennell 28 41**		7
24	IsthN	H	Basildon United	278	W 2 - 0	Fennell 17 Nkosi 89	12	8
27	IsthN	A	Witham Town	259	W 1 - 0	Fennell 20	7	9
31	**FAT3Q**	**A**	**Biggleswade Town**		**L 0 - 1**			10
Nov 4	IsthN	A	AFC Sudbury	252	D 1 - 1	Debell 90	5	11

Goalscorers	LGE	FAC	FAT	SG	HAT	PEN	1Q	2Q	45+	3Q	4Q	90+	T
TOTALS	10	0	3		0	0	4	3	1	2	2	1	13
Fennell	3		2	4			2	2			1		5
Adlington-Pile	1			1					1				1
Craddock	1			1			1						1
Debell	1			1								1	1
Gregan	1			1						1			1
Humphrey	1			1			1						1
Nkosi	1			1							1		1
Okoh	1			1						1			1
Osei-Owusu			1	1				1					1

HISTON MATCH RESULTS 2020-21

Date	Comp	H/A	Opponents	Att:	Result	Goalscorers	Pos	No.
Sept 12	**FACP**	**A**	**Biggleswade**	**71**	**L 0 - 1**			1
19	IsthN	A	Heybridge Swifts	247	W 2 - 1	Harradine 32 42	5	2
29	IsthN	H	Soham Town Rangers	292	L 1 - 2	Rolph 47	10	3
Oct 3	IsthN	A	Witham Town	82	W 2 - 1	Rolph 5 Lewis 90	5	4
6	IsthN	A	Dereham Town	202	D 0 - 0		2	5
Oct 17	**FAT2Q**	**H**	**Leek Town**	**226**	**L 1 - 2**	**Gould 7**		6
24	IsthN	A	Great Waking Rovers	159	W 4 - 3	Gould 29 Dawkin 35 47 Rolph 77	2	7
27	IsthN	H	Romford	172	L 1 - 2	Lewis 57	3	8

Goalscorers	LGE	FAC	FAT	SG	HAT	PEN	1Q	2Q	45+	3Q	4Q	90+	T
TOTALS	10	0	1		0	0	2	4	0	3	1	1	11
Rolph	3			3			1			1	1		3
Dawkins	2			1				1		1			2
Gould	1		1	2			1	1					2
Harradine	2			1				2					2
Lewis	2			2						1		1	2

HULLBRIDGE SPORTS MATCH RESULTS 2020-21

Date	Comp	H/A	Opponents	Att:	Result	Goalscorers	Pos	No.
Sept 1	**FACEP**	**H**	**Hadley**		**L 0 - 2**			1
19	IsthN	A	Witham Town	119	W 7 - 0	Simon-Parson 3 (og) Fitzer 35 90 Okunja 50 Scarborough 55 Watson 80 86	1	2
26	**FAT1Q**	**H**	**Ashford Town (Mx)**		**L 0 - 1**			3
Oct 3	IsthN	A	AFC Sudbury	247	W 3 - 0	Cocklin 22 Watson 75 Wright 85	1	4
6	IsthN	A	Heybridge Swifts	175	L 0 - 5		3	5
10	IsthN	H	Tilbury	230	L 1 - 2	Scarborough 47	8	6
24	IsthN	A	Felixstowe & Walton United	393	L 0 - 2		10	7

Goalscorers	LGE	FAC	FAT	SG	HAT	PEN	1Q	2Q	45+	3Q	4Q	90+	T
TOTALS	11	0	0		0	0	2	1	0	3	5	0	11
Watson	3			2							3		3
Fitzer	2			1				1			1		2
Scarborough	2			1						2			2
Cocklin	1			1			1						1
Okunja	1			1						1			1
Opponent	1			1			1						1
Wright	1			1							1		1

MALDON & TIPTREE MATCH RESULTS 2020-21

Date	Comp	H/A	Opponents	Att:	Result	Goalscorers	Pos	No.
Sept 12	**FACP**	**H**	**Hertford Town**	**230**	**W 1 - 0**	**William-Bushell 60**		1
19	IsthN	A	Soham Town Rangers	146	D 1 - 1	Barnwell 54	8	2
22	**FAC1Q**	**A**	**Haverhill Rovers**	**298**	**W 3 - 0**	**William-Bushell 45 Cracknell 50 Kemp 64**		3
26	IsthN	H	Brentwood Town	173	D 1 - 1	Stokes 51	10	4
Oct 3	**FAC2Q**	**H**	**Grays Athletic**	**251**	**D 2 - 2**	**Vyse 52 OG 86 (Won 5-4 on pens)**		5
6	IsthN	A	Canvey Island	313	W 1 - 0	Vyse 59	8	6
10	IsthN	H	Felixstowe & Walton United	224	W 3 - 0	Vyse 13 64 67 (pen)	2	7
13	**FAC3Q**	**A**	**Braintree Town**		**W 1 - 0**	**Hasanally 75**		8
17	**FAT2Q**	**H**	**Grays Athletic**	**319**	**W 4 - 1**	**Vyse 18 (pen) William-Bushall 43 Hasanally 44 Kaid 82**		9
24	**FAC4Q**	**H**	**Haringey Borough**	**382**	**W 1 - 0**	**Barnwell 88 (pen)**		10
27	IsthN	H	Tilbury	286	W 3 - 1	Barnwell 7 William-Bushall 14 Kemp 28	2	11
31	**FAT3Q**	**H**	**Kingstonian**	**256**	**W 3 - 2**	**Barnwell 17 29 Kaid 71**		12
Nov 8	**FAC1P**	**H**	**Morecambe**		**L 0 - 1**			13
Dec 9	**FAT1P**	**A**	**Enfield Town**	**335**	**D 2 - 2**	**Barnwell 77 Kaid 90 (Won 4-3 on pens)**		14
15	**FAT2P**	**H**	**Bognor Regis Town**	**184**	**W 2 - 1**	**Cracknell 61 Barnwell 90+3**		15

Goalscorers	LGE	FAC	FAT	SG	HAT	PEN	1Q	2Q	45+	3Q	4Q	90+	T
TOTALS	9	8	11		1	3	5	4	1	10	6	2	28
Barnwell	2	1	4	6		1	2	1		1	2	1	7
Vyse	4	1	1	4	1	2	2			4			6
William-Bushell	1	2	1	4			1	1	1	1			4
Kaid			3	3							2	1	3
Cracknell		1	1	2						2			2
Hasanally		1	1	2			1				1		2
Kemp	1	1		2			1			1			2
Opponent		1		1							1		1
Stokes	1			1						1			1

ROMFORD MATCH RESULTS 2020-21

Date	Comp	H/A	Opponents	Att:	Result	Goalscorers	Pos	No.
Sept 1	**FACEP**	**A**	**Sawbridgeworth Town**		**L 1 - 2**	**Toussaint 67**		1
19	IsthN	A	Canvey Island	336	D 0 - 0		13	2
26	IsthN	H	Aveley	202	L 0 - 1		14	3
30	IsthN	H	Basildon United	183	**W** 1 - 0	Graham 87	6	4
Oct 3	IsthN	A	Great Wakering Rovers	171	L 0 - 3		11	5
7	IsthN	H	Witham Town	167	L 1 - 2	May 58	14	6
10	IsthN	A	Grays Athletic	368	D 1 - 1	Newton 16	15	7
17	**FAT2Q**	**A**	**Tooting & Mitcham United**	**400**	**L 0 - 2**			8
27	IsthN	A	Histon	172	**W** 2 - 1	Abnett 55 Graham 58	14	9

Goalscorers	LGE	FAC	FAT	SG	HAT	PEN	1Q	2Q	45+	3Q	4Q	90+	T
TOTALS	5	1	0		0	0	1	0	0	4	1	0	6
Graham	2			2						1	1		2
May	1			1						1			1
Abnett	1			1						1			1
Newton	1			1			1						1
Toussaint		1		1						1			1

SOHAM TOWN RANGERS MATCH RESULTS 2020-21

Date	Comp	H/A	Opponents	Att:	Result	Goalscorers	Pos	No.
Sept 12	**FACP**	**H**	**St Neots Town**	**203**	**W 3 - 2**	**Walter 4 Andrews T 48 Mulready 80**		1
19	IsthN	H	Maldon & Tiptree	146	D 1 - 1	Watson 61	9	2
21	**FAC1Q**	**A**	**Hashtag United**	**300**	**D 1 - 1**	**Rogers 35 (Lost 2-4 pens)**		3
26	**FAT1Q**	**H**	**Corby Town**	**131**	**L 0 - 3**			4
29	IsthN	A	Histon	292	**W** 2 - 1	Andrews T 11 35	5	5
Oct 7	IsthN	A	Cambridge City	306	L 1 - 2	Kelly 15	11	6
10	IsthN	H	Heybridge Swifts	136	**W** 1 - 0	Andrews T 53	4	7
24	IsthN	H	Grays Athletic	168	**W** 1 - 0	Watson 37	3	8
27	IsthN	A	AFC Sudbury	191	L 0 - 1		4	9
31	IsthN	A	Tilbury	210	L 1 - 2	Carden 38	6	10

Goalscorers	LGE	FAC	FAT	SG	HAT	PEN	1Q	2Q	45+	3Q	4Q	90+	T
TOTALS	7	4	0		0	0	3	4	0	3	1	0	11
Andrews T	3	1		3			1	1		2			4
Watson	2			2				1		1			2
Carden	1			1				1					1
Kelly	1			1			1						1
Mulready		1		1							1		1
Rogers		1		1				1					1
Walter		1		1			1						1

TILBURY MATCH RESULTS 2020-21

Date	Comp	H/A	Opponents	Att:	Result	Goalscorers	Pos	No.
Sept 12	**FACP**	**A**	**Coggeshall Town**	**171**	**L 0 - 2**			1
19	IsthN	A	Cambridge City	250	**W** 1 - 0	Moses 14	7	2
26	IsthN	H	Dereham Town	205	**W** 2 - 0	Moses 36 Agyakwa 49	1	3
Oct 6	IsthN	H	Grays Athletic	367	L 0 - 1		4	4
10	IsthN	A	Hullbridge Sports	230	**W** 2 - 1	Scarborough 20 (og) Noble 45	1	5
13	IsthN	H	Great Wakering Rovers	161	D 3 - 3	Smith L 17 Ogunwamide 82 84	1	6
17	**FAT2Q**	**A**	**Aylesbury United**	**197**	**D 2 - 2**	**Brodie 4 Moses 84 (Lost 2-4 on pens)**		7
19	IsthN	A	Aveley	397	**W** 3 - 0	Stokes T 21 Moses 82 (pen) Brodie 86	1	8
27	IsthN	A	Maldon & Tiptree	286	L 1 - 3	Stokes M 25 (og)	1	9
31	IsthN	H	Soham Town Rangers	210	**W** 2 - 1	Moses 45 (pen) Burns 90	1	10

Goalscorers	LGE	FAC	FAT	SG	HAT	PEN	1Q	2Q	45+	3Q	4Q	90+	T
TOTALS	14	0	2		0	2	5	2	2	1	5	1	16
Moses	4		1	5		2	1	1	1		2		5
Brodie	1		1	2			1				1		2
Ogunwamide	2			1							2		2
Opponent	2			2			1	1					2
Agyakwa	1			1						1			1
Burns	1			1								1	1
Noble	1			1					1				1
Smith L	1			1			1						1
Stokes	1			1			1						1

WITHAM TOWN MATCH RESULTS 2020-21

Date	Comp	H/A	Opponents	Att:	Result	Goalscorers	Pos	No.
Sept 12	**FACP**	**A**	**Grays Athletic**	**223**	**L 0 - 1**			1
19	IsthN	H	Hullbridge Sports	119	L 0 - 7		20	2
26	**FAT1Q**	**H**	**Hanwell Town**	**104**	**L 0 - 2**			3
29	IsthN	A	Bury Town	400	L 0 - 5		20	4
Oct 3	IsthN	H	Histon	82	L 1 - 2	Akpele 57	20	5
7	IsthN	A	Romford	167	**W** 2 - 1	Simon-Parson 39 Akpele 44	20	6
10	IsthN	H	Great Wakering Rovers	110	L 0 - 2		20	7
24	IsthN	A	Aveley	318	L 2 - 4	Adeniji 29 Akpele 85	20	8
27	IsthN	H	Heybridge Swifts	259	L 0 - 1		20	9
31	IsthN	A	AFC Sudbury	226	L 2 - 5	Willis 77 Simon-Parson 79	20	10

Goalscorers	LGE	FAC	FAT	SG	HAT	PEN	1Q	2Q	45+	3Q	4Q	90+	T
TOTALS	7	0	0		0	0	0	3	0	1	3	0	7
Akpele	3			3				1		1	1		3
Simon-Parson	2			2				1			1		2
Adeniji	1			1				1					1
Willis	1			1							1		1

ASHFORD TOWN (MIDDX) MATCH RESULTS 2020-21

Date	Comp	H/A	Opponents	Att:	Result	Goalscorers	Pos	No.
Sept 12	**FACP**	**A**	**Southall**	**130**	**L 1 - 2**	**Pearce 14 (og)**		1
19	IsthSC	A	Chalfont St Peter	82	W 1 - 0	Humphreys 57	7	2
26	**FAT1Q**	**A**	**Hullbridge Sports**		**W 1 - 0**	**Duff 90**		3
29	IsthSC	H	Tooting & Mitcham United	153	L 0 - 2		11	4
Oct 6	IsthSC	A	Uxbridge	94	D 0 - 0		9	5
10	IsthSC	H	South Park	123	W 3 - 1	Duff 3 87 Bunyan 60	6	6
13	IsthSC	A	Northwood	120	W 2 - 0	Duff 45 Humphreys 70	3	7
17	**FAT2Q**	**H**	**Whitstable Town**	**163**	**W 1 - 0**	**Bunyan 8**		8
24	IsthSC	A	Harlow Town	230	W 2 - 1	French 2 Sweeney 87	2	9
27	IsthSC	H	Chertsey Town	400	L 0 - 3			10
31	**FAT3Q**	**A**	**Hastings United**	**400**	**D 1 - 1**	**Bunyan 63 (Lost 2-4 on pens)**		11
Nov 3	IsthSC	A	Barking	101	L 0 - 1		8	12

Goalscorers	LGE	FAC	FAT	SG	HAT	PEN	1Q	2Q	45+	3Q	4Q	90+	T
TOTALS	8	1	3		0	0	4	0	1	3	3	1	12
Duff	3		1	3			1		1		1	1	4
Bunyan	1		2	3			1			2			3
Humphreys	2			2						1	1		2
French	1			1			1						1
Opponent		1		1			1						1
Sweeney	1			1							1		1

BARKING MATCH RESULTS 2020-21

Date	Comp	H/A	Opponents	Att:	Result	Goalscorers	Pos	No.
Sept 12	**FACP**	**H**	**Heybridge Swifts**	**129**	**W 2 - 0**	**Fallah 28 59**		1
19	IsthSC	H	Marlow	79	D 2 - 2	Moore 72 Dadson 80	10	2
22	**FAC1Q**	**H**	**Dunstable Town**	**105**	**W 6 - 1**	**Dadson 7 47 49 Douglas 29 (og) GB-Dumaka 41 Anderson 89**		3
26	**FAT1Q**	**A**	**AFC Sudbury**	**178**	**W 2 - 1**	**Dadson 28 31**		4
Oct 3	**FAC2Q**	**H**	**Kings Langley**	**197**	**D 2 - 2**	**Dadson 9 Dixon 74 (Won 3-2 on pens)**		5
6	IsthSC	A	Chalfont St Peter	87	L 0 - 2		18	6
10	IsthSC	H	FC Romania	87	L 1 - 2	Green 8	20	7
13	**FAC3Q**	**A**	**Hartley Wintney**	**391**	**L 1 - 5**	**Westendorf 19**		8
17	**FAT2Q**	**H**	**Harlow Town**	**107**	**W 1 - 0**	**GB-Dumaka 86**		9
20	IsthSC	A	Ware	152	L 1 - 3	Luke 37	20	10
24	IsthSC	A	Westfield	188	W 1 - 0	Westendorf 72	17	11
27	IsthSC	H	Waltham Abbey	103	W 3 - 0	Sheehan-Cozens 16 Tweed 20 Luke 61		12
31	**FAT3Q**	**H**	**Sittingbourne**	**158**	**D 1 - 1**	**Westendorf 14 (Won 4-3 on pens)**		13
Nov 3	IsthSC	H	Ashford Town (Mx)	101	W 1 - 0	GB-Dumaka 89	12	14
Dec 8	**FAT1P**	**A**	**Carshalton Athletic**	**396**	**L 0 - 3**			15

Goalscorers	LGE	FAC	FAT	SG	HAT	PEN	1Q	2Q	45+	3Q	4Q	90+	T
TOTALS	9	11	4		1	0	7	6	0	4	7	0	24
Dadson	1	4	2	4	1		2	2		2	1		7
GB-Dumaka	1	1	1	3				1			2		3
Westendorf	1	1	1	3			2				1		3
Fallah		2		1				1		1			2
Luke	2			2				1		1			2
Anderson		1		1							1		1
Dixon		1		1							1		1
Green	1			1			1						1
Moore	1			1							1		1
Opponent		1		1				1					1
Sheehan-Cozens	1			1			1						1
Tweed	1			1			1						1

BEDFONT SPORTS MATCH RESULTS 2020-21

Date	Comp	H/A	Opponents	Att:	Result	Goalscorers	Pos	No.
Sept 12	**FACP**	**H**	**Hassocks**	**71**	**W 3 - 1**	**Esprit 3 56 (pen) Sanders 75**		1
19	IsthSC	A	Hanwell Town	198	L 0 - 1		14	2
22	**FAC1Q**	**H**	**Lewes**	**113**	**W 3 - 1**	**Diomande 6 Edwards 54 Postance 90**		3
26	IsthSC	H	Ware	67	L 2 - 3	Sanders 22 (pen) 48	16	4
Oct 3	**FAC2Q**	**H**	**Carshalton Athletic**	**174**	**W 2 - 0**	**Edwards 63 78**		5
10	IsthSC	A	Chipstead	159	W 5 - 0	Sandars 15 43 90 Postance 42 Edwards 73	13	6
13	**FAC3Q**	**H**	**Canvey Island**	**237**	**L 0 - 2**			7
17	**FAT2Q**	**H**	**Coggeshall Town**	**92**	**D 0 - 0**	**(Lost 5-6 on pens)**		8
20	IsthSC	H	Chalfont St Peter	91	W 2 - 1	Opoku-Boateng 31 Weight 60	12	9
24	IsthSC	H	Marlow	121	W 1 - 0	Kinsella 33	9	10
27	IsthSC	A	Tooting & Mitcham United	331	L 0 - 3			11

Goalscorers	LGE	FAC	FAT	SG	HAT	PEN	1Q	2Q	45+	3Q	4Q	90+	T
TOTALS	10	8	0		1	2	5	3	0	6	2	2	18
Sanders	5	1		3	1	1	2	1		1	1	1	6
Edwards	1	3		3						3	1		4
Esprit		2		1		1	1			1			2
Postance	1	1		2				1				1	2
Diomande		1		1			1						1

Goalscorers	LGE	FAC	FAT	SG	HAT	PEN	1Q	2Q	45+	3Q	4Q	90+	T
Kinsella	1			1				1					1
Opoku-Boateng	1			1			1						1
Weight	1			1						1			1

BRACKNELL TOWN MATCH RESULTS 2020-21

Date	Comp	H/A	Opponents	Att:	Result	Goalscorers	Pos	No.
Sept 12	**FACP**	**A**	**Badshot Lea**	**257**	**W 2 - 0**	**Platt 60 Coles 82**		1
19	IsthSC	H	Chipstead	226	W 2 - 0	Herbert 44 Soares 83	2	2
22	**FAC1Q**	**A**	**Ashford United**	**243**	**W 4 - 1**	**Bowerman 11 66 (pen) Herbert 20 90**		3
26	IsthSC	A	Uxbridge	130	D 2 - 2	Bowerman 21 Genovesi 43	2	4
Oct 3	**FAC2Q**	**H**	**Marlow**	**389**	**D 2 - 2**	**Bowerman 18 52 (Won 4-3 on pens)**		5
6	IsthSC	A	Chertsey Town	400	W 2 - 1	Bowerman 2 Bayliss 88	1	6
10	IsthSC	H	Chalfont St Peter	382	W 4 - 0	Platt 10 Grant 32 Bowerman 39 Bayliss 74	1	7
13	**FAC3Q**	**A**	**Haringey Borough**	**347**	**L 1 - 5**	**Knight 54**		8
17	**FAT2Q**	**H**	**Sevenoaks Town**	**204**	**W 2 - 0**	**Bowerman 52 (pen) Ishmael 77**		9
25	IsthSC	A	FC Romania	160	W 4 - 2	Bayliss 3 Bowerman 41 77 Grant 67	2	10
Dec 8	**FAT1P**	**A**	**Salisbury**	**402**	**W 1 - 0**	**Rees 17**		11
15	**FAT2P**	**H**	**Havant & Waterlooville**	**324**	**L 2 - 3**	**Bowerman 32 90+6 (pen)**		12

Goalscorers	LGE	FAC	FAT	SG	HAT	PEN	1Q	2Q	45+	3Q	4Q	90+	T
TOTALS	14	9	5		0	3	8	6	0	6	6	2	28
Bowerman	5	4	3	8		3	4	3		3	1	1	12
Bayliss	3			3			1				2		3
Herbert	1	2		2			1	1				1	3
Grant	2			2				1		1			2
Platt	1	1		2			1			1			2

Goalscorers	LGE	FAC	FAT	SG	HAT	PEN	1Q	2Q	45+	3Q	4Q	90+	T
Coles		1		1							1		1
Genovesi	1			1				1					1
Ishmael			1	1							1		1
Knight		1		1						1			1
Rees			1	1			1						1
Soares	1			1							1		1

CHALFONT ST PETER MATCH RESULTS 2020-21

Date	Comp	H/A	Opponents	Att:	Result	Goalscorers	Pos	No.
Sept 12	**FACP**	**A**	**Oxhey Jets**	**148**	**W 1 - 0**	**Ibie 90**		1
19	IsthSC	H	Ashford Town (Mx)	82	L 0 - 1		15	2
22	**FAC1Q**	**H**	**Farnborough**	**178**	**L 2 - 3**	**Boxer 3 Ibie 11**		3
26	**FAT1Q**	**A**	**Hythe Town**	**178**	**L 0 - 3**			4
Oct 3	IsthSC	H	Ware	110	L 0 - 1		17	5
6	IsthSC	H	Barking	87	W 2 - 0	Hunt 49 Ibie 84	11	6
10	IsthSC	A	Bracknell Town	382	L 0 - 4		17	7
20	IsthSC	A	Bedfont Sports	91	L 1 - 2	Ibie 36 (pen)	19	8
24	IsthSC	H	Hanwell Town	157	W 1 - 0	James 89 (pen)	14	9
27	IsthSC	A	Hertford Town	212	L 1 - 2	Kalu 88		10
31	IsthSC	A	Harlow Town	158	W 1 - 0	Cathline 79	14	11

Goalscorers	LGE	FAC	FAT	SG	HAT	PEN	1Q	2Q	45+	3Q	4Q	90+	T
TOTALS	6	3	0		0	2	2	1	0	1	4	1	9
Ibie	2	2		4		1	1	1			1	1	4
Boxer		1		1			1						1
Cathline	1			1							1		1
Hunt	1			1						1			1
James	1			1		1					1		1
Kalu	1			1							1		1

CHERTSEY TOWN MATCH RESULTS 2020-21

Date	Comp	H/A	Opponents	Att:	Result	Goalscorers	Pos	No.
Sept 12	**FACP**	**H**	**Abbey Rangers**	**400**	**W 2 - 0**	**Duffy 71 (pen) Baxter 90**		1
19	IsthSC	H	Uxbridge	353	W 1 - 0	Baxter 81	8	2
22	**FAC1Q**	**H**	**Leatherhead**	**400**	**D 0 - 0**	**(Won 5-4 on pens)**		3
Oct 3	**FAC2Q**	**A**	**Haringey Borough**	**266**	**L 0 - 2**			4
6	IsthSC	H	Bracknell Town	400	L 1 - 2	MacLaren	12	5
10	IsthSC	A	Northwood	218	W 3 - 1	Baxter 33 Abosogun 53 MacLaren 81	7	6
13	IsthSC	A	South Park	106	D 2 - 2	Baxter 42 Duffy 90	8	7
17	**FAT2Q**	**H**	**Berkhamsted**	**340**	**L 1 - 2**	**Day 56**		8
20	IsthSC	H	Marlow	378	L 0 - 3		11	9
24	IsthSC	H	Hertford Town	400	W 4 - 1	Baxter 16 82 Abisogun 32 Day 69	6	10
27	IsthSC	A	Ashford Town (Mx)	400	W 3 - 0	Baxter 30 34 85		11

Goalscorers	LGE	FAC	FAT	SG	HAT	PEN	1Q	2Q	45+	3Q	4Q	90+	T
TOTALS	14	2	1		1	1	1	5	0	2	6	2	17
Baxter	8	1		6	1		1	4			3	1	9
Abosogun	2			2				1		1			2
Day	1		1	2						1	1		2
Duffy	1	1		2		1					1	1	2
MacLaren	2			2							1		2

CHIPSTEAD MATCH RESULTS 2020-21

Date	Comp	H/A	Opponents	Att:	Result	Goalscorers	Pos	No.
Sept 12	**FACP**	**A**	**Ramsgate**	**400**	**W 3 - 0**	**Cripps 45 Beadle 58 Bell 60**		1
19	IsthSC	A	Bracknell Town	226	L 0 - 2		17	2
22	**FAC1Q**	**H**	**Deal Town**	**157**	**D 1 - 1**	**McAllister 87 (Won 4-2 on pens)**		3
26	IsthSC	H	Westfield	99	L 1 - 4	Collins 50	20	4
Oct 3	**FAC2Q**	**H**	**East Grinstead Town**	**277**	**W 1 - 0**	**Collins 34**		5
6	IsthSC	A	Harlow Town	156	W 3 - 2	Beadle 2 Collins 6 74	16	6
10	IsthSC	H	Bedfont Sports	159	L 0 - 5		19	7
13	**FAC3Q**	**A**	**Hayes & Yeading United**	**369**	**D 0 - 0**	**(Lost 2-4 on pens)**		8
17	**FAT2Q**	**H**	**Three Bridges**	**132**	**L 1 - 2**	**Membrillera 32**		9
20	IsthSC	A	Waltham Abbey	121	D 1 - 1	Dickson 60	16	10
24	IsthSC	A	Uxbridge	82	W 3 - 1	Boulter 14 Dickson 60 Membrillera 90	13	11
27	IsthSC	H	South Park	105	W 3 - 1	Grant 19 Splatt 45 Moody 69 (pen)		12
31	IsthSC	H	Hanwell Town	137	L 1 - 3	Grant 17	12	13

Goalscorers	LGE	FAC	FAT	SG	HAT	PEN	1Q	2Q	45+	3Q	4Q	90+	T
TOTALS	12	5	1		0	1	5	2	2	5	3	1	18
Collins	3	1		3			1	1		1	1		4
Beadle	1	1		2			1			1			2
Dickson	2			2						2			2
Grant	2			1			2						2
Membrillera	1		1	2				1				1	2
Bell		1		1						1			1
Boulter	1			1			1						1
Cripps		1		1					1				1
McAllister		1		1							1		1
Moody	1			1		1					1		1
Splatt	1			1					1				1

FC ROMANIA MATCH RESULTS 2020-21

Date	Comp	H/A	Opponents	Att:	Result	Goalscorers	Pos	No.
Sept 12	**FACP**	**H**	**Brentwood Town**	**78**	**L 0 - 1**			1
19	IsthSC	A	Harlow Town	177	L 0 - 2		18	2
29	IsthSC	A	Northwood	131	L 0 - 1		19	3
Oct 7	IsthSC	H	Tooting & Mitcham United	86	L 0 - 1		20	4
10	IsthSC	A	Barking	87	W 2 - 1	Hurdebei 43 Filip 84	16	5
17	**FAT2Q**	**A**	**Hastings United**	**377**	**L 0 - 3**			6
25	IsthSC	H	Bracknell Town	160	L 2 - 4	Sighiartau 22 Da Silva 86	19	7
27	IsthSC	A	Hanwell Town	169	W 3 - 2	Sighiartau 10 16 Da Silva 42		8
31	IsthSC	A	Staines Town	181	L 1 - 3	Armoo 6	16	9

Goalscorers	LGE	FAC	FAT	SG	HAT	PEN	1Q	2Q	45+	3Q	4Q	90+	T
TOTALS	8	0	0		0	0	4	2	0	0	2	0	8
Sighiartau	3			2			3						3
Da Silva	2			2				1			1		2
Armoo	1			1			1						1
Filip	1			1							1		1
Hurdebei	1			1				1					1

HANWELL TOWN MATCH RESULTS 2020-21

Date	Comp	H/A	Opponents	Att:	Result		Goalscorers	Pos	No.
Sept 12	**FACP**	**H**	**Spelthorne Sports**	**175**	**W**	**4 - 1**	**Obi 34 Herring 45 72 Chendlik 89**		1
19	IsthSC	H	Bedfont Sports	198	W	1 - 0	Duncan 69	9	2
22	**FAC1Q**	**A**	**Haywards Heath Town**	**155**	**W**	**1 - 0**	**Crichlow 12**		3
26	**FAT1Q**	**A**	**Witham Town**	**104**	**W**	**2 - 0**	**Chendlik 23 (pen) Crichlow 61**		4
Oct 3	**FAC2Q**	**H**	**Hartley Wintney**	**280**	**L**	**3 - 4**	**Obi 5 19 (pen) 45**		5
6	IsthSC	A	Westfield	95	W	3 - 2	Laney 13 Obi 90 90 (pen)	4	6
10	IsthSC	H	Staines Town	283	L	2 - 4	Robinson 84 90	10	7
13	IsthSC	A	Harlow Town	128	W	3 - 0	Obi 9 20 55 (pen)	4	8
17	**FAT2Q**	**H**	**Aveley**	**201**	**D**	**1 - 1**	**Obi 69 (Lost 7-8 on pens)**		9
20	IsthSC	H	Northwood	209	D	1 - 1	Obi 45	3	10
24	IsthSC	A	Chalfont St Peter	157	L	0 - 1		7	11
27	IsthSC	H	FC Romania	169	L	2 - 3	Obi 21 Killeen 56		12
31	IsthSC	A	Chipstead	137	W	3 - 1	Robinson 47 Obi 56 Chendlik 90+3 (pen)	7	13

Goalscorers	LGE	FAC	FAT	SG	HAT	PEN	1Q	2Q	45+	3Q	4Q	90+	T
TOTALS	15	8	3		2	5	7	2	3	5	5	4	26
Obi	8	4	1	8	2	3	5	1	2	2	1	2	13
Chendlik	1	1	1	3		2		1			1	1	3
Robinson	3			2						1	1	1	3
Crichlow		1	1	2			1			1			2
Herring		2		1					1		1		2
Duncan	1			1							1		1
Killeen	1			1						1			1
Laney	1			1			1						1

HARLOW TOWN MATCH RESULTS 2020-21

Date	Comp	H/A	Opponents	Att:	Result		Goalscorers	Pos	No.
Sept 1	**FACEP**	**H**	**Enfield**	**260**	**W**	**5 - 1**	**Gyamfi 12 Alcock 50 Biler 57 Mackie 68 Taylor 88 (og)**		1
12	**FACP**	**H**	**Sporting Bengal United**	**157**	**W**	**3 - 0**	**Gyamfi 6 87 Kay 64**		2
19	IsthSC	H	FC Romania	177	W	2 - 0	Mackie 31 Gyamfi 48	3	3
22	**FAC1Q**	**H**	**Waltham Abbey**	**337**	**L**	**0 - 1**			4
Oct 3	IsthSC	A	Tooting & Mitcham United	295	L	0 - 1		7	5
6	IsthSC	H	Chipstead	156	L	2 - 3	Menga 11 Kayembe 45	10	6
10	IsthSC	A	Hertford Town	305	L	0 - 1		14	7
13	IsthSC	H	Hanwell Town	128	L	0 - 3		16	8
17	**FAT2Q**	**A**	**Barking**	**107**	**L**	**0 - 1**			9
24	IsthSC	H	Ashford Town (Mx)	230	L	1 - 2	Gyamfi 43	20	10
27	IsthSC	A	Ware	249	L	1 - 6	Phillips 87		11
31	IsthSC	H	Chalfont St Peter	158	L	0 - 1		20	12

Goalscorers	LGE	FAC	FAT	SG	HAT	PEN	1Q	2Q	45+	3Q	4Q	90+	T
TOTALS	8	6	0		0	0	3	2	1	4	4	0	14
Gyamfi	2	3		4			2	1		1	1		5
Mackie	1	1		2				1			1		2
Alcock	1			1						1			1
Biler	1			1						1			1
Kay		1		1						1			1
Kayembe	1			1					1				1
Menga	1			1			1						1
Opponent		1		1							1		1
Phillips	1			1							1		1

HERTFORD TOWN MATCH RESULTS 2020-21

Date	Comp	H/A	Opponents	Att:	Result	Goalscorers	Pos	No.
Sept 12	**FACP**	**H**	**Maldon & Tiptree**	**230**	**L 0 - 1**			1
19	IsthSC	A	Tooting & Mitcham	315	W 2 - 1	Jagdev 9 Ogbonna 28	6	2
Oct 6	IsthSC	A	Staines Town	97	L 0 - 1		13	3
10	IsthSC	H	Harlow Town	305	W 1 - 0	Faniyan 40 (pen)	8	4
13	IsthSC	H	Waltham Abbey	152	L 1 - 2	Symes 54	10	5
17	**FAT2Q**	**A**	**Faversham Town**	**212**	**L 1 - 4**	**Faniyan 8**		6
20	IsthSC	A	Westfield	101	W 3 - 1	Gymer 54 66 Ogbonna 74	7	7
24	IsthSC	A	Chertsey Town	400	L 1 - 4	Faniyan 26	10	8
27	IsthSC	H	Chalfont St Peter	212	W 2 - 1	Faniyan 4 35		9

Goalscorers	LGE	FAC	FAT	SG	HAT	PEN	1Q	2Q	45+	3Q	4Q	90+	T
TOTALS	10	0	1		0	1	3	4	0	3	1	0	11
Faniyan	4		1	3		1	2	3					5
Gymer	2			1						2			2
Ogbonna	2			2				1			1		2
Jagdev	1			1			1						1
Symes	1			1						1			1

MARLOW MATCH RESULTS 2020-21

Date	Comp	H/A	Opponents	Att:	Result	Goalscorers	Pos	No.
Sept 12	**FACP**	**H**	**North Leigh**	**201**	**W 2 - 0**	**Samuel 35 Brown 84**		1
19	IsthSC	A	Barking	79	D 2 - 2	Artwell 40 57	11	2
22	**FAC1Q**	**A**	**Frimley Green**	**300**	**D 1 - 1**	**Romeo 74 (Won 4-1 on pens)**		3
29	IsthSC	H	Staines Town	123	W 3 - 0	Clark 4 Bell 7 Rogers 37	2	4
Oct 3	**FAC2Q**	**A**	**Bracknell Town**	**389**	**D 2 - 2**	**Brown 61 (pen) Clark 72 (Lost 3-4 on pens)**		5
6	IsthSC	A	Waltham Abbey	93	L 1 - 2	Rogers 35	8	6
10	IsthSC	H	Westfield	190	D 3 - 3	Clark 8 32 72	11	7
17	**FAT2Q**	**A**	**Phoenix Sports**	**63**	**W 2 - 0**	**Romeo 31 Clark 49**		8
20	IsthSC	A	Chertsey Town	378	W 3 - 0	Clark 24 75 90	9	9
24	IsthSC	A	Bedfont Sports	121	L 0 - 1		11	10
27	IsthSC	H	Uxbridge	121	W 4 - 0	Clark 24 Samuel 33 Chapple 45 Stewart 89		11
Nov 3	**FAT3Q**	**H**	**Berkhamsted**	**230**	**W 2 - 1**	**Brown 58 Rogers 89**		12
Dec 8	**FAT1P**	**H**	**Nuneaton Borough**	**135**	**L 1 - 4**	**Clark 75 (pen)**		13

Goalscorers	LGE	FAC	FAT	SG	HAT	PEN	1Q	2Q	45+	3Q	4Q	90+	T
TOTALS	16	5	5		2	2	4	9	1	4	8	1	26
Clark	8	1	2	6	2	1	3	3		1	4	1	11
Brown		2	1	3		1				2	1		3
Rogers	2		1	3				2			1		3
Artwell	2			1				1		1			2
Romeo		1	1	2				1			1		2
Samuel	1	1		2				2					2
Bell	1			1			1						1
Chapple	1			1					1				1
Stewart	1			1							1		1

NORTHWOOD MATCH RESULTS 2020-21

Date	Comp	H/A	Opponents	Att:	Result	Goalscorers	Pos	No.
Sept 12	**FACP**	**H**	**Slimbridge**	**153**	**D 1 - 1**	**Dickson 32 (Won 4-2 on pens)**		1
19	IsthSC	A	Westfield	140	L 0 - 3		20	2
22	**FAC1Q**	**A**	**Burnham**	**237**	**L 0 - 1**			3
26	**FAT1Q**	**H**	**Basildon United**	**111**	**D 1 - 1**	**Sharman 85 (Won 4-3 on pens)**		4
29	IsthSC	H	FC Romania	131	W 1 - 0	Totesaut 10 (pen)	13	5
Oct 6	IsthSC	A	South Park	33	L 2 - 3	Ward 4 Totesaut 41	15	6
10	IsthSC	H	Chertsey Town	218	L 1 - 3	Odelusi 23	18	7
13	IsthSC	H	Ashford Town (Mx)	120	L 0 - 2		18	8
17	**FAT2Q**	**H**	**Heybridge Swifts**	**151**	**D 3 - 3**	**Graca 72 Totesaut 79 El-Droubi 90**		9
20	IsthSC	A	Hanwell Town	209	D 1 - 1	Isaac 55	15	10
24	IsthSC	A	Waltham Abbey	142	L 1 - 5	Morgan-Cummings 10	18	11
27	IsthSC	H	Staines Town	145	L 1 - 2	Muhemba 85		12

Goalscorers	LGE	FAC	FAT	SG	HAT	PEN	1Q	2Q	45+	3Q	4Q	90+	T
TOTALS	7	1	4		0	1	3	3	0	1	4	1	12
Totesaut	2		1	3		1	1	1			1		3
Dickson		1		1				1					1
El-Droubi			1	1								1	1
Graca			1	1							1		1
Isaac	1			1						1			1
Morgan-Cummings	1			1			1						1
Muhemba	1			1							1		1
Odelusi	1			1				1					1
Sharman			1	1							1		1
Ward	1			1			1						1

SOUTH PARK MATCH RESULTS 2020-21

Date	Comp	H/A	Opponents	Att:	Result	Goalscorers	Pos	No.
Sept 12	**FACP**	**A**	**Hythe Town**	**163**	**W 2 - 1**	**French 51 Lalor-Dell 67**		1
19	IsthSC	A	Waltham Abbey	105	L 0 - 2		19	2
22	**FAC1Q**	**H**	**Bognor Regis Town**	**202**	**D 2 - 2**	**Lalor-Dell 6 Dukali 37 (Lost 2-4 on pens)**		3
26	**FAT1Q**	**H**	**Three Bridges**	**111**	**L 0 - 1**			4
Oct 6	IsthSC	H	Northwood	33	W 3 - 2	Lalor-Dell 6 60 Dukali 83	14	5
10	IsthSC	A	Ashford Town (Mx)	123	L 1 - 3	Brefo 12	15	6
13	IsthSC	H	Chertsey Town	106	D 2 - 2	Bobumurodov 22 Lalor-Dell 75	13	7
17	IsthSC	A	Staines Town	142	D 4 - 4	Bobumurodov 15 Lalor-Dell 36 (pen) 45 James-Lewis 70	13	8
24	IsthSC	H	Ware	64	L 1 - 4	Savage 22	16	9
27	IsthSC	A	Chipstead	105	L 1 - 3	Lalor-Dell 90		10

Goalscorers	LGE	FAC	FAT	SG	HAT	PEN	1Q	2Q	45+	3Q	4Q	90+	T
TOTALS	13	3	0		0	1	6	2	1	3	3	1	16
Lalor-Dell	6	2		6		1	2	1	1	2	1	1	8
Bobumurodov	2			2			2						2
Dukali	1	1		2				1			1		2
Brefo	1			1			1						1
French	1			1						1			1
James-Lewis	1			1							1		1
Savage	1			1			1						1

STAINES TOWN MATCH RESULTS 2020-21

Date	Comp	H/A	Opponents	Att:	Result		Goalscorers	Pos	No.
Sept 12	**FACP**	**H**	**Guildford City**	**151**	**W**	**2 - 1**	**Taylor-Crossdale 6 (pen) Hattabi 83**		1
19	IsthSC	H	Ware	129	W	3 - 2	Osei-Obengo 4 66 Adom 69	5	2
22	**FAC1Q**	**H**	**Walton Casuals**	**239**	**L**	**1 - 2**	**Osei-Obengo 34 (pen)**		3
26	**FAT1Q**	**A**	**Waltham Abbey**	**100**	**L**	**2 - 3**	**Osei-Obengo 15 Everett 67**		4
29	IsthSC	A	Marlow	123	L	0 - 3		12	5
Oct 6	IsthSC	H	Hertford Town	97	W	1 - 0	Everett 47	7	6
10	IsthSC	A	Hanwell Town	283	W	4 - 2	Oyebola 44 Jewers 55 Eweka 66 Adom 89	4	7
17	IsthSC	H	South Park	142	D	4 - 4	Robinson 34 55 71 Krabbendom 50 (pen)	4	8
24	IsthSC	H	Tooting & Mitcham United	204	L	0 - 4		8	9
27	IsthSC	A	Northwood	145	W	2 - 1	Oyebola 38 Osei-Obengo 90		10
31	IsthSC	H	FC Romania	181	W	3 - 1	Eweka 4 Oyebola 70 Luther 90	2	11

Goalscorers	LGE	FAC	FAT	SG	HAT	PEN	1Q	2Q	45+	3Q	4Q	90+	T
TOTALS	17	3	2		1	3	4	4	0	7	5	2	22
Osei-Obengo	3	1	1	4		1	2	1		1		1	5
Oyebola	3			3				2			1		3
Robinson	3			1	1			1		1	1		3
Adom	2			2							2		2
Everett	1		1	2						2			2
Eweka	2			2			1			1			2
Hattabi		1		1							1		1
Jewers	1			1						1			1
Krabbendom	1			1		1				1			1
Luther	1			1								1	1
Taylor-Crossdale		1		1		1	1						1

TOOTING & MITCHAM UNITED MATCH RESULTS 2020-21

Date	Comp	H/A	Opponents	Att:	Result		Goalscorers	Pos	No.
Sept 12	**FACP**	**H**	**Fisher**	**398**	**D**	**2 - 2**	**Christie 30 Stewart 80 (Lost 1-3 on pens)**		1
19	IsthSC	H	Hertford Town	315	L	1 - 2	Rose 42	13	2
26	**FAT1Q**	**A**	**AFC Dunstable**	**97**	**W**	**2 - 1**	**Waters 40 Clarke 88**		3
29	IsthSC	A	Ashford Town (Mx)	153	W	2 - 0	Rose 76 Stewart 80	6	4
Oct 3	IsthSC	H	Harlow Town	295	W	1 - 0	Williams 42	2	5
7	IsthSC	A	FC Romania	86	W	1 - 0	Rose 89	1	6
10	IsthSC	H	Waltham Abbey	400	L	0 - 1		3	7
17	**FAT2Q**	**H**	**Romford**	**400**	**W**	**2 - 0**	**Walters 33 Williams 71**		8
24	IsthSC	A	Staines Town	204	W	4 - 0	Walters 21 Simpson 76 Rose 81 Williams 90	3	9
27	IsthSC	H	Bedfont Sports	331	W	3 - 0	Williams 24 77 Rose 38 (pen)		10
31	**FAT3Q**	**A**	**Bognor Regis Town**	**486**	**L**	**0 - 2**			11

Goalscorers	LGE	FAC	FAT	SG	HAT	PEN	1Q	2Q	45+	3Q	4Q	90+	T
TOTALS	12	2	4		0	1	1	7	0	0	9	1	18
Rose	5			5		1		2			3		5
Williams	4		1	4				2			2	1	5
Stewart	1	1		2							2		2
Walters	1		1	2			1	1					2
Christie		1		1				1					1
Clarke			1	1							1		1
Simpson	1			1							1		1
Waters			1	1				1					1

UXBRIDGE MATCH RESULTS 2020-21

Date	Comp	H/A	Opponents	Att:	Result		Goalscorers	Pos	No.
Sept 12	**FACP**	**A**	**Sheppey United**	**235**	**L**	**1 - 4**	**Haugh 65**		1
19	IsthSC	A	Chertsey Town	353	L	0 - 1		16	2
26	IsthSC	H	Bracknell Town	130	D	2 - 2	Martin 78 Bitmead 84	13	3
Oct 6	IsthSC	H	Ashford Town (Mx)	94	D	0 - 0		17	4
10	IsthSC	A	Ware	169	W	2 - 1	Bitmead 33 Bates 44	12	5
17	**FAT2Q**	**H**	**Waltham Abbey**	**137**	**W**	**2 - 1**	**Bates 63 Hedley 89**		6
24	IsthSC	H	Chipstead	82	L	1 - 3	Fenton 7	15	7
27	IsthSC	A	Marlow	121	L	0 - 4			8
Nov 3	**FAT3Q**	**H**	**Hayes & Yeading United**	**251**	**W**	**2 - 1**	**Talla 12 Bunting 88**		9
Dec 8	**FAT1P**	**H**	**Cray Wanderers**	**102**	**L**	**1 - 3**	**Martin 12**		10

Goalscorers	LGE	FAC	FAT	SG	HAT	PEN	1Q	2Q	45+	3Q	4Q	90+	T
TOTALS	5	1	5		0	0	3	2	0	2	4	0	11
Bates	1		1	2				1		1			2
Bitmead	2			2				1			1		2
Martin	1		1	2			1				1		2
Bunting			1	1							1		1
Fenton	1			1			1						1
Haugh		1		1						1			1
Hedley			1	1							1		1
Talla			1	1			1						1

WALTHAM ABBEY MATCH RESULTS 2020-21

Date	Comp	H/A	Opponents	Att:	Result		Goalscorers	Pos	No.
Sept 12	**FACP**	**H**	**Woodford Town**	**178**	**W**	**1 - 0**	**McKenzie 45**		1
19	IsthSC	H	South Park	105	W	2 - 0	Koranteng 6 Hallett 85	4	2
22	**FAC1Q**	**A**	**Harlow Town**	**337**	**W**	**1 - 0**	**Domafriyie 26**		3
26	**FAT1Q**	**H**	**Staines Town**	**100**	**W**	**3 - 2**	**Hallett 36 (pen) Daveney 50 Daniel 71**		4
Oct 3	**FAC2Q**	**A**	**Bury Town**	**400**	**L**	**1 - 4**	**Gordon 81**		5
6	IsthSC	H	Marlow	93	W	2 - 1	Holland 20 Hallett 83	3	6
10	IsthSC	A	Tooting & Mitcham United	400	W	1 - 0	Hallett 14 (pen)	2	7
13	IsthSC	A	Hertford Town	152	W	2 - 1	Dear 9 Holland 31	1	8
17	**FAT2Q**	**A**	**Uxbridge**	**137**	**L**	**1 - 2**	**McKenzie 34 (pen)**		9
20	IsthSC	H	Chipstead	121	D	1 - 1	Holland 30	1	10
24	IsthSC	H	Northwood	142	W	5 - 1	Hallett 11 21 34 Holland 25 Koranteng 66	1	11
27	IsthSC	A	Barking	103	L	0 - 3			12
31	IsthSC	H	Westfield	108	L	0 - 2		1	13

Goalscorers	LGE	FAC	FAT	SG	HAT	PEN	1Q	2Q	45+	3Q	4Q	90+	T
TOTALS	13	3	4		1	3	7	6	1	2	4	0	20
Hallett	6		1	5	1	2	3	2			2		7
Holland	4			4			2	2					4
Koranteng	2			2			1			1			2
McKenzie		1	1	2		1		1	1				2
Daniel			1	1							1		1
Daveney			1	1						1			1
Dear	1			1			1						1
Domafriyie		1		1				1					1
Gordon		1		1							1		1

WARE MATCH RESULTS 2020-21

Date	Comp	H/A	Opponents	Att:	Result	Goalscorers	Pos	No.
Sept 1	**FACEP**	**A**	**Southend Manor**	**200**	**W 5 - 0**	**Rose 15 75 Kendall 46 61 Adu-Donyinah 77**		1
12	**FACP**	**A**	**Canvey Island**	**216**	**L 0 - 2**			2
19	IsthSC	A	Staines Town	129	L 2 - 3	Rose 16 Hope 25	12	3
26	IsthSC	A	Bedford Sports	67	W 3 - 2	Bruno 42 53 (pens) Adamson 50	10	4
Oct 3	IsthSC	A	Chalfont St Peter	110	W 1 - 0	Rose 26	3	5
10	IsthSC	H	Uxbridge	169	L 1 - 2	Rumens 24	9	6
17	**FAT2Q**	**A**	**Burgess Hill Town**	**250**	**L 0 - 2**			7
20	IsthSC	H	Barking	152	W 3 - 1	Rose 28 Milner 47 Crowter 70	6	8
24	IsthSC	A	South Park	64	W 4 - 1	Adu-Donyinah 33 62 Rose 42 Simms 90	4	9
27	IsthSC	H	Harlow Town	249	W 6 - 1	Wade 4 36 74 Arthur 14 29 Titchmarsh 83		10

Goalscorers	LGE	FAC	FAT	SG	HAT	PEN	1Q	2Q	45+	3Q	4Q	90+	T
TOTALS	20	5	0		1	2	4	9	0	6	5	1	25
Rose	4	2		5			2	3			1		6
Adu-Donyinah	2	1		2				1		1	1		3
Wade	3			1	1		1	1			1		3
Arthur	2			1			1	1					2
Bruno	2			1		2		1		1			2
Kendall		2		1						2			2
Adamson	1			1						1			1
Crowter	1			1							1		1
Hope	1			1				1					1
Milner	1			1						1			1
Rumens	1			1				1					1
Simms	1			1								1	1
Titchmarsh	1			1							1		1

WESTFIELD MATCH RESULTS 2020-21

Date	Comp	H/A	Opponents	Att:	Result	Goalscorers	Pos	No.
Sept 12	**FACP**	**H**	**Frimley Green**	**143**	**D 2 - 2**	**Janaway 74 (og) Dede 89 (Lost 3-5 on pens)**		1
19	IsthSC	H	Northwood	140	W 3 - 0	Tajs 43 Goather-Braithwaite 60 Dede 68 (pen)	1	2
26	IsthSC	A	Chipstead	99	W 4 - 1	Goather-Braithwaite 25 29 Dede 66 90	1	3
Oct 6	IsthSC	H	Hanwell Town	95	L 2 - 3	Hill 30 Dede 41	2	4
10	IsthSC	A	Marlow	190	D 3 - 3	Goather-Braithwaite 14 51 84	5	5
17	**FAT2Q**	**A**	**Felixstowe & Walton United**	**266**	**L 0 - 5**			6
20	IsthSC	H	Hertford Town	101	L 1 - 3	King 45	10	7
24	IsthSC	H	Barking	188	L 0 - 1		12	8
31	IsthSC	A	Waltham Abbey	108	W 2 - 0	Hamilton-Olise 20 Goather-Braithwaite 25	11	9

Goalscorers	LGE	FAC	FAT	SG	HAT	PEN	1Q	2Q	45+	3Q	4Q	90+	T
TOTALS	15	2	0		0	1	2	6	1	3	4	1	17
Goather-Braithwaite	7			4			1	3		2	1		7
Dede	4	1		4		1		1		1	2	1	5
Hamilton-Olise	1			1			1						1
Hill	1			1				1					1
King	1			1					1				1
Oppenent		1		1							1		1
Tajs	1			1				1					1

ASHFORD UNITED MATCH RESULTS 2020-21

Date	Comp	H/A	Opponents	Att:	Result	Goalscorers	Pos	No.
Sept 12	**FACP**	**H**	**Whitehawk**	**239**	**W 2 - 0**	**Wisson 8 Condon 26**		1
19	IsthSE	H	Phoenix Sports	234	L 1 - 2	Ter Horst 27	15	2
22	**FAC1Q**	**H**	**Bracknell Town**	**243**	**L 1 - 4**	**Anidugbe 60 (og)**		3
26	IsthSE	A	Ramsgate	394	W 2 - 1	Stone 33 Wisson 89	10	4
Oct 6	IsthSE	A	Sittingbourne	240	D 2 - 2	Gorham 39 Anidugbe 81 (pen)	10	5
10	IsthSE	H	East Grinstead Town	320	L 0 - 3		15	6
17	**FAT2Q**	**A**	**Hythe United**	**388**	**D 2 - 2**	**Kwayie 1 Fagg 70 (Lost 6-7 on pens)**		7
20	IsthSE	H	Whyteleafe	202	W 2 - 0	Steventon 7 Ter Horst 25	9	8
27	IsthSE	H	Sevenoaks Town	290	L 2 - 3	Fagg 8 Anidugbe 59		9

Goalscorers	LGE	FAC	FAT	SG	HAT	PEN	1Q	2Q	45+	3Q	4Q	90+	T
TOTALS	9	3	2		0	1	4	5	0	2	3	0	14
Anidugbe	2			2		1				1	1		2
Fagg	1		1	2			1				1		2
Ter Horst	2			2				2					2
Wisson	1	1		2			1				1		2
Condon		1		1				1					1
Gorham	1			1				1					1
Kwayie			1	1			1						1
Opponent		1		1						1			1
Steventon	1			1			1						1
Stone	1			1				1					1

BURGESS HILL TOWN MATCH RESULTS 2020-21

Date	Comp	H/A	Opponents	Att:	Result	Goalscorers	Pos	No.
Sept 12	**FACP**	**H**	**Holland & Blair**		**P - P**			1
19	IsthSE	A	Hythe Town	161	L 2 - 3	Laing 28 Brown 83 (og)	13	2
23	**FAC1Q**	**A**	**Cray Valley PM**	**154**	**L 1 - 3**	**Laing 66 (pen)**		3
26	IsthSE	H	Haywards Heath Town	341	D 1 - 1	Williams-Bowers 8	14	4
Oct 3	IsthSE	A	Sevenoaks Town	171	L 0 - 1		15	5
6	IsthSE	H	Phoenix Sports	223	W 2 - 0	Miller 56 Ndozid 67	11	6
10	IsthSE	A	Whitstable Town	369	L 0 - 1		12	7
17	**FAT2Q**	**H**	**Ware**	**250**	**W 2 - 0**	**Smith-Joseph 6 Ndozid 15 (pen)**		8
24	IsthSE	H	Ramsgate	286	L 0 - 3		18	9
27	IsthSE	A	Whyteleafe	310	L 0 - 5			10
31	**FAT3Q**	**H**	**Harrow Borough**	**190**	**W 4 - 1**	**Cooper 45 Harding 57 59 Smith-Joseph 89**		11
Dec 8	**FAT1P**	**A**	**Margate**			**Walkover**		12
15	**FAT2P**	**A**	**Welwyn Garden City**	**216**	**L 1 - 2**	**Cooper 73**		13

Goalscorers	LGE	FAC	FAT	SG	HAT	PEN	1Q	2Q	45+	3Q	4Q	90+	T
TOTALS	5	1	7		0	2	3	1	1	5	3	0	13
Cooper			2	2					1		1		2
Harding			2	1						2			2
Laing	1	1		2		1		1		1			2
Ndozid	1		1	2		1	1			1			2
Smith-Joseph			2	2			1				1		2
Miller	1			1						1			1
Opponent	1			1							1		1
Williams-Bowers	1			1			1						1

CHICHESTER CITY MATCH RESULTS 2020-21

Date	Comp	H/A	Opponents	Att:	Result		Goalscorers	Pos	No.
Sept 14	**FACP**	**A**	**Basingstoke Town**		**D**	**2 - 2**	**Penny 45 Clack 69 (Won 3-1 on pens)**		1
19	IsthSE	H	Ramsgate	208	L	1 - 3	Clack 65	17	2
22	**FAC1Q**	**H**	**Cribbs**	**274**	**W**	**3 - 1**	**Pashley 58 Clack 67 Prichard 90**		3
26	IsthSE	A	Whyteleafe	175	L	0 - 1		17	4
Oct 3	**FAC2Q**	**H**	**Risborough Rangers**	**343**	**W**	**2 - 1**	**Haitham 67 Rowlatt 76**		5
6	IsthSE	A	VCD Athletic	96	L	1 - 4	Hutchings 11	18	6
10	IsthSE	H	Haywards Heath Town	263	W	3 - 2	Iordache 17 76 77	17	7
13	**FAC3Q**	**H**	**Tonbridge Angels**	**400**	**L**	**1 - 2**	**Haitham 29**		8
17	**FAT2Q**	**A**	**Brentwood Town**	**301**	**L**	**2 - 3**	**Iordache 3 Heath 5**		9
24	IsthSE	A	Herne Bay	400	W	2 - 1	Iordache 13 Dunn 20	13	10

Goalscorers	LGE	FAC	FAT	SG	HAT	PEN	1Q	2Q	45+	3Q	4Q	90+	T
TOTALS	7	8	2		1	0	6	1	1	4	4	1	17
Iordache	4		1	3	1		3				2		5
Clack	1	2		3						2	1		3
Haitham		2		2				1		1			2
Dunn	1			1			1						1
Heath			1	1			1						1
Hutchings	1			1			1						1
Pashley		1		1						1			1
Penny		1		1					1				1
Prichard		1		1								1	1
Rowlatt		1		1							1		1

CRAY VALLEY PAPER MILL MATCH RESULTS 2020-21

Date	Comp	H/A	Opponents	Att:	Result		Goalscorers	Pos	No.
Sept 12	**FACP**	**H**	**VCD Athletic**	**182**	**W**	**6 - 0**	**Dymond 12 Yusuff 24 52 Ibrahiym 32 Babalola 59 Adeyemo 83**		1
19	IsthSE	A	Hastings United	400	D	0 - 0		9	2
23	**FAC1Q**	**H**	**Burgess Hill Town**	**154**	**W**	**3 - 1**	**Dymond 28 Babalola 39 Gayle 45**		3
26	IsthSE	H	Sittingbourne	243	W	2 - 1	Smith 39 Ibrahiym 50	4	4
Oct 3	**FAC2Q**	**A**	**Harrow Borough**	**153**	**W**	**5 - 1**	**Yusuff 32 (pen) Gayle 60 Dymond 67 Adeyemo 80 Attenborough-Warren 85**		5
6	IsthSE	H	Faversham Town	148	L	1 - 2	Adeyemo 76	12	6
10	IsthSE	A	Whyteleafe	279	D	2 - 2	Hasler 59 90	11	7
13	**FAC3Q**	**H**	**Aveley**	**301**	**W**	**2 - 0**	**Yusuff 48 90**		8
17	**FAT2Q**	**A**	**Whyteleafe**	**227**	**D**	**0 - 0**	**(Lost 2-3 on pens)**		9
24	**FAC4Q**	**A**	**Maidenhead United**	**0**	**W**	**3 - 2**	**Yusuff 30 Dymond 44 Babalola 90+3**		10
27	IsthSE	A	Whitstable Town	271	D	1 - 1	Hill 90		11
Nov 7	**FAC1P**	**A**	**Havant & Waterlooville**	**0**	**L**	**0 - 1**			12

Goalscorers	LGE	FAC	FAT	SG	HAT	PEN	1Q	2Q	45+	3Q	4Q	90+	T
TOTALS	6	19	0		0	1	0	9	1	7	5	4	25
Yusuff		6		4		1		3		2		1	6
Dymond		4		4				3		1			4
Adeyemo	1	2		3							4		3
Babalola		3		3				1		1		1	3
Gayle		2		2					1	1			2
Hasler	2			1						1		1	2
Ibrahiym	1	1		2				1		1			2
Attenborough-Warren		1		1							1		1
Hill	1			1								1	1
Smith	1			1				1					1

EAST GRINSTEAD TOWN MATCH RESULTS 2020-21

Date	Comp	H/A	Opponents	Att:	Result	Goalscorers	Pos	No.
Sept 12	**FACP**	**H**	**Phoenix Sports**	**208**	**W 3 - 2**	**Theophanous 4 35 Amoo 45**		1
19	IsthSE	A	Haywards Heath Town	230	W 4 - 1	Uwezu 18 (pen) Cowlings 33 (og) Theophanous 52 Amoo 59	1	2
22	**FAC1Q**	**H**	**Worthing**	**273**	**D 3 - 3**	**Theophanous 52 80 Thompson 84 (Won 4-3 on pens)**		3
Oct 3	**FAC2Q**	**A**	**Chipstead**	**277**	**L 0 - 1**			4
6	IsthSE	H	Ramsgate	155	W 4 - 1	Theophanous 3 18 Thompson 24 Clohessy 82	4	5
10	IsthSE	A	Ashford United	320	W 3 - 0	Theophanous 48 53 Wedgeworth 85	2	6
17	**FAT2Q**	**A**	**Sittingbourne**	**175**	**L 0 - 1**			7
24	IsthSE	H	Whitstable Town	295	D 2 - 2	Clohessy 55 Sawogo 90	3	8
27	IsthSE	A	Phoenix Sports	92	W 2 - 1	Theophanous 3 Andrews 29 (og)		9
Nov 3	IsthSE	A	VCD Athletic	211	D 1 - 1	Uwezu 45	3	10

Goalscorers	LGE	FAC	FAT	SG	HAT	PEN	1Q	2Q	45+	3Q	4Q	90+	T
TOTALS	16	6	0		0	1	5	4	2	6	4	1	22
Theophanous	6	4		6			4	1		4	1		10
Amoo	1	1		2					1	1			2
Clohessy	2			2						1	1		2
Opponent	2			2				2					2
Thompson	1	1		2				1			1		2
Uwezu	2			2		1	1		1				2
Sawogo	1			1								1	1
Wedgeworth	1			1							1		1

FAVERSHAM TOWN MATCH RESULTS 2020-21

Date	Comp	H/A	Opponents	Att:	Result	Goalscorers	Pos	No.
Sept 12	**FACP**	**H**	**Eastbourne Town**	**220**	**D 1 - 1**	**Harding 34 (Won 6-5 on pens)**		1
21	**FAC1Q**	**A**	**Carshalton Athletic**	**334**	**L 0 - 5**			2
26	IsthSE	H	Hastings United	236	D 0 - 0		13	3
Oct 3	IsthSE	A	Sittingbourne	326	W 3 - 0	Denny 9 Bewick 67 Okoh 84	6	4
6	IsthSE	A	Cray Valley PM	148	W 2 - 1	Chambers 2 Oluwasemo 90+3	3	5
10	IsthSE	H	Sevenoaks Town	298	D 1 - 1	Harding 87	6	6
17	**FAT2Q**	**H**	**Hertford Town**	**212**	**W 4 - 1**	**Bourne 14 Ogboe 42 (pen) Harding 52 90**		7
24	IsthSE	A	Whitehawk	400	D 1 - 1	Harding 58	7	8
27	IsthSE	H	VCD Athletic	224	W 1 - 0	Ogboe 40		9
31	**FAT3Q**	**H**	**Haringey Borough**	**228**	**L 1 - 2**	**Hogan 72**		10

Goalscorers	LGE	FAC	FAT	SG	HAT	PEN	1Q	2Q	45+	3Q	4Q	90+	T
TOTALS	8	1	5		0	1	3	3	0	3	3	2	14
Harding	2	1	2	4				1		2	1	1	5
Ogboe	1		1	2		1		2					2
Bewick	1			1						1			1
Bourne			1	1			1						1
Chambers	1			1			1						1
Denny	1			1			1						1
Hogan			1	1							1		1
Okoh	1			1							1		1
Oluwasemo	1			1								1	1

HASTINGS UNITED MATCH RESULTS 2020-21

Date	Comp	H/A	Opponents	Att:	Result		Goalscorers	Pos	No.
Sept 12	**FACP**	**H**	**Herne Bay**	**400**	**W**	**1 - 0**	**Dixon 83**		1
19	IsthSE	H	Cray Valley PM	400	D	0 - 0		10	2
22	**FAC1Q**	**H**	**Chesham United**	**384**	**D**	**0 - 0**	**(Won 6-5 on pens)**		3
26	IsthSE	A	Faversham Town	236	D	0 - 0		12	4
Oct 3	**FAC2Q**	**H**	**Ebbsfleet United**		**D**	**2 - 2**	**Pogue 60 Adams 86 (Lost 1-4 on pens)**		5
6	IsthSE	A	Haywards Heath Town	159	W	5 - 1	Adams 22 45 Pogue 49 52 79	9	6
10	IsthSE	H	VCD Athletic	400	W	2 - 1	Adams 25 Chalmers 70	5	7
17	**FAT2Q**	**H**	**FC Romania**	**377**	**W**	**3 - 0**	**Pope 7 Elphick 32 Chalmers 56**		8
20	IsthSE	H	Three Bridges	400	W	3 - 0	Pope 10 68 Rodari 82	2	9
24	IsthSE	A	Sevenoaks Town	300	W	1 - 0	Worrall 56	1	10
27	IsthSE	H	Whitehawk	400	W	2 - 1	Pogue 51 Pope 78	1	11
31	**FAT3Q**	**H**	**Ashford Town (Mx)**	**400**	**D**	**1 - 1**	**Worrall 43 (Won 4-2 on pens)**		12
Dec 8	**FAT1P**	**A**	**Aveley**	**139**	**L**	**0 - 1**			13

Goalscorers	LGE	FAC	FAT	SG	HAT	PEN	1Q	2Q	45+	3Q	4Q	90+	T
TOTALS	13	3	4		1	0	3	3	1	6	7	0	20
Pogue	4	1		3	1					4	1		5
Adams	3	1		3			1	1	1		1		4
Pope	3		1	3			2				2		4
Chalmers	1		1	2						1	1		2
Worrall	1		1	2				1		1			2
Dixon		1		1							1		1
Elphick			1	1				1					1
Rodari	1			1							1		1

HAYWARDS HEATH TOWN MATCH RESULTS 2020-21

Date	Comp	H/A	Opponents	Att:	Result		Goalscorers	Pos	No.
Sept 12	**FACP**	**A**	**Broadbridge Heath**			**P - P**			1
19	IsthSE	H	East Grinstead Town	230	L	1 - 4	Morrison 90	18	2
22	**FAC1Q**	**H**	**Hanwell Town**	**155**	**L**	**0 - 1**			3
26	IsthSE	A	Burgess Hill Town	341	D	1 - 1	Clark 3	16	4
Oct 3	IsthSE	H	Whitstable Town	145	L	0 - 2		17	5
6	IsthSE	H	Hastings United	159	L	1 - 5	Cotton 59	17	6
10	IsthSE	A	Chichester City	263	L	2 - 3	Cotton 42 (pen) Dalhouse 51	19	7
17	**FAT2Q**	**H**	**Welwyn Garden City**	**163**	**L**	**1 - 4**	**Akehurst 45**		8

Goalscorers	LGE	FAC	FAT	SG	HAT	PEN	1Q	2Q	45+	3Q	4Q	90+	T
TOTALS	5	0	1		0	1	1	1	1	2	0	1	6
Cotton	2			2		1		1		1			2
Akehurst			1	1					1				1
Clark	1			1			1						1
Dalhouse	1			1						1			1
Morrison	1			1								1	1

HERNE BAY MATCH RESULTS 2020-21

Date	Comp	H/A	Opponents	Att:	Result	Goalscorers	Pos	No.
Sept 12	**FACP**	**A**	**Hastings United**	**400**	**L 0 - 1**			1
19	IsthSE	H	Whyteleafe	368	L 1 - 4	Dawodu 69	19	2
26	IsthSE	A	Phoenix Sports	178	W 3 - 0	Walters 7 Ansah 90+1 Grant 90+5	8	3
Oct 3	IsthSE	H	Whitehawk	383	W 3 - 1	Harvey 82 90 Ansah 90	4	4
10	IsthSE	A	Hythe Town	263	L 0 - 1		9	5
17	**FAT2Q**	**A**	**VCD Athletic**	**128**	**W 2 - 1**	**Dawodu 56 Edgar 73**		6
24	IsthSE	H	Chichester City	400	L 1 - 2	Ansah 40	11	7
27	IsthSE	A	Ramsgate	400	D 1 - 1	Walters 25		8
31	**FAT3Q**	**A**	**Hitchin Town**	**443**	**L 1 - 3**	**Ansah 8**		9

Goalscorers	LGE	FAC	FAT	SG	HAT	PEN	1Q	2Q	45+	3Q	4Q	90+	T
TOTALS	9	0	3		0	0	2	2	0	1	3	4	12
Ansah	3		1	4			1	1				2	4
Dawodu	1		1	2						1	1		2
Harvey	2			1							1	1	2
Walters	2			2			1	1					2
Edgar			1	1							1		1
Grant	1			1								1	1

HYTHE TOWN MATCH RESULTS 2020-21

Date	Comp	H/A	Opponents	Att:	Result	Goalscorers	Pos	No.
Sept 12	**FACP**	**H**	**South Park**	**163**	**L 1 - 2**	**Gordon 82**		1
19	IsthSE	H	Burgess Hill Town	161	W 3 - 2	Phillip 7 49 Collin 90	5	2
26	**FAT1Q**	**H**	**Chalfont St Peter**	**178**	**W 3 - 0**	**Collin 8 45 77**		3
Oct 3	IsthSE	H	Phoenix Sports	212	L 0 - 4		13	4
7	IsthSE	A	Hythe Town	207	D 2 - 2	Collin 27 Smith 86	14	5
10	IsthSE	H	Herne Bay	263	W 1 - 0	Oldaker 46	8	6
13	IsthSE	A	Whitstable Town	255	W 6 - 0	Flisher 18 (pen) Brown 38 41 54 Smith 50 Walmsley 66	2	7
17	**FAT2Q**	**H**	**Ashford United**	**388**	**D 2 - 2**	**Walmsley 72 Wynter 89 (Won 7-6 on pens)**		8
24	IsthSE	A	Haywards Heath Town	230	L 2 - 4	Beckwith 39 Dembele 90	5	9
31	**FAT3Q**	**A**	**Royston Town**	**290**	**L 0 - 2**			10

Goalscorers	LGE	FAC	FAT	SG	HAT	PEN	1Q	2Q	45+	3Q	4Q	90+	T
TOTALS	14	1	5		2	1	3	4	1	5	5	2	20
Collin	2		3	3	1		1	1	1		1	1	5
Brown	3			1	1			2		1			3
Phillip	2			1			1			1			2
Smith	2			2						1	1		2
Walmsley	1		1	2						1	1		2
Beckwith	1			1				1					1
Dembele	1			1								1	1
Flisher	1			1		1	1						1
Gordon		1		1							1		1
Oldaker	1			1						1			1
Wynter			1	1							1		1

PHOENIX SPORTS MATCH RESULTS 2020-21

Date	Comp	H/A	Opponents	Att:	Result	Goalscorers	Pos	No.
Sept 1	**FACEP**	**A**	**Lancing**	**204**	**D 3 - 3**	**Chin 17 20 Gaggin 25 (Won 11-10 on pens)**		1
12	**FACP**	**A**	**East Grinstead Town**	**208**	**L 2 - 3**	**Duah-Kessie 80 Dyer 90**		2
19	IsthSE	A	Ashford United	234	W 2 - 1	Duah-Kessie 73 Andrews 82	7	3
26	IsthSE	H	Herne Bay	178	L 0 - 3		11	4
Oct 3	IsthSE	A	Hythe Town	212	W 4 - 0	Ansah 52 Fitchett 57 Bryon 77 Chin 83	5	5
6	IsthSE	A	Burgess Hill Town	223	L 0 - 2		7	6
10	IsthSE	H	Whitehawk	186	L 0 - 2		10	7
17	**FAT2Q**	**H**	**Marlow**	**63**	**L 0 - 2**			8
24	IsthSE	A	Three Bridges	141	L 0 - 6		14	9
27	IsthSE	H	East Grinstead Town	92	L 1 - 2	Young 36		10

Goalscorers	LGE	FAC	FAT	SG	HAT	PEN	1Q	2Q	45+	3Q	4Q	90+	T
TOTALS	7	5	0		0	0	2	2	0	2	5	1	12
Chin	1	2		2			2				1		3
Duah-Kessie	1	1		2							2		2
Andrews	1			1							1		1
Ansah	1			1						1			1
Bryon	1			1							1		1
Dyer		1		1								1	1
Fitchett	1			1						1			1
Gaggin		1		1				1					1
Young	1			1				1					1

RAMSGATE MATCH RESULTS 2020-21

Date	Comp	H/A	Opponents	Att:	Result	Goalscorers	Pos	No.
Sept 12	**FACP**	**H**	**Chipstead**	**400**	**L 0 - 3**			1
19	IsthSE	A	Chichester City	208	W 3 - 1	Chapman 47 Nikah 59 62	4	2
26	IsthSE	H	Ashford United	394	L 1 - 2	Wilson 78 (og)	6	3
Oct 6	IsthSE	A	East Grinstead Town	155	L 1 - 4	Arnold 78	14	4
10	IsthSE	H	Three Bridges	400	L 1 - 2	Chapman 45	16	5
24	IsthSE	A	Burgess Hill Town	286	W 3 - 0	Carey 34 Ajayi 37 Miller 56	10	6
27	IsthSE	H	Herne Bay	400	D 1 - 1	Chapman 75		7
31	**FAT3Q**	**A**	**Enfield Town**	**415**	**L 1 - 8**	**Ajayi 57**		8

Goalscorers	LGE	FAC	FAT	SG	HAT	PEN	1Q	2Q	45+	3Q	4Q	90+	T
TOTALS	10	0	1		0	0	0	2	1	5	3	0	11
Chapman	3			3					1	1	1		3
Ajayi	1		1	2				1		1			2
Nikah	2			1						2			2
Arnold	1			1							1		1
Carey	1			1				1					1
Miller	1			1						1			1
Opponent	1			1							1		1

SEVENOAKS TOWN MATCH RESULTS 2020-21

Date	Comp	H/A	Opponents	Att:	Result	Goalscorers	Pos	No.
Sept 12	**FACP**		**CB Hounslow United**		**A - A**			1
19	IsthSE	H	Three Bridges	137	**W** 4 - 1	De Silva 45 Thompson 71 75 Bessey-Saldanha 90	2	2
22	**FAC1Q**	**A**	**Corinthian**		**L 1 - 3**	**Bessey-Saldanha 17**		3
26	IsthSE	A	Whitehawk	274	D 1 - 1	Parkinson 76	3	4
Oct 3	IsthSE	H	Burgess Hill Town	171	**W** 1 - 0	Parkinson 74	2	5
7	IsthSE	H	Hythe Town	207	D 2 - 2	Richardson-Brown 31 De Silva 80 (pen)	2	6
10	IsthSE	A	Faversham Town	298	D 1 - 1	Ripley 90	3	7
17	**FAT2Q**	**A**	**Bracknell Town**	**204**	**L 0 - 2**			8
24	IsthSE	H	Hastings Town	300	L 0 - 1		8	9
27	IsthSE	A	Ashford United	290	**W** 3 - 2	Sawyer 4 Gunner 6 Ripley 90+5		10
31	IsthSE	A	Haywards Heath Town	173	D 2 - 2	Thompson 7 Taylor 89	5	11

Goalscorers	LGE	FAC	FAT	SG	HAT	PEN	1Q	2Q	45+	3Q	4Q	90+	T
TOTALS	14	1	0		0	1	4	1	1	0	6	3	15
Thompson	3			2			1				2		3
Bessey-Saldanha	1	1		2			1					1	2
De Silva	2			2		1			1		1		2
Parkinson	2			2							2		2
Ripley	2			2								2	2
Gunner	1			1			1						1
Richardson-Brown	1			1				1					1
Sawyer	1			1			1						1
Taylor	1			1							1		1

SITTINGBOURNE MATCH RESULTS 2020-21

Date	Comp	H/A	Opponents	Att:	Result	Goalscorers	Pos	No.
Sept 12	**FACP**	**A**	**Deal Town**	**287**	**L 1 - 4**	**Rowland 86**		1
19	IsthSE	H	Whitstable Town	263	**W** 3 - 2	Drury 19 (pen) Rowland 40 Goodger 75	6	2
22	IsthSE	A	Cray Valley PM	243	L 1 - 2	Drury 76	9	3
Oct 3	IsthSE	H	Faversham Town	326	L 0 - 3		12	4
6	IsthSE	H	Ashford United	240	D 2 - 2	Rowland 29 45	13	5
17	**FAT2Q**	**H**	**East Grinstead Town**	**175**	**W 1 - 0**	**Flisher 73**		6
24	IsthSE	H	Whyteleafe	161	L 2 - 3	Caney-Bryan 1 Rowland 74	17	7
31	**FAT3Q**	**A**	**Barking**	**158**	**D 1 - 1**	**Rowland 29 (Lost 3-4 on pens)**		8

Goalscorers	LGE	FAC	FAT	SG	HAT	PEN	1Q	2Q	45+	3Q	4Q	90+	T
TOTALS	8	1	2		0	1	2	3	1	0	5	0	11
Rowland	4	1	1	5				3	1		2		6
Drury	2			2		1	1				1		2
Caney-Bryan	1			1			1						1
Flisher			1	1							1		1
Goodger	1			1							1		1

THREE BRIDGES MATCH RESULTS 2020-21

Date	Comp	H/A	Opponents	Att:	Result	Goalscorers	Pos	No.
Sept 12	**FACP**	**A**	**Cobham**	**70**	**D 1 - 1**	**Lovegrove 63 (Lost 3-4 on pens)**		1
19	IsthSE	A	Sevenoaks Town	137	L 1 - 4	Barbary 14	19	2
26	**FAT1Q**	**A**	**South Park**	**111**	**W 1 - 0**	**Barbary 90**		3
Oct 3	IsthSE	H	VCD Athletic	129	L 0 - 4		19	4
6	IsthSE	H	Whitstable Town	91	L 2 - 3	O'Neill 23 Tolfrey 38	19	5
10	IsthSE	A	Ramsgate	400	W 2 - 1	Tolfrey 8 O'Neill 81 (pen)	18	6
17	**FAT2Q**	**A**	**Chipstead**	**132**	**W 2 - 1**	**O'Neill 19 Lovegrove 36**		7
20	IsthSE	A	Hastings Town	400	L 0 - 3		18	8
24	IsthSE	H	Phoenix Sports	141	W 6 - 0	Hall 1 Tolfrey 38 68 Sesay 50 Barbary 74 Lansdale 83	12	9
31	**FAT3Q**	**A**	**Needham Market**	**189**	**L 1 - 4**	**Tolfrey 56**		10

Goalscorers	LGE	FAC	FAT	SG	HAT	PEN	1Q	2Q	45+	3Q	4Q	90+	T
TOTALS	11	1	4		0	0	4	4	0	3	4	1	16
Tolfrey	4		1	4			1	2		1	1		5
Barbary	2		1	3			1				1	1	3
O'Neill	2		1	3			1	1			1		3
Lovegrove		1	1	2				1		1			2
Hall	1			1			1						1
Lansdale	1			1							1		1
Sesay	1			1						1			1

VCD ATHLETIC MATCH RESULTS 2020-21

Date	Comp	H/A	Opponents	Att:	Result	Goalscorers	Pos	No.
Sept 12	**FACP**	**A**	**Cray Valley PM**	**182**	**L 0 - 6**			1
19	IsthSE	H	Whitehawk	169	W 2 - 1	Hudson 85 88 (pen)	8	2
26	IsthSE	A	Whitstable Town	221	W 4 - 1	Probets 54 Edwards 56 Elliott 68 Vines 75	1	3
Oct 3	IsthSE	A	Three Bridges	129	W 4 - 0	El-Mogharbel 30 Dawson 42 Bingham 50 Vines 59	1	4
6	IsthSE	H	Chichester City	96	W 4 - 1	Adesite 19 58 Dawson 63 Vines 66	1	5
10	IsthSE	A	Hastings United	400	L 1 - 2	Hysi 84	1	6
17	**FAT2Q**	**H**	**Herne Bay**	**128**	**L 1 - 2**	**Adesite 71**		7
27	IsthSE	A	Faversham Town	224	L 0 - 1		2	8
31	IsthSE	H	Whitstable Town	126	W 2 - 0	Elliott 32 62	2	9
Nov 3	IsthSE	H	East Grinsatead Town	211	D 1 - 1	Elliott 62	2	10

Goalscorers	LGE	FAC	FAT	SG	HAT	PEN	1Q	2Q	45+	3Q	4Q	90+	T
TOTALS	18	0	1		0	1	1	3	0	9	6	0	19
Elliott	4			3				1		2	1		4
Adesite	2		1	2			1			1	1		3
Vines	3			3						2	1		3
Dawson	2			2				1		1			2
Hudson	2			1		1					2		2
Bingham	1			1						1			1
Edwards	1			1						1			1
El-Mogharbel	1			1				1					1
Hysi	1			1							1		1
Probets	1			1						1			1

WHITEHAWK MATCH RESULTS 2020-21

Date	Comp	H/A	Opponents	Att:	Result	Goalscorers	Pos	No.
Sept 12	**FACP**	**A**	**Ashford United**	**239**	**L 0 - 2**			1
19	IsthSE	A	VCD Athletic	169	L 1 - 2	Hamilton 5	16	2
26	IsthSE	H	Sevenoaks Town	274	D 1 - 1	Abdulla 30	15	3
Oct 3	IsthSE	A	Herne Bay	383	L 1 - 3	Kamurasi 25 (og)	16	4
10	IsthSE	A	Phoenix Sports	186	**W** 2 - 0	Rodrigues 22 (pen) Abdulla 83 (pen)	13	5
17	**FAT2Q**	**H**	**Barton Rovers**	**400**	**W 2 - 1**	**Muggeridge 12 Rodrigues 28**		6
24	IsthSE	H	Faversham Town	400	D 1 - 1	Hamilton 61	16	7
27	IsthSE	A	Hastings United	400	L 1 - 2	Cotton 85		8
31	**FAT3Q**	**H**	**Cray Wanderers**	**390**	**L 0 - 3**			9

Goalscorers	LGE	FAC	FAT	SG	HAT	PEN	1Q	2Q	45+	3Q	4Q	90+	T
TOTALS	7	0	2		0	2	3	3	0	1	2	0	9
Abdulla	2			2		1		1			1		2
Hamilton	2			2			1			1			2
Rodrigues	1		1	2		1	1	1					2
Cotton	1			1							1		1
Muggeridge			1	1			1						1

	LGE	FAC	FAT	SG	HAT	PEN	1Q	2Q	45+	3Q	4Q	90+	T
Opponent	1			1				1					1

WHITSTABLE TOWN MATCH RESULTS 2020-21

Date	Comp	H/A	Opponents	Att:	Result	Goalscorers	Pos	No.
Sept 12	**FACP**	**A**	**Carshalton Athletic**	**326**	**L 1 - 5**	**Rowe 87**		1
19	IsthSE	A	Sittingbourne	263	L 2 - 3	Jadama 3 Medley 90	14	2
26	IsthSE	H	VCD Athletic	221	L 1 - 4	Millbank 32	19	3
Oct 3	IsthSE	A	Hatwards Heath	145	**W** 2 - 0	Rowe 18 Jadama 37	11	4
6	IsthSE	A	Three Bridges	91	**W** 3 - 2	Millbank 45 90 Cham 90	8	5
10	IsthSE	H	Burgess Hill Town	369	**W** 1 - 0	Jadama 17	4	6
13	IsthSE	H	Hythe Town	255	L 0 - 6		5	7
17	**FAT2Q**	**A**	**Ashford Town (Mx)**	**163**	**L 0 - 1**			8
24	IsthSE	A	East Grinstead Town	295	D 2 - 2	Medley 36 Millbank 81	6	9
27	IsthSE	H	Cray Valley PM	271	D 1 - 1	Jadama 29		10
31	IsthSE	A	VCD Athletic	126	L 0 - 2		7	11

Goalscorers	LGE	FAC	FAT	SG	HAT	PEN	1Q	2Q	45+	3Q	4Q	90+	T
TOTALS	12	1	0		0	0	3	4	1	0	2	3	13
Jadama	4			4			2	2					4
Millbank	4			3				1	1		1	1	4
Medley	2			2				1				1	2
Rowe	1	1		2			1				1		2
Cham	1			1								1	1

	LGE	FAC	FAT	SG	HAT	PEN	1Q	2Q	45+	3Q	4Q	90+	T

WHYTELEAFE MATCH RESULTS 2020-21

Date	Comp	H/A	Opponents	Att:	Result		Goalscorers	Pos	No.
Sept 1	**FACEP**	**A**	**Glebe**	**232**	**W**	**3 - 1**	**Gondoh 25 70 (pen) Owusu 30**		1
12	**FACP**	**H**	**Bearsted**	**205**	**W**	**4 - 0**	**Hibbert 4 74 Gondoh 12 Orome 40**		2
19	IsthSE	A	Herne Bay	368	W	4 - 1	Gondoh 10 20 (pens) Hibbert 37 43	3	3
22	**FAC1Q**	**H**	**Binfield**	**253**	**W**	**2 - 0**	**Gondoh 37 62**		4
26	IsthSE	H	Chichester City	175	W	1 - 0	Watson 49	2	5
Oct 5	**FAC2Q**	**A**	**Burnham**	**248**	**W**	**3 - 1**	**Orome 27 Watson 45 Thompson 90**		6
10	IsthSE	H	Cray Valley PM	279	D	2 - 2	Hibbert 27 40	7	7
13	**FAC3Q**	**H**	**Concord Rangers**	**400**	**L**	**1 - 2**	**Gondoh 2**		8
17	**FAT2Q**	**H**	**Cray Valley PM**	**227**	**D**	**0 - 0**	**(Won 3-2 on pens)**		9
20	IsthSE	A	Ashford United	202	L	0 - 2		8	10
24	IsthSE	A	Sittingbourne	161	W	3 - 2	Hibbert 53 68 Gondoh 58	4	11
27	IsthSE	H	Burgess Hill Town	310	W	5 - 0	Watson 4 24 65 86 Hibbert 14		12
31	**FAT3Q**	**A**	**Chesham United**		**D**	**2 - 2**	**Watson 8 24 (Lost 2-3 on pens)**		13

Goalscorers	LGE	FAC	FAT	SG	HAT	PEN	1Q	2Q	45+	3Q	4Q	90+	T
TOTALS	15	13	2		1	3	8	11	1	5	4	1	30
Gondoh	3	6		6		3	4	2		2	1		9
Hibbert	7	2		5			2	4		1	2		9
Watson	5	1	2	4	1		2	2	1	2	1		8
Orome		2		2				2					2
Owusu		1		1				1					1
Thompson		1		1								1	1

NORTHERN PREMIER LEAGUE 2020-21

PREMIER	P	W	D	L	F	A	GD	Pts
1 Mickleover FC	10	7	1	2	23	11	12	22
2 Basford United	9	6	1	2	15	9	6	19
3 Buxton	8	5	2	1	22	11	11	17
4 Warrington Town	9	5	1	3	16	11	5	16
5 Witton Albion	7	5	0	2	13	7	6	15
6 South Shields	9	4	3	2	12	8	4	15
7 Whitby Town	9	4	2	3	15	14	1	14
8 Matlock Town	6	4	1	1	10	4	6	13
9 Atherton Collieries	8	4	1	3	13	8	5	13
10 Gainsborough Trinity	8	4	0	4	13	12	1	12
11 Scarborough Athletic	8	3	2	3	10	11	-1	11
12 Lancaster City	7	2	4	1	12	10	2	10
13 FC United of Manchester	7	2	4	1	9	7	2	10
14 Radcliffe FC	9	3	1	5	15	23	-8	10
15 Nantwich Town	6	2	3	1	9	9	0	9
16 Morpeth Town	7	2	3	2	9	10	-1	9
17 Hyde United	6	1	3	2	5	6	-1	6
18 Stalybridge Celtic	9	1	3	5	7	17	-10	6
19 Ashton United	7	1	2	4	5	13	-8	5
20 Bamber Bridge	9	1	1	7	6	17	-11	4
21 Grantham Town	8	0	3	5	5	14	-9	3
22 Stafford Rangers	8	0	1	7	3	15	-12	1

SOUTH/EAST	P	W	D	L	F	A	GD	Pts
1 Leek Town	8	6	1	1	26	9	17	19
2 Loughborough Dynamo	8	6	1	1	16	9	7	19
3 Newcastle Town	8	5	2	1	17	9	8	17
4 Kidsgrove Athletic	7	5	1	1	13	7	6	16
5 Chasetown	9	5	1	3	18	13	5	16
6 Worksop Town	7	4	2	1	20	9	11	14
7 Belper Town	9	4	2	3	25	15	10	14
8 Stamford	7	3	4	0	20	6	14	13
9 Lincoln United	7	4	1	2	21	11	10	13
10 Ilkeston Town	7	4	1	2	17	14	3	13
11 Carlton Town	9	3	2	4	13	14	-1	11
12 Sutton Coldfield Town	8	3	2	3	13	22	-9	11
13 Frickley Athletic	8	3	0	5	14	14	0	9
14 Stocksbridge Park Steels	9	3	0	6	16	25	-9	9
15 Cleethorpes Town	8	2	2	4	14	14	0	8
16 Glossop North End	9	2	2	5	7	21	-14	8
17 Spalding United	8	2	1	5	11	14	-3	7
18 Sheffield FC	6	1	1	4	4	10	-6	4
19 Wisbech Town	8	1	0	7	5	26	-21	3
20 Market Drayton Town	8	0	0	8	2	30	-28	0

NORTH/WEST	P	W	D	L	F	A	GD	Pts
1 Colne	9	7	1	1	20	9	11	22
2 Ramsbottom United	8	6	1	1	19	9	10	19
3 Workington	9	5	4	0	19	9	10	19
4 Clitheroe	9	5	3	1	15	9	6	18
5 Dunston	7	5	1	1	13	8	5	16
6 Marine	7	5	0	2	16	5	11	15
7 Runcorn Linnets	8	4	3	1	15	11	4	15
8 Marske United	5	3	2	0	14	5	9	11
9 Tadcaster Albion	8	3	2	3	13	10	3	11
10 City of Liverpool FC	9	3	1	5	19	21	-2	10
11 Kendal Town	12	2	4	6	11	22	-11	10
12 Widnes	9	2	2	5	8	15	-7	8
13 Mossley	7	2	1	4	10	11	-1	7
14 Trafford	7	1	4	2	8	11	-3	7
15 Prescot Cables	9	2	1	6	11	15	-4	7
16 Pickering Town	9	2	1	6	8	19	-11	7
17 Brighouse Town	8	1	2	5	13	20	-7	5
18 Pontefract Collieries	8	1	2	5	8	22	-14	5
19 Ossett United	8	1	1	6	6	15	-9	4

ASHTON UNITED MATCH RESULTS 2020-21

Date	Comp	H/A	Opponents	Att:	Result	Goalscorers	Pos	No.
Sept 12	**FACP**	**H**	**Squires Gate**	**236**	**W 2 - 0**	**Lynch 29 Wilson 72**		1
19	NPLP	A	Stafford Rangers	595	W 1 - 0	Pritchard 13	7	2
22	**FAC1Q**	**A**	**Scarborough Athletic**		**W 2 - 0**	**Bentham 9 Hardcastle 88**		3
29	NPLP	H	South Shields	285	D 3 - 3	Alli 25 Raynes 28 Wilson 66 (pen)	8	4
Oct 3	**FAC2Q**	**H**	**South Shields**	**310**	**L 0 - 4**			5
6	NPLP	H	Bamber Bridge	209	D 0 - 0		8	6
10	NPLP	A	Matlock Town	532	L 1 - 4	Hardcastle 27	14	7
13	NPLP	A	Atherton Collieries	420	L 0 - 1		16	8
17	NPLP	H	Mickleover	258	L 0 - 3		18	9
31	**FAT3Q**	**H**	**Clitheroe**	**253**	**W 1 - 0**	**Brewster 45**		10
Nov 3	NPLP	A	Whitby Town	264	L 0 - 2		19	11
Dec 8	**FAT1P**	**H**	**South Shields**		**W 2 - 1**	**Baird 55 Raynes 82**		12
15	**FAT2P**	**H**	**York City**		**D 3 - 3**	**Alli 19 Macadam 55 Lynch 76 (Won 4-2 on pens)**		13
19	**FAT3P**	**H**	**Kettering Town**		**L 1 - 2**	**Almond 36 (pen)**		14

Goalscorers	LGE	FAC	FAT	SG	HAT	PEN	1Q	2Q	45+	3Q	4Q	90+	T
TOTALS	5	4	7		0	2	3	5	1	3	4	0	16
Alli	1		1	2			1	1					2
Hardcastle	1	1		2				1			1		2
Lynch		1	1	2				1			1		2
Raynes	1		1	2				1			1		2
Wilson	1	1		2		1				1	1		2
Almond			1	1		1		1					1
Baird			1	1						1			1
Bentham		1		1			1						1
Brewster			1	1					1				1
Macadam			1	1						1			1
Pritchard	1			1			1						1

ATHERTON COLLIERIES MATCH RESULTS 2020-21

Date	Comp	H/A	Opponents	Att:	Result	Goalscorers	Pos	No.
Sept 19	NPLP	H	Scarborough Athletic	405	L 0 - 2		18	1
22	**FAC1Q**	**H**	**Bamber Bridge**			**Walkover**		2
26	NPLP	A	Grantham Town	231	W 2 - 1	Peet 40 Sambor 85 (pen)	12	3
29	NPLP	A	Warrington Town	420	L 0 - 2		16	4
Oct 3	**FAC2Q**	**A**	**Guiseley**		**L 0 - 4**			5
13	NPLP	H	Ashton United	420	W 1 - 0	Glass 30	12	6
17	NPLP	H	Stalybridge Celtic	360	D 1 - 1	Cusani 6	11	7
20	NPLP	H	Bamber Bridge	301	W 5 - 0	Darr 25 (pen) 38 Lafferty 35 Rokka 37 Banister 73	7	8
24	NPLP	A	Witton Ablion	443	L 1 - 2	Glass 71	8	9
27	NPLP	A	Stafford Rangers	457	W 3 - 0	Glass 29 Rokka 45 Smith 72		10
Nov 4	**FAT3Q**	**H**	**City of Liverpool**	**294**	**L 0 - 3**			11

Goalscorers	LGE	FAC	FAT	SG	HAT	PEN	1Q	2Q	45+	3Q	4Q	90+	T
TOTALS	13	0	0		0	2	1	7	1	0	4	0	13
Glass	3			3				2			1		3
Darr	2			1		1		2					2
Rokka	2			2				1	1				2
Banister	1			1							1		1
Cusani	1			1			1						1
Lafferty	1			1				1					1
Peet	1			1				1					1
Sambor	1			1		1					1		1
Smith	1			1							1		1

BAMBER BRIDGE MATCH RESULTS 2020-21

Date	Comp	H/A	Opponents	Att:	Result	Goalscorers	Pos	No.
Sept 19	NPLP	H	Matlock Town	397	W 1 - 0	Burton 66	8	1
22	**FAC1Q**	**A**	**Atherton Collieries**			**Walkover for Atherton Collieries**		2
Oct 6	NPLP	A	Ashton United	209	D 0 - 0		11	3
10	NPLP	H	South Shields	450	L 1 - 3	Dudley 16	15	4
13	NPLP	A	Radcliffe	342	L 1 - 2	Thomason 76	17	5
17	NPLP	A	Basford United	271	L 1 - 2	Forbes 68	19	6
20	NPLP	A	Atherton Colleries	301	L 0 - 5		19	7
24	NPLP	H	Buxton	325	L 1 - 2	O'Reilly 84	19	8
27	NPLP	H	Gainsborough Trinity	240	L 0 - 1			9
31	**FAT3Q**	**A**	**Radcliffe**	**447**	**W 2 - 1**	**Dudley 17 Roache 48**		10
Nov 3	NPLP	A	Morpeth Town	300	L 1 - 2	Thomason 81	20	11
Dec 12	**FAT1P**	**A**	**Witton Albion**	**300**	**L 0 - 2**			12

Goalscorers	LGE	FAC	FAT	SG	HAT	PEN	1Q	2Q	45+	3Q	4Q	90+	T
TOTALS	6	0	2		0	0	2	0	0	1	5	0	8
Dudley	1		1	2			2						2
Thomason	2			2							2		2
Burton	1			1							1		1
Forbes	1			1							1		1
O'Reilly	1			1							1		1
Roache			1	1						1			1

BASFORD UNITED MATCH RESULTS 2020-21

Date	Comp	H/A	Opponents	Att:	Result	Goalscorers	Pos	No.
Sept 19	NPLP	H	Warrington Town	318	L 0 - 2		19	1
22	**FAC1Q**	**A**	**Chasetown**	**266**	**L 1 - 2**	**Richards 27**		2
26	NPLP	A	Lancaster City	196	W 2 - 1	Galinski 26 Howes 52	13	3
29	NPLP	A	Matlock Town	444	D 2 - 2	Richards 38 Thornhill 65	10	4
Oct 3	NPLP	A	Witton Albion	246	L 0 - 2		12	5
10	NPLP	A	Radcliffe	446	W 3 - 0	Wilson 9 Richards 50 Thornhill 56 (pen)	8	6
17	NPLP	H	Bamber Bridge	271	W 2 - 1	Thornhill 10 James 14	5	7
20	NPLP	H	Stafford Rangers	257	W 1 - 0	Galinski 71	3	8
24	NPLP	A	Stalybridge Celtic	343	W 1 - 0	Chettle 37	2	9
27	NPLP	H	Scarborough Athletic	401	W 4 - 1	Galinski 18 Marshall 35 63 Richards 47	1	10
31	**FAT3Q**	**H**	**Alvechurch**	**291**	**W 2 - 1**	**Hines 86 Marshall 89**		11
Dec 8	**FAT1P**	**H**	**Rushall Olympic**		**W 5 - 0**	**Wilson 11 Gascoigne 24 Marshall 49 Chettle 58 James 70**		12
12	**FAT2P**	**H**	**Felixstowe & Walton United**	**247**	**W 3 - 0**	**Galinski 30 Marshall 70 (pen) Chettle 77**		13
19	**FAT3P**	**A**	**Peterborough Sports**		**L 2 - 3**	**Wilson 3 Richards 41**		14

Goalscorers	LGE	FAC	FAT	SG	HAT	PEN	1Q	2Q	45+	3Q	4Q	90+	T
TOTALS	15	1	12		0	2	6	8	0	8	6	0	28
Marshall	2		3	4		1		1		2	2		5
Richards	3	1	1	5				3		2			5
Galinski	3		1	4			1	2			1		4
Chettle	1		2	3				1		1	1		3
Thornhill	3			3		1	1			2			3
Wilson	1		2	3			3						3
James	1		1	2			1				1		2
Gascoigne			1	1				1					1
Hines			1	1							1		1
Howes	1			1						1			1

BUXTON MATCH RESULTS 2020-21

Date	Comp	H/A	Opponents	Att:	Result		Goalscorers	Pos	No.
Sept 19	NPLP	H	Radcliffe	395	W	4 - 2	Walshaw 18 Dawson 37 De Girolamo 53 (pen) O'Grady 76	2	1
22	**FAC1Q**	**H**	**Belper Town**	**317**	**W**	**7 - 0**	**Hurst 8 Walshaw 19 21 51 De Girolamo 62 69 80**		
26	NPLP	H	Whitby Town	346	D	2 - 2	King 14 De Girolamo 53 (pen)	4	2
29	NPLP	A	Nantwich Town	363	L	1 - 3	De Girolamo 6	7	3
Oct 3	**FAC2Q**	**H**	**Stafford Rangers**	**401**	**D**	**0 - 0**	**(Lost 2-4 on pens)**		4
10	NPLP	A	Stalybridge Celtic	409	W	4 - 0	De Girolamo 12 75 (pen) Killock 24 Clarke 60	4	
13	NPLP	H	Scarborough Athletic	427	W	4 - 1	Walshaw 27 39 75 King 84	2	5
20	NPLP	H	Mickleover	368	D	2 - 2	De Girolamo 32 45	5	6
24	NPLP	A	Bamber Bridge	325	W	2 - 1	De Girolamo 21 Dawson 29	4	7
31	**FAT3Q**	**A**	**Brighouse Town**	**276**	**W**	**2 - 0**	**Walsahw 55 Styche 90**		
Nov 3	NPLP	H	Stafford Rangers	288	W	3 - 1	Elliott 39 De Girolamo 62 Styche 77	3	8
Dec 8	**FAT1P**	**H**	**City of Liverpool**		**L**	**1 - 2**	**De Girolamo 80**		9

Goalscorers	LGE	FAC	FAT	SG	HAT	PEN	1Q	2Q	45+	3Q	4Q	90+	T
TOTALS	22	7	3		3	3	8	7	1	7	7	2	32
De Girolamo	9	3	1	9	1	3	3	1	1	4	4		13
Walshaw	4	3	1	4	2		3	2		2	1		8
Dawson	2			2				2					2
King	2			2			1				1		2
Styche	1		1	2								2	2
Clarke	1			1						1			1
Elliott	1			1				1					1
Hurst		1		1			1						1
Killock	1			1				1					1
O'Grady	1			1							1		1

FC UNITED OF MANCHESTER MATCH RESULTS 2020-21

Date	Comp	H/A	Opponents	Att:	Result		Goalscorers	Pos	No.
Sept 19	NPLP	H	Nantwich Town	547	D	1 - 1	Ennis 63	9	1
22	**FAC1Q**	**H**	**Pontefract Collieries**	**534**	**W**	**6 - 2**	**Ennis 4 31 (pen) Linney 10 Cockerline 16 Donohue 35 Morris 87**		2
26	NPLP	H	Scarborough Athletic	600	D	0 - 0		15	3
29	NPLP	A	Hyde United	600	D	2 - 2	Jones 21 Doyle 66	14	4
Oct 3	**FAC2Q**	**A**	**Curzon Ashton**		**W**	**2 - 1**	**Linney 11 Ennis 71**		5
17	NPLP	H	Stafford Rangers	600	W	2 - 1	Cockerline 40 Fowler 71	13	6
20	NPLP	H	Lancaster City	600	D	1 - 1	Cockerline 50	12	7
24	**FAC4Q**	**H**	**Guiseley**	**600**	**W**	**2 - 1**	**Ennis 10 (pen) Sinclair-Smith 90**		8
27	NPLP	A	South Shields	300	L	0 - 1			9
31	**FAT3Q**	**H**	**Marske United**	**600**	**L**	**2 - 3**	**Jones 13 Fowler 89**		10
Nov 3	NPLP	H	Warrington Town	600	W	3 - 1	Sinclair-Smith 9 38 Jones 25	13	11
7	**FAC1P**	**H**	**Doncaster Rovers**		**L**	**1 - 5**	**Linney 30**		12
									13

Goalscorers	LGE	FAC	FAT	SG	HAT	PEN	1Q	2Q	45+	3Q	4Q	90+	T
TOTALS	9	11	2		0	2	8	6	0	3	4	1	22
Ennis	1	4		4		2	2	1		1	1		5
Cockerline	2	1		3			1	1		1			3
Jones	2		1	3			2	1					3
Linney		3		3			2	1					3
Sinclair-Smith	2	1		2			1	1				1	3
Fowler	1		1	2							2		2
Donohue		1		1				1					1
Doyle	1			1						1			1
Morris		1		1							1		1

GAINSBOROUGH TRINITY MATCH RESULTS 2020-21

Date	Comp	H/A	Opponents	Att:	Result	Goalscorers	Pos	No.
Sept 19	NPLP	H	Hyde United	583	W 2 - 0	Fyfe 22 Smith 66	3	1
22	**FAC1Q**	**A**	**AFC Mansfield**	**201**	**L 0 - 3**			2
26	NPLP	A	Warrington Town	416	L 0 - 3		14	3
29	NPLP	H	Whitby Town	421	W 5 - 1	Orlando-Young 7 10 62 83 Grant 54	4	4
Oct 17	NPLP	H	Witton Albion	594	L 1 - 3	Orlando-Young 4	12	5
20	NPLP	H	Stalybridge Celtic	421	W 3 - 2	Woolford 29 Fyfe 37 39	10	6
24	NPLP	A	Radcliffe	500	L 1 - 2	Ainge 42	13	7
27	NPLP	A	Bamber Bridge	240	W 1 - 0	Ainge 80		8
31	**FAT3Q**	**A**	**Peterborough Sports**		**L 2 - 4**	**Ainge 34 Greaves 54**		9
Nov 3	NPLP	H	South Shields	557	L 0 - 1		10	10

Goalscorers	LGE	FAC	FAT	SG	HAT	PEN	1Q	2Q	45+	3Q	4Q	90+	T
TOTALS	13	0	2		0	0	4	5	0	4	2	0	15
Orlando-Young	5			2			3			1	1		5
Ainge	2		1	3				2			1		3
Fyfe	3			2			1	2					3
Grant	1			1						1			1
Greaves			1	1						1			1
Smith	1			1						1			1
Woolford	1			1				1					1

GRANTHAM TOWN MATCH RESULTS 2020-21

Date	Comp	H/A	Opponents	Att:	Result	Goalscorers	Pos	No.
Sept 19	NPLP	A	Morpeth Town	403	D 1 - 1	Worsfold 53	10	1
22	**FAC1Q**	**H**	**Rushall Olympic**	**232**	**D 2 - 2**	**Dyer 16 Kianga 25 (Won 3-1 on pens)**		2
26	NPLP	H	Atherton Collieries	231	L 1 - 2	Doran 68	16	3
29	NPLP	H	Stafford Rangers	201	D 1 - 1	Holland 67	18	4
Oct 3	**FAC2Q**	**H**	**Matlock Town**	**349**	**L 0 - 1**			5
10	NPLP	A	Whitby Town	387	L 0 - 2		20	6
17	NPLP	H	Lancaster City	216	L 2 - 4	Young 21 Hardy 71	20	7
20	NPLP	H	Matlock Town	182	L 0 - 1		20	8
24	NPLP	A	Mickleover	425	L 0 - 3		20	9
31	**FAT3Q**	**A**	**Yaxley**	**119**	**W 2 - 0**	**Hardy 17 (pen) Campbell 76**		10
Nov 3	NPLP	H	Stalybridge Celtic	201	D 0 - 0		21	11
Dec 10	**FAT1P**	**H**	**St Ives Town**		**L 3 - 4**	**Hardy 10 36 Worsfold 28**		12

Goalscorers	LGE	FAC	FAT	SG	HAT	PEN	1Q	2Q	45+	3Q	4Q	90+	T
TOTALS	5	2	5		0	1	4	3	0	2	3	0	12
Hardy	1		3	3		1	2	1			1		4
Worsfold	1		1	2				1		1			2
Campbell			1	1							1		1
Doran	1			1							1		1
Dyer		1		1			1						1
Holland	1			1						1			1
Kianga		1		1				1					1
Young	1			1			1						1

HYDE UNITED MATCH RESULTS 2020-21

Date	Comp	H/A	Opponents	Att:	Result	Goalscorers	Pos	No.
Sept 19	NPLP	A	Gainsborough Trinity	583	L 0 - 2		20	1
22	**FAC1Q**	**A**	**West Allotment Celtic**	**145**	**W 5 - 0**	**Lane 15 Tongue 23 65 James 47 Walker 73 (og)**		2
26	NPLP	H	South Shields	587	D 0 - 0		18	3
29	NPLP	H	FC United of Manchester	600	D 2 - 2	Tongue 19 Lane 41	19	4
Oct 3	**FAC2Q**	**H**	**AFC Fylde**	**404**	**L 2 - 4**	**Hollins 24 Morris 84**		5
10	NPLP	A	Stafford Rangers	578	W 2 - 0	Lane 34 (pen) Uche 90	13	6
27	NPLP	A	Mickleover	221	L 0 - 1			7
31	**FAT3Q**	**H**	**Frickley Athletic**	**273**	**W 2 - 1**	**James 30 Hollins 59**		8
Nov 3	NPLP	H	Lancaster City	305	D 1 - 1	Hollins 7	17	9
Dec 12	**FAT1P**	**A**	**Marine**	**400**	**L 0 - 1**			10

Goalscorers	LGE	FAC	FAT	SG	HAT	PEN	1Q	2Q	45+	3Q	4Q	90+	T
TOTALS	5	7	2		0	1	3	5	0	3	2	1	14
Hollins	1	1	1	3			1	1		1			3
Lane	2	1		3		1	1	2					3
Tongue	1	2		2			1	1		1			3
James		1	1	2				1		1			2
Morris		1		1							1		1
Opponent		1		1							1		1
Uche	1			1								1	1

LANCASTER CITY MATCH RESULTS 2020-21

Date	Comp	H/A	Opponents	Att:	Result	Goalscorers	Pos	No.
Sept 19	NPLP	A	Stalybridge Celtic	370	D 1 - 1	Kilfin 83	11	1
22	**FAC1Q**	**H**	**Runcorn Town**	**273**	**D 0 - 0**	**(Won 4-3 on pens)**		2, 3
26	NPLP	H	Basford United	196	L 1 - 2	Teague 30	17	4
29	NPLP	H	Morpeth Town	200	D 2 - 2	Turner 7 Norris 11	17	5
Oct 3	**FAC2Q**	**A**	**Skelmersdale United**		**L 1 - 2**	**Bailey C 52**		6
17	NPLP	A	Grantham Town	216	W 4 - 2	Kilfin 7 Bailey S 16 Bailey C 19 Norris 64	15	7, 8
20	NPLP	A	FC United of Manchester	600	D 1 - 1	Kilfin 55	14	9
24	NPLP	H	Warrington Town	197	W 2 - 1	Norris 66 Holland-Wilkinson 72	11	10
31	**FAT3Q**	**A**	**Warrington Town**	**406**	**D 1 - 1**	**Cowperthwaite 90 (Lost 3-4 on pens)**		11, 12
Nov 3	NPLP	A	Hyde United	305	D 1 - 1	Holland-Wilkinson 4	12	13

Goalscorers	LGE	FAC	FAT	SG	HAT	PEN	1Q	2Q	45+	3Q	4Q	90+	T
TOTALS	12	1	1		0	0	6	1	0	4	2	1	14
Kilfin	3			3			1			1	1		3
Norris	3			3			1			2			3
Bailey C	1	1		2			1			1			2
Holland-Wilkinson	2			2			1				1		2
Bailey S	1			1			1						1
Cowperthwaite			1	1								1	1
Teague	1			1				1					1
Turner	1			1			1						1

MATLOCK TOWN MATCH RESULTS 2020-21

Date	Comp	H/A	Opponents	Att:	Result	Goalscorers	Pos	No.
Sept 19	NPLP	A	Bamber Bridge	397	L 0 - 1		15	1
22	**FAC1Q**	**A**	**Quorn**	**295**	**W 2 - 0**	**Hughes 63 85**		2
26	NPLP	H	Stafford Rangers	453	W 2 - 0	Hughes 62 Greenfield 72	9	3
29	NPLP	H	Basford United	444	D 2 - 2	Kendall 45 Hughes 67	9	4
Oct 3	**FAC2Q**	**A**	**Grantham Town**	**349**	**W 1 - 0**	**Dolan 79**		5
10	NPLP	H	Ashton United	532	W 4 - 1	Walker 5 (pen) Wilson 38 (og) Byrne 66 Hughes 79	5	6
13	**FAC3Q**	**A**	**Guiseley**		**L 0 - 2**			7
17	NPLP	A	South Shields	300	W 1 - 0	Byrne 70	4	8
20	NPLP	A	Grantham Town	182	W 1 - 0	Walker 24 (pen)	2	9
Nov 3	**FAT3Q**	**A**	**Coalville Town**	**362**	**D 3 - 3**	**Kendall 47 Harris 54 Walker 84 (Won 4-2 on pens)**		10
Dec 8	**FAT1P**	**A**	**Coleshill Town**		**L 2 - 5**	**Qualter 41 Walker 89**		11
								12

Goalscorers	LGE	FAC	FAT	SG	HAT	PEN	1Q	2Q	45+	3Q	4Q	90+	T
TOTALS	10	3	5		0	2	1	3	1	6	7	0	18
Hughes	3	2		4						3	2		5
Walker	2		2	4		2	1	1			2		4
Byrne	2			2						1	1		2
Kendall	1		1	2					1	1			2
Dolan		1		1							1		1
Greenfield	1			1							1		1
Harris			1	1						1			1
Opponent	1			1				1					1
Qualter			1	1				1					1

MICKLEOVER FC MATCH RESULTS 2020-21

Date	Comp	H/A	Opponents	Att:	Result	Goalscorers	Pos	No.
Sept 19	NPLP	A	South Shields	600	L 0 - 3		22	1
22	**FAC1Q**	**A**	**Leek Town**	**400**	**W 2 - 1**	**Beavon 27 Bacon 49**		2
26	NPLP	H	Morpeth Town	307	L 1 - 2	Beavon 47	21	3
29	NPLP	H	Witton Albion	237	W 2 - 1	Milner 36 Wright 87	15	4
Oct 3	**FAC2Q**	**H**	**Newark**	**432**	**W 4 - 1**	**Beavon 33 Wright 69 79 Bacon 90**		5
10	NPLP	H	Warrington Town	425	W 3 - 2	Watt 36 Bacon 61 Beavon 80	11	6
13	**FAC3Q**	**A**	**St Albans City**		**D 1 - 1**	**Bacon 52 (Lost 4-5 on pens)**		7
17	NPLP	A	Ashton United	258	W 3 - 0	Butler 5 Beavon 16 Bennet 61	6	8
20	NPLP	A	Buxton	368	D 2 - 2	Watt 22 Bacon 43	8	9
24	NPLP	H	Grantham Town	425	W 3 - 0	Beavon 40 Bacon 53 Webb 82 (pen)	6	10
27	NPLP	H	Hyde United	221	W 1 - 0	Milner 55	3	11
31	**FAT3Q**	**H**	**Dereham Town**	**203**	**W 5 - 0**	**Webb 3 57 Beavon 60 77 Satchwell 90**		12
Nov 3	NPLP	A	Nantwich Town	301	W 4 - 0	Watt 18 Bennett 47 Webb 60 Verma 84	1	13
Dec 8	**FAT1P**	**A**	**Hitchin Town**	**203**	**L 0 - 3**			14
19	NPLP	H	Radcliffe	207	W 4 - 1	Watt 29 Bacon 75 90 (pen) Wright 87 (pen)	1	15

Goalscorers	LGE	FAC	FAT	SG	HAT	PEN	1Q	2Q	45+	3Q	4Q	90+	T
TOTALS	23	7	5		0	3	5	7	0	11	9	3	35
Bacon	5	3		7		1		1		4	1	2	8
Beavon	4	2	2	7			1	3		2	2		8
Watt	4			4			2	2					4
Webb	2		2	3		1	1			2	1		4
Wright	2	2		3		1					4		4
Bennett	2			2						2			2
Milner	2			2				1		1			2
Butler	1			1			1						1
Satchwell			1	1								1	1
Verma	1			1							1		1

MORPETH TOWN MATCH RESULTS 2020-21

Date	Comp	H/A	Opponents	Att:	Result	Goalscorers	Pos	No.
Sept 19	NPLP	H	Grantham Town	403	D 1 - 1	Johnson 39	12	1
22	**FAC1Q**	**A**	**City of Liverpool**	**200**	**W 3 - 0**	**Foalle 34 76 Henderson 84**		2
26	NPLP	A	Mickleover	307	W 2 - 1	Noble 17 Johnson 68	7	3
29	NPLP	A	Lancaster City	200	D 2 - 2	Henderson 53 Finnigan 90	6	4
Oct 3	**FAC2Q**	**A**	**Southport**		**L 1 - 2**	**Henderson 18**		5
20	NPLP	A	South Shields	300	D 0 - 0		15	6
24	NPLP	A	Whitby Town	316	L 1 - 2	Hutchinson 83	16	7
27	NPLP	A	Stalybridge Celtic	259	L 1 - 3	Foalle 24		8
31	**FAT3Q**	**H**	**Whitby Town**	**300**	**W 3 - 1**	**Henderson 30 Sayer 37 (pen) Noble 39**		9
Nov 3	NPLP	H	Bamber Bridge	300	W 2 - 1	Sayer 18 (pen) Reid 36	16	10
Dec 8	**FAT1P**	**A**	**Runcorn Linnets**	**270**	**D 2 - 2**	**Hutchinson 27 Foalle 41 (Won 3-2 on pens)**		11
15	**FAT2P**	**A**	**Blyth Spartans**			**Walkover**		12
19	**FAT3P**	**H**	**Notts County**		**L 0 - 3**			13

Goalscorers	LGE	FAC	FAT	SG	HAT	PEN	1Q	2Q	45+	3Q	4Q	90+	T
TOTALS	9	4	5		0	2	3	9	0	1	4	1	18
Henderson	2	2	1	5			1	1		1	2		5
Foalle	1	2	1	3				3			1		4
Johnson	2			2				1			1		2
Noble	1		1	2			1	1					2
Sayer	1		1	2		2	1	1					2
Finnigan	1			1								1	1
Hutchinson			1	1				1					1
Reid	1			1				1					1

NANTWICH TOWN MATCH RESULTS 2020-21

Date	Comp	H/A	Opponents	Att:	Result	Goalscorers	Pos	No.
Sept 19	NPLP	A	FC United of Manchester	547	D 1 - 1	Cooke 68	13	1
22	**FAC1Q**	**A**	**Tividale**	**137**	**W 4 - 2**	**Saunders 4 (pen) 63 Malkin 20 49**		2
26	NPLP	H	Stalybridge Celtic	520	W 3 - 0	Stair 28 Heath 68 Haywood 90	2	3
29	NPLP	H	Buxton	363	W 2 - 1	Lawrie 86 (pen) Stair 88	3	4
Oct 3	**FAC2Q**	**H**	**Barwell**	**225**	**W 1 - 0**	**Mwasile 43**		5
13	**FAC3Q**	**A**	**Marine**	**397**	**L 1 - 4**	**Cooke 59**		6
17	NPLP	A	Scarborough Athletic	600	D 1 - 1	Heath 78	7	7
20	NPLP	A	Warrington Town	467	D 2 - 2	Mwasile 21 Heath 85	9	8
31	**FAT3Q**	**A**	**Redditch United**	**341**	**W 3 - 2**	**Saunders 49 87 Haywood 56**		9
Nov 3	NPLP	H	Mickleover	301	L 0 - 4		15	10
Dec 8	**FAT1P**	**H**	**Workington**	**272**	**W 3 - 1**	**Saunders 20 McGowan 31 90**		11
15	**FAT2P**	**A**	**Witton Albion**	**351**	**W 5 - 2**	**McGowan 28 41 Harrison 55 Webb 67 Walsh 90**		12
19	**FAT3P**	**H**	**Herford**	**433**	**L 0 - 1**			13

Goalscorers	LGE	FAC	FAT	SG	HAT	PEN	1Q	2Q	45+	3Q	4Q	90+	T
TOTALS	9	6	11		0	2	4	6	0	6	7	3	26
Saunders		2	3	3		1	2	1		1	1		5
McGowan			4	2				3				1	4
Heath	3			3							3		3
Cooke	1	1		2						1	1		2
Haywood	1		1	2						1		1	2
Malkin		2		1			1			1			2
Mwasile	1	1		2			1	1					2
Stair	2			2				1			1		2
Harrison			1	1						1			1
Lawrie	1			1		1					1		1
Walsh			1	1								1	1
Webb			1	1						1			1

RADCLIFFE FC MATCH RESULTS 2020-21

Date	Comp	H/A	Opponents	Att:	Result	Goalscorers	Pos	No.
Sept 19	NPLP	A	Buxton	395	L 2 - 4	Crothers 31 (pen) Navarro 57	17	1
22	**FAC1Q**	**H**	**Workington**	**309**	**W 5 - 3**	**Owens 27 90 Crothers 71 90 Akpro 79**		2
26	NPLP	H	Witton Albion	424	L 1 - 4	Crothers 79	22	3
Oct 3	**FAC2Q**	**A**	**Farsley Celtic**		**L 1 - 2**	**Hall 61**		4
6	NPLP	A	South Shields	300	W 3 - 1	Akpro 1 83 Hall 60	15	5
10	NPLP	H	Basford United	446	L 0 - 3		18	6
13	NPLP	H	Bamber Bridge	342	W 2 - 1	Cole 16 Akpro 48	13	7
17	NPLP	A	Warrington Town	476	L 1 - 2	Akpro 68	14	8
24	NPLP	H	Gainsborough Trinity	500	W 2 - 1	Owens 17 74	14	9
27	NPLP	H	Whitby Town	377	D 3 - 3	Cole 5 Hall 50 87		10
31	**FAT3Q**	**H**	**Bamber Bridge**	**447**	**L 1 - 2**	**Akpro 45**		11
Dec 19	NPLP	A	Mickleover	207	L 1 - 4	Owens 51 (pen)	14	12

Goalscorers	LGE	FAC	FAT	SG	HAT	PEN	1Q	2Q	45+	3Q	4Q	90+	T
TOTALS	15	6	1		0	2	4	2	1	6	5	4	22
Akpro	4	1	1	5			1		1	1	2	1	6
Owens	3	2		3		1	1	1		1		2	5
Crothers	2	2		3		1		1			2	1	4
Hall	3	1		3						3	1		4
Cole	2			2			2						2
Navarro	1			1						1			1

SCARBOROUGH ATHLETIC MATCH RESULTS 2020-21

Date	Comp	H/A	Opponents	Att:	Result	Goalscorers	Pos	No.
Sept 19	NPLP	A	Atherton Collieries	405	W 2 - 0	Cartman 1 54	4	1
22	**FAC1Q**	**H**	**Ashton United**		**L 0 - 2**			2
26	NPLP	A	FC United of Manchester	600	D 0 - 0		6	3
29	NPLP	A	Stalybridge Celtic	313	W 3 - 0	Cartman 3 Barrett 22 44	2	4
Oct 10	NPLP	A	Witton Albion	441	L 0 - 1		7	5
13	NPLP	A	Buxton	427	L 1 - 4	Cartman 52	7	6
17	NPLP	H	Nantwich Town	600	D 1 - 1	Cartman 54 (pen)	9	7
20	NPLP	H	Whitby Town	600	W 2 - 1	Coulson 26 Cartman 82	6	8
27	NPLP	A	Basford United	401	L 1 - 4	Coulson 76		9
31	**FAT3Q**	**H**	**Witton Albion**			**Walkover for Witton.**		10

Goalscorers	LGE	FAC	FAT	SG	HAT	PEN	1Q	2Q	45+	3Q	4Q	90+	T
TOTALS	10	0	0		0	1	3	2	0	3	2	0	10
Cartman	6			5		1	2			3	1		6
Barrett	2			1			1	1					2
Coulson	2			2				1			1		2

SOUTH SHIELDS MATCH RESULTS 2020-21

Date	Comp	H/A	Opponents	Att:	Result	Goalscorers	Pos	No.
Sept 19	NPLP	H	Mickleover Sports	600	W 3 - 0	Lowe 2 Shaw 68 Gilchrist 90	1	1
22	**FAC1Q**	**A**	**Warrington Town**	**426**	**D 0 - 0**	**(Won 6-5 on pens)**		2
26	NPLP	A	Hyde United	587	D 0 - 0		3	3
29	NPLP	A	Ashton United	285	D 3 - 3	Gilchrist 57 78 Briggs 76	5	4
Oct 3	**FAC2Q**	**A**	**Ashton United**	**310**	**W 4 - 0**	**Gilchrist 25 Osei 33 Briggs 69 Ross 86**		5
6	NPLP	H	Radcliffe FC	300	L 1 - 3	Kempster 32	6	6
10	NPLP	A	Bamber Bridge	450	W 3 - 1	Gilchrist 4 33 60	3	7
13	**FAC3Q**	**A**	**Southport**		**D 1 - 1**	**Osei 74 (Won 4-2 on pens)**		8
17	NPLP	H	Matlock Town	300	L 0 - 1		8	9
20	NPLP	H	Morpeth Town	300	D 0 - 0		11	10
24	**FAC4Q**	**H**	**FC Halifax**	**300**	**W 2 - 0**	**Osei 38 Briggs 71**		11
27	NPLP	H	FC United of Manchester	300	W 1 - 0	Gillies 83		12
31	**FAT3Q**	**H**	**Colne**	**300**	**W 1 - 0**	**Briggs 54**		13
Nov 3	NPLP	A	Gainsborough Trinity	557	W 1 - 0	Briggs 66 (pen)	6	14
7	**FAC1P**	**A**	**Cheltenham Town**		**L 1 - 3**	**Osei 18**		15
Dec 8	**FAT1P**	**A**	**Ashton United**		**L 1 - 2**	**Sterry 66**		16

Goalscorers	LGE	FAC	FAT	SG	HAT	PEN	1Q	2Q	45+	3Q	4Q	90+	T
TOTALS	12	8	2		1	1	3	5	0	5	8	1	22
Gilchrist	6	1		4	1		1	2		2	1	1	7
Briggs	2	2	1	5		1				2	3		5
Osei		4		4			1	2			1		4
Gillies	1			1							1		1
Kempster	1			1				1					1
Lowe	1			1			1						1
Ross		1		1							1		1
Shaw	1			1							1		1
Sterry			1	1						1			1

STAFFORD RANGERS MATCH RESULTS 2020-21

Date	Comp	H/A	Opponents	Att:	Result	Goalscorers	Pos	No.
Sept 19	NPLP	H	Ashton United	595	L 0 - 1		16	1
22	**FAC1Q**	**A**	**Worcester City**	**300**	**W 3 - 2**	**Kenton 32 Cuff 36 75**		2
26	NPLP	A	Matlock Town	453	L 0 - 2		20	3
29	NPLP	A	Grantham Town	201	D 1 - 1	Holland 50 (og)	20	4
Oct 3	**FAC2Q**	**A**	**Buxton**	**401**	**D 0 - 0**	**(Won 4-2 on pens)**		5
10	NPLP	H	Hyde United		L 0 - 2		21	6
13	**FAC3Q**	**H**	**Hereford**	**585**	**W 3 - 1**	**Cuff 28 82 Coyle 90**		7
17	NPLP	A	FC United of Manchester	600	L 1 - 2	Sebbeh-Njie 27	22	8
20	NPLP	A	Basford United	257	L 0 - 1		22	9
24	**FAC4Q**	**H**	**Skelmersdale United**	**600**	**L 1 - 4**	**Cuff 78**		10
27	NPLP	H	Atherton Collieries	457	L 0 - 3			11
31	**FAT3Q**	**A**	**St Ives Town**	**156**	**D 1 - 1**	**Cuff 13 (Lost 1-4 on pens)**		12
Nov 3	NPLP	A	Buxton	288	L 1 - 3	Candlin 86	22	13

Goalscorers	LGE	FAC	FAT	SG	HAT	PEN	1Q	2Q	45+	3Q	4Q	90+	T
TOTALS	3	7	1		0	0	1	4	0	1	4	1	11
Cuff		5	1	4			1	2			3		6
Candlin	1			1							1		1
Coyle		1		1								1	1
Kenton		1		1				1					1
Opponent	1			1						1			1
Sebbeh-Njie	1			1				1					1

STALYBRIDGE CELTIC MATCH RESULTS 2020-21

Date	Comp	H/A	Opponents	Att:	Result	Goalscorers	Pos	No.
Sept 12	**FACP**	**A**	**Stocksbridge Park Steels**	**361**	**W 3 - 1**	**Burke 12 Prifti 60 Deacon 90**		1
19	NPLP	H	Lancaster City	370	D 1 - 1	Doyle 40	14	2
22	**FAC1Q**	**H**	**Bishop Auckland**	**332**	**W 3 - 0**	**Burke 22 Freedman 51 Salmon 77**		3
26	NPLP	A	Nantwich Town	520	L 0 - 3		19	4
29	NPLP	H	Scarborough Athletic	313	L 0 - 3		21	5
Oct 3	**FAC2Q**	**H**	**Longridge Town**	**448**	**L 2 - 3**	**Harris 72 Ustabas 87**		6
10	NPLP	H	Buxton	409	L 0 - 4		21	7
17	NPLP	A	Atherton Collieries	360	D 1 - 1	Goodwin 26	21	8
20	NPLP	A	Gainsborough Trinity	421	L 2 - 3	Ustabas 14 Doyle 43	21	9
24	NPLP	H	Basford United	343	L 0 - 1		21	10
27	NPLP	H	Morpeth Town	259	W 3 - 1	Salmon 23 Sephton 26 Makinson 33		11
31	**FAT3Q**	**A**	**Marine**	**400**	**L 2 - 3**	**Hawley 36 Ustabus 48**		12
Nov 3	NPLP	A	Grantham Town	201	D 0 - 0		18	13

Goalscorers	LGE	FAC	FAT	SG	HAT	PEN	1Q	2Q	45+	3Q	4Q	90+	T
TOTALS	7	8	2		0	0	3	7	0	3	3	1	17
Ustabas	1	1	1	3			1			1	1		3
Burke		2		2			2						2
Doyle	2			2				2					2
Salmon	1	1		2				1			1		2
Deacon		1		1								1	1
Freedman		1		1						1			1
Goodwin	1			1				1					1
Harris		1		1							1		1
Hawley			1	1				1					1
Makinson	1			1				1					1
Prifti		1		1						1			1
Sephton	1			1				1					1

WARRINGTON TOWN MATCH RESULTS 2020-21

Date	Comp	H/A	Opponents	Att:	Result	Goalscorers	Pos	No.
Sept 19	NPLP	A	Basford United	318	W 2 - 0	Dunn 29 Dixon 41 (pen)	5	1
22	**FAC1Q**	**H**	**South Shields**	**426**	**D 0 - 0**	**(Lost 5-6 on pens)**		2
26	NPLP	H	Gainsborough Trinity	416	W 3 - 0	Dixon 16 67 (pen) Amis 41	1	3
29	NPLP	H	Atherton Collieries	420	W 2 - 0	Roberts 50 Amis 67	1	4
Oct 3	NPLP	H	Whitby Town	273	W 1 - 0	Regan 45	1	5
10	NPLP	A	Mickleover Sports	425	L 2 - 3	Amis 12 Buckley 90	1	6
17	NPLP	H	Radcliffe	476	W 2 - 1	Dixon 12 (pen) Duffy 40	1	7
20	NPLP	H	Nantwich Town	467	D 2 - 2	Dunn 48 Amis 90	1	8
24	NPLP	A	Lancaster City	197	L 1 - 2	Buckley 77	1	9
31	**FAT3Q**	**H**	**Lancaster City**	**406**	**D 1 - 1**	**Buckley 28 (Won 4-3 on pens)**		10
Nov 3	NPLP	A	FC United of Manchester	600	L 1 - 3	Duffy 14	4	11
Dec 8	**FAT1P**	**A**	**Marske United**		**L 1 - 3**	**Gumbs 27**		12

Goalscorers	LGE	FAC	FAT	SG	HAT	PEN	1Q	2Q	45+	3Q	4Q	90+	T
TOTALS	16	0	2		0	3	3	7	1	4	1	2	18
Amis	4			4			1	1		1		1	4
Dixon	4			3		3	2	1		1			4
Buckley	2		1	3				1			1	1	3
Duffy	2			2				2					2
Dunn	2			2				1		1			2
Gumbs			1	1				1					1
Regan	1			1					1				1
Roberts	1			1						1			1

WHITBY TOWN MATCH RESULTS 2020-21

Date	Comp	H/A	Opponents	Att:	Result		Goalscorers	Pos	No.
Sept 19	NPLP	A	Witton Albion	378	W	2 - 0	Rowe 57 Cobain 87	6	1
22	**FAC1Q**	**H**	**Warrington Rylands**		**D**	**1 - 1**	**Martin 90 (Lost 3-4 on pens)**		2
26	NPLP	A	Buxton	346	D	2 - 2	Giles 79 Hazel 81	5	3
29	NPLP	A	Gainsborough Trinity	421	L	1 - 5	Hazel 46	11	4
Oct 3	NPLP	A	Warrington Town	273	L	0 - 1		11	5
10	NPLP	H	Grantham Town	387	W	2 - 0	Fewster 19 30	9	6
20	NPLP	A	Scarborough Athletic	600	L	1 - 2	Hazel 11 (pen)	13	7
24	NPLP	H	Morpeth Town	316	W	2 - 1	Hazel 14 35	9	8
27	NPLP	A	Radcliffe	377	D	3 - 3	Cooke 10 Giles 29 55 (pen)	10	9
31	**FAT3Q**	**A**	**Morpeth Town**	**300**	**L**	**1 - 3**	**Giles 42**		10
Nov 3	NPLP	H	Ashton United	264	W	2 - 0	Giles 58 (pen) Fewster 80	7	11

Goalscorers	LGE	FAC	FAT	SG	HAT	PEN	1Q	2Q	45+	3Q	4Q	90+	T
TOTALS	15	1	1		0	3	4	4	0	4	4	1	17
Giles	4		1	4		2		2		2	1		5
Hazel	5			4		1	2	1		1	1		5
Fewster	3			2			1	1			1		3
Cobain	1			1							1		1
Cooke	1			1			1						1
Martin		1		1								1	1
Rowe	1			1						1			1

WITTON ALBION MATCH RESULTS 2020-21

Date	Comp	H/A	Opponents	Att:	Result		Goalscorers	Pos	No.
Sept 19	NPLP	H	Whitby Town	378	L	0 - 2		21	1
22	**FAC1Q**	**A**	**Whitley Bay**	**253**	**L**	**2 - 3**	**Jones 12 Wardle 85**		2
26	NPLP	A	Radcliffe	424	W	4 - 1	Bakkor 5 8 33 Jones 85	8	3
29	NPLP	A	Mickleover	237	L	1 - 2	Smart 89	13	4
Oct 3	NPLP	H	Basford United	246	W	2 - 0	Carr 3 (og) McNulty 7	5	5
10	NPLP	H	Scarborough Athletic	441	W	1 - 0	Bakkor 53	2	6
17	NPLP	A	Gainsborough Trinity	594	W	3 - 1	Baldwin 7 Owens 54 Hooper 89	2	7
24	NPLP	H	Atherton Collieries	443	W	2 - 1	Jones 2 Foley 15 (pen)	3	8
31	**FAT3Q**	**A**	**Scarborough Athletic**				**Walkover**		9
Dec 12	**FAT1P**	**H**	**Bamber Bridge**	**300**	**W**	**2 - 0**	**Jones 24 Baldwin 34**		10
15	**FAT2P**	**H**	**Nantwich Town**	**351**	**L**	**2 - 5**	**Bakkor 8 Hopley 90**		11

Goalscorers	LGE	FAC	FAT	SG	HAT	PEN	1Q	2Q	45+	3Q	4Q	90+	T
TOTALS	13	2	4		1	1	9	3	0	2	4	1	19
Bakkor	4		1	3	1		3	1		1			5
Jones	2	1	1	3			2	1			1		4
Baldwin	1		1	2			1	1					2
Foley	1			1		1	1						1
Hooper	1			1							1		1
Hopley			1	1								1	1
McNulty	1			1			1						1
Opponent	1			1			1						1
Owens	1			1						1			1
Smart	1			1							1		1
Wardle		1		1							1		1

BRIGHOUSE TOWN MATCH RESULTS 2020-21

Date	Comp	H/A	Opponents	Att:	Result		Goalscorers	Pos	No.
Sept 12	**FACP**	**A**	**Runcorn Town**	**183**	**D**	**1 - 1**	**Church 74 (Lost 4-5 on pens)**		1
19	NPLNW	H	Clitheroe	327	L	1 - 2	Church 58	14	2
26	NPLNW	A	Marske United	297	L	0 - 3		19	3
Oct 5	NPLNW	H	Runcorn Linnets	346	D	3 - 3	Church 36 51 Grant 39	13	4
10	NPLNW	H	Bighouse Town	395	L	2 - 5	Harris 16 Clarke 65	18	5
17	**FAT2Q**	**A**	**Kendal Town**	**210**	**L**	**0 - 1**	**Brighouse reinstated after Kendal fielded ineligible players.**		6
20	NPLNW	A	Pickering Town	134	L	0 - 1		19	7
24	NPLNW	H	Pontefract Collieries	400	**W**	2 - 0	Boyle 9 39	16	8
31	**FAT3Q**	**H**	**Buxton**	**276**	**L**	**0 - 2**			9
Dec 19	NPLNW	H	Workington	192	D	2 - 2	Racchi 12 Clarke 90	17	10

Goalscorers	LGE	FAC	FAT	SG	HAT	PEN	1Q	2Q	45+	3Q	4Q	90+	T
TOTALS	10	1	0		0	0	3	3	0	3	1	1	11
Church	3	1		3				1		2	1		4
Boyle	2			1			1	1					2
Clarke	2			2						1		1	2
Grant	1			1				1					1
Harris	1			1			1						1
Racchi	1			1			1						1

CITY OF LIVERPOOL MATCH RESULTS 2020-21

Date	Comp	H/A	Opponents	Att:	Result		Goalscorers	Pos	No.
Sept 12	**FACP**	**A**	**Glossop North End**	**350**	**W**	**3 - 0**	**Nevitt 30 Kinsella 61 Hazelhurst 76**		1
19	NPLNW	H	Marske United	397	L	2 - 4	Burke 41 (pen) Hazelhurst 83	16	2
22	**FAC1Q**	**H**	**Morpeth Town**	**200**	**L**	**0 - 3**			3
29	NPLNW	A	Kendal Town	78	L	0 - 1		16	4
Oct 3	NPLNW	A	Workington	393	L	2 - 5	Hazelhurst 15 (pen) McGrath 86	19	5
10	NPLNW	A	Brighouse Town	396	**W**	5 - 2	Burke 31 45 (pen) Rigby 48 Nevitt 69 78	15	6
13	NPLNW	A	Prescot Cables		D	2 - 2	McCarten 19 75	14	7
20	NPLNW	H	Trafford	269	**W**	1 - 0	McCarten 79	9	8
24	NPLNW	A	Colne	281	L	2 - 4	McDonald 56 Burke 90 (pen)	10	9
Nov 4	**FAT3Q**	**A**	**Atherton Collieries**	**294**	**W**	**3 - 0**	**Reid 7 Hazelhurst 31 Bryant 51**		10
Dec 8	**FAT1P**	**A**	**Buxton**		**W**	**2 - 1**	**Hazelhurst 20 87**		11
15	**FAT2P**	**A**	**Darlington**		**L**	**0 - 2**			12
19	NPLNW	H	Pontefract Collieries	287	**W**	4 - 1	Hazelhurst 11 Rigby 20 Grey 24 Bryant 60	10	13
26	NPLNW	H	Marine	400	L	1 - 2	Hinnigan 49	10	14

Goalscorers	LGE	FAC	FAT	SG	HAT	PEN	1Q	2Q	45+	3Q	4Q	90+	T
TOTALS	19	3	5		0	3	6	5	1	6	8	1	27
Hazelhurst	3	1	3	6		1	3	1			3		7
Burke	4			3		2		2	1			1	4
McCarten	3			2			1				2		3
Nevitt	2	1		2				1			2		3
Bryant	1		1	2						2			2
Rigby	2			2			1			1			2
Grey	1			1				1					1
Hinnigan	1			1						1			1
Kinsella		1		1						1			1
McDonald	1			1						1			1
McGrath	1			1							1		1
Reid			1	1			1						1

CLITHEROE MATCH RESULTS 2020-21

Date	Comp	H/A	Opponents	Att:	Result	Goalscorers	Pos	No.
Sept 12	**FACP**	**A**	**Warrington Rylands**	**275**	**L 0 - 1**			1
19	NPLNW	A	Brighouse Town	327	**W** 2 - 1	Priestly 71 89	5	2
26	NPLNW	H	Prescot Cables	372	**W** 1 - 0	Dent 62	3	3
Oct 3	NPLNW	H	Trafford	400	D 2 - 2	Cummings 30 Gaul 65 (pen)	4	4
6	NPLNW	A	Mossley	361	**W** 3 - 1	Adams 3 Wilkins 24 Feeney 78	1	5
10	NPLNW	A	Runcorn Linnets	305	D 1 - 1	Hobson 50	4	6
13	NPLNW	H	Ramsbottom United	400	**W** 3 - 1	Wilkins 12 Adams 35 Cummings 50	2	7
17	**FAT2Q**	**A**	**Dunston**	**212**	**W 1 - 0**	**Adams 47**		8
20	NPLNW	A	Workington	400	L 1 - 2	Smalley 22	3	9
31	**FAT3Q**	**A**	**Ashton United**	**253**	**L 0 - 1**			10
Dec 22	NPLNW	H	Kendal Town	375	D 1 - 1	Adams 43	5	11
26	NPLNW	A	Widnes	148	**W** 1 - 0	Priestly 71	4	12

Goalscorers	LGE	FAC	FAT	SG	HAT	PEN	1Q	2Q	45+	3Q	4Q	90+	T
TOTALS	15	0	1		0	1	3	4	0	5	4	0	16
Adams	3		1	4			1	2		1			4
Priestly	3			2							3		3
Cummings	2			2				1		1			2
Wilkins	2			2			1	1					2
Dent	1			1						1			1

Goalscorers	LGE	FAC	FAT	SG	HAT	PEN	1Q	2Q	45+	3Q	4Q	90+	T
Feeney	1			1							1		1
Gaul	1			1		1				1			1
Hobson	1			1						1			1
Smalley	1			1			1						1

COLNE MATCH RESULTS 2020-21

Date	Comp	H/A	Opponents	Att:	Result	Goalscorers	Pos	No.
Sept 12	**FACP**	**H**	**Prescot Cables**	**270**	**L 0 - 2**			1
26	NPLNW	A	Dunston	198	**W** 1 - 0	Russell 19 (pen)	6	2
29	NPLNW	A	Marine	243	**W** 2 - 1	Cooke 21 40	6	3
Oct 3	NPLNW	A	Colne	300	**W** 1 - 0	Cooke 70	3	4
6	NPLNW	H	Workington	213	L 0 - 1		5	5
10	NPLNW	A	Widnes		D 1 - 1	Dean 10	6	6
13	NPLNW	H	Pontefract Collieries	149	**W** 6 - 2	Webb-Foster 9 Dean 13 50 Cooke 30 32 Dodd 66	3	7
17	**FAT2Q**	**A**	**Widnes**		**W 4 - 3**	**Cooke 55 71 86 Williams 56**		8
24	NPLNW	H	City of Liverpool	281	**W** 4 - 2	Cooke 25 Webb-Foster 60 74 Williams 72	3	9
31	**FAT3Q**	**A**	**South Shields**	**300**	**L 0 - 1**			10
Dec 19	NPLNW	H	Prescot Cables	200	**W** 2 - 0	Webb-Foster 23 77 (pen)	3	11
26	NPLNW	H	Kendal Town	200	**W** 3 - 2	Webb-Foster 5 57 Dean 88	1	12

Goalscorers	LGE	FAC	FAT	SG	HAT	PEN	1Q	2Q	45+	3Q	4Q	90+	T
TOTALS	20	0	4		1	2	6	5	0	6	7	0	24
Cooke	6		3	5	1		1	4		1	3		9
Webb-Foster	7			4		1	2	1		2	2		7
Dean	4			3			2			1	1		4
Williams	1		1	2						1	1		2
Dodd	1			1						1			1

Goalscorers	LGE	FAC	FAT	SG	HAT	PEN	1Q	2Q	45+	3Q	4Q	90+	T
Russell	1			1		1	1						1

DUNSTON MATCH RESULTS 2020-21

Date	Comp	H/A	Opponents	Att:	Result	Goalscorers	Pos	No.
Sept 12	**FACP**	**A**	**Whitley Bay**			**Walkover for Whitley Bay**		1
19	NPLNW	H	Marine	186	W 2 - 1	Joyce 62 (og) Galbraith 82 (pen)	6	2
26	NPLNW	H	Colne	198	L 0 - 1		7	3
29	NPLNW	A	Ossett United	236	W 2 - 0	Heslop 74 Fitzpatrick 82	4	4
Oct 3	NPLNW	A	Pickering Town	108	W 1 - 0	Fitzpatrick 31	2	5
6	NPLNW	H	Tadcaster Albion	231	D 1 - 1	Thear 43	2	6
10	NPLNW	H	Prescot Cables	198	W 3 - 2	There 40 Hall 78 Elliott 86	1	7
17	**FAT2Q**	**H**	**Clitheroe**	212	L 0 - 1			8

Goalscorers	LGE	FAC	FAT	SG	HAT	PEN	1Q	2Q	45+	3Q	4Q	90+	T
TOTALS	9	0	0		0	1	0	3	0	1	5	0	9
Fitzpatrick	2			2				1			1		2
Thear	2			2				2					2
Elliott	1			1							1		1
Galbraith	1			1		1					1		1
Hall	1			1							1		1
Heslop	1			1							1		1
Opponent	1			1						1			1

KENDAL TOWN MATCH RESULTS 2020-21

Date	Comp	H/A	Opponents	Att:	Result	Goalscorers	Pos	No.
Sept 12	**FACP**	**H**	**Bishop Auckland**	**257**	**L 0 - 5**			1
19	NPLNW	A	Prescot Cables	400	L 0 - 2		17	2
26	NPLNW	H	Workington	325	D 0 - 0		13	3
29	NPLNW	H	City of Liverpool	78	W 1 - 0	Hodgson 80	9	4
Oct 6	NPLNW	A	Trafford	200	L 0 - 2		11	5
10	NPLNW	A	Pickering Town	166	W 1 - 0	Livingston 9	7	6
17	**FAT2Q**	**H**	**Brighouse Town**	**210**	**W 1 - 0**	**Jaaskelainen 35**		7
20	NPLNW	A	Ramsbottom United	273	D 2 - 2	Hodgson 53 Fagan 90	8	8
24	NPLNW	H	Runcorn Linnets	210	L 2 - 3	Humphrey 6 Birch 55	8	9
27	NPLNW	H	Mossley	144	D 2 - 2	Rodriquez 70 89		10
31	NPLNW	H	Tadcaster Albion	150	L 0 - 3		10	11
Dec 19	NPLNW	H	Marine	146	L 0 - 4		11	12
22	NPLNW	A	Clitheroe	375	D 1 - 1	Rodriquez 55	11	13
26	NPLNW	A	Colne	200	L 2 - 3	Keenan 17 Humphrey 46	11	14

Goalscorers	LGE	FAC	FAT	SG	HAT	PEN	1Q	2Q	45+	3Q	4Q	90+	T
TOTALS	11	0	1		0	0	3	1	0	4	3	1	12
Rodriquez	3			2						1	2		3
Hodgson	2			2						1	1		2
Humphrey	2			2			1			1			2
Birch	1			1						1			1
Fagan	1			1								1	1
Jaaskelainen			1	1				1					1
Keenan	1			1			1						1
Livingston	1			1			1						1

MARINE MATCH RESULTS 2020-21

Date	Comp	H/A	Opponents	Att:	Result		Goalscorers	Pos	No.
Sept 12	FACP	H	Barnoldswick Town	323	W	2 - 1	Wignall 87 Hmami 90		1
19	NPLNW	A	Dunstan	186	L	1 - 2	Cummins 40	15	2
22	FAC1Q	A	Frickley Athletic	202	W	1 - 0	Raven 72		3
26	FAT1Q	A	Tadcaster Albion	221	W	3 - 1	Howard 7 Cummins 37 62		4
29	NPLNW	H	Colne	243	L	1 - 2	Touray 58	15	5
Oct 3	FAC2Q	A	Runcorn Linnets	331	D	1 - 1	Cummins 54 (Won 4-3 on pens)		6
7	NPLNW	A	Widnes		W	2 - 0	Hmami 6 33	14	7
10	NPLNW	H	Tadcaster Albion	298	W	2 - 0	Hmami 34 Touray 38	8	8
13	FAC3Q	H	Nantwich Town	397	W	4 - 1	Hmami 4 61 Miley 68 85		9
17	FAT2Q	H	Mossley	260	W	5 - 0	Touray 63 73 76 Cummins 87 Kuemo 90		10
24	FAC4Q	A	Chester		W	1 - 0	Barrigan 81 (pen)		11
27	NPLNW	H	Pickering Town	287	W	4 - 0	Hmami 25 Touray 43 Kuemo 62 Cummins 71	9	12
31	FAT3Q	H	Stalybridge Celtic	400	W	3 - 2	Cummins 17 63 Miley 45		13
Nov 7	FAC1P	A	Colchester United		D	1 - 1	Miley 22 (Won 5-3 on Pens)		14
28	FAC2P	H	Havant & Waterlooville		W	1 - 0	Cummins 120		15
Dec 12	FAT1P	H	Hyde United	400	W	1 - 0	Wignall 65		16
15	FAT2P	H	Southport	400	L	0 - 1			17
19	NPLNW	A	Kendal Town	146	W	4 - 0	Devline 63 Hmami 79 Kengni 86 90	6	18
26	NPLNW	A	City of Liverpool	400	W	2 - 1	Miley 14 Kengni 77	6	19
Jan 9	FAC3P	H	Tottenham Hotspur		L	0 - 5	Marine sold 32,202 virtual tickets for this match.		20

Goalscorers	LGE	FAC	FAT	SG	HAT	PEN	1Q	2Q	45+	3Q	4Q	90+	T
TOTALS	16	11	12		1	1	6	7	1	9	12	4	39
Cummins	2	2	5	6			1	2		3	2	1	9
Hmami	5	3		6			2	3		1	1	1	8
Touray	3		3	4	1			2		2	2		6
Miley	1	3	1	3			2		1		2		5
Kengni	3			2							2	1	3
Kuemo	1		1	2						1		1	2
Wignall		1	1	2						1	1		2
Barrigan		1		1		1					1		1
Devline	1			1						1			1
Howard			1	1			1						1
Raven		1		1							1		1

MARSKE UNITED MATCH RESULTS 2020-21

Date	Comp	H/A	Opponents	Att:	Result		Goalscorers	Pos	No.
Sept 12	FACP	A	Crook Town	300	W	2 - 0	Gott 58 (pen) Burgess 77		1
19	NPLNW	A	City of Liverpool	397	W	4 - 2	Boyes 8 Tymon 18 27 86	2	2
22	FAC1Q	H	Trafford	300	W	1 - 0	Burgess 86		3
26	NPLNW	H	Brighouse Town	297	W	3 - 0	Boyes 10 Round 53 Tymon 86	1	4
Oct 3	FAC2Q	H	Consett	361	W	6 - 0	Butterworth 29 42 Boyes 31 56 Tymon 54 63		5
6	NPLNW	A	Pontefract Collieries	167	D	1 - 1	Tymon 90	6	6
10	NPLNW	H	Trafford	362	W	5 - 1	Wheatley 6 16 Tymon 9 56 Round 66	5	7
13	FAC3Q	H	Blyth Spartans	400	W	1 - 0	Boyes 58		8
17	FAT2Q	A	Stocksbridge PS	230	W	4 - 0	Smith 28 36 Butterworth 45 Tymon 76		9
20	NPLNW	H	Ossett United	369	D	1 - 1	Butterworth 49	6	10
24	FAC4Q	A	Brackley Town		L	1 - 5	Tymon 7		11
31	FAT3Q	A	FC United of Manchester	600	W	3 - 2	Boyes 19 84 Maloney 90		12
Dec 8	FAT1P	H	Warrington Town		W	3 - 1	Tymon 15 Round 52 Boyes 78		13
15	FAT2P	A	Spennymoor Town		L	2 - 6	Boyes 27 Tymon 87		14

Goalscorers	LGE	FAC	FAT	SG	HAT	PEN	1Q	2Q	45+	3Q	4Q	90+	T
TOTALS	14	11	12		1	1	9	6	1	11	8	2	37
Tymon	7	3	3	9	1		4	1		3	4	1	13
Boyes	2	3	4	7			3	2		2	2		9
Butterworth	1	2	1	3				1	1	2			4
Round	2		1	3						3			3
Burgess		2		2							2		2
Smith			2	1				2					2
Wheatley	2			1			2						2
Gott		1		1		1				1			1
Maloney			1	1								1	1

MOSSLEY MATCH RESULTS 2020-21

Date	Comp	H/A	Opponents	Att:	Result	Goalscorers	Pos	No.
Sept 12	**FACP**	**H**	**St Helens Town**	**399**	**W 3 - 0**	**Shenton 11 53 Richardson 23**		1
19	NPLNW	H	Ossett United	400	W 2 - 0	Keogh 21 Shenton 51	3	2
22	**FAC1Q**	**H**	**Ramsbottom United**	**371**	**W 2 - 1**	**Shenton 21 Mulvey 64**		3
26	NPLNW	H	Pickering Town	400	W 4 - 1	Waller 8 Shenton 30 Evans 61 66	2	4
29	NPLNW	H	Runcorn Linnets	337	L 1 - 2	Waller 49	3	5
Oct 3	**FAC2Q**	**H**	**Tadcaster Albion**	**400**	**D 1 - 1**	**Fitzgerald 18 (Lost 3-4 on pens)**		6
6	NPLNW	H	Clitheroe	361	L 1 - 3	McLaughlin 83	7	7
10	NPLNW	A	Workington	400	L 0 - 2		10	8
17	**FAT2Q**	**A**	**Marine**	**260**	**L 0 - 5**			9
27	NPLNW	A	Kendal Town	144	D 2 - 2	Brown 15 Fitzgerald 35		10
31	NPLNW	A	Widnes		L 0 - 1		11	11

Goalscorers	LGE	FAC	FAT	SG	HAT	PEN	1Q	2Q	45+	3Q	4Q	90+	T
TOTALS	10	6	0		0	0	6	3	0	5	2	0	16
Shenton	2	3		4			2	1		1	1		5
Evans	2			1						2			2
Fitzgerald	1	1		2			1	1					2
Waller	2			2			1			1			2
Brown	1			1			1						1

Goalscorers	LGE	FAC	FAT	SG	HAT	PEN	1Q	2Q	45+	3Q	4Q	90+	T
Keogh	1			1			1						1
McLaughlin	1			1							1		1
Mulvey		1		1						1			1
Richardson		1		1				1					1

OSSETT UNITED MATCH RESULTS 2020-21

Date	Comp	H/A	Opponents	Att:	Result	Goalscorers	Pos	No.
Sept 12	**FACP**	**A**	**Consett**	**300**	**D 2 - 2**	**Purewal 15 (og) Stockdill 39 (Lost 4-5 on pens)**		1
19	NPLNW	A	Mossley	400	L 0 - 2		18	2
26	**FAT1Q**	**H**	**Ramsbottom United**	**346**	**L 0 - 2**			3
29	NPLNW	H	Dunston	236	L 0 - 2		19	4
Oct 3	NPLNW	H	Colne	300	L 0 - 1		18	5
6	NPLNW	A	Pickering Town	135	L 1 - 2	Green 58	19	6
10	NPLNW	A	Ramsbottom United	393	L 1 - 2	Haswell 27	19	7
13	NPLNW	H	Widnes	230	W 3 - 2	Connolly 27 Normanton 82 Stockdill 84	16	8
20	NPLNW	A	Marske United	369	D 1 - 1	Stockdill 79	16	9
24	NPLNW	H	Workington	400	L 0 - 3		17	10

Goalscorers	LGE	FAC	FAT	SG	HAT	PEN	1Q	2Q	45+	3Q	4Q	90+	T
TOTALS	6	2	0		0	0	2	2	0	1	3	0	8
Stockdill	2	1		3				1			2		3
Connolly	1			1			1						1
Green	1			1						1			1
Haswell	1			1				1					1
Normanton	1			1							1		1

Goalscorers	LGE	FAC	FAT	SG	HAT	PEN	1Q	2Q	45+	3Q	4Q	90+	T
Opponent		1		1			1						1

PICKERING TOWN MATCH RESULTS 2020-21

Date	Comp	H/A	Opponents	Att:	Result	Goalscorers	Pos	No.
Sept 1	**FACEP**	**A**	**Penrith**	**161**	**L 2 - 3**	**Warrilow 36 Brooksby 58**		1
19	NPLNW	H	Workington	159	D 2 - 2	Warrilow 5 Brooksey 44	7	2
26	NPLNW	A	Mossley	400	L 1 - 4	Clappison 25	14	3
29	NPLNW	A	Ramsbottom United	222	L 0 - 3		14	4
Oct 3	NPLNW	H	Dunston	108	L 0 - 1		14	5
6	NPLNW	H	Ossett United	135	W 2 - 1	Barnes 21 Jessop 80	12	6
10	NPLNW	H	Kendal Town	166	L 0 - 1		13	7
17	**FAT2Q**	**H**	**Trafford**	**124**	**W 1 - 0**	**Barnes 60**		8
20	NPLNW	H	Brighouse Town	134	W 1 - 0	Jessop 28	10	9
27	NPLNW	A	Marine	287	L 0 - 4			10
31	**FAT3Q**	**H**	**Runcorn Linnets**	**166**	**L 1 - 4**	**Jessop 46**		11
Nov 3	NPLNW	H	Pontefract Collieries	139	L 2 - 3	Osborne 9 Barnes 56	14	12

Goalscorers	LGE	FAC	FAT	SG	HAT	PEN	1Q	2Q	45+	3Q	4Q	90+	T
TOTALS	8	2	2		0	0	3	4	0	4	1	0	12
Barnes	2		1	3			1			2			3
Jessop	2		1	3				1		1	1		3
Brooksey	1	1		2				1		1			2
Warrilow	1	1		2			1	1					2
Clappison	1			1				1					1
Osborne	1			1			1						1

PONTEFRACT COLLIERIES MATCH RESULTS 2020-21

Date	Comp	H/A	Opponents	Att:	Result	Goalscorers	Pos	No.
Sept 12	**FACP**	**A**	**Hebburn Town**	**300**	**D 2 - 2**	**Reeves 14 (pen) Keane 64 (Won 5-3 on pens)**		1
19	NPLNW	H	Runcorn Linnets	253	D 1 - 1	Modest 86	9	2
22	**FAC1Q**	**A**	**FC United of Manchester**	**534**	**L 2 - 6**	**Modest 46 Keane 52**		3
29	NPLNW	A	Tadcaster Albion	317	L 0 - 3		13	4
Oct 3	NPLNW	A	Ramsbottom United	186	L 0 - 3		13	5
6	NPLNW	H	Marske United	167	D 1 - 1	Ibrahimi 85 (pen)	14	6
13	NPLNW	A	Colne (6)	149	L 2 - 6	Reeves 2 74	17	7
17	**FAT2Q**	**H**	**Workington**	**191**	**L 1 - 4**	**Reeves 90**		8
24	NPLNW	A	Brighouse Town	400	L 0 - 2		19	9
Nov 3	NPLNW	A	Pickering Town	139	W 3 - 2	Reeves 48 (pen) Modest 69 78	16	10
Dec 19	NPLNW	A	City of Liverpool	287	L 1 - 4	Lazenby 82	18	11

Goalscorers	LGE	FAC	FAT	SG	HAT	PEN	1Q	2Q	45+	3Q	4Q	90+	T
TOTALS	8	4	1		0	3	2	0	0	4	6	1	13
Reeves	3	1	1	4		2	2			1	1	1	5
Modest	3	1		3						1	3		4
Keane		2		2						2			2
Ibrahimi	1			1		1					1		1
Lazenby	1			1							1		1

PRESCOT CABLES MATCH RESULTS 2020-21

Date	Comp	H/A	Opponents	Att:	Result	Goalscorers	Pos	No.
Sept 12	**FACP**	**A**	**Colne**	**270**	**W 2 - 0**	**Unsworth 18 (og) Edgar 45**		1
19	NPLNW	H	Kendal Town	400	W 2 - 0	Monaghan 6 Fleming 90	4	2
22	**FAC1Q**	**A**	**Sunderland RCA**	**207**	**W 4 - 0**	**Monaghan 54 Corness 90 White 90 Hamilton 90**		3
26	NPLNW	A	Clitheroe	372	L 0 - 1		5	4
Oct 3	**FAC2Q**	**A**	**Darlington**		**D 2 - 2**	**McMilan 56 Edgar 84 (pen) (Lost 4-5 on pens)**		5
10	NPLNW	A	Dunston (2)	198	L 2 - 3	Edgar 68 Hamilton 74	14	6
13	NPLNW	H	City of Liverpool		D 2 - 2	Edgar 57 (pen) Hamilton 72	13	7
27	NPLNW	A	Tadcaster Albion	211	L 1 - 3	Monaghan 7		8
31	NPLNW	A	Ramsbottom United	314	L 1 - 2	Rainford 33	16	9
Nov 4	NPLNW	A	Widnes		W 3 - 1	Dean 4 Rainford 33 McMilan 45	11	10
Dec 19	NPLNW	A	Colne	200	L 0 - 2		14	11
26	NPLNW	H	Runcorn Linnets	400	L 0 - 1		15	12

Goalscorers	LGE	FAC	FAT	SG	HAT	PEN	1Q	2Q	45+	3Q	4Q	90+	T
TOTALS	11	8	0		0	2	4	2	2	4	3	4	19
Edgar	2	2		4		2			1	1	2		4
Hamilton	2	1		3						1	1	1	3
Monaghan	2	1		3			2			1			3
McMilan	1	1		2					1	1			2
Rainford	2			2				2					2
Corness		1		1								1	1
Dean	1			1			1						1
Fleming	1			1								1	1
Opponent		1		1			1						1
White		1										1	1

RAMSBOTTOM UNITED MATCH RESULTS 2020-21

Date	Comp	H/A	Opponents	Att:	Result	Goalscorers	Pos	No.
Sept 12	**FACP**	**H**	**Irlam**	**306**	**W 4 - 1**	**Fawns 55 Thompson 62 Kennedy 66 (pen) O'Brien 69**		1
19	NPLNW	A	Widnes	122	W 4 - 1	Hampson 16 Fawns 33 Gonzales 50 Burns 90 (pen)	1	2
22	**FAC1Q**	**A**	**Mossley**	**371**	**L 1 - 2**	**Fawns 60**		3
26	**FAT1Q**	**A**	**Ossett United**	**346**	**W 2 - 0**	**Gonzales 47 Thompson 51**		4
29	NPLNW	H	Pickering Town	222	W 3 - 0	Gonzales 12 56 Osi-Efa 83	1	5
Oct 3	NPLNW	H	Pontefract Collieries	186	W 3 - 0	O'Brien 12 14 Gonzales 65	1	6
10	NPLNW	H	Ossett United	393	W 2 - 1	Donaldson 44 Osi-Efa 90	2	7
13	NPLNW	A	Clitheroe (4)	400	L 1 - 3	Donaldson 45	4	8
17	**FAT2Q**	**A**	**Worksop Town**	**298**	**D 4 - 4**	**Rouse 24 45 Gonzales 55 Fawns 69 (lost 4-5 on pens)**		9
20	NPLNW	H	Kendal Town	273	D 2 - 2	Gonzales 52 Fawns 75	4	10
24	NPLNW	A	Tadcaster Albion	317	W 2 - 1	Rouse 21 Kennedy 78	2	11
31	NPLNW	H	Prescot Cables	314	W 2 - 1	Donaldson 12 Harrison 86	1	12

Goalscorers	LGE	FAC	FAT	SG	HAT	PEN	1Q	2Q	45+	3Q	4Q	90+	T
TOTALS	19	5	6		0	2	6	3	2	11	6	2	30
Gonzales	5		2	6			1			6			7
Fawns	2	2	1	5				1		2	2		5
Donaldson	3			3			1	1	1				3
O'Brien	2	1		2			2				1		3
Rouse	1		2	2			1	1	1				3
Kennedy	1	1		2		1				1	1		2
Osi-Efa	2			2							1	1	2
Thompson		1	1	2						2			2
Burns	1			1		1						1	1
Hampson	1			1			1						1
Harrison	1			1							1		1

RUNCORN LINNETS MATCH RESULTS 2020-21

Date	Comp	H/A	Opponents	Att:	Result	Goalscorers	Pos	No.
Sept 12	**FACP**	**H**	**Albion Sports**	**384**	**W 2 - 0**	**Nolan 29 Lindfield 37**	10	1
19	NPLNW	A	Pontefract Collieries	253	D 1 - 1	Lindfield 6	10	2
22	**FAC1Q**	**A**	**West Auckland**	**194**	**D 0 - 0**	**(Won 3-2 on pens)**		3
29	NPLNW	A	Mossley	337	W 2 - 1	Lindfield 15 Brooke 23	3	4
Oct 3	**FAC2Q**	**H**	**Marine**	**331**	**D 1 - 1**	**Sherlock 90 (pen) (Lost 3-4 on pens)**		5
5	NPLNW	A	Brighouse Town	346	D 3 - 3	Sherlock 56 90 (pens) Brizell 90	8	6
10	NPLNW	H	Clitheroe	305	D 1 - 1	O'Mahoney 62	9	7
17	**FAT2Q**	**A**	**Sheffield**	**281**	**W 3 - 2**	**Lindfield 45 Brooke 57 O'Mahoney 90**		8
20	NPLNW	H	Tadcaster Albion	235	W 4 - 2	Lindfield 50 (pen) 66 Crilly 77 Murray 90	7	9
24	NPLNW	A	Kendal Town	210	W 3 - 2	Brooke 31 Downes 52 Murray 74	6	10
31	**FAT3Q**	**A**	**Pickering Town**	**166**	**W 4 - 1**	**Murray 17 81 90 Welsh 36 (pen)**		11
Dec 8	**FAT1P**	**H**	**Morpeth Town**	**270**	**D 2 - 2**	**Murray 59 Brooke 63 (Lost 2-3 on pens)**		12
19	NPLNW	H	Widnes	284	L 0 - 1		7	13
26	NPLNW	A	Prescot Cables	400	W 1 - 0	Murray 27	7	14

Goalscorers	LGE	FAC	FAT	SG	HAT	PEN	1Q	2Q	45+	3Q	4Q	90+	T
TOTALS	15	3	9		1	5	3	6	1	8	3	6	27
Murray	3		4	5	1		1	1		1	2	2	7
Lindfield	4	1	1	5		1	2	1	1	2			6
Brooke	2		2	4				2		2			4
Sherlock	2	1		2		3				1		2	3
O'Mahoney	1		1	2						1		1	2
Brizell	1			1								1	1
Crilly	1			1							1		1
Downes	1			1						1			1
Nolan		1		1				1					1
Welsh			1	1		1		1					1

TADCASTER ALBION MATCH RESULTS 2020-21

Date	Comp	H/A	Opponents	Att:	Result	Goalscorers	Pos	No.
Sept 12	**FACP**	**A**	**Guisborough Town**	**300**	**W 2 - 1**	**Thompson 20 Ifeanyi 45**		1
19	NPLNW	A	Trafford	400	D 0 - 0		11	2
22	**FAC1Q**	**H**	**Litherland REMYCA**	**191**	**W 7 - 2**	**Thompson 8 27 Ifeanyi 63 74 Pandor 85 Roper 85 Crook 90**		3
26	**FAT1Q**	**H**	**Marine**	**221**	**L 1 - 3**	**Russell 22**		4
29	NPLNW	H	Pontefract Collieries	317	W 3 - 0	Bailey 42 (og) Sanyang 67 Russell 69	7	5
Oct 3	**FAC2Q**	**A**	**Mossley**	**400**	**D 1 - 1**	**Ifeanyi 13 (Won 4-3 on pens)**		6
6	NPLNW	A	Dunston	231	D 1 - 1	Pandor 70	9	7
10	NPLNW	A	Marine	298	L 0 - 2		12	8
13	**FAC3Q**	**A**	**Darlington**		**L 1 - 6**	**Crook 74**		9
20	NPLNW	A	Runcorn Linnets	235	L 2 - 4	Sousa 15 Thompson 71	14	10
24	NPLNW	H	Ramsbottom United	317	L 1 - 2	Thompson 37	14	11
27	NPLNW	H	Prescot Cables	211	W 3 - 1	Russell 9 Milne 47 Thompson 71		12
31	NPLNW	A	Kendal Town	150	W 3 - 0	Ifeanyi 45 Thompson 60 Russell 74	8	13

Goalscorers	LGE	FAC	FAT	SG	HAT	PEN	1Q	2Q	45+	3Q	4Q	90+	T
TOTALS	13	11	1		0	0	6	3	2	4	9	1	25
Thompson	4	3		6			2	2		1	2		7
Ifeanyi		4		3			1		1	1	1		4
Russell	3		1	4			2				2		4
Crook		2		2							1	1	2
Pandor	1	1		2							2		2
Ifeanyi	1			1					1				1
Milne	1			1						1			1
Opponent	1			1				1					1
Roper		1		1							1		1
Sanyang	1			1						1			1
Sousa	1			1			1						1

TRAFFORD MATCH RESULTS 2020-21

Date	Comp	H/A	Opponents	Att:	Result	Goalscorers	Pos	No.
Sept 12	**FACP**	**A**	**Wythenshawe Amateurs**	**300**	**W 4 - 1**	**Ford 16 Morgan 45 Mulholland 69 Elstone 89**		1
19	NPLNW	H	Tadcaster Albion	400	D 0 - 0		12	2
22	**FAC1Q**	**A**	**Marske United**	**300**	**L 0 - 1**			3
29	NPLNW	A	Workington	400	D 2 - 2	Hazeldine 21 Roberts 35	12	4
Oct 3	NPLNW	A	Clitheroe	400	D 2 - 2	Hazeldine 6 58	12	5
6	NPLNW	H	Kendal Town	200	W 2 - 0	Morgan 7 Halfacre 68	8	6
10	NPLNW	A	Marske United	362	L 1 - 5	Morgan 74	11	7
17	**FAT2Q**	**A**	**Pickering Town**	**124**	**L 0 - 1**			8
20	NPLNW	A	City of Liverpool	269	L 0 - 1		13	9
24	NPLNW	H	Widnes	200	D 1 - 1	Barlow 53	9	10

Goalscorers	LGE	FAC	FAT	SG	HAT	PEN	1Q	2Q	45+	3Q	4Q	90+	T
TOTALS	8	4	0		0	0	4	1	1	2	4	0	12
Hazeldine	3			2			2			1			3
Morgan	2	1		3			1		1		1		3
Barlow	1			1						1			1
Elstone		1		1							1		1
Ford		1		1			1						1
Halfacre	1			1							1		1
Mulholland		1		1							1		1
Roberts	1			1				1					1

WIDNES MATCH RESULTS 2020-21

Date	Comp	H/A	Opponents	Att:	Result	Goalscorers	Pos	No.
Sept 12	**FACP**	**H**	**Longridge Town**	**153**	**L 2 - 3**	**Steele 17 Rainford 78**		1
19	NPLNW	H	Ramsbottom United	122	L 1 - 4	Steele 47	19	2
Oct 7	NPLNW	H	Marine		L 0 - 2		17	3
10	NPLNW	H	Colne		D 1 - 1	Steele 38	17	4
13	NPLNW	A	Ossett United	230	L 2 - 3	Towey 2 Steele 25	18	5
17	**FAT2Q**	**H**	**Colne**		**L 3 - 4**	**Sambor 24 64 Jennings 28**		6
24	NPLNW	A	Trafford	200	D 1 - 1	Southworth 16	18	7
31	NPLNW	H	Mossley		W 1 - 0	Sargent 51	15	8
Nov 4	NPLNW	H	Prescot Cables		L 1 - 3	McNally 12	16	9
Dec 19	NPLNW	A	Runcorn Linnets	284	W 1 - 0	Banister 88	12	10
26	NPLNW	H	Clitheroe	148	L 0 - 1		12	11

Goalscorers	LGE	FAC	FAT	SG	HAT	PEN	1Q	2Q	45+	3Q	4Q	90+	T
TOTALS	8	2	3		0	0	4	4	0	3	2	0	13
Steele	3	1		4			1	2		1			4
Sambor			2	1				1		1			2
Banister	1			1							1		1
Jennings			1	1				1					1
McNally	1			1			1						1
Rainford		1		1							1		1
Sargent	1			1						1			1
Southworth	1			1			1						1
Towey	1			1			1						1

WORKINGTON MATCH RESULTS 2020-21

Date	Comp	H/A	Opponents	Att:	Result		Goalscorers	Pos	No.
Sept 12	**FACP**	**A**	**Knaresborough Town**	**255**	**W**	**3 - 1**	**Tinnion 9 Allison 42 80**		1
19	NPLNW	A	Pickering Town	159	D	2 - 2	Allison 78 Jerome 79	8	2
22	**FAC1Q**	**A**	**Radcliffe**	**309**	**L**	**3 - 5**	**Allison 12 Jerome 46 Carroll 66**		3
26	NPLNW	A	Kendal Town	325	D	0 - 0			4
29	NPLNW	H	Trafford	400	D	2 - 2	Allison 15 Bowman 45	11	5
Oct 3	NPLNW	H	City of Liverpool	393	W	5 - 2	Jerome 11 51 Brockbank 24 Lightfoot 67 Potts 71	7	6
6	NPLNW	A	Colne	213	W	1 - 0	Allison 61 (pen)	4	7
10	NPLNW	H	Mossley	400	W	2 - 0	Allison 21 Symington 83	3	8
17	**FAT2Q**	**A**	**Pontefract Collieries**	**191**	**W**	**4 - 1**	**Bowman 4 45 Hubbold 23 Wordsworth 58**		9
20	NPLNW	H	Clitheroe	400	W	2 - 1	Jerome 56 90	2	10
24	NPLNW	A	Ossett United	400	W	3 - 0	Allison 44 Jerome 48 Smith 56	1	11
31	**FAT3Q**	**A**	**Glossop North End**	**313**	**W**	**1 - 0**	**Tinnion 4**		12
Dec 8	**FAT1P**	**A**	**Nantwich Town**	**272**	**L**	**1 - 3**	**Tinnion 77 (pen)**		13
19	NPLNW	A	Brighouse Town	192	D	2 - 2	Jerome 47 Smith 59	2	14

Goalscorers	LGE	FAC	FAT	SG	HAT	PEN	1Q	2Q	45+	3Q	4Q	90+	T
TOTALS	19	6	6		0	2	7	4	2	11	6	1	31
Allison	5	3		7		1	3	2		1	2		8
Jerome	7	1		5			1			5	1	1	8
Bowman	1		2	2			1		2				3
Tinnion		1	2	3		1	2				1		3
Smith	2			2						2			2
Brockbank	1			1				1					1
Carroll		1		1						1			1
Hubbold			1	1				1					1
Lightfoot	1			1						1			1
Potts	1			1							1		1
Symington	1			1							1		1
Wordsworth			1	1						1			1

BELPER TOWN MATCH RESULTS 2020-21

Date	Comp	H/A	Opponents	Att:	Result		Goalscorers	Pos	No.
Sept 12	**FACP**	**A**	**Sutton Coldfield Town**	**249**	**W**	**1 - 0**	**Gregory 24**		1
19	NPLSE	H	Market Drayton Town	398	W	4 - 0	Bennett 4 (og) Simms 18 (og) McDonnell 61 Nelthorpe 86 (pen)	4	2
22	**FAC1Q**	**A**	**Buxton**	**317**	**L**	**0 - 7**			3
26	NPLSE	H	Chasetown	373	L	0 - 1			4
29	NPLSE	A	Frickley Athletic	209	W	4 - 1	McDonnell 9 Wright 18 South 21 Ridley 78	2	5
Oct 3	NPLSE	A	Glossop North End	241	W	2 - 1	Wright 25 Crouz 37	1	6
6	NPLSE	H	Sutton Coldfield Town	353	W	7 - 1	Robinson 21 McDonnell 29 33 Wright 38 Robson 41 73 Peterson 67	1	7
10	NPLSE	H	Worksop Town	400	D	2 - 2	Crouz 11 Nelthorpe 52 (pen)	1	8
13	NPLSE	A	Stocksbridge PS	211	L	3 - 4	Crouz 6 Wright 51 Litchfield 65	1	9
17	**FAT2Q**	**A**	**Newcastle Town**	**214**	**D**	**2 - 2**	**McDonnell 35 Wright 45 (lost 4-5 on pens)**		10
24	NPLSE	A	Cleethorpes Town	347	L	0 - 2		7	11
31	NPLSE	H	Spalding United	400	D	3 - 3	Crouz 4 McDonnell 36 Chilaka 49	6	12

Goalscorers	LGE	FAC	FAT	SG	HAT	PEN	1Q	2Q	45+	3Q	4Q	90+	T
TOTALS	25	1	2		0	2	9	9	1	6	3	0	28
McDonnell	5		1	5			1	4		1			6
Wright	4		1	5			1	2	1	1			5
Crouz	4			4			3	1					4
Nelthorpe	2			2		2				1	1		2
Opponent	2			1			2						2
Robson	2			1				1			1		2
Chilaka	1			1						1			1
Litchfield	1			1						1			1
Peterson	1			1						1			1
Ridley	1			1							1		1
Robinson	1			1			1						1
South	1			1			1						1
Gregory		1		1				1					1

CARLTON TOWN MATCH RESULTS 2020-21

Date	Comp	H/A	Opponents	Att:	Result	Goalscorers	Pos	No.
Sept 2	**FACEP**	**H**	**Loughborough University**	**176**	**D 1 - 1**	**Clark 75 (Won 4-2 on pens)**		1
12	**FACP**	**A**	**GNG Oadby Town**			**Walkover**		2
19	NPLSE	H	Lincoln United	190	L 1 - 3	Blake 53	15	3
22	**FAC1Q**	**A**	**Banbury United**	**369**	**L 0 - 1**			4
26	NPLSE	A	Spalding United	136	L 0 - 2		18	5
29	NPLSE	A	Sutton Coldfield United	167	D 0 - 0		18	6
Oct 3	NPLSE	A	Frickley Athletic	128	W 3 - 0	Everington 35 (og) Opoku 84 Davie 90	13	7
6	NPLSE	H	Wisbech Town	122	W 4 - 0	Clark 33 Opoku 54 (pen) Thomas 57 Whitton 75	7	8
10	NPLSE	A	Newcastle Town	200	L 1 - 6	Thomas 15	11	9
13	NPLSE	H	Stamford	173	D 1 - 1	Daft 21	12	10
17	**FAT2Q**	**A**	**Evesham United**	**269**	**L 0 - 2**			11
24	NPLSE	H	Leek Town	163	L 1 - 2	Opoku 8	14	12
31	NPLSE	A	Sheffield	208	W 2 - 0	Opoku 17 (pen) Davie 62	11	13

Goalscorers	LGE	FAC	FAT	SG	HAT	PEN	1Q	2Q	45+	3Q	4Q	90+	T
TOTALS	13	1	0		0	2	4	2	0	4	3	1	14
Opoku	4			4		2	2			1	1		4
Clark	1	1		2				1			1		2
Davie	2			2						1		1	2
Thomas	2			2			1			1			2
Blake	1			1						1			1
Daft	1			1			1						1
Opponent	1			1				1					1
Whitton	1			1							1		1

CHASETOWN MATCH RESULTS 2020-21

Date	Comp	H/A	Opponents	Att:	Result	Goalscorers	Pos	No.
Sept 12	**FACP**	**A**	**Kidsgrove Athletic**	**327**	**W 1 - 0**	**Langston 64**		1
19	NPLSE	H	Frickley Athletic	310	L 2 - 3	Kirton 21 Butlin 34	12	2
22	**FAC1Q**	**H**	**Basford United**	**266**	**W 2 - 1**	**Butlin 9 Wynter 55**		3
26	NPLSE	A	Belper Town	373	W 1 - 0	Langston 73	10	4
28	NPLSE	A	Market Drayton Town	222	W 3 - 1	Butlin 15 27 Langston 90	4	5
Oct 3	**FAC2Q**	**H**	**AFC Telford United**	**369**	**D 1 - 1**	**Butlin 45 (Lost 4-5 on pens)**		6
6	NPLSE	H	Kidsgrove Athletic	172	L 1 - 3	Butlin 55	12	7
10	NPLSE	A	Spalding United	190	W 3 - 1	Curtis 36 Taylor 59 Butlin 80	9	8
17	**FAT2Q**	**A**	**Yaxley**			**Walkover forYaxley**		9
24	NPLSE	H	Stamford	281	D 2 - 2	Langston 62 83	10	10
27	NPLSE	A	Ilkeston Town	309	L 1 - 2	Haddaway 33		11
31	NPLSE	H	Stocksbridge PS	204	W 2 - 1	Hayward 4 Lund 79	10	12
Nov 3	NPLSE	H	Newcastle Town	213	W 3 - 0	Butlin 35 73 O'Callaghan 43	5	13

Goalscorers	LGE	FAC	FAT	SG	HAT	PEN	1Q	2Q	45+	3Q	4Q	90+	T
TOTALS	18	4	0		0	0	4	6	1	5	5	1	22
Butlin	7	2		7			2	3	1	1	2		9
Langston	4	1		4						2	2	1	5
Curtis	1			1				1					1
Haddaway	1			1				1					1
Hayward	1			1			1						1
Kirton	1			1			1						1
Lund	1			1							1		1
O'Callaghan	1			1				1					1
Taylor	1			1						1			1
Wynter		1		1						1			1

CLEETHORPES TOWN MATCH RESULTS 2020-21

Date	Comp	H/A	Opponents	Att:	Result	Goalscorers	Pos	No.
Sept 12	**FACP**	**H**	**AFC Mansfield**	**238**	**L 0 - 1**			1
19	NPLSE	H	Ilkeston Town	400	L 2 - 3	Middleton 47 Vernon 90 (pen)	13	2
26	NPLSE	A	Glossop North End	254	L 1 - 2	Vernon 40	15	3
20	NPLSE	A	Lincoln United	253	D 1 - 1	Walker 15	15	4
Oct 3	NPLSE	A	Loughborough Dynamo	152	D 1 - 1	Vernon 17	16	5
10	NPLSE	A	Leek Town	400	L 2 - 3	Touray-Sisay 43 Middleton 63	16	6
13	NPLSE	H	Spalding United	303	W 3 - 1	Vernon 26 Venney 48 Hannah 82	15	7
17	**FAT2Q**	**A**	**City of Liverpool**			**Walkover for City of Liverpool**		8
20	NPLSE	A	Wisbech Town	110	L 2 - 3	Robertson 15 Vernon 21	17	9
24	NPLSE	H	Belper Town	347	W 2 - 0	Robertson 21 Vernon 38	13	10

Goalscorers	LGE	FAC	FAT	SG	HAT	PEN	1Q	2Q	45+	3Q	4Q	90+	T
TOTALS	14	0	0		0	1	5	4	0	3	1	1	14
Vernon	6			6		1	2	3				1	6
Middleton	2			2						2			2
Robertson	2			2			2						2
Hannah	1			1							1		1
Touray-Sisay	1			1				1					1
Venney	1			1						1			1
Walker	1			1			1						1

FRICKLEY ATHLETIC MATCH RESULTS 2020-21

Date	Comp	H/A	Opponents	Att:	Result	Goalscorers	Pos	No.
Sept 12	**FACP**	**H**	**Newcastle Benfield**	**222**	**W 3 - 1**	**Blake 6 Grayson 45 Wightwick 90**		1
19	NPLSE	A	Chasetown	310	W 3 - 2	Miller 37 Jarman 53 Margetts 90 (pen)	7	2
22	**FAC1Q**	**H**	**Marine**	**202**	**L 0 - 1**			3
26	NPLSE	A	Newcastle Town	188	L 0 - 1		11	4
29	NPLSE	H	Belper Town	209	L 1 - 4	Margetts 63	14	5
Oct 3	NPLSE	H	Carlton Town	128	L 0 - 3		15	6
10	NPLSE	A	Wisbech Town	208	W 4 - 0	Margetts 21 45 Williams 81 90	13	7
13	NPLSE	H	Sheffield	220	L 1 - 2	Margetts 67	14	8
20	NPLSE	A	Glossop North End	176	L 1 - 2	Margetts 27 (pen)	16	9
24	NPLSE	H	Market Drayton Town	176	W 4 - 0	Margetts 42 45 (pen) Tomlinson 71 Williams 85	11	10
31	**FAT3Q**	**A**	**Hyde United**	**273**	**L 1 - 2**	**Everington 4**		11

Goalscorers	LGE	FAC	FAT	SG	HAT	PEN	1Q	2Q	45+	3Q	4Q	90+	T
TOTALS	14	3	1		0	3	3	3	3	3	3	3	18
Margetts	8			6		3	1	2	2	2		1	8
Williams	3			2							2	1	3
Blake		1		1			1						1
Everington			1	1			1						1
Grayson		1		1					1				1
Jarman	1			1						1			1
Miller	1			1				1					1
Tomlinson	1			1							1		1
Wightwick		1		1								1	1

GLOSSOP NORTH END MATCH RESULTS 2020-21

Date	Comp	H/A	Opponents	Att:	Result	Goalscorers	Pos	No.
Sept 12	**FACP**	**H**	**City of Liverpool**	**350**	**L 0 - 3**			1
19	NPLSE	A	Stamford	294	L 0 - 5		19	2
26	NPLSE	H	Cleethorpes Town	254	W 2 - 1	Burey 47 Fosu-Mensah 71	13	3
29	NPLSE	H	Newcastle Town	184	D 0 - 0		11	4
Oct 3	NPLSE	H	Belper Town	241	L 1 - 2	Fitton 29	14	5
6	NPLSE	A	Worksop Town	347	L 1 - 5	Fosu-Mensah 4	14	6
10	NPLSE	H	Kidsgrove Athletic	333	D 0 - 0		15	7
13	NPLSE	A	Loughborough Dynamo	104	L 1 - 2	Brown 5	16	8
20	NPLSE	H	Frickley Athletic	176	W 2 - 1	Burey 56 61	13	9
24	NPLSE	A	Lincoln United	239	L 0 - 5		16	10
31	**FAT3Q**	**H**	**Workington**	**313**	**L 0 - 1**			11

Goalscorers	LGE	FAC	FAT	SG	HAT	PEN	1Q	2Q	45+	3Q	4Q	90+	T
TOTALS	7	0	0		0	0	2	1	0	3	1	0	7
Burey	3			2						3			3
Fosu-Mensah	2			2			1				1		2
Brown	1			1			1						1
Fitton	1			1				1					1

ILKESTON TOWN MATCH RESULTS 2020-21

Date	Comp	H/A	Opponents	Att:	Result	Goalscorers	Pos	No.
Sept 12	**FACP**	**H**	**Shepshed Dynamo**	**363**	**W 3 - 0**	**Troke 10 (pen) Goodson 27 69**		1
19	NPLSE	A	Cleethorpes Town	400	W 3 - 2	Watson 14 Troke 58 Goodson 73	8	2
22	**FAC1Q**	**A**	**Coventry Sphinx**	**247**	**W 2 - 0**	**Lee 77 Thomas 86**		3
29	NPLSE	H	Stamford	393	D 2 - 2	Troke 18 74 (pens)	10	4
Oct 3	**FAC2Q**	**H**	**Hanley Town**	**398**	**W 4 - 1**	**Goodson 35 82 Watson 37 Troke 87 (pen)**		5
6	NPLSE	A	Spalding United	200	W 2 - 1	Goodson 6 54	8	6
10	NPLSE	A	Market Drayton Town	233	W 5 - 1	Troke 12 81 Goodson 62 77 Reid 90	6	7
13	**FAC3Q**	**H**	**Alvechurch**	**400**	**W 1 - 0**	**Brown-Hill 47**		8
17	**FAT2Q**	**H**	**Kempston Rovers**	**370**	**W 2 - 1**	**Troke 63 70**		9
20	NPLSE	A	Newcastle Town	150	L 1 - 4	Troke 34 (pen)	9	10
24	**FAC4Q**	**H**	**Hartlepool United**	**400**	**L 0 - 6**			11
27	NPLSE	H	Chasetown	309	W 2 - 1	Troke 48 Maguire 68		12
31	**FAT3Q**	**A**	**AFC Rushden & Diamonds**			**Walkover for AFC Rushden & Diamonds**		13
Nov 3	NPLSE	H	Leek Town	374	L 2 - 3	Troke 10 Wilson 90	10	14

Goalscorers	LGE	FAC	FAT	SG	HAT	PEN	1Q	2Q	45+	3Q	4Q	90+	T
TOTALS	17	10	2		0	5	6	5	0	6	11	2	29
Troke	8	2	2	8		5	4	1		3	4		12
Goodson	5	4		5			1	2		2	4		9
Watson	1	1		2			1	2					2
Brown-Hill		1		1						1			1
Lee		1		1							1		1
Maguire	1			1							1		1
Reid	1			1								1	1
Thomas		1		1							1		1
Wilson	1			1								1	1

KIDSGROVE ATHLETIC MATCH RESULTS 2020-21

Date	Comp	H/A	Opponents	Att:	Result	Goalscorers	Pos	No.
Sept 12	**FACP**	**H**	**Chasetown**	**327**	**L 0 - 1**		9	1
19	NPLSE	A	Stocksbridge Park Steels	147	W 1 - 0	Adu-Gyamfi 81	9	2
26	**FAT1Q**	**A**	**Cambridge City**	**212**	**W 3 - 2**	**Lovatt 46 72 Adu-Gyamfi 49**		3
29	NPLSE	H	Leek Town	400	W 1 - 0	Diskin 40	5	4
Oct 6	NPLSE	A	Chasetown	172	W 3 - 1	Malbon 12 22 65	3	5
10	NPLSE	A	Glossop North End	333	D 0 - 0		7	6
13	NPLSE	H	Market Drayton Town	289	W 3 - 0	Lovatt 7 Bromfield 54 Diskin 79	2	7
17	**FAT2Q**	**A**	**Daventry Town**		**W 2 - 0**	**Whieldon 21 Adu-Gyamfi 38**		8
20	NPLSE	A	Sutton Coldfield Town	143	L 3 - 5	Diskin 42 Malbon 70 Hickman 88	5	9
24	NPLSE	H	Sheffield	280	W 2 - 1	Diskin 11 (pen) Turner 22 (og)	4	10
31	**FAT3Q**	**A**	**Stratford Town**		**W 3 - 1**	**Adu-Gyamfi 4 Bergin 10 Diskin 66 (pen)**		11
Dec 12	**FAT1P**	**H**	**Stamford**	**198**	**L 0 - 2**			12

Goalscorers	LGE	FAC	FAT	SG	HAT	PEN	1Q	2Q	45+	3Q	4Q	90+	T
TOTALS	13	0	8		1	2	8	3	0	5	5	0	21
Diskin	4		1	5		2	1	2		1	1		5
Adu-Gyamfi	1		3	4			1	1		1	1		4
Malbon	4			2	1		2			1	1		4
Lovatt	1		2	2			1			1	1		3
Bergin			1	1			1						1
Bromfield	1			1						1			1
Hickman	1			1							1		1
Opponent	1			1			1						1
Whieldon			1	1			1						1

LEEK TOWN MATCH RESULTS 2020-21

Date	Comp	H/A	Opponents	Att:	Result	Goalscorers	Pos	No.
FACP	**FACP**	**H**	**Sporting Khalsa**	**400**	**W 2 - 1**	**Wakefield 18 Bell 65**		1
19	NPLSE	H	Wisbech Town	378	W 5 - 0	Grice 23 Stevenson 25 55 75 Saxon 70	1	2
22	**FAC1Q**	**H**	**Mickleover**	**400**	**L 1 - 2**	**Short 20**		3
29	NPLSE	A	Kidsgrove Athletic	400	L 0 - 1		12	4
Oct 3	NPLSE	A	Sutton Coldfield Town	181	D 1 - 1	Bell 60	10	5
6	NPLSE	H	Market Drayton Town	331	W 6 - 0	Grice 6 71 Bell 44 Wakefield 54 Kirby 75 81	5	6
10	NPLSE	H	Cleethorpes Town	400	W 3 - 2	Stevenson 52 Saxon 77 Kirby 84	5	7
17	**FAT2Q**	**A**	**Histon**	**226**	**W 2 - 1**	**Saxon 68 90**		8
20	NPLSE	H	Stocksbridge PS	363	W 6 - 2	Bell 14 22 Grice 51 Grocott 54 Saxon 61 Short 90	3	9
24	NPLSE	A	Carlton Town	163	W 2 - 1	Trickett-Smith 54 Ashman 69	3	10
31	**FAT3Q**	**A**	**Evesham United**	**271**	**L 2 - 3**	**Saxon 62 Kirby 70**		11
Nov 3	NPLSE	A	Ilkeston Town	374	W 3 - 2	Trickett-Smith 54 79 Grocott 63	1	12

Goalscorers	LGE	FAC	FAT	SG	HAT	PEN	1Q	2Q	45+	3Q	4Q	90+	T
TOTALS	26	3	4		1	0	5	3	0	12	11	2	33
Bell	4	1		4			2	1		2			5
Saxon	3		2	4						1	3	1	5
Grice	4			3			1	1		1	1		4
Kirby	3		1	3							4		4
Stevenson	4			2	1			1		2	1		4
Trickett-Smith	3			2						2	1		3
Grocott	2			2						2			2
Short	1	1		2			1					1	2
Wakefield	1	1		2			1			1			2
Ashman	1			1							1		1
Saxon			1	1						1			1

LINCOLN UNITED MATCH RESULTS 2020-21

Date	Comp	H/A	Opponents	Att:	Result		Goalscorers	Pos	No.
Sept 12	**FACP**	**A**	**West Bridgford**				**Walkover for West Bridgford**		1
19	NPLSE	A	Carlton Town	190	W	3 - 1	Smith R 28 90 McMenery 73	6	2
29	NPLSE	H	Cleethorpes Town	253	D	1 - 1	Park 57	9	3
Oct 3	NPLSE	H	Stocksbridge Park Steels	156	L	3 - 4	Cotton 42 (pen) 70 Smith R 83	11	4
6	NPLSE	A	Stamford	240	L	1 - 5	Cotton 6 (pen)	13	5
10	NPLSE	A	Sutton Coldfield Town	331	W	6 - 0	McMenemy 13 43 Foster 18 Park 46 Cotton 70 (pen) Chapman 72	10	6
13	NPLSE	A	Wisbech Town	209	W	2 - 0	Cotton 9 (pen) Park 39	9	7
17	**FAT2Q**	**A**	**Stamford**	**288**	**L**	**1 - 2**	**Cotton 76 (pen)**		8
24	NPLSE	H	Glossop North End	239	W	5 - 0	Cotton 8 59 McMenemy 9 32 Janssen 87	8	9

Goalscorers	LGE	FAC	FAT	SG	HAT	PEN	1Q	2Q	45+	3Q	4Q	90+	T
TOTALS	21	0	1		0	5	6	5	0	3	7	1	22
Cotton	7		1	6		5	3	1		1	3		8
McMenery	5			3			2	2			1		5
Park	3			3				1		2			3
Smith R	3			2				1			1	1	3
Chapman	1			1							1		1
Foster	1			1			1						1
Janssen	1			1							1		1

LOUGHBOROUGH DYNAMO MATCH RESULTS 2020-21

Date	Comp	H/A	Opponents	Att:	Result		Goalscorers	Pos	No.
Sept 12	**FACP**	**A**	**Lutterworth Town**	**238**	**W**	**6 - 0**	**Matthews 37 Steadman 45 Garnett 52 59 Demidh 80 89**		1
19	NPLSE	A	Worksop Town	339	L	2 - 6	Steadman 54 Smith 61	17	2
22	**FAC1Q**	**A**	**Nuneaton Borough**	**311**	**L**	**1 - 2**	**Burrows 22**		3
26	NPLSE	A	Stocksbridge Park Steels	127	W	2 - 0	Gordon 16 Burrows 23 (pen)	12	4
29	NPLSE	H	Spalding United	120	W	1 - 0	Demidh 82	6	5
Oct 3	NPLSE	H	Cleethorpes Town	152	D	1 - 1	Burrows 61	3	6
10	NPLSE	A	Sheffield	400	W	2 - 1	Burrows 45 51 (pens)	8	7
13	NPLSE	H	Glossop North End (15)	104	W	2 - 1	Matthews 49 Norris 60	3	8
17	**FAT2Q**	**H**	**Bury Town**	**120**	**W**	**1 - 0**	**Steadman 89**		9
19	NPLSE	A	Market Drayton Town	132	W	3 - 0	Smith 18 Demidh 66 Burrows 90	1	10
24	NPLSE	H	Wisbech Town	175	W	3 - 0	Riley 23 Burrows 45 Collins 90	1	11
31	**FAT3Q**	**H**	**Bedford Town**	**169**	**L**	**1 - 3**	**Matthews 35**		12

Goalscorers	LGE	FAC	FAT	SG	HAT	PEN	1Q	2Q	45+	3Q	4Q	90+	T
TOTALS	16	7	2		0	3	3	4	3	9	4	2	25
Burrows	6	1		6		3	1	1	2	2		1	7
Demidh	2	2		3						1	3		4
Matthews	1	1	1	3				2		1			3
Steadman	1	1	1	3					1	1	1		3
Garnett		2		1						2			2
Smith	2			2			1			1			2
Collins	1			1								1	1
Gordon	1			1			1						1
Norris	1			1						1			1
Riley	1			1				1					1

MARKET DRAYTON TOWN MATCH RESULTS 2020-21

Date	Comp	H/A	Opponents	Att:	Result	Goalscorers	Pos	No.
Sept 12	**FACP**	**H**	**Tividale**	**122**	**L 0 - 1**			1
19	NPLSE	A	Belper Town	398	L 0 - 4		18	2
26	**FAT1Q**	**H**	**Bury Town**	**78**	**L 0 - 1**			3
28	NPLSE	H	Chasetown	222	L 1 - 3	Hands 24 (pen)	19	4
Oct 6	NPLSE	A	Leek Town	331	L 0 - 6		19	5
10	NPLSE	H	Ilkeston	233	L 1 - 5	Barnsley 87	19	6
13	NPLSE	A	Kidsgrove Athletic	289	L 0 - 3		19	7
19	NPLSE	H	Loughborough Dynamo	132	L 0 - 3		20	8
24	NPLSE	A	Frickley Athletic	176	L 0 - 4		20	9
31	NPLSE	H	Sutton Coldfield Town	88	L 0 - 2		20	10

Goalscorers	LGE	FAC	FAT	SG	HAT	PEN	1Q	2Q	45+	3Q	4Q	90+	T
TOTALS	2	0	0		0	1	0	1	0	0	1	0	2
Barnsley	1			1							1		1
Hands	1			1		1		1					1

NEWCASTLE TOWN MATCH RESULTS 2020-21

Date	Comp	H/A	Opponents	Att:	Result	Goalscorers	Pos	No.
Sept 12	**FACP**	**H**	**Halesowen Town**	**214**	**L 1 - 2**	**McLean 42**		1
19	NPLSE	H	Sheffield FC	223	D 0 - 0		10	2
26	NPLSE	H	Frickley Athletic	188	**W** 1 - 0	Askey 73	2	3
29	NPLSE	A	Glossop North End	184	D 0 - 0		7	4
Oct 3	NPLSE	A	Wisbech Town	157	**W** 3 - 2	Van Der Laan 57 McLean 72 82	2	5
10	NPLSE	H	Carlton Town	200	**W** 6 - 1	Berks 12 (pen) 58 McLean 25 (pen) Chimenes 69 Morley 83 Vale 89	2	6
17	**FAT2Q**	**H**	**Belper Town**	**214**	**D 2 - 2**	**McLean 47 Berks 58 (Won 5-4 on pens)**		7
20	NPLSE	H	Ilkeston Town	150	**W** 4 - 1	McLean 6 39 (pen) Melhado 50 Berks 70	2	8
24	NPLSE	A	Stocksbridge PS	173	**W** 3 - 2	McLean 8 (pen) 19 Baxter 33	2	9
31	**FAT3Q**	**H**	**Nuneaton Borough**	**301**	**L 0 - 2**			10
Nov 3	NPLSE	A	Chasetown	213	L 0 - 3		3	11

Goalscorers	LGE	FAC	FAT	SG	HAT	PEN	1Q	2Q	45+	3Q	4Q	90+	T
TOTALS	17	1	2		0	4	4	4	0	5	7	0	20
McLean	7	1	1	6		3	3	3		1	2		9
Berks	3		1	3		1	1			2	1		4
Askey	1			1							1		1
Baxter	1			1				1					1
Chimenes	1			1							1		1
Melhado	1			1						1			1
Morley	1			1							1		1
Vale	1			1							1		1
Van Der Laan	1			1						1			1

SHEFFIELD FC MATCH RESULTS 2020-21

Date	Comp	H/A	Opponents	Att:	Result	Goalscorers	Pos	No.
Sept 12	**FACP**	**A**	**Holbeach United**	**151**	**W 4 - 0**	**Newsham 19 27 42 Viggars 61**		**1**
19	NPLSE	A	Newcastle Town	223	D 0 - 0		11	2
22	**FAC1Q**	**A**	**Coalville Town**	**223**	**L 0 - 2**			**3**
29	NPLSE	H	Stocksbridge Park Steels	400	L 0 - 3		16	4
Oct 10	NPLSE	H	Loughborough Dynamo	400	L 1 - 2	Newsham 90	18	5
13	NPLSE	A	Frickley Athletic	220	W 2 - 1	Newsham 35 Cribley 79	18	6
17	**FAT2Q**	**H**	**Runcorn Linnets**	**281**	**L 2 - 3**	**Prior 6 Grayson 75**		**7**
24	NPLSE	A	Kidsgrove Athletic	280	L 1 - 2	Purkiss 72	18	8
31	NPLSE	H	Carlton Town	208	L 0 - 2		18	9

Goalscorers	LGE	FAC	FAT	SG	HAT	PEN	1Q	2Q	45+	3Q	4Q	90+	T
TOTALS	4	4	2		1	0	2	3	0	1	3	1	10
Newsham	2	3		3	1		1	3				1	5
Cribley	1			1							1		1
Grayson			1	1							1		1
Prior			1	1			1						1
Viggars		1		1						1			1
Purkiss	1			1							1		1

SPALDING UNITED MATCH RESULTS 2020-21

Date	Comp	H/A	Opponents	Att:	Result	Goalscorers	Pos	No.
Sept 12	**FACEP**	**H**	**Barton Town**	**152**	**L 1 - 3**	**Floyd 7**		**1**
19	NPLSE	H	Sutton Coldfield	122	W 3 - 0	Brownhill 8 Weir-Daley 24 Goddard 44	5	2
26	NPLSE	H	Carlton Town	136	W 2 - 0	Clarke 3 62	1	3
29	NPLSE	A	Loughborough Dynamo	120	L 0 - 1		3	4
Oct 6	NPLSE	H	Ilkeston Town	200	L 1 - 2	Floyd 85	10	5
10	NPLSE	H	Chasetown	190	L 1 - 3	Weir-Daley 71	12	6
13	NPLSE	A	Cleethorpes Town	303	L 1 - 3	Johnson 84	13	7
17	**FAT2Q**	**H**	**Bedford Town**	**224**	**L 0 - 1**			**8**
24	NPLSE	A	Worksop Town	374	L 0 - 2		17	9
31	NPLSE	A	Belper Town	400	D 3 - 3	Brownhill 25 Weir-Daley 45 Ranger 59	17	10

Goalscorers	LGE	FAC	FAT	SG	HAT	PEN	1Q	2Q	45+	3Q	4Q	90+	T
TOTALS	11	1	0		0	0	3	3	1	2	3	0	12
Weir-Daley	3			3				1	1		1		3
Brownhill	2			2			1	1					2
Clarke	2			1			1			1			2
Floyd	1	1		2			1				1		2
Goddard	1			1				1					1
Johnson	1			1							1		1
Ranger	1			1						1			1

STAMFORD MATCH RESULTS 2020-21

Date	Comp	H/A	Opponents	Att:	Result	Goalscorers	Pos	No.
Sept 12	**FACP**	**H**	**Diss Town**	**237**	**W 4 - 0**	**Chitiza 77 Blunden 79 Challinor 81 McGoven 90**		1
19	NPLSE	H	Glossop North End	294	W 5 - 0	Chitiza 11 Matwasa 27 Limb 61 Vince 64 (pen) Siddons 79	2	2
22	**FAC1Q**	**H**	**AFC Sudbury**	**309**	**W 4 - 0**	**Matwasa 38 Blunden 44 84 Hicks 87**		3
29	NPLSE	A	Ilkeston Town	393	D 2 - 2	Morgan 4 Challinor 68	8	4
Oct 3	**FAC2Q**	**A**	**Royston Town**	**422**	**D 2 - 2**	**Chitiza 78 Morgan 84 (Lost 2-4 on pens)**		5
6	NPLSE	H	Lincoln United	240	W 5 - 1	Duffy 21 Matwasa 47 Siddons 73 84 Bartle 76	6	6
10	NPLSE	H	Stocksbridge	311	W 5 - 0	Matwasa 19 Siddons 41 51 Limb 72 Hicks 79	3	7
13	NPLSE	A	Carlton Town	173	D 1 - 1	Wright 77	4	8
17	**FAT2Q**	**H**	**Lincoln United**	**288**	**W 2 - 1**	**Siddons 14 Challinor 80**		9
20	NPLSE	H	Worksop Town	377	D 0 - 0		6	10
24	NPLSE	A	Chasetown	281	D 2 - 2	Morgan 6 19 (pen)	6	11
31	**FAT3Q**	**A**	**Stourbridge**	**572**	**W 3 - 0**	**Siddons 8 Chitiza 35 Morgan 89 (pen)**		12
Dec 12	**FAT1P**	**A**	**Kidsgrove Athletic**	**198**	**W 2 - 0**	**Siddons 38 Vince 82**		13
15	**FAT2P**	**H**	**Kidderminster Harriers**		**W 1 - 0**	**Morgan 19**		14
	FAT3P		**Bye**					15
Jan 19	**FAT4P**	**H**	**Hereford**		**L 0 - 2**			16

Goalscorers	LGE	FAC	FAT	SG	HAT	PEN	1Q	2Q	45+	3Q	4Q	90+	T
TOTALS	20	10	8		0	3	9	6	0	4	18	1	38
Siddons	5		3	6			2	2		1	3		8
Morgan	3	1	2	5		2	4				2		6
Chitiza	1	2	1	4			1	1			2		4
Matwasa	3	1		4			1	2		1			4
Blunden		3		2				1			2		3
Challinor	1	1	1	3							3		3
Hicks	1	1		2							2		2
Limb	2			2						1	1		2
Vince	1		1	2		1				1	1		2
Bartle	1			1							1		1
Duffy	1			1			1						1
McGoven		1		1								1	1
Wright	1			1							1		1

STOCKSBRIDGE PARK STEELS MATCH RESULTS 2020-21

Date	Comp	H/A	Opponents	Att:	Result	Goalscorers	Pos	No.
Sept 12	**FACP**	**H**	**Stalybridge Celtic**	**361**	**L 1 - 3**	**Ruthven 31**		1
19	NPLSE	H	Kidsgrove Athletic	147	L 0 - 1		14	2
26	NPLSE	H	Loughborough Dynamo	127	L 0 - 2		16	3
29	NPLSE	A	Sheffield	400	W 3 - 0	Nodder 24 Mangham 32 Reay 45	13	4
Oct 3	NPLSE	A	Lincoln United	156	W 4 - 3	Reay 7 Lumsden 60 67 Whitham 84	8	5
10	NPLSE	A	Stamford	311	L 0 - 5		14	6
13	NPLSE	H	Belper Town	211	W 4 - 3	Lumsden 33 Nodder 59 Mangham 82 84	11	7
17	**FAT2Q**	**H**	**Marske United**	**230**	**L 0 - 4**			8
20	NPLSE	A	Leek Town	363	L 2 - 6	Mangham 8 Ruthven 76	11	9
24	NPLSE	H	Newcastle Town	173	L 2 - 3	Fielding 22 Mangham 56	12	10
31	NPLSE	A	Chasetown	204	L 1 - 2	Cope 71	14	11

Goalscorers	LGE	FAC	FAT	SG	HAT	PEN	1Q	2Q	45+	3Q	4Q	90+	T
TOTALS	16	1	0		0	0	3	4	1	4	5	0	17
Mangham	5			4			1	1		1	2		5
Lumsden	3			2				1		2			3
Nodder	2			2				1		1			2
Reay	2			2			1		1				2
Ruthven	1	1		2				1			1		2
Cope	1			1							1		1
Fielding	1			1			1						1
Whitham	1			1							1		1

SUTTON COLDFIELD TOWN MATCH RESULTS 2020-21

Date	Comp	H/A	Opponents	Att:	Result	Goalscorers	Pos	No.
Sept 12	**FACP**	**H**	**Belper Town**	**249**	**L 0 - 1**			1
19	NPLSE	A	Spalding United	122	L 0 - 3		16	2
29	NPLSE	H	Carlton Town	167	D 0 - 0		17	3
Oct 3	NPLSE	H	Leek Town	181	D 1 - 1	Zia 51	17	4
6	NPLSE	A	Belper Town	353	L 1 - 7	Leek 16 (pen)	17	5
10	NPLSE	H	Lincoln United	331	L 0 - 6		17	6
13	NPLSE	A	Worksop Town	360	**W** 4 - 2	Ahenkorah 18 Francis 35 Preston 44 Leek 89	17	7
17	**FAT2Q**	**H**	**Dereham Town**	**283**	**L 2 - 3**	**Beresford 70 Shaw 85**		8
20	NPLSE	H	Kidsgrove Athletic	143	**W** 5 - 3	Nesbitt 48 Shaw 72 74 86 Hilton 90	14	9
31	NPLSE	A	Market Drayton Town	88	**W** 2 - 0	Nesbitt 20 24	12	10

Goalscorers	LGE	FAC	FAT	SG	HAT	PEN	1Q	2Q	45+	3Q	4Q	90+	T
TOTALS	13	0	2		1	1	3	3	0	2	6	1	15
Shaw	3		1	2	1						4		4
Nesbitt	3			2			1	1		1			3
Leek	2			2		1	1				1		2
Ahenkorah	1			1			1						1
Beresford			1	1							1		1
Francis	1			1				1					1
Hilton	1			1								1	1
Preston	1			1				1					1
Zia	1			1						1			1

WISBECH TOWN MATCH RESULTS 2020-21

Date	Comp	H/A	Opponents	Att:	Result	Goalscorers	Pos	No.
Sept 12	**FACP**	**A**	**Haverhill Rovers**	**170**	**L 3 - 4**	**Adams 19 Edge 68 Vieira 84**		1
19	NPLSE	A	Leek Town	378	L 0 - 5		20	2
29	NPLSE	H	Worksop Town	210	L 0 - 3		20	3
Oct 3	NPLSE	H	Newcastle Town	157	L 2 - 3	Vieira 49 Maddison 90	20	4
6	NPLSE	A	Carlton Town	122	L 0 - 4		20	5
10	NPLSE	H	Fickley Athletic		L 0 - 4		20	6
13	NPLSE	A	Lincoln United	209	L 0 - 2		20	7
17	**FAT2Q**	**H**	**Coleshill Town**	**164**	**L 1 - 2**	**Grogan 90**		8
20	NPLSE	H	Cleethorpes Town	110	**W** 3 - 2	Edge 35 75 (pen) Adams 83	19	9
24	NPLSE	A	Loughborough Dynamo	175	L 0 - 3		19	10

Goalscorers	LGE	FAC	FAT	SG	HAT	PEN	1Q	2Q	45+	3Q	4Q	90+	T
TOTALS	5	3	1		0	1	1	1	0	1	4	2	9
Edge	2	1		2		1		1			2		3
Adams	1	1		2			1				1		2
Vieira	1	1		2						1	1		2
Grogan			1	1								1	1
Maddison	1			1								1	1

WORKSOP TOWN MATCH RESULTS 2020-21

Date	Comp	H/A	Opponents	Att:	Result	Goalscorers	Pos	No.
Sept 12	**FACP**	**A**	**Ansley Nomads**	**300**	**W 2 - 1**	**Hinsley 4 Redford 40**		1
19	NPLSE	H	Loughborough Dynamo	339	W 6 - 2	Redford 9 23 68 (pen) 70 (pen) Hinsley 41 Opponent 45	3	2
22	**FAC1Q**	**A**	**Westfields**	**240**	**W 3 - 1**	**Redford 32 (pen) Smythe 38 Hinsley 45**		3
29	NPLSE	A	Wisbech Town	210	W 3 - 0	Dunn 34 Redford 50 Hinsley 82	2	4
Oct 3	**FAC2Q**	**H**	**Chester**	**293**	**D 2 - 2**	**Radford 31 Broadhead 74**		5
6	NPLSE	H	Glossop North End	347	W 5 - 1	Allott 25 36 Broadhead 31 Hinsley 61 Cromack 80	2	6
10	NPLSE	A	Belper Town	400	D 2 - 2	Hinsley 45 Curti 82 (og)	4	7
13	NPLSE	H	Sutton Coldfield Town	360	L 2 - 4	Hinsley 8 Jemson 86	7	8
17	**FAT2Q**	**H**	**Ramsbottom United**	**298**	**D 4 - 4**	**Greenhough 5 Baxendale 14 Allott 22 Brown 87 (Won 5-4 on pens)**		9
20	NPLSE	A	Stamford	377	D 0 - 0		7	10
24	NPLSE	H	Spalding United	374	W 2 - 0	Gibbens 35 Allott 57 (pen)	5	11
31	**FAT3Q**	**A**	**St Neots Town**	**371**	**L 1 - 6**	**Dunn 11**		12

Goalscorers	LGE	FAC	FAT	SG	HAT	PEN	1Q	2Q	45+	3Q	4Q	90+	T
TOTALS	20	7	5		1	4	7	11	3	3	8	0	32
Hinsley	5	2		7			2	1	2	1	1		7
Redford	5	2		4	1	3	1	3		1	2		7
Alott	3		1	3		1	1	2		1			4
Broadhead	1	1		2				1			1		2
Dunn	1		1	2			1	1					2
Opponent	2			2					1		1		2
Baxendale			1	1			1						1
Brown			1	1							1		1
Cromack	1			1							1		1
Gibbens	1			1				1					1
Greenhough			1	1			1						1
Jemson	1			1							1		1
Radford		1		1				1					1
Smythe		1		1				1					1

SOUTHERN LEAGUE 2020-21

PREMIER CENTRAL	P	W	D	L	F	A	GD	Pts
1 Coalville Town	7	5	2	0	21	5	16	17
2 Needham Market	7	5	2	0	17	7	10	17
3 Stratford Town	8	5	0	3	17	16	1	15
4 Rushall Olympic	8	3	4	1	14	12	2	13
5 Tamworth	7	3	3	1	13	8	5	12
6 Redditch United	8	3	3	2	14	11	3	12
7 Stourbridge	8	2	5	1	10	7	3	11
8 Royston Town	8	2	5	1	12	11	1	11
9 Kings Langley	9	2	5	2	11	11	0	11
10 Hitchin Town	7	3	1	3	12	14	-2	10
11 St Ives Town	6	3	1	2	11	13	-2	10
12 Peterborough Sports	6	2	3	1	10	5	5	9
13 AFC Rushden & Diamonds	7	2	3	2	14	11	3	9
14 Lowestoft Town	7	2	3	2	8	9	-1	9
15 Nuneaton Borough	8	2	2	4	14	13	1	8
16 Biggleswade Town	8	2	2	4	13	17	-4	8
17 Alvechurch	9	2	2	5	12	16	-4	8
18 Banbury United	7	2	2	3	9	13	-4	8
19 Bromsgrove Sporting	8	2	2	4	9	17	-8	8
20 Hednesford Town	8	2	1	5	12	16	-4	7
21 Leiston	8	1	2	5	11	21	-10	5
22 Barwell	7	1	1	5	6	17	-11	4

PREMIER SOUTH	P	W	D	L	F	A	GD	Pts
1 Poole Town	7	6	1	0	16	7	9	19
2 Tiverton Town	7	6	0	1	21	4	17	18
3 Salisbury	7	5	2	0	17	7	10	17
4 Truro City	8	5	1	2	17	9	8	16
5 Metropolitan Police	8	4	2	2	14	11	3	14
6 Swindon Supermarine	7	4	0	3	12	10	2	12
7 Chesham United	7	3	3	1	6	4	2	12
8 Taunton Town	6	3	2	1	8	5	3	11
9 Hendon	8	3	2	3	12	10	2	11
10 Hayes & Yeading United	7	2	4	1	11	8	3	10
11 Gosport Borough	7	2	2	3	11	9	2	8
12 Walton Casuals	6	2	1	3	8	13	-5	7
13 Wimborne Town	6	2	1	3	5	12	-7	7
14 Hartley Wintney	6	1	3	2	5	9	-4	6
15 Weston-super-Mare	6	1	2	3	8	10	-2	5
16 Harrow Borough	7	1	2	4	11	14	-3	5
17 Yate Town	8	1	2	5	8	17	-9	5
18 Farnborough	8	1	1	6	7	16	-9	4
19 Dorchester Town	7	1	1	5	5	17	-12	4
20 Beaconsfield Town	7	0	2	5	4	14	-10	2

DIVISION ONE CENTRAL	P	W	D	L	F	A	GD	Pts
1 Corby Town	7	5	0	2	15	8	7	15
2 Bedworth United	8	4	3	1	16	15	1	15
3 St Neots Town	8	3	4	1	23	12	11	13
4 Aylesbury United	7	4	1	2	16	11	5	13
5 Bedford Town	7	3	3	1	9	6	3	12
6 Daventry Town	8	4	0	4	13	15	-2	12
7 Halesowen Town	7	3	2	2	20	10	10	11
8 Berkhamsted	6	3	2	1	13	5	8	11
9 Barton Rovers	8	3	2	3	16	13	3	11
10 AFC Dunstable	7	3	2	2	10	9	1	11
11 Welwyn Garden City	6	3	1	2	10	8	2	10
12 Kidlington	6	2	3	1	10	6	4	9
13 Coleshill Town	8	3	0	5	7	11	-4	9
14 Wantage Town	8	3	0	5	13	20	-7	9
15 Yaxley	6	2	2	2	13	14	-1	8
16 Thame United	7	2	1	4	12	10	2	7
17 Kempston Rovers	8	1	3	4	11	18	-7	6
18 Biggleswade FC	7	2	0	5	7	16	-9	6
19 North Leigh	7	1	3	3	5	17	-12	6
20 Didcot Town	8	2	0	6	7	22	-15	6

DIVISION ONE SOUTH	P	W	D	L	F	A	GD	Pts
1 Cirencester Town	9	8	0	1	26	4	22	24
2 AFC Totton	9	6	2	1	22	8	14	20
3 Basingstoke Town	7	5	1	1	23	13	10	16
4 Winchester City	7	5	0	2	14	8	6	15
5 Slimbridge	9	4	2	3	22	21	1	14
6 Paulton Rovers	9	4	1	4	15	14	1	13
7 Willand Rovers	8	4	1	3	14	13	1	13
8 Highworth Town	8	4	1	3	11	14	-3	13
9 Frome Town	7	3	2	2	12	7	5	11
10 Larkhall Athletic	7	3	1	3	11	11	0	10
11 Bristol Manor Farm	7	3	1	3	12	14	-2	10
12 Sholing	5	3	0	2	9	6	3	9
13 Evesham United	6	2	2	2	5	7	-2	8
14 Cinderford Town	7	2	1	4	10	21	-11	7
15 Thatcham Town	8	1	3	4	8	13	-5	6
16 Bideford AFC	6	0	4	2	7	9	-2	4
17 Moneyfields	4	1	0	3	7	7	0	3
18 Melksham Town	6	1	0	5	5	14	-9	3
19 Barnstaple Town	6	0	2	4	9	22	-13	2
20 Mangotsfield United	7	0	0	7	4	20	-16	0

AFC RUSHDEN & DIAMONDS MATCH RESULTS 2020-21

Date	Comp	H/A	Opponents	Att:	Result		Goalscorers	Pos	No.
Sept 19	SthPC	A	Nuneaton Borough	596	D	1 - 1	Smith L 33 (pen)	9	1
22	**FAC1Q**	**H**	**Newark**	**450**	**L**	**0 - 5**			2
26	SthPC	H	Barwell	343	D	1 - 1	Slinn 82	14	3
29	SthPC	H	Hitchin Town	379	W	7 - 1	Wreh 9 11 17 20 Collard 67 Smith L 77 Akubuine 90+1	7	4
Oct 6	SthPC	A	Leiston	214	D	2 - 2	Lorraine 34 Smith L 71		5
10	SthPC	A	Bromsgrove Sporting	600	L	0 - 1		12	6
17	SthPC	H	Hednesford Town	410	W	2 - 1	Smith L 16 Fairlamb 69	4	7
24	SthPC	A	Coalville Town	500	L	1 - 4	Hughes 79	10	8
31	**FAT3Q**	**H**	**Ilkeston Town**		**W/O**				9
Dec 8	**FAT1P**	**H**	**Peterborough Sports**	**252**	**L**	**1 - 5**	**Collard 49**		10

Goalscorers	LGE	FAC	FAT	SG	HAT	PEN	1Q	2Q	45+	3Q	4Q	90+	T
TOTALS	14	0	1		1	1	5	2	0	1	5	1	15
Smith L	4			4		1	1	1			2		4
Wreh	4			1	1		4						4
Collard	1		1	1						1			2
Akubuine	1			1								1	1
Fairlamb	1			1							1		1
Hughes	1			1							1		1
Lorraine	1			1				1					1
Slinn	1			1							1		1

ALVECHURCH MATCH RESULTS 2020-21

Date	Comp	H/A	Opponents	Att:	Result		Goalscorers	Pos	No.
Sept 19	SthPC	A	Hitchin Town	425	L	1 - 5	Cook 61 (pen)	22	1
22	**FAC1Q**	**A**	**Shifnal Town**	**320**	**W**	**2 - 0**	**Wakeling 20 76**		2
26	SthPC	H	Royston Town	226	D	2 - 2	Wakeling 46 Hull 77	20	3
29	SthPC	H	Stratford Town	248	L	1 - 3	Wakeling 14 (pen)	21	4
Oct 3	**FAC2Q**	**H**	**Kidderminster Harriers**	**445**	**D**	**2 - 2**	**Cook 3 Hull 57 (Won 4-2 on pens)**		5
6	SthPC	A	Barwell	159	W	5 - 0	Delfouneso 24 (og) Wakeling 40 43 63 Hamilton 85		6
10	SthPC	H	Tamworth	461	W	1 - 0	Monteiro 45	11	7
13	**FAC3Q**	**A**	**Ilkeston**	**400**	**L**	**0 - 1**			8
17	SthPC	A	Biggleswade Town	177	L	1 - 2	McFarlane 16	16	9
24	SthPC	H	Needham Market	226	L	1 - 2	Lloyd 8	17	10
26	SthPC	A	Stourbridge	600	D	0 - 0			11
31	**FAT3Q**	**A**	**Basford United**	**291**	**L**	**1 - 2**	**Cook 90+1**		12
Nov 3	SthPC	H	Nuneaton Borough	402	L	0 - 2		17	13

Goalscorers	LGE	FAC	FAT	SG	HAT	PEN	1Q	2Q	45+	3Q	4Q	90+	T
TOTALS	12	4	1		0	2	5	3	1	4	3	1	17
Wakeling	5	2		4		1	2	2		2	1		7
Cook	1	1	1	3		1	1			1		1	2
Hull	1	1		2						1	1		2
Hamilton	1			1							1		1
Lloyd	1			1			1						1
McFarlane	1			1			1						1
Monteiro	1			1					1				1
Opponent	1			1				1					1

BANBURY UNITED MATCH RESULTS 2020-21

Date	Comp	H/A	Opponents	Att:	Result		Goalscorers	Pos	No.
Sept 19	SthPC	A	Royston Town	377	D	2 - 2	Welch 31 (og) Parr 83 (og)	7	1
22	**FAC1Q**	**H**	**Carlton Town**	**369**	**W**	**1 - 0**	**Rasulo 78**		2
26	SthPC	H	Redditch United	471	L	0 - 1		17	3
29	SthPC	H	Hednesford Town	351	W	2 - 0	Henshall 20 Langmead 81	10	4
Oct 3	**FAC2Q**	**A**	**Leamington**		**W**	**1 - 0**	**Langmead 17**		5
6	SthPC	A	Nuneaton Borough	353	W	2 - 1	Rasulo 61 (pen) 82		6
10	SthPC	H	Needham Market	506	D	1 - 1	Langmead 76	7	7
13	**FAC3Q**	**A**	**Peterborough Sports**	**471**	**D**	**1 - 1**	**(Won 7-6 on pens)**		8
17	SthPC	A	Coalville Town	510	L	1 - 6	Landers 4	13	9
24	**FAC4Q**	**H**	**Bury Town**		**W**	**2 - 1**	**Self 80 Landers 83**		10
27	SthPC	A	Kings Langley	259	L	1 - 2	Landers 2	14	11
31	**FAT3Q**	**A**	**Tamworth**	**355**	**L**	**1 - 2**			12
Nov 7	**FAC1P**	**H**	**Canvey Island**		**L**	**1 - 2**	**Johnson 68**		13

Goalscorers	LGE	FAC	FAT	SG	HAT	PEN	1Q	2Q	45+	3Q	4Q	90+	T
TOTALS	9	6	1		0	1	4	1	0	1	8	0	16
Landers	2	1		3			2				1		3
Langmead	2	1		3			1				2		3
Rasulo	2	1		2		1				1	2		3
Opponent	2			1				1			1		2
Henshall	1			1			1						1
Johnson		1		1							1		1
Self		1		1							1		1

BARWELL MATCH RESULTS 2020-21

Date	Comp	H/A	Opponents	Att:	Result		Goalscorers	Pos	No.
Sept 19	SthPC	H	Lowestoft Town	249	L	1 - 2	Hickey 32 (pen)	17	1
22	**FAC1Q**	**H**	**Bedworth United**	**206**	**W**	**3 - 1**	**Williams 74 76 Hickey 90+2 (pen)**		2
26	SthPC	A	AFC Rushden & Diamonds	343	D	1 - 1	Ashmore 8	18	3
29	SthPC	A	Tamworth	372	L	1 - 2	Williams 19	19	4
Oct 3	**FAC2Q**	**A**	**Nantwich Town**	**225**	**L**	**0 - 1**			5
6	SthPC	H	Alvechurch	159	L	0 - 5			6
10	SthPC	A	Peterborough Sports	247	L	0 - 3		22	7
17	SthPC	H	Nuneaton Borough	585	W	2 - 1	Davidson-Miller 46 Williams 85	20	8
27	SthPC	H	Rushall Olympic	239	L	1 - 3	Hickey 49	21	9
31	**FAT3Q**	**A**	**Rushall Olympic**	**308**	**L**	**1 - 4**	**Hollis 53**		10

Goalscorers	LGE	FAC	FAT	SG	HAT	PEN	1Q	2Q	45+	3Q	4Q	90+	T
TOTALS	6	3	1		0	2	2	1	0	3	3	1	10
Williams	2	2		3			1				3		4
Hickey	2	1		3		2		1		1		1	3
Ashmore	1			1			1						1
Davidson-Miller	1			1						1			1
Hollis			1	1						1			1

BIGGLESWADE TOWN MATCH RESULTS 2020-21

Date	Comp	H/A	Opponents	Att:	Result	Goalscorers	Pos	No.
Sept 19	SthPC	A	St Ives Town	217	L 0 - 1		19	1
22	**FAC1Q**	**A**	**Leiston**	**175**	**L 1 - 5**			2
26	SthPC	H	Bromsgrove Sporting	175	L 0 - 1		21	3
29	SthPC	H	Leiston	110	**W** 7 - 4	Giles 19 72 82 Neal 26 62 78 Chambers-Parrillon 33	14	4
Oct 3	SthPC	A	Stourbridge	591	D 2 - 2	Lopes 40 Giles 70	10	5
6	SthPC	A	Royston Town	256	D 1 - 1	Parr 40 (og)		6
10	SthPC	A	Redditch United	553	L 1 - 4	Neal 1	15	7
17	SthPC	H	Alvechurch	177	**W** 2 - 1	Neal 54 Giles 55	11	8
24	SthPC	A	Tamworth	523	L 0 - 3		15	9
31	**FAT3Q**	**H**	**Heybridge Swifts**	**133**	**W 1 - 0**	**Furlong 56**		10
Dec 8	**FAT1P**	**H**	**Bedford Town**	**201**	**D 0 - 0**	**(Lost 3-4 on pens)**		11

Goalscorers	LGE	FAC	FAT	SG	HAT	PEN	1Q	2Q	45+	3Q	4Q	90+	T
TOTALS	13	1	1		2	0	2	4	0	4	4	0	15
Giles	5			3	1		1			1	3		5
Neal	5			3	1		1	1		2	1		5
Chambers-Parrillon	1			1				1					1
Furlong			1	1						1			1
Lopes	1			1				1					1
Opponent	1			1				1					1

BROMSGROVE SPORTING MATCH RESULTS 2020-21

Date	Comp	H/A	Opponents	Att:	Result	Goalscorers	Pos	No.
Sept 19	SthPC	H	Coalville Town	569	D 1 - 1	Broadhurst 90 (pen)	10	1
22	**FAC1Q**	**H**	**Stratford Town**	**472**	**L 1 - 2**			2
26	SthPC	A	Bigglewade Town	175	**W** 1 - 0	Ward 83	5	3
29	SthPC	A	Rushall Olympic	435	L 3 - 4	Pendley 39 (og) Lait 65 Taylor 70	12	4
Oct 6	SthPC	H	Tamworth	600	D 2 - 2	Cowley 14 Taylor 17		5
10	SthPC	H	AFC Rushden & Diamonds	600	**W** 1 - 0	Taylor 14	8	6
17	SthPC	A	Needham Market	301	L 0 - 3		12	7
24	SthPC	H	Hitchin Town	600	L 0 - 2		16	8
27	SthPC	A	Hednesford Town	596	L 1 - 5	Richards 32		9
31	**FAT3Q**	**H**	**Coleshill Town**	**482**	**L 0 - 1**			10

Goalscorers	LGE	FAC	FAT	SG	HAT	PEN	1Q	2Q	45+	3Q	4Q	90+	T
TOTALS	9	1	0		0	1	3	2	0	1	2	1	10
Taylor	3			3			2				1		3
Broadhurst	1			1		1						1	1
Cowley	1			1			1						1
Lait	1			1						1			1
Opponent	1			1				1					1
Richards	1			1				1					1
Ward	1			1							1		1

COALVILLE TOWN MATCH RESULTS 2020-21

Date	Comp	H/A	Opponents	Att:	Result	Goalscorers	Pos	No.
Sept 12	**FACP**	**A**	**Boston Town**	**130**	**W 3 - 0**	**Berridge 31 Pierpoint 69 Kee 82 (pen)**		**1**
19	SthPC	A	Bromsgrove Sporting	569	D 1 - 1	Berridge 50	11	2
22	**FAC1Q**	**H**	**Sheffield**	**369**	**W 2 - 0**	**Thwaites 15 (og) Thomas 68**		**3**
26	SthPC	H	Leiston	281	W 4 - 1	Robertson 39 Taylor 39 Shaw 54 Berridge 63	2	4
29	SthPC	H	Redditch United	265	D 1 - 1	Kee 69	8	5
Oct 3	**FAC2Q**	**H**	**Alfreton Town**	**437**	**L 1 - 2**	**Berridge 64**		**6**
6	SthPC	A	Hednesford Town	311	W 3 - 0	Shaw 20 Berridge 34 Kee 50		7
10	SthPC	A	Rushall Olympic	447	W 2 - 0	Shaw 39 Whittall 72 (og)	1	8
17	SthPC	H	Banbury United	510	W 6 - 1	Eggleton 27 Berridge 30 Shaw 62 Kee 68 73 Smith 79	1	9
24	SthPC	H	AFC Rushden & Diamonds	500	W 4 - 1	McGlinchey 17 Berridge 51 63 Shaw 70	1	10
Nov 3	**FAT3Q**	**H**	**Matlock Town**	**362**	**D 3 - 3**	**Berridge 7 36 85 (Lost 2-4 on pens)**		**11**

Goalscorers	LGE	FAC	FAT	SG	HAT	PEN	1Q	2Q	45+	3Q	4Q	90+	T
TOTALS	21	6	3		1	1	4	7	0	9	10	0	30
Berridge	6	2	3	8	1		1	4		5	1		11
Kee	4	1		4		1				1	4		5
Shaw	5			5			1	1		2	1		5
Opponent	1	1		2			1				1		2
Eggleton	1			1				1					1
McGlinchey	1			1			1						1
Pierpoint		1		1							1		1
Robertson	1			1				1					1
Smith	1			1							1		1
Taylor	1			1						1			1
Thomas		1		1							1		1

HEDNESFORD TOWN MATCH RESULTS 2020-21

Date	Comp	H/A	Opponents	Att:	Result	Goalscorers	Pos	No.
Sept 19	SthPC	H	Stourbridge	600	L 1 - 4	Glover 33	21	1
22	**FAC1Q**	**H**	**Long Eaton United**	**342**	**W 3 - 2**	**Glover 41 90+2 Turner 60**		**2**
26	SthPC	A	Lowestoft Town	200	D 0 - 0		19	3
29	SthPC	A	Banbury United	351	L 0 - 2		20	4
Oct 3	**FAC2Q**	**H**	**Halesowen Town**	**600**	**D 0 - 0**	**(Lost 3-5 on pens)**		**5**
6	SthPC	H	Coalville Town	311	L 0 - 3			6
10	SthPC	H	Stratford Town	479	W 4 - 2	Turner 30 90+3 Dodds 33 Sweeney 35	19	7
17	SthPC	A	AFC Rushden & Diamonds	410	L 1 - 2	Sweeney 76	19	8
24	SthPC	A	Royston Town	354	L 1 - 2	Turner 19 (pen)	20	9
27	SthPC	H	Bromsgrove Sporting	596	W 5 - 1	Dodds 45+2 67 Turner 51 Rowley 79 Bailey 86		10
31	**FAT3Q**	**A**	**Corby Town**	**391**	**W 2 - 1**	**Dwyer 57 Hallahan 60**		**11**
Dec 8	**FAT1P**	**A**	**Welwyn Garden City**	**119**	**L 1 - 3**	**Dwyer 9**		**12**

Goalscorers	LGE	FAC	FAT	SG	HAT	PEN	1Q	2Q	45+	3Q	4Q	90+	T
TOTALS	12	3	3		0	1	2	5	1	5	3	2	18
Turner	4	1		4		1	1	1		2		1	5
Dodds	3			2				1	1	1			3
Glover	1	2		2				2				1	3
Dwyer			2	2			1			1			2
Sweeney	2			2				1			1		2
Bailey	1			1							1		1
Hallahan			1	1						1			1
Rowley	1			1							1		1

HITCHIN TOWN MATCH RESULTS 2020-21

Date	Comp	H/A	Opponents	Att:	Result		Goalscorers	Pos	No.
Sept 19	SthPC	H	Alvechurch	425	W	5 - 1	Eadie 4 (pen) Stead 23 68 Brown 62 Gouldbourne 80	1	1
21	**FAC1Q**	**H**	**Needham Market**	**410**	**W**	**3 - 0**	**Marsh 14 Stead 69 79**		2
26	SthPC	A	Stourbridge	600	L	0 - 1		9	3
29	SthPC	A	AFC Rushden & Diamonds	379	L	1 - 7	Marsh 35	15	4
Oct 3	**FAC2Q**	**A**	**St Albans Town**	**0**	**L**	**0 - 5**			5
10	SthPC	H	Leiston	523	D	2 - 2	Eadie 74 Marsh 86	18	6
17	SthPC	A	Stratford Town	355	W	2 - 1	Brown 12 Gouldbourne 45	17	7
24	SthPC	A	Bromsgrove Sporting	600	W	2 - 0	Marsh 45+1 Stead 75	7	8
26	SthPC	H	Royston Town	600	L	0 - 2			9
31	**FAT3Q**	**H**	**Herne Bay**	**443**	**W**	**3 - 1**	**Barker 34 Marsh 48 Stead 84**		10
Dec 8	**FAT1P**	**H**	**Mickleover Sports**	**203**	**W**	**3 - 0**	**Brown 25 45 74**		11
12	**FAT2P**	**H**	**Peterborough Sports**	**385**	**L**	**0 - 4**			12

Goalscorers	LGE	FAC	FAT	SG	HAT	PEN	1Q	2Q	45+	3Q	4Q	90+	T
TOTALS	12	3	6		1	1	4	3	3	2	9	0	21
Stead	3	2	1	4			1				5		6
Brown	2		3	3	1		1	1	1	1	1		5
Marsh	3	1	1	5			1	1	1	1	1		5
Eadie	2			2		1	1				1		2
Gouldbourne	2			2					1		1		2
Barker			1	1				1					1

KINGS LANGLEY MATCH RESULTS 2020-21

Date	Comp	H/A	Opponents	Att:	Result		Goalscorers	Pos	No.
Sept 19	SthPC	A	Stratford Town	285	L	1 - 2	Toiny-Pendred 66	18	1
22	**FAC1Q**	**H**	**FC Clacton**	**277**	**D**	**1 - 1**	**Johnson 42 (Won 4-2 on pens)**		2
26	SthPC	H	Nuneaton Borough	390	W	3 - 2	Toiny-Pendred 12 Wadkins 56 Parkes 89	10	3
29	SthPC	H	St Ives Town	293	D	2 - 2	Crawford 42 Wood 51	11	4
Oct 3	**FAC2Q**	**A**	**Barking**	**197**	**D**	**2 - 2**	**Wadkins 80 86 (Lost 2-3 on pens)**		5
6	SthPC	A	Peterborough Sports	178	D	1 - 1	Parkes 32		6
10	SthPC	H	Lowestoft Town	483	D	1 - 1	Crawford 10	14	7
17	SthPC	A	Stourbridge	600	D	0 - 0		15	8
24	SthPC	A	Rushall Olympic	449	D	1 - 1	Connolly 65	12	9
27	SthPC	H	Banbury United	259	W	2 - 1	Toiny-Pendred 14 Connolly 81		10
31	**FAT3Q**	**H**	**Brightlingsea Regent**	**236**	**W**	**4 - 1**	**Wadkins 18 Williams 29 49 Wood 65**		11
Nov 3	SthPC	A	Leiston	164	L	0 - 1		9	12
Dec 8	**FAT1P**	**A**	**St Neots**	**270**	**L**	**1 - 3**			13

Goalscorers	LGE	FAC	FAT	SG	HAT	PEN	1Q	2Q	45+	3Q	4Q	90+	T
TOTALS	11	3	4		0	0	4	4	0	6	4	0	18
Wadkins	1	2	1	3			1			1	2		4
Toiny-Pendred	3			3			2			1			3
Connolly	2			2						1	1		2
Crawford	2			2			1	1					2
Parkes	2			2				1			1		2
Williams			2	1				1		1			2
Wood	1		1	2						2			2
Johnson		1		1				1					1

LEISTON MATCH RESULTS 2020-21

Date	Comp	H/A	Opponents	Att:	Result		Goalscorers	Pos	No.
Sept 12	**FACP**	**H**	**Halstead Town**	**174**	**W**	**5 - 0**	**Jackson 5 (pen) 23 Eaton-Collins 19 Eagle 83 Davies 88**		1
19	SthPC	H	Rushall Olympic	213	L	0 - 1		20	2
22	**FAC1Q**	**H**	**Biggleswade United**	**175**	**W**	**5 - 1**	**Davies 6 34 72 84 Eaton-Collins 50**		3
26	SthPC	A	Coalville Town	281	L	1 - 4	Barnes 72	22	4
29	SthPC	A	Biggleswade Town	110	L	4 - 7	Davies 13 Squire 49 (og) Jackson 65 71 (pen)	22	5
Oct 3	**FAC2Q**	**A**	**Leighton Town**	**300**	**W**	**2 - 1**	**Jackson 5 (pen) Davies 14**		6
6	SthPC	H	AFC Rushden & Diamonds	214	D	2 - 2	Switters 20 Davies 65		7
10	SthPC	A	Hitchin Town	523	D	2 - 2	Jackson 15 Davies 71	21	8
13	**FAC3Q**	**H**	**AFC Telford United**	**334**	**D**	**0 - 0**	**(Won 9-8 on pens)**		9
17	SthPC	H	Peterborough Sports	226	L	1 - 4	Eaton-Collins 38	22	10
24	**FAC4Q**	**H**	**Barnet**	**600**	**L**	**2 - 3**	**Davies 9 Connors 19 (og)**		11
27	SthPC	A	St Ives Town	156	L	0 - 1			12
31	**FAT3Q**	**H**	**Worthing**	**134**	**D**	**4 - 4**	**Jackson 9 35 Barnes 58 82 (Won 4-2 on pens)**		13
Nov 3	SthPC	H	Kings Langley	164	W	1 - 0	Eaton-Collins 79	21	14
Dec 12	**FAT1P**	**A**	**Needham Market**	**230**	**L**	**1 - 2**	**Barnes**		15

Goalscorers	LGE	FAC	FAT	SG	HAT	PEN	1Q	2Q	45+	3Q	4Q	90+	T
TOTALS	11	14	5		0	3	11	4	0	5	9	0	30
Davies	3	7		7			4	1		1	4		10
Jackson	3	3	2	5		3	4	2		1	1		8
Barnes	1		3	3						1	2		4
Eaton-Collins	2	2		4			1	1		1	1		4
Opponent	1	1		2			1			1			2
Switters	1			1			1						1
Eagle		1		1							1		1

LOWESTOFT TOWN MATCH RESULTS 2020-21

Date	Comp	H/A	Opponents	Att:	Result		Goalscorers	Pos	No.
Sept 19	SthPC	A	Barwell	249	W	2 - 1	Zielonka 45 78 (pens)	3	1
22	**FAC1Q**	**H**	**Avery**	**275**	**L**	**2 - 3**	**Reed 38 McIntosh 69**		2
26	SthPC	H	Hednesford Town	200	D	0 - 0		6	3
29	SthPC	H	Peterborough Sports	216	W	1 - 0	Reed 88	5	4
Oct 3	SthPC	A	Needham Market	365	L	1 - 3	Reed 29	5	5
10	SthPC	A	Kings Langley	483	D	1 - 1	Oppong 71	10	6
17	SthPC	H	Rushall Olympic	343	D	1 - 1	Tann 5	9	7
24	SthPC	H	Stratford Town	341	L	2 - 3	Zielonka 24 Higgs 48	11	8
31	**FAT3Q**	**H**	**Lewes**	**236**	**W**	**3 - 1**	**Higgs 16 54 Parsons 44**		9
Dec 8	FAT1P	H	Cheshunt	200	L	0 - 3			10

Goalscorers	LGE	FAC	FAT	SG	HAT	PEN	1Q	2Q	45+	3Q	4Q	90+	T
TOTALS	8	2	3		0	2	2	4	1	2	4	0	13
Higgs	1		2	2			1			2			3
Reed	2	1		3				2			1		3
Zielonka	3			2		2		1	1		1		3
McIntosh		1									1		1
Oppong	1			1							1		1
Parsons			1	1				1					1
Tann	1			1			1						1

NEEDHAM MARKET MATCH RESULTS 2020-21

Date	Comp	H/A	Opponents	Att:	Result		Goalscorers	Pos	No.
Sept 19	SthPC	A	Redditch United	442	D	1 - 1	Hunt 38	12	1
21	**FAC1Q**	**A**	**Hitchin Town**	**410**	**L**	**0 - 3**			2
26	SthPC	H	Stratford Town	232	W	4 - 2	Fowkes 12 15 Heath 49 Page 50	3	3
29	SthPC	H	Royston Town	265	W	3 - 1	Fowkes 12 82 Lawrence 22	1	4
Oct 3	SthPC	H	Lowestoft Town	365	W	3 - 1	Dye 14 Lawrence 18 Page 67	1	5
10	SthPC	A	Banbury United	506	D	1 - 1	Ingram 80	2	6
17	SthPC	H	Bromsgrove Sporting	301	W	3 - 0	Page 37 53 Hunt 68	2	7
24	SthPC	A	Alvechurch	226	W	2 - 1	Mills 12 Ingram 83 (pen)	2	8
31	**FAT3Q**	**H**	**Three Bridges**	**189**	**W**	**4 - 1**	**Fowkes 32 Collard 36 Marsden 48 75**		9
Dec 12	**FAT1P**	**H**	**Leiston**	**230**	**W**	**2 - 1**	**Fowkes 13 Dye 33**		10
15	**FAT2P**	**A**	**Gloucester City**		**L**	**2 - 4**	**Pollard 40 Fowkes 53**		11

Goalscorers	LGE	FAC	FAT	SG	HAT	PEN	1Q	2Q	45+	3Q	4Q	90+	T
TOTALS	17	0	8		0	1	8	6	0	6	5	0	25
Fowkes	4		3	5			4	1		1	1		7
Page	4			3				1		3			4
Dye	1		1	2			1	1					2
Hunt	2			2				1			1		2
Ingram	2			2		1					2		2
Lawrence	2			2			2						2
Marsden			2	1						1	1		2
Collard			1	1				1					1
Heath	1			1						1			1
Mills	1			1			1						1
Pollard			1	1				1					1

NUNEATON BOROUGH MATCH RESULTS 2020-21

Date	Comp	H/A	Opponents	Att:	Result		Goalscorers	Pos	No.
Sept 19	SthPC	H	AFC Rushden & Diamonds	596	D	1 - 1	Brown 70	13	1
22	**FAC1Q**	**H**	**Loughborough Dynamo**	**311**	**W**	**2 - 1**	**Kelly 36 Shamsi 72**		2
26	SthPC	A	Kings Langley	390	L	2 - 3	Lita 47 54	16	3
28	SthPC	A	Stourbridge	573	D	1 - 1	Shamsi 14	16	4
Oct 3	**FAC2Q**	**H**	**Stratford Town**	**488**	**W**	**2 - 1**	**Bassett 46 Lita 82**		5
6	SthPC	H	Banbury United	353	L	1 - 2	Lita 25		6
13	**FAC3Q**	**A**	**Bury Town**	**400**	**L**	**0 - 2**			7
17	SthPC	A	Barwell	585	L	1 - 2	Edjenguele 27	21	8
20	SthPC	H	St Ives Town	305	W	6 - 2	Shamsi 26 37 53 (pen) 82 90+1 Kaziboni 70	18	9
24	SthPC	A	Redditch United	580	L	0 - 2		19	10
31	**FAT3Q**	**A**	**Newcastle Town**	**301**	**W**	**2 - 0**	**Kelly 57 Kelly-Evans 61**		11
Nov 3	SthPC	A	Alvechurch	402	W	2 - 0	Bassett 14 Lita 55 (pen)	15	12
Dec 8	**FAT1P**	**A**	**Marlow**	**135**	**W**	**4 - 1**	**Baker 20 51 Lita 42 Kelly 73**		13
15	**FAT2P**	**A**	**Kettering Town**		**L**	**1 - 5**	**Kettle 21 (RC - Breeden (Gk) 8)**		14

Goalscorers	LGE	FAC	FAT	SG	HAT	PEN	1Q	2Q	45+	3Q	4Q	90+	T
TOTALS	14	4	7		0	2	4	6	0	8	6	1	25
Shamsi	6	1		3		1	1	2		1	2	1	7
Lita	4	1	1	5		1		2		3	1		6
Kelly		1	2	3				1		1	1		3
Baker			2	1			1			1			2
Bassett	1	1		2			1			1			2
Brown	1			1							1		1
Edjenguele	1			1				1					1
Kaziboni	1			1							1		1
Kelly-Evans			1	1						1			1
Kettle			1	1			1						1

PETERBOROUGH SPORTS MATCH RESULTS 2020-21

Date	Comp	H/A	Opponents	Att:	Result		Goalscorers	Pos	No.
Sept 19	SthPC	H	Tamworth	295	D	1 - 1	Sembie-Ferris 43	14	1
22	**FAC1Q**	**H**	**Enfield Town**	**233**	**D**	**2 - 2**	**McGowan 30 Jones 52 (Won 5-4 on pens)**		2
26	SthPC	A	Rushall Olympic	346	D	1 - 1	Sani 50	15	3
29	SthPC	A	Lowestoft Town	216	L	0 - 1		17	4
Oct 3	**FAC2Q**	**H**	**Stansted**	**216**	**W**	**4 - 2**	**Moreman 10 30 90+2 Sani 12**		5
6	SthPC	H	Kings Langley	178	D	1 - 1	Moreman 17		6
10	SthPC	H	Barwell	247	W	3 - 0	Sani 4 Malone 30 Lawlor 33	13	7
13	**FAC3Q**	**H**	**Banbury United**	**471**	**D**	**1 - 1**	**Nicholson (Lost 6-7 on pens)**		8
17	SthPC	A	Leiston	226	W	4 - 1	Sani 14 McCammon 43 Nichlson 45 58	5	9
31	**FAT3Q**	**H**	**Gainsborough Trinity**	**213**	**W**	**4 - 2**	**Moreman 4 Malone 17 Sani 56 Baker 66 (og)**		10
Dec 8	**FAT1P**	**A**	**AFC Rushden & Diamonds**	**252**	**W**	**5 - 1**	**Sani 11 42 49 Sembie-Ferris 31 Nicholson 80**		11
12	**FAT2P**	**A**	**Hitchin Town**	**385**	**W**	**4 - 0**	**Hilliard 11 Sembie-Ferris 45 68 Jarvis 84**		12
19	**FAT3P**	**H**	**Basford United**		**W**	**3 - 2**	**Sembie-Ferris 16 Jones 73 Nicholson 75**		13
Jan 16	**FAT4P**	**A**	**Bath City**		**W**	**1 - 0**	**Jones 45+2**		14
Feb 6	**FAT5P**	**A**	**Oxford City**		**L**	**0 - 2**			15

Goalscorers	LGE	FAC	FAT	SG	HAT	PEN	1Q	2Q	45+	3Q	4Q	90+	T
TOTALS	10	7	17		2	0	10	8	3	6	5	1	34
Sani	3	1	4	5	1		4	1		3			8
Moreman	1	3	1	3	1		3	1				1	5
Nicholson	2	1	2	5					1	1	2		5
Sembie-Ferris	1		4	5			1	2	1		1		5
Jones		1	2	3					1	1	1		3
Malone	1		1	2			1	1					2
Hilliard			1	1			1						1
Jarvis			1	1							1		1
Lawlor	1			1				1					1
McCammon	1			1				1					1
McGowan		1		1				1					1
Opponent			1	1						1			1

REDDITCH UNITED MATCH RESULTS 2020-21

Date	Comp	H/A	Opponents	Att:	Result		Goalscorers	Pos	No.
Sept 19	SthPC	H	Needham Market	442	D	1 - 1	Clement 17	15	1
22	**FAC1Q**	**A**	**Hanley Town**	**320**	**L**	**2 - 3**			2
26	SthPC	A	Banbury United	471	W	1 - 0	Clement 82	7	3
29	SthPC	A	Coalville Town	265	D	1 - 1	Nassunculo 65	9	4
Oct 6	SthPC	H	Rushall Olympic	472	D	3 - 3	Clement 2 Cameron 14 Nassunculo 66		5
10	SthPC	H	Biggleswade Town	553	W	4 - 1	Clement 8 34 Cameron 54 Johnston 83	3	6
17	SthPC	A	St Ives Town	156	L	1 - 3	Clement 21	6	7
24	SthPC	H	Nuneaton Borough	580	W	2 - 0	Hillman 43 Nassunculo 90	4	8
27	SthPC	A	Stratford Town	530	L	1 - 2	Copp 65		9
31	**FAT3Q**	**H**	**Nantwich Town**	**341**	**L**	**2 - 3**	**Hillmans 53 90**		10

Goalscorers	LGE	FAC	FAT	SG	HAT	PEN	1Q	2Q	45+	3Q	4Q	90+	T
TOTALS	14	2	2		0	0	5	2	0	5	2	2	18
Clement	6			5			4	1			1		6
Hillman	1		2	2				1		1		1	3
Nassunculo	3			3						2		1	3
Cameron	2			2			1			1			2
Copp	1			1						1			1
Johnston	1			1							1		1

ROYSTON TOWN MATCH RESULTS 2020-21

Date	Comp	H/A	Opponents	Att:	Result	Goalscorers	Pos	No.
Sept 12	**FACP**	**H**	**Newmarket Town**	**310**	**W 6 - 0**	**Edwards 2 44 65 83 Mentis Galliford 85**		1
19	SthPC	H	Banbury United	377	D 2 - 2	Castiglione 32 Adams 54	8	2
22	**FAC1Q**	**H**	**Wroxham**	**330**	**W 2 - 0**	**Edwards Galliford**		3
26	SthPC	A	Alvechurch	226	D 2 - 2	Adams 75 90+3	13	4
29	SthPC	A	Needham Market	265	L 1 - 3	Edwards 51	18	5
Oct 3	**FAC2Q**	**H**	**Stamford**	**422**	**D 2 - 2**	**Adams 19 45 (Won 4-2 on pens)**		6
6	SthPC	H	Biggleswade Town	256	D 1 - 1	Watkins 88		7
10	SthPC	H	Stourbridge	362	D 1 - 1	Edwards 14	17	8
13	**FAC3Q**	**A**	**Bishop's Stortford**	**600**	**L 0 - 3**			9
17	SthPC	A	Tamworth	521	D 1 - 1	Adams 55	18	10
24	SthPC	H	Hednesford Town	354	W 2 - 1	Williams 14 Edwards 21 (pen)	13	11
26	SthPC	A	Hitchin Town	600	W 2 - 0	Adams 66 Rotimi 75		12
31	**FAT3Q**	**H**	**Hythe Town**	**290**	**W 2 - 0**	**Adams 24 (pen) 44**		13
Dec 8	**FAT1P**	**H**	**Tamworth**	**179**	**W 3 - 1**	**Murray 4 Bridges 22 Parr 53**		14
15	**FAT2P**	**A**	**Brackley Town**	**159**	**L 2 - 3**	**Adams 22 Mentis 48**		15

Goalscorers	LGE	FAC	FAT	SG	HAT	PEN	1Q	2Q	45+	3Q	4Q	90+	T
TOTALS	12	10	7		0	2	8	4	2	7	5	1	29
Adams	5	2	3	7		1	1	2	1	3	1	1	10
Edwards	3	5		5		1	4	1	1	2	1		8
Galliford		2		1							1		2
Mentis		1	1	2						1			2
Bridges			1	1			1						1
Castiglione	1			1				1					1
Murray			1	1			1						1
Parr			1	1						1			1
Rotimi	1			1							1		1
Watkins	1			1							1		1
Williams	1			1			1						1

RUSHALL OLYMPIC MATCH RESULTS 2020-21

Date	Comp	H/A	Opponents	Att:	Result	Goalscorers	Pos	No.
Sept 19	SthPC	A	Leiston	213	W 1 - 0	Whittall 79	5	1
22	**FAC1Q**	**A**	**Grantham Town**	**242**	**D 2 - 2**	**Reid 8 Zari 90+3 (Lost 1-3 on pens)**		2
26	SthPC	H	Peterborough Sports	346	D 1 - 1	Whittall 87	8	3
29	SthPC	H	Bromsgrove Sporting	435	W 4 - 3	Whittall 20 Zazi 28 Sawyers 83 Calder 89	4	4
Oct 6	SthPC	A	Redditch United	472	D 3 - 3	Whittall 78 Zazi 82 Moore 90+5		5
10	SthPC	H	Coalville Town	447	L 0 - 2		9	6
17	SthPC	A	Lowestoft Town	343	D 1 - 1	Mantom 87	8	7
24	SthPC	H	Kings Langley	449	D 1 - 1	Whittall 17	8	8
27	SthPC	A	Barwell	239	W 3 - 1	Pendley 4 Hewlett 17 Usher-Shipway 37		9
31	**FAT3Q**	**H**	**Barwell**	**308**	**W 4 - 1**	**Opponent 21 Reid 59 Whittall (pen) Glover**		10
Dec 8	**FAT1P**	**A**	**Basford United**	**0**	**L 0 - 5**			11

Goalscorers	LGE	FAC	FAT	SG	HAT	PEN	1Q	2Q	45+	3Q	4Q	90+	T
TOTALS	14	2	4		0	1	6	2	0	1	7	2	20
Whittall	5		1	6		1	2				3		6
Zazi	2	1		3				1			1	1	3
Reid		1	1	2			1			1			2
Calder	1			1							1		1
Glover			1	1									1
Hewlett	1			1			1						1
Mantom	1			1							1		1
Moore	1			1								1	1
Pednley	1			1			1						1
Opponent			1	1			1						1
Sawyers	1			1							1		1
Usher-Shipway	1			1				1					1

ST IVES TOWN MATCH RESULTS 2020-21

Date	Comp	H/A	Opponents	Att:	Result		Goalscorers	Pos	No.
Sept 19	SthPC	H	Biggleswade Town	217	W	1 - 0	Richards 73	6	1
22	**FAC1Q**	**A**	**Brantham Athletic**	**130**	**L**	**0 - 1**			2
26	SthPC	A	Tamworth	339	L	2 - 4	Richards 57 Seymour-Shove 82	12	3
29	SthPC	A	Kings Langley	293	D	2 - 2	Gyasi 2 47	13	4
Oct 17	SthPC	H	Redditch United	156	W	3 - 1	Richards 35 Hicks 54 75	14	5
20	SthPC	A	Nuneaton Borough	305	L	2 - 6	Parker 12 (pen) Ballinger 43	17	6
27	SthPC	H	Leiston	156	W	1 - 0	Gyasi 90+1	11	7
31	**FAT3Q**	**H**	**Stafford Rangers**	**156**	**D**	**1 - 1**	**Williams 89 (pen) (Won 4-1 on pens)**		8
Dec 10	**FAT1P**	**A**	**Grantham Town**		**W**	**4 - 3**	**Richards 35 (pen) Ysasi 45 Solkhon 90 (pen) Hotter 90**		9
15	**FAT2P**	**A**	**Leamington**		**L**	**0 - 5**			10

Goalscorers	LGE	FAC	FAT	SG	HAT	PEN	1Q	2Q	45+	3Q	4Q	90+	T
TOTALS	11	0	5		0	3	2	3	1	3	4	3	16
Richards	3		1	4		1		2		1	1		4
Gyasi	3			2			1			1		1	3
Hicks	2			1						1	1		2
Ballinger	1			1				1					1
Hotter			1	1								1	1
Parker	1			1		1	1						1
Seymour-Shove	1			1							1		1
Solkhon			1	1								1	1
Williams			1	1		1					1		1
Ysasi			1	1					1				1

STOURBRIDGE MATCH RESULTS 2020-21

Date	Comp	H/A	Opponents	Att:	Result		Goalscorers	Pos	No.
Sept 19	SthPC	A	Hednesford Town	600	W	4 - 1	Mills 21 45 Landell 71 76	2	1
22	**FAC1Q**	**A**	**Tamworth**	**380**	**D**	**3 - 3**	**Mills 50 Knights 57 Landell 75 (Lost 4-5 on pens)**		2
26	SthPC	H	Hitchin Town	600	W	1 - 0	Fletcher 37	1	3
28	SthPC	H	Nuneaton Borough	573	D	1 - 1	Birch 5	2	4
Oct 3	SthPC	H	Biggleswade Town	591	D	2 - 2	Brown 5 Birch 90+4	2	5
6	SthPC	A	Stratford Town	345	L	1 - 2	Knights 59		6
10	SthPC	A	Royston Town	362	D	1 - 1	Mills 31 (pen)	4	7
17	SthPC	H	Kings Langley	600	D	0 - 0		3	8
26	SthPC	H	Alvechurch	600	D	0 - 0		6	9
31	**FAT3Q**	**H**	**Stamford**	**572**	**L**	**0 - 3**			10

Goalscorers	LGE	FAC	FAT	SG	HAT	PEN	1Q	2Q	45+	3Q	4Q	90+	T
TOTALS	10	3	0		0	1	3	2	1	1	2	1	13
Mills	3	1		3		1	1	1	1	1			4
Landell	2	1		2							3		3
Birch	2			2			1					1	2
Knights	1	1		2						2			2
Brown	1			1			1						1
Fletcher	1			1				1					1

STRATFORD TOWN MATCH RESULTS 2020-21

Date	Comp	H/A	Opponents	Att:	Result	Goalscorers	Pos	No.
Sept 19	SthPC	H	Kings Langley	285	W 2 - 1	Isaac 68 Grocott 83 (pen)	4	1
22	**FAC1Q**	**A**	**Bromsgrove Sporting**	**472**	**W 2 - 1**	**Grocott 57 87**		2
26	SthPC	A	Needham Market	232	L 2 - 4	Curtis 70 Glover 87	11	3
29	SthPC	A	Alvechurch	248	W 3 - 1	Howards 6 Grocott 21 (pen) Sammons 25	6	4
Oct 3	**FAC2Q**	**A**	**Nuneaton Borough**	**488**	**L 1 - 2**	**Williams 89**		5
6	SthPC	H	Stourbridge	345	W 2 - 1	Grocott 48 (pen) Williams 70		6
10	SthPC	A	Hednesford Town	479	L 2 - 4	Powell 67 Andoh 90+1	5	7
17	SthPC	H	Hitchin Town	355	L 1 - 2	Heaven 67	10	8
24	SthPC	A	Lowestoft Town	341	W 3 - 2	Williams 12 28 Powell 90	5	9
27	SthPC	H	Redditch United	530	W 2 - 1	Powell 29 Sammons 39	3	10
31	**FAT3Q**	**H**	**Kidsgrove Athletic**	**198**	**L 1 - 3**	**Sammons 76**		11

Goalscorers	LGE	FAC	FAT	SG	HAT	PEN	1Q	2Q	45+	3Q	4Q	90+	T
TOTALS	17	3	1		0	3	3	4	0	4	8	2	21
Grocott	3	2		4		3	1			2	2		5
Williams	3	1		3			1	1			2		4
Powell	3			3				1		1		1	3
Sammons	2		1	3				2			1		3
Andoh	1			1								1	1
Curtis	1			1							1		1
Glover	1			1							1		1
Heaven	1			1						1			1
Howards	1			1			1						1
Isaac	1			1							1		1

TAMWORTH MATCH RESULTS 2020-21

Date	Comp	H/A	Opponents	Att:	Result	Goalscorers	Pos	No.
Sept 19	SthPC	A	Peterborough Sports	295	D 1 - 1	Cullinane-Liburd 41	16	1
22	**FAC1Q**	**H**	**Stourbridge**	**380**	**D 3 - 3**	**Beswick 2 Graham 80 89 (Won 5-4 on pens)**		2
26	SthPC	H	St Ives Town	339	W 4 - 2	Beswick 59 (pen) Gough 86 Graham 89 McDonald 90	4	3
29	SthPC	H	Barwell	372	W 2 - 1	McDonald 24 McDonagh 39	3	4
Oct 3	**FAC2Q**	**H**	**Evesham United**	**496**	**W 3 - 1**	**McDonald 2 Yafai 21 Gordon 31**		5
6	SthPC	A	Bromsgrove Sporting	600	D 2 - 2	McDonald 90 90+4		6
10	SthPC	A	Alvechurch	461	L 0 - 1		6	7
13	**FAC3Q**	**A**	**Oxford City**		**L 1 - 6**	**Gordon 90**		8
17	SthPC	H	Royston Town	521	D 1 - 1	Cox 58	7	9
24	SthPC	H	Biggleswade Town	523	W 3 - 0	Ryan 50 Bewsick 63 (pen) Walters 90+4	3	10
31	**FAT3Q**	**H**	**Banbury United**	**355**	**W 2 - 1**	**McDonald 36 40**		11
Dec 8	**FAT1P**	**A**	**Royston Town**	**179**	**L 1 - 3**	**Ryan 6**		12

Goalscorers	LGE	FAC	FAT	SG	HAT	PEN	1Q	2Q	45+	3Q	4Q	90+	T
TOTALS	13	7	3		0	2	4	6	0	4	4	5	23
McDonald	4	1	2	5			1	3				3	7
Beswick	2	1		3		2	1			2			3
Graham	1	2		2							3		3
Gordon		2		2				1				1	2
Ryan	1		1	2			1			1			2
Cox	1			1						1			1
Cullinane-Liburd	1			1				1					1
Gough	1			1							1		1
McDonagh	1			1				1					1
Walters	1			1								1	1
Yafai		1		1			1						1

BEACONSFIELD TOWN MATCH RESULTS 2020-21

Date	Comp	H/A	Opponents	Att:	Result	Goalscorers	Pos	No.
Sept 19	SthPS	H	Poole Town	69	L 1 - 2	Ewington 65	17	1
21	**FAC1Q**	**H**	**Harrow Borough**	**220**	**L 0 - 2**			2
28	SthPS	H	Gosport Borough	120	L 0 - 2		17	3
Oct 3	SthPS	A	Salisbury	391	L 0 - 1		19	4
6	SthPS	A	Hartley Wintney	242	D 1 - 1	Ewington 72		5
10	SthPS	H	Heading & Hayes United		D 0 - 0		18	6
24	SthPS	A	Farnborough	413	L 1 - 4	Louis 15	20	7
26	SthPS	H	Harrow Borough	192	L 1 - 4	Minhas 18	20	8
31	**FAT3Q**	**A**	**Aveley**		**L 0 - 3**			9

Goalscorers	LGE	FAC	FAT	SG	HAT	PEN	1Q	2Q	45+	3Q	4Q	90+	T
TOTALS	4	0	0		0	0	2	0	0	1	1	0	4
Ewington	2			2						1	1		2
Louis	1			1			1						1
Minhas	1			1			1						1

CHESHAM UNITED MATCH RESULTS 2020-21

Date	Comp	H/A	Opponents	Att:	Result	Goalscorers	Pos	No.
Sept 19	SthPS	H	Gosport Borough	520	D 0 - 0		14	1
22	**FAC1Q**	**A**	**Hastings United**	**384**	**D 0 - 0**	**(Lost 5-6 on pens)**		2
26	SthPS	A	Wimborne Town	259	W 1 - 0	Clayton 80	9	3
29	SthPS	H	Hartley Wintney	373	D 0 - 0		7	4
Oct 6	SthPS	A	Harrow Borough	227	W 2 - 1	Kirby 45 Rolfe 73		5
10	SthPS	H	Swindon Supermarine	552	L 0 - 1		9	6
17	SthPS	A	Yate Town	213	W 1 - 0	Cass 10	6	7
27	SthPS	A	Hayes & Yeading United	305	D 2 - 2	Cass 59 Kirby 80		8
31	**FAT3Q**	**H**	**Whyteleafe**	**315**	**D 2 - 2**	**Clayton 47 Unknown 90 (Won 3-2 on pens)**		9
Dec 8	**FAT1P**	**A**	**Weston-s-Mare**		**W 3 - 1**			10
15	**FAT2P**	**A**	**Aveley**		**W 3 - 1**	**Brown 15 Joseph 59 Pearce 90+2**		11
19	**FAT3P**	**H**	**Torquay United**		**L 0 - 1**			12

Goalscorers	LGE	FAC	FAT	SG	HAT	PEN	1Q	2Q	45+	3Q	4Q	90+	T
TOTALS	6	0	7		0	0	2	0	1	3	3	1	13
Cass	2			2			1			1			2
Clayton	1		1	2						1	1		2
Kirby	2			2					1		1		2
Brown			1	1			1						1
Joseph			1	1						1			1
Pearce			1	1								1	1
Rolfe	1			1							1		1

DORCHESTER TOWN MATCH RESULTS 2020-21

Date	Comp	H/A	Opponents	Att:	Result	Goalscorers	Pos	No.
Sept 19	SthPS	H	Weston-s-Mare	401	L 1 - 3	Wilson 7	19	1
22	**FAC1Q**	**A**	**Christchurch**	**300**	**L 1 - 2**			2
26	SthPS	A	Yate Town	238	L 1 - 4	Bayston 90	18	3
29	SthPS	H	Wimborne Town	267	D 0 - 0		16	4
Oct 10	SthPS	H	Tiverton Town	362	W 1 - 0	Ngoy 86	15	5
17	SthPS	A	Swindon Supermarine	331	L 0 - 2		16	6
24	SthPS	H	Salisbury	600	L 1 - 6	Ngoy 29 (pen)	17	7
27	SthPS	A	Taunton Town	476	L 1 - 2	Koszela 20		8
31	**FAT3Q**	**H**	**Gosport Borough**	**247**	**W 2 - 1**			9
Dec 5	**FAT1P**	**A**	**Swindon Supermarine**	**289**	**L 2 - 3**			10

Goalscorers	LGE	FAC	FAT	SG	HAT	PEN	1Q	2Q	45+	3Q	4Q	90+	T
TOTALS	5	1	4		0	1	2	1	0	0	1	1	10
Ngoy	2			2		1		1			1		2
Bayston	1			1								1	1
Koszela	1			1			1						1
Wilson	1			1			1						1

FARNBOROUGH MATCH RESULTS 2020-21

Date	Comp	H/A	Opponents	Att:	Result	Goalscorers	Pos	No.
Sept 12	**FACP**	**H**	**Lymington Town**	**232**	**D 0 - 0**	**(Won 4-3 on pens)**		1
19	SthPS	H	Swindon Supermarine	362	L 1 - 3	Agongo 90	20	2
22	**FAC1Q**	**A**	**Chalfont St Peter**	**178**	**W 3 - 2**	**Cullen 27 Paget 78 (pen) Leggett 90**		3
26	SthPS	A	Gosport Borough	403	L 0 - 4		19	4
30	SthPS	H	Yate Town	228	D 0 - 0		17	5
Oct 3	**FAC2Q**	**H**	**Tonbridge Angels**	**382**	**L 0 - 1**			6
6	SthPS	A	Wimborne Town	160	L 1 - 2	Miller 46		7
10	SthPS	H	Taunton Town	421	L 0 - 1		20	8
17	SthPS	A	Tiverton Town	267	L 1 - 3	Fearn 90	20	9
24	SthPS	H	Beaconsfield Town	413	W 4 - 1	Fearn 25 53 Ellias-Fernandes 30 Owens 36	15	10
27	SthPS	A	Hendon	238	L 0 - 2			11
31	**FAT3Q**	**A**	**Frome Town**	**253**	**L 0 - 3**			12

Goalscorers	LGE	FAC	FAT	SG	HAT	PEN	1Q	2Q	45+	3Q	4Q	90+	T
TOTALS	7	3	0		0	1	0	4	0	2	1	3	10
Fearn	3			2				1		1		1	3
Agongo	1			1								1	1
Cullen		1		1				1					1
Ellias-Fernandes	1			1				1					1
Leggett		1		1								1	1
Miller	1			1						1			1
Owens	1			1				1					1
Paget		1		1		1					1		1

GOSPORT BOROUGH MATCH RESULTS 2020-21

Date	Comp	H/A	Opponents	Att:	Result	Goalscorers	Pos	No.
Sept 19	SthPS	A	Chesham United	520	D 0 - 0		15	1
23	**FAC1Q**	**A**	**Tavistock**	**223**	**D 2 - 2**	**(Won 5-3 on pens)**		2
26	SthPS	H	Farnborough	403	W 4 - 0	Wooden 22 Tarbuck 33 McCreadie 53 Suraci 74	4	3
29	SthPS	A	Beaconsfield Town	120	W 2 - 0	Suraci 72 88	1	4
Oct 3	**FAC2Q**	**H**	**Hereford**	**501**	**L 1 - 3**			5
7	SthPS	H	Walton Casuals	323	L 2 - 3	Wooden 60 Oxlade-Chamberlain 90+4	4	6
10	SthPS	A	Metropolitan Police	160	L 1 - 3	Wooden 50	10	7
17	SthPS	H	Harrow Borough	490	D 2 - 2	Lewis 23 45	9	8
27	SthPS	A	Poole Town	492	L 0 - 1			9
31	**FAT3Q**	**A**	**Dorchester Town**	**247**	**L 1 - 2**			10

Goalscorers	LGE	FAC	FAT	SG	HAT	PEN	1Q	2Q	45+	3Q	4Q	90+	T
TOTALS	11	3	1		0	0	1	2	1	3	3	1	15
Suraci	3			2							3		3
Wooden	3			3			1			2			3
Lewis	2			1				1	1				2
McCreadie	1			1						1			1
Oxlaide-Chamberlain	1			1								1	1
Tarbuck	1			1				1					1

HARROW BOROUGH MATCH RESULTS 2020-21

Date	Comp	H/A	Opponents	Att:	Result	Goalscorers	Pos	No.
Sept 12	**FACP**	**A**	**Langney Wanderers**	**120**	**D 1 - 1**	**Moore 70 (Won 3-2 on pens)**		1
19	SthPS	A	Truro City	425	L 0 - 1		18	2
21	**FAC1Q**	**A**	**Beaconsfield Town**	**220**	**W 2 - 0**	**Ferdinand 13 19**		3
26	SthPS	H	Salisbury	169	L 1 - 2	Moore 64	17	4
29	SthPS	A	Metropolitan Police	111	L 2 - 5	Keita 70 Charles-Smith 90	19	5
Oct 3	**FAC2Q**	**H**	**Cray Valley PM**	**153**	**L 1 - 5**	**Keita 43 (pen)**		6
6	SthPS	H	Chesham United	227	L 1 - 2	Ferdinand 31		7
10	SthPS	H	Weston-s-Mare	176	D 1 - 1	Moore 17	19	8
17	SthPS	A	Gosport Borough	490	D 2 - 2	O'Connor 40 Ferdinand 90	19	9
26	SthPS	A	Beaconsfield Town	192	W 4 - 1	O'Connor 19 37 Ferdinand 74 Wynter 87	14	10
31	**FAT3Q**	**A**	**Burgess Hill Town**	**190**	**L 1 - 4**	**Ferdinand 42**		11

Goalscorers	LGE	FAC	FAT	SG	HAT	PEN	1Q	2Q	45+	3Q	4Q	90+	T
TOTALS	11	4	1		0	1	4	5	0	1	4	2	16
Ferdinand	3	2	1	5			2	2			1	1	6
Moore	2	1		3			1			1	1		3
O'Connor	3			2			1	2					3
Keita	1	1		2		1		1			1		2
Charles-Smith	1			1								1	1
Wynter	1			1							1		1

HARTLEY WINTNEY MATCH RESULTS 2020-21

Date	Comp	H/A	Opponents	Att:	Result	Goalscorers	Pos	No.
Sept 12	**FACP**	**H**	**Hamworthy United**	**299**	**W 1 - 0**			1
19	SthPS	A	Walton Casuals	150	D 1 - 1	Smith 21 (pen)	9	2
22	**FAC1Q**	**H**	**Erith & Belvedere**	**254**	**W 5 - 0**			3
29	SthPS	A	Chesham United	373	D 0 - 0		14	4
Oct 3	**FAC2Q**	**A**	**Hanwell Town**	**280**	**W 5 - 3**	**Smith 39 (pen) Eshun 51 84 Parker 78 (pen) 90**		5
6	SthPS	H	Beaconsfield Town	242	D 1 - 1	Argent 40		6
10	SthPS	A	Hendon	291	L 0 - 4		17	7
13	**FAC3Q**	**H**	**Barking**	**391**	**W 3 - 1**	**Flemming 48 (og) Burt 50 Argent 61**		8
17	SthPS	H	Salisbury	462	L 0 - 2		17	9
24	**FAC4Q**	**A**	**Dagenham & Redbridge**		**L 0 - 1**			10
27	SthPS	H	Yate Town	270	W 3 - 1	Smith 20 (pen) Parker 49 Wright 87		11
31	**FAT3Q**	**H**	**Poole Town**	**255**	**L 1 - 4**			12

Goalscorers	LGE	FAC	FAT	SG	HAT	PEN	1Q	2Q	45+	3Q	4Q	90+	T
TOTALS	5	14	1		0	4	2	2	0	4	4	1	20
Parker	1	2		2		1				1	1	1	3
Smith	2	1		3		3	2	1					3
Eshun		2		1						1	1		2
Wright	1	1		2							2		2
Argent	1			1				1					1
Burt		1		1						1			1
Opponent		1		1						1			1

HAYES & YEADING UNITED MATCH RESULTS 2020-21

Date	Comp	H/A	Opponents	Att:	Result	Goalscorers	Pos	No.
Sept 19	SthPS	H	Taunton Town	246	D 1 - 1	Rowe 87	9	1
22	**FAC1Q**	**A**	**Margate**	**205**	**W 2 - 1**	**Rowe 36 52**		2
26	SthPS	A	Poole Town	260	L 1 - 2	Amartey 64	13	3
29	SthPS	H	Swindon Supermarine	188	W 3 - 1	Williams 19 Amartey 76 Cunningham 76	10	4
Oct 3	**FAC2Q**	**H**	**Bognor Regis Town**	**301**	**W 5 - 0**	**Robinson 48 Greco 51 69 Amartey 65 Donnelly 74**		5
6	SthPS	A	Hendon	237	D 1 - 1	Amartey 73		6
10	SthPS	A	Beaconsfield Town	252	D 0 - 0		11	7
13	**FAC3Q**	**H**	**Chipstead**	**269**	**D 0 - 0**	**(Won 4-2 on pens)**		8
17	SthPS	H	Truro City	300	W 3 - 1	Amartey 38 90 Sheppard 85	8	9
24	**FAC4Q**	**A**	**Wealdstone**		**W 2 - 0**	**Amartey 26 Rowe 62**		10
27	SthPS	H	Chesham United	305	D 2 - 2	Amartey 31 Rowe 62		11
31	**FAT3Q**	**A**	**Uxbridge**	**251**	**L 1 - 2**	**Amartey 39**		12
Nov 8	**FAC1P**	**H**	**Carlisle United**		**D 2 - 2**	**Rowe 104 Nasha 108 (Lost 3-4 on pens)**		13

Goalscorers	LGE	FAC	FAT	SG	HAT	PEN	1Q	2Q	45+	3Q	4Q	90+	T
TOTALS	11	11	1		0	0	1	5	0	7	7	3	23
Amartey	6	2	1	8				4		2	2	1	9
Rowe	2	4		5				1		3	1	1	6
Greco		2		1						1	1		2
Cunningham	1			1							1		1
Donnelly		1		1							1		1
Nasha		1		1								1	1
Robinson		1		1						1			1
Sheppard	1			1							1		1
Williams	1			1			1						1

HENDON MATCH RESULTS 2020-21

Date	Comp	H/A	Opponents	Att:	Result	Goalscorers	Pos	No.
Sept 19	SthPS	A	Salisbury	524	D 2 - 2	Corcoran 20 Brooks 71	6	1
22	**FAC1Q**	**A**	**Crawley Down Gatwick**		**W 2 - 1**	**Clarke 76 Brooks 88**		2
26	SthPS	H	Truro City	336	L 0 - 4		15	3
29	SthPS	A	Walton Casuals	187	W 3 - 1	White 7 Lucien 25 Olarerin 64	12	4
Oct 3	**FAC2Q**	**H**	**Maidstone United**	**310**	**L 0 - 1**			5
6	SthPS	H	Hayes & Yeading United	237	D 1 - 1	Clarke 21		6
10	SthPS	H	Hartley Wintney	291	W 4 - 0	White 3 24 Byron 50 Clarke 52	7	7
17	SthPS	A	Poole Town	476	L 0 - 1		11	8
27	SthPS	H	Farnborough	238	W 2 - 0	Lucien 8 White 26		9
31	**FAT3Q**	**A**	**Corinthian-Casuals**	**407**	**L 4 - 5**	**Lucien 16 (pen) Brewer 40 Byron 66 Grant 89**		10
Nov 3	SthPS	A	Metropolitan Police	159	L 0 - 1		9	11

Goalscorers	LGE	FAC	FAT	SG	HAT	PEN	1Q	2Q	45+	3Q	4Q	90+	T
TOTALS	**12**	**2**	**4**		**0**	**1**	**6**	**4**	**0**	**4**	**4**	**0**	**18**
White	4			3			2	2					4
Clarke	2	1		3			1			1	1		3
Lucien	2		1	3		1	2	1					3
Brooks	1	1		2							2		2
Byron	1		1	2						2			2
Brewer			1	1				1					1
Corcoran	1			1			1						1
Grant			1	1							1		1
Olarerin	1			1						1			1

METROPOLITAN POLICE MATCH RESULTS 2020-21

Date	Comp	H/A	Opponents	Att:	Result	Goalscorers	Pos	No.
Sept 19	SthPS	H	Yate Town	134	D 1 - 1	Blackmore 14	10	1
23	**FAC1Q**	**A**	**Sutton Common Rovers**	**300**	**W 3 - 1**			2
26	SthPS	A	Weston-s-Mare	535	D 1 - 1	Johnson 16	11	3
29	SthPS	H	Harrow Borough	111	W 5 - 2	Mazzone 15 33 (pen) 75 Knight 17 Blackmore 63	5	4
Oct 3	**FAC2Q**	**H**	**Walton Casuals**	**287**	**L 1 - 2**			5
6	SthPS	A	Swindon Supermarine	232	L 1 - 2	Knight 49		6
10	SthPS	H	Gosport Borough	160	W 3 - 1	Mazzone 11 81 Shroll 45	5	7
17	SthPS	A	Taunton Town	487	W 2 - 1	Shroll 24 Blackmore 60	4	8
27	SthPS	A	Walton Casuals	199	L 0 - 3			9
31	**FAT3Q**	**A**	**Felixstowe & Walton United**	**322**	**L 1 - 3**	**Cursons 37**		10
Nov 3	SthPS	H	Hendon	159	W 1 - 0	Mazzone 49	5	11

Goalscorers	LGE	FAC	FAT	SG	HAT	PEN	1Q	2Q	45+	3Q	4Q	90+	T
TOTALS	**14**	**4**	**1**		**1**	**1**	**5**	**3**	**1**	**4**	**2**	**0**	**19**
Mazzone	6			3	1	1	2	1		1	2		6
Blackmore	3			3			1			2			3
Knight	2			2			1			1			2
Shroll	2			2				1	1				2
Johnson	1			1			1						1
Cursons			1	1				1					1

POOLE TOWN MATCH RESULTS 2020-21

Date	Comp	H/A	Opponents	Att:	Result	Goalscorers	Pos	No.
Sept 19	SthPS	A	Beaconsfield Town	69	W 2 - 1	Rowe 35 Lee 55	4	1
26	SthPS	H	Hayes & Yeading United	260	W 2 - 1	Rowe 24 Lee 69	3	2
Oct 3	**FAC2Q**	**A**	**Chippenham Town**		**D 2 - 2**	**(Lost 4-5 on pens)**		3
6	SthPS	H	Truro City	321	W 2 - 1	Lee 35 Carmichael 58		4
10	SthPS	A	Salisbury	600	D 2 - 2	Whisken 7 Lee 35 (pen)	3	5
17	SthPS	H	Hendon	476	W 1 - 0	Carmichael 45	2	6
24	SthPS	A	Yate Town	237	W 6 - 2	Carmichael 10 Moore 14 22 Spetch 50 Lee 59 Jerrard 90+32		7
27	SthPS	H	Gosport Borough	492	W 1 - 0	Lee 66	1	8
31	**FAT3Q**	**A**	**Hartley Wintney**	**255**	**W 4 - 1**			9
Dec 8	**FAT1P**	**H**	**Willand Rovers**	**257**	**W 3 - 1**			10
19	**FAT2P**	**A**	**Maidstone United**		**L 0 - 2**			11

Goalscorers	LGE	FAC	FAT	SG	HAT	PEN	1Q	2Q	45+	3Q	4Q	90+	T
TOTALS	16	2	7		0	0	4	4	1	5	1	1	25
Lee	6			6				2		3	1		6
Carmichael	3			3			1		1	1			3
Moore	2			1			2						2
Rowe	2			2				2					2
Jerrard	1			1								1	1
Spetch	1			1						1			1
Whisken	1			1			1						1

SALISBURY MATCH RESULTS 2020-21

Date	Comp	H/A	Opponents	Att:	Result	Goalscorers	Pos	No.
Sept 19	SthPS	H	Hendon	524	D 2 - 2	Brooks 1 Perry 60 (og)	7	1
23	**FAC1Q**	**A**	**Kidlington**	**236**	**D 1 - 1**	**(Lost 2-4 on pens)**		2
26	SthPS	A	Harrow Borough	169	W 2 - 1	Diaz 71 Brooks 76	8	3
Oct 3	SthPS	H	Beaconsfield Town	391	W 1 - 0	Fitchett 25	4	4
10	SthPS	H	Poole Town	600	D 2 - 2	Baker 67 Brooks 88	8	5
17	SthPS	A	Hartley Wintney	462	W 2 - 0	Diaz 40 Fitchett 73	5	6
24	SthPS	A	Dorchester Town	600	W 6 - 1	Baker 9 44 Ball 49 Kennedy 66 Knowles 77 (pen) Brooks 89	3	7
27	SthPS	H	Weston-s-Mare	594	W 2 - 1	Davis 45+2 (pen) Roberts 59		8
31	**FAT3Q**	**H**	**Tiverton Town**	**519**	**W 6 - 0**			9
Dec 8	**FAT1P**	**H**	**Bracknell Town**	**402**	**L 0 - 1**			10

Goalscorers	LGE	FAC	FAT	SG	HAT	PEN	1Q	2Q	45+	3Q	4Q	90+	T
TOTALS	17	1	6		0	1	2	3	1	5	6	0	24
Brooks	4			4			1				3		4
Baker	3			2			1	1		1			3
Diaz	2			2				1			1		2
Fitchett	2			2				1			1		2
Ball	1			1						1			1
Davis	1			1					1				1
Kennedy	1			1						1			1
Knowles	1			1		1					1		1
Opponent	1			1						1			1
Roberts	1			1						1			1

SWINDON SUPERMARINE MATCH RESULTS 2020-21

Date	Comp	H/A	Opponents	Att:	Result	Goalscorers	Pos	No.
Sept 19	SthPS	A	Farnborough	362	W 3 - 1	Williams 36 McDonagh 49 Kotwica 70	2	1
22	**FAC1Q**	**H**	**Shepton Mallet**	**194**	**W 3 - 0**			2
26	SthPS	H	Tiverton Town	245	L 1 - 2	Campbell 2	10	3
29	SthPS	A	Hayes & Yeading United	188	L 1 - 3	Campbell 62	13	4
Oct 3	**FAC2Q**	**A**	**Weston-s-Mare**	**319**	**D 2 - 2**	**(Lost 2-4 on pens)**		5
6	SthPS	H	Metropolitan Police	232	W 2 - 1	Kotwica 28 46		6
10	SthPS	A	Chesham United	552	W 1 - 0	McDonagh 59	4	7
17	SthPS	H	Dorchester Town	331	W 2 - 0	Dunstan 59 (og) Liddlard 86	3	8
24	SthPS	H	Truro City	352	L 2 - 3	Hooper 6 Williams 87	5	9
31	**FAT3Q**	**A**	**Highworth Town**	**302**	**W 3 - 2**			10
Dec 5	**FAT1P**	**H**	**Dorchester Town**	**289**	**W 3 - 2**			11
12	**FAT2P**	**H**	**Carshalton Athletic**	**281**	**D 0 - 0**	**(Won 5-4 on pens)**		12
19	**FAT3P**	**A**	**Bath City**		**L 0 - 4**			13

Goalscorers	LGE	FAC	FAT	SG	HAT	PEN	1Q	2Q	45+	3Q	4Q	90+	T
TOTALS	12	5	6		0	0	2	2	0	5	3	0	23
Kotwica	3			2				1		1	1		3
Campbell	2			2			1			1			2
McDonagh	2			2						2			2
Williams	2			2				1			1		2
Hooper	1			1			1						1
Liddlard	1			1							1		1
Opponent	1			1						1			1

TAUNTON TOWN MATCH RESULTS 2020-21

Date	Comp	H/A	Opponents	Att:	Result	Goalscorers	Pos	No.
Sept 19	SthPS	A	Hayes & Yeading United	246	D 1 - 1	Holmes 43	11	1
22	**FAC1Q**	**H**	**Wantage Town**	**349**	**W 5 - 0**			2
26	SthPS	H	Walton Casuals	427	W 2 - 0	Holmes 60 87	7	3
29	SthPS	A	Truro City	515	D 1 - 1	Grimes 29	6	4
Oct 3	**FAC2Q**	**A**	**Tiverton Town**	**560**	**W 5 - 3**			5
10	SthPS	A	Farnborough	421	W 1 - 0	Howe 72	6	6
13	**FAC3Q**	**H**	**Truro City**	**584**	**W 4 - 2**			7
17	SthPS	H	Metropolitan Police	487	L 1 - 2	Howe 89	10	8
24	**FAC4Q**	**A**	**Tonbridge Angels**		**L 0 - 5**			9
27	SthPS	H	Dorchester Town	476	W 2 - 1	Holmes 40 Chamberlain 47		10
Nov 3	**FAT3Q**	**H**	**Truro City**		**L 2 - 4**			11

Goalscorers	LGE	FAC	FAT	SG	HAT	PEN	1Q	2Q	45+	3Q	4Q	90+	T
TOTALS	8	14	2		0	0	0	3	0	2	3	0	24
Holmes	4			3				2		1	1		4
Howe	2			2							2		2
Grimes	1			1				1					1
Chamberlain	1			1						1			1

TIVERTON TOWN MATCH RESULTS 2020-21

Date	Comp	H/A	Opponents	Att:	Result	Goalscorers	Pos	No.
Sept 19	SthPS	H	Wimborne Town	302	W 5 - 0	Fletcher 39 45 83 Bastin 43 Hayfield 74	1	1
23	**FAC1Q**	**H**	**Bideford**	**331**	**W 2 - 0**			2
26	SthPS	A	Swindon Supermarine	245	W 2 - 1	Peck 15 Lam 88	1	3
30	SthPS	H	Weston-s-Mare	334	W 3 - 1	Lewington 6 Lam 52 Fletcher 90+4 (pen)	1	4
Oct 3	**FAC2Q**	**H**	**Taunton Town**	**560**	**L 3 - 5**			5
6	SthPS	A	Yate Town	220	W 3 - 0	Fletcher 7 Morison 42 Watkins 61	1	6
10	SthPS	A	Dorchester Town	362	L 0 - 1		1	7
17	SthPS	H	Farnborough	267	W 3 - 1	Morison 11 Fletcher 17 Shepherd 40	1	8
24	SthPS	H	Walton Casuals	264	W 5 - 0	Fletcher 8 (pen) 86 Morison 17 Hayfield 62 Lewington 82	1	9
31	**FAT3Q**	**A**	**Salisbury**	**519**	**L 0 - 6**			10

Goalscorers	LGE	FAC	FAT	SG	HAT	PEN	1Q	2Q	45+	3Q	4Q	90+	T
TOTALS	21	5	0		1	2	7	4	1	3	5	1	26
Fletcher	8			5	1	2	3	1	1		2	1	8
Morison	3			3			2	1					3
Hayfield	2			2						1	1		2
Lam	2			2						1	1		2
Lewington	2			2			1				1		2
Bastin	1			1				1					1
Peck	1			1			1						1
Shepherd	1			1				1					1
Watkins	1			1						1			1

TRURO CITY MATCH RESULTS 2020-21

Date	Comp	H/A	Opponents	Att:	Result	Goalscorers	Pos	No.
Sept 19	SthPS	H	Harrow Borough	425	W 1 - 0	Neal 73	5	1
22	**FAC1Q**	**A**	**Tadley Calleva**	**297**	**W 1 - 0**	**Battle 45**		2
26	SthPS	A	Hendon	336	W 4 - 0	Riley-Lowe 14 Rooney 59 Harvey 65 Neal 79	2	3
29	SthPS	H	Taunton Town	515	D 1 - 1	Rooney 35	2	4
Oct 3	**FAC2Q**	**H**	**Hungerford Town**	**257**	**W 4 - 0**	**Palmer Rooney Neal Harvey**		5
6	SthPS	A	Poole Town	321	L 1 - 2	Neal 64		6
10	SthPS	H	Yate Town	429	W 2 - 0	Richards 5 Battle 84	2	7
13	**FAC3Q**	**A**	**Taunton Town**	**584**	**L 2 - 4**			8
17	SthPS	A	Hayes & Yeading United	300	L 1 - 3	Graffiti 71 (og)	7	9
24	SthPS	A	Swindon Supermarine	352	W 3 - 2	Lee 68 (og) Battle 78 Harvey 90	4	10
27	SthPS	H	Wimborne Town	365	W 4 - 1	Richards 6 45 Rooney 16 Harvey 23	4	11
Nov 3	**FAT3Q**	**A**	**Taunton Town**	**427**	**W 4 - 2**			12
Dec 5	**FAT1P**	**A**	**Moneyfields**	**237**	**W 5 - 1**			13
19	**FAT2P**	**A**	**Concord Rangers**		**W 2 - 1**	**Harvey 52 Battle 63**		14

Goalscorers	LGE	FAC	FAT	SG	HAT	PEN	1Q	2Q	45+	3Q	4Q	90+	T
TOTALS	17	7	11		0	0	4	2	2	6	5	1	35
Harvey	3	1	1	5				1		2		1	5
Battle	2	1	1	4					1	1	2		4
Neal	3	1		4						1	2		4
Rooney	3	1		4			1	1		1			4
Richards	3			2			2		1				3
Opponent	2			2						1	1		2
Palmer		1		1									1
Riley-Lowe	1			1			1						1

WALTON CASUALS MATCH RESULTS 2020-21

Date	Comp	H/A	Opponents	Att:	Result	Goalscorers	Pos	No.
Sept 19	SthPS	H	Hartley Wintney	150	D 1 - 1	Coombes 67 (pen)	12	1
22	**FAC1Q**	**A**	**Staines Town**	**238**	**W 2 - 1**	**Unknown 68 79**		2
26	SthPS	A	Taunton Town	427	L 0 - 2		14	3
29	SthPS	H	Hendon	187	L 1 - 3	Odunalke 85	15	4
Oct 3	**FAC2Q**	**A**	**Metropolitan Police**	**287**	**W 2 - 1**			5
7	SthPS	A	Gosport Borough	323	W 3 - 2	Nicholas 3 65 Akers 57	14	6
13	**FAC3Q**	**A**	**Sholing**	**341**	**L 2 - 5**			7
24	SthPS	A	Tiverton Town	264	L 0 - 5			8
27	SthPS	H	Metropolitan Police	199	W 3 - 0	Coombes 58 72 Lamont 90+1 (pen)		9
31	**FAT3Q**	**H**	**Folkestone Invicta**	**203**	**W 2 - 1**	**Coombes 8 90**		10

Goalscorers	LGE	FAC	FAT	SG	HAT	PEN	1Q	2Q	45+	3Q	4Q	90+	T
TOTALS	8	6	2		0	2	2	0	0	4	2	2	16
Coombes	3		2	3		1	1			2	1	1	5
Nicholas	2			2			1			1			2
Akers	1			1						1			1
Lamont	1			1		1						1	1
Odunalke	1			1							1		1

WESTON-SUPER-MARE MATCH RESULTS 2020-21

Date	Comp	H/A	Opponents	Att:	Result	Goalscorers	Pos	No.
Sept 19	SthPS	A	Dorchester Town	401	W 3 - 1	Waite 35 Knowles 41 Laird 53	3	1
22	**FAC1Q**	**A**	**Cowes Sports**	**300**	**W 5 - 0**	**Knowles (x2) Jagger-Cane Humphries Thomas**		2
26	SthPS	H	Metropolitan Police	535	D 1 - 1	Jones 35	6	3
30	SthPS	A	Tiverton Town	334	L 1 - 3	Laird 87	11	4
Oct 3	**FAC2Q**	**H**	**Swindon Supermarine**	**319**	**D 2 - 2**	**Symons 40 Avery 88 (Won 4-2 on pens)**		5
10	SthPS	A	Harrow Borough	176	D 1 - 1	McCootie 24	12	6
13	**FAC3Q**	**H**	**Larkhall Athletic**	**584**	**W 6 - 0**			7
17	SthPS	H	Wimborne Town	581	L 1 - 2	Waite 3	13	8
24	**FAC4Q**	**A**	**Eastleigh**		**L 1 - 3**	**Knowles 81**		9
27	SthPS	A	Salisbury	594	L 1 - 2	Grubb 8		10
31	**FAT3Q**	**H**	**Larkhall Athletic**		**W 2 - 1**			11
Dec 8	**FAT1P**	**H**	**Chesham United**		**L 1 - 3**			12

Goalscorers	LGE	FAC	FAT	SG	HAT	PEN	1Q	2Q	45+	3Q	4Q	90+	T
TOTALS	8	14	3		0	0	2	4	0	1	2	0	25
Knowles	1	3		2				1			1		4
Laird	2			2						1	1		2
Waite	2			2			1	1					2
Avery		1											1
Grubb	1			1			1						1
Humphries		1											1
Jagger-Cane		1											1
Jones	1			1				1					1
McCootie	1			1				1					1
Symons		1											1
Thomas		1											1

WIMBORNE TOWN MATCH RESULTS 2020-21

Date	Comp	H/A	Opponents	Att:	Result	Goalscorers	Pos	No.
Sept 12	**FACP**	**H**	**AFC Portchester**	**180**	**W 3 - 0**			1
19	SthPS	A	Tiverton Town	302	L 0 - 5		21	2
22	**FAC1Q**	**A**	**Barnstaple Town**	**147**	**W 3 - 2**			3
26	SthPS	H	Chesham Town	259	L 0 - 1		20	4
29	SthPS	A	Dorchester Town	267	D 0 - 0		17	5
Oct 3	**FAC2Q**	**H**	**Melksham Town**	**183**	**D 0 - 0**	**(Won 5-4 on pens)**		6
6	SthPS	H	Farnborough	160	W 2 - 1	Shepherd 80 89		7
13	**FAC3Q**	**H**	**Maidstone United**	**323**	**D 2 - 2**	**Gunson 38 90+ (Won 3-1 on pens)**		8
17	SthPS	A	Weston-s-Mare	581	W 2 - 1	Young 67 Beale 77	12	9
24	**FAC4Q**	**A**	**Boreham Wood**		**L 0 - 2**			10
27	SthPS	A	Truro City	365	L 1 - 4	Beale 53		11

Goalscorers	LGE	FAC	FAT	SG	HAT	PEN	1Q	2Q	45+	3Q	4Q	90+	T
TOTALS	5	8	0		0	0	0	1	0	2	3	1	13
Beale	2			2						1	1		2
Gunson		2		1				1				1	2
Shepherd	2			1							2		2
Young	1			1						1			1

YATE TOWN MATCH RESULTS 2020-21

Date	Comp	H/A	Opponents	Att:	Result	Goalscorers	Pos	No.
Sept 19	SthPS	A	Metropolitan Police	134	D 1 - 1	Fisher 65 (og)	13	1
22	**FAC1Q**	**H**	**Bristol Manor Farm**	**303**	**L 1 - 2**			2
26	SthPS	H	Dorchester Town	238	W 4 - 1	Williams 14 Turl 25 Lewis 47 Fleetwood 58	5	3
30	SthPS	A	Farnborough	228	D 0 - 0		6	4
Oct 6	SthPS	H	Tiverton Town	220	L 0 - 3			5
17	SthPS	H	Chesham United	213	L 0 - 1		14	6
24	SthPS	H	Poole Town	237	L 2 - 6	Beckinsale 4 60	14	7
27	SthPS	A	Hartley Wintney	270	L 1 - 3	Norman 13		8

Goalscorers	LGE	FAC	FAT	SG	HAT	PEN	1Q	2Q	45+	3Q	4Q	90+	T
TOTALS	8	1	0		0	0	3	1	0	4	0	0	9
Beckinsale	2			1			1			1			2
Fleetwood	1			1						1			1
Lewis	1			1						1			1
Norman	1			1			1						1
Opponent	1			1						1			1
Turl	1			1				1					1
Williams	1			1			1						1

AFC DUNSTABLE MATCH RESULTS 2020-21

Date	Comp	H/A	Opponents	Att:	Result	Goalscorers	Pos	No.
Sept 1	**FACEP**	**H**	**Hallen**	**48**	**W 4 - 0**			1
12	**FACP**	**A**	**Thatcham Town**	**129**	**W 5 - 1**			2
19	SthD1C	A	Biggleswade	151	L 0 - 2		16	3
22	**FAC1Q**	**A**	**Merstham**	**177**	**D 2 - 2**	**Baker 48 Christie 85 (pen) (Won 7-6 on pens)**		4
26	**FAT1Q**	**H**	**Tooting & Mitcham United**	**97**	**L 1 - 2**	**Campbell 52**		5
29	SthD1C	H	Didcot Town	83	W 1 - 0	Campbell 7	11	6
Oct 3	**FAC2Q**	**H**	**Hemel Hempstead Town**	**214**	**L 1 - 2**			7
6	SthD1C	A	Wantage Town	72	L 1 - 3	Christie 90+2		8
10	SthD1C	A	Bedworth United	207	D 1 - 1	Christie 43	16	9
13	SthD1C	H	Corby Town	143	W 2 - 0	Christie 8 Elliot 31	11	10
24	SthD1C	H	St Neots Town	169	D 2 - 2	McClelland 38 81	11	11
31	SthD1C	H	Halesowen Town	169	W 3 - 1	Christie 22 (pen) Forsyth 26 (og) Newman 29	8	12

Goalscorers	LGE	FAC	FAT	SG	HAT	PEN	1Q	2Q	45+	3Q	4Q	90+	T
TOTALS	10	12	1		0	2	3	5	0	2	2	1	23
Christie	4	1		5		2	2	1			1	1	5
Campbell	1		1	2			1			1			2
McClelland	2			1				1			1		2
Baker		1		1						1			1
Elliot	1			1				1					1
Newman	1			1				1					1
Opponent	1			1				1					1

AYLESBURY UNITED MATCH RESULTS 2020-21

Date	Comp	H/A	Opponents	Att:	Result	Goalscorers	Pos	No.
Sept 12	**FACP**	**H**	**Long Crendon**	**197**	**W 3 - 0**	**Riddick 3 Hogg 38 Wood 89 (RC - Hopwood (Gk) 75)**		1
19	SthD1C	A	Corby Town	400	W 1 - 0	Hogg 39	6	2
22	**FAC1Q**	**H**	**Moneyfields**	**112**	**D 2 - 2**	**Stobbs 59 Hogg 85 (pen) (Lost 3-4 on pens)**		3
30	SthD1C	H	Wantage Town	107	W 4 - 2	Rudd 26 48 Akintunde 64 French 90+2	3	4
Oct 3	SthD1C	H	Daventry Town	112	W 3 - 2	Akintunde 34 Deacon 76 Hercules 90+3 (pen)	2	5
6	SthD1C	A	Berkhamsted	242	L 2 - 3	Deacon 36 77		6
10	SthD1C	A	Coleshill Town	166	W 4 - 1	Rudd 15 39 O'Connor 34 Ball 87	1	7
17	**FAT2Q**	**H**	**Tilbury**	**197**	**D 2 - 2**	**Akintunde 21 (pen) 40 (Won 4-2 on pens)**		8
28	SthD1C	H	Bedford Town	181	D 0 - 0			9
Nov 1	**FAT3Q**	**H**	**Margate**	**243**	**L 2 - 4**	**Jones 10 69**		10

Goalscorers	LGE	FAC	FAT	SG	HAT	PEN	1Q	2Q	45+	3Q	4Q	90+	T
TOTALS	14	5	4		0	3	4	8	0	3	6	2	23
Akintunde	2		2	3		1	1	2		1			4
Rudd	4			2			1	2		1			4
Deacon	3			2				1			2		3
Hogg	1	2		3		1		2			1		3
Jones			2	1			1				1		2
Ball	1			1							1		1
French	1			1								1	1
Hercules	1			1		1						1	1
O'Connor	1			1				1					1
Riddick		1		1			1						1
Stobbs		1		1						1			1
Wood		1		1							1		1

BARTON ROVERS MATCH RESULTS 2020-21

Date	Comp	H/A	Opponents	Att:	Result	Goalscorers	Pos	No.
Sept 12	**FACP**	**A**	**Bowers & Pitsea**	**155**	**L 1 - 5**	**Opponent 81**		**1**
19	SthD1C	H	Coleshill Town	128	**W** 1 - 0	Tshikuna 90	7	2
26	SthD1C	A	Halesowen Town	400	D 1 - 1	Tshikuna 21	4	3
29	SthD1C	A	Bedworth United	137	L 3 - 4	Tshikuna 39 44 Regis 84	7	4
Oct 3	SthD1C	A	Bedford Town	334	D 1 - 1	Osobu 84		5
6	SthD1C	H	Kempston Rovers	155	**W** 3 - 0	Bell 62 Vincent 68 Regis 90+1		6
10	SthD1C	A	Daventry Town	130	**W** 5 - 3	Tshikuna 3 Connor 15 Bell 47 Dummett 80 Regis 90	2	7
17	**FAT2Q**	**A**	**Whitehawk**	**400**	**L 1 - 2**	**Dummett 66**		**8**
24	SthD1C	H	Corby Town	202	L 1 - 2	Vincent 27 (pen)	6	9
Nov 3	SthD1C	H	St Neots Town	221	L 1 - 2	Smith 22	9	10

Goalscorers	LGE	FAC	FAT	SG	HAT	PEN	1Q	2Q	45+	3Q	4Q	90+	T
TOTALS	16	1	1		0	1	4	3	0	3	5	3	18
Tshikuna	5			4			2	2				1	5
Regis	3			3							1	2	3
Bell	2			2						2			2
Dummett	1		1	2						1	1		2
Vincent	2			2		1		1			1		2
Connor	1			1			1						1
Opponent		1		1							1		1
Osobu	1			1							1		1
Smith	1			1			1						1

BEDFORD TOWN MATCH RESULTS 2020-21

Date	Comp	H/A	Opponents	Att:	Result	Goalscorers	Pos	No.
Sept 12	**FACP**	**A**	**Daventry Town**	**206**	**L 0 - 1**			**1**
19	SthD1C	A	Thame United	178	L 0 - 3		19	2
29	SthD1C	H	Berkhamsted	315	D 1 - 1	Walker 8	17	3
Oct 3	SthD1C	H	Barton Rovers	334	D 1 - 1	Watson 90	19	4
6	SthD1C	A	Biggleswade	204	**W** 2 - 0	Mackhail-Smith 60 Watson 70		5
10	SthD1C	H	North Leigh	337	**W** 4 - 1	Mackhail-Smith 24 Harriott 28 Sanders 60 Howe 79	7	6
17	**FAT2Q**	**A**	**Spalding United**	**224**	**W 1 - 0**	**Howe 38**		**7**
24	SthD1C	A	Yaxley	278	**W** 1 - 0	Tomlinson 66	7	8
28	SthD1C	A	Aylesbury United	181	D 0 - 0			9
31	**FAT3Q**	**A**	**Loughborough Dynamo**	**169**	**W 3 - 1**	**Setchell 35 Summerfield 53 Hitchcock 67 (pen)**		**10**
Dec 8	**FAT1P**	**A**	**Biggleswade Town**	**201**	**D 0 - 0**	**(Won 5-3 on pens)**		**11**
15	**FAT2P**	**A**	**Alfreton Town**			**Match postponed - Alfreton progressed to the third round.**		**12**

Goalscorers	LGE	FAC	FAT	SG	HAT	PEN	1Q	2Q	45+	3Q	4Q	90+	T
TOTALS	9	0	4		0	1	1	4	0	5	2	1	13
Howe	1		1	2				1			1		2
Mackhail-Smith	2			2				1		1			2
Watson	2			2							1	1	2
Harriott	1			1				1					1
Sanders	1			1						1			1
Tomlinson	1			1						1			1
Walker	1			1			1						1
Setchell			1	1				1					1
Summerfield			1	1						1			1
Hitchcock			1	1		1				1			1

BEDWORTH UNITED MATCH RESULTS 2020-21

Date	Comp	H/A	Opponents	Att:	Result	Goalscorers	Pos	No.
Sept 12	**FACP**	**A**	**Racing Club Warwick**	**283**	**D 1 - 1**	**Truslove (Won 3-2 on pens)**		1
19	SthD1C	A	St Neots Town	281	D 1 - 1	Piggon 54	9	2
22	**FAC1Q**	**A**	**Barwell**	**206**	**L 1 - 3**	**Pigeon (pen)**		3
26	SthD1C	A	Wantage Town	88	W 3 - 1	Webster 7 (og) John 31 Dawson 80	3	4
29	SthD1C	H	Barton Rovers	137	W 4 - 3	Piggon 25 45 Parrott 30 Walton 64	1	5
Oct 3	SthD1C	H	Thame United	157	W 3 - 2	Piggon 18 48 Barnett 85	1	6
7	SthD1C	A	Corby Town	399	L 0 - 4			7
10	SthD1C	H	AFC Dunstable	207	D 1 - 1	Keen 47	3	8
17	**FAT2Q**	**H**	**St Neots Town**	**154**	**L 1 - 4**			9
24	SthD1C	A	Kidlington	81	D 1 - 1	Dawson 60	3	10
Nov 3	SthD1C	H	Welwyn Garden City	153	W 3 - 2	Rowe 60 Piggon 82 Blythe 90+3	2	11

Goalscorers	LGE	FAC	FAT	SG	HAT	PEN	1Q	2Q	45+	3Q	4Q	90+	T
TOTALS	16	2	1		0	1	4	3	1	6	3	1	19
Piggon	6	1		5		1	2	1	1	2	1		7
Dawson	2			2						1	1		2
Barnett	1			1							1		1
Blythe	1			1								1	1
John	1			1				1					1
Keen	1			1						1			1
Opponent	1			1			1						1
Parrott	1			1				1					1
Rowe	1			1						1			1
Truslove		1		1			1						1
Walton	1			1						1			1

BERKHAMSTED MATCH RESULTS 2020-21

Date	Comp	H/A	Opponents	Att:	Result	Goalscorers	Pos	No.
Sept 12	**FACP**	**A**	**Cribbs**	**90**	**L 0 - 2**			1
19	SthD1C	H	North Leigh	165	D 1 - 1	Bangura 83	10	2
29	SthD1C	A	Bedford Town	315	D 1 - 1	Toomey 2	14	3
Oct 3	SthD1C	H	Coleshill Town	149	L 0 - 1		18	4
6	SthD1C	H	Aylesbury United	242	W 3 - 2	Toomey 14 86 88		5
10	SthD1C	H	Wantage Town	234	W 5 - 0	Lopes 13 Hartley 55 (og) Bangura 72 Toomey 76 Verney 87	6	6
17	**FAT2Q**	**A**	**Chertsey Town**	**340**	**W 2 - 1**	**Bangura 18 Balogun 78**		7
24	SthD1C	A	Didcot Town	214	W 3 - 0	Bangura 7 87 Kirkpatrick 11	5	8
Nov 3	**FAT3Q**	**A**	**Marlow**	**230**	**L 1 - 2**	**Chapple 47 (og)**		9

Goalscorers	LGE	FAC	FAT	SG	HAT	PEN	1Q	2Q	45+	3Q	4Q	90+	T
TOTALS	13	0	3		1	0	6	0	0	2	8	0	16
Bangura	4		1	4			2				3		5
Toomey	5			3	1		2				3		5
Opponent	1		1	2						2			2
Balogun			1	1							1		1
Kirkpatrick	1			1			1						1
Lopes	1			1			1						1
Verney	1			1							1		1

BIGGLESWADE MATCH RESULTS 2020-21

Date	Comp	H/A	Opponents	Att:	Result	Goalscorers	Pos	No.
Sept 12	**FACP**	**H**	**Histon**	**203**	**W 1 - 0**	**Fleming 25**		1
19	SthD1C	H	AFC Dunstable	151	W 2 - 0	Fleming 9 Mason 78	4	2
22	**FAC1Q**	**A**	**Ely City**	**196**	**W 2 - 1**	**Mason 15 Drakulic 58**		3
26	**FAT1Q**	**A**	**Evesham United**	**271**	**L 1 - 2**	**Gauge 76**		4
29	SthD1C	A	Welwyn Garden City	146	L 0 - 3		10	5
Oct 3	**FAC2Q**	**A**	**Canvey Island**	**289**	**D 2 - 2**	**Johnson 34 (pen) Bailey 62 (Lost 3-4 on pens)**		6
6	SthD1C	H	Bedford Town	204	L 0 - 2			7
10	SthD1C	H	Kidlington	128	L 1 - 3	Coles 14	18	8
19	SthD1C	A	Coleshill Town	164	L 0 - 2		19	9
27	SthD1C	A	St Neots Town	350	L 1 - 4	Coles 61		10

Goalscorers	LGE	FAC	FAT	SG	HAT	PEN	1Q	2Q	45+	3Q	4Q	90+	T
TOTALS	4	5	1		0	1	3	2	0	3	2	0	10
Coles	2			2			1			1			2
Fleming	1	1		2			1	1					2
Mason	1	1		2			1				1		2
Bailey		1		1						1			1
Drakulic		1		1						1			1
Gauge			1	1							1		1
Johnson		1		1		1		1					1

COLESHILL TOWN MATCH RESULTS 2020-21

Date	Comp	H/A	Opponents	Att:	Result	Goalscorers	Pos	No.
Sept 12	**FACP**	**A**	**Coventry Sphinx**	**150**	**D 0 - 0**	**(Lost 3-4 pens)**		1
19	SthD1C	A	Barton Rovers	128	L 0 - 1		13	2
28	SthD1C	H	Corby Town	204	L 0 - 1		19	3
Oct 3	SthD1C	A	Berkhamsted	149	W 1 - 0	Mannion 33	13	4
6	SthD1C	A	Thame United	101	L 1 - 4	Dubidat 40		5
10	SthD1C	H	Aylesbury United	166	L 1 - 4	Dubidat 30	19	6
17	**FAT2Q**	**A**	**Wisbech Town**	**164**	**W 2 - 1**	**Tongue 48 Dubidat 61**		7
19	SthD1C	H	Biggleswade	164	W 2 - 0	Dainty 63 Brogan 90	14	8
24	SthD1C	A	North Leigh	134	L 0 - 1		15	9
31	**FAT3Q**	**A**	**Bromsgrove Sporting**	**482**	**W 1 - 0**			10
Nov 2	SthD1C	H	Wantage Town	247	W 2 - 0	Willis 47 Harrison 79	13	11
Dec 8	**FAT1P**	**H**	**Matlock Town**	**0**	**W 5 - 2**	**Yates 18 (og) Tonge 32 61 Willis 57 Dainty 76**		12
15	**FAT2P**	**H**	**AFC Telford United**	**30**	**L 1 -10**	**Dainty 52**		13

Goalscorers	LGE	FAC	FAT	SG	HAT	PEN	1Q	2Q	45+	3Q	4Q	90+	T
TOTALS	7	0	9		0	0	1	4	0	7	2	1	16
Dainty	1		2	3						2	1		3
Dubidat	2		1	3				2		1			3
Tongue			3	2				1		2			3
Willis	1		1	2						2			2
Brogan	1			1								1	1
Harrison	1			1							1		1
Mannion	1			1				1					1
Opponent			1	1			1						1

CORBY TOWN MATCH RESULTS 2020-21

Date	Comp	H/A	Opponents	Att:	Result	Goalscorers	Pos	No.
Sept 12	**FACP**	**A**	**Mildenhall Town**	**175**	**D 1 - 1**	**Wise 28 (Lost 3-4 pens)**		1
19	SthD1C	H	Aylesbury United	400	L 0 - 1		14	2
26	**FAT1Q**	**A**	**Soham Town Rangers**	**131**	**W 3 - 0**	**Harty 6 Watson 12 (og) Diggin 58 (pen)**		3
28	SthD1C	A	Coleshill Town	204	W 1 - 0	Diggin 35	9	4
Oct 7	SthD1C	H	Bedworth United	399	W 4 - 0	Westwood 25 Diggin 47 (pen) 57 Crawford 74	6	5
10	SthD1C	H	Halesowen Town	400	W 4 - 3	Crawford 60 62 Wise 69 Furey 82	4	6
13	SthD1C	A	AFC Dunstable	143	L 0 - 2		4	7
17	**FAT2Q**	**H**	**Halesowen Town**	**400**	**W 1 - 0**			8
24	SthD1C	A	Barton Rovers	202	W 2 - 1	Tague 52 Crawford 57	2	9
28	SthD1C	H	Daventry Town	400	W 4 - 1	White 6 Yorston 8 Sandy 17 Crawford 80	1	10
31	**FAT3Q**	**H**	**Hednesford Town**	**391**	**L 1 - 2**			11

Goalscorers	LGE	FAC	FAT	SG	HAT	PEN	1Q	2Q	45+	3Q	4Q	90+	T
TOTALS	15	1	5		0	2	5	3	0	7	4	0	21
Crawford	5			4						3	2		5
Diggin	3		1	3		2		1		3			4
Wise	1	1		2				1			1		2
Furey	1			1							1		1
Harty			1				1						1

Goalscorers	LGE	FAC	FAT	SG	HAT	PEN	1Q	2Q	45+	3Q	4Q	90+	T
Opponent			1	1			1						1
Sandy	1			1			1						1
Tague	1			1						1			1
Westwood	1			1				1					1
White	1			1			1						1
Yorston	1			1			1						1

DAVENTRY TOWN MATCH RESULTS 2020-21

Date	Comp	H/A	Opponents	Att:	Result	Goalscorers	Pos	No.
Sept 12	**FACP**	**H**	**Bedford Town**	**206**	**W 1 - 0**	**Bowen 90 (pen)**		1
19	SthD1C	H	Kidlington	124	W 1 - 0	Creaney 13	8	2
22	**FAC1Q**	**H**	**Evesham United**	**195**	**L 0 - 2**			3
29	SthD1C	A	Kempston Rovers	75	W 1 - 0	Childs 57		4
Oct 3	SthD1C	A	Aylesbury United	112	L 2 - 3	Bowen 11 Orosz 18		5
10	SthD1C	H	Barton Rovers	130	L 3 - 5	Bowen 58 64 Orosz 67	11	6
17	**FAT2Q**	**H**	**Kidsgrove Athletic**		**L 0 - 2**			7
24	SthD1C	A	Halesowen Town	400	L 0 - 2		14	8
28	SthD1C	A	Corby Town	400	L 1 - 4	Bowen 85		9
31	SthD1C	H	Kempston Rovers	150	W 2 - 1	Ball 71 Emery 90+2	13	10
Nov 4	SthD1C	H	Didcot Town	120	W 3 - 0	Bowen 17 38 Orosz 68	6	11

Goalscorers	LGE	FAC	FAT	SG	HAT	PEN	1Q	2Q	45+	3Q	4Q	90+	T
TOTALS	13	1	0		0	1	4	1	0	4	3	2	14
Bowen	6	1		5		1	2	1		2	1	1	7
Orosz	3			3			1			1	1		3
Ball	1			1							1		1
Childs	1			1						1			1
Creaney	1			1			1						1

Goalscorers	LGE	FAC	FAT	SG	HAT	PEN	1Q	2Q	45+	3Q	4Q	90+	T
Emery	1			1								1	1

DIDCOT TOWN MATCH RESULTS 2020-21

Date	Comp	H/A	Opponents	Att:	Result	Goalscorers	Pos	No.
Sept 12	**FACP**	**H**	**Royal Wootton Bassett**	**283**	**L 1 - 2**	**Humphries**		1
19	SthD1C	H	Kempston Rovers	195	**W** 4 - 1	Thomas 17 37 Dark 41 Jeacock 73	3	2
26	SthD1C	H	Thame United	224	**W** 2 - 1	Thomas 40 Jeacock 63	1	3
29	SthD1C	A	AFC Dunstable	83	L 0 - 1		2	4
Oct 3	SthD1C	A	Yaxley	99	L 1 - 2	Ferguson 90	3	5
6	SthD1C	H	Kidlington	184	L 0 - 3			6
10	SthD1C	A	St Neots Town	228	L 0 - 8		13	7
17	**FAT2Q**	**A**	**Kidlington**	**170**	**L 1 - 2**	**Jeacock 60**		8
24	SthD1C	H	Berkhamsted	214	L 0 - 3		17	9
Nov 4	SthD1C	A	Daventry Town	120	L 0 - 3		19	10

Goalscorers	LGE	FAC	FAT	SG	HAT	PEN	1Q	2Q	45+	3Q	4Q	90+	T
TOTALS	7	1	1		0	0	1	3	0	2	1	1	9
Jeacock	2		1	3						2	1		3
Thomas	3			2			1	2					3
Dark	1			1				1					1
Ferguson	1			1								1	1
Humphries		1		1									1

HALESOWEN TOWN MATCH RESULTS 2020-21

Date	Comp	H/A	Opponents	Att:	Result	Goalscorers	Pos	No.
Sept 12	**FACP**	**A**	**Newcastle Town**	**214**	**W 2 - 1**	**Gregory 81 Holmes 86**		1
19	SthD1C	H	Yaxley	400	**W** 7 - 1	Gregory 26 31 36 Manning 53 Cobourne 57 (pen) Yates 76 Westwood 78	1	2
22	**FAC1Q**	**A**	**West Bridgford**	**287**	**W 1 - 0**	**Gregory**		3
26	SthD1C	H	Barton Rovers	400	D 1 - 1	Cobourne 15 (pen)	2	4
30	SthD1C	A	Kidlington	104	D 1 - 1	Molyneux 59	5	5
Oct 3	**FAC2Q**	**A**	**Hednesford Town**	**600**	**D 0 - 0**	**(Won 5-3 on pens)**		6
6	SthD1C	H	North Leigh	400	**W** 5 - 0	Ali 25 Molyneux 48 Hawker 49 Manning 51 Holmes 71		7
10	SthD1C	A	Corby Town	400	L 3 - 4	Molyneux 10 Cobourne 13 (pen) 25	5	8
13	**FAC3Q**	**A**	**Cambridge City**	**400**	**L 0 - 2**			9
17	**FAT2Q**	**A**	**Corby Town**	**400**	**L 0 - 1**			10
24	SthD1C	H	Daventry Town	400	**W** 2 - 0	Molyneux 18 McCone 66	4	11
31	SthD1C	A	AFC Dunstable	169	L 1 - 3	Westwood 80 (pen)	7	12

Goalscorers	LGE	FAC	FAT	SG	HAT	PEN	1Q	2Q	45+	3Q	4Q	90+	T
TOTALS	20	3	0		1	4	4	5	0	7	6	0	23
Gregory	3	2		3	1			3			1		5
Cobourne	4			3		3	2	1		1			4
Molyneux	4			4			2			2			4
Holmes	1	1		2							2		2
Manning	2			2						2			2

Goalscorers	LGE	FAC	FAT	SG	HAT	PEN	1Q	2Q	45+	3Q	4Q	90+	T
Westwood	2			2		1					2		2
Ali	1			1				1					1
Hawker	1			1						1			1
McCone	1			1						1			1
Yates	1			1							1		1

KEMPSTON ROVERS MATCH RESULTS 2020-21

Date	Comp	H/A	Opponents	Att:	Result		Goalscorers	Pos	No.
Sept 12	**FACP**	**A**	**Long Melford**	**132**	**D**	**0 - 0**	**(Lost 2-4 pens)**		1
19	SthD1C	A	Didcot Town	195	L	1 - 4	Magagada 8	18	2
29	SthD1C	H	Daventry Town	75	L	0 - 1		20	3
Oct 3	SthD1C	H	Wantage Town	80	**W**	3 - 2	Hunte 23 61 Baker 76	15	4
6	SthD1C	A	Barton Rovers	155	L	0 - 3			5
10	SthD1C	H	Yaxley	102	D	3 - 3	Baker 7 Ladipo 41 Slama 62	17	6
17	**FAT2Q**	**A**	**Ilkeston Town**	**370**	**L**	**1 - 2**	**Magagada 36**		7
24	SthD1C	A	Welwyn Garden City	145	D	1 - 1	Slama 49	18	8
27	SthD1C	H	Kidlington	76	D	2 - 2	Baker 60 Akinbobola 88		9
31	SthD1C	A	Daventry Town	150	L	1 - 2	Akinbobola 81	17	10

Goalscorers	LGE	FAC	FAT	SG	HAT	PEN	1Q	2Q	45+	3Q	4Q	90+	T
TOTALS	11	0	1		0	0	2	3	0	4	3	0	12
Baker	3			3			1			1	1		3
Akinbobola	2			2							2		2
Hunte	2			1				1		1			2
Magagada	1		1	2			1	1					2
Slama	2			2						2			2
Ladipo	1			1				1					1

KIDLINGTON MATCH RESULTS 2020-21

Date	Comp	H/A	Opponents	Att:	Result		Goalscorers	Pos	No.
Sept 12	**FACP**	**H**	**Thame United**	**152**	**W**	**1 - 0**			1
19	SthD1C	A	Daventry Town	124	L	0 - 1		15	2
23	**FAC1Q**	**H**	**Salisbury**	**236**	**D**	**1 - 1**	**(Won 4-2 on pens)**		3
30	SthD1C	H	Halesowen Town	104	D	1 - 1	Davidge 44	16	4
Oct 3	**FAC2Q**	**H**	**Bristol Manor Farm**	**294**	**D**	**1 - 1**	**(Lost 6-7 on pens)**		5
6	SthD1C	A	Didcot Town	184	**W**	3 - 0	Whitehead 27 Harvey 70 Yusuf 73		6
10	SthD1C	A	Biggleswade	128	**W**	3 - 1	Robertson 20 Mattimore 50 Harvey 78	8	7
17	**FAT2Q**	**H**	**Didcot Town**	**170**	**W**	**2 - 1**			8
24	SthD1C	H	Bedworth United	81	D	1 - 1	Gillett 86	10	9
27	SthD1C	A	Kempston Rovers	76	D	2 - 2	Davidge 4 Harvey 32		10
31	**FAT3Q**	**A**	**Moneyfields**		**L**	**2 - 3**			11

Goalscorers	LGE	FAC	FAT	SG	HAT	PEN	1Q	2Q	45+	3Q	4Q	90+	T
TOTALS	10	3	4		0	0	2	3	0	1	4	0	17
Harvey	3			3				1			2		3
Davidge	2			2			1	1					2
Gillett	1			1							1		1
Mattimore	1			1						1			1
Robertson	1			1			1						1
Whitehead	1			1				1					1
Yusuf	1			1							1		1

NORTH LEIGH MATCH RESULTS 2020-21

Date	Comp	H/A	Opponents	Att:	Result	Goalscorers	Pos	No.
Sept 12	**FACP**	**A**	**Marlow**	**201**	**L 0 - 2**			1
19	SthD1C	A	Berkhamsted	165	D 1 - 1	Mills 56	11	2
26	**FAT1Q**	**A**	**Melksham Town**	**253**	**D 3 - 3**	**Opponent 10 Learoyd 16 Seacole 51 (Won 5-4 on pens)**		3
29	SthD1C	H	Thame United	110	D 0 - 0		15	4
Oct 6	SthD1C	A	Halesowen Town	400	L 0 - 5			5
10	SthD1C	A	Bedford Town	337	L 1 - 4	Mills 61	20	6
17	**FAT2Q**	**A**	**Thatcham Town**	**186**	**W 4 - 2**			7
20	SthD1C	H	St Neots Town	150	D 2 - 2	Seacole 29 Learoyd 90+1	20	8
24	SthD1C	H	Coleshill Town	134	W 1 - 0	Seacole 90	16	9
27	SthD1C	A	Yaxley	69	L 0 - 5			10
30	**FAT3Q**	**A**	**Wantage Town**	**398**	**W 4 - 1**			11
Dec 8	**FAT1P**	**H**	**Frome Town**		**L 0 - 1**			12

Goalscorers	LGE	FAC	FAT	SG	HAT	PEN	1Q	2Q	45+	3Q	4Q	90+	T
TOTALS	5	0	11		0	0	2	1	0	3	0	2	16
Seacole	2		1	3				1		1		1	3
Learoyd	1		1	2			1					1	2
Mills	2			2						2			2
Opponent			1	1			1						1

ST NEOTS MATCH RESULTS 2020-21

Date	Comp	H/A	Opponents	Att:	Result	Goalscorers	Pos	No.
Sept 2	**FACEP**	**A**	**Pinchbeck United**	**98**	**W 4 - 0**	**Lobjoit 36 61 O'Hara 13 Dickens 15**		1
12	**FACP**	**A**	**Soham Town Rangers**	**203**	**L 2 - 3**	**Lobjoit 27 36**		2
19	SthD1C	H	Bedworth United	281	D 1 - 1	Lobjoit 42	12	3
26	SthD1C	A	Yaxley	142	D 2 - 2	Smith 34 Lobjoit 67	10	4
Oct 10	SthD1C	H	Didcot Town (9)	228	W 8 - 0	Watkins 2 Robbins 20 36 Worman 29 Bennett 46 Amu 76 84 Goode 88	14	5
13	SthD1C	H	Welwyn Garden City	230	L 2 - 3	Robbins 19 Amu 58	15	6
17	**FAT2Q**	**A**	**Bedworth United**	**154**	**W 4 - 1**			7
20	SthD1C	A	North Leigh	150	D 2 - 2	Worman 56 76	12	8
24	SthD1C	A	AFC Dunstable	169	D 2 - 2	Simper 65 Lobjoit 70	12	9
27	SthD1C	H	Biggleswade	350	W 4 - 1	Dickens 15 Worman 34 57 Battersby 69		10
31	**FAT3Q**	**H**	**Worksop Town**	**371**	**W 6 - 1**	**Simper 45 Lobjoit 50 83 Worman 59 71 Robbins 75**		11
Nov 3	SthD1C	A	Barton Rovers	221	W 2 - 1	Robbins 34 Worman 38	3	12
Dec 8	**FAT1P**	**H**	**Kings Langley**	**270**	**W 3 - 1**			13
15	**FAT2P**	**A**	**Hereford**	**285**	**L 0 - 3**			14

Goalscorers	LGE	FAC	FAT	SG	HAT	PEN	1Q	2Q	45+	3Q	4Q	90+	T
TOTALS	23	6	6		0	0	6	10	1	9	9	0	35
Lobjoit	3	4	2	6				4		3	2		9
Worman	6		2	5				3		3	2		8
Robbins	4		1	4			2	2			1		5
Amu	3			2						1	2		3
Dickens	1	1		2			2						2
Simper	1		1	2					1	1			2
Battersby	1			1							1		1
Bennett	1			1						1			1
Goode	1			1							1		1
O'Hara		1		1			1						1
Smith	1			1				1					1
Watkins	1			1			1						1

THAME UNITED MATCH RESULTS 2020-21

Date	Comp	H/A	Opponents	Att:	Result	Goalscorers	Pos	No.
Sept 12	**FACP**	**A**	**Kidlington**	**152**	**L 0 - 1**			1
19	StHD1C	H	Bedford Town	178	W 3 - 0	Blake 28 Hackett 47 West 90	2	2
26	StHD1C	A	Didcot Town	224	L 1 - 2	Hackett 60	5	3
29	StHD1C	A	North Leigh	110	D 0 - 0		6	4
Oct 3	StHD1C	A	Bedworth United	157	L 2 - 3	Mepham 36 Blake 43		5
6	StHD1C	H	Coleshill Town	101	W 4 - 1	Goss 1 3 90+3 Blake 57		6
10	StHD1C	H	Welwyn Garden City	147	L 0 - 1		9	7
17	**FAT2Q**	**H**	**Cirencester Town**	**160**	**W 4 - 1**			8
24	StHD1C	A	Wantage Town	125	L 2 - 3	Blake 15 (pen) Hackett 75 (pen)	13	9
31	**FAT3Q**	**H**	**Wimborne Town**			**Match cancelled - Thame United progress.**		10
Dec 8	**FAT1P**	**H**	**Bognor Regis Town**	**161**	**L 2 - 5**			11

Goalscorers	LGE	FAC	FAT	SG	HAT	PEN	1Q	2Q	45+	3Q	4Q	90+	T
TOTALS	12	0	6		1	2	3	2	0	4	0	3	18
Blake	4			4		1	1	1		2			4
Goss	3			1	1		2					1	3
Hackett	3			3		1				2		1	3
Mepham	1			1				1					1
West	1			1								1	1

WANTAGE TOWN MATCH RESULTS 2020-21

Date	Comp	H/A	Opponents	Att:	Result	Goalscorers	Pos	No.
Sept 12	**FACP**	**H**	**Windsor**	**132**	**W 3 - 2**	**Knight 20 60 Killie 87**		1
19	StHD1C	H	Welwyn Garden City	90	W 2 - 0	Alexander 6 Knight 74	5	2
22	**FAC1Q**	**A**	**Taunton Town**	**349**	**L 0 - 5**			3
26	StHD1C	H	Bedworth United	88	L 1 - 3	Knight 48	9	4
30	StHD1C	A	Aylesbury United	107	L 2 - 4	Sheppard 40 90	12	5
Oct 63	StHD1C	A	Kempston Rovers	80	L 2 - 3	Alexander 22 Ballard 38	14	6
6	StHD1C	H	AFC Dunstable	72	W 3 - 1	Alexander 13 Mahon 52 82		7
10	StHD1C	A	Berkhamsted	234	L 0 - 5		12	8
17	**FAT2Q**	**A**	**Sholing**	**174**	**W 2 - 0**	**Hamilton 25 Knight 30**		9
24	StHD1C	H	Thame United	125	W 3 - 2	Middleshurst 12 Hamilton 44 Knight 89 (pen)	9	10
30	**FAT3Q**	**H**	**North Leigh**	**398**	**L 1 - 4**	**Knight 55**		11
Nov 2	StHD1C	A	Coleshill Town	247	L 0 - 2		14	12

Goalscorers	LGE	FAC	FAT	SG	HAT	PEN	1Q	2Q	45+	3Q	4Q	90+	T
TOTALS	13	3	3		0	1	5	5	0	4	4	1	19
Knight	3	2	2	6		1	1	1		3	2		7
Alexander	3			3			3						3
Hamilton	1		1	2				2					2
Mahon	2			1						1	1		2
Sheppard	2			1				1				1	2
Ballard	1			1				1					1
Killie		1		1							1		1
Middlehurst	1			1			1						1

WELWYN GARDEN CITY MATCH RESULTS 2020-21

Date	Comp	H/A	Opponents	Att:	Result	Goalscorers	Pos	No.
Sept 12	**FACP**	**H**	**Saffron Walden Town**	**181**	**W 2 - 0**			1
19	SthD1C	A	Wantage Town	90	L 0 - 2		17	2
22	**FAC1Q**	**H**	**Bishop's Stortford**	**210**	**D 1 - 1**	**(Lost 3-4 on pens)**		3
29	SthD1C	H	Biggleswade	146	W 3 - 0	Ironton 25 90 Bailey 78	8	4
Oct 10	SthD1C	A	Thame United (5)	147	W 1 - 0	Opoku 67	10	5
13	SthD1C	A	St Neots Town	230	W 3 - 2	Bailey 70 82 (pen) Close 85	5	6
17	**FAT2Q**	**A**	**Haywards Heath Town**	**163**	**W 4 - 1**			7
24	SthD1C	H	Kempston Rovers	145	D 1 - 1	Vasey 6	8	8
31	**FAT3Q**	**A**	**Horsham**	**473**	**D 1 - 1**	**(Won 5-3 on pens)**		9
Nov 3	SthD1C	A	Bedworth United	153	L 2 - 3	Templeton 16 (og) Vasey 24	11	10
Dec 8	**FAT1P**	**H**	**Hednesford Town**	**119**	**W 3 - 1**			11
15	**FAT2P**	**H**	**Burgess Hill Town**	**216**	**W 2 - 1**	**Close 7 Mensah 31**		12
19	**FAT3P**	**H**	**Aldershot Town**		**L 1 - 5**	**Kinoshi 85**		13

Goalscorers	LGE	FAC	FAT	SG	HAT	PEN	1Q	2Q	45+	3Q	4Q	90+	T
TOTALS	10	3	11		0	1	3	3	0	1	5	1	24
Bailey	3			2		1					3		3
Close	1		1	2			1				1		2
Ironton	2			1				1				1	2
Vasey	2			2			1	1					2
Kinoshi			1	1							1		1
Mensah			1	1				1					1
Opoku	1			1						1			1
Opponent	1			1			1						1

YAXLEY MATCH RESULTS 2020-21

Date	Comp	H/A	Opponents	Att:	Result	Goalscorers	Pos	No.
Sept 12	**FACP**	**H**	**Stowmarket Town**	**133**	**L 1 - 2**	**Waumsley 90+4**		1
19	SthD1C	A	Halesowen Town	400	L 1 - 7	Sanders 33	20	2
26	SthD1C	H	St Neots Town	142	D 2 - 2	Gothard 2 MacLeod 26	13	3
Oct 3	SthD1C	H	Didcot Town	99	W 2 - 1	MacLeod 13 Sanders 69	8	4
10	SthD1C	A	Kempston Rovers	102	D 3 - 3	Waumsley 30 79 Hook 90	15	5
17	**FAT2Q**	**H**	**Chasetown**			**Match cancelled - Yaxley progressed to the next round.**		6
24	SthD1C	H	Bedford Town	278	L 0 - 1		19	7
27	SthD1C	H	North Leigh	69	W 5 - 0	Cotton 23 36 57 MacLeod 29 Waumsley 55		8
31	**FAT3Q**	**H**	**Grantham Town**	**119**	**L 0 - 2**			9

Goalscorers	LGE	FAC	FAT	SG	HAT	PEN	1Q	2Q	45+	3Q	4Q	90+	T
TOTALS	13	1	0		1	0	2	6	0	2	2	2	14
Waumsley	3	1		3				1		1	1	1	4
Cotton	3			1	1			2		1			3
MacLeod	3			3			1	2					3
Sanders	2			2				1			1		2
Gothard	1			1			1						1
Hook	1			1								1	1

AFC TOTTON MATCH RESULTS 2020-21

Date	Comp	H/A	Opponents	Att:	Result		Goalscorers	Pos	No.
Sept 12	**FACP**	**A**	**Binfield**	**220**	**L**	**1 - 5**	**Feeney 4**		1
19	SthD1S	H	Barnstaple Town	326	**W**	3 - 0	Masterton 40 Byrne 45 Feeney 85	2	2
26	SthD1S	H	Bideford	234	D	1 - 1	Williams 38	1	3
30	SthD1S	A	Willand Rovers	98	**W**	5 - 0	Williams 11 68 Feeney 39 Read 69 Taylor 75	1	4
Oct 6	SthD1S	H	Winchester City	368	L	1 - 2	Williams 40		5
10	SthD1S	H	Bristol Manor Farm	375	**W**	3 - 0	Taylor 17 Williams 35 45	3	6
17	**FAT2Q**	**H**	**Frome Town**	**252**	**D**	**2 - 2**	**Oatley (Fk) Masterton (Fk) (Lost 5-6 on pens)**		7
21	SthD1S	A	Larkhall Athletic	105	**W**	3 - 1	Feeney 39 Taylor 73 Kasimu 90+2	1	8
24	SthD1S	A	Basingstoke Town	400	**W**	3 - 2	Feeney 27 Read 42 Griffin 75	1	9
31	SthD1S	A	Thatcham Town	227	**W**	2 - 1	Griffin 65 Kasimu 77	2	10
Nov 3	SthD1S	A	Frome Town	367	D	1 - 1	Kasimu 64	2	11

Goalscorers	LGE	FAC	FAT	SG	HAT	PEN	1Q	2Q	45+	3Q	4Q	90+	T
TOTALS	22	1	2		0	0	3	8	2	2	7	1	25
Williams	6			4			1	3	1		1		6
Feeney	4	1		4			1	3			1		5
Kasimu	3			3						1	1	1	3
Taylor	3			3			1				2		3
Griffin	2			2						1	1		2
Masterton	1		1	2				1					2
Read	2			2				1			1		2
Byrne	1			1					1				1
Oatley			1	1									1

BARNSTPLE TOWN MATCH RESULTS 2020-21

Date	Comp	H/A	Opponents	Att:	Result		Goalscorers	Pos	No.
Sept 12	**FACP**	**H**	**Helston Athletic**	**115**	**W**	**2 - 0**	**Clarke Bello 80**		1
19	SthD1S	A	AFC Totton	326	L	0 - 3		19	2
22	**FAC1Q**	**H**	**Wimborne Town**	**147**	**L**	**2 - 3**	**Cooper (pen) Clarke 90**		3
29	SthD1S	H	Cinderford Town	121	L	2 - 3	Cooper 40 82	19	4
Oct 3	SthD1S	H	Basingstoke Town	107	D	2 - 2	Ofori 14 Cooper 53	18	5
6	SthD1S	A	Bristol Manor Farm	210	D	2 - 2	Ofori 17 Hopcroft 40		6
10	SthD1S	A	Slimbridge	83	L	1 - 4	Bello 62	19	7
17	**FAT2Q**	**A**	**Larkhall Athletic**	**120**	**L**	**0 - 5**			8
24	SthD1S	H	Willand Rovers	170	L	2 - 8	Bello 8 Guppy 80 (og)	19	9

Goalscorers	LGE	FAC	FAT	SG	HAT	PEN	1Q	2Q	45+	3Q	4Q	90+	T
TOTALS	9	4	0		0	1	3	2	0	2	3	1	13
Cooper	3	1		3		1		1		1	1		4
Bello	2	1		3			1			1	1		3
Clarke		2		1								1	2
Ofori	2			2			2						2
Hopcroft	1			1				1					1
Opponent	1			1							1		1

BASINGSTOKE TOWN MATCH RESULTS 2020-21

Date	Comp	H/A	Opponents	Att:	Result	Goalscorers	Pos	No.
Sept 1	**FACEP**	**H**	**Bournemouth**	**200**	**D 1 - 1**	**(Won 5-4 on pens)**		1
14	**FACP**	**H**	**Chichester City**		**D 2 - 2**	**Wilson 33 Hallahan 43 (pen) (Lost 1-3 on pens)**		2
19	SthD1S	A	Slimbridge	148	W 6 - 3	Reid 55 Hallahan 67 73 Palmer 69 76 Ive 90+2	1	3
30	SthD1S	A	Larkhall Athletic	125	W 2 - 1	Hallahan 18 90+4 (pen)	3	4
Oct 3	SthD1S	A	Barnstaple Town	107	D 2 - 2	Palmer 43 Armsworth 62	3	5
6	SthD1S	H	Sholing	248	W 2 - 1	Reid 25 53		6
10	SthD1S	A	Cinderford Town	172	W 6 - 3	Wilson 22 46 54 Cook 32 Ive 44 Hallahan 90	1	7
17	**FAT2Q**	**A**	**Moneyfields**	**198**	**L 1 - 2**	**Cook 34**		8
24	SthD1S	H	AFC Totton	400	L 2 - 3	Zubar 73 (og) Cook 90+6	4	9
27	SthD1S	H	Mangotsfield United	400	W 3 - 0	Wilson 5 Reid 6 Dallimore 35		10

Goalscorers	LGE	FAC	FAT	SG	HAT	PEN	1Q	2Q	45+	3Q	4Q	90+	T
TOTALS	23	3	1		1	2	4	8	0	6	4	4	27
Hallahan	5	1		4		2	1	1		1	1	2	6
Wilson	4	1		3	1		2	1		2			5
Reid	4			3			1	1		2			4
Cook	2		1	3				2				1	3
Palmer	3			2				1			2		3
Ive	2			2				1				1	2
Armsworth	1			1						1			1
Dallimore	1			1				1					1
Opponent	1			1							1		1

BIDEFORD MATCH RESULTS 2020-21

Date	Comp	H/A	Opponents	Att:	Result	Goalscorers	Pos	No.
Sept 12	**FACP**	**H**	**Wells City**	**234**	**W 3 - 0**	**Down 9 Brown 13 (og) Roseenquest 81**	9	1
19	SthD1S	H	Larkhall Athletic	236	D 2 - 2	Turner 13 (pen) 40	9	2
23	**FAC1Q**	**A**	**Tiverton Town**	**331**	**L 0 - 2**			3
26	SthD1S	A	AFC Totton	234	D 1 - 1	Turner 63	12	4
30	SthD1S	A	Paulson Rovers	91	L 0 - 1		14	5
Oct 3	SthD1S	H	Slimbridge	179	D 2 - 2	Carter 42 82	14	6
6	SthD1S	H	Frome Town	152	L 0 - 1			7
10	SthD1S	H	Thatcham Town	227	D 2 - 2	Carter 74 Rosenquest 90	18	8
17	**FAT2Q**	**H**	**Slimbridge**	**200**	**W 3 - 2**	**Down 11 Carter 26 29**		9
31	**FAT3Q**	**A**	**Yate Town**			**Walkover**		10
Dec 5	**FAT1P**	**A**	**Evesham United**	**309**	**D 1 - 1**	**Wilson (Lost 4-5 on pens)**		11

Goalscorers	LGE	FAC	FAT	SG	HAT	PEN	1Q	2Q	45+	3Q	4Q	90+	T
TOTALS	7	3	4		0	1	4	4	0	1	4	1	14
Carter	3		2	3				3			2		5
Turner	3			2		1	1	1		1			3
Down		1	1	2			2						2
Rosenquest	1	1		2							1	1	2
Opponent		1		1			1						1
Wilson			1	1							1		1

BRISTOL MANOR FARM MATCH RESULTS 2020-21

Date	Comp	H/A	Opponents	Att:	Result	Goalscorers	Pos	No.
Sept 12	**FACP**	**A**	**Cadbury Heath**	**172**	**W 5 - 1**	**Bryant 30 Grubb x2 Leigh-Gilchrist x2**		1
19	SthD1S	H	Cirencester Town	230	L 0 - 2		17	2
22	**FAC1Q**	**A**	**Yate Town**	**303**	**W 2 - 1**	**Vowles 20 Bamford 60**		3
26	SthD1S	H	Highworth Town	176	W 3 - 2	Leigh-Gilchrist 12 Vowles 29 90	11	4
30	SthD1S	A	Slimbridge	156	W 3 - 1	Vowles 7 20 (pen) 83	7	5
Oct 3	**FAC2Q**	**A**	**Kidlington**	**294**	**D 1 - 1**	**Bryant (Won 7-6 on pens)**		6
6	SthD1S	H	Barnstaple Town	210	D 2 - 2	Day 45 Bamford 53		7
10	SthD1S	A	AFC Totton	375	L 0 - 3		12	8
13	**FAC3Q**	**H**	**Cray Wanderers**	**392**	**D 3 - 3**	**Day Bryant Vowles 70 (Lost 2-4 on pens)**		9
17	**FAT2Q**	**A**	**Willand Rovers**	**157**	**L 1 - 2**	**Bamford**		10
20	SthD1S	A	Winchester City	178	L 2 - 3	Adams 35 Spencer 64	12	11
Nov 3	SthD1S	A	Thatcham Town	165	W 2 - 1	Adams 7 45	11	12

Goalscorers	LGE	FAC	FAT	SG	HAT	PEN	1Q	2Q	45+	3Q	4Q	90+	T
TOTALS	12	11	1		1	1	5	3	2	3	2	1	24
Vowles	5	2		4	1	1	3	1			2	1	7
Adams	3			2			1	1	1				3
Bamford	1	1	1	3						2			3
Bryant		3		3				1					3
Leigh-Gilchrist	1	2		2			1						3
Day	1	1		2					1				2
Grubb		2		1									2
Spencer	1			1						1			1

CINDERFORD TOWN MATCH RESULTS 2020-21

Date	Comp	H/A	Opponents	Att:	Result	Goalscorers	Pos	No.
Sept 12	**FACP**	**A**	**Brimscombe & Thrupp**	**177**	**W 2 - 1**	**Drew Lomety**		1
19	SthD1S	H	Moneyfields	140	W 2 - 1	Drew 26 47	5	2
22	**FAC1Q**	**H**	**Royal Wootton Bassett**	**184**	**D 2 - 2**	**Alder Davies(Lost 5-6 on pens)**		3
29	SthD1S	A	Barnstaple Town	121	W 3 - 2	Drew 6 71 (pens) Davies 90+2	4	4
Oct 3	SthD1S	A	Cirencester Town	145	L 0 - 4		8	5
6	SthD1S	H	Paulson Rovers	122	L 0 - 5			6
10	SthD1S	H	Basingstoke Town	172	L 3 - 6	Spurrier 41 75 Gibbons 77	13	7
17	**FAT2Q**	**A**	**Mangotsfield United**	**174**	**W 2 - 1**	**MacDonald Gibbons**		8
24	SthD1S	A	Evesham United	245	D 1 - 1	Drew 45	14	9
27	SthD1S	H	Winchester City	153	L 1 - 2	Alder 14		10

Goalscorers	LGE	FAC	FAT	SG	HAT	PEN	1Q	2Q	45+	3Q	4Q	90+	T
TOTALS	10	4	2		0	0	3	1	1	1	3	1	16
Drew	5	1		4			2		1	1	1		6
Alder	1	1		2			1						2
Davies	1	1		2								1	2
Gibbons	1		1	2							1		2
Spurrier	2			1				1			1		2
Lomety		1		1									1
MacDonald			1	1									1

CIRENCESTER TOWN MATCH RESULTS 2020-21

Date	Comp	H/A	Opponents	Att:	Result	Goalscorers	Pos	No.
Sept 12	**FACP**	**A**	**Flackwell Heath**	**95**	**W 3 - 0**	**Dennis 60 Parsons 63 (pen) Anderson 89**		1
19	SthD1S	A	Bristol Manor Farm	230	W 2 - 0	James 48 50	4	2
22	**FAC1Q**	**A**	**Saltash United**		**L 1 - 3**	**Gabriel 25 (pen)**		3
26	**FAT1Q**	**H**	**Paulton Rovers**	**100**	**D 1 - 1**	**Gray 76 (Won 5-4 on pens)**		4
29	SthD1S	H	Thatcham Town	96	W 2 - 0	Brennan 52 Nelmes 57	2	5
Oct 3	SthD1S	H	Cinderford Town	145	W 4 - 0	Parsons 12 30 Spurrier 19 (og) Gray 46	1	6
6	SthD1S	A	Melksham Town	302	W 4 - 0	Gray 4 Parsons 26 Dennis 73 Nelmes 80	1	7
10	SthD1S	H	Sholing	194	L 0 - 2		2	8
17	**FAT2Q**	**A**	**Thame United**	**160**	**L 1 - 4**	**Parsons 14**		9
24	SthD1S	A	Frome Town	325	W 2 - 1	Bennett 10 Dennis 65	2	10
27	SthD1S	H	Willand Rovers	220	W 3 - 0	Irving 7 Shepherd 62 Parsons 75		11
31	SthD1S	A	Mangotsfield United	230	W 3 - 0	Parsons 25 45 Bennett 86	1	12
Nov 4	SthD1S	A	Paulton Rovers	138	W 6 - 1	Turley 24 Parsons 45 50 Twiggs 57 (og) Gabriel 81 Anderson 89	1	13

Goalscorers	LGE	FAC	FAT	SG	HAT	PEN	1Q	2Q	45+	3Q	4Q	90+	T
TOTALS	26	4	2		0	2	7	4	2	11	8	0	32
Parsons	8	1	1	7		1	3	2	2	2	1		10
Dennis	2	1		3						2	1		3
Gray	2		1	3			1			1	1		3
Anderson	1	1		2							2		2
Bennett	2			2			1				1		2
Gabriel	1	1		2		1		1			1		2
James	2			1						2			2
Nelmes	2			2						1	1		2
Opponent	2			2			1			1			2
Brennan	1			1						1			1
Irving	1			1			1						1
Shepherd	1			1						1			1
Turley	1			1				1					1

EVESHAM UNITED MATCH RESULTS 2020-21

Date	Comp	H/A	Opponents	Att:	Result	Goalscorers	Pos	No.
Sept 19	SthD1S	H	Sholing	252	L 0 - 3		20	1
22	**FAC1Q**	**A**	**Daventry Town**	**195**	**W 2 - 0**	**Lucas 23 Basford 72**		2
26	**FAT1Q**	**H**	**Biggleswade**	**271**	**W 2 - 1**	**Basford 2 (pen) 60**		3
29	SthD1S	A	Frome Town	286	D 2 - 2	Lucas 27 31	17	4
Oct 3	**FAC2Q**	**A**	**Tamworth**	**496**	**L 1 - 3**	**Horrell 55 (pen)**		5
5	SthD1S	H	Larkhall Athletic	183	L 0 - 1		18	6
10	SthD1S	A	Winchester City	244	W 1 - 0	Hunt 21	15	7
17	**FAT2Q**	**H**	**Carlton Town**	**269**	**W 2 - 0**	**Paddock 18 Lymn 24**		8
21	SthD1S	A	Paulton Rovers	117	W 1 - 0	Lucas 85	12	9
24	SthD1S	H	Cinderford Town	245	D 1 - 1	Horrell 52	12	10
31	**FAT3Q**	**H**	**Leek Town**	**271**	**W 3 - 2**	**Franklin 14 25 55**		11
Dec 5	**FAT1P**	**H**	**Bideford**	**309**	**D 1 - 1**	**Lucas 76 (Won 5-4 on pens)**		12
14	**FAT2P**	**H**	**Boston United**	**370**	**L 0 - 3**			13

Goalscorers	LGE	FAC	FAT	SG	HAT	PEN	1Q	2Q	45+	3Q	4Q	90+	T
TOTALS	5	3	8		1	2	5	4	0	4	3	0	16
Lucas	3	1	1	3			1	2			2		5
Basford		1	2	2		1	1			1	1		3
Franklin			3	1	1		1	1		1			3
Horrell	1	1		2		1				2			2
Hunt	1			1			1						1
Lymn			1	1				1					1
Paddock			1	1			1						1

FROME TOWN MATCH RESULTS 2020-21

Date	Comp	H/A	Opponents	Att:	Result	Goalscorers	Pos	No.
Sept 12	**FACP**	**H**	**Bodmin Town**	**245**	**W 3 - 0**	**Simpson x3**		1
19	SthD1S	A	Mangotsfield Town	220	W 1 - 0	Mannings 63	7	2
22	**FAC1Q**	**H**	**AFC Stoneham**	**238**	**W 4 - 1**	**Jackson O'Loughlin Simpson Davies**		3
29	SthD1S	H	Evesham United	286	D 2 - 2	Jackson 8 Monks 89	6	4
Oct 3	**FAC2Q**	**H**	**Larkhall Athletic**	**345**	**D 1 - 1**	**Davies (Lost 3-4 on pens)**		5
6	SthD1S	A	Bideford	152	W 1 - 0	Simpson 27		6
10	SthD1S	A	Willand Rovers	145	L 1 - 2	Davies 34	11	7
17	**FAT2Q**	**A**	**AFC Totton**	**252**	**D 2 - 2**	**Davies Mannings (Won 6-5 on pens)**		8
20	SthD1S	H	Highworth Town	298	W 5 - 0	Simpson 3 68 Witcombe 63 Davis 80 Ollis 90+2	5	9
24	SthD1S	H	Cirencester Town	325	L 1 - 2	Hobbs 21	8	10
31	**FAT3Q**	**H**	**Farnborough**	**253**	**W 3 - 0**	**Mannings x2 Davies**		11
Nov 3	SthD1S	H	AFC Totton	367	D 1 - 1	Simpson 7	9	12
Dec 8	**FAT1P**	**A**	**North Leigh**		**W 1 - 0**	**Davies**		13
15	**FAT2P**	**H**	**Hampton & Richmond B.**			**Walkover**		14
23	**FAT3P**	**A**	**Maidstone United**			**Walkover for Maidstone - Frome unable to fulfil fixture**		15

Goalscorers	LGE	FAC	FAT	SG	HAT	PEN	1Q	2Q	45+	3Q	4Q	90+	T
TOTALS	12	8	6		3	0	4	2	0	2	3	1	26
Simpson	4	4		5	3		2	1			1		8
Davies	1	2	3	4				1					6
Mannings	1		3	3						1			4
Jackson	1	1		2			1						2
Davis	1			1							1		1
Hobbs	1			1			1						1
Monks	1			1							1		1
O'Loughlin		1		1									1
Ollis	1			1								1	1
Witcombe	1			1						1			1

HIGHWORTH TOWN MATCH RESULTS 2020-21

Date	Comp	H/A	Opponents	Att:	Result	Goalscorers	Pos	No.
Sept 12	**FACP**	**A**	**Holmer Green**	**166**	**W 2 - 0**			1
19	SthD1S	H	Willand Rovers	165	W 1 - 0	Edenborough 86	8	2
23	**FAC1Q**	**H**	**Melksham Town**	**149**	**D 1 - 1**	**(Lost 4-5 on pens)**		3
26	SthD1S	A	Bristol Manor Farm	176	L 2 - 3	McGhee-Parsons 25 Edenborough 49	9	4
29	SthD1S	A	Sholing	150	L 2 - 3	Cheetham 44 Stanners 48	10	5
Oct 3	SthD1S	H	Paulton Rovers	78	W 2 - 1	Selman 13 Dean 87	7	6
7	SthD1S	H	Slimbridge	135	D 2 - 2	Jackson 29 Morrison 80	8	7
10	SthD1S	A	Melksham Town	397	W 1 - 0	McGhee-Parsons 32	5	8
17	**FAT2Q**	**H**	**Winchester City**	**124**	**W 2 - 1**			9
20	SthD1S	A	Frome Town	298	L 0 - 5			10
24	SthD1S	H	Winchester City	128	W 1 - 0	Edenborough 83	6	11
31	**FAT3Q**	**H**	**Swindon Supermarine**	**302**	**L 2 - 3**			12

Goalscorers	LGE	FAC	FAT	SG	HAT	PEN	1Q	2Q	45+	3Q	4Q	90+	T
TOTALS	11	3	4		0	0	1	3	0	3	4	0	18
Edenborough	3			3						1	2		3
McGhee-Parsons	2			2				1		1			2
Cheetham	1			1				1					1
Dean	1			1							1		1
Jackson	1			1				1					1
Morrison	1			1							1		1
Selman	1			1			1						1
Stanners	1			1						1			1

LARKHALL ATHLETIC MATCH RESULTS 2020-21

Date	Comp	H/A	Opponents	Att:	Result	Goalscorers	Pos	No.
Sept 12	**FACP**	**A**	**Newton Abbot Spurs**	**190**	**W 4 - 0**	**Powell x3 Demkiv**		1
19	SthD1S	A	Bideford	236	D 2 - 2	Norris 47 Camm 56	10	2
23	**FAC1Q**	**H**	**Bitton AFC**	**221**	**W 3 - 2**	**Powell x2 Lambert**		3
26	SthD1S	A	Willand Rovers	105	L 0 - 2		15	4
30	SthD1S	H	Basingstoke Town	125	L 1 - 2	Lambert 74	16	5
Oct 3	**FAC2Q**	**A**	**Frome Town**	**345**	**D 1 - 1**	**Powell (Won 4-3 on pens)**		6
5	SthD1S	A	Evesham Town	183	W 1 - 0	Lambert 38	11	7
10	SthD1S	H	Mangotsfield United	210	W 3 - 0	Powell 32 Baker 37 Tumelty 39	10	8
13	**FAC3Q**	**A**	**Weston-s-Mare**	**584**	**L 0 - 6**			9
17	**FAT2Q**	**H**	**Barnstaple Town**	**120**	**W 5 - 0**	**Baker Powell x2 (1 pen) Tumelty Thompson**		10
21	SthD1S	H	AFC Totton	105	L 1 - 3	Powell 15	11	11
24	SthD1S	A	Paulton Rovers	136	W 3 - 2	Baker 89 Britton 90 Thompson 90+1	10	12
31	**FAT3Q**	**A**	**Weston-s-Mare**		**L 1 - 2**	**Lambert 71**		13

Goalscorers	LGE	FAC	FAT	SG	HAT	PEN	1Q	2Q	45+	3Q	4Q	90+	T
TOTALS	11	8	6		1	1	1	4	0	2	3	2	25
Powell	2	6	2	5	1	1	1	1					10
Lambert	2	1	1	4				1			2		4
Baker	2		1	3				1			1		3
Thompson	1		1	2								1	2
Tumelty	1		1	2				1					2
Britton	1			1								1	1
Camm	1			1						1			1
Demkiv		1		1									1
Norris	1			1						1			1

MANGOTSFIELD UNITED MATCH RESULTS 2020-21

Date	Comp	H/A	Opponents	Att:	Result	Goalscorers	Pos	No.
Sept 12	**FACP**	**A**	**Tavistock**	**161**	**L 1 - 2**	**Kelly 64**		1
19	SthD1S	H	Frome Town	220	L 0 - 1		15	2
29	SthD1S	A	Winchester City	158	L 1 - 5	Simons 56	20	3
Oct 6	SthD1S	H	Willand Rovers	148	L 1 - 2	Simons 44		4
10	SthD1S	A	Larkhall Athletic	210	L 0 - 3		20	5
17	**FAT2Q**	**H**	**Cinderford Town**	**174**	**L 1 - 2**	**Binding 77**		6
24	SthD1S	H	Slimbridge	165	L 2 - 3	Noad 43 Nderemani 84	20	7
27	SthD1S	A	Basingstoke Town	400	L 0 - 3			8
31	SthD1S	H	Cirencester Town	230	L 0 - 3		20	9

Goalscorers	LGE	FAC	FAT	SG	HAT	PEN	1Q	2Q	45+	3Q	4Q	90+	T
TOTALS	4	1	1		0	0	0	2	0	2	2	0	6
Simons	2			2				1		1			2
Binding			1	1							1		1
Kelly		1		1						1			1
Nderemani	1			1							1		1
Noad	1			1				1					1

MELKSHAM TOWN MATCH RESULTS 2020-21

Date	Comp	H/A	Opponents	Att:	Result	Goalscorers	Pos	No.
Sept 12	**FACP**	**A**	**Exmouth Town**	**297**	**W 2 - 0**			1
19	SthD1S	H	Winchester City	390	L 1 - 2	Ormrod 55	13	2
23	**FAC1Q**	**A**	**Highworth Town**	**149**	**D 1 - 1**	**(Won 5-4 on pens)**		3
26	**FAT1Q**	**H**	**North Leigh**	**253**	**D 3 - 3**	**(Lost 4-5 on pens)**		4
29	SthD1S	A	Moneyfields	113	W 2 - 0	Ball 39 40	8	5
Oct 3	**FAC2Q**	**A**	**Wimborne Town**	**183**	**D 0 - 0**	**(Lost 4-5 on pens)**		6
6	SthD1S	H	Cirencester Town	302	L 0 - 4			7
10	SthD1S	H	Highworth Town (8)	397	L 0 - 1		17	8
21	SthD1S	A	Slimbridge	126	L 2 - 4	Barcelos 16 50	17	9
24	SthD1S	A	Thatcham Town	162	L 0 - 3		18	10

Goalscorers	LGE	FAC	FAT	SG	HAT	PEN	1Q	2Q	45+	3Q	4Q	90+	T
TOTALS	5	3	3		0	0	1	2	0	2	0	0	11
TBall	2			1				2					2
Barcelos	2			1			1			1			2
Ormrod	1			1						1			1

MONEYFIELDS MATCH RESULTS 2020-21

Date	Comp	H/A	Opponents	Att:	Result	Goalscorers	Pos	No.
Sept 12	**FACP**	**H**	**Camberley Town**	**164**	**W 4 - 2**	**Barker 28 Briggs 63 Hutchings 75 Roberts 86**		1
19	SthD1S	A	Cinderford Town	140	L 1 - 2	Barker 62	14	2
22	**FAC1Q**	**A**	**Aylesbury United**	**112**	**D 2 - 2**	**Hutchings 54 (pen) 68 (Won 4-3 on pens)**		3
29	SthD1S	H	Melksham Town	113	L 0 - 2		18	4
Oct 3	**FAC2Q**	**H**	**Cray Wanderers**	**194**	**L 2 - 6**			5
6	SthD1S	A	Thatcham Town	124	W 5 - 1	Hutchings 2 17 Bailey 32 Roberts 35 76		6
17	**FAT2Q**	**H**	**Basingstoke Town**	**196**	**W 2 - 1**	**Roberts x2**		7
31	**FAT3Q**	**H**	**Kidlington**		**W 3 - 2**	**Roberts 41 90+1 Hutchings 90+4**		8
Dec 5	**FAT1P**	**H**	**Truro City**	**237**	**L 1 - 5**			9

Goalscorers	LGE	FAC	FAT	SG	HAT	PEN	1Q	2Q	45+	3Q	4Q	90+	T
TOTALS	6	8	6		0	1	2	4	0	3	4	2	20
Roberts	2	1	4	4				2			2	1	7
Hutchings	2	3	1	4		1	2			1	2	1	6
Barker	1	1		2				1		1			2
Bailey	1			1				1					1
Briggs		1		1						1			1

PAULTON ROVERS MATCH RESULTS 2020-21

Date	Comp	H/A	Opponents	Att:	Result	Goalscorers	Pos	No.
Sept 12	**FACP**	**A**	**Saltash United**	**166**	**L 0 - 1**			1
19	SthD1S	A	Thatcham Town	132	D 0 - 0		11	2
26	**FAT1Q**	**A**	**Cirencester Town**	**100**	**D 1 - 1**	**Cottle 37 (Lost 4-5 pens)**		3
30	SthD1S	H	Bideford	91	W 1 - 0	O'Hare 90	9	4
Oct 3	SthD1S	A	Highworth Town	78	L 1 - 2	Gay 11	10	5
6	SthD1S	A	Cinderford Town	122	W 5 - 0	Felix 14 Hailston 25 43 Gay 61 Ibrahim 90		6
21	SthD1S	H	Evesham United	117	L 0 - 1		7	7
24	SthD1S	H	Larkhall Athletic	136	L 2 - 3	Allan 42 Cottle 85	9	8
31	SthD1S	H	Slimbridge	125	W 3 - 1	Deakin 34 (og) O'Hare 67 Hailston 69	6	9
Nov 4	SthD1S	H	Cirencester Town	138	L 1 - 6	O'Hare 83	6	10

Goalscorers	LGE	FAC	FAT	SG	HAT	PEN	1Q	2Q	45+	3Q	4Q	90+	T
TOTALS	13	0	1		0	0	2	5	0	2	3	2	14
Hailston	3			2				2			1		3
O'Hare	3			3						1	1	1	3
Cottle	1		1	2				1			1		2
Gay	2			2			1			1			2
Allan	1			1				1					1
Felix	1			1			1						1
Ibrahim	1			1								1	1
Opponent	1			1				1					1

SHOLING MATCH RESULTS 2020-21

Date	Comp	H/A	Opponents	Att:	Result	Goalscorers	Pos	No.
Sept 12	**FACP**	**A**	**Bemerton Heath Harlequins**	**101**	**W 1 - 0**	**Green 55**		1
19	SthD1S	A	Evesham United	252	W 3 - 0	Herbert 22 Mason 25 Green 39	3	2
22	**FAC1Q**	**A**	**Fairford Town**	**150**	**W 2 - 1**	**Mason 58 (pen) Watts 81**		3
26	SthD1S	H	Slimbridge	220	L 0 - 2		10	4
29	SthD1S	H	Highworth Town	150	W 3 - 2	Green 38 90+2 McLean 41	3	5
Oct 3	**FAC2Q**	**A**	**Saltash United**	**300**	**W 3 - 1**	**Mason 11 40 (pen) 60**		6
6	SthD1S	A	Basingstoke Town	248	L 1 - 2	Green 82		7
10	SthD1S	A	Cirencester Town	194	W 2 - 0	Targett 81 McLean 86	8	8
13	**FAC3Q**	**H**	**Walton Casuals**	**341**	**W 5 - 2**	**Green 4 38 Wagstaffe 47 Mason 52 (pen) Targett 68**		9
17	**FAT2Q**	**H**	**Wantage Town**	**174**	**L 0 - 2**			10
24	**FAC4Q**	**H**	**Torquay United**	**400**	**L 0 - 2**			11

Goalscorers	LGE	FAC	FAT	SG	HAT	PEN	1Q	2Q	45+	3Q	4Q	90+	T
TOTALS	9	11	0		1	3	3	6	0	5	5	1	20
Green	4	3		5			1	3		1	1	1	7
Mason	1	5		4	1	3	1	2		3			6
McLean	2			2				1			1		2
Targett	1	1		2							2		2
Herbert	1			1			1						1
Wagstaffe		1		1						1			1
Watts		1		1							1		1

SLIMBRIDGE MATCH RESULTS 2020-21

Date	Comp	H/A	Opponents	Att:	Result		Goalscorers	Pos	No.
Sept 12	**FACP**	**A**	**Northwood**	**153**	**D**	**1 - 1**	**Martin 80 (Lost 2-4 on pens)**		1
19	SthD1S	H	Basingstoke Town	148	L	3 - 6	Martin 3 King 18 Mbunga 44	18	2
26	SthD1S	A	Sholing	220	**W**	2 - 0	Mbunga 36 Malshanskyj 74	8	3
30	SthD1S	H	Bristol Manor Farm	156	L	1 - 3	King 34 (pen)	12	4
Oct 3	SthD1S	A	Bideford	179	D	2 - 2	Hawes 5 Malshanskyj 11	11	5
7	SthD1S	A	Highworth Town	135	D	2 - 2	Malshanskyj 43 Flo 60	12	6
10	SthD1S	H	Barnstaple Town	83	**W**	4 - 1	Flo 13 40 White 61 Hawes 89	9	7
17	**FAT2Q**	**A**	**Bideford**	**200**	**L**	**2 - 3**	**Malshanskyj 17 King 67**		8
21	SthD1S	H	Melksham Town	126	**W**	4 - 2	White 8 Hawes 45 Mbunga 49 Martin 90+3	5	9
24	SthD1S	A	Mangotsfield United	165	**W**	3 - 2	Malshanskyj 20 Flo 79 King 90+2	3	10
31	SthD1S	A	Paulton Rovers	125	L	1 - 3	Hawes 44	5	11

Goalscorers	LGE	FAC	FAT	SG	HAT	PEN	1Q	2Q	45+	3Q	4Q	90+	T
TOTALS	22	1	2		0	1	8	6	1	4	4	2	25
Malshanskyj	4		1	5			3	1			1		5
Flo	4			3			1	1		1	1		4
Hawes	4			4			1	1	1		1		4
King	3		1	4		1	1	1		1		1	4
Martin	2	1		3			1				1	1	3
Mbunga	3			3				2		1			3
White	2			2			1			1			2

THATCHAM TOWN MATCH RESULTS 2020-21

Date	Comp	H/A	Opponents	Att:	Result		Goalscorers	Pos	No.
Sept 12	**FACP**	**H**	**AFC Dunstable**	**129**	**L**	**1 - 5**	**Lynch 74 (pen)**		1
19	SthD1S	H	Paulton Rovers	132	D	0 - 0		12	2
29	SthD1S	A	Cirencester Town	96	L	0 - 2		16	3
Oct 3	SthD1S	A	Willand Rovers	70	D	0 - 0		15	4
6	SthD1S	H	Moneyfields	124	L	1 - 5	Alves 6		5
10	SthD1S	A	Bideford (15)	227	D	2 - 2	Lynch 55 77	14	6
17	**FAT2Q**	**H**	**North Leigh**	**186**	**L**	**2 - 4**	**Gwavava 3 Branker 19**		7
24	SthD1S	H	Melksham Town	162	**W**	3 - 0	Lynch 64 80 90+4	15	8
31	SthD1S	H	AFC Totton	227	L	1 - 2	Smith 2	15	9
Nov 3	SthD1S	H	Bristol Manor Farm	165	L	1 - 2	Lynch 18	15	10

Goalscorers	LGE	FAC	FAT	SG	HAT	PEN	1Q	2Q	45+	3Q	4Q	90+	T
TOTALS	8	1	2		1	1	5	0	0	2	3	1	11
Lynch	6	1		4	1	1	1			2	3	1	7
Alves	1			1			1						1
Branker			1	1			1						1
Gwavava			1	1			1						1
Smith	1			1			1						1

WILLAND ROVERS MATCH RESULTS 2020-21

Date	Comp	H/A	Opponents	Att:	Result	Goalscorers	Pos	No.
Sept 2	**FACEP**	**H**	**Bridport**	**192**	**W 2 - 1**	**Skeet 37 Veal 60**		1
12	**FACP**	**A**	**Shepton Mallet**	**224**	**L 0 - 1**			2
19	SthD1S	A	Highworth Town	165	L 0 - 1		16	3
26	SthD1S	H	Larkhall Athletic	105	W 2 - 0	Rosenwald 28 Pike 84	5	4
30	SthD1S	H	AFC Totton	98	L 0 - 5		13	5
Oct 3	SthD1S	H	Thatcham Town	70	D 0 - 0		12	6
6	SthD1S	A	Mangotsfield United	148	W 2 - 1	Kempster 50 Reay 56		7
10	SthD1S	H	Frome Town	145	W 2 - 1	Reay 19 Mouldon 75	6	8
17	**FAT2Q**	**H**	**Bristol Manor Farm**	**157**	**W 2 - 1**			9
24	SthD1S	A	Barnstaple Town	170	W 8 - 2	Richards 11 45 90 Rosenwald 16 Rice 47 Mouldon 85 Griffith 86 Skeet 90	5	10
27	SthD1S	A	Circenster Town	220	L 0 - 3			11
Dec 8	**FAT1P**	**A**	**Poole Town**	**257**	**L 1 - 3**			12

Goalscorers	LGE	FAC	FAT	SG	HAT	PEN	1Q	2Q	45+	3Q	4Q	90+	T
TOTALS	14	2	3		1	0	3	2	1	4	4	2	19
Richards	3			1	1		1		1			1	3
Mouldon	2			2							2		2
Reay	2			2			1			1			2
Rosenwald	2			2			1	1					2
Skeet	1	1		2				1				1	2
Griffith	1			1							1		1
Kempster	1			1						1			1
Pike	1			1							1		1
Rice	1			1						1			1
Veal		1		1						1			1

WINCHESTER CITY MATCH RESULTS 2020-21

Date	Comp	H/A	Opponents	Att:	Result	Goalscorers	Pos	No.
Sept 12	**FACP**	**H**	**Corsham Town**	**163**	**W 2 - 0**	**Smith Purdy**		1
19	SthD1S	A	Melksham Town	390	W 2 - 1	Mitford 45 Barron 78	6	2
22	**FAC1Q**	**H**	**Clevedon Town**	**218**	**W 3 - 2**	**Mitford x2 Smith**		3
29	SthD1S	H	Mangotsfield United	158	W 5 - 1	Balmer 2 9 Barron 61 Douglas 65 Smith M 90	1	4
Oct 3	**FAC2Q**	**A**	**Bath City**		**L 2 - 3**	**Opponent Mitford**		5
6	SthD1S	A	AFC Totton	368	W 2 - 1	Carr 11 Griggs 70		6
10	SthD1S	H	Evesham United	244	L 0 - 1		7	7
17	**FAT2Q**	**A**	**Highworth Town**	**124**	**L 1 - 2**	**Flooks**		8
20	SthD1S	H	Bristol Manor Farm	178	W 3 - 2	Balmer 2 77 McCormick 51	3	9
24	SthD1S	A	Highworth Town	128	L 0 - 1		7	10
27	SthD1S	A	Cinderford Town	153	W 2 - 1	Balmer 29 Flooks 56		11

Goalscorers	LGE	FAC	FAT	SG	HAT	PEN	1Q	2Q	45+	3Q	4Q	90+	T
TOTALS	14	7	1		0	0	4	1	1	4	3	1	22
Balmer	5			3			3	1			1		5
Mitford	1	3		3					1				4
Smith M	1	2		3								1	3
Barron	2			2						1	1		2
Flooks	1		1	2						1			2
Carr	1			1			1						1
Douglas	1			1						1			1
Griggs	1			1							1		1
McCormick	1			1						1			1
Opponent		1		1									1
Purdy		1		1									1

COMBINED COUNTIES LEAGUE

PREMIER	P	W	D	L	F	A	GD	Pts
1 Sutton Common Rovers	13	11	2	0	35	6	29	35
2 Badshot Lea	14	10	1	3	32	19	13	31
3 Spelthorne Sports	15	9	2	4	36	13	23	29
4 Hanworth Villa	10	8	2	0	28	10	18	26
5 Southall	12	8	1	3	31	12	19	25
6 Ascot United	13	7	3	3	33	18	15	24
7 Knaphill	14	7	3	4	28	22	6	24
8 Banstead Athletic	14	5	5	4	17	14	3	20
9 Abbey Rangers	12	5	2	5	22	15	7	17
10 Sheerwater	13	5	2	6	19	17	2	17
11 Cobham	12	5	2	5	21	22	-1	17
12 Camberley Town	10	5	0	5	10	14	-4	15
13 Egham Town	13	4	2	7	19	26	-7	14
14 Redhill	13	4	2	7	23	32	-9	14
15 Colliers Wood United	14	3	3	8	17	31	-14	12
16 Frimley Green	13	3	2	8	20	36	-16	11
17 Raynes Park Vale	11	3	1	7	13	26	-13	10
18 CB Hounslow United	10	1	3	6	12	25	-13	6
19 Guildford City	9	1	1	7	8	20	-12	4
20 Molesey	15	1	1	13	6	52	-46	4

DIVISION ONE	P	W	D	L	F	A	GD	Pts
1 Farnham Town	12	10	1	1	28	11	17	31
2 Walton & Hersham	12	8	2	2	36	9	27	26
3 Westside	11	8	0	3	26	12	14	24
4 Tooting Bec	11	7	2	2	27	12	15	23
5 FC Deportivo Galicia	11	6	2	3	28	15	13	20
6 Dorking Wanderers Res	13	6	2	5	27	26	1	20
7 Epsom & Ewell	11	6	1	4	20	11	9	19
8 Kensington & Ealing Boro	12	6	1	5	33	25	8	19
9 Fleet Spurs	13	6	1	6	19	20	-1	19
10 British Airways	12	5	2	5	18	19	-1	17
11 Chessington & Hook United	15	5	2	8	19	36	-17	17
12 Bedfont & Feltham	12	4	2	6	19	26	-7	14
13 Godalming Town	14	4	2	8	21	32	-11	14
14 Jersey Bulls	4	4	0	0	10	3	7	12
15 Sandhurst Town	11	4	0	7	10	26	-16	12
16 Eversley & California	12	3	2	7	18	23	-5	11
17 Cove	11	3	2	6	13	22	-9	11
18 AFC Hayes	7	3	1	3	12	14	-2	10
19 Ash United	10	2	1	7	22	26	-4	7
20 Bagshot	12	0	0	12	9	47	-38	0

EAST MIDLANDS LEAGUE

PREMIER	P	W	D	L	F	A	GD	Pts
1 Ollerton Town	12	9	2	1	35	5	30	29
2 Sherwood Colliery	9	9	0	0	34	8	26	27
3 Belper United	13	8	1	4	36	23	13	25
4 Eastwood C FC	12	8	0	4	24	17	7	24
5 Clifton All Whites	11	6	1	4	25	16	9	19
6 Rainworth MW	10	6	1	3	19	15	4	19
7 Hucknall Town	9	6	0	3	27	13	14	18
8 Kimberley MW	12	5	1	6	28	25	3	16
9 Clipstone	11	4	3	4	22	19	3	15
10 Heanor Town	10	5	0	5	19	20	-1	15
11 Dunkirk	10	4	2	4	20	19	1	14
12 Barrow Town	12	4	1	7	22	39	-17	13
13 Shirebrook Town	12	3	3	6	14	30	-16	12
14 Gedling MW	8	3	1	4	16	17	-1	10
15 West Bridgford	10	2	4	4	12	16	-4	10
16 Ingles	12	2	3	7	12	29	-17	9
17 Graham St Prims	9	2	2	5	7	17	-10	8
18 Borrowash Victoria	11	2	2	7	9	24	-15	8
19 Teversal	11	2	0	9	8	29	-21	6
20 Radford	6	1	1	4	6	14	-8	4

EASTERN COUNTIES LEAGUE

	PREMIER	P	W	D	L	F	A	GD	Pts
1	Wroxham	10	10	0	0	28	8	20	30
2	Norwich United	11	9	2	0	24	9	15	29
3	Brantham Athletic	11	6	4	1	21	13	8	22
4	Walsham Le Willows	12	6	3	3	30	21	9	21
5	Ely City	12	5	5	2	12	8	4	20
6	Kirkley & Pakefield	11	6	1	4	21	23	-2	19
7	Stanway Rovers	12	4	4	4	25	17	8	16
8	Hadleigh United	11	4	4	3	16	14	2	16
9	Mildenhall Town	8	4	3	1	19	10	9	15
10	FC Clacton	10	4	3	3	22	16	6	15
11	Stowmarket Town	7	4	3	0	10	5	5	15
12	Gorleston	10	5	0	5	16	20	-4	15
13	Newmarket Town	10	3	1	6	16	22	-6	10
14	Swaffham Town	13	3	1	9	16	27	-11	10
15	Whitton United	9	3	0	6	17	22	-5	9
16	Godmanchester Rovers	12	2	3	7	14	22	-8	9
17	Woodbridge Town	11	2	2	7	16	22	-6	8
18	Haverhill Rovers	11	2	1	8	9	28	-19	7
19	Long Melford	8	1	2	5	12	19	-7	5
20	Thetford Town	11	1	0	10	6	24	-18	3

	DIVISON ONE NORTH	P	W	D	L	F	A	GD	Pts
1	Fakenham Town	11	9	2	0	34	8	26	29
2	Ipswich Wanderers	10	9	1	0	33	9	24	28
3	March Town United	11	9	0	2	32	11	21	27
4	Lakenheath	10	7	1	2	30	12	18	22
5	Sheringham	13	6	3	4	32	26	6	21
6	Leiston Res	10	7	0	3	22	20	2	21
7	Great Yarmouth Town	13	6	1	6	25	27	-2	19
8	Mulbarton Wanderers	10	5	3	2	27	7	20	18
9	Downham Town	11	6	0	5	24	19	5	18
10	Diss Town	12	4	3	5	27	27	0	15
11	Framlingham Town	11	4	1	6	26	29	-3	13
12	Needham Market Res	12	4	1	7	24	34	-10	13
13	Kings Lynn Town Res	11	4	0	7	28	32	-4	12
14	Cornard United	12	3	2	7	20	28	-8	11
15	AFC Sudbury Res	10	3	2	5	15	27	-12	11
16	Debenham LC	10	3	1	6	12	21	-9	10
17	Norwich CBS	10	1	6	3	19	18	1	9
18	Haverhill Borough	11	1	1	9	7	27	-20	4
19	Wisbech St Mary	14	1	0	13	16	71	-55	3

	DIVISION ONE SOUTH	P	W	D	L	F	A	GD	Pts
1	Newbury Forest	10	7	1	2	21	16	5	22
2	Athletic Newham	12	5	6	1	20	13	7	21
3	White Ensign	10	6	2	2	22	14	8	20
4	Wivenhoe Town	11	6	1	4	20	14	6	19
5	Little Oakley	8	6	0	2	23	12	11	18
6	Frenford	11	5	2	4	22	14	8	17
7	Wormley Rovers	10	5	2	3	17	14	3	17
8	Benfleet	10	5	2	3	25	26	-1	17
9	Coggeshall United	11	4	3	4	14	14	0	15
10	Barkingside	9	4	1	4	12	12	0	13
11	Hackney Wick	14	3	4	7	23	30	-7	13
12	Burnham Ramblers	10	3	2	5	18	21	-3	11
13	Halstead Town	9	2	3	4	21	17	4	9
14	Holland	7	1	3	3	8	12	-4	6
15	Harwich & Parkeston	11	0	5	6	10	20	-10	5
16	Brimsdown	10	1	2	7	17	40	-23	5
17	May & Baker	5	1	1	3	8	12	-4	4

ESSEX SENIOR LEAGUE

	PREMIER	P	W	D	L	F	A	GD	Pts
1	Hashtag United	12	10	1	1	29	10	19	31
2	Stansted	15	9	2	4	27	19	8	29
3	Walthamstow	12	9	0	3	35	16	19	27
4	Cockfosters	11	8	2	1	29	9	20	26
5	Saffron Walden Town	15	6	5	4	34	16	18	23
6	Hadley	8	7	0	1	23	9	14	21
7	Hoddesdon Town	13	6	1	6	25	25	0	19
8	West Essex	12	5	2	5	27	20	7	17
9	Takeley	11	5	1	5	34	19	15	16
10	Enfield	14	4	2	8	22	29	-7	14
11	Redbridge	9	4	1	4	19	19	0	13
12	Sporting Bengal United	13	4	1	8	16	27	-11	13
13	St Margaretsbury	11	3	3	5	11	25	-14	12
14	Sawbridgeworth Town	15	3	3	9	23	47	-24	12
15	Ilford	11	2	4	5	20	27	-7	10
16	Southend Manor	12	6	1	5	19	33	-14	10*
17	Woodford Town	13	1	1	11	11	29	-18	4
18	Clapton Football Club	11	0	4	7	13	38	-25	4

HELLENIC LEAGUE

	PREMIER	P	W	D	L	F	A	GD	Pts
1	Flackwell Heath	7	6	0	1	16	4	12	18
2	Binfield	7	5	2	0	18	7	11	17
3	Reading City	9	5	2	2	15	10	5	17
4	Bishops Cleeve	8	5	0	3	15	8	7	15
5	Brimscombe & Thrupp	6	4	2	0	18	5	13	14
6	Fairford Town	9	4	1	4	17	13	4	13
7	Holmer Green	8	4	1	3	14	11	3	13
8	Longlevens	7	3	3	1	12	9	3	12
9	Easington Sports	7	4	0	3	12	11	1	12
10	Virginia Water	8	3	2	3	10	10	0	11
11	Burnham	7	2	3	2	8	11	-3	9
12	Windsor	9	2	2	5	17	19	-2	8
13	Lydney Town	7	2	2	3	9	14	-5	8
14	Westfields	5	2	1	2	5	5	0	7
15	Royal Wootton Bassett Town	8	1	4	3	8	12	-4	7
16	Tuffley Rovers	7	2	0	5	7	16	-9	6
17	Ardley United	10	1	1	8	8	20	-12	4
18	Shrivenham	9	1	0	8	4	28	-24	3

	DIVISION ONE EAST	P	W	D	L	F	A	GD	Pts
1	Wokingham & Emmbrook	8	6	2	0	22	2	20	20
2	Holyport	9	5	2	2	17	12	5	17
3	Wallingford Town	10	5	2	3	15	13	2	17
4	Risborough Rangers	6	6	0	0	24	2	22	15*
5	Milton United	7	4	1	2	19	13	6	13
6	Long Crendon	6	4	1	1	12	7	5	13
7	Kidlington Reserves	8	3	3	2	19	15	4	12
8	Penn & Tylers Green	5	3	1	1	12	7	5	10
9	AFC Aldermaston	7	3	1	3	11	14	-3	10
10	Abingdon United	9	3	1	5	13	17	-4	10
11	Langley	8	2	2	4	15	26	-11	8
12	Chalvey Sports	8	2	1	5	11	19	-8	7
13	Abingdon Town	8	1	1	6	9	18	-9	4
14	Woodley United	6	1	0	5	8	22	-14	3
15	Thame Rangers	11	1	0	10	12	32	-20	3

	DIVISION ONE WEST	P	W	D	L	F	A	GD	Pts
1	Malvern Town	11	10	0	1	38	14	24	30
2	Thornbury Town	9	5	3	1	19	9	10	18
3	Newent Town	9	5	2	2	20	15	5	17
4	Hereford Lads Club	9	5	1	3	26	10	16	16
5	Malmesbury Victoria	10	4	4	2	20	10	10	16
6	Hereford Pegasus	10	5	1	4	16	17	-1	16
7	Clanfield 85	8	4	3	1	13	7	6	15
8	Cheltenham Saracens	7	3	2	2	17	13	4	11
9	Bourton Rovers	7	3	1	3	14	17	-3	10
10	Wellington	9	3	0	6	17	19	-2	9
11	Stonehouse Town	8	3	0	5	9	18	-9	9
12	Shortwood United	8	2	2	4	8	13	-5	8
13	Moreton Rangers	12	1	4	7	14	30	-16	7
14	Tytherington Rocks	9	2	0	7	14	23	-9	6
15	Cirencester Town Dev'	8	0	1	7	9	39	-30	1

	DIVISION TWO EAST	P	W	D	L	F	A	GD	Pts
1	Flackwell Heath Res	6	4	1	1	21	10	11	13
2	Holmer Green Dev	5	4	0	1	19	11	8	12
3	Wokingham & Emmbrook Res	4	3	1	0	12	1	11	10
4	Watlington Town	5	3	1	1	16	12	4	10
5	Westfield FC Res	4	3	0	1	13	11	2	9
6	Chalfont Wasps	4	2	1	1	6	9	-3	7
7	Yateley United	2	2	0	0	10	4	6	6
8	FC Beaconsfield	5	1	3	1	11	11	0	6
9	Chalvey Sports Res	4	1	1	2	11	12	-1	4
10	Chinnor	6	1	1	4	17	22	-5	4
11	Hazlemere Sports	3	1	0	2	3	6	-3	3
12	Penn & Tylers Green Dev	4	0	1	3	8	14	-6	1
13	Taplow United	2	0	0	2	3	7	-4	0
14	Stokenchurch	3	0	0	3	3	12	-9	0
15	Cove U23	3	0	0	3	4	15	-11	0

HELLENIC LEAGUE

	DIVISION TWO NORTH	P	W	D	L	F	A	GD	Pts
1	Heyford Athletic	4	4	0	0	14	1	13	12
2	Thame United Res	6	3	2	1	8	4	4	11
3	Aston Clinton	6	3	1	2	12	11	1	10
4	Buckingham Athletic Dev	4	3	0	1	11	8	3	9
5	Headington Amateurs	5	2	2	1	12	9	3	8
6	Southam United	3	2	1	0	9	7	2	7
7	Ardley United Dev	4	2	0	2	10	9	1	6
8	Easington Sports Dev	4	1	2	1	11	6	5	5
9	Adderbury Park	3	1	1	1	6	6	0	4
10	Long Crendon Res	5	1	1	3	6	14	-8	4
11	Risborough Rangers Res	3	0	2	1	5	6	-1	2
12	Banbury United Dev	2	0	1	1	2	4	-2	1
13	Old Bradwell United Dev	3	0	1	2	3	6	-3	1
14	Kidlington Dev	6	0	0	6	3	21	-18	0

	DIVISION TWO SOUTH	P	W	D	L	F	A	GD	Pts
1	Hungerford Town Swifts	6	6	0	0	24	4	20	18
2	Highworth Town Res	5	3	1	1	15	3	12	10
3	Kintbury Rangers	3	3	0	0	14	4	10	9
4	Swindon Supermarine Dev	5	3	0	2	7	9	-2	9
5	Letcombe	5	2	2	1	13	3	10	8
6	Shrivenham Dev	6	2	0	4	10	15	-5	6
7	Clanfield (85) Dev	6	1	2	3	12	16	-4	5
8	Wantage Town Dev	2	1	1	0	4	3	1	4
9	Woodcote Stoke Row	4	1	1	2	10	21	-11	4
10	Abingdon United Dev	4	1	0	3	2	8	-6	3
11	Wallingford Town AFC Res	5	1	0	4	9	16	-7	3
12	AFC Aldermaston Res	3	1	0	2	2	10	-8	3
13	Woodstock Town	4	1	0	3	4	13	-9	3
14	Faringdon Town	2	0	1	1	2	3	-1	1

	DIVISION TWO WEST	P	W	D	L	F	A	GD	Pts
1	Slimbridge Res	6	5	0	1	20	5	15	15
2	Kington Town	6	4	0	2	17	12	5	12
3	Malvern Town Dev	4	3	1	0	13	6	7	10
4	Hartpury University	5	3	1	1	16	13	3	10
5	Shipston Excelsior	3	3	0	0	8	3	5	9
6	Tuffley Rovers Dev	6	2	2	2	23	20	3	8
7	SC Inkberrow	3	2	0	1	17	4	13	6
8	Shortwood United Res	6	2	0	4	17	17	0	6
9	Fairford Town Res	5	2	0	3	10	17	-7	6
10	Cricklade Town Res	5	2	0	3	8	17	-9	6
11	Newent Town Res	6	1	2	3	12	21	-9	5
12	Moreton Rangers Dev	4	1	1	2	6	11	-5	4
13	Evesham United Dev	5	0	1	4	6	16	-10	1
14	Bourton Rovers Res	4	0	0	4	3	14	-11	0

MIDLAND LEAGUE

PREMIER	P	W	D	L	F	A	GD	Pts
1 Sporting Khalsa	11	8	2	1	31	16	15	26
2 Stourport Swifts	13	7	2	4	32	19	13	23
3 Long Eaton United	8	7	1	0	31	4	27	22
4 Newark	10	6	3	1	19	9	10	21
5 Lye Town	15	5	5	5	25	22	3	20
6 Romulus	10	5	4	1	13	6	7	19
7 Gresley Rovers	11	6	1	4	23	21	2	19
8 Tividale	15	5	4	6	29	29	0	19
9 Coventry United	9	6	0	3	23	15	8	18
10 A F C Wulfrunians	10	4	5	1	14	9	5	17
11 Walsall Wood	10	4	2	4	18	13	5	14
12 Coventry Sphinx	10	4	2	4	19	15	4	14
13 Racing Club Warwick	9	2	4	3	16	15	1	10
14 Worcester City	12	2	4	6	14	21	-7	10
15 Heather St. John's	11	2	2	7	10	26	-16	8
16 Boldmere St Michaels	6	2	1	3	10	15	-5	7
17 Highgate United	8	1	2	5	15	18	-3	5
18 Haughmond	10	0	1	9	10	40	-30	1
19 Selston	10	0	1	9	12	51	-39	1

DIVISION ONE	P	W	D	L	F	A	GD	Pts
1 Lichfield City	15	10	2	3	33	13	20	32
2 Leicester Road	11	8	2	1	27	5	22	26
3 Ashby Ivanhoe	12	8	2	2	33	17	16	26
4 Hinckley AFC	12	7	3	2	26	19	7	24
5 Kirby Muxloe	12	7	3	2	24	21	3	24
6 Nuneaton Griff	14	6	3	5	20	18	2	21
7 Heath Hayes	13	6	3	4	21	20	1	21
8 Stapenhill	11	6	2	3	22	12	10	20
9 Atherstone Town	13	6	2	5	28	21	7	20
10 Uttoxeter Town	11	6	1	4	25	15	10	19
11 Brocton	13	4	5	4	26	20	6	17
12 Chelmsley Town	15	5	2	8	25	31	-6	17
13 Studley	10	3	3	4	21	15	6	12
14 Rocester	12	3	3	6	22	24	-2	12
15 Coventry Copsewood	13	3	2	8	23	38	-15	11
16 Stafford Town	14	3	2	9	20	38	-18	11
17 Cadbury Athletic	11	2	1	8	14	36	-22	7
18 G N P Sports	11	1	3	7	10	26	-16	6
19 Paget Rangers	13	2	0	11	12	43	-31	6

DIVISION TWO	P	W	D	L	F	A	GD	Pts
1 Solihull United	8	7	1	0	28	6	22	22
2 Knowle	9	5	2	2	21	14	7	17
3 Coton Green	9	5	0	4	23	12	11	15
4 F C Stratford	8	4	3	1	20	15	5	15
5 Hampton	8	4	3	1	13	12	1	15
6 Barnt Green Spartak	8	4	2	2	23	16	7	14
7 Coventry Alvis	9	4	1	4	21	17	4	13
8 Alcester Town	8	3	3	2	11	13	-2	12
9 Feckenham	5	3	1	1	14	12	2	10
10 Earlswood Town	6	3	0	3	15	15	0	9
11 Northfield Town	9	2	3	4	9	18	-9	9
12 Boldmere Sports & Social Falcons	8	2	2	4	13	14	-1	8
13 Lane Head	9	2	2	5	13	23	-10	8
14 Bolehall Swifts	10	2	0	8	8	20	-12	6
15 Redditch Borough	7	1	1	5	11	21	-10	4
16 Fairfield Villa	5	0	0	5	5	20	-15	0

DIVISION THREE	P	W	D	L	F	A	GD	Pts
1 Kenilworth Sporting	8	7	0	1	26	7	19	21
2 Inkberrow	8	6	1	1	32	15	17	19
3 Central Ajax	7	6	0	1	22	7	15	18
4 Enville Athletic	9	5	2	2	16	12	4	17
5 Coventrians	7	5	0	2	29	13	16	15
6 A F C Solihull	8	4	1	3	30	20	10	13
7 Upton Town	6	4	1	1	14	11	3	13
8 Sutton United	7	4	0	3	26	13	13	12
9 F C Shush	7	4	0	3	22	18	4	12
10 Welland	7	3	1	3	16	14	2	10
11 Tamworth Academy	5	3	0	2	16	8	8	9
12 Leamington Hibernian	8	1	2	5	15	30	-15	5
13 W L V Sport	9	1	1	7	7	23	-16	4
14 Continental Star	8	1	1	6	12	30	-18	4
15 Birmingham Tigers	7	1	0	6	13	27	-14	3
16 Castle Vale Town	9	0	0	9	12	60	-48	0

NORTH WEST COUNTIES LEAGUE

	PREMIER	P	W	D	L	F	A	GD	Pts
1	Avro	8	5	1	2	23	9	14	16
2	Warrington Rylands 1906	5	4	1	0	15	4	11	13
3	Northwich Victoria	7	4	1	2	12	9	3	13
4	Irlam	9	4	0	5	13	20	-7	12
5	Runcorn Town	6	3	2	1	14	7	7	11
6	Hanley Town	7	3	2	2	12	9	3	11
7	Winsford United	5	3	1	1	18	7	11	10
8	Congleton Town	5	3	1	1	9	8	1	10
9	Bootle	3	3	0	0	14	5	9	9
10	1874 Northwich	5	3	0	2	12	8	4	9
11	Burscough	3	2	1	0	8	5	3	7
12	Padiham	6	2	1	3	12	16	-4	7
13	Longridge Town	4	2	0	2	9	5	4	6
14	Ashton Athletic	5	2	0	3	10	16	-6	6
15	Whitchurch Alport	7	1	3	3	10	19	-9	6
16	Barnoldswick Town	8	2	0	6	11	26	-15	6
17	Charnock Richard	4	1	1	2	7	9	-2	4
18	Skelmersdale United	4	1	0	3	5	9	-4	3
19	Squires Gate	9	1	0	8	15	29	-14	3
20	Litherland REMYCA	4	0	1	3	7	16	-9	1

	DIVISION ONE SOUTH	P	W	D	L	F	A	GD	Pts
1	Vauxhall Motors	8	7	1	0	19	6	13	22
2	Wythenshawe Town	7	7	0	0	29	3	26	21
3	Sandbach United	8	5	1	2	23	16	7	16
4	Stockport Town	8	4	2	2	20	6	14	14
5	West Didsbury & Chorlton	6	4	1	1	18	11	7	13
6	Cheadle Heath Nomads	9	3	3	3	20	17	3	12
7	New Mills	6	3	2	1	6	5	1	11
8	Stone Old Alleynians	6	3	1	2	13	9	4	10
9	Barnton	6	3	1	2	10	7	3	10
10	Abbey Hey	7	3	1	3	13	11	2	10
11	Cheadle Town	7	2	2	3	12	10	2	8
12	Alsager Town	7	2	1	4	8	14	-6	7
13	Cammell Laird 1907	7	2	0	5	6	10	-4	6
14	Maine Road	7	2	0	5	9	16	-7	6
15	St Martins	9	1	2	6	9	29	-20	5
16	Ellesmere Rangers	4	1	0	3	4	12	-8	3
17	Abbey Hulton United	7	0	3	4	9	22	-13	3
18	Wythenshawe Amateurs	5	0	2	3	4	8	-4	2
19	Eccleshall	4	0	1	3	4	24	-20	1

	DIVISION ONE NORTH	P	W	D	L	F	A	GD	Pts
1	Bury AFC	7	5	1	1	22	11	11	16
2	Lower Breck	4	4	0	0	15	3	12	12
3	AFC Darwen	7	4	0	3	20	16	4	12
4	Cleator Moor Celtic	9	3	3	3	21	20	1	12
5	AFC Liverpool	4	3	1	0	15	7	8	10
6	Prestwich Heys	5	3	1	1	13	9	4	10
7	Steeton	7	3	1	3	13	11	2	10
8	Golcar United	8	3	1	4	14	15	-1	10
9	Ashton Town	8	3	1	4	14	18	-4	10
10	Bacup Borough	3	3	0	0	9	2	7	9
11	Garstang	7	3	0	4	14	19	-5	9
12	Pilkington	5	2	2	1	11	11	0	8
13	AFC Blackpool	5	2	0	3	12	16	-4	6
14	Chadderton	7	1	2	4	12	19	-7	5
15	Holker Old Boys	3	1	0	2	8	10	-2	3
16	Atherton LR	3	1	0	2	3	5	-2	3
17	Nelson	6	1	0	5	11	19	-8	3
18	Daisy Hill	5	1	0	4	7	18	-11	3
19	St Helens Town	3	0	1	2	5	10	-5	1

NORTHERN COUNTIES EAST LEAGUE

PREMIER	P	W	D	L	F	A	GD	Pts
1 Yorkshire Amateur	11	9	2	0	36	9	27	29
2 Bridlington Town	9	7	0	2	39	15	24	21
3 Liversedge	7	7	0	0	25	3	22	21
4 Garforth Town	9	7	0	2	22	12	10	21
5 Maltby Main	10	5	3	2	23	17	6	18
6 AFC Mansfield	9	5	2	2	26	9	17	17
7 Handsworth	12	5	2	5	28	31	-3	17
8 Grimsby Borough	10	5	1	4	28	22	6	16
9 Barton Town	11	4	2	5	16	25	-9	14
10 Albion Sports	9	4	1	4	14	14	0	13
11 Eccleshill United	11	4	1	6	14	18	-4	13
12 Penistone Church	7	4	0	3	17	11	6	12
13 Hemsworth Miners Welfare	7	4	0	3	8	5	3	12
14 Goole AFC	11	3	2	6	13	34	-21	11
15 Silsden AFC	10	3	1	6	16	22	-6	10
16 Thackley	11	2	2	7	13	24	-11	8
17 Staveley Miners Welfare	6	2	1	3	9	10	-1	7
18 Knaresborough Town	9	2	1	6	9	18	-9	7
19 Bottesford Town	11	1	1	9	15	39	-24	4
20 Athersley Recreation	10	1	0	9	9	42	-33	3

DIVISION ONE	P	W	D	L	F	A	GD	Pts
1 Emley AFC	10	8	2	0	27	9	18	26
2 Campion	11	8	0	3	36	19	17	24
3 Winterton Rangers	9	7	1	1	34	11	23	22
4 North Ferriby	10	7	1	2	20	9	11	22
5 Retford FC	13	6	3	4	29	23	6	21
6 Brigg Town	11	6	2	3	32	19	13	20
7 Rossington Main	12	5	3	4	29	24	5	18
8 Skegness Town	8	5	1	2	17	12	5	16
9 Parkgate	10	5	1	4	26	28	-2	16
10 Hall Road Rangers	10	4	2	4	17	20	-3	14
11 Hallam	8	4	1	3	21	17	4	13
12 Nostell Miners Welfare	12	4	0	8	20	28	-8	12
13 Glasshoughton Welfare	12	3	2	7	22	21	1	11
14 Armthorpe Welfare	12	3	2	7	21	35	-14	11
15 Swallownest	8	3	1	4	16	17	-1	10
16 Dronfield Town	11	3	1	7	17	28	-11	10
17 Harrogate Railway Athletic	8	2	3	3	16	25	-9	9
18 East Hull	10	2	1	7	10	33	-23	7
19 Worsbrough Bridge Athletic	13	1	3	9	14	35	-21	6
20 Selby Town	6	1	0	5	9	20	-11	3

NORTHERN LEAGUE

DIVISION ONE	P	W	D	L	F	A	GD	Pts
1 Hebburn Town	12	11	0	1	49	11	38	33
2 Stockton Town	12	8	3	1	32	8	24	27
3 Consett	12	9	0	3	32	19	13	27
4 North Shields	11	8	2	1	27	12	15	26
5 Newton Aycliffe	12	6	4	2	31	15	16	22
6 Newcastle Benfield	13	7	1	5	35	23	12	22
7 Whitley Bay	11	7	1	3	27	18	9	22
8 Shildon	11	6	3	2	26	11	15	21
9 Thornaby	11	6	2	3	19	22	-3	20
10 Whickham	13	5	2	6	18	21	-3	17
11 West Auckland Town	13	5	2	6	21	29	-8	17
12 Ashington	11	5	1	5	23	24	-1	16
13 Sunderland RCA	12	4	1	7	25	23	2	13
14 Northallerton Town	13	3	3	7	10	30	-20	12
15 Sunderland Ryhope C.W.	10	3	2	5	11	18	-7	11
16 Guisborough Town	12	2	3	7	20	35	-15	9
17 Penrith	11	3	0	8	15	34	-19	9
18 Bishop Auckland	12	1	2	9	12	30	-18	5
19 Seaham Red Star	11	1	2	8	10	31	-21	5
20 Billingham Town	13	1	0	12	14	43	-29	3

DIVISION TWO	P	W	D	L	F	A	GD	Pts
1 West Allotment Celtic	12	7	3	2	25	16	9	24
2 Crook Town	12	7	2	3	33	17	16	23
3 Carlisle City	11	7	2	2	25	17	8	23
4 Billingham Synthonia	11	7	1	3	31	11	20	22
5 Tow Law Town	12	6	2	4	22	19	3	20
6 Bedlington Terriers	11	6	2	3	19	16	3	20
7 Birtley Town	13	5	5	3	18	19	-1	20
8 Easington Colliery	10	7	1	2	32	17	15	19*
9 Newcastle University	11	5	4	2	17	15	2	19
10 Redcar Athletic	11	5	3	3	19	14	5	18
11 Heaton Stannington	12	4	5	3	26	15	11	17
12 Chester-Le-Street	12	5	2	5	29	20	9	17
13 Brandon United	12	4	3	5	20	27	-7	15
14 Willington	13	5	0	8	19	27	-8	15
15 Esh Winning	12	5	0	7	22	31	-9	15
16 Ryton & Crawcrook Albion	14	3	3	8	21	26	-5	12
17 Sunderland West End	12	3	2	7	15	30	-15	11
18 Jarrow	12	3	1	8	17	31	-14	10
19 Washington	10	2	2	6	18	29	-11	8
20 Durham City	13	0	1	12	19	50	-31	1

SOUTH WEST PENINSULA LEAGUE

PREMIER EAST	P	W	D	L	F	A	GD	Pts
1 Torpoint Athletic	15	11	1	3	40	21	19	34
2 Ivybridge Town	15	11	0	4	50	14	36	33
3 Millbrook AFC	11	10	1	0	43	8	35	31
4 Brixham AFC	14	9	3	2	43	16	27	30
5 IlfracombeTown	12	9	1	2	48	9	39	28
6 Torridgeside AFC	12	8	2	2	50	23	27	26
7 Newton Abbot Spurs	13	8	2	3	35	19	16	26
8 Dartmouth AFC	15	8	2	5	32	36	-4	26
9 Elmore AFC	14	7	1	6	39	29	10	22
10 Sidmouth Town	12	6	1	5	31	27	4	19
11 Torrington AFC	14	5	3	6	43	38	5	18
12 Cullompton Rangers	14	5	3	6	34	30	4	18
13 Honiton Town	15	5	2	8	38	31	7	17
14 Crediton United	14	5	1	8	30	27	3	16
15 Bovey Tracey	14	4	1	9	39	44	-5	13
16 Plymouth Marjon	15	3	3	9	35	42	-7	12
17 Elburton Villa	13	3	2	8	32	33	-1	11
18 Axminster Town	12	3	1	8	29	29	0	10
19 Holsworthy AFC	14	2	2	10	16	31	-15	8
20 Stoke Gabriel	18	0	0	18	7	207	-200	0

PREMIER WEST	P	W	D	L	F	A	GD	Pts
1 Mousehole	15	12	2	1	52	8	44	38
2 Saltash United	15	12	2	1	59	22	37	38
3 Camelford	13	10	2	1	35	13	22	32
4 Falmouth Town	13	10	0	3	52	16	36	30
5 Dobwalls	14	9	2	3	35	16	19	29
6 Bodmin Town	15	8	3	4	41	19	22	27
7 Wadebridge Town	15	8	2	5	45	40	5	26
8 Newquay	17	7	4	6	34	28	6	25
9 Liskeard Athletic	13	8	0	5	45	22	23	24
10 St Austell	15	7	3	5	30	31	-1	24
11 Helston Athletic	10	5	4	1	30	22	8	19
12 Porthleven	13	5	1	7	18	29	-11	16
13 Sticker	17	5	1	11	30	48	-18	16
14 St Dennis	18	4	3	11	35	52	-17	15
15 Wendron United	13	4	1	8	23	40	-17	13
16 St Blazey	8	3	2	3	18	14	4	11
17 Penzance	15	3	1	11	21	49	-28	10
18 Callington Town	13	1	1	11	14	54	-40	4
19 Launceston	12	1	0	11	13	51	-38	3
20 Godolphin Atlantic	16	0	2	14	14	70	-56	-1*

SOUTHERN COMBINATION LEAGUE

PREMIER	P	W	D	L	F	A	GD	Pts
1 Saltdean United	14	9	4	1	35	15	20	31
2 Horley Town	12	8	2	2	33	12	21	26
3 Pagham	13	7	5	1	31	14	17	26
4 Eastbourne Town	14	8	2	4	30	20	10	26
5 AFC Uckfield Town	14	7	3	4	17	14	3	24
6 Crawley Down Gatwick	11	7	1	3	23	15	8	22
7 Newhaven	10	6	2	2	24	8	16	20
8 Lancing	11	6	2	3	30	20	10	20
9 Lingfield	12	5	5	2	21	16	5	20
10 Loxwood	14	6	1	7	26	23	3	19
11 Steyning Town	13	6	0	7	18	19	-1	18
12 Hassocks	13	6	0	7	25	33	-8	18
13 Alfold	11	5	2	4	22	16	6	17
14 Little Common	12	4	3	5	20	23	-3	15
15 Broadbridge Heath	13	5	0	8	24	28	-4	15
16 Peacehaven & Telscombe	13	4	2	7	19	20	-1	14
17 Eastbourne United	14	4	1	9	12	39	-27	13
18 Langney Wanderers	12	2	1	9	11	31	-20	7
19 Horsham YMCA	13	1	2	10	13	31	-18	5
20 East Preston	13	0	2	11	11	48	-37	2

DIVISION ONE	P	W	D	L	F	A	GD	Pts
1 Bexhill United	11	10	1	0	34	9	25	31
2 Littlehampton Town	10	9	1	0	48	9	39	28
3 AFC Varndeanians	10	7	2	1	23	12	11	23
4 Midhurst & Easebourne	12	7	1	4	24	20	4	22
5 Shoreham	12	6	2	4	26	18	8	20
6 Worthing United	9	6	0	3	10	10	0	18
7 Mile Oak	11	5	0	6	25	27	-2	15
8 Wick	10	4	2	4	21	19	2	14
9 Billingshurst	11	3	4	4	17	27	-10	13
10 Roffey	12	3	2	7	19	23	-4	11
11 Storrington	12	3	1	8	13	24	-11	10
12 Arundel	10	2	3	5	19	29	-10	9
13 Seaford Town	10	2	2	6	11	17	-6	8
14 Selsey	9	2	2	5	7	14	-7	8
15 Hailsham Town	10	2	1	7	12	34	-22	7
16 Oakwood	11	1	2	8	11	28	-17	5

DIVISION TWO	P	W	D	L	F	A	GD	Pts
1 Rustington	10	8	1	1	34	8	26	25
2 Upper Beeding	11	7	4	0	25	8	17	25
3 Copthorne	10	7	0	3	24	12	12	21
4 TD Shipley	8	6	2	0	26	5	21	20
5 St Francis Rangers	11	5	2	4	25	21	4	17
6 Montpelier Villa	9	4	2	3	20	12	8	14
7 Jarvis Brook	9	4	1	4	17	15	2	13
8 Worthing Town	10	3	4	3	15	16	-1	13
9 Charlwood	10	4	1	5	17	21	-4	13
10 Littlehampton United	11	3	1	7	21	29	-8	10
11 Bosham	10	2	2	6	15	25	-10	8
12 Brighton Electricity	11	2	2	7	12	30	-18	8
13 Ferring	12	2	1	9	15	31	-16	7
14 Rottingdean Village	10	2	1	7	7	40	-33	7

SOUTHERN COUNTIES EAST LEAGUE

PREMIER	P	W	D	L	F	A	GD	Pts
1 Chatham Town	11	10	0	1	60	18	42	30
2 Corinthian	11	10	0	1	38	16	22	30
3 Tunbridge Wells	12	8	2	2	24	14	10	26
4 Sheppey United	9	8	1	0	28	14	14	25
5 Beckenham Town	13	7	3	3	33	18	15	24
6 Balham	12	6	3	3	18	13	5	21
7 Hollands & Blair	11	6	3	2	15	12	3	21
8 Erith Town	12	6	2	4	26	20	6	20
9 Glebe	12	5	2	5	23	22	1	17
10 Deal Town	11	4	4	3	14	11	3	16
11 Bearsted	13	5	1	7	28	39	-11	16
12 Fisher	11	4	3	4	15	15	0	15
13 Welling Town	11	4	1	6	18	25	-7	13
14 Punjab United	12	4	1	7	20	29	-9	13
15 Crowborough Ath	11	3	3	5	14	20	-6	12
16 Canterbury City	12	3	1	8	17	34	-17	10
17 Erith & Belvedere	11	2	3	6	18	23	-5	9
18 AFC Croydon Ath	12	2	3	7	14	27	-13	9
19 Lordswood	13	2	2	9	13	29	-16	8
20 K Sports	11	1	4	6	10	18	-8	7
21 Tower Hamlets	13	0	2	11	17	46	-29	2

DIVISION ONE	P	W	D	L	F	A	GD	Pts
1 SC Thamesmead	8	7	0	1	24	10	14	21
2 Kennington	6	6	0	0	27	3	24	18
3 Rochester Utd	7	5	2	0	16	6	10	17
4 Holmesdale	6	5	0	1	20	9	11	15
5 Rusthall	8	5	0	3	21	14	7	15
6 Greenways	7	4	0	3	13	12	1	12
7 Croydon	7	3	2	2	17	19	-2	11
8 Snodland Town	7	3	1	3	9	16	-7	10
9 Kent Football Utd	8	2	2	4	8	14	-6	8
10 Stansfeld	6	2	1	3	18	18	0	7
11 Lydd Town	5	2	1	2	14	15	-1	7
12 Forest Hill Park	7	2	1	4	9	13	-4	7
13 Sutton Athletic	7	2	1	4	11	19	-8	7
14 Lewisham Borough	7	1	3	3	6	9	-3	6
15 FC Elmstead	8	1	1	6	10	23	-13	4
16 Bridon Ropes	7	0	2	5	5	16	-11	2
17 Meridian VP	7	0	1	6	6	18	-12	1

SPARTAN SOUTH MIDLANDS LEAGUE

	PREMIER	P	W	D	L	F	A	GD	Pts
1	Biggleswade United	14	9	1	4	38	24	14	28
2	Oxhey Jets	12	7	4	1	39	16	23	25
3	Eynesbury Rovers	12	8	1	3	35	18	17	25
4	Colney Heath	12	7	4	1	24	15	9	25
5	Potton United	13	7	2	4	29	22	7	23
6	Newport Pagnell Town	13	6	4	3	34	21	13	22
7	Leighton Town	10	7	1	2	24	11	13	22
8	Harpenden Town	11	7	1	3	28	20	8	22
9	Harefield United	12	7	0	5	23	24	-1	21
10	Baldock Town	12	6	1	5	21	18	3	19
11	Aylesbury Vale Dynamos	10	6	1	3	22	20	2	19
12	Crawley Green	14	5	2	7	28	35	-7	17
13	Leverstock Green	11	5	1	5	19	17	2	16
14	Dunstable Town	13	4	4	5	23	31	-8	16
15	Arlesey Town	10	4	0	6	14	20	-6	12
16	Edgware Town	10	3	1	6	19	29	-10	10
17	Tring Athletic	15	3	0	12	20	37	-17	9
18	North Greenford United	10	2	2	6	13	20	-7	8
19	Broadfields United	11	2	1	8	11	19	-8	7
20	Wembley	12	1	2	9	9	29	-20	5
21	London Colney	11	1	1	9	13	40	-27	4

	DIVISION ONE	P	W	D	L	F	A	GD	Pts
1	Shefford Town & Campton	11	8	1	2	29	11	18	25
2	Milton Keynes Irish	9	7	1	1	32	11	21	22
3	London Lions	9	7	1	1	18	7	11	22
4	St Panteleimon	10	7	0	3	31	15	16	21
5	Buckingham Athletic	11	5	2	4	24	14	10	17
6	Ampthill Town	9	5	2	2	21	17	4	17
7	Stotfold	10	5	1	4	23	17	6	16
8	Bedford	9	4	4	1	16	13	3	16
9	Rayners Lane	11	5	1	5	19	21	-2	16
10	New Salamis	8	3	4	1	23	9	14	13
11	Winslow United	9	4	1	4	19	17	2	13
12	Langford	12	3	1	8	17	32	-15	10
13	Enfield Borough	6	2	0	4	19	19	0	6
14	Park View	9	2	0	7	9	25	-16	6
15	Amersham Town	8	1	1	6	6	16	-10	4
16	Hillingdon Borough	8	1	0	7	4	37	-33	3
17	London Tigers	9	0	0	9	8	37	-29	0

	DIVISION TWO	P	W	D	L	F	A	GD	Pts
1	Old Bradwell United	8	5	2	1	22	7	15	17
2	Pitstone & Ivinghoe	5	5	0	0	14	4	10	15
3	Codicote	7	4	1	2	19	11	8	13
4	MK Gallacticos	7	4	0	3	12	12	0	12
5	Berkhamsted Raiders	6	3	1	2	18	14	4	10
6	Berkhamsted Comrades	7	3	1	3	14	10	4	10
7	New Bradwell St Peter	7	3	0	4	16	12	4	9
8	Bovingdon	5	3	0	2	13	9	4	9
9	Buckingham United	5	2	1	2	15	9	6	7
10	Totternhoe	4	2	1	1	8	6	2	7
11	Aston Clinton	6	2	1	3	14	14	0	7
12	Sarratt	5	2	0	3	11	16	-5	6
13	Tring Corinthians AFC	7	1	2	4	10	15	-5	5
14	Mursley United	6	1	0	5	4	25	-21	3
15	The 61 FC (Luton)	5	0	0	5	3	29	-26	0

UNITED COUNTIES LEAGUE

PREMIER	P	W	D	L	F	A	GD	Pts
1 Anstey Nomads	10	9	1	0	32	5	27	28
2 Loughborough University	13	8	2	3	42	17	25	26
3 Lutterworth Town	14	8	2	4	36	22	14	26
4 Quorn	12	7	4	1	41	18	23	25
5 Shepshed Dynamo	10	7	2	1	25	9	16	23
6 Rugby Town	11	7	1	3	31	11	20	22
7 Wellingborough Town	14	5	5	4	23	23	0	20
8 Harborough Town	12	5	3	4	19	19	0	18
9 Northampton ON Chenecks	13	5	2	6	28	24	4	17
10 Rothwell Corinthians	13	4	5	4	20	20	0	17
11 Boston Town	12	5	1	6	25	15	10	16
12 Deeping Rangers	9	5	1	3	14	17	-3	16
13 Holbeach United	10	4	3	3	21	11	10	15
14 G.N.G Oadby Town	12	4	3	5	18	24	-6	15*
15 Cogenhoe United	9	4	2	3	19	13	6	14
16 Desborough Town	12	4	2	6	21	36	-15	14
17 Leicester Nirvana	11	3	0	8	9	23	-14	9*
18 Sleaford Town	12	1	1	10	9	46	-37	4
19 Pinchbeck United	12	0	2	10	7	43	-36	2
20 Peterborough Northern Star	13	0	2	11	10	54	-44	2

DIVISION ONE	P	W	D	L	F	A	GD	Pts
1 Long Buckby AFC	12	10	1	1	43	11	32	31
2 Melton Town	12	10	0	2	52	14	38	30
3 St Andrews	11	9	0	2	42	10	32	27
4 Bugbrooke St.Michael	14	7	4	3	32	25	7	25
5 Harrowby United	10	7	2	1	27	10	17	23
6 Blackstones	12	6	2	4	27	19	8	20
7 Aylestone Park	11	5	2	4	45	21	24	17
8 Saffron Dynamo	12	5	2	5	23	26	-3	17
9 Whittlesey Athletic	12	3	6	3	25	23	2	15
10 Huntingdon Town	13	4	3	6	18	26	-8	15
11 Northampton Sileby Rangers	10	5	2	3	18	12	6	14*
12 Holwell Sports	11	4	2	5	23	19	4	14
13 Lutterworth Athletic	11	3	4	4	28	25	3	13
14 Birstall United Social	14	4	1	9	25	50	-25	13
15 Wellingborough Whitworth	13	3	3	7	24	47	-23	12
16 Bourne Town	9	3	3	3	14	18	-4	9*
17 Raunds Town	11	2	2	7	19	35	-16	8
18 Irchester United	12	1	4	7	20	45	-25	7
19 Burton Park Wanderers	11	1	2	8	12	40	-28	5
20 Rushden & Higham United	11	1	1	9	12	53	-41	4

WESSEX LEAGUE

PREMIER	P	W	D	L	F	A	GD	Pts
1 Hamworthy United	14	12	1	1	50	9	41	37
2 Lymington Town	12	11	0	1	23	4	19	33
3 Horndean	13	10	1	2	32	15	17	31
4 Fareham Town	11	8	2	1	33	12	21	26
5 Blackfield & Langley	13	8	1	4	27	20	7	25
6 Christchurch	11	7	2	2	23	8	15	23
7 Fleet Town	14	6	4	4	28	20	8	22
8 AFC Stoneham	12	7	0	5	35	15	20	21
9 AFC Portchester	12	6	1	5	20	15	5	19
10 Bashley	12	6	0	6	19	22	-3	18
11 Tadley Calleva	11	5	2	4	17	18	-1	17
12 Baffins Milton Rovers	13	3	4	6	21	25	-4	13
13 Bournemouth	14	3	3	8	15	39	-24	12
14 Hamble Club	13	2	5	6	16	23	-7	11
15 Brockenhurst	10	3	2	5	10	20	-10	11
16 Shaftesbury	12	3	1	8	19	34	-15	10
17 Cowes Sports	11	2	2	7	16	24	-8	8
18 Portland United	15	2	2	11	16	51	-35	8
19 Alresford Town	13	1	4	8	14	39	-25	7
20 Amesbury Town	12	0	1	11	5	26	-21	1

DIVISION ONE	P	W	D	L	F	A	GD	Pts
1 Laverstock & Ford	14	11	3	0	47	18	29	36
2 Alton	11	9	1	1	29	14	15	28
3 Folland Sports	12	7	2	3	33	17	16	23
4 United Services Portsmouth	10	7	0	3	30	13	17	21
5 Bemerton Heath Harlequins	11	6	3	2	25	18	7	21
6 Newport (IOW)	11	6	1	4	29	19	10	19
7 Andover Town	12	5	4	3	25	22	3	19
8 Ringwood Town	12	5	2	5	25	30	-5	17
9 Verwood Town	11	4	4	3	20	17	3	16
10 Hythe & Dibden	11	4	4	3	19	21	-2	16
11 Andover New Street	12	4	3	5	16	20	-4	15
12 Petersfield Town	10	4	2	4	15	19	-4	14
13 Downton	14	3	2	9	20	29	-9	11
14 Fawley AFC	11	3	1	7	15	27	-12	10
15 East Cowes Victoria	12	2	4	6	13	29	-16	10
16 Romsey Town	8	3	0	5	11	13	-2	9
17 Whitchurch United	11	3	0	8	18	32	-14	9
18 New Milton Town	11	2	2	7	19	27	-8	8
19 Totton & Eling	12	1	0	11	10	34	-24	3

WEST MIDLANDS (REGIONAL) LEAGUE

PREMIER	P	W	D	L	F	A	GD	Pts
1 Shifnal Town	8	7	0	1	20	4	16	21
2 Worcester Raiders	7	6	1	0	25	8	17	19
3 Shawbury United	9	5	2	2	22	15	7	17
4 Littleton	7	5	1	1	20	7	13	16
5 Bilston Town Community FC	7	5	1	1	17	7	10	16
6 Wolverhampton Casuals	9	4	1	4	16	21	-5	13
7 Wolverhampton Sporting Com	6	3	1	2	13	12	1	10
8 Wednesfield	6	3	0	3	16	14	2	9
9 Dudley Town	4	2	1	1	9	3	6	7
10 OJM Black Country Rangers	3	2	1	0	7	2	5	7
11 Pershore Town 88	5	1	3	1	12	13	-1	6
12 Cradley Town	7	2	0	5	12	17	-5	6
13 Darlaston Town (1874)	8	2	0	6	7	20	-13	6
14 Dudley Sports	6	1	2	3	11	10	1	5
15 AFC Bridgnorth	8	1	2	5	12	22	-10	5
16 Bewdley Town	4	1	1	2	14	15	-1	4
17 Wem Town	9	1	1	7	10	30	-20	4
18 Smethwick Rangers	7	0	0	7	6	29	-23	0

DIVISION ONE	P	W	D	L	F	A	GD	Pts
1 Tipton Town	8	5	1	2	18	11	7	16
2 Gornal Athletic	7	5	1	1	16	9	7	16
3 A F C Bentley	5	5	0	0	18	3	15	15
4 Allscott Heath	6	5	0	1	22	8	14	15
5 Droitwich Spa	7	4	2	1	27	16	11	14
6 Sikh Hunters	7	4	1	2	21	18	3	13
7 Gornal Colts	6	3	1	2	17	13	4	10
8 Bromyard Town	6	3	0	3	15	11	4	9
9 Old Wulfrunians	6	3	0	3	12	15	-3	9
10 Wyrley	7	2	2	3	9	14	-5	8
11 Wellington Amateurs	6	2	0	4	13	15	-2	6
12 Wrens Nest	7	1	1	5	7	25	-18	4
13 Willenhall Town	8	0	3	5	10	19	-9	3
14 F C Darlaston	5	1	0	4	5	14	-9	3
15 Team Dudley	4	0	0	4	3	12	-9	0
16 Bustleholme	3	0	0	3	3	13	-10	0

DIVISION TWO	P	W	D	L	F	A	GD	Pts
1 Bilbrook Santos	6	6	0	0	24	2	22	18
2 Kidderminster Harriers Academy	5	4	0	1	16	7	9	12
3 Nineveh Stallions	4	3	0	1	11	3	8	9
4 Crown FC	5	2	2	1	8	6	2	8
5 Punjab United	4	2	1	1	7	9	-2	7
6 Warstones Wanderers	4	1	2	1	7	7	0	5
7 Shawbury United U23	5	1	1	3	7	13	-6	4
8 Worcester Raiders Reserves	3	1	0	2	2	2	0	3
9 Edgbaston Spartans	5	1	0	4	5	12	-7	3
10 A F C Birmingham	3	1	0	2	5	14	-9	3
11 Cannock United	6	0	0	6	7	24	-17	0

WESTERN LEAGUE

PREMIER		P	W	D	L	F	A	GD	Pts
1	Plymouth Parkway	13	11	2	0	50	10	40	35
2	Tavistock	11	8	1	2	34	18	16	25
3	Exmouth Town	11	8	0	3	32	16	16	24
4	Clevedon Town	13	7	3	3	26	18	8	24
5	Cribbs	12	7	2	3	24	16	8	23
6	Westbury United	12	7	2	3	22	17	5	23
7	Street	13	7	1	5	33	26	7	22
8	Roman Glass St George	12	7	0	5	19	15	4	21
9	Buckland Athletic	15	6	3	6	23	22	1	21
10	Bridgwater Town	12	6	1	5	23	20	3	19
11	Bitton	8	6	0	2	29	13	16	18
12	Bradford Town	14	5	3	6	28	29	-1	18
13	Shepton Mallet	11	4	4	3	20	19	1	16
14	Keynsham Town	13	4	3	6	18	21	-3	15
15	Brislington	12	4	2	6	22	29	-7	14
16	Cadbury Heath	10	4	0	6	18	23	-5	12
17	Wellington	14	3	3	8	15	29	-14	12
18	Odd Down (BATH)	14	3	1	10	15	43	-28	10
19	Hallen	14	2	3	9	25	37	-12	9
20	Bridport	10	1	0	9	6	31	-25	3
21	Chipping Sodbury Town	12	0	2	10	9	39	-30	2

DIVISION ONE		P	W	D	L	F	A	GD	Pts
1	Corsham Town	10	9	1	0	35	13	22	28
2	Welton Rovers	11	8	2	1	29	12	17	26
3	Calne Town	9	8	0	1	23	6	17	24
4	Ashton & Backwell United	10	7	2	1	26	14	12	23
5	Wincanton Town	12	6	2	4	26	20	6	20
6	Warminster Town	11	6	1	4	27	16	11	19
7	Radstock Town	10	6	0	4	23	19	4	18
8	Wells City	10	5	1	4	19	17	2	16
9	Bishop Sutton	10	5	1	4	17	18	-1	16
10	Almondsbury	11	5	1	5	18	24	-6	16
11	Lebeq United	9	4	2	3	20	17	3	14
12	Portishead Town	10	4	2	4	16	14	2	14
13	Sherborne Town	11	4	1	6	17	19	-2	13
14	Bristol Telephones	9	4	0	5	20	21	-1	12
15	Hengrove Athletic	9	3	3	3	10	12	-2	12
16	Cheddar	10	4	0	6	21	24	-3	12
17	Bishops Lydeard	11	1	1	9	12	28	-16	4
18	Oldland Abbotonians	9	1	0	8	8	23	-15	3
19	Longwell Green Sports	10	0	1	9	11	34	-23	1
20	Devizes Town	10	0	1	9	11	38	-27	1

NATIONAL LEAGUE SYSTEM REGIONAL FEEDER TABLES 2020-21

UNLESS OTHERWISE STATED, TABLES AS THEY WERE WHEN EACH LEAGUE TERMINATED THE SEASON DUE TO COVID.

ANGLIAN COMBINATION

Step 7 - promotes to Eastern Counties League.

PREMIER DIVISION	P	W	D	L	F	A	GD	Pts
1 Harleston Town	9	8	1	0	35	8	27	25
2 UEA	10	8	1	1	26	14	12	25
3 Caister	10	7	1	2	23	11	12	22
4 Norwich CEYMS	11	5	4	2	27	21	6	19
5 Dussindale & Hellesdon Rovers	11	5	2	4	28	24	4	17
6 Waveney	8	5	0	3	18	12	6	15
7 Long Stratton	10	4	2	4	17	15	2	14
8 Mattishall	10	3	4	3	20	20	0	13
9 Acle United	11	4	1	6	19	31	-12	13
10 Mundford	11	3	3	5	18	25	-7	12
11 Scole United	9	3	2	4	18	18	0	11
12 Wroxham Res	9	3	2	4	23	24	-1	11
13 Blofield United	11	3	1	7	15	26	-11	10
14 Beccles Town	9	2	2	5	18	25	-7	8
15 Thorpe St Andrew	12	1	4	7	18	33	-15	7
16 Bradenham Wands	11	1	2	8	15	31	-16	5

DIVISION ONE	P	W	D	L	F	A	GD	Pts
1 Heacham	10	9	0	1	33	7	26	27
2 Aylsham	12	9	0	3	34	15	19	27
3 Attleborough Town	11	8	1	2	32	14	18	25
4 Yelverton	9	7	1	1	25	13	12	22
5 East Harling	12	6	4	2	23	12	11	22
6 Stalham Town	11	7	1	3	27	20	7	22
7 Wymondham Town	11	5	3	3	28	23	5	18
8 Sprowston Athletic	10	5	1	4	23	15	8	16
9 Norwich United U21	11	4	3	4	25	23	2	15
10 Easton	11	4	3	4	18	19	-1	15
11 Gorleston Res	12	3	4	5	30	26	4	13
12 Bungay Town	11	4	0	7	14	24	-10	12
13 Watton United	11	1	2	8	8	24	-16	5
14 Kirkley & Pakefield Res	10	1	1	8	6	20	-14	4
15 Thetford Rovers	10	1	0	9	13	46	-33	3
16 Fakenham Town Res	10	0	0	10	3	41	-38	0

DIVISION TWO	P	W	D	L	F	A	GD	Pts
1 Wells Town	12	9	2	1	47	16	31	29
2 Holt United	10	7	1	2	25	11	14	22
3 Martham	11	7	1	3	24	14	10	22
4 North Walsham Town	11	6	0	5	25	23	2	18
5 Gayton United	11	4	4	3	26	23	3	16
6 Brandon Town	8	5	0	3	20	20	0	15
7 Castle Acre Swifts	10	5	0	5	19	24	-5	15
8 Loddon United	11	4	2	5	28	22	6	14
9 Buxton	11	4	2	5	19	27	-8	14
10 Reepham Town	11	3	3	5	22	19	3	12
11 Caister Res	11	3	1	7	25	31	-6	10
12 Beccles Caxton	10	3	1	6	19	30	-11	10
13 Swaffham Town Res	11	3	1	7	17	40	-23	10
14 Earsham	8	1	0	7	6	22	-16	3

DIVISION THREE	P	W	D	L	F	A	GD	Pts
1 AC Mill Lane	10	8	1	1	39	11	28	25
2 Gt Yarmouth Town Res	11	8	0	3	34	15	19	24
3 Norwich CEYMS Res	10	7	2	1	21	13	8	23
4 Beccles Town Res	11	5	3	3	25	20	5	18
5 Aylsham Res	10	6	0	4	16	13	3	18
6 Poringland Wands	10	4	5	1	20	12	8	17
7 Long Stratton Res	10	5	2	3	30	24	6	17
8 Dussindale & Hellesdon R Res	11	4	4	3	19	12	7	16
9 Attleborough Town Res	11	5	0	6	25	22	3	15
10 Mattishall Res	11	4	2	5	45	32	13	14
11 South Walsham	11	4	1	6	25	25	0	13
12 Hempnall	9	4	1	4	28	33	-5	13
13 Costessey Sports	9	3	2	4	25	22	3	11
14 Waveney Res	10	0	4	6	13	25	-12	4
15 Bradenham Wands Res	9	1	1	7	11	34	-23	4
16 Horsford United	11	0	0	11	10	73	-63	0

DIVISION FOUR	P	W	D	L	F	A	GD	Pts
1 UEA Res	12	10	0	2	41	11	30	30
2 Mutford & Wrentham	10	9	0	1	25	6	19	27
3 Dersingham Rovers	11	8	1	2	43	15	28	25
4 Scole United Res	12	7	2	3	31	17	14	23
5 Norton Athletic	9	5	0	4	24	17	7	15
6 Thorpe St Andrew Res	9	4	2	3	24	21	3	14
7 Longham	9	4	2	3	25	23	2	14
8 Belton	10	4	1	5	24	31	-7	13
9 Hemsby	9	3	3	3	28	19	9	12
10 Mulbarton Wands Res	10	3	2	5	25	29	-4	11
11 Acle United Res	10	2	1	7	17	28	-11	7
12 Harleston Town Res	10	2	1	7	14	44	-30	7
13 Holt United Res	10	2	0	8	20	36	-16	6
14 Mundford Res	11	0	1	10	10	54	-44	1

DIVISION FIVE NORTH	P	W	D	L	F	A	GD	Pts
1 Wells Town Res	11	9	0	2	58	17	41	27
2 Easton Res	12	9	1	2	46	11	35	26*
3 Briston	9	7	1	1	39	17	22	22
4 Cromer Youth OB	11	6	3	2	49	24	25	21
5 AFC Lynn Napier	10	6	2	2	30	25	5	20
6 Gayton United Res	10	5	2	3	31	23	8	17
7 Norwich Eagles	11	5	1	5	40	40	0	16
8 Dussindale & Hellesdon R A	10	4	2	4	19	32	-13	14
9 Hindringham	11	4	1	6	23	30	-7	13
10 Narborough	11	4	1	6	21	35	-14	13
11 Stalham Town Res	12	3	1	8	19	39	-20	10
12 Reepham Town Res	12	2	2	8	21	36	-15	8
13 Necton	12	1	3	8	18	52	-34	6
14 Thorpe Village	10	0	2	8	6	39	-33	2

DIVISION FIVE SOUTH	P	W	D	L	F	A	GD	Pts
1 Celt Rangers	10	9	1	0	67	12	55	28
2 Carlton Colville Town	9	8	1	0	33	11	22	25
3 Freethorpe Res	9	6	2	1	34	4	30	20
4 Yelverton Res	11	6	1	4	20	18	2	19
5 Tacolneston	9	6	0	3	28	16	12	18
6 AC Mill Lane Res	10	6	0	4	25	17	8	18
7 Blofield United Res	9	5	1	3	23	25	-2	16
8 East Harling Res	11	4	3	4	27	16	11	15
9 Martham Res	10	4	2	4	24	18	6	14
10 Shrublands	11	4	0	7	27	24	3	12
11 Bungay Town Res	9	2	3	4	16	19	-3	9
12 Poringland Wands Res	9	2	0	7	9	41	-32	6
13 Wymondham Town Res	12	1	0	11	15	48	-33	3
14 Thetford Rovers Res	11	0	0	11	6	85	-79	0

BEDFORDSHIRE COUNTY LEAGUE

Step 7 - promotes to Spartan South Midlands League

PREMIER DIVISION	P	W	D	L	F	A	GD	Pts
1 Elstow Abbey	9	6	1	2	20	5	15	19
2 AFC Oakley	8	6	0	2	34	11	23	18
3 Flitwick Town	8	5	1	2	20	13	7	16
4 Marston Shelton Rovers	8	5	1	2	20	16	4	16
5 Cranfield United	8	5	1	2	19	16	3	16
6 Queens Park Crescents	7	5	0	2	16	10	6	15
7 Biggleswade Res	7	4	1	2	18	9	9	13
8 Crawley Green Res	8	4	1	3	15	16	-1	13
9 Caldecote	8	4	0	4	15	14	1	12
10 Stevington	7	3	2	2	12	8	4	11
11 Bedford Albion	7	3	0	4	11	14	-3	9
12 Riseley Sports	9	2	1	6	8	16	-8	7
13 Shefford Town & Campton Res	6	2	0	4	6	15	-9	6
14 AFC Kempston Town & Bedford C	9	1	1	7	13	21	-8	4
15 Wilstead	9	1	1	7	9	38	-29	4
16 Biggleswade United U23	8	1	1	6	14	28	-14	3*

DIVISION ONE 'A'	P	W	D	L	F	A	GD	Pts
1 Lea Sports PSG	7	5	0	2	25	12	13	15
2 Stotfold Development	6	5	0	1	22	14	8	15
3 Eaton Park Rangers	7	5	0	2	17	15	2	15
4 Langford Res	8	5	0	3	26	11	15	14*
5 Arlesey Town U23	6	4	1	1	17	11	6	13
6 St Joseph's (Saturday)	6	4	0	2	22	12	10	12
7 Kempston Athletic	7	4	0	3	24	9	15	11*
8 Ickwell & Old Warden	5	2	0	3	10	16	-6	6
9 Totternhoe Res	4	1	0	3	6	12	-6	3
10 AFC Kempston Town & BC Res	7	1	0	6	8	29	-21	3
11 Houghton Athletic	7	0	1	6	9	31	-22	1
12 Wilstead Res	4	0	0	4	2	16	-14	-1*

DIVISION ONE 'B'	P	W	D	L	F	A	GD	Pts
1 Henlow	7	6	1	0	22	10	12	19
2 Sharnbrook	6	5	1	0	19	4	15	16
3 Stopsley United	5	3	0	2	26	6	20	9
4 Ampthill Town Dev	6	3	0	3	21	15	6	9
5 Flitwick Town Res	6	3	0	3	11	13	-2	9
6 The Pines (Luton)	4	2	0	2	13	13	0	6
7 Sporting Lewsey Park	6	2	0	4	11	13	-2	6
8 AFC Oakley Res	4	2	0	2	10	12	-2	6
9 Pitstone & Ivinghoe Res	5	2	0	3	12	19	-7	6
10 Bedford Sports Athletic	4	1	1	2	7	13	-6	4
11 Cranfield United Res	5	0	1	4	7	16	-9	1
12 The 61 FC (Luton) Res	4	0	0	4	5	30	-25	0

BRIGHTON, WORTHING & DISTRICT LEAGUE

DIVISION ONE	P	W	D	L	F	A	GD	Pts
1 Lancing United	15	12	2	1	82	20	62	38
2 Broadwater Athletic	15	11	3	1	56	21	35	36
3 Angmering Village Res	15	10	3	2	45	25	20	33
4 Ovingdean	15	9	3	3	43	26	17	30
5 The Lectern Lights	15	9	2	4	46	24	22	29
6 Diversity United	15	7	5	3	51	20	31	26
7 Hangleton	15	7	5	3	46	35	11	26
8 The View Saturday	15	6	4	5	34	30	4	22
9 Clarendon Athletic	15	5	4	6	28	38	-10	19
10 AFC Broadwater	15	5	3	7	33	57	-24	18
11 Preston Park	15	5	2	8	33	42	-9	17
12 Worthing Town Res	15	3	4	8	25	34	-9	13
13 Boys Brigade Old Boys	15	4	1	10	29	52	-23	13
14 Goring St Theresa's	15	3	3	9	18	41	-23	12
15 AFC Fernhurst	15	1	2	12	16	49	-33	5
16 St Marys	15	0	0	15	13	84	-71	0

Resumed the league in Spring 2021 and as none of the clubs had played each other twice at that point it was decided that to conclude the season, clubs would only play each other once.

BRISTOL & SUBURBAN LEAGUE

PREMIER DIVISION ONE	P	W	D	L	F	A	GD	Pts
1 Stoke Gifford United	8	4	3	1	25	12	13	15
2 Old Cothamians	7	5	0	2	23	14	9	15
3 Parson Street Old Boys	6	4	0	2	25	12	13	12
4 Filton Athletic	5	3	2	0	8	3	5	11
5 AFC Mangotsfield	7	3	1	3	15	14	1	10
6 Stoke Rangers	7	3	1	3	19	20	-1	10
7 Lawrence Weston Athletic	7	3	1	3	11	14	-3	10
8 Bristol Spartak	5	3	0	2	8	8	0	9
9 Easton Cowboys	4	2	1	1	8	7	1	7
10 North Bristol United	6	1	3	2	9	12	-3	6
11 Rockleaze Rangers Res	6	2	0	4	11	15	-4	6
12 Old Georgians	6	1	0	5	4	11	-7	3
13 St Aldhelms	6	1	0	5	5	20	-15	3
14 Avonmouth	2	0	0	2	1	10	-9	0

LOCKDOWN A	P	W	D	L	F	A	GD	Pts
1 Old Cothamians	5	4	1	0	19	9	10	13
2 Bristol Spartak	5	2	2	1	11	9	2	8
3 Lawrence Weston Athletic	5	1	4	0	7	6	1	7
4 Parson Street Old Boys	5	0	3	2	10	13	-3	3
5 Easton Cowboys	5	0	3	2	8	12	-4	3
6 AFC Mangotsfield	5	0	3	2	6	12	-6	3

LOCKDOWN B	P	W	D	L	F	A	GD	Pts
1 Almondsbury Res	5	5	0	0	20	2	18	15
2 Stoke Rangers	5	4	0	1	19	7	12	12
3 North Bristol United	5	3	0	2	12	6	6	9
4 Rockleaze Rangers Res	5	2	0	3	5	11	-6	6
5 MPK Lofts	5	1	0	4	5	13	-8	3
6 St Aldhelms	5	0	0	5	2	24	-22	0

LOCKDOWN C	P	W	D	L	F	A	GD	Pts
1 Redbridge Saturday	5	3	2	0	13	5	8	11
2 Bristol Bilbao	5	3	2	0	17	10	7	11
3 Ridings High	5	3	0	2	9	9	0	9
4 Wessex Wanderers	5	1	1	3	10	10	0	4
5 Jamaica Bell, The	5	0	3	2	6	8	-2	3
6 AFC Brislington Res	5	1	0	4	7	20	-13	3

LOCKDOWN D	P	W	D	L	F	A	GD	Pts
1 Bromley Heath United Res	5	4	1	0	16	5	11	13
2 Southmead CS Athletic	5	3	0	2	8	7	1	9
3 Keynsham Town A	5	2	0	3	8	11	-3	6
4 Cosmos UK	5	1	2	2	9	10	-1	5
5 Old Cothamians Res	5	1	2	2	6	10	-4	5
6 Stockwood Wanderers Res	5	0	3	2	8	12	-4	3

LOCKDOWN E	P	W	D	L	F	A	GD	Pts
1 Rockleaze Rangers A	5	4	1	0	15	4	11	13
2 Easton Cowboys Res	5	2	2	1	19	14	5	8
3 Imperial Res	5	2	1	2	10	20	-10	7
4 Park Knowle	5	2	0	3	10	9	1	6
5 AFC Mangotsfield Res	5	1	2	2	10	14	-4	5
6 Wanderers Saturday	5	1	0	4	5	8	-3	3

LOCKDOWN F	P	W	D	L	F	A	GD	Pts
1 AFC Whitchurch	5	4	0	1	15	6	9	12
2 Parson Street OB Res	5	3	2	0	15	8	7	11
3 Fishponds Old Boys	5	3	0	2	16	15	1	9
4 Rockleaze Rangers B	5	1	1	3	11	14	-3	4
5 Corinthian Sports	4	1	1	2	10	14	-4	4
6 St Vallier	4	0	0	4	8	18	-10	0

LOCKDOWN G	P	W	D	L	F	A	GD	Pts
1 Bristol Phoenix	4	3	1	0	15	6	9	10
2 Old Georgians Res	4	2	2	0	8	4	4	8
3 Stokeside	4	1	1	2	7	9	-2	4
4 Broad Plain House Res	4	1	0	3	9	7	2	3
5 Lawrence Weston Athletic Res	4	1	0	3	4	17	-13	3

LOCKDOWN H	P	W	D	L	F	A	GD	Pts
1 Wessex Wanderers Res	5	4	1	0	22	8	14	13
2 Rockleaze Rangers C	5	3	0	2	15	8	7	9
3 Bedminster Down	5	2	2	1	15	13	2	8
4 Long Ashton Victoria	5	1	2	2	13	13	0	5
5 Socius United	5	1	2	2	11	19	-8	5
6 Brandon Sports	5	0	1	4	8	23	-15	1

LOCKDOWN I	P	W	D	L	F	A	GD	Pts
1 Redbridge Saturday Res	4	3	0	1	16	5	11	9
2 Ashton FC	4	3	0	1	15	4	11	9
3 Bromley Heath United A	4	2	1	1	11	10	1	7
4 Easton Cowboys A	4	1	0	3	5	15	-10	3
5 Brentry Athletic	4	0	1	3	3	16	-13	1
6 Cutters Friday A	0	0	0	0	0	0	0	0

LOCKDOWN J	P	W	D	L	F	A	GD	Pts
1 Suburban Phoenix	5	5	0	0	24	3	21	15
2 Corinthian Sports Res	5	2	2	1	12	10	2	8
3 Eastville Rangers	5	2	1	2	10	13	-3	7
4 Fishponds Old Boys Res	5	2	1	2	10	15	-5	7
5 TC Sports	5	1	1	3	9	13	-4	4
6 Kellaway Rangers	5	0	1	4	2	13	-11	1

BRISTOL PREMIER COMBINATION LEAGUE

PREMIER DIVISION	P	W	D	L	F	A	GD	Pts
1 Winterbourne United	9	6	1	2	36	16	20	19
2 Hallen Res	6	6	0	0	30	10	20	18
3 Nicholas Wanderers	5	4	1	0	16	5	11	13
4 Cribbs Res	5	4	0	1	24	11	13	12
5 Olveston United	6	4	0	2	15	5	10	12
6 AEK Boco Res	7	3	1	3	18	15	3	10
7 Totterdown United	7	3	1	3	20	19	1	10
8 Shaftesbury Crusade	7	3	0	4	15	20	-5	9
9 Seymour United	5	2	0	3	8	9	-1	6
10 Longwell Green Sports Res	7	1	3	3	14	19	-5	6
11 Highridge United	7	1	2	4	10	21	-11	5
12 Lebeq	7	1	1	5	6	33	-27	4
13 Chipping Sodbury Town Res	5	1	0	4	9	20	-11	3
14 Pucklechurch Sports	7	0	2	5	13	31	-18	2

DIVISION ONE	P	W	D	L	F	A	GD	Pts
1 Bradley Stoke Town	8	4	2	2	23	13	10	14
2 Wick Res	5	4	0	1	12	9	3	12
3 Iron Acton	5	3	1	1	20	14	6	10
4 Mendip Broadwalk Res	6	3	1	2	11	10	1	10
5 Cribbs A	4	3	0	1	20	14	6	9
6 DRG SV Frenchay	5	2	2	1	10	5	5	8
7 St Nicholas	4	2	1	1	10	8	2	7
8 Greyfriars Athletic	9	2	1	6	22	27	-5	7
9 De Veys	6	2	1	3	13	18	-5	7
10 Nicholas Wanderers Res	4	2	0	2	10	9	1	6
11 Hambrook	4	2	0	2	7	12	-5	6
12 Oldland Abbotonians Res	4	0	1	3	5	16	-11	1
13 Shirehampton Res	4	0	0	4	4	12	-8	0

CAMBRIDGESHIRE COUNTY LEAGUE

STEP 7 - promotes to Eastern Counties League.

PREMIER DIVISION	P	W	D	L	F	A	GD	Pts
1 West Wratting	9	7	1	1	26	11	15	22
2 Great Shelford	8	6	2	0	17	7	10	20
3 Eaton Socon	10	6	2	2	23	17	6	20
4 Witchford 96	10	5	3	2	24	19	5	18
5 Eynesbury United	8	5	2	1	20	12	8	17
6 Foxton	9	4	3	2	16	11	5	15
7 Over Sports	8	4	1	3	13	10	3	13
8 Cambridge University Press	9	3	2	4	14	17	-3	11
9 Cherry Hinton	7	3	1	3	12	12	0	10
10 Linton Granta	8	3	0	5	14	15	-1	9
11 Comberton United	9	3	0	6	19	24	-5	9
12 Hemingfords United	8	2	2	4	12	16	-4	8
13 Ely City Res	9	1	2	6	15	26	-11	5
14 Gamlingay United	9	0	4	5	7	13	-6	4
15 Fulbourn Institute	9	0	1	8	6	28	-22	1

SENIOR A	P	W	D	L	F	A	GD	Pts
1 Isleham United	9	7	1	1	23	10	13	22
2 AFC Barley Mow	11	6	3	2	37	20	17	21
3 Eaton Socon Res	11	6	3	2	25	16	9	21
4 March Town United Res	10	7	0	3	26	22	4	21
5 Somersham Town	8	6	1	1	23	15	8	19
6 Orwell	9	6	0	3	22	12	10	18
7 Huntingdon United	8	4	3	1	20	13	7	15
8 Whittlesford United	10	3	2	5	22	30	-8	11
9 Bluntisham Rangers	12	3	2	7	15	28	-13	11
10 Cottenham United	9	3	1	5	20	21	-1	10
11 Bassingbourn	6	2	1	3	13	15	-2	7
12 Thaxted Rangers	9	2	1	6	16	20	-4	7
13 Milton	7	2	0	5	12	19	-7	6
14 Soham Town Rangers FC Res	8	1	0	7	11	26	-15	3
15 Hundon F.C.	9	1	0	8	10	28	-18	3

SENIOR B	P	W	D	L	F	A	GD	Pts
1 Fordham	11	9	1	1	25	9	16	28
2 Newmarket Town F.C Res	11	8	1	2	38	12	26	25
3 Brampton	9	7	1	1	24	10	14	22
4 Houghton & Wyton	9	5	3	1	25	13	12	18
5 Cherry Hinton Res	8	5	1	2	21	12	9	16
6 Sawston Rovers	11	4	2	5	32	26	6	14
7 Linton Granta Res	9	4	1	4	23	18	5	13
8 Hardwick FC	9	4	0	5	19	15	4	12
9 Cambridge Uni Press Res	11	3	2	6	14	17	-3	11
10 Duxford United	10	2	4	4	17	18	-1	10
11 Lakenheath F.C. Res	7	2	1	4	14	22	-8	7
12 St Ives Rangers	10	1	2	7	11	40	-29	5
13 Wisbech St Mary Res	9	1	1	7	17	51	-34	4
14 Fulbourn Institute Res	8	1	0	7	9	26	-17	3

DIVISION ONE A	P	W	D	L	F	A	GD	Pts
1 Comberton United Res	7	7	0	0	32	6	26	21
2 Harston	7	5	1	1	20	6	14	16
3 Clare Town F.C.	8	5	1	2	20	12	8	16
4 Great Shelford Res	7	4	1	2	12	9	3	13
5 Debden	7	4	0	3	12	10	2	12
6 West Wratting Res	6	4	0	2	14	13	1	12
7 Barrington Barrington	9	3	2	4	19	23	-4	11
8 Steeple Morden	10	3	2	5	16	23	-7	11
9 Meldreth	8	2	0	6	9	19	-10	6
10 Milton Res	8	1	3	4	7	20	-13	6
11 Mott MacDonald	7	1	2	4	10	12	-2	5
12 Cambourne Rovers	6	0	0	6	5	23	-18	0

DIVISION ONE B	P	W	D	L	F	A	GD	Pts
1 Swavesey Institute	10	6	1	3	28	15	13	19
2 AFC Walpole	6	6	0	0	20	4	16	18
3 Outwell Swifts	6	6	0	0	16	6	10	18
4 Hemingfords United Res	10	5	1	4	27	15	12	16
5 Fenstanton	11	5	0	6	23	28	-5	15
6 Over Sports Res	8	3	2	3	10	10	0	11
7 Alconbury	7	3	1	3	12	12	0	10
8 Ely City 'A'	7	2	1	4	10	16	-6	7
9 Burwell Swifts	7	2	0	5	10	17	-7	6
10 Godmanchester Rovers Res	4	1	1	2	9	11	-2	4
11 Chatteris Town	7	1	1	5	7	16	-9	4
12 Gamlingay United Res	7	1	0	6	5	27	-22	3

Central Midlands Premier North action - Clay Cross Town v Staveley MW Reserves. Photos Bill Wheatcroft.

DIVISION TWO A	P	W	D	L	F	A	GD	Pts
1 Melbourn FC	9	6	3	0	24	5	19	21
2 Buckden	8	5	2	1	43	9	34	17
3 Guilden Morden	7	5	1	1	30	11	19	16
4 Foxton Res	7	5	1	1	26	15	11	16
5 Great Paxton 's	9	4	0	5	14	24	-10	12
6 Litlington Athletic	9	3	2	4	17	17	0	11
7 Whittlesford United Res	8	3	1	4	21	14	7	10
8 Linton Granta A	8	3	1	4	19	18	1	10
9 Puddlebrook 68 F.C.	5	2	1	2	12	13	-1	7
10 Papworth	9	2	1	6	14	31	-17	7
11 Haverhill Rovers F.C. Res	4	1	1	2	5	9	-4	4
12 Steeple Morden Res	9	0	0	9	4	63	-59	0

DIVISION TWO B	P	W	D	L	F	A	GD	Pts
1 March Town United A	9	7	1	1	36	11	25	22
2 Benwick Athletic	8	6	1	1	28	12	16	19
3 Soham United Youths	9	6	1	2	27	16	11	19
4 Burwell Tigers Men	9	5	1	3	18	14	4	16
5 Wimblington	10	4	2	4	25	27	-2	14
6 Exning United F.C.	8	4	1	3	30	18	12	13
7 Guyhirn	9	4	0	5	18	25	-7	12
8 Wisbech Town Acorns	10	2	1	7	8	33	-25	7
9 Fordham Res	10	2	0	8	19	31	-12	6
10 Chatteris Town Res	8	1	0	7	13	35	-22	3

DIVISION THREE A	P	W	D	L	F	A	GD	Pts
1 Hardwick FC Res	7	7	0	0	38	10	28	21
2 Abington United	7	5	1	1	32	17	15	16
3 Clare Town F.C. Res	9	4	2	3	15	18	-3	14
4 Sawston United Youth	7	4	1	2	13	5	8	13
5 Orwell Res	8	4	1	3	23	19	4	13
6 Sawston Rovers Res	6	4	0	2	27	15	12	12
7 Kedington F.C.	8	3	3	2	21	23	-2	12
8 Hundon F.C. Res	8	3	2	3	13	13	0	11
9 Duxford United Res	9	2	1	6	22	35	-13	7
10 Girton United	7	2	1	4	20	35	-15	7
11 Harston Res	8	1	0	7	10	22	-12	3
12 Guilden Morden Second	8	0	2	6	8	30	-22	2

DIVISION THREE B	P	W	D	L	F	A	GD	Pts
1 Longstanton FC	9	7	1	1	33	15	18	22
2 Stretham	9	6	2	1	32	12	20	20
3 Cherry Hinton A	8	6	1	1	41	13	28	19
4 Crusaders 2019	9	6	0	3	19	17	2	18
5 Oakington Vikings	8	5	1	2	27	16	11	16
6 Isleham United Res	10	4	3	3	26	18	8	15
7 Barton Mills F.C.	8	3	3	2	16	7	9	12
8 Histon Hornets	9	3	2	4	25	21	4	11
9 Cottenham United Res	8	2	0	6	14	32	-18	6
10 The Eagle (Ely)	6	1	1	4	12	14	-2	4
11 Eaton Socon A	9	0	0	9	12	47	-35	0
12 Mott MacDonald Res	7	0	0	7	3	48	-45	0

DIVISION THREE C	P	W	D	L	F	A	GD	Pts
1 Needingworth United	9	7	0	2	30	12	18	21
2 Witchford 96 Res	8	5	0	3	31	16	15	15
3 AFC Christchurch Magpies	8	4	1	3	19	16	3	13
4 Manea United	10	4	0	6	18	20	-2	12
5 March Academy	9	3	3	3	15	17	-2	12
6 Little Downham & Pymoor Swifts Res	7	3	2	2	20	19	1	11
7 Houghton & Wyton Res	7	3	2	2	18	17	1	11
8 Bluntisham Rangers Res	8	3	1	4	22	25	-3	10
9 Somersham Town Res	7	2	3	2	17	20	-3	9
10 Littleport Town	7	1	3	3	10	21	-11	6
11 Doddington United	10	1	3	6	18	35	-17	6

CENTRAL MIDLANDS LEAGUE

Step 7 - promotes to Northern Counties East League & East Midlands Counties League

PREMIER DIVISION NORTH	P	W	D	L	F	A	GD	Pts
1 Clay Cross Town	7	6	0	1	31	4	27	18
2 Retford United	7	6	0	1	17	9	8	18
3 AFC Bentley	8	5	1	2	22	12	10	16
4 Dinnington Town	9	5	0	4	16	18	-2	15
5 Harworth Colliery	5	4	1	0	6	1	5	13
6 Sutton Rovers 2007	10	4	1	5	20	16	4	13
7 Thorne Colliery	8	4	0	4	10	8	2	12
8 Newark Town	5	3	1	1	14	5	9	10
9 Kiveton Miners Welfare	10	3	1	6	16	37	-21	10
10 St Josephs Rockware of Worksop	6	2	2	2	16	14	2	8
11 Collingham	6	2	1	3	14	13	1	7
12 Crowle Colts	5	2	0	3	4	10	-6	6
13 Staveley Miners Welfare Res	6	1	1	4	7	13	-6	4
14 AFC Phoenix	8	1	1	6	6	21	-15	4
15 Boynton Sports	8	1	0	7	8	26	-18	3

PREMIER DIVISION SOUTH	P	W	D	L	F	A	GD	Pts
1 Blidworth Welfare	11	10	1	0	35	11	24	31
2 Pinxton	9	7	1	1	36	16	20	22
3 Rowsley '86	10	7	1	2	31	21	10	22
4 Mickleover Res	8	5	1	2	21	12	9	16
5 Underwood Villa	9	5	0	4	19	18	1	15
6 Ashland Rovers	10	5	0	5	23	25	-2	15
7 Linby Colliery Welfare	9	3	3	3	22	13	9	12
8 Holbrook St Michaels	7	3	2	2	18	16	2	11
9 Hilton Harriers	10	3	1	6	14	22	-8	10
10 South Normanton Athletic	7	3	0	4	15	14	1	9
11 Mansfield Hosiery Mills	6	3	0	3	5	13	-8	9
12 Sherwood Colliery Res	8	2	1	5	15	17	-2	7
13 Nottingham	9	2	1	6	17	29	-12	7
14 Holbrook Sports	3	1	0	2	4	6	-2	3
15 Teversal Res	9	1	0	8	11	25	-14	3
16 Arnold Town	9	1	0	8	9	37	-28	3

DIVISION ONE CENTRAL	P	W	D	L	F	A	GD	Pts
1 Wirksworth Ivanhoe	12	9	2	1	31	17	14	29
2 Bakewell Town	12	8	4	0	41	7	34	28
3 Cromford & Wirksworth Town	12	7	2	3	26	10	16	23
4 Woodhouse Colts	12	6	1	5	33	25	8	19
5 Kilburn	12	4	1	7	18	28	-10	13
6 Ashland Rovers Res	12	1	1	10	7	47	-40	4
7 Holbrook St Michaels Res	12	0	3	9	6	28	-22	3

Holbrook Sports Res, Pinxton Dev and South Normanton Athletic Res did not take part when the division was restarted in the Spring 2021 and their previous results were expunged.

DIVISION ONE NORTH	P	W	D	L	F	A	GD	Pts
1 Sheffield Res	14	13	1	0	49	18	31	40
2 Glapwell	14	10	1	3	30	11	19	31
3 Harworth Colliery Res	14	6	3	5	43	30	13	21
4 780 JLC	14	6	2	6	37	36	1	20
5 Bessacarr	14	4	4	6	32	31	1	16
6 Thorne Colliery Dev	14	4	2	8	24	37	-13	14
7 Newark Town Dev	14	3	1	10	17	48	-31	10
8 Ollerton Town Res	14	2	2	10	17	38	-21	8

Shirebrook Soliders did not take part when the division was restarted in the Spring 2021 and their previous results were expunged.

DIVISION ONE SOUTH	P	W	D	L	F	A	GD	Pts
1 Long Eaton United Com	10	10	0	0	30	5	25	30
2 Melbourne Dynamo	10	6	0	4	29	13	16	18
3 Selston Res	10	4	0	6	19	24	-5	12
4 Pass Move Grin Acad	10	4	0	6	15	25	-10	11*
5 Ripley Town	10	3	1	6	17	31	-14	10
6 Clifton All Whites Dev	10	2	1	7	17	29	-12	7
7 Heanor Town Res								
8 Linby Colliery Welfare Res								

Underwood Villa Res did not take part when the division was restarted in the Spring 2021 and their previous results were expunged.

CHESHIRE LEAGUE

Step 7 - promotes to North West Counties League.

PREMIER DIVISION	P	W	D	L	F	A	GD	Pts
1 F.C. St. Helens	9	8	1	0	39	9	30	25
2 GPSO	7	4	1	2	12	7	5	13
3 Whaley Bridge Athletic	5	4	0	1	13	9	4	12
4 Congleton Town Res.	6	4	0	2	10	9	1	12
5 Broadheath Central FC	7	2	4	1	16	15	1	10
6 Altrincham FC Res.	6	2	3	1	15	13	2	9
7 Billinge	7	3	0	4	13	15	-2	9
8 Lostock Gralam	6	3	0	3	10	12	-2	9
9 Winstanley Warriors	8	2	2	4	20	24	-4	8
10 Egerton FC	6	2	1	3	20	11	9	7
11 Crewe FC	5	2	1	2	13	18	-5	7
12 Middlewich Town	9	2	1	6	9	23	-14	7
13 Eagle Sports	6	1	3	2	11	13	-2	6
14 Daten FC	6	1	2	3	8	12	-4	5
15 Knutsford	2	1	0	1	2	3	-1	3
16 Poynton FC	5	1	0	4	3	16	-13	3
17 Garswood United	4	0	1	3	5	10	-5	1

LEAGUE ONE	P	W	D	L	F	A	GD	Pts
1 Knowsley South	22	17	1	4	74	30	44	52
2 Denton Town	22	14	2	6	53	23	30	46*
3 Vulcan FC	22	12	3	7	41	41	0	39
4 Partington Village	22	12	1	9	48	29	19	37
5 Parklands	22	12	1	9	41	46	-5	37
6 Styal FC	22	11	2	9	35	39	-4	35
7 Cheadle Heath Nomads Res.	22	10	4	8	53	44	9	34
8 Winnington Avenue Y.C. 94	22	10	4	8	47	40	7	33*
9 Windle Labour F.C	22	9	1	12	38	44	-6	28
10 Newton Athletic	22	6	4	12	34	54	-20	22
11 Maine Road Res.	22	2	5	15	35	75	-40	11
12 Moore United	22	1	4	17	27	61	-34	7

Ashton Athletic Res. and Malpas FC did not take part when the division was restarted in the Spring 2021 and their previous results were expunged.

LEAGUE TWO	P	W	D	L	F	A	GD	Pts
1 Blacon Youth	20	16	4	0	84	15	69	52
2 Whalley Range FC	19	15	3	1	90	33	57	48*
3 Wyth. Amateurs FC Res.	20	11	3	6	46	33	13	36
4 Holmes Chapel	20	11	2	7	61	40	21	35
5 Pilkington Res.	20	11	2	7	46	45	1	35
6 St Helens Town Res.	20	10	1	9	49	70	-21	31
7 Sandbach United Res.	20	9	1	10	44	48	-4	28
8 West Didsbury & Chorlton Res.	20	7	1	12	35	30	5	22
9 Golborne Sports	19	3	3	13	34	56	-22	12*
10 Rylands Res.	20	3	2	15	33	99	-66	11
11 Hartford FC	20	1	2	17	22	75	-53	5

Nantwich Town Res. did not take part when the division was restarted in the Spring 2021 and their previous results were expunged.

Golborne Sports v Whalley Range was abandoned and was not played again after the FA found both teams at fault of not controlling their players.

CORNWALL COMBINATION

	P	W	D	L	F	A	GD	Pts
1 Ruan Minor	7	6	1	0	26	4	22	19
2 Ludgvan	8	5	2	1	27	10	17	17
3 Helston Athletic Thirds	11	5	2	4	27	20	7	17
4 Penryn Athletic Res	9	5	2	2	20	13	7	17
5 Wendron United Thirds	12	4	4	4	25	28	-3	16
6 Pendeen Rovers	10	4	3	3	24	14	10	15
7 Illogan RBL Res	10	4	3	3	25	19	6	15
8 Holman SC	10	5	0	5	31	29	2	15
9 Hayle Res	9	4	2	3	33	20	13	14
10 Rosudgeon	9	4	2	3	26	22	4	14
11 Marazion	6	4	1	1	22	12	10	13
12 St Agnes Res	11	4	1	6	17	29	-12	13
13 St Day Res	8	3	0	5	20	20	0	9
14 RNAS Culdrose	9	2	2	5	9	20	-11	8
15 Lizard Argyle	9	2	1	6	16	34	-18	7
16 Perranporth	10	0	0	10	4	58	-54	0

DEVON & EXETER LEAGUE

When the league was restarted in the Spring 2021 those clubs who chose not to take part had their previous results expunged.

PREMIER DIVISION EAST	P	W	D	L	F	A	GD	Pts
1 Lyme Regis	8	6	1	1	35	15	20	19
2 Feniton	8	5	2	1	19	11	8	17
3 Kentisbeare	8	2	1	5	17	24	-7	7
4 Dawlish United	8	2	1	5	9	23	-14	7
5 Chard Town Res	8	1	3	4	6	13	-7	6

PREMIER DIVISION WEST	P	W	D	L	F	A	GD	Pts
1 Lapford	12	10	1	1	53	13	40	31
2 Thorverton	12	8	2	2	35	16	19	26
3 Elmore Res	12	6	3	3	28	15	13	21
4 Chagford	12	4	3	5	25	37	-12	15
5 Alphington Res	12	3	4	5	19	25	-6	13
6 Newtown Res	12	3	2	7	24	33	-9	11
7 Hatherleigh Town	12	0	1	11	7	52	-45	1

DIVISION ONE EAST	P	W	D	L	F	A	GD	Pts
1 Exmouth Rovers	14	13	1	0	38	10	28	40
2 Otterton	14	9	1	4	41	36	5	28
3 East Budleigh	14	8	1	5	44	29	15	25
4 Teignmouth Res	12	6	2	4	30	23	7	19*
5 Clyst Valley Res	14	5	3	6	32	42	-10	18
6 Lyme Regis Res	13	4	1	8	25	29	-4	13
7 Dunkeswell Rovers	14	2	1	11	19	38	-19	6*
8 Lympstone	13	1	2	10	7	29	-22	5

DIVISION ONE WEST	P	W	D	L	F	A	GD	Pts
1 Halwill	12	8	2	2	38	15	23	26
2 Newton St Cyres	12	8	2	2	33	17	16	26
3 Alphington 3rd	12	6	0	6	28	33	-5	18
4 Bow Amateur Athletic Club	12	5	1	6	24	28	-4	15*
5 Winkleigh	12	5	1	6	32	19	13	14*
6 Westexe Park Rangers	12	4	1	7	23	45	-22	13
7 Tedburn St Mary	12	2	1	9	15	36	-21	7

DIVISION TWO EAST	P	W	D	L	F	A	GD	Pts
1 Ottery St Mary AFC Res	14	11	1	2	43	16	27	34
2 Axminster Town Res	14	12	1	1	68	12	56	33*
3 Cranbrook	14	7	1	6	58	42	16	22
4 Millwey Rise	14	5	5	4	21	20	1	19*
5 Pinhoe	14	3	4	7	26	61	-35	13
6 Exeter United	14	3	4	7	24	33	-9	12*
7 East Budleigh Res	14	3	2	9	25	58	-33	11
8 Feniton Res	14	2	2	10	26	49	-23	8

DIVISION TWO WEST	P	W	D	L	F	A	GD	Pts
1 Central	12	8	3	1	25	15	10	27
2 Devon Yeoman	12	8	2	2	34	19	15	26
3 Okehampton Argyle Res	12	6	3	3	31	15	16	21
4 Bampton Res	12	5	3	4	37	21	16	17*
5 South Zeal United	12	4	2	6	29	24	5	14
6 Hemyock	12	3	2	7	18	30	-12	11
7 Culm United	12	0	1	11	12	62	-50	0*

DIVISION THREE EAST	P	W	D	L	F	A	GD	Pts
1 Winchester Res	12	11	1	0	37	15	22	34
2 Dawlish United Res	12	9	0	3	46	17	29	27
3 Awliscombe	12	7	1	4	28	22	6	22
4 Topsham Town Res	12	5	0	7	20	20	0	14*
5 Offwell Rangers FC	12	2	2	8	13	24	-11	8
6 Cranbrook United	12	2	2	8	7	27	-20	8
7 Devon Yeoman Res	12	2	2	8	15	41	-26	8

DIVISION THREE WEST	P	W	D	L	F	A	GD	Pts
1 Bradninch	15	12	1	2	57	27	30	37
2 Broadclyst Res	15	9	4	2	42	21	21	31
3 Cullompton Rangers Res	16	9	1	6	39	23	16	28
4 Witheridge Res	15	8	1	6	46	29	17	25
5 Elmore 3rd	16	6	3	7	48	45	3	21
6 Central Res	15	6	2	7	37	40	-3	20
7 Chagford Res	15	4	2	9	28	47	-19	14
8 Amory Green Rovers	13	2	3	8	27	48	-21	9
9 Halwill Res	16	2	3	11	18	62	-44	8*

DIVISION FOUR CENTRAL	P	W	D	L	F	A	GD	Pts
1 Kenn Valley United	18	16	0	2	85	35	50	48
2 Thorverton Res	18	12	2	4	69	47	22	38
3 Beacon Knights FC	18	9	3	6	45	37	8	30
4 Priory	18	7	7	4	50	44	6	28
5 Newton St Cyres Res	18	8	3	7	44	44	0	27
6 Cranbrook United Res	18	7	5	6	46	45	1	26
7 City Raiders AFC	18	5	4	9	39	58	-19	19
8 Whipton & Pinhoe Res	17	4	4	9	51	44	7	16
9 Tedburn St Mary Res	17	4	3	10	29	40	-11	15
10 Exeter Panthers AFC	18	1	1	16	26	90	-64	4

DIVISION FOUR EAST	P	W	D	L	F	A	GD	Pts
1 Ottery St Mary AFC 3rd	14	12	2	0	40	14	26	38
2 HT Dons	14	10	0	4	45	26	19	30
3 Dawlish United 3rd	14	10	0	4	36	25	11	30
4 Falcons FC	14	8	2	4	28	24	4	26
5 Otterton Res	14	5	1	8	41	32	9	16
6 Bradninch Ress	14	4	1	9	38	59	-21	13
7 Lympstone Res	14	3	2	9	26	31	-5	11
8 Exmouth Town 3rd	14	0	0	14	15	58	-43	0

DEVON FOOTBALL LEAGUE

Step 7 - promotes to the South West Peninsula League.

NORTH-EAST DIVISION	P	W	D	L	F	A	GD	Pts
1 Exwick Villa	11	8	2	1	34	13	21	26
2 Newtown	10	5	3	2	25	14	11	18
3 Teignmouth	9	5	2	2	35	17	18	17
4 Topsham Town	9	4	5	0	19	9	10	17
5 Alphington	11	5	2	4	17	13	4	17
6 Braunton	7	4	2	1	17	11	6	14
7 Exmouth Town Res	8	4	1	3	14	14	0	13
8 St Martins	11	4	1	6	13	20	-7	13
9 University of Exeter	4	4	0	0	17	3	14	12
10 Liverton United	10	2	5	3	16	19	-3	11
11 Budleigh Salterton	11	2	3	6	23	30	-7	9
12 Clyst Valley	9	1	2	6	13	27	-14	5
13 Chudleigh Athletic	10	1	2	7	15	37	-22	5
14 Heavitree United	10	0	2	8	5	36	-31	2

Bovey Tracey Res (after 3 games) and Witheridge (6 games) both resigned from the league - their results were expunged.

SOUTH-WEST DIVISION	P	W	D	L	F	A	GD	Pts
1 Ottery St Mary	13	12	1	0	53	7	46	37
2 Okehampton Argyle	12	10	1	1	48	9	39	31
3 Buckland Athletic Res	11	10	0	1	55	2	53	30
4 Plymstock United	10	7	0	3	30	16	14	21
5 Paignton Saints	10	7	0	3	31	18	13	21
6 Newton Abbot Spurs Res	13	6	2	5	30	20	10	20
7 Lakeside Athletic	10	5	1	4	22	30	-8	16
8 Plympton Athletic	9	5	0	4	19	16	3	15
9 Roselands	11	4	1	6	28	22	6	13
10 Plymouth Argyle Dev	10	4	1	5	14	17	-3	13
11 Kingsteignton Athletic	9	3	1	5	16	29	-13	10
12 Bere Alston United	10	3	0	7	12	20	-8	9
13 Paignton Villa	11	2	0	9	11	41	-30	6
14 Totnes & Dartington Sports	12	2	0	10	12	53	-41	6
15 Watcombe Wanderers	9	1	0	8	8	31	-23	3
16 Waldon Athletic	10	0	0	10	5	63	-58	0

DORSET FOOTBALL LEAGUE

SENIOR DIVISION	P	W	D	L	F	A	GD	Pts
1 Sturminster Marshall	8	7	0	1	20	4	16	21
2 Wincanton Town Res	7	5	0	2	13	11	2	15
3 Tisbury United	5	4	1	0	13	5	8	13
4 Mere Town	5	4	0	1	11	8	3	12
5 Dorchester Sports Res	7	4	0	3	15	15	0	12
6 Cranborne	6	3	1	2	9	9	0	10
7 Broadstone	5	3	0	2	10	7	3	9
8 Chickerell United	6	3	0	3	17	15	2	9
9 Stalbridge	4	2	1	1	14	10	4	7
10 Merley Cobham Sports Res	7	2	1	4	12	17	-5	7
11 Poole Borough	7	2	0	5	6	8	-2	6
12 Beaminster	5	1	0	4	7	13	-6	3
13 Hamworthy Recreation Res	6	0	0	6	6	16	-10	0
14 Westland Sports Res	6	0	0	6	6	21	-15	0

DORSET PREMIER LEAGUE

Step 7 - promotes to the Wessex League.

	P	W	D	L	F	A	GD	Pts
1 Merley Cobham Sports	9	9	0	0	42	10	32	27
2 Westland Sports	8	7	0	1	20	6	14	21
3 Sherborne Town Res	9	5	1	3	14	12	2	16
4 Balti Sports	11	5	1	5	24	29	-5	16
5 Gillingham Town	7	5	0	2	20	9	11	15
6 Dorchester Sports	9	4	2	3	14	13	1	14
7 Bournemouth Sports	9	4	2	3	16	19	-3	14
8 Swanage Town & Herston	7	4	1	2	19	14	5	13
9 Blandford United	5	3	1	1	21	9	12	10
10 Hamworthy Recreation	6	3	1	2	19	9	10	10
11 Holt United	5	2	0	3	12	14	-2	6
12 Portland United Res	9	1	3	5	12	22	-10	6
13 Shaftesbury Town Res	8	2	0	6	13	24	-11	6
14 Sturminster Newton United	7	1	2	4	11	22	-11	5
15 Bridport Res	8	1	0	7	12	27	-15	3
16 Wareham Rangers	9	0	0	9	4	34	-30	0

EAST CORNWALL LEAGUE

	P	W	D	L	F	A	GD	Pts
1 Mount Gould	12	12	0	0	81	5	76	36
2 Torpoint Athletic 3rd	11	9	0	2	29	4	25	27
3 St Dominick	10	6	3	1	40	13	27	21
4 St Stephen	8	6	0	2	26	16	10	18
5 Plymouth Marjon Res	12	5	2	5	23	23	0	17
6 St Newlyn East AFC	9	4	2	3	23	16	7	14
7 St Minver	7	4	1	2	18	9	9	13
8 St Blazey Res	9	4	1	4	16	22	-6	13
9 Veryan	11	3	2	6	23	37	-14	11
10 St Cleer	7	3	0	4	11	10	1	9
11 Looe Town	6	2	1	3	8	25	-17	7
12 Padstow United	11	2	1	8	16	45	-29	7
13 Foxhole Stars	9	0	3	6	8	23	-15	6*
14 St Teath	9	2	0	7	11	51	-40	6
15 Roche	7	1	1	5	5	19	-14	4
16 Newquay Res	8	1	1	6	17	37	-20	-2

EAST SUSSEX LEAGUE

PREMIER DIVISION	P	W	D	L	F	A	GD	Pts
1 Crowhurst	9	5	2	2	20	16	4	17
2 St Leonards Social	9	4	3	2	21	14	7	15
3 Northiam 75	9	4	2	3	26	20	6	14
4 Wadhurst United	7	3	2	2	19	18	1	11
5 Battle Town	5	3	1	1	10	5	5	10
6 Punnetts Town	6	3	1	2	14	13	1	10
7 Rock-A-Nore (Old Hastings)	7	3	1	3	10	15	-5	10
8 Hawkhurst United	5	2	1	2	14	16	-2	7
9 Robertsbridge United	7	1	2	4	17	20	-3	5
10 Bexhill Town	8	0	1	7	6	20	-14	1

DIVISION ONE	P	W	D	L	F	A	GD	Pts
1 South Coast Athletico	7	5	1	1	28	12	16	16
2 The Junior Club Tackleway	7	5	1	1	18	4	14	16
3 Bexhill Amateur Athletic Club	5	4	1	0	10	5	5	13
4 Rye Town	8	4	0	4	18	11	7	12
5 Sedlescombe Rangers Res	7	2	2	3	10	12	-2	8
6 Battle Town Res	6	1	2	3	7	14	-7	5
7 Sidley United Res	8	1	2	5	9	24	-15	5
8 Peche Hill Select	4	1	1	2	7	9	-2	4
9 Victoria Baptists	6	0	2	4	7	23	-16	2

DIVISION TWO	P	W	D	L	F	A	GD	Pts
1 Little Common Res	8	8	0	0	44	7	37	24
2 SC Pass Move Arrows	5	4	0	1	26	5	21	12
3 Bexhill Rovers	6	4	0	2	23	15	8	12
4 Catsfield	4	3	1	0	13	6	7	10
5 Herstmonceux	9	3	1	5	25	37	-12	10
6 Westfield Res	7	4	0	3	36	20	16	9*
7 St Leonards Social Res	5	2	0	3	11	16	-5	6
8 Northiam 75 Res	6	1	0	5	13	30	-17	6*
9 Peche Hill Select Res	8	2	0	6	16	43	-27	6
10 Mountfield United	6	0	0	6	6	34	-28	0

DIVISION THREE	P	W	D	L	F	A	GD	Pts
1 AFC Hollington	6	5	0	1	17	6	11	15
2 Bexhill Amateur Athletic Club Res	6	4	0	2	11	6	5	12
3 Sandhurst	4	3	1	0	15	3	12	10
4 Old Town Lions	5	3	1	1	16	11	5	10
5 Hastings United Youth	6	3	0	3	10	14	-4	9
6 Hawkhurst United Res	6	2	0	4	16	16	0	6
7 Hampden Park	7	2	0	5	17	22	-5	6
8 The Junior Club Tackleway Res	4	1	0	3	8	14	-6	3
9 Robertsbridge United Res	4	0	0	4	8	26	-18	0

DIVISION FOUR	P	W	D	L	F	A	GD	Pts
1 Hooe	9	5	3	1	39	17	22	18
2 Icklesham Casuals	8	6	0	2	25	14	11	18
3 Welcroft Park Rangers	7	5	0	2	18	15	3	15
4 Sovereign Saints Res	8	4	2	2	26	20	6	14
5 Orington	9	2	3	4	23	25	-2	9
6 Battle Town Third	7	2	2	3	16	14	2	8
7 Parkfield	7	2	1	4	20	21	-1	7
8 Magham Down	6	2	1	3	12	22	-10	7
9 Sedlescombe Rangers Dev	8	2	0	6	10	28	-18	6
10 West Hill United	5	1	0	4	8	21	-13	3

DIVISION FIVE	P	W	D	L	F	A	GD	Pts
1 AFC Hollington Res	5	4	1	0	24	6	18	13
2 Hastings Comets	5	4	0	1	17	8	9	12
3 Wadhurst United Res	5	3	1	1	12	17	-5	10
4 Herstmonceux Res	7	3	0	4	15	18	-3	9
5 Ticehurst	5	2	0	3	18	17	1	6
6 Welcroft Park Rangers Res	7	2	0	5	22	26	-4	6
7 Hampden Park U23	8	2	0	6	11	27	-16	3

ESSEX & SUFFULK BORDER LEAGUE

Step 7 - promotes to the Eastern Counties League.

PREMIER DIVISION	P	W	D	L	F	A	GD	Pts
1 Gas Recreation	12	9	1	2	36	14	22	28
2 Colne Athletic	13	7	3	3	27	24	3	24
3 Stanway Pegasus	10	7	1	2	25	15	10	22
4 Great Bentley	10	6	2	2	31	17	14	20
5 Little Oakley Res	14	5	4	5	32	26	6	19
6 Tiptree Heath	10	6	0	4	24	20	4	18
7 Sudbury Sports	9	5	2	2	31	13	18	17
8 West Bergholt	11	6	2	3	26	19	7	17*
9 White Notley	9	5	1	3	28	19	9	16
10 Dedham Old Boys	10	4	2	4	13	17	-4	14
11 Alresford Colne Rangers	12	4	2	6	17	30	-13	14
12 Brantham Athletic Res	10	3	2	5	20	23	-3	11
13 Hatfield Peverel	11	3	1	7	22	31	-9	10
14 Earls Colne	9	1	6	2	13	16	-3	9
15 Barnston	8	2	0	6	9	23	-14	9*
16 Lawford Lads	10	1	3	6	10	31	-21	6
17 Felixstowe & Walton United Res	10	1	1	8	17	32	-15	4
18 Flitch United	8	0	3	5	6	17	-11	3

DIVISION ONE	P	W	D	L	F	A	GD	Pts
1 Belle Vue Social Club	9	8	0	1	27	6	21	24
2 Silver End United	10	8	0	2	24	10	14	24
3 FC Clacton Res	10	7	2	1	35	14	21	23
4 Tiptree Jobserve	8	7	1	0	33	9	24	22
5 Alresford Colne Rangers Res	11	6	2	3	41	19	22	20
6 Stanway Pegasus Res	10	6	0	4	24	19	5	18
7 Coggeshall United Res	10	5	2	3	19	13	6	17
8 Dunmow Town	7	5	0	2	28	8	20	15
9 Shrub End United	9	4	1	4	22	33	-11	13
10 Cressing United	8	3	1	4	16	13	3	10
11 Mersea Island	9	3	1	5	25	29	-4	10
12 Gosfield United	9	3	1	5	14	21	-7	10
13 Stanway Rovers Res	7	2	1	4	15	21	-6	7
14 Hedinghams United	11	2	0	9	16	31	-15	6
15 Holland A	11	1	2	8	18	45	-27	5
16 Boxted Lodgers	10	1	0	9	7	45	-38	3
17 West Bergholt Res	7	0	0	7	9	37	-28	0

DIVISION TWO	P	W	D	L	F	A	GD	Pts
1 Harwich & Parkeston Res	12	10	1	1	41	21	20	31
2 Lawford Lads Res	11	7	3	1	32	16	16	24
3 Cavendish F.C.	9	8	0	1	30	15	15	24
4 Tollesbury	10	6	3	1	33	15	18	21
5 Tiptree Jobserve Res	11	5	2	4	20	22	-2	17
6 Hatfield Peverel Res	10	5	1	4	33	25	8	16
7 Gas Recreation Res	9	5	0	4	22	23	-1	15
8 Great Bentley Res	9	5	0	4	13	16	-3	15
9 Rowhedge	7	3	3	1	10	5	5	12
10 Brightlingsea Town	9	3	1	5	20	19	1	10
11 Dedham Old Boys Res	10	2	4	4	12	21	-9	10
12 Stanway Athletic	10	2	1	7	16	27	-11	7
13 St Osyth	11	1	3	7	12	20	-8	6
14 Oyster	10	1	3	6	14	27	-13	6
15 Harwich Rangers	10	1	1	8	12	38	-26	4
16 Brantham Athletic F.C. 'A'	8	0	2	6	10	20	-10	2

DIVISION THREE	P	W	D	L	F	A	GD	Pts
1 Thorpe Athletic	10	8	1	1	36	12	24	25
2 Barnston Res	10	7	1	2	53	22	31	22
3 Felsted Rovers	9	7	0	2	37	14	23	21
4 Sporting Rebels	11	6	3	2	29	25	4	21
5 Kelvedon Social	7	6	1	0	29	5	24	19
6 Wormingford Wanderers	9	6	0	3	30	10	20	18
7 Colne Athletic Res	10	6	0	4	28	15	13	18
8 Ramsey & Mistley	12	6	0	6	39	30	9	18
9 Flitch United Res	9	5	1	3	29	27	2	16
10 University of Essex	5	4	1	0	25	7	18	13
11 Little Clacton	11	3	0	8	27	39	-12	9
12 Langham Lodgers	9	2	1	6	12	30	-18	7
13 Abbey Fields	11	1	1	9	22	43	-21	4
14 Oyster Res	8	1	0	7	16	28	-12	3
15 Tiptree Heath Res	8	1	0	7	8	39	-31	3
16 Hedinghams United Res	9	0	0	9	6	80	-74	0

DIVISION FOUR	P	W	D	L	F	A	GD	Pts
1 Frinton & Walton	9	9	0	0	74	4	70	27
2 Ramsey & Mistley Res	11	8	3	0	37	10	27	27
3 Dovercourt Rovers	10	8	1	1	38	12	26	25
4 Gosfield United Res	10	7	1	2	47	13	34	22
5 New Field	11	7	1	3	32	14	18	22
6 Great Bentley A	10	4	3	3	23	15	8	15
7 Boxted Lodgers Res	11	4	3	4	24	29	-5	15
8 Kelvedon Social A	9	4	2	3	12	16	-4	14
9 Stillwaters	8	4	1	3	22	28	-6	13
10 Mersea Island Res	10	4	0	6	24	30	-6	12
11 Cavendish F.C. Res	11	3	2	6	28	29	-1	11
12 FC Clacton A	9	3	1	5	17	26	-9	10
13 Bradfield Rovers	12	2	2	8	11	37	-26	8
14 Wethersfield	10	2	1	7	15	37	-22	7
15 Tollesbury Res	11	1	1	9	16	45	-29	4
16 Parkeston Welfare Park	12	1	0	11	8	83	-75	3

ESSEX OLYMPIAN LEAGUE

Step 7 - promotes to the Eastern Counties League. Final tables were ranked on PPG - W - D.

PREMIER DIVISION	P	W	D	L	PPG	Pts
1 Buckhurst Hill	18	16	1	1	2.72	49
2 Basildon Town	17	10	3	4	1.94	33
3 Catholic United	18	9	4	5	1.72	31
4 Bishop's Stortford Swifts	18	9	3	6	1.67	30
5 Sungate	15	7	4	4	1.67	25
6 Leigh Ramblers	16	8	1	7	1.56	25
7 Hutton	17	7	5	5	1.53	26
8 Rayleigh Town	15	7	1	7	1.47	22
9 Harold Wood Athletic	17	7	2	8	1.35	23
10 Springfield	17	4	6	7	1.06	18
11 Canning Town	15	3	3	9	0.80	12
12 Kelvedon Hatch	16	3	3	10	0.75	12
13 Shenfield A.F.C.	18	4	1	13	0.72	13
14 Old Southendian	15	2	3	10	0.60	9

DIVISION ONE	P	W	D	L	PPG	Pts
1 Ongar Town	16	13	2	1	2.56	41
2 Galleywood	16	12	0	4	2.25	36
3 Manford Way	16	11	1	4	2.12	34
4 Runwell Sports	16	8	2	6	1.81	29*
5 Snaresbrook	17	10	1	6	1.65	28*
6 Toby	18	9	2	7	1.61	29
7 Old Chelmsfordians	16	6	3	7	1.31	21
8 Ramsden Scotia	17	6	3	8	1.24	21
9 Chingford Athletic	19	5	4	10	1.00	19
10 Rayleigh Town Res	18	3	3	12	0.67	12
11 Herongate Athletic	17	3	2	12	0.65	11
12 Shoebury Town	16	3	1	12	0.62	10

DIVISION TWO	P	W	D	L	PPG	Pts
1 Leigh Town	14	9	4	1	2.36	33*
2 Beacon Hill Rovers	18	12	2	4	2.11	38
3 Epping Town	18	11	4	3	2.06	37
4 Wakering Sports	17	10	1	6	1.82	31
5 Corinthians	17	9	2	6	1.71	29
6 Laindon Orient	18	9	3	6	1.67	30
7 Old Southendian Res	14	5	4	5	1.36	19
8 Harold Wood Athletic Res	15	5	4	6	1.27	19
9 Ryan	16	4	5	7	1.06	17
10 Rochford Town	17	2	6	9	0.65	11*
11 May & Baker E.C.'A'	16	2	1	13	0.44	7
12 AS Rawreth	16	1	2	13	0.31	5

DIVISION THREE	P	W	D	L	PPG	Pts
1 ACD United	16	14	0	2	2.62	42
2 Manford Way Res	16	12	2	2	2.38	38
3 Hutton Res	20	14	2	4	2.20	44
4 Wakebury	18	12	1	5	2.06	37
5 Basildon Town Res	17	9	3	5	1.76	30
6 Hullbridge Sports 'A'	19	8	4	7	1.47	28
7 Collier Row	19	7	1	11	1.16	22
8 Lakeside United	17	6	1	10	1.12	19
9 Buckhurst Hill Res	15	4	0	11	0.80	12
10 Corinthians Res	14	2	4	8	0.71	10
11 Toby Res	16	2	2	12	0.50	8
12 Leigh Town Res	13	0	0	13	0	0

DIVISION FOUR	P	W	D	L	PPG	Pts
1 Catholic United Res	15	14	0	1	2.80	42
2 Hashtag United Dev	15	11	2	2	2.33	35
3 Wakering Sports Res	15	9	2	4	1.93	29
4 Ongar Town Res	14	7	1	6	1.57	22
5 Sungate Res	16	8	1	7	1.56	25
6 Galleywood Res	12	5	3	4	1.50	18
7 Chingford Athletic Res	15	7	1	7	1.47	22
8 Laindon Orient Res	17	6	4	7	1.29	22
9 Shenfield A.F.C. Res	15	4	1	10	0.87	13
10 Leytonstone United	15	3	3	9	0.80	12
11 Old Chelmsfordians Res	17	4	1	12	0.76	13
12 Canning Town Res	14	1	3	10	0.43	6

DIVISION FIVE	P	W	D	L	PPG	Pts
1 Wakering Sports 'A'	15	12	2	1	2.53	38
2 Springfield Res	14	11	0	3	2.36	33
3 Roydon	15	10	1	4	2.07	31
4 Collier Row Res	17	9	2	6	1.88	32*
5 Bishop's Stortford Swifts Res	15	9	1	5	1.87	28
6 Old Barkabbeyans	16	8	2	6	1.62	26
7 Newbury Forest Res	13	6	1	6	1.46	19
8 Epping Town Res	16	7	1	8	1.38	22
9 Shoebury Town Res	15	6	1	8	1.27	19
10 Herongate Athletic Res	16	4	1	11	0.81	13
11 Leigh Ramblers Res	13	3	1	9	0.77	10
12 Runwell Sports Res	16	3	2	11	0.69	11
13 AS Rawreth Res	15	2	1	12	0.27	4

GLOUCESTERSHIRE COUNTY LEAGUE

Step 7 - promotes to the Western League and the Hellenic League.

	P	W	D	L	F	A	GD	Pts
1 AEK Boco	6	5	0	1	11	8	3	15
2 Sharpness	7	4	2	1	16	5	11	14
3 Patchway Town	5	4	1	0	13	5	8	13
4 Wick	6	4	1	1	13	6	7	13
5 Rockleaze Rangers	6	4	1	1	13	7	6	13
6 Gala Wilton	5	3	1	1	13	4	9	10
7 Frampton United	5	3	1	1	9	5	4	10
8 Shirehampton	5	2	2	1	9	5	4	8
9 Broadwell Amateurs	4	1	2	1	3	3	0	5
10 Hardwicke	5	1	2	2	7	8	-1	5
11 Ruardean Hill Rangers	5	1	1	3	5	9	-4	4
12 Bromley Heath United	5	1	0	4	6	13	-7	3
13 Quedgeley Wanderers	6	0	2	4	8	18	-10	2
14 Hanham Athletic	6	0	2	4	4	18	-14	2
15 Little Stoke	4	0	1	3	4	10	-6	1
16 Henbury	6	0	1	5	3	13	-10	1

GLOUCESTERSHIRE NORTHERN SENIOR LEAGUE

	P	W	D	L	F	A	GD	Pts
1 English Bicknor	10	7	2	1	29	12	17	23
2 Andoversford	11	7	2	2	23	13	10	23
3 Bredon	9	6	2	1	28	6	22	20
4 Cheltenham Civil Service	10	5	2	3	18	14	4	17
5 Whitecroft	10	5	1	4	15	16	-1	16
6 Brockworth Albion	9	4	2	3	13	7	6	14
7 Cam Bulldogs	11	3	5	3	12	14	-2	14
8 Chalford	8	4	1	3	19	11	8	13
9 Harrow Hill	9	4	1	4	19	12	7	13
10 Charlton Rovers	9	4	1	4	16	14	2	13
11 Longlevens Res	8	3	2	3	15	13	2	11
12 Woolaston	6	3	0	3	11	17	-6	9
13 Upton St Leonards	7	2	0	5	10	17	-7	6
14 Taverners	10	2	0	8	11	23	-12	6
15 Leonard Stanley	11	1	3	7	11	47	-36	6
16 Berkeley Town	8	0	2	6	4	18	-14	2

HAMPSHIRE PREMIER LEAGUE

Step 7 - promotes to the Wessex League.

SENIOR DIVISION	P	W	D	L	F	A	GD	Pts
1 Bush Hill	14	11	1	2	62	16	46	34
2 Locks Heath	16	10	3	3	42	16	26	33
3 Infinity	13	8	5	0	41	17	24	29
4 Paulsgrove	10	9	1	0	49	14	35	28
5 Fleetlands	12	8	3	1	43	13	30	27
6 Hayling United	14	7	2	5	47	29	18	23
7 Overton United	15	7	1	7	31	37	-6	22
8 Stockbridge	13	6	2	5	20	26	-6	20
9 Clanfield	13	4	1	8	31	29	2	13
10 Colden Common	11	3	3	5	32	26	6	12
11 Liphook United	9	4	0	5	22	26	-4	12
12 Liss Athletic	12	4	0	8	30	47	-17	12
13 Winchester Castle	11	2	2	7	11	28	-17	8
14 Chamberlayne Athletic	11	0	5	6	13	42	-29	5
15 Sway	11	1	1	9	14	68	-54	4
16 Lyndhurst	13	0	0	13	12	66	-54	0

DIVISION ONE	P	W	D	L	F	A	GD	Pts
1 Moneyfields Res	10	9	1	0	41	8	33	28
2 Denmead F.C.	9	6	1	2	26	13	13	19
3 QK Southampton	9	5	2	2	35	24	11	17
4 Harvest Home	8	5	1	2	23	11	12	16
5 South Wonston Swifts	11	5	1	5	24	18	6	16
6 Silchester	9	5	1	3	23	21	2	16
7 Andover New Street Swifts	12	6	2	4	26	18	8	14*
8 Broughton	9	4	2	3	20	25	-5	14
9 Upham	10	4	2	4	20	26	-6	14
10 Kingsclere	10	4	0	6	18	29	-11	12
11 Michelmersh & Timsbury	10	3	2	5	24	26	-2	11
12 AFC Netley	8	3	1	4	21	18	3	10
13 Headley United	10	3	1	6	19	23	-4	10
14 Clarendon	10	0	2	8	11	38	-27	2
15 AFC Petersfield	9	0	1	8	7	40	-33	1

HOPE VALLEY AMATEUR LEAGUE

PREMIER DIVISION		P	W	D	L	F	A	GD	Pts
1	High Lane	21	17	2	2	93	33	60	53
2	Furness Vale	20	16	2	2	70	34	36	50
3	Chapel Town	20	14	3	3	68	30	38	45
4	Tansley Juniors	20	10	3	7	46	36	10	33
5	Buxworth	20	10	1	9	46	50	-4	31
6	Bamford	20	9	1	10	53	56	-3	28
7	Fairfield FC	21	6	4	11	44	53	-9	22
8	Dove Holes	20	6	4	10	31	46	-15	22
9	Ashover	20	6	1	13	41	61	-20	19
10	Baslow	20	4	1	15	48	75	-27	13
11	Youlgrave Utd	20	1	2	17	20	86	-66	5

Ashover (stripes) 1 - 2 Fairfield . Photos Bill Wheatcroft.

HERTS SENIOR COUNTY LEAGUE

Step 7 - promotes to the Spartan South Midlands League.

PREMIER DIVISION	P	W	D	L	F	A	GD	Pts
1 Belstone	10	8	1	1	29	7	22	25
2 Wingate & Finchley Dev	10	7	2	1	28	14	14	23
3 Royston Town FC Res	12	7	1	4	30	16	14	22
4 Letchworth Garden City Eagles	11	5	4	2	30	15	15	19
5 Bush Hill Rangers FC	11	5	4	2	23	16	7	19
6 Cuffley Seniors	10	4	4	2	24	16	8	16
7 Harefield United Res	9	5	0	4	15	14	1	15
8 Glenn Sports	9	4	1	4	20	28	-8	13
9 Ware Sports FC	10	3	3	4	21	19	2	12
10 Welwyn Garden City U23	11	3	3	5	11	20	-9	12
11 Cockfosters Res	10	3	1	6	15	22	-7	10
12 Chipperfield Corinthians	9	2	3	4	11	18	-7	9
13 Hatfield Town	9	2	2	5	10	16	-6	8
14 Sandridge Rovers	10	2	2	6	8	19	-11	8
15 Hoddesdon Town Res	10	2	1	7	19	38	-19	7
16 Colney Heath Res	9	1	2	6	10	26	-16	5

DIVISION ONE	P	W	D	L	F	A	GD	Pts
1 Oracle Components	10	8	0	2	26	15	11	24
2 Oxhey	11	7	1	3	24	19	5	22
3 Hatfield United	9	6	3	0	24	13	11	21
4 Tring Athletic Res	9	5	2	2	19	12	7	17
5 Bovingdon Res	9	5	0	4	22	16	6	15
6 Standon & Puckeridge FC Blues	8	4	2	2	12	7	5	14
7 Buntingford Town	9	4	1	4	13	15	-2	13
8 Aldenham FC	10	4	1	5	18	24	-6	13
9 Sun Sports Watford	8	3	3	2	17	10	7	12
10 Hinton	11	4	0	7	18	23	-5	12
11 Wheathampstead Wanderers	10	3	2	5	16	25	-9	11
12 Hertford Heath	9	2	4	3	18	18	0	10
13 Evergreen FC	9	3	1	5	10	11	-1	10
14 Old Parmiterians	10	3	1	6	13	20	-7	10
15 Bushey Rangers	8	0	3	5	5	11	-6	3
16 Knebworth	8	1	0	7	5	21	-16	3

DIVISION TWO	P	W	D	L	F	A	GD	Pts
1 Tring Town AFC	10	7	0	3	19	14	5	21
2 Hemel Hempstead Rovers	8	6	2	0	29	10	19	20
3 Waltham Abbey Res	8	6	1	1	25	7	18	19
4 Hadley Saturday Veterans	10	6	1	3	28	25	3	19
5 Broxbourne Badgers	8	5	2	1	26	17	9	17
6 Chipperfield Corinthians Res	9	5	1	3	22	18	4	16
7 Lemsford	7	3	2	2	22	13	9	11
8 Sandridge Rovers Res	8	3	1	4	15	15	0	10
9 Letchworth Garden City Eagles Res	9	3	1	5	16	18	-2	10
10 Baldock Town FC Res	8	2	2	4	14	20	-6	8
11 Oxhey Res	6	2	0	4	9	15	-6	6
12 Ware Sports FC Res	7	2	0	5	11	18	-7	6
13 Wormley Rovers Res	9	2	0	7	18	26	-8	6
14 Cuffley Seniors Res	7	1	0	6	10	21	-11	3
15 Oxhey Jets Dev	6	0	1	5	6	33	-27	1

DIVISION THREE	P	W	D	L	F	A	GD	Pts
1 Stevenage Borough Com	8	6	1	1	29	8	21	19
2 Hatfield Athletic	7	6	1	0	27	9	18	19
3 Oxhey Jets Vets	9	5	3	1	27	13	14	18
4 Hatfield Town U23	8	5	1	2	21	11	10	16
5 Sarratt Res	9	5	1	3	25	18	7	16
6 Mill End Sports	8	5	1	2	21	14	7	16
7 Hinton Res	9	4	2	3	18	18	0	14
8 Harpenden Rovers	9	4	1	4	17	18	-1	13
9 Buntingford Town Res	9	2	4	3	18	18	0	10
10 Lemsford Res	9	2	3	4	12	22	-10	9
11 Evergreen FC Res	9	2	2	5	14	21	-7	8
12 Hemel Hempstead Rovers Res	8	1	4	3	16	26	-10	7
13 Knebworth Res	9	2	1	6	13	28	-15	7
14 Bedmond Sports FC	6	1	2	3	6	15	-9	5
15 Bovingdon A	7	1	1	5	8	22	-14	4
16 Stanmore Jafferys	6	0	0	6	8	19	-11	0

HUMBER PREMIER LEAGUE

Step 7 - promotes to Northern Counties East League.

PREMIER DIVISION	P	W	D	L	F	A	GD	Pts
1 Beverley Town	15	14	0	1	51	15	36	42
2 LIV Supplies Sat HPL	15	9	4	2	44	22	22	31
3 Westella & Willerby AFC	15	8	4	3	39	26	13	28
4 Hull United Seniors	15	9	1	5	38	27	11	28
5 South Cave United	15	8	4	3	26	15	11	28
6 Hedon Rangers FC	15	8	1	6	30	28	2	25
7 Pocklington Town	15	6	4	5	38	22	16	22
8 Barton Town FC Res	15	6	2	7	28	29	-1	20
9 Driffield Junior Football Club	15	6	2	7	31	43	-12	20
10 Sculcoates Amateurs	15	5	4	6	28	27	1	19
11 Reckitts AFC s	15	4	4	7	25	31	-6	16
12 Chalk Lane Sat	15	5	1	9	29	39	-10	16
13 Hornsea Town	15	5	1	9	30	53	-23	16
14 Hessle Rangers	15	4	3	8	26	39	-13	15
15 Walkington AFC	15	3	5	7	22	35	-13	14
16 North Ferriby Res	15	0	0	15	17	51	-34	0

DIVISION ONE	P	W	D	L	F	A	GD	PPG	Pts
1 Cherry Burton F.C	11	8	1	2	43	18	25	2.27	25
2 East Riding Rangers	12	8	2	2	30	22	8	2.17	26
3 St Marys AFC	12	6	3	3	42	22	20	1.75	21
4 Brandesburton AFC	11	6	1	4	36	25	11	1.73	19
5 Easington United	11	5	3	3	25	23	2	1.64	18
6 Hessle Sporting Club	11	5	3	3	28	18	10	1.64	18
7 Blackburn Athletic	9	4	2	3	24	14	10	1.56	14
8 Goole United AFC	11	4	3	4	21	23	-2	1.36	15
9 Bridlington Town Res	12	5	1	6	24	32	-8	1.33	16
10 Driffield Evening Institute AFC	8	2	1	5	12	17	-5	0.88	7
11 Reckitts AFC Res	12	2	4	6	12	36	-24	0.83	10
12 Beverley Town Res	12	2	2	8	21	34	-13	0.67	8
13 Sproatley Juniors	12	1	2	9	21	55	-34	0.42	5

Resumed the league in Spring 2021 and as none of the clubs had played each other twice at that point it was decided that to conclude the season, clubs would only play each other once. However, not all games were played in Division One so the final table was based on points per game.

KENT COUNTY LEAGUE

Step 7 - promotes to the Southern Counties East League.

PREMIER DIVISION	P	W	D	L	F	A	GD	Pts
1 Kings Hill	9	7	0	2	27	13	14	21
2 New Romney	9	6	0	3	14	10	4	18
3 Farnborough Old Boys Guild	8	5	2	1	22	6	16	17
4 Hawkinge Town	9	5	1	3	22	20	2	16
5 Fleetdown United	8	5	1	2	14	12	2	16
6 Peckham Town	8	4	2	2	16	12	4	14
7 Borden Village	8	4	2	2	9	10	-1	14
8 Tudor Sports	8	4	1	3	14	13	1	13
9 Staplehurst Monarchs United	8	3	3	2	19	13	6	12
10 K Sports Res	9	3	0	6	18	25	-7	9
11 Stansfeld (Oxford & Bermondsey)	9	3	0	6	10	20	-10	9
12 Bromleians	8	2	2	4	10	13	-3	8
13 Otford United	10	2	2	6	17	23	-6	8
14 Ide Hill	6	2	0	4	12	12	0	6
15 Faversham Strike Force	8	1	2	5	8	18	-10	5
16 Crockenhill	9	1	2	6	14	26	-12	5

DIV. ONE CENTRAL & EAST	P	W	D	L	F	A	GD	Pts
1 Larkfield and New Hythe Wanderers	8	7	0	1	28	11	17	21
2 Hollands & Blair Res	8	4	2	2	19	11	8	14
3 Snodland Town Res	7	4	1	2	19	12	7	13
4 Sturry	6	4	1	1	17	11	6	13
5 Ashford	7	3	2	2	20	22	-2	11
6 Rochester City	8	3	2	3	17	21	-4	11
7 Cuxton 1991	6	3	1	2	18	10	8	10
8 Tenterden Town	7	3	1	3	17	19	-2	10
9 Rusthall Res	8	3	1	4	16	19	-3	10
10 Whitstable Town Res	8	3	1	4	24	28	-4	10
11 Lordswood Res	9	1	3	5	19	23	-4	6
12 Thanet United	9	0	4	5	15	26	-11	4
13 Guru Nanak	7	1	1	5	11	27	-16	4

DIVISION ONE WEST	P	W	D	L	F	A	GD	Pts
1 HFSP Ten-Em-Bee	7	6	0	1	21	7	14	18
2 Halls	9	5	2	2	14	9	5	17
3 Red Velvet	7	5	1	1	22	9	13	16
4 Welling Park	8	5	0	3	17	11	6	15
5 Metrogas	7	4	1	2	13	5	8	13
6 Chipstead	7	3	1	3	15	11	4	10
7 AFC Mottingham	6	3	0	3	6	10	-4	9
8 Belvedere	6	2	1	3	6	11	-5	7
9 South East Athletic	8	1	2	5	10	19	-9	5
10 Sutton Athletic Res	8	1	2	5	10	21	-11	5
11 Bexley	8	2	1	5	7	13	-6	4*
12 Club Langley	5	0	1	4	3	18	-15	1

LEICESTERSHIRE SENIOR LEAGUE

Step 7 - promotes to the East Midlands Counties League.

PREMIER DIVISION	P	W	D	L	F	A	GD	Pts
1 Friar Lane & Epworth	10	7	1	2	29	15	14	22
2 Ashby Ivanhoe Knights	11	7	1	3	16	13	3	22
3 Sileby Town	8	7	0	1	32	7	25	21
4 Cottesmore A	7	6	1	0	18	7	11	19
5 Allexton & New Parks	7	5	0	2	24	12	12	15
6 Rugby Borough	7	4	1	2	18	12	6	13
7 County Hall	10	4	1	5	20	27	-7	13
8 Hathern	8	4	0	4	19	9	10	12
9 Ellistown	5	3	1	1	10	6	4	10
10 Blaby & Whetstone	9	3	1	5	15	20	-5	10
11 FC GNG	9	3	0	6	13	23	-10	9
12 Desford	9	2	2	5	16	20	-4	8
13 Thurnby Rangers	11	2	1	8	13	34	-21	7
14 Fleckney Athletic	10	1	2	7	14	27	-13	5
15 FC Khalsa GAD	9	0	2	7	8	33	-25	2

DIVISION ONE	P	W	D	L	F	A	GD	Pts
1 Highfield Rangers	14	8	3	3	26	20	6	27
2 Northfield Emerald	9	8	0	1	48	16	32	24
3 Ingles Res	8	6	1	1	25	13	12	19
4 Saffron Dynamo Res	11	6	0	5	18	15	3	18
5 Earl Shilton Albion	10	5	2	3	29	23	6	17
6 Anstey Town	7	5	0	2	12	6	6	15
7 Kirby Muxloe Res	8	4	1	3	26	21	5	13
8 Magna 73	8	4	1	3	21	16	5	13
9 Friar Lane & Epworth Res	8	4	0	4	13	15	-2	12
10 Birstall United Social Res	10	3	2	5	18	25	-7	11
11 Holwell Sports Res	9	1	2	6	12	21	-9	5
12 Loughborough	6	0	2	4	5	18	-13	2
13 Barrow Town Res	7	0	2	5	11	28	-17	2
14 Lutterworth Town Res	9	0	0	9	10	37	-27	0

DIVISION TWO NORTH & EAST	P	W	D	L	F	A	GD	Pts
1 Asfordby	8	7	0	1	32	7	25	21
2 Bottesford	6	4	1	1	18	9	9	13
3 Sporting Markfield	5	4	0	1	15	9	6	12
4 Sileby Town Res	6	3	0	3	20	14	6	9
5 Sutton Bonington	6	2	2	2	7	8	-1	8
6 Rothley Imperial	4	2	0	2	5	8	-3	6
7 2nd Royal Anglian Regiment	5	1	2	2	3	13	-10	5
8 Coalville Town Ravens	7	1	1	5	5	11	-6	4
9 Cottesmore AFC Dev	6	1	1	4	8	15	-7	4
10 Thurnby Rangers Dev	5	0	1	4	6	25	-19	1

DIVISION TWO SOUTH & WEST	P	W	D	L	F	A	GD	Pts
1 Barlestone St Giles	8	7	0	1	27	9	18	21
2 Burbage Old Boys	6	6	0	0	31	4	27	18
3 Kibworth Town	6	5	0	1	19	12	7	15
4 Dunton & Broughton United	8	3	2	3	14	13	1	11
5 St Andrews Res	7	3	1	3	17	20	-3	10
6 Rugby Borough Res	8	3	0	5	21	22	-1	9
7 Desford Res	7	2	1	4	6	16	-10	7
8 Blaby & Whetstone Res	7	1	0	6	8	26	-18	0*
9 AFC North Kilworth	7	0	0	7	4	25	-21	0

LINCOLNSHIRE LEAGUE

Step 7 - promotes to the Northern Counties East League.

PREMIER DIVISION	P	W	D	L	F	A	GD	Pts
1 Epworth Town Colts AFC	9	8	1	0	28	6	22	25
2 Louth Town	9	7	1	1	28	14	14	22
3 Wyberton	12	6	2	4	31	17	14	20
4 Immingham Town	8	6	1	1	37	8	29	19
5 Grantham Town Academy	7	5	2	0	27	10	17	17
6 Keelby United	11	4	2	5	15	28	-13	17*
7 Tetney Rovers	7	4	2	1	19	11	8	16*
8 Lincoln Moorlands Railway AFC	10	4	4	2	24	19	5	15*
9 Grimsby Borough Res	11	4	2	5	25	17	8	14
10 Lincoln United Dev	9	4	0	5	16	16	0	12
11 Nunsthorpe Tavern	8	3	2	3	19	23	-4	11
12 Horncastle Town	7	2	2	3	15	16	-1	8
13 Nettleham	7	2	0	5	13	23	-10	6
14 Appleby Frodingham	8	2	0	6	15	28	-13	6
15 Brigg Town CIC	11	1	3	7	12	28	-16	6
16 Bottesford Town Dev	10	2	1	7	16	32	-16	4*
17 Sleaford Town Junior FC	10	0	1	9	9	53	-44	1

LIVERPOOL PREMIER LEAGUE

Step 7 - promotes to the North West Counties League.

All games pre COVID suspension were expunged. In spring 2021 clubs then played each other once to form the tables below.

PREMIER DIVISION	P	W	D	L	F	A	GD	Pts
1 Liverpool NALGO	10	7	3	0	33	11	22	24
2 Waterloo Dock	10	7	2	1	34	17	17	23
3 BRNESC	10	6	3	1	32	17	15	21
4 Quarry Bank Old Boys	10	6	2	2	33	15	18	20
5 Page Celtic	10	5	1	4	25	21	4	16
6 MSB Woolton	10	4	0	6	18	22	-4	12
7 Knotty Ash	10	3	1	6	15	26	-11	10
8 Sefton Athletic	10	3	0	7	15	30	-15	9
9 East Villa	10	2	2	6	22	32	-10	8
10 Liver Academy	10	2	1	7	15	26	-11	7
11 Old Xaverians	10	2	1	7	6	31	-25	7

The Lute resigned after 5 matches - results expunged.

DIVISION ONE	P	W	D	L	F	A	GD	Pts
1 The Empress	14	9	3	2	49	21	28	30
2 FC Bernie Mays	14	9	1	4	42	18	24	28*
3 FC Garston	14	5	7	2	38	23	15	22*
4 Halewood Apollo	14	6	3	5	36	22	14	21
5 Marshalls Roby	14	5	4	5	27	28	-1	19
6 Stoneycroft	14	5	3	6	28	39	-11	18
7 Alumni	14	4	1	9	19	38	-19	13
8 BRNESC Res	14	2	0	12	14	64	-50	6

DIVISION TWO	P	W	D	L	F	A	GD	Pts
1 Warbreck	16	12	2	2	55	23	32	38
2 FC Marsden	16	11	2	3	54	17	37	35
3 Waterloo Grammar School Old Boys	16	10	2	4	50	26	24	32
4 Gilmour	16	9	3	4	41	31	10	30
5 Bluecoat FC	16	8	4	4	35	21	14	28
6 ROMA	16	7	1	8	39	38	1	22
7 Red Rum Development	16	3	3	10	18	46	-28	12
8 Formby Town U18	16	1	2	13	18	30	-12	5
9 Botanic	16	1	1	14	27	105	-78	4

MANCHESTER LEAGUE

Step 7 - Promotes to the North West Counties League.

PREMIER DIVISION	P	W	D	L	F	A	GD	Pts
1 Stockport Georgians	9	8	0	1	43	14	29	24
2 Hindsford	8	5	1	2	21	15	6	16
3 Springhead	7	4	3	0	23	17	6	15
4 Rochdale Sacred Heart	7	4	1	2	18	12	6	13
5 Pennington	7	4	1	2	16	12	4	13
6 Manchester Gregorians	8	3	2	3	21	14	7	11
7 Bolton County	6	3	1	2	14	9	5	10
8 Royton Town	9	3	1	5	19	28	-9	10
9 Old Altrinchamians	6	3	0	3	16	13	3	9
10 Chadderton Res	9	3	0	6	19	28	-9	9
11 Dukinfield Town	6	2	2	2	8	5	3	8
12 Walshaw Sports Club	7	1	5	1	15	15	0	8
13 Heywood St James	5	1	2	2	11	15	-4	5
14 Heyside	7	1	0	6	8	29	-21	3
15 Beechfield United	9	0	1	8	12	38	-26	1

DIVISION ONE	P	W	D	L	F	A	GD	Pts
1 Elton Vale	8	6	1	1	31	12	19	19
2 Atherton Town	6	4	0	2	18	14	4	12
3 Moorside Rangers	6	3	2	1	11	9	2	11
4 Bolton Lads and Girls Club	8	3	2	3	19	18	1	11
5 Middleton Colts	7	3	2	2	14	20	-6	11
6 Govan Athletic	7	3	1	3	16	9	7	10
7 Uppermill	7	3	1	3	20	20	0	10
8 Tintwistle Athletic	5	3	0	2	15	10	5	9
9 Boothstown	7	2	1	4	13	20	-7	7
10 Altrincham Hale	3	1	0	2	6	6	0	3
11 Wilmslow Albion	4	1	0	3	10	18	-8	3
12 East Manchester	8	1	0	7	10	27	-17	3

DIVISION TWO	P	W	D	L	F	A	GD	Pts
1 Bolton United	7	7	0	0	35	9	26	21
2 Rochdale Sacred Heart Res	8	6	1	1	59	10	49	19
3 Hindsford Res	9	6	1	2	42	12	30	19
4 Astley and Tyldesley	8	5	1	2	26	20	6	16
5 AFC Monton	6	3	2	1	23	8	15	11
6 Leigh Genesis	9	3	2	4	28	32	-4	11
7 Avro Res	7	3	1	3	26	14	12	10
8 Breightmet United	7	2	1	4	15	23	-8	7
9 Hindley Juniors	8	1	2	5	18	37	-19	5
10 Hollinwood	6	1	0	5	10	44	-34	3
11 Oldham Community	11	0	1	10	12	85	-73	1

DIVISION THREE	P	W	D	L	F	A	GD	Pts
1 Dukinfield Town Res	8	7	0	1	18	5	13	21
2 Elton Vale Res	6	5	1	0	20	7	13	16
3 Atherton Town Res	9	6	1	2	24	18	6	15*
4 Walshaw Sports Club Res	6	4	0	2	17	10	7	12
5 Uppermill Res	7	4	0	3	11	14	-3	12
6 Stockport Georgians Res	8	2	2	4	18	23	-5	8
7 Springhead Res	6	2	1	3	12	12	0	7
8 Manchester Gregorians Res	7	2	1	4	13	20	-7	7
9 Altrincham Hale Res	7	1	2	4	13	18	-5	5
10 Bolton County Res	7	1	1	5	10	14	-4	4
11 Royton Town Res	5	0	3	2	16	18	-2	3

DIVISION FOUR	P	W	D	L	F	A	GD	Pts
1 AFC Monton Res	10	8	2	0	53	11	42	26
2 Beechfield United 'A'	8	6	0	2	38	16	22	18
3 Boothstown Res	8	5	2	1	20	10	10	17
4 Dukinfield Town	7	4	0	3	26	15	11	12
5 Old Altrinchamians Res	7	4	0	3	25	21	4	12
6 Heywood St James Res	6	3	2	1	26	14	12	11
7 Pennington Res	7	3	1	3	24	17	7	10
8 Tintwistle Athletic Res	5	3	1	1	13	9	4	10
9 Moorside Rangers Res	9	2	2	5	24	28	-4	8
10 Atherton Town 'A'	8	1	0	7	14	41	-27	3
11 Leigh Genesis Res	6	1	0	5	10	41	-31	3
12 Heyside Res	9	0	0	9	17	67	-50	0

DIVISION FIVE	P	W	D	L	F	A	GD	Pts
1 Govan Athletic Res	8	5	1	2	32	11	21	16
2 Pennington 'A'	9	5	0	4	22	19	3	15
3 Bolton Lads and Girls Club Res	7	5	0	2	24	22	2	15
4 Dukinfield Town 'A'	6	4	1	1	19	11	8	13
5 Astley and Tyldesley Res	7	2	3	2	11	19	-8	9
6 Leigh Genesis 'A'	6	2	2	2	12	18	-6	8
7 Bolton United Res	6	2	0	4	13	17	-4	6
8 Wilmslow Albion Res	4	1	0	3	6	11	-5	3
9 Uppermill 'A'	8	0	1	7	14	27	-13	1

MID SUSSEX LEAGUE

Step 7 - Promotes to the Southern Combination.

It was decided to split the Premier Division & Championship in two (Top and Bottom ranked on points-per-game before the COVID suspension) with teams playing each other once. Results from before the lockdown were expunged but points for six games at each team's pre-pause points-per-game rate were awarded in advance of the resumption.

PREMIER DIVISION	P	W	D	L	F	A	GD	Pts
1 Lindfield	12	8	1	3	36	24	12	25
2 Sidley United	9	7	1	1	31	11	20	22
3 Hollington United	10	7	0	3	30	16	14	21
4 Balcombe	10	6	0	4	31	19	12	18
5 Willingdon Athletic	9	5	1	3	20	20	0	16
6 Forest Row	8	5	0	3	26	14	12	15
7 Eastbourne Rangers	12	5	0	7	17	33	-16	15
8 Sporting Lindfield	10	4	2	4	13	19	-6	14
9 Ringmer AFC	10	4	1	5	21	32	-11	13
10 Westfield	9	4	0	5	26	21	5	12
11 Cuckfield Rangers	10	3	1	6	17	20	-3	10
12 Rotherfield	9	3	0	6	11	28	-17	9
13 Sedlescombe Rangers	9	2	1	6	15	21	-6	7
14 AFC Uckfield Town II	9	0	2	7	11	27	-16	2

PREMIER DIVISION (Top)	P	W	D	L	F	A	GD	Pts
1 Hollington United	6	4	1	1	12	5	7	26
2 Balcombe	6	4	2	0	23	8	15	25
3 Sidley United	6	2	1	3	5	12	-7	22
4 Forest Row	6	2	3	1	18	7	11	21
5 Lindfield	6	2	0	4	10	13	-3	19
6 Willingdon Athletic	6	1	3	2	10	15	-5	17
7 Sporting Lindfield	6	1	0	5	8	26	-18	12

PREMIER DIVISION (Bottom)	P	W	D	L	F	A	GD	Pts
1 Ringmer AFC	6	5	1	0	22	6	16	24
2 Eastbourne Rangers	6	3	2	1	15	7	8	19
3 Westfield	6	3	1	2	16	10	6	18
4 Cuckfield Rangers	6	3	2	1	15	8	7	17
5 Sedlescombe Rangers	6	3	0	3	12	15	-3	14
6 Rotherfield	6	0	1	5	4	26	-22	7
7 AFC Uckfield Town II	6	0	1	5	3	15	-12	3

CHAMPIONSHIP	P	W	D	L	F	A	GD	Pts
1 Southwick 1882	8	8	0	0	26	8	18	24
2 Crawley Devils	9	7	0	2	30	13	17	21
3 Holland Sports	8	6	1	1	31	8	23	19
4 West Hoathly	10	3	5	2	17	11	6	14
5 Ridgewood	9	4	2	3	20	20	0	14
6 Reigate Priory	9	4	1	4	27	15	12	13
7 Mile Oak II	7	4	0	3	17	17	0	12
8 Roffey II	9	4	0	5	16	21	-5	12
9 Polegate Town	10	3	1	6	17	21	-4	10
10 Hurstpierpoint	10	3	1	6	21	39	-18	10
11 Ashurst Wood	10	2	3	5	33	29	4	9
12 Sovereign Saints	8	2	2	4	15	21	-6	8
13 Peacehaven & Telscombe II	8	2	1	5	17	37	-20	7
14 Copthorne II	9	1	1	7	8	35	-27	4

CHAMPIONSHIP (Top)	P	W	D	L	F	A	GD	Pts
1 Southwick 1882	6	6	0	0	25	3	22	36
2 Holland Sports	6	5	0	1	16	4	12	30
3 Crawley Devils	6	1	2	3	8	15	-7	19
4 Reigate Priory	6	2	2	2	7	11	-4	17
5 West Hoathly	6	2	1	3	5	11	-6	16
6 Mile Oak II	6	1	1	4	3	9	-6	15
7 Ridgewood	6	0	2	4	5	16	-11	12

CHAMPIONSHIP (Bottom)	P	W	D	L	F	A	GD	Pts
1 Roffey II	6	3	2	1	12	7	5	19
2 Sovereign Saints	6	3	1	2	9	7	2	16
3 Hurstpierpoint	6	3	0	3	8	9	-1	15
4 Ashurst Wood	6	2	2	2	11	16	-5	14
5 Peacehaven & Telscombe II	6	2	1	3	7	9	-2	13
6 Polegate Town	6	2	0	4	12	10	2	12
7 Copthorne II	6	3	0	3	7	8	-1	12

DIVISION ONE	P	W	D	L	F	A	GD	Pts
1 Buxted	18	13	0	5	48	29	19	39
2 Burgess Hill Albion	18	10	3	5	30	22	8	33
3 Montpelier Villa AFC II	18	10	1	7	46	30	16	31
4 Balcombe II	18	9	2	7	30	31	-1	29
5 AFC Acorns	18	8	3	7	37	34	3	27
6 AFC Varndeanians II	18	6	6	6	30	33	-3	24
7 Godstone	18	6	3	9	37	40	-3	21
8 Cuckfield Town	18	5	4	9	26	33	-7	19
9 Lindfield II	18	5	3	10	25	40	-15	18
10 Ardingly	18	4	3	11	25	42	-17	15

DIVISION TWO NORTH	P	W	D	L	F	A	GD	Pts
1 Ifield Sports	16	12	1	3	57	17	40	34*
2 Royal Earlswood	16	8	2	6	36	38	-2	29*
3 Reigate Priory II	16	9	1	6	37	35	2	28
4 South Park A	16	7	4	5	46	28	18	25
5 DCK Maidenbower	16	7	1	8	36	44	-8	22
6 Stones	16	7	1	8	35	49	-14	22
7 Galaxy	16	7	2	7	30	34	-4	20*
8 A.F.C. Gatton	16	5	4	7	36	34	2	19
9 Crawley Devils II	16	2	0	14	27	61	-34	6

DIVISION TWO SOUTH	P	W	D	L	F	A	GD	Pts
1 Cuckfield Rangers II	18	15	1	2	51	14	37	46
2 Ditchling	18	13	1	4	53	27	26	40
3 Eastbourne Rangers II	18	12	1	5	52	27	25	37
4 Burgess Hill Rhinos	18	9	4	5	46	35	11	31
5 Ringmer AFC II	18	7	4	7	39	42	-3	25
6 Willingdon Athletic II	18	7	2	9	29	27	2	23
7 AFC Hurst	18	6	2	10	33	37	-4	20
8 Fletching	18	4	6	8	32	48	-16	18
9 Portslade Athletic	18	5	1	12	20	42	-22	16
10 AFC Varndeanians III	18	1	0	17	12	68	-56	3

DIVISION THREE NORTH	P	W	D	L	F	A	GD	Pts
1 Pound Hill	18	15	0	3	47	24	23	45
2 Nutley	18	11	3	4	46	32	14	36
3 Dormansland Rockets	18	11	2	5	57	26	31	35
4 Forest Row II	18	10	2	6	45	29	16	32
5 AFC Acorns II	18	9	1	8	41	39	2	28
6 Crawley United	18	7	2	9	33	37	-4	23
7 Ashurst Wood II	18	5	4	9	32	40	-8	19
8 Horsted Keynes	18	4	2	12	24	51	-27	14
9 Horley A.F.C.	18	3	4	11	35	52	-17	13
10 Rotherfield II	18	3	4	11	21	51	-30	13

DIVISION THREE SOUTH	P	W	D	L	F	A	GD	Pts
1 FC Sporting	18	15	3	0	51	20	31	48
2 Newick	18	14	1	3	62	28	34	43
3 Lancing United II	18	10	1	7	41	48	-7	31
4 Ringmer AFC III	18	8	3	7	46	29	17	27
5 Brighton & Sussex Medical School	18	8	2	8	41	34	7	26
6 Ansty Sports & Social Club	18	7	2	9	37	37	0	23
7 Ridgewood II	18	5	4	9	29	44	-15	19
8 Peacehaven & Telscombe III	18	5	4	9	35	39	-4	18*
9 Polegate Town II	18	3	3	12	34	58	-24	12
10 Wivelsfield Green	18	2	3	13	17	56	-39	9

DIVISION FOUR NORTH	P	W	D	L	F	A	GD	Pts
1 Ifield Albion	18	15	2	1	51	15	36	47
2 Cuckfield Town II	18	11	5	2	39	21	18	38
3 Hartfield	18	10	2	6	49	36	13	32
4 Balcombe III	18	8	6	4	40	31	9	30
5 Handcross Village	18	8	3	7	34	21	13	27
6 Ifield	18	8	1	9	41	37	4	25
7 Lindfield III	18	7	4	7	39	47	-8	25
8 Horsham Athletic	18	5	1	12	34	44	-10	16
9 Copthorne A	18	1	7	10	25	50	-25	10
10 Fairfield	18	0	3	15	19	69	-50	3

DIVISION FOUR SOUTH	P	W	D	L	F	A	GD	Pts
1 Barcombe	18	16	1	1	66	18	48	49
2 Scaynes Hill	18	11	4	3	49	26	23	37
3 Eastbourne Athletic	18	8	7	3	35	23	12	31
4 Uckfield United	17	8	2	7	47	28	19	26
5 Keymer & Hassocks	18	8	2	8	30	37	-7	26
6 Hurstpierpoint II	18	7	2	9	36	57	-21	23
7 Buxted II	18	6	3	9	22	34	-12	21
8 Burgess Hill Albion II	18	5	3	10	23	34	-11	18
9 Ditchling II	17	3	3	11	26	45	-19	12
10 Maresfield Village	18	2	3	13	17	49	-32	9

DIVISION FIVE NORTH EAST	P	W	D	L	F	A	GD	Pts
1 Old Oxted Town	18	11	2	5	62	25	37	35
2 West Hoathly Res	18	10	2	6	39	29	10	32
3 East Grinstead Meads II	18	9	4	5	30	26	4	31
4 East Grinstead Town III	18	9	2	7	31	24	7	29
5 Ardingly Res	18	8	4	6	31	37	-6	28
6 Ashurst Wood III	18	7	5	6	38	32	6	26
7 Holland Sports II	18	8	0	10	41	40	1	24
8 Caterham	18	6	3	9	35	42	-7	21
9 Lindfield IV	18	6	2	10	28	46	-18	20
10 Galaxy III	18	3	2	13	24	58	-34	11

DIVISION FIVE NORTH WEST	P	W	D	L	F	A	GD	Pts
1 Furnace Green United	18	15	0	3	88	25	63	45
2 Cuckfield Rangers Dev	18	13	1	4	63	27	36	42*
3 Galaxy II	18	14	3	1	57	21	36	41*
4 Horley A.F.C. Res	18	9	2	7	42	47	-5	29
5 Athletico Shrublands	18	9	2	7	44	41	3	26*
6 East Grinstead Meads	18	6	3	9	53	66	-13	21
7 Reigate Priory A	18	5	3	10	36	50	-14	18
8 Crawley United II	18	3	3	12	35	85	-50	12
9 Stones Res	18	3	2	13	29	53	-24	11
10 Scaynes Hill III	18	3	1	14	33	65	-32	10

DIVISION FIVE SOUTH	P	W	D	L	F	A	GD	Pts
1 Scaynes Hill II	16	10	3	3	37	20	17	33
2 Portslade Athletic II	16	10	1	5	43	28	15	31
3 Lectern Lights II	16	8	3	5	39	26	13	27
4 Willingdon Athletic III	16	7	3	6	36	26	10	24
5 Fairfield II	16	7	3	6	28	30	-2	24
6 Fletching II	16	7	1	8	43	46	-3	22
7 Ringmer AFC IV	16	5	4	7	39	42	-3	19
8 Newick II	16	4	5	7	26	40	-14	17
9 Hurstpierpoint III	16	1	3	12	18	51	-33	6

MIDDLESEX COUNTY LEAGUE

Step 7 - Promotes to the various Step 6 divisions.

PREMIER DIVISION	P	W	D	L	F	A	GD	Pts
1 Brentham	6	4	2	0	18	11	7	14
2 London Samurai United	6	4	2	0	14	9	5	14
3 Pitshanger Dynamo	5	3	1	1	14	9	5	10
4 Indian Gymkhana	7	2	4	1	10	7	3	10
5 Hilltop	6	3	0	3	17	17	0	9
6 Cricklewood Wanderers	6	2	0	4	9	15	-6	9*
7 Clapton Community	4	2	1	1	6	4	2	7
8 NW London	6	1	3	2	7	8	-1	6
9 Sporting Hackney	5	2	0	3	12	15	-3	6
10 Kensington Dragons	5	2	2	1	12	8	4	5*
11 Larkspur Rovers	5	1	2	2	11	7	4	5
12 CB Hounslow United Res	5	1	1	3	10	13	-3	4
13 PFC Victoria London	3	0	1	2	2	7	-5	1
14 Stonewall	5	0	1	4	9	21	-12	1

DIVISION ONE CENTRAL & EAST	P	W	D	L	F	A	GD	Pts
1 FC Soma	6	5	1	0	21	7	14	16
2 Jolof Sports Club	6	4	1	1	20	12	8	13
3 Edmonton Rangers Wolves	6	4	0	2	19	8	11	12
4 The Wilberforce Wanderers	6	3	3	0	21	11	10	12
5 FC Roast	5	4	0	1	12	7	5	12
6 Priory Park Rangers	5	4	0	1	12	7	5	12
7 Camden & Islington	6	3	0	3	22	12	10	9
8 OIR FC	6	2	1	3	13	20	-7	9*
9 Stonewall Res	7	2	2	3	11	13	-2	8
10 Bruce Castle United	6	2	2	2	20	19	1	7*
11 North London	8	1	0	7	18	34	-16	3
12 FC Marylebone	7	0	2	5	10	22	-12	2
13 Eastfield	6	0	0	6	4	31	-27	0

DIVISION ONE NORTH WEST	P	W	D	L	F	A	GD	Pts
1 Springfield	7	5	1	1	14	10	4	16
2 Kodak Harrow	6	5	0	1	19	8	11	15
3 Harrow Bhoys	6	4	0	2	13	8	5	12
4 AFC Hanwell & Hayes	6	3	2	1	23	10	13	11
5 Speedy United	8	3	2	3	15	15	0	11
6 AVA	4	3	0	1	11	6	5	9
7 AEK London	6	2	2	2	16	9	7	8
8 Sporting Duet Academy	5	2	1	2	13	9	4	7
9 London Rangers	6	2	1	3	12	14	-2	7
10 Stones (Wealdstone)	5	1	1	3	8	11	-3	4
11 Starlight	7	1	1	5	8	33	-25	4
12 Pitshanger Dynamo Res	8	0	1	7	8	27	-19	1

DIVISION ONE SOUTH WEST	P	W	D	L	F	A	GD	Pts
1 FC Deportivo Galicia Res	7	6	1	0	25	7	18	19
2 Southall Athletic	6	3	1	2	19	13	6	10
3 Hillingdon	5	3	1	1	14	9	5	10
4 Hayes & Hillingdon	7	3	1	3	20	18	2	10
5 Ruislip Town	6	3	1	2	13	11	2	10
6 Brentham Res	6	2	1	3	14	13	1	9*
7 Claygate Royals	3	2	0	1	9	6	3	6
8 South Kilburn	5	1	3	1	6	6	0	6
9 AFC Southall	4	1	1	2	6	7	-1	4
10 Newmont	6	1	2	3	12	17	-5	4*
11 Wembley City	6	1	1	4	11	23	-12	4
12 Boston Manor	7	1	1	5	7	26	-19	4

NORTH BUCKS & DISTRICT LEAGUE

PREMIER DIVISION	P	W	D	L	F	A	GD	Pts
1 Great Horwood	11	10	0	1	30	16	14	30
2 Hanslope	11	8	3	0	35	10	25	27
3 Aylesbury Vale Dynamos	11	6	0	5	24	20	4	18
4 Stewkley Team	11	5	2	4	18	19	-1	17
5 Towcester Town	11	5	1	5	32	23	9	16
6 Bletchley Park	11	4	4	3	21	16	5	16
7 Marsh Gibbon	11	4	4	3	18	14	4	16
8 Potterspury	11	5	1	5	25	23	2	16
9 Olney FC	11	3	3	5	28	27	1	12
10 City Colts	11	3	1	7	24	37	-13	10
11 Clean Slate	11	2	1	8	21	46	-25	7
12 Stoke Hammond BT	11	1	0	10	15	40	-25	3

INTERMEDIATE	P	W	D	L	F	A	GD	Pts
1 Willen	11	9	0	2	53	21	32	27
2 Milton Keynes Irish Athletic	11	9	0	2	46	14	32	27
3 Grendon Rangers	11	8	1	2	33	17	16	25
4 Twyford United	11	7	1	3	40	20	20	22
5 Mursley United	11	6	0	5	18	34	-16	18
6 AFC Santander	11	5	0	6	22	26	-4	15
7 Hanslope Res	11	3	2	6	24	33	-9	11
8 Tattenhoe	11	3	2	6	13	25	-12	11
9 Great Linford	11	3	2	6	15	34	-19	11
10 New Bradwell St Peter Res	11	3	1	7	18	27	-9	10
11 Deanshanger Athletic	11	3	0	8	18	33	-15	9
12 Buckingham United Res	11	2	1	8	22	38	-16	7

DIVISION ONE	P	W	D	L	F	A	GD	Pts
1 Silverstone F.C.	11	9	2	0	37	9	28	29
2 Westbury	11	8	2	1	30	10	20	26
3 Potterspury Res	11	8	1	2	22	15	7	25
4 MK Wanderers	11	6	3	2	29	13	16	21
5 Towcester Town Res	11	7	0	4	21	9	12	21
6 Yardley Gobion F.C.	11	5	2	4	23	18	5	17
7 Clean Slate FS 10	11	5	1	5	21	27	-6	16
8 Great Horwood Res	11	3	2	6	25	30	-5	11
9 Newport Pagnell Athletic	11	3	1	7	18	25	-7	10
10 Steeple Claydon	11	2	1	8	16	20	-4	7
11 AFC Santander Res	11	1	1	9	8	30	-22	4
12 Syresham	11	1	0	10	6	50	-44	3

DIVISION TWO	P	W	D	L	F	A	GD	Pts
1 Stony Stratford Town	11	10	0	1	50	10	40	30
2 MK Wanderers	11	8	2	1	45	22	23	26
3 Olney Res	11	7	2	2	27	16	11	23
4 Newport Pagnell Athletic Res	11	6	3	2	29	26	3	21
5 Bletchley Park Res	11	6	1	4	25	26	-1	19
6 Deanshanger Athletic Res	11	4	3	4	25	17	8	15
7 Silverstone F.C. Res	11	4	3	4	21	29	-8	15
8 City Colts Res	11	4	2	5	27	18	9	14
9 Stewkley Res	11	4	1	6	22	31	-9	13
10 Marsh Gibbon Res	11	2	1	8	26	39	-13	7
11 Twyford United Res	11	2	0	9	18	45	-27	6
12 Yardley Gobion F.C. Res	11	0	0	11	9	45	-36	0

NORTH DEVON LEAGUE

PREMIER DIVISION	P	W	D	L	F	A	GD	Pts
1 North Molton Sports Club	20	20	0	0	42	10	32	60
2 Boca Seniors	20	15	2	3	53	25	28	47
3 Fremington	20	13	4	3	28	25	3	43
4 Kilkhampton	20	9	4	7	26	45	-19	31
5 Hartland Clovelly FC	20	9	2	9	23	53	-30	29
6 Bradworthy	20	9	0	11	27	36	-9	27
7 Holsworthy Res	20	8	1	11	30	56	-26	22*
8 Park United	17	6	1	10	42	9	33	19
9 Appledore	18	6	1	11	37	10	27	19
10 Braunton Res	16	1	1	14	9	12	-3	4
11 Ilfracombe Town Res	17	0	0	17	5	41	-36	0

SENIOR DIVISION	P	W	D	L	F	A	GD	Pts
1 Barnstaple Town Res	18	18	0	0	86	12	74	54
2 North Molton Sports Club Res	18	15	1	2	59	25	34	46
3 Northam Lions	18	12	1	5	58	41	17	37
4 Combe Martin	18	9	2	7	59	45	14	29
5 Torrington Res	18	9	2	7	32	49	-17	29
6 Torridgeside Res	18	7	2	9	25	42	-17	23
7 Shebbear United	18	7	1	10	21	42	-21	19*
8 Landkey Town	17	3	2	12	16	15	1	11
9 Fremington Res	18	3	1	14	17	78	-61	10
10 Braunton 3rds	17	0	0	17	6	30	-24	0

INTERMEDIATE ONE	P	W	D	L	F	A	GD	Pts
1 Barnstaple FC	20	18	2	0	72	21	51	56
2 Chittlehampton	20	15	4	1	37	15	22	49
3 Appledore Lions	20	13	3	4	63	32	31	42
4 Eastside	20	13	0	7	45	32	13	39
5 Putford	20	9	4	7	52	54	-2	31
6 Barum United	20	8	2	10	35	55	-20	23*
7 South Molton	20	7	1	12	29	86	-57	22
8 Lynton	20	6	3	11	41	47	-6	18*
9 Merton	20	4	1	15	28	56	-28	13
10 Appledore Res	19	4	0	15	16	9	7	12
11 SAS Equalizers	19	1	2	16	14	25	-11	5

INTERMEDIATE TWO	P	W	D	L	F	A	GD	Pts
1 Woolsery	20	19	0	1	99	15	84	57
2 Woolacombe	20	14	1	5	60	34	26	43
3 Kingsley Wizards	20	13	3	4	62	58	4	42
4 Hartland Clovelly Res	20	9	3	8	38	54	-16	30
5 Combe Martin Res	20	10	2	8	34	43	-9	29*
6 Park Rangers	20	10	1	9	43	48	-5	28*
7 Northam Lions Res	20	8	1	11	28	59	-31	25
8 Torridgeside 3rds	20	7	2	11	40	53	-13	23
9 High Bickington	20	7	1	12	31	62	-31	22
10 Braunton 4ths	19	5	0	14	27	18	9	15
11 Bridgerule	19	0	0	19	7	25	-18	0

INTERMEDIATE THREE	P	W	D	L	F	A	GD	Pts
1 Hartland Clovelly 3rds	18	15	0	3	81	29	52	45
2 Sandymere Blues	18	14	0	4	65	24	41	42
3 Ashwater	18	13	0	5	59	44	15	39
4 Kingsley Park	18	11	1	6	52	42	10	34
5 Taw Park	18	10	0	8	48	51	-3	30
6 Bideford AFC Res	18	9	2	7	47	53	-6	29
7 Bradworthy Res	18	5	1	12	30	61	-31	16
8 Morwenstow Res	18	4	2	12	31	67	-36	14
9 Shebbear United Res	18	4	0	14	25	68	-43	9*
10 Braunton 5ths	18	1	2	15	15	14	1	5

NORTH RIDING LEAGUE

Step 7 - promotes to the Northern League.

PREMIER DIVISION	P	W	D	L	F	A	GD	Pts
1 Boro Rangers	9	9	0	0	37	5	32	27
2 Redcar Town	11	9	0	2	32	10	22	27
3 Redcar Newmarket	11	7	1	3	36	26	10	22
4 Yarm & Eaglescliffe	11	6	3	2	33	21	12	21
5 BEADS	10	6	0	4	24	23	1	18
6 St. Mary's 1947	10	4	4	2	21	18	3	16
7 Kader	11	3	3	5	25	33	-8	12
8 Staithes Athletic	9	3	0	6	12	23	-11	9
9 Thirsk Falcons	8	1	4	3	17	21	-4	7
10 Grangetown Boys Club	8	2	0	6	12	22	-10	6
11 Thornaby Dubliners	9	2	0	7	11	22	-11	6
12 Bedale	6	0	4	2	9	14	-5	4
13 Fishburn Park	8	1	1	6	12	24	-12	4
14 Stokesley SC	7	1	0	6	2	21	-19	3

DIVISION ONE	P	W	D	L	F	A	GD	Pts
1 Redcar Athletic Res	9	7	1	1	47	11	36	22
2 Cleveland	7	5	1	1	17	9	8	16
3 Loftus Athletic	7	5	0	2	32	19	13	15
4 Nunthorpe	8	4	3	1	20	14	6	15
5 Boro Rangers Res	7	3	3	1	23	14	9	12
6 New Marske	10	3	1	6	15	24	-9	10
7 Lealholm	5	3	0	2	9	11	-2	9
8 Whitby Fishermens Society	5	2	0	3	12	17	-5	6
9 T.I.B.S.	8	2	0	6	18	24	-6	6
10 Great Ayton United	7	2	0	5	10	17	-7	6
11 Northallerton Town Res	6	1	2	3	8	20	-12	5
12 Wolviston	4	1	1	2	11	12	-1	4
13 Kader Res	7	1	0	6	11	41	-30	3

NORTHANTS COMBINATION

Step 7 - promotes to the United Counties League.

PREMIER DIVISION	P	W	D	L	F	A	GD	Pts
1 Harpole	9	7	0	2	22	9	13	21
2 Kettering Nomads	6	6	0	0	21	5	16	18
3 Wollaston Victoria	7	5	0	2	27	14	13	15
4 Heyford Athletic	8	4	0	4	17	24	-7	12
5 Roade	5	3	2	0	16	8	8	11
6 Moulton	8	3	2	3	17	18	-1	11
7 Corby Pegasus	9	3	2	4	16	23	-7	11
8 Corby Stewarts & Lloyds	8	3	0	5	12	14	-2	9
9 Woodford United	8	2	2	4	14	14	0	8
10 Rothwell FC Aztec	7	2	2	3	17	20	-3	8
11 Earls Barton United	7	2	1	4	16	19	-3	7
12 James King Blisworth	7	2	1	4	12	16	-4	7
13 Thrapston Town	6	2	0	4	17	19	-2	6
14 Spratton	7	1	0	6	10	31	-21	3

DIVISION ONE	P	W	D	L	F	A	GD	Pts
1 Wootton St George	7	5	2	0	23	7	16	17
2 AFC Houghton Magna	7	4	2	1	22	10	12	14
3 Medbourne	7	4	2	1	16	10	6	14
4 Roade Res	9	4	1	4	21	14	7	13
5 Corby White Hart Loco's	8	4	1	3	18	12	6	13
6 Northampton Spartak	9	4	1	4	27	28	-1	13
7 Corby Strip Mills	7	4	0	3	16	9	7	12
8 West Haddon Albion	7	2	4	1	18	17	1	10
9 Bugbrooke St Michaels 'A'	9	3	1	5	13	16	-3	10
10 Finedon Volta	7	3	0	4	12	24	-12	9
11 Moulton Future Elite Sports	5	2	1	2	14	12	2	7
12 Higham Town	8	2	1	5	12	28	-16	7
13 Corby Ravens	4	1	1	2	6	9	-3	4
14 Milton	8	0	1	7	5	27	-22	1

NORTHERN ALLIANCE

Step 7 - promotes to the Northern League.

PREMIER DIVISION	P	W	D	L	F	A	GD	Pts
1 AFC Killingworth	9	8	0	1	35	9	26	24
2 Cullercoats	11	7	1	3	29	15	14	22
3 Wallington	8	7	0	1	27	14	13	21
4 Seaton Delaval	11	6	0	5	22	18	4	18
5 Blyth Town	9	5	2	2	20	13	7	17
6 Newcastle Chemfica	11	5	2	4	25	21	4	17
7 Winlaton Vulcans	8	5	0	3	23	17	6	15
8 Ponteland United	8	4	0	4	18	18	0	12
9 Whitley Bay A	8	3	2	3	10	13	-3	11
10 Newcastle Blue Star	10	4	1	5	24	17	7	10*
11 Gateshead Rutherford	7	3	1	3	18	17	1	10
12 AFC New Fordley	6	2	3	1	5	4	1	9
13 Percy Main Amateurs	11	2	2	7	15	33	-18	8
14 Alnwick Town	10	2	1	7	18	30	-12	7
15 North Shields Athletic	10	0	2	8	11	39	-28	2
16 Shankhouse	7	0	1	6	3	25	-22	1

DIVISION ONE	P	W	D	L	F	A	GD	Pts
1 Prudhoe Youth Club	14	11	1	2	43	20	23	34
2 Haltwhistle Jubilee	10	9	1	0	41	15	26	28
3 Cramlington United	9	7	0	2	32	9	23	21
4 Whitley Bay Sporting Club	10	6	2	2	26	14	12	20
5 Hexham	10	5	2	3	31	17	14	17
6 Red Row Welfare	12	5	1	6	26	25	1	16
7 Rothbury	9	5	0	4	12	21	-9	15
8 Bedlington	9	4	1	4	29	30	-1	13
9 Hebburn Town U23	8	4	0	4	17	15	2	12
10 Seaton Burn	9	3	2	4	13	28	-15	11
11 Wallsend Boys Club	12	3	3	6	29	33	-4	9*
12 Whitburn & Cleadon	7	3	0	4	10	14	-4	9
13 Gosforth Bohemian	10	1	3	6	15	28	-13	6
14 FC United of Newcastle	11	2	0	9	18	32	-14	6
15 Forest Hall	8	1	0	7	6	26	-20	3
16 Felling Magpies	6	0	0	6	7	28	-21	0

DIVISION TWO	P	W	D	L	F	A	GD	Pts
1 Newcastle Independent	9	8	0	1	34	9	25	24
2 Newcastle University Res	11	7	1	3	28	17	11	19*
3 AFC Newbiggin	10	5	4	1	19	14	5	19
4 Cramlington Town	11	5	3	3	22	22	0	18
5 Willington Quay Saints	9	5	2	2	16	12	4	17
6 Stobswood Welfare	12	5	2	5	25	25	0	17
7 West Jesmond	7	5	1	1	27	14	13	16
8 Newcastle East End	8	4	2	2	17	10	7	14
9 Ponteland United Res	11	3	5	3	18	18	0	14
10 Wideopen & District	11	4	2	5	21	24	-3	14
11 Ellington	9	3	4	2	13	11	2	13
12 Spittal Rovers	11	3	1	7	20	22	-2	10
13 Newcastle Blue Star Res	10	1	2	7	11	35	-24	5
14 Gateshead Redheugh 1957	8	0	3	5	12	20	-8	3
15 Ashington Res	7	1	0	6	11	23	-12	3
16 Seaton Sluice	8	1	0	7	12	30	-18	3

NOTTINGHAMSHIRE SENIOR LEAGUE

Step 7 - promotes to the Northern Counties East and Midlands Counties Leagues.

PREMIER DIVISION	P	W	D	L	F	A	GD	Pts
1 Bingham Town	7	7	0	0	40	6	34	21
2 Wollaton	8	6	2	0	22	6	16	20
3 AFC Dunkirk	8	6	2	0	23	8	15	20
4 Woodthorpe Park Rangers	9	6	1	2	23	13	10	19
5 Stapleford Town	9	5	2	2	28	16	12	17
6 Ilkeston Town FCB	7	4	2	1	21	11	10	14
7 Southwell City	11	4	2	5	29	20	9	14
8 Cotgrave	7	4	1	2	18	13	5	13
9 Sandiacre Town	8	4	1	3	17	16	1	13
10 Bilborough Town	10	3	2	5	17	25	-8	11
11 Aslockton & Orston	7	2	2	3	12	22	-10	8
12 Awsworth Villa	6	2	1	3	8	11	-3	7
13 Attenborough	7	2	1	4	12	28	-16	7
14 Keyworth United	8	2	0	6	19	24	-5	6
15 FC Cavaliers	9	2	0	7	11	29	-18	6
16 Burton Joyce	7	1	1	5	8	17	-9	4
17 Magdala Amateurs	7	0	2	5	10	21	-11	2
18 Calverton Miners Welfare	7	0	0	7	5	37	-32	0

DIVISION ONE	P	W	D	L	F	A	GD	Pts
1 FC Sez	11	9	2	0	34	14	20	29
2 Ruddington Village	11	6	3	2	29	19	10	21
3 AFC Top Valley	8	6	2	0	22	12	10	20
4 United Grays	11	6	1	4	34	21	13	19
5 Radcliffe Olympic	13	5	4	4	26	19	7	19
6 Ravenshead	9	6	1	2	22	17	5	19
7 Gedling Southbank	11	5	2	4	35	24	11	17
8 Southwell City Res	13	4	3	6	24	27	-3	15
9 Hucknall Town Res	10	4	1	5	29	22	7	13
10 Meden Vale Colts	9	4	1	4	18	22	-4	13
11 Beeston	9	3	3	3	22	14	8	12
12 Wollaton Res	12	4	0	8	34	35	-1	12
13 West Bridgford AFC	8	2	4	2	11	11	0	10
14 Stapleford Town Res	7	2	3	2	14	17	-3	9
15 Radford Res	10	3	0	7	12	39	-27	9
16 Bridgford United	10	2	2	6	18	33	-15	8
17 Kimberley Miners Welfare Res	11	2	0	9	13	29	-16	6
18 Kirton Brickworks	9	2	0	7	11	33	-22	6

DIVISION TWO NORTH	P	W	D	L	F	A	GD	Pts
1 FC Geordie	10	8	0	2	57	17	40	24
2 Ravenshead Reds	10	5	4	1	25	16	9	19
3 FC Mansfield	9	5	3	1	33	15	18	18
4 Quarrydale United	9	5	2	2	26	20	6	17
5 Trent Vineyard	8	5	1	2	18	15	3	16
6 Beeston Old Boys Association	6	5	0	1	22	7	15	15
7 United Grays Community	9	5	0	4	27	20	7	15
8 Bilborough Town	8	4	2	2	25	22	3	14
9 Pythian Res	11	4	1	6	22	37	-15	13
10 Blidworth Welfare Red	8	3	2	3	17	17	0	11
11 AFC Creswell	7	3	1	3	15	16	-1	10
12 Beeston	10	2	3	5	19	33	-14	9
13 Arnold Town Res	11	1	0	10	18	40	-22	3
14 Ballers	8	0	1	7	13	46	-33	1
15 Brinsley	6	0	0	6	8	24	-16	0

DIVISION TWO SOUTH	P	W	D	L	F	A	GD	Pts
1 Pythian	11	9	2	0	47	17	30	29
2 Keyworth United Res	10	9	1	0	43	12	31	28
3 East Leake Robins	10	9	0	1	55	15	40	27
4 AC United	11	6	2	3	39	22	17	20
5 Bingham Town Res	10	6	1	3	34	24	10	19
6 Burton Joyce Res	9	5	1	3	22	24	-2	16
7 Elston United	7	4	1	2	22	10	12	13
8 Ruddington Village Res	8	3	2	3	21	27	-6	11
9 Barrowby	5	3	1	1	14	8	6	10
10 Fernwood Foxes	9	2	3	4	20	23	-3	9
11 AFC Colsterworth Sports & Social	7	2	0	5	15	27	-12	6
12 Cotgrave Res	11	1	3	7	24	44	-20	6
13 Rushcliffe	11	1	1	9	20	36	-16	4
14 Long Bennington	8	1	1	6	15	32	-17	4
15 West Bridgford AFC Res	8	1	1	6	16	37	-21	4
16 Aslockton & Orston Res	9	0	0	9	7	56	-49	0

OXFORDSHIRE SENIOR LEAGUE

Step 7 - promotes to the Hellenic League.

PREMIER DIVISION	P	W	D	L	F	A	GD	Pts
1 Marston Saints	9	8	1	0	26	10	16	25
2 Yarnton	10	7	1	2	28	19	9	22
3 Kennington Athletic	9	6	1	2	27	13	14	19
4 Bure Park FC	10	6	0	4	34	24	10	18
5 Cropredy	7	5	2	0	28	7	21	17
6 Launton Sports	9	5	1	3	18	10	8	16
7 Charlton United	11	4	1	6	16	22	-6	13
8 Garsington	10	4	0	6	18	20	-2	12
9 Hanborough	9	3	1	5	15	21	-6	10
10 Summertown Stars AFC	9	3	0	6	29	28	1	9
11 Mansfield Road	9	3	0	6	17	24	-7	9
12 Freeland	9	1	2	6	7	24	-17	5
13 Chesterton	9	0	0	9	8	49	-41	0

DIVISION ONE	P	W	D	L	F	A	GD	Pts
1 Bicester Hallions	10	9	1	0	39	5	34	28
2 Eynsham Association	11	8	1	2	30	20	10	25
3 Middleton Cheney	11	6	1	4	26	26	0	19
4 Kirtlington FC	10	5	1	4	29	23	6	16
5 Adderbury Park Res	9	5	1	3	23	18	5	16
6 Chalgrove Cavaliers	10	5	1	4	22	26	-4	16
7 Ashton Folly	10	3	4	3	26	18	8	13
8 Horspath	10	4	1	5	20	31	-11	13
9 Bicester Town Colts	10	3	0	7	25	33	-8	9
10 "Kidlington FC A	9	2	1	6	14	19	-5	7
11 Woodstock Town	10	2	0	8	12	24	-12	6
12 Oxford Irish Athletic	10	1	2	7	13	36	-23	5

DIVISION TWO	P	W	D	L	F	A	GD	Pts
1 Easington Sports Clan	11	8	3	0	25	12	13	27
2 Kennington Athletic Res	10	8	2	0	41	10	31	26
3 Chinnor Res	8	6	2	0	39	8	31	20
4 Cropredy Dev	10	6	0	4	51	23	28	18
5 Launton Sports Res	10	6	0	4	22	18	4	18
6 Heyford Athletic Res	9	4	4	1	22	7	15	16
7 Hanborough Res	11	4	2	5	21	26	-5	14
8 Chesterton Res	12	3	3	6	25	39	-14	12
9 Yarnton Res	9	3	2	4	20	21	-1	11
10 Charlton United Res	9	3	1	5	21	29	-8	10
11 Summertown Stars AFC Res	11	2	3	6	15	27	-12	9
12 Marston Saints Res	10	2	1	7	12	35	-23	7
13 Mansfield Road Res	8	2	0	6	17	30	-13	6
14 Bicester Hallions Res	10	0	1	9	10	56	-46	1

PETERBOROUGH & DISTRICT LEAGUE

Step 7 - promotes to the United Counties League.

PREMIER DIVISION	P	W	D	L	F	A	GD	Pts
1 Stilton United	11	8	2	1	37	10	27	26
2 Netherton United	10	7	1	2	45	10	35	22
3 Moulton Harrox	6	6	0	0	21	6	15	18
4 Crowland Town	8	6	0	2	19	6	13	18
5 Peterborough North End Sports	9	5	2	2	15	12	3	17
6 FC Parson Drove	8	5	1	2	18	8	10	15*
7 Holbeach United Res	9	3	6	0	24	15	9	15
8 ICA Sports	9	3	2	4	19	12	7	11
9 Uppingham Town	9	2	4	3	20	20	0	10
10 Long Sutton Athletic	8	3	1	4	16	18	-2	10
11 Eye United	8	2	2	4	15	23	-8	8
12 Ketton	10	2	2	6	16	28	-12	8
13 Leverington Sports	10	1	4	5	16	24	-8	7
14 Cardea	11	2	1	8	17	44	-27	7
15 Stamford Lions	6	0	2	4	5	16	-11	5*
16 Oakham United	8	0	0	8	3	54	-51	0

DIVISION ONE	P	W	D	L	F	A	GD	Pts
1 Wittering Premiair	10	9	0	1	53	15	38	30*
2 Oundle Town	11	8	1	2	30	18	12	25
3 Warboys Town	11	7	0	4	31	16	15	21
4 Stamford Belvedere	9	5	2	2	32	11	21	17
5 Whittlesey Athletic Res	9	5	1	3	18	14	4	16
6 FC Peterborough	9	5	0	4	16	25	-9	15
7 Tydd	9	4	1	4	20	17	3	13
8 Moulton Harrox Res	10	4	1	5	30	29	1	13
9 Rippingale & Folkingham	9	4	1	4	20	26	-6	13
10 Eunice Huntingdon	10	4	1	5	20	28	-8	13
11 Pinchbeck United Res	9	3	1	5	15	24	-9	10
12 Thorpe Wood Rangers	8	3	0	5	11	21	-10	9
13 Crowland Town Res	10	2	1	7	11	30	-19	7
14 Peterborough Northern Star Res	9	2	1	6	12	17	-5	6*
15 Kings Cliffe	8	2	0	6	15	32	-17	6
16 NECI	5	0	1	4	8	19	-11	1

DIVISION TWO	P	W	D	L	F	A	GD	Pts
1 Ramsey Town	10	9	0	1	42	7	35	27
2 Wisbech Town Res	9	7	0	2	31	14	17	21
3 Deeping Rangers Res	7	6	1	0	23	6	17	19
4 Glinton & Northborough	9	5	1	3	27	24	3	16
5 Wittering Premiair Res	10	5	1	4	26	30	-4	16
6 Farcet United	9	5	0	4	39	21	18	15
7 Orton Rangers	8	4	1	3	19	16	3	13
8 Stamford Belvedere Res	8	4	1	3	19	25	-6	13
9 Long Sutton Athletic Res	9	4	0	5	18	21	-3	12
10 Netherton United Res	8	3	0	5	33	19	14	9
11 Holbeach United Sports	6	2	0	4	9	15	-6	9*
12 Peterborough Polonia	8	2	0	6	17	27	-10	9*
13 Parkside	9	2	1	6	13	32	-19	7
14 FC Hampton	9	0	3	6	17	34	-17	3
15 Oakham United Res	7	0	1	6	10	52	-42	-1

DIVISION THREE	P	W	D	L	F	A	GD	Pts
1 Stanground Sports	10	9	0	1	51	10	41	27
2 Weldon United	10	7	2	1	40	16	24	23
3 Casterton	7	6	1	0	34	7	27	22*
4 Stilton United Res	9	6	2	1	32	9	23	20
5 FC Peterborough Res	9	6	0	3	23	16	7	18
6 Peterborough City	9	5	1	3	32	25	7	16
7 Cardea Res	10	5	0	5	40	25	15	15
8 Wittering Premiair 'A'	9	4	2	3	30	26	4	14
9 Tydd Res	8	3	0	5	19	32	-13	9
10 Kings Cliffe Res	8	3	0	5	16	34	-18	9
11 Huntingdon Rovers	9	3	0	6	20	47	-27	9
12 Dreams	9	2	0	7	25	36	-11	6
13 Leverington Sports Res	10	2	0	8	21	40	-19	6
14 FC Hampton Res	10	2	0	8	24	44	-20	6
15 Stamford Lions Res	7	0	0	7	8	48	-40	-1*

DIVISION FOUR	P	W	D	L	F	A	GD	Pts
1 Sawtry	9	7	2	0	39	10	29	23
2 Deeping United	8	7	1	0	51	9	42	22
3 Netherton United 'A'	11	6	2	3	25	19	6	20
4 Uppingham Town Res	8	4	3	1	23	11	12	15
5 Whittlesey Athletic 'A'	10	3	5	2	30	16	14	14
6 Huntingdon Town	10	4	2	4	33	27	6	14
7 Park Farm Pumas	9	4	1	4	21	23	-2	13
8 Long Sutton Athletic 'A'	9	4	1	4	17	22	-5	13
9 Thurlby Tigers	6	3	1	2	17	16	1	10
10 Warboys Town Res	11	3	1	7	19	36	-17	10
11 Cambridge	8	2	2	4	17	25	-8	8
12 Parkside Res	9	1	0	8	10	46	-36	3
13 Orton Rangers Res	10	0	1	9	12	54	-42	1

DIVISION FIVE	P	W	D	L	F	A	GD	Pts
1 Sutton Bridge United	11	8	2	1	41	19	22	26
2 Thorpe Wood Rangers Res	8	8	0	0	47	13	34	24
3 Rippingale & Folkingham Res	11	7	3	1	33	17	16	23*
4 Langtoft United	7	6	1	0	45	6	39	19
5 Wittering Premiair 'B'	11	6	0	5	38	27	11	18
6 Deeping United Res	11	6	0	5	32	27	5	18
7 Oundle Town Res	10	5	2	3	36	20	16	17
8 NECI Res	8	5	0	3	26	22	4	15
9 Ramsey Town Res	10	3	2	5	22	31	-9	11
10 Weldon United Res	9	3	0	6	22	23	-1	9
11 Dreams Res	10	3	0	7	23	52	-29	9
12 Kings Cliffe 'A'	8	2	1	5	11	27	-16	7
13 Park Farm Pumas Res	10	2	0	8	22	43	-21	6
14 Holbeach Bank	11	1	1	9	18	58	-40	4
15 FC Hampton 'A'	9	1	0	8	16	47	-31	3

PLYMOUTH & WEST DEVON LEAGUE

PREMIER DIVISION	P	W	D	L	F	A	GD	Pts
1 Millbridge	16	15	1	0	69	19	50	46
2 Plymouth Hope	16	9	4	3	47	42	5	31
3 University of Plymouth	16	8	2	6	46	33	13	26
4 Signal Box Oak Villa	16	8	1	7	53	44	9	25
5 Saltram Athletic	16	7	1	8	44	50	-6	22
6 Plymouth Vaults	16	6	2	8	40	41	-1	20
7 Pennycross SC	16	6	1	9	37	36	1	19*
8 Signal Box Oak Villa Res	16	5	0	11	34	54	-20	15*
9 Horrabridge Rangers	16	1	2	13	21	66	-45	5

DIVISION ONE	P	W	D	L	F	A	GD	Pts
1 Morley Rangers	16	12	2	2	81	22	59	38
2 DC Auto Repairs	16	10	3	3	57	25	32	33
3 Tamar View	16	10	2	4	62	32	30	32
4 Hooe Rovers	16	9	3	4	49	20	29	30
5 Princetown	16	7	2	7	46	39	7	23
6 Millbridge Res	16	7	0	9	41	54	-13	21
7 Torpoint Athletic 4ths	16	5	1	10	32	53	-21	16
8 Tavistock Rovers	16	4	0	12	39	67	-28	12
9 Plymouth United	16	1	1	14	26	121	-95	4

DIVISION TWO	P	W	D	L	F	A	GD	Pts
1 Mainstone Social FC	14	14	0	0	98	12	86	42
2 Mountwise AFC	14	12	0	2	107	9	98	36
3 FC Tavyside	14	8	2	4	63	30	33	26
4 Plymouth Parkway Res	14	6	2	6	48	58	-10	20
5 Belgrave	14	5	2	7	51	50	1	17
6 Roborough Rangers	14	5	2	7	34	59	-25	17
7 Horrabridge Rangers Res	14	0	2	12	24	113	-89	2
8 Castle Loyale	14	0	2	12	19	113	-94	2

SHEFFIELD & HALLAMSHIRE LEAGUE

Step 7 - promotes to the Northern Counties East League.

PREMIER DIVISION	P	W	D	L	F	A	GD	Pts
1 Dodworth Miners Welfare	9	7	1	1	29	5	24	22
2 Swinton Athletic	7	7	0	0	24	4	20	21
3 North Gawber Colliery	9	4	2	3	26	15	11	14
4 Ecclesfield Red Rose 1915	9	4	2	3	21	12	9	14
5 Oughtibridge W.M.S.C.	8	4	1	3	15	19	-4	13
6 Wakefield	6	4	0	2	14	8	6	12
7 Penistone Church Res	7	4	0	3	14	12	2	12
8 Hepworth United	8	4	0	4	12	15	-3	12
9 Wombwell Main	5	3	0	2	13	12	1	9
10 Jubilee Sports	5	2	0	3	6	13	-7	6
11 Stocksbridge Park Steels Res	9	2	0	7	13	26	-13	6
12 Sheffield Town	5	1	0	4	8	11	-3	3
13 Houghton Main	6	1	0	5	13	25	-12	3
14 High Green Villa	6	1	0	5	12	24	-12	3
15 Davys	5	1	0	4	2	21	-19	3

DIVISION ONE	P	W	D	L	F	A	GD	Pts
1 Handsworth Res	6	5	1	0	24	6	18	16
2 Denaby Main	7	4	3	0	15	6	9	15
3 Kiveton Park	6	4	0	2	19	9	10	12
4 Wombwell Town	5	3	1	1	13	6	7	10
5 South Kirkby Colliery	6	3	1	2	10	13	-3	10
6 South Elmsall United Services	6	3	0	3	14	13	1	9
7 AFC Dronfield	4	2	1	1	6	6	0	7
8 Athersley Recreation Res	8	2	1	5	13	17	-4	7
9 Sheffield Union	4	2	0	2	8	9	-1	6
10 Sheffield Medics	5	1	1	3	7	8	-1	4
11 Kinsley Boys	3	1	0	2	3	7	-4	3
12 New Bohemians	5	1	0	4	5	22	-17	3
13 Wombwell Main Res	7	0	1	6	8	23	-15	1

DIVISION TWO	P	W	D	L	F	A	GD	Pts
1 Caribbean Sports	8	8	0	0	32	8	24	24
2 Swinton Athletic Res	8	6	1	1	33	13	20	19
3 Millmoor Juniors	8	5	3	0	32	10	22	18
4 Silkstone United	7	6	0	1	20	10	10	18
5 Houghton Main Dev	7	2	2	3	14	20	-6	8
6 Sheffield Lane Top	8	2	2	4	13	20	-7	8
7 Kiveton Park Res	6	2	0	4	16	17	-1	6
8 Stocksbridge Park Steels Dev	6	2	0	4	20	23	-3	6
9 Wakefield EFP	4	1	1	2	6	14	-8	4
10 Bank End AFC	6	1	1	4	6	17	-11	4
11 Parkgate Res	8	1	0	7	12	21	-9	3
12 Thurcroft	6	0	0	6	5	36	-31	0

SHROPSHIRE COUNTY LEAGUE

Step 7 - promotes to the West Midlands (regional) League.

PREMIER DIVISION	P	W	D	L	F	A	GD	Pts
1 Steam Wagon United	10	9	0	1	47	14	33	27
2 Ludlow	10	7	1	2	42	12	30	22
3 Shrewsbury Juniors	9	6	1	2	41	21	20	19
4 Dawley Town	7	6	0	1	32	12	20	18
5 Church Stretton Town	9	5	0	4	34	21	13	15
6 AMS FC	6	5	0	1	16	7	9	15
7 Newport Town	9	4	1	4	30	28	2	13
8 Gobowen Celtic	7	3	1	3	11	22	-11	10
9 Shrewsbury Up & Comers	11	2	4	5	14	30	-16	10
10 Shifnal Town	7	3	0	4	16	21	-5	9
11 Wrockwardine Wood Juniors	9	3	0	6	15	25	-10	9
12 Madeley Sports	10	2	1	7	22	51	-29	7
13 AFC Bridgnorth	9	1	1	7	11	36	-25	4
14 Albrighton	9	0	0	9	4	35	-31	0

SOMERSET COUNTY LEAGUE

Step 7 - promotes to the Western League.

PREMIER DIVISION	P	W	D	L	F	A	GD	Pts
1 Nailsea & Tickenham	8	7	1	0	28	5	23	22
2 Worle	9	5	2	2	24	15	9	17
3 Watchet Town	8	5	1	2	17	8	9	16
4 Chilcompton Sports	7	5	0	2	20	4	16	15
5 Clevedon United	7	5	0	2	21	8	13	15
6 Middlezoy Rovers	8	4	1	3	20	13	7	13
7 Clutton	8	3	4	1	8	8	0	13
8 Westfield	9	3	1	5	19	27	-8	10
9 Mendip Broadwalk	7	3	0	4	16	16	0	9
10 Fry Club	7	2	2	3	13	15	-2	8
11 Keynsham Town Res	6	2	2	2	7	9	-2	8
12 Nailsea United	8	2	1	5	14	22	-8	7
13 Stockwood Wanderers	7	1	3	3	6	12	-6	6
14 Ilminster Town	8	1	3	4	15	24	-9	6
15 Stockwood Green	7	2	0	5	9	26	-17	6
16 Chard Town	10	1	1	8	13	38	-25	4

DIVISION ONE	P	W	D	L	F	A	GD	Pts
1 Staplegrove	9	6	1	2	21	18	3	19
2 Saltford	8	5	2	1	17	11	6	17
3 Wells City Res	7	5	1	1	18	9	9	16
4 Winscombe	6	4	2	0	16	8	8	14
5 Uphill Castle	7	4	0	3	24	13	11	12
6 Somerton Town	8	3	2	3	17	13	4	11
7 Middlezoy Rovers Res	7	3	2	2	15	14	1	11
8 Burnham United	7	3	3	1	12	8	4	10*
9 Street FC Res	7	3	1	3	11	10	1	10
10 Wrington Redhill	8	2	2	4	12	15	-3	8
11 Minehead AFC	9	1	4	4	6	13	-7	7
12 Welton Rovers Res	8	2	1	5	12	20	-8	7
13 Nailsea & Tickenham Res	5	0	3	2	6	10	-4	3
14 Timsbury Athletic	7	1	0	6	9	23	-14	3
15 Yatton & Cleeve United	7	0	2	5	14	25	-11	2

DIVISION TWO	P	W	D	L	F	A	GD	Pts
1 Ashton & Backwell United Res	7	5	1	1	17	4	13	16
2 Peasedown Miners Welfare	9	4	3	2	22	15	7	15
3 Cheddar Res	6	4	1	1	17	7	10	13
4 Castle Cary	9	4	1	4	25	25	0	13
5 Hutton	7	3	3	1	14	6	8	12
6 AFC Brislington	7	4	0	3	22	18	4	12
7 Chew Magna	7	3	2	2	20	18	2	11
8 Glastonbury	7	3	2	2	16	16	0	11
9 Radstock Town Res	6	2	2	2	16	15	1	8
10 Portishead Town Res	5	2	1	2	7	6	1	7
11 Imperial	6	1	2	3	8	14	-6	5
12 Long Ashton	7	0	1	6	7	25	-18	1
13 Fry Club Res	7	0	1	6	7	29	-22	1

DIVISION THREE	P	W	D	L	F	A	GD	Pts
1 Cutters Friday	7	6	1	0	20	4	16	19
2 Ashcott	7	5	2	0	22	8	14	17
3 Banwell	6	5	1	0	32	5	27	16
4 Bishops Lydeard Res	7	5	0	2	22	15	7	15
5 Clevedon United Res	7	4	2	1	12	12	0	14
6 Nailsea United Res	9	4	1	4	25	22	3	13
7 Somerton Town Res	8	2	3	3	12	15	-3	9
8 Winscombe Res	3	2	0	1	6	5	1	6
9 Draycott	5	2	0	3	15	15	0	6
10 Combe St Nicholas	5	1	1	3	12	15	-3	4
11 Burnham United Res	6	0	4	2	6	9	-3	4
12 Yatton & Cleeve United Res	7	1	1	5	8	25	-17	4
13 Congresbury	6	1	0	5	6	21	-15	3
14 Tunley Athletic	6	0	2	4	5	18	-13	2
15 Stockwood Green Res	5	0	0	5	6	20	-14	0

SOUTH DEVON LEAGUE

PREMIER DIVISON	P	W	D	L	F	A	GD	Pts
1 The Windmill FC (Devon)	10	7	2	1	29	10	19	23
2 Meadowbrook Athletic	9	7	1	1	34	17	17	22
3 Salcombe Town	10	6	1	3	37	23	14	19
4 Ipplepen Athletic	9	5	3	1	24	12	12	18
5 Buckfastleigh Rangers	8	5	1	2	22	14	8	16
6 Torbay Police	10	4	2	4	30	28	2	14
7 Ivybridge Town Res	10	4	1	5	27	29	-2	13
8 Broadmeadow ST	12	3	3	6	20	34	-14	12
9 Watts Blake Bearne	8	3	2	3	21	17	4	11
10 Newton Abbot 66	10	3	2	5	21	27	-6	11
11 East Allington United	9	3	2	4	17	25	-8	11
12 Brixham AFC Res	10	2	4	4	17	29	-12	10
13 Elburton Villa Res	9	2	3	4	15	24	-9	9
14 Plympton Athletic Res	8	2	1	5	12	20	-8	7
15 Barton Athletic	7	2	0	5	12	13	-1	6
16 Buckland Athletic 3rd	9	2	0	7	9	25	-16	6

DIVISION ONE	P	W	D	L	F	A	GD	Pts
1 Galmpton United	10	9	0	1	53	10	43	27
2 Ashburton Association	10	8	2	0	52	15	37	26
3 Upton Athletic	12	8	0	4	26	24	2	24
4 Paignton Saints Res	9	7	0	2	38	14	24	21
5 Abbotskerswell	9	6	1	2	30	17	13	19
6 Kingsteignton Athletic Res	8	6	0	2	25	12	13	18
7 Beesands Rovers	10	4	2	4	27	28	-1	14
8 Chudleigh Athletic Res	10	4	1	5	26	26	0	13
9 Buckfastleigh Rangers Res	10	3	0	7	17	39	-22	9
10 Kingskerswell & Chelston	8	2	0	6	16	21	-5	6
11 Harbertonford	8	1	0	7	13	26	-13	3
12 Waldon Athletic Res	8	0	0	8	8	51	-43	0
13 Paignton Villa Res	10	0	0	10	10	58	-48	0

DIVISION TWO	P	W	D	L	F	A	GD	Pts
1 Ilsington Villa	12	9	0	3	51	30	21	27
2 Newton Abbot Spurs 3rd	10	8	0	2	39	21	18	24
3 Ipplepen Athletic Res	9	7	0	2	38	13	25	21
4 Babbacombe Corinthians	9	6	0	3	43	11	32	18
5 Dittisham United	10	5	1	4	41	24	17	16
6 Barton Athletic Res	11	5	1	5	37	40	-3	16
7 Newton Rovers	9	5	1	3	25	28	-3	16
8 Torquay Town	11	5	0	6	51	43	8	15
9 Watcombe Wanderers Res	9	5	0	4	20	24	-4	15
10 Dartmouth Res	9	4	1	4	18	16	2	13
11 East Allington United Res	11	3	0	8	25	69	-44	9
12 Torbay Police Res	8	2	1	5	16	24	-8	7
13 Broadhempston United	10	1	1	8	15	39	-24	4
14 Bishopsteignton United	10	1	0	9	22	59	-37	0*

DIVISION THREE	P	W	D	L	F	A	GD	Pts
1 Brixham Town FC	9	8	1	0	44	6	38	25
2 Totnes & Dartington SC Res	9	8	0	1	39	12	27	24
3 Galmpton United Res	9	5	1	3	20	14	6	16
4 Chudleigh Athletic 3rds	7	5	0	2	17	10	7	15
5 Liverton United Res	7	4	1	2	22	11	11	13
6 Watts Blake Bearne Res	5	4	0	1	16	6	10	12
7 Torquay Town Res	8	3	2	3	17	18	-1	11
8 Newton Abbot 66 Res	8	3	2	3	13	15	-2	11
9 Kingsbridge & Kellaton United	6	3	1	2	13	17	-4	10
10 Paignton Saints 3rds	9	3	1	5	15	22	-7	10
11 Teign Village	8	2	1	5	13	23	-10	7
12 South Brent FC	9	1	2	6	14	24	-10	5
13 Babbacombe Corinthians Res	8	1	1	6	11	25	-14	4
14 Newton Rovers Res	9	1	1	7	4	36	-32	4
15 Kingsteignton Athletic 3rd	7	1	0	6	9	28	-19	3

ST PIRAN LEAGUE

Step 7 - promotes to the South West Peninsula League.

EAST DIVISION	P	W	D	L	F	A	GD	Pts
1 Bude Town	12	8	3	1	54	14	40	27
2 Polperro	10	7	2	1	30	12	18	23
3 Launceston Res	11	6	2	3	31	24	7	20
4 Torpoint Athletic Res	10	6	1	3	31	17	14	19
5 AFC St Austell Res	10	6	1	3	30	25	5	19
6 Saltash Borough	13	5	3	5	39	31	8	18
7 St Mawgan	8	5	2	1	20	11	9	17
8 Saltash United Res	11	5	2	4	30	23	7	17
9 Liskeard Athletic Res	10	4	2	4	20	29	-9	14
10 Lanreath	10	3	3	4	20	30	-10	12
11 Callington Town Res	11	3	1	7	24	38	-14	10
12 Millbrook Res	10	2	3	5	10	18	-8	9
13 Sticker Res	12	3	0	9	23	42	-19	9
14 Morwenstow	10	2	1	7	25	33	-8	7
15 St Dennis Res	8	0	0	8	7	47	-40	0

WEST DIVISION	P	W	D	L	F	A	GD	Pts
1 Illogan RBL	10	9	0	1	39	12	27	27
2 Mousehole	11	8	1	2	30	14	16	25
3 Helston Athletic Res	11	7	1	3	33	16	17	22
4 Mullion	10	7	1	2	25	15	10	22
5 Hayle	11	5	2	4	25	26	-1	17
6 Penryn Athletic	10	5	1	4	22	15	7	16
7 St Ives Town	9	5	1	3	19	13	6	16
8 St Day	11	5	1	5	21	28	-7	16
9 St Agnes	8	2	2	4	12	15	-3	8
10 Redruth United	7	2	2	3	12	19	-7	8
11 Wendron United Res	9	2	1	6	14	22	-8	7
12 Falmouth Town Res	12	2	0	10	13	30	-17	6
13 Perranwell	9	2	0	7	11	29	-18	6
14 Porthleven Res	10	1	1	8	14	36	-22	4

STAFFORDSHIRE SENIOR LEAGUE

Step 7 - promotes to the North West Counties League.

After the COVID suspension of the league, it was decided that teams should only play each other once in the season. Where teams had already played each other twice, the second match played was expunged.

PREMIER DIVISION	P	W	D	L	F	A	GD	Pts
1 Foley Meir	16	12	3	1	57	17	40	39
2 AFC Alsager	16	12	1	3	45	20	25	37
3 Redgate Clayton	16	11	2	3	52	20	32	35
4 Ball Haye Green	16	10	2	4	43	36	7	32
5 Wolstanton United	16	8	5	3	24	14	10	29
6 Buxton	16	8	1	7	45	39	6	25
7 Alsager Town Res	16	7	3	6	26	23	3	24
8 Audley & District	16	7	2	7	30	32	-2	23
9 Walsall Phoenix	16	6	4	6	32	28	4	22
10 Leek C.S.O.B.	16	6	2	8	25	25	0	20
11 Eastwood Hanley	16	6	2	8	25	36	-11	20
12 Ashbourne	16	5	2	9	32	39	-7	17
13 Abbey Hulton United	16	4	4	8	25	34	-9	16
14 Hanley Town Res	16	4	3	9	23	35	-12	15
15 Silverdale Athletic	16	4	3	9	33	47	-14	15
16 Brereton Social	16	4	2	10	17	26	-9	14
17 Cheadle Town	16	1	1	14	9	72	-63	4

DIVISION ONE	P	W	D	L	F	A	GD	Pts
1 Shenstone Pathfinder	14	13	0	1	57	12	45	39
2 City of Stoke	14	12	0	2	46	20	26	36
3 Lichfield City Casuals	14	9	3	2	39	17	22	30
4 Milton United	14	9	2	3	44	17	27	29
5 Madeley White Star	14	9	1	4	50	15	35	28
6 Wolstanton United Res	14	7	4	3	31	15	16	25
7 Chesterton A.F.C	14	6	1	7	32	37	-5	19
8 Redgate Clayton Res	14	5	3	6	24	26	-2	18
9 Audley & District Res	14	5	1	8	25	37	-12	16
10 Hawkins Sports	14	3	4	7	30	45	-15	13
11 Whittington	14	4	1	9	21	52	-31	13
12 Cheadle Town Res	14	3	3	8	21	29	-8	12
13 Leek C.S.O.B. Res	14	3	2	9	18	30	-12	11
14 Ball Haye Green	14	3	1	10	16	45	-29	10
15 Eastwood Hanley	14	1	0	13	26	83	-57	3

DIVISION TWO	P	W	D	L	F	A	GD	Pts
1 Foley Meir	14	12	1	1	59	24	35	37
2 FC 41	14	9	2	3	46	17	29	29
3 Stone Old Alleynians Res	14	8	3	3	62	27	35	27
4 City of Stoke Res	14	8	3	3	48	34	14	27
5 Cresswell Wanderers	14	8	2	4	54	23	31	26
6 Abbey Hulton United	14	8	1	5	36	24	12	25
7 Sikh Hunters	14	7	1	6	42	40	2	22
8 Walsall Phoenix Res	14	6	3	5	46	29	17	21
9 AFC Alsager	14	5	4	5	39	33	6	19
10 Milton United	14	5	3	6	30	34	-4	18
11 Stapenhill Swans	14	5	1	8	42	34	8	16
12 Wyrley Res	14	5	0	9	36	36	0	15
13 Blurton Reds	14	5	0	9	25	52	-27	15
14 Whittington Res	14	1	0	13	11	83	-72	3
15 Huthman FC	14	1	0	13	16	102	-86	3

SUFFOLK & IPSWICH LEAGUE

Step 7 - promotes to Eastern Counties League.

SENIOR DIVISION	P	W	D	L	F	A	GD	Pts
1 Benhall St Mary	9	7	1	1	21	5	16	22
2 Halesworth Town	9	7	0	2	30	8	22	21
3 Bildeston Rangers	10	6	1	3	29	22	7	19
4 Claydon	9	5	2	2	25	11	14	17
5 Trimley Red Devils	10	5	2	3	25	17	8	17
6 Henley Athletic	6	5	0	1	19	14	5	15
7 East Bergholt United	9	4	2	3	20	19	1	14
8 Bourne Vale United	9	4	1	4	19	20	-1	13
9 Ransomes Sports	7	4	0	3	15	14	1	12
10 Crane Sports	7	3	2	2	17	10	7	11
11 Old Newton United	7	3	2	2	12	12	0	11
12 Haughley United	9	2	3	4	18	22	-4	9
13 Coplestonians	8	2	1	5	13	22	-9	7
14 Westerfield United	8	1	2	5	7	23	-16	5
15 Capel Plough	7	1	1	5	9	17	-8	4
16 Leiston St Margarets	10	1	0	9	7	32	-25	3
17 Achilles	8	0	2	6	5	23	-18	2

DIVISION ONE	P	W	D	L	F	A	GD	Pts
1 Wickham Market	9	8	0	1	24	13	11	24
2 Tattingstone United	10	6	2	2	23	9	14	20
3 Sporting 87	9	6	2	1	23	12	11	20
4 Stowupland Falcons	9	4	1	4	18	17	1	13
5 Bacton United 89	10	4	1	5	20	21	-1	13
6 Bedricks Worth	6	3	2	1	18	13	5	11
7 Coddenham Athletic	4	2	1	1	11	6	5	7
8 Southwold Town	4	2	1	1	9	8	1	7
9 Stanton	5	2	0	3	11	11	0	6
10 Grundisburgh	6	1	1	4	8	13	-5	4
11 A.F.C. Kesgrave	10	0	3	7	13	35	-22	3
12 Barham Athletic	3	0	0	3	0	8	-8	0
13 Wenhaston United	5	0	0	5	4	16	-12	0

DIVISION TWO	P	W	D	L	F	A	GD	Pts
1 Ufford Sports	10	5	2	3	21	15	6	17
2 Elmswell	6	5	0	1	19	7	12	15
3 Melton United	8	5	0	3	19	12	7	15
4 Saxmundham Sports	8	5	0	3	17	20	-3	15
5 A.F.C. YourShirts	8	4	2	2	22	13	9	14
6 Woolverstone United	6	4	1	1	16	4	12	13
7 Cockfield United	8	4	1	3	27	16	11	13
8 Bramford Road Old Boys	7	3	2	2	14	10	4	11
9 Thurston	9	3	0	6	17	30	-13	9
10 Somersham	5	2	1	2	7	10	-3	7
11 Ipswich Athletic	8	1	1	6	8	32	-24	4
12 Kirton Athletic	4	1	0	3	6	8	-2	3
13 Stonham Aspal	7	0	0	7	6	22	-16	0

DIVISION THREE	P	W	D	L	F	A	GD	Pts
1 Bramford United	9	9	0	0	46	10	36	27
2 Bardwell Sports	9	7	1	1	46	13	33	22
3 Witnesham Wasps	9	7	1	1	26	10	16	22
4 Kesgrave Kestrels	8	5	1	2	28	16	12	16
5 Unity	10	4	2	4	16	25	-9	14
6 Stage	9	3	4	2	24	23	1	13
7 Great Blakenham Chequers	9	3	2	4	25	29	-4	11
8 A.F.C. Wanderers	9	4	2	3	29	28	1	10*
9 Ipswich Exiles	8	3	1	4	15	20	-5	10
10 Laxfield	9	2	1	6	12	17	-5	7
11 Occold	9	1	4	4	16	28	-12	7
12 Wortham	9	2	1	6	23	40	-17	7
13 Hope Church	10	1	3	6	15	31	-16	6
14 Aldeburgh Town	9	0	1	8	13	44	-31	1

SURREY COUNTY INTERMEDIATE LEAGUE (WESTERN)

	P	W	D	L	F	A	GD	Pts
1 Hersham	12	10	1	1	37	12	25	31
2 Hambledon	12	7	3	2	33	18	15	24
3 University of Surrey	12	7	1	4	37	27	10	22
4 Cranleigh	12	6	3	3	40	14	26	21
5 West End Village	12	6	3	3	36	27	9	21
6 Manorcroft United	12	5	3	4	18	14	4	18
7 Ottershaw	12	5	3	4	24	23	1	18
8 Chiddingfold	12	4	4	4	15	24	-9	16
9 Keens Park Rangers	12	4	3	5	28	19	9	15
10 Lightwater United	12	3	3	6	18	25	-7	12
11 Shottermill & Haslemere	12	3	3	6	15	23	-8	12
12 Milford & Witley	12	2	1	9	14	39	-25	7
13 Knaphill Athletic	12	0	1	11	11	61	-50	1

SURREY ELITE INTERMEDIATE LEAGUE

Step 7 - promotes to the Combined Counties League.

PREMIER DIVISION	P	W	D	L	F	A	GD	Pts
1 Merrow	9	7	0	2	22	12	10	21
2 Battersea Ironsides	7	5	1	1	24	13	11	16
3 Horsley.	7	5	1	1	22	13	9	16
4 Farleigh Rovers	6	5	1	0	14	7	7	16
5 AFC Cubo	7	5	0	2	17	7	10	15
6 Spartans Youth Adult	8	4	1	3	15	13	2	13
7 NPL Saturday	9	4	1	4	16	21	-5	13
8 Staines Lammas	9	3	1	5	21	22	-1	10
9 Guildford United	6	2	1	3	14	15	-1	7
10 Worcester Park	8	1	3	4	14	19	-5	6
11 Lyne Seniors	8	2	0	6	12	23	-11	6
12 AFC Royal Holloway	8	1	2	5	9	18	-9	5
13 Ripley Village	5	0	2	3	5	9	-4	2
14 AFC Spelthorne Sports Club	7	0	2	5	7	20	-13	2

SURREY SOUTH EASTERN COMBINATION INTERMEDITE LEAGUE

DIVISION ONE	P	W	D	L	F	A	GD	Pts
1 AFC Walcountians	22	19	1	2	64	20	44	58
2 Frenches Athletic	22	12	4	6	44	32	12	40
3 Sporting 50	22	10	4	8	41	32	9	37*
4 Earlsfield United	22	10	2	10	45	39	6	35*
5 FC Tooting Bec	22	10	3	9	37	38	-1	33
6 West Fulham	22	10	2	10	44	37	7	32
7 Kew Park Rangers	22	8	4	10	39	52	-13	28
8 Westminster Casuals	22	7	4	11	21	28	-7	25
9 Wandgas Sport	22	7	4	11	41	58	-17	25
10 Goldfingers	22	5	3	14	33	52	-19	24*
11 Balham	22	10	3	9	46	46	0	21*
12 AFC Ewell	22	5	4	13	35	56	-21	19

THAMES VALLEY LEAGUE

Step 7 - promotes to the Hellenic and the Combined Counties Leagues.

PREMIER DIVISION	P	W	D	L	F	A	GD	Pts
1 Finchampstead	26	19	5	2	59	23	36	62
2 Berks County	26	18	4	4	54	23	31	58
3 Burghfield	26	17	5	4	58	37	21	56
4 Maidenhead Town	26	13	5	8	44	45	-1	44
5 Newbury	26	12	7	7	39	39	0	43
6 Reading City U23	26	12	5	9	58	43	15	41
7 Richings Park	26	13	1	12	39	54	-15	40
8 Mortimer	26	10	9	7	36	40	-4	39
9 Wraysbury Village	26	12	1	13	39	50	-11	37
10 Westwood Wanderers	26	10	3	13	25	31	-6	33
11 Windlesham & Chobham	26	8	5	13	27	51	-24	29
12 Marlow United	26	6	1	19	27	52	-25	19
13 Cookham Dean	26	3	4	19	14	29	-15	12*
14 Woodley United Royals	26	1	1	24	9	11	-2	4

Woodley United Royals did not take part when the league resumed after the COVID suspension. The 5 matches they had played before the suspension were not expunged, whilst their remaining 21 matches were awarded to the opposition.

DIVISION ONE	P	W	D	L	F	A	GD	Pts
1 Reading YMCA	20	19	0	1	42	17	25	57
2 Wargrave	20	17	1	2	58	24	34	52
3 FC Imaan Lions	20	12	1	7	59	46	13	37
4 Slough Heating Laurencians	20	10	4	6	44	26	18	34
5 Eldon Celtic	20	10	2	8	40	35	5	32
6 Hurst	20	10	2	8	35	33	2	32
7 Rotherfield United	20	8	2	10	34	38	-4	26
8 Mortimer	20	6	2	12	32	48	-16	20
9 Westwood Wanderers	20	5	1	14	31	39	-8	16
10 Holyport	20	4	0	16	41	57	-16	12
11 Cookham Dean	20	1	1	18	13	66	-53	4

DIVISION TWO	P	W	D	L	F	A	GD	Pts
1 Henley Town	18	14	1	3	60	22	38	43
2 Goring United	18	12	1	5	57	24	33	37
3 Maidenhead Town	18	12	1	5	51	33	18	37
4 Richings Park	18	10	4	4	46	38	8	34
5 Berks County	17	9	3	5	39	29	10	30
6 Datchet	17	7	2	8	46	45	1	23
7 Phoenix Old Boys	18	4	6	8	30	49	-19	18
8 Twyford & Ruscombe	18	3	3	12	40	74	-34	12
9 Hurst	18	3	3	12	30	47	-17	11*
10 Windlesham & Chobham	18	2	2	14	14	52	-38	7*

DIVISION THREE	P	W	D	L	F	A	GD	Pts
1 Hambleden	20	18	1	1	55	17	38	55
2 Maidenhead Town 'A'	20	15	2	3	33	16	17	47
3 AFC Winkfield	20	13	3	4	37	33	4	42
4 Goring United	20	11	1	8	28	31	-3	34
5 Westwood Wanderers Dev	20	11	0	9	19	26	-7	33
6 Pangbourne	20	9	3	8	19	26	-7	30
7 White Eagles	20	10	0	10	18	33	-15	30
8 Phoenix Old Boys	20	8	2	10	24	40	-16	26
9 Woodley United 'A'	20	2	4	14	9	7	2	10
10 Robertswood	20	2	3	15	10	8	2	9
11 Taplow United	20	0	3	17	3	18	-15	3

DIVISION FOUR	P	W	D	L	F	A	GD	Pts
1 Burghfield	20	12	7	1	62	27	35	43
2 Reading City Dev	20	14	3	3	76	32	44	42*
3 Reading YMCA Rapids	20	12	4	4	46	26	20	40
4 Berks County Rovers	20	10	1	9	40	51	-11	31
5 Braybrooke	20	8	6	6	39	50	-11	30
6 Harchester Hawks	20	8	4	8	38	38	0	28
7 Phoenix Old Boys Dev	20	7	7	6	40	43	-3	28
8 Henley Town Dev	20	8	3	9	66	52	14	27
9 Finchampstead Dev	20	7	4	9	39	44	-5	25
10 Farnham Royal Mavericks	20	2	1	17	18	43	-25	10*
11 AFC Corinthians	20	2	0	18	17	75	-58	6

WEARSIDE LEAGUE

Step 7 - promotes to the Northern League.

DIVISION ONE	P	W	D	L	F	A	GD	Pts
1 Boldon Community Association	14	13	0	1	61	16	45	39
2 Horden Community Welfare	11	8	0	3	44	10	34	24
3 Chester-le-Street United	11	8	0	3	36	17	19	24
4 Silksworth Colliery Welfare	11	7	1	3	23	12	11	22
5 Darlington Town	10	7	1	2	19	13	6	22
6 Durham Corinthians	11	7	0	4	26	23	3	21
7 Darlington Railway Athletic	14	6	2	6	22	26	-4	20
8 Wolviston	10	6	0	4	23	27	-4	18
9 Richmond Town	10	5	2	3	22	15	7	17
10 Farringdon Detached	11	4	2	5	23	26	-3	14
11 Norton & Stockton Ancients	10	4	0	6	17	19	-2	12
12 Washington United	10	3	2	5	18	23	-5	11
13 Windscale	8	3	1	4	16	21	-5	10
14 Hartlepool	15	3	1	11	16	40	-24	10
15 Annfield Plain	10	2	2	6	12	43	-31	8
16 Coxhoe Athletic	11	2	1	8	15	26	-11	7
17 Gateshead Leam Rangers	11	2	1	8	13	27	-14	7
18 West Auckland Tunns	12	1	2	9	11	33	-22	5

DIVISION TWO	P	W	D	L	F	A	GD	Pts
1 Shildon Res	16	13	1	2	70	14	56	40
2 Shotton Colliery	16	13	0	3	64	20	44	39
3 Durham United	16	11	1	4	64	29	35	34
4 Polton	16	10	3	3	49	27	22	33
5 Durham Corinthians Res	16	9	3	4	46	23	23	30
6 Sunderland West End and Uni	16	9	1	6	34	25	9	28
7 Hylton Colliery Welfare	16	8	2	6	44	35	9	26
8 South Moor	16	8	1	7	46	35	11	25
9 Washington Res	16	7	3	6	43	37	6	24
10 Wheatley Hill WMC	16	7	2	7	41	53	-12	22
11 Cockerton Club	16	6	1	9	36	57	-21	19
12 Wynyard Village	16	6	0	10	39	46	-7	18
13 Durham FC	16	5	2	9	52	50	2	17
14 Ryhope Colliery Welfare U23	16	5	2	9	23	32	-9	17
15 Hurworth Albion	16	4	0	12	22	80	-58	12
16 Doxford Park	16	3	1	12	31	69	-38	10
17 Hetton Juniors	16	0	1	15	13	85	-72	1

AFC Durham (8 games) and Simonside (12) withdrew from the division - results expunged.

Resumed the division in Spring 2021 and as none of the clubs had played each other twice at that point it was decided that to conclude the season, clubs would only play each other once.

WEST CHESHIRE LEAGUE

Step 7 - promotes to the North West Counties League.

DIVISION ONE	P	W	D	L	F	A	GD	Pts
1 South Liverpool	15	13	2	0	52	16	36	41
2 Mersey Royal	15	11	3	1	52	21	31	36
3 Mossley Hill Athletic	15	11	3	1	41	19	22	36
4 Newton	15	7	1	7	34	33	1	22
5 Ashville	15	6	3	6	25	20	5	21
6 Marshalls	15	6	3	6	34	34	0	21
7 Vauxhall Motors Res	15	6	3	6	26	27	-1	21
8 Chester Nomads	15	6	3	6	33	40	-7	21
9 Maghull	15	6	2	7	37	36	1	20
10 Upton AA	15	5	3	7	24	32	-8	18
11 Redgate Rovers	15	5	2	8	26	32	-6	17
12 Prescot Cables Res	15	5	2	8	24	31	-7	17
13 Capenhurst Villa	15	4	5	6	17	24	-7	17
14 Rainhill Town	15	3	3	9	19	36	-17	12
15 Ellesmere Port Town	15	2	4	9	18	42	-24	10
16 Aintree Villa	15	3	0	12	19	38	-19	9

DIVISION TWO	P	W	D	L	F	A	GD	Pts
1 FC Bootle St Edmund's	15	15	0	0	53	15	38	45
2 Heswall	15	13	0	2	50	18	32	39
3 Poulton Vics	15	13	0	2	40	17	23	39
4 West Kirby	15	11	0	4	34	28	6	33
5 South Sefton Borough	15	9	1	5	52	34	18	28
6 Cheshire Lines	15	6	4	5	29	20	9	22
7 Maghull Reserve	15	6	3	6	22	20	2	21
8 Mossley Hill Athletic Res	15	6	1	8	28	34	-6	19
9 South Liverpool Res	15	6	1	8	26	37	-11	19
10 Marine Res	15	5	1	9	31	42	-11	16
11 Litherland Remyca Dev	15	4	4	7	30	43	-13	16
12 Rainhill Town Res	15	4	3	8	29	27	2	15
13 Mallaby	15	3	3	9	25	40	-15	12
14 Ashville Res	15	2	4	9	21	37	-16	10
15 Poulton Royal	15	2	2	11	22	49	-27	8
16 Neston Nomads	15	1	1	13	18	49	-31	4

DIVISION THREE	P	W	D	L	F	A	GD	Pts
1 Helsby	16	14	0	2	60	12	48	42
2 Runcorn Sports	16	12	4	0	48	12	36	40
3 Rainford United	16	12	1	3	51	27	24	37
4 Marshalls Res	16	10	2	4	58	30	28	32
5 Heswall Res	16	9	3	4	29	22	7	30
6 Bootle Res	16	9	2	5	44	29	15	29
7 Willaston	16	9	2	5	39	30	9	29
8 Aintree Villa Res	16	7	3	6	24	32	-8	24
9 Capenhurst Villa Res	16	6	5	5	32	39	-7	23
10 Sutton Athletics	16	6	4	6	45	28	17	22
11 Mersey Harps	16	6	3	7	39	42	-3	21
12 West Kirby Res	16	6	1	9	22	28	-6	19
13 Chester Nomads Res	16	4	2	10	24	36	-12	14
14 Poulton Vics Res	16	4	2	10	30	51	-21	14
15 Neston Nomads Res	16	2	0	14	17	60	-43	6
16 Poulton Royal Res	16	1	2	13	20	48	-28	5
17 Ellesmere Port Town Res	16	1	0	15	14	70	-56	3

The league resumed in Spring 2021 and it was decided that each team should play each other once. For those that had already played twice the aggregate score was taken to represent the single match result.

WEST LANCASHIRE LEAGUE

Step 7 - promotes to the North West Counties League.

PREMIER DIVISION	P	W	D	L	F	A	GD	Pts
1 Turton	8	5	0	3	19	11	8	15
2 Thornton Cleveleys	6	4	2	0	19	6	13	14
3 Fulwood Amateurs	7	4	1	2	20	14	6	13
4 Euxton Villa	5	4	0	1	13	4	9	12
5 Coppull United	7	3	3	1	15	11	4	12
6 Blackpool Wren Rovers	6	4	0	2	11	9	2	12
7 Poulton	8	3	1	4	25	14	11	10
8 Hurst Green	7	3	1	3	16	16	0	10
9 Burscough Richmond	6	3	0	3	12	16	-4	9
10 Lytham Town	5	2	1	2	12	11	1	7
11 Slyne-with-Hest	5	2	1	2	13	17	-4	7
12 Tempest United	6	2	0	4	13	13	0	6
13 Vickerstown	4	1	0	3	4	8	-4	3
14 Southport Hesketh	4	1	0	3	7	15	-8	3
15 CMB	5	1	0	4	4	20	-16	3
16 Whitehaven	7	1	0	6	6	24	-18	3

DIVISION ONE	P	W	D	L	F	A	GD	Pts
1 Askam United	7	6	1	0	17	5	12	19
2 Hesketh Bank	7	4	1	2	15	12	3	13
3 Stoneclough	5	4	0	1	10	7	3	12
4 Millom	7	4	0	3	17	17	0	12
5 Lostock St Gerards	7	3	2	2	16	14	2	11
6 Ulverston Rangers	6	3	1	2	11	10	1	10
7 Horwich St Mary's Victoria	5	3	0	2	14	16	-2	9
8 Eagley	7	2	1	4	21	17	4	7
9 Wyre Villa	6	2	1	3	14	14	0	7
10 Milnthorpe Corinthians	5	2	1	2	10	10	0	7
11 Crooklands Casuals	7	2	0	5	10	17	-7	6
12 Haslingden St Mary's	5	1	2	2	11	12	-1	5
13 Croston Sports Club	5	1	1	3	8	10	-2	4
14 Kendal County	4	1	0	3	5	11	-6	3
15 Hawcoat Park	7	0	3	4	11	18	-7	3

DIVISION TWO	P	W	D	L	F	A	GD	Pts
1 Carnforth Rangers	7	6	1	0	25	7	18	19
2 Galgate	8	5	2	1	22	14	8	17
3 Burnley United	7	5	1	1	20	8	12	16
4 Walney Island	8	5	1	2	28	17	11	16
5 Rossendale	5	4	1	0	20	9	11	13
6 Chipping	8	3	2	3	24	22	2	11
7 Charnock Richard Res	7	2	3	2	17	14	3	9
8 Furness Rovers	5	3	0	2	12	12	0	9
9 Cartmel & District	7	2	3	2	9	12	-3	9
10 Storeys of Lancaster	7	1	4	2	15	18	-3	7
11 Garstang Res	7	2	1	4	15	27	-12	7
12 Kendal United	6	1	1	4	15	17	-2	4
13 Freckleton	5	1	0	4	14	18	-4	3
14 Dalton United	5	0	2	3	5	13	-8	2
15 Burscough Dynamo	6	0	1	5	7	20	-13	1
16 Cadley	6	0	1	5	8	28	-20	1

WEST SUSSEX LEAGUE

PREMIER DIVISION	P	W	D	L	F	A	GD	Pts
1 Capel	7	6	1	0	24	6	18	19
2 West Chiltington	6	5	0	1	17	6	11	15
3 Upper Beeding Res	7	4	0	3	13	10	3	12
4 Lavant	7	3	1	3	12	25	-13	10
5 Rudgwick	8	2	3	3	17	14	3	9
6 Sompting	5	2	2	1	12	7	5	8
7 The Unicorn Bognor Regis	5	2	1	2	11	15	-4	7
8 Stedham United	6	1	2	3	8	14	-6	5
9 Southwater	6	1	1	4	10	15	-5	4
10 Newtown Villa	7	0	1	6	9	21	-12	1

CHAMPIONSHIP NORTH	P	W	D	L	F	A	GD	Pts
1 Slinfold	8	4	1	3	21	12	9	13
2 Partridge Green	8	3	3	2	26	12	14	12
3 Ewhurst	8	3	3	2	18	12	6	12
4 Pulborough	7	4	0	3	16	22	-6	12
5 Wisborough Green	8	3	1	4	13	19	-6	10
6 Westcott (1935)	6	2	3	1	9	11	-2	9
7 Barns Green	6	2	2	2	12	12	0	8
8 Cowfold	4	2	1	1	6	6	0	7
9 Horsham Crusaders	7	2	1	4	12	16	-4	7
10 Billingshurst Res	6	1	1	4	9	20	-11	4

CHAMPIONSHIP SOUTH	P	W	D	L	F	A	GD	Pts
1 Barnham Trojans	6	3	3	0	20	5	15	12
2 Petworth	4	4	0	0	11	6	5	12
3 AFC Southbourne	7	3	2	2	24	14	10	11
4 Harting	7	3	1	3	12	18	-6	10
5 Watersfield	7	3	0	4	16	15	1	9
6 Hunston Community Club	8	1	4	3	17	16	1	7
7 Sidlesham	4	2	1	1	9	9	0	7
8 Storrington Community Res	6	1	1	4	8	20	-12	4
9 East Dean	5	1	0	4	9	23	-14	3

WEST YORKSHIRE LEAGUE

Step 7 - promotes to the Northern Counties East League.

All games pre COVID suspension were expunged. In spring 2021 clubs then played each other once to form the tables below.

PREMIER DIVISION	P	W	D	L	F	A	GD	Pts
1 Beeston St Anthony	8	7	0	1	24	10	14	21
2 Boroughbridge	8	5	1	2	18	9	9	16
3 Hall Green United	8	5	0	3	18	16	2	15
4 Horbury Town	8	4	2	2	11	9	2	14
5 Field	8	3	1	4	10	13	-3	10
6 Huddersfield Amateur	8	3	0	5	12	20	-8	9
7 Robin Hood Athletic	8	2	1	5	10	15	-5	7
8 Headingley AFC	8	2	1	5	12	18	-6	7
9 Hunslet	8	2	0	6	10	15	-5	6

Carlton Athletic, Ilkley Town, Knaresborough Town, Sherburn White Rose and Whitkirk Wanderers all withdrew - results expunged.

DIVISION ONE	P	W	D	L	F	A	GD	Pts
1 Rawdon Old Boys	10	7	3	0	40	12	28	24
2 Kirk Deighton Rangers	10	6	2	2	18	14	4	20
3 G&C Hartshead	10	5	3	2	16	12	4	18
4 Wyke Wanderers	10	3	5	2	12	9	3	14
5 Otley Town	10	4	2	4	8	14	-6	14
6 Salts	10	3	3	4	14	10	4	12
7 Pool AFC	10	3	3	4	16	16	0	12
8 Wetherby Athletic	10	3	3	4	10	22	-12	12
9 Aberford Albion	10	3	2	5	15	25	-10	11
10 East End Park	10	2	2	6	12	15	-3	8
11 Shelley	10	1	2	7	9	21	-12	5

Featherstone Colliery, Glasshoughton Rock and Oxenhope Recreation all withdrew - results expunged.

DIVISION TWO	P	W	D	L	F	A	GD	Pts
1 Brighouse Sports	11	9	0	2	33	17	16	27
2 Swillington Saints Welfare	11	8	1	2	39	17	22	22*
3 Old Centralians	11	7	1	3	32	26	6	22
4 Kellingley Welfare	11	7	0	4	31	17	14	21
5 Leeds Modernians	11	7	0	4	17	19	-2	21
6 Rothwell Juniors	11	6	0	5	36	25	11	18
7 Ripon City	11	5	2	4	26	19	7	17
8 Laund Hill FC	11	5	0	6	15	18	-3	15
9 Altofts	11	5	0	6	22	30	-8	15
10 Overthorpe Sports Club	11	4	0	7	19	26	-7	12
11 Tingley Athletic FC 1st	11	1	0	10	9	41	-32	3
12 Howden Clough	11	0	0	11	9	33	-24	0

Harrogate Railway Athletic withdrew - results expunged.

WILTSHIRE SENIOR LEAGUE

Step 7 - promotes to the Western League.

		P	W	D	L	F	A	GD	Pts
1	Pewsey Vale	14	12	1	1	44	9	35	37
2	Melksham Town Res	15	10	1	4	46	16	30	31
3	Royal Wootton Bassett Town Dev	12	9	1	2	31	17	14	28
4	Wroughton	10	8	0	2	38	14	24	24
5	Frome Collegians	13	7	0	6	33	21	12	21
6	Odd Down Res	14	6	1	7	26	34	-8	19
7	Cricklade Town	9	6	0	3	18	13	5	18
8	Trowbridge Town	12	6	0	6	22	20	2	18
9	Shrewton United	12	5	2	5	32	28	4	17
10	Corsham Town Res	13	5	2	6	25	30	-5	17
11	Malmesbury Victoria Dev	13	4	2	7	25	31	-6	14
12	Purton	8	4	1	3	20	19	1	13
13	Stratton Juniors	9	2	1	6	13	28	-15	7
14	Marlborough Town	8	1	0	7	8	24	-16	3
15	Devizes Town Res	12	1	0	11	8	33	-25	3
16	Ludgershall Sports	12	1	0	11	10	62	-52	3

YORK LEAGUE

Step 7 - promotes to the Northern Counties East League.

	PREMIER DIVISION	P	W	D	L	F	A	GD	Pts
1	Dunnington	10	8	2	0	30	4	26	26
2	Tadcaster Magnets	11	5	5	1	30	17	13	20
3	Wigginton Grasshoppers	8	5	2	1	17	5	12	17
4	Dringhouses	6	5	0	1	22	13	9	15
5	Huntington Rovers	8	4	2	2	18	16	2	14
6	Thorpe United	9	4	2	3	14	12	2	14
7	Old Malton St Marys	8	3	2	3	20	14	6	11
8	Strensall Tigers	9	3	2	4	20	18	2	11
9	Rawcliffe	7	3	1	3	10	9	1	10
10	F1 Racing	10	2	2	6	17	31	-14	8
11	Poppleton United	9	2	1	6	25	37	-12	7
12	Kirkbymoorside	7	2	1	4	10	23	-13	7
13	Easingwold Town	11	1	3	7	11	25	-14	6
14	Hemingbrough United	7	0	1	6	9	29	-20	1

	DIVISION ONE	P	W	D	L	F	A	GD	Pts
1	Tockwith	7	7	0	0	36	7	29	21
2	Osbaldwick	9	7	0	2	41	13	28	21
3	Malt Shovel	7	6	0	1	53	10	43	18
4	Haxby Town	9	5	1	3	41	25	16	16
5	Bishopthorpe United	5	2	2	1	19	12	7	8
6	Brooklyn	8	2	2	4	15	17	-2	8
7	Pocklington Town Res	4	2	1	1	10	2	8	7
8	Cliffe	7	1	1	5	15	42	-27	4
9	Stamford Bridge	3	1	0	2	11	10	1	3
10	Harrison Signs	9	1	0	8	7	69	-62	3
11	Riccall United	8	0	1	7	7	48	-41	1

	DIVISION TWO	P	W	D	L	F	A	GD	Pts
1	Cawood	7	5	2	0	25	10	15	17
2	Wombleton Wanderers	6	4	2	0	26	5	21	14
3	The Beagle	5	4	1	0	16	5	11	13
4	Wheldrake	9	3	3	3	25	27	-2	12
5	Clifford Seniors	5	3	0	2	14	11	3	9
6	Bubwith White Swan	5	3	0	2	8	12	-4	9
7	Rufforth United	5	2	0	3	15	16	-1	6
8	Pollington	7	1	0	6	12	27	-15	3
9	Civil Service (York)	6	0	2	4	16	27	-11	2
10	Heslington	7	0	2	5	9	26	-17	2

	DIVISION THREE	P	W	D	L	F	A	GD	Pts
1	Wilberfoss AFC	8	6	0	2	30	11	19	18
2	Fulford Football Club	7	5	1	1	26	14	12	16
3	Garforth LG Team	6	5	0	1	22	7	15	15
4	Duncombe Park	7	4	1	2	17	14	3	13
5	York St John University	9	4	0	5	25	35	-10	12
6	Walnut Tree	5	3	1	1	19	13	6	10
7	Copmanthorpe	9	3	0	6	23	26	-3	9
8	Helperby United	5	2	0	3	16	16	0	6
9	Church Fenton FC	7	2	0	5	17	27	-10	6
10	Crayke United	8	1	1	6	16	43	-27	4
11	Barmby Moor	5	1	0	4	11	16	-5	3

	DIVISION FOUR	P	W	D	L	F	A	GD	Pts
1	South Milford	8	8	0	0	59	11	48	24
2	Howden AFC	6	5	0	1	42	9	33	15
3	Kellingley Welfare Res	7	5	0	2	21	14	7	15
4	Sporting Knavesmire	8	4	2	2	23	21	2	14
5	Marton Abbey	6	3	2	1	24	11	13	11
6	Elvington Harriers	5	3	1	1	20	17	3	10
7	York Railway Institute	7	2	2	3	23	28	-5	8
8	London NE Railway Builders	7	1	1	5	12	38	-26	4
9	Thirsk Falcons Dev	5	1	0	4	21	32	-11	3
10	Bishop Wilton	8	1	0	7	13	40	-27	3
11	Selby Olympia	7	0	0	7	10	47	-37	0

YORKSHIRE AMATEUR LEAGUE

	SUPREME DIVISION	P	W	D	L	F	A	GD	Pts
1	Horsforth St. Margarets	28	26	0	2	107	38	69	78
2	Farsley Celtic Juniors	28	21	2	5	109	40	69	65
3	Littletown FC	28	17	2	9	79	64	15	53*
4	Route One Rovers	28	15	7	6	108	63	45	52
5	Wortley FC	28	17	3	8	85	55	30	51*
6	Athletico	28	13	7	8	88	75	13	46
7	Leeds City FC	28	11	7	10	54	69	-15	40
8	Toller FC	28	12	3	13	72	71	1	39
9	Ryburn United	28	9	6	13	50	63	-13	33
10	Stanley United	28	7	7	14	70	93	-23	28
11	Alwoodley FC	28	8	4	16	40	71	-31	28
12	Leeds Medics & Dentists	28	6	5	17	43	67	-24	23
13	Calverley United	28	9	2	17	51	70	-19	20*
14	Lower Hopton	28	4	4	20	37	91	-54	16
15	Drighlington	28	4	3	21	43	106	-63	15

Steeton withdrew - results expunged.

	PREMIER DIVISION	P	W	D	L	F	A	GD	Pts
1	Middleton FC	22	19	2	1	132	30	102	59
2	Mount St Marys	22	15	4	3	71	34	37	49
3	Golcar United	22	13	5	4	70	45	25	44
4	Morley Town AFC	22	11	3	8	58	57	1	36
5	Nostell M.W.	21	11	2	8	56	56	0	35
6	Collegians	22	9	3	10	50	62	-12	30
7	St Bedes AFC	22	9	2	11	55	66	-11	29
8	White Rose	21	9	1	11	46	64	-18	25*
9	Ealandians	22	7	2	13	50	63	-13	23
10	Wibsey	22	6	3	13	44	56	-12	18*
11	Shire Academics	22	6	0	16	48	89	-41	18
12	Stanningley Old Boys	22	1	3	18	33	91	-58	6

Gildersome Spurs O.B. withdrew - results expunged.

ENGLAND C

Due to COVID-19 there were no fixtures during the 2020-21 season

RESULTS SUMMARY 1979 - 2021	P	W	D	L	F	A
Barbados	1	1	0	0	2	0
Belgium	6	3	1	2	8	7
Bermuda	1	1	0	0	6	1
Bosnia & Herzegovina	1	0	0	1	2	6
Cyprus U21	1	0	0	1	1	2
Czech Republic U21	1	0	2	0	2	2
Finland U21	4	2	0	2	4	5
Estonia	1	1	0	0	1	0
Estonia U23	4	3	0	1	7	5
Grenada	1	0	1	0	1	1
Gibraltar	4	3	0	1	8	7
Holland	19	14	5	0	40	8
Hungary	2	0	1	1	3	5
Iraq	1	0	0	1	1	5
Irish Premier League XI	1	0	0	1	1	3
Italy	18	5	8	4	24	22
Jordan U23	1	1	0	0	1	0
Latvia U23	1	0	0	1	0	1
Malta	1	1	0	0	4	0
Norway U21	1	0	0	1	1	2
Panjab	1	1	0	0	2	1
Poland	1	1	0	0	2	1
Portugal	1	0	0	1	0	1
Republic of Ireland	13	10	0	3	30	11
Republic of Ireland U21	1	1	0	0	2	1
Republic of Ireland Amateurs	1	0	0	1	2	4
Russia	1	0	0	1	0	4
Scotland	15	10	3	2	30	15
Slovakia U21/U23	3	0	0	3	3	9
Sparta Prague B	1	0	2	0	2	2
Turkey U23	2	0	0	2	0	3
Ukraine	1	1	0	0	2	0
USA	2	1	1	0	2	1
Wales	24	13	7	4	34	20
Wales C	2	1	1	0	5	4
TOTALS	**139**	**74**	**32**	**34**	**233**	**160**

ENGLAND'S RESULTS 1979 - 2021

Date	Venue	Score
BARBADOS		
02.06.08	Bridgetown	2 - 0
BELGIUM		
11.02.03	KV Ostend	1 - 3
04.11.03	Darlington	2 - 2
15.11.05	FC Racing Jets	2 - 0
19.05.09	Oxford United	0 - 1
09.02.11	Luton Town	1 - 0
12.09.12	Gemeentalijk Sportstadion	2 - 1
BERMUDA		
04.06.13	Hamilton	6 - 1
BOSNIA & HERZEGOVINA		
16.09.08	Grbavia Stadium	2 - 6
CYPRUS U21		
17.02.15	Larnaca	1 - 2
CZECH REPUBLIC UNDER-21		
19.11.13	Home	2 - 2
ESTONIA		
12.10.10		1 - 0
UNDER-23		
18.11.14	FC Halifax Town	4 - 2
15.11.16	A Le Coq Arena, Tallinn	2 - 1
10.10.18	Leyton Orient FC	1 - 0
05.06.19	Kadrioru Stadium	0 - 2
FINLAND UNDER-21		
14.04.93	Woking	1 - 3
30.05.94	Aanekoski	0 - 2
01.06.07	FC Hakka	1 - 0
15.11.07	Helsinki	2 - 0
GIBRALTAR		
27.04.82	Gibraltar	3 - 2
31.05.95	Gibraltar	3 - 2
21.05.08	Colwyn Bay	1 - 0
15.11.11	Gibraltar	1 - 3
GRENADA		
31.05.08	St. George's	1 - 1
HOLLAND		
03.06.79	Stafford	1 - 0
07.06.80	Zeist	2 - 1
09.06.81	Lucca	2 - 0
03.06.82	Aberdeen	1 - 0
02.06.83	Scarborough	6 - 0
05.06.84	Palma	3 - 3
13.06.85	Vleuten	3 - 0
20.05.87	Kirkaldy	4 - 0
11.04.95	Aalsmeer	0 - 0
02.04.96	Irthlingborough	3 - 1
18.04.97	Appingedam	0 - 0
03.03.98	Crawley	2 - 1
30.03.99	Genemuiden	1 - 1
21.03.00	Northwich	1 - 0
22.03.01	Wihemina FC	3 - 0
24.04.02	Yeovil Town	1 - 0
25.03.03	BV Sparta 25	0 - 0
16.02.05	Woking	3 - 0
29.11.06	Burton Albion	4 - 1
HUNGARY		
15.09.09	Szekesfehervar	1 - 1
28.05.14	Budapest	2 - 4
IRAQ		
27.05.04	Macclesfield	1 - 5
IRISH PREMIER LEAGUE XI		
13.02.07	Glenavon FC	1 - 3
ITALY		
03.06.80	Zeist	2 - 0
13.06.81	Montecatini	1 - 1
01.06.82	Aberdeen	0 - 0
31.05.83	Scarborough	2 - 0
09.06.84	Reggio Emilia	0 - 1
11.06.85	Houten	2 - 2
18.05.87	Dunfermline	1 - 2
29.01.89	La Spezia	1 - 1
25.02.90	Solerno	0 - 2
05.03.91	Kettering	0 - 0
01.03.99	Hayes	4 - 1
01.03.00	Padova	1 - 1
20.11.02	AC Cremonese	3 - 2
11.02.04	Shrewsbury	1 - 4
10.11.04	US Ivrea FC	1 - 0
15.02.06	Cambridge United	3 - 1
12.11.08	Benevento	2 - 2
28.02.12	Fleetwood Town	1 - 1
JORDAN UNDER-23		
04.03.14	Jordan	1 - 0
LATVIA UNDER-23		
10.09.13	Latvia	0 - 1
MALTA UNDER-21		
17.02.09	Malta	4 - 0
NORWAY UNDER-21		
01.06.94	Slemmestad	1 - 2
PANJAB		
28.05.17	Solihull Moors	1 - 2
POLAND		
17.11.09	Gradiszk Wielpolski	2 - 1
PORTUGAL		
19.05.11	Sixfields Stadium	0 - 1
REPUBLIC OF IRELAND		
24.05.86	Kidderminster	2 - 1
26.05.86	Nuneaton	2 - 1
25.05.90	Dublin	2 - 1
27.05.90	Cork	3 - 0
27.02.96	Kidderminster	4 - 0
25.02.97	Dublin	0 - 2
16.05.02	Boston	1 - 2
20.05.03	Merthyr Tydfil	4 - 0
18.05.04	Deverondale	2 - 3
24.05.05	Cork	1 - 0
23.05.06	Eastbourne Boro'	2 - 0
22.05.07	Clachnacuddin	5 - 0
26.05.10	Waterford United	2 - 1
UNDER-21		
01.06.15	Galway	2 - 1
AMATEURS		
27.05.18	Whitehall Stadium	2 - 4
RUSSIA		
05.06.12	Russia	0 - 4
SCOTLAND		
31.05.79	Stafford	5 - 1
05.06.80	Zeist	2 - 4
11.06.81	Empoli	0 - 0
05.06.82	Aberdeen	1 - 1
04.06.83	Scarborough	2 - 1
07.06.84	Modena	2 - 0
15.06.85	Harderwijk	1 - 3
23.05.87	Dunfermline	2 - 1
18.05.02	Kettering	2 - 0
24.05.03	Carmarthen Town	0 - 0
23.05.04	Deverondale	3 - 1
28.05.05	Cork	3 - 2
27.05.06	Eastbourne Boro'	2 - 0
25.05.07	Ross County	3 - 0
22.05.08	Colwyn Bay	1 - 0
SLOVAKIA UNDER-21/23		
24.05.14	Slovakia	0 - 1
05.06.16	Sutton United	3 - 4
08.11.17	Ziar nad Hronon Stadium	0 - 4
SPARTA PRAGUE B		
21.05.14	Prague	2 - 2
TURKEY U23		
05.02.13	Dartford FC	0 - 1
14.10.14	Istanbul	0 - 2
UKRAINE		
22.03.16	Kiev	2 - 0
USA		
20.03.02	Stevenage Boro.	2 - 1
09.06.04	Charleston USA	0 - 0
WALES		
27.03.84	Newtown	1 - 2
26.03.85	Telford	1 - 0
18.03.86	Merthyr Tydfil	1 - 3
17.03.87	Gloucester	2 - 2
15.03.88	Rhyl	2 - 0
21.03.89	Kidderminster	2 - 0
06.03.90	Merthyr Tydfil	0 - 0
17.05.91	Stafford	1 - 2
03.03.92	Aberystwyth	1 - 0
02.03.93	Cheltenham	2 - 1
22.02.94	Bangor	2 - 1
28.02.95	Yeovil Town	1 - 0
23.05.99	St Albans	2 - 1
16.05.00	Llanelli	1 - 1
13.02.01	Rushden & Dia.	0 - 0
14.05.02	Boston	1 - 1
22.05.03	Merthyr Tydfil	2 - 0
20.05.04	Keith FC	0 - 2
26.05.05	Cork	1 - 0
25.05.06	Eastbourne Boro'	1 - 1
27.05.07	Clachnacuddin	3 - 0
21.02.08	Exeter City	2 - 1
24.05.08	Rhyl	3 - 0
15.09.10	Newtown FC	2 - 2
WALES C		
20.03.18	Barry FC	3 - 2
20.03.19	Salford City FC	2 - 2

GOALSCORERS 1979 - 2021

13 GOALS...
Carter, Mark

7 GOALS...
Cole, Mitchell

6 GOALS...
Ashford, Noel

5 GOALS...
Davison, Jon
Williams, Colin

4 GOALS...
Culpin, Paul
D'Sane, Roscoe
Johnson, Jeff
Mackhail-Smith, Craig
Norwood, James

3 GOALS...
Adamson, David
Guinan, Steve
Grayson,Neil
Hatch, Liam
Kirk, Jackson
Morison, Steve
Morrison, Michael
Okenabirhie, Fejiri (Hatrick)
Opponents
Taylor, Matt
Watkins, Dale

2 GOALS...
Alford, Carl
Barnes-Homer, Matthew
Barrett, Keith
Bishop, Andrew
Burgess, Andrew
Casey, Kim
Cordice, Neil
Elding, Anthony
Gray, Andre
Hayles, Barry
Hill, Kenny
Howell, David
John, Louis
McQueen, Darren
Mutrie, Les
Patmore, Warren
Pearson, Matty
Richards, Justin
Seddon, Gareth
Southam, Glen
Watson, John
Weatherstone, Simon
Whitbread, Barry
Yiadom, Andy

1 GOAL...
Agana, Tony
Anderson, Dale
Ashton, John
Beautyman, Harry
Benson, Paul
Berry
Blackburn, Chris
Boardman, Jon
Bogle, Omar
Bolton, Jimmy
Boyd, George
Bradshaw, Mark
Briscoe, Louis
Brown, Paul
Browne, Corey
Carey-Bertram, Daniel
Carr, Michael
Cavell, Paul
Charles, Lee
Charley, Ken
Charnock, Kieran
Constable, James
Crittenden, Nick
Davies, Paul
Day, Matt
Densmore, Shaun
Drummond, Stewart
Fleming, Andrew
Franks, Franks
Furlong, Paul
Grant, John
Guthrie, Kurtis
Harrad, Shaun
Hine, Mark
Holland, Jack
Holroyd, Chris
Humphreys, Delwyn
Howells, Jake
Jackson, Kayden
Jackson, Marlon
James, Kingsley
Jennings, Connor
Kennedy, John
Kerr, Scott
Kimmins,Ged
King, Simon
Leworthy, David
Lowe, Jamal
McDougald, Junior
McFadzean, Kyle
Mayes, Bobby
Moore, Neil
Moore, Luke
Newton, Sean
O'Keefe, Eamon
Oli, Dennis
Pavey, Alfie
Penn, Russell
Pennell, Luke
Pitcher, Geoff
Porter, Max
Ricketts, Sam
Robbins, Terry
Roberts, Jordan
Robinson, Mark
Roddis,Nick
Rodgers, Luke
Rodman, Alex
Rogers, Paul
Ryan, Tim
Sarcevic, Antoni
Sellars, Neil
Shaw, John
Sheldon, Gareth
Simpson, Josh
Sinclair, Dean
Smith, Ian
Smith, Ossie
Spencer, Scott
Stansfield, Adam
Stephens, Mickey
Stott, Steve
Taylor, Steve
Thurgood, Stuart
Tubbs, Matthew
Venables, David
Walker, Thomas
Watkins, Adam
Way, Darren
Webb, Paul
Whitehouse, Elliott
Wilcox, Russ
Willoughby, Kurt

MANAGERS 1979 - 2021

		P	W	D	L	F	A	*Win%
1979	Howard Wilkinson	2	2	0	0	6	1	-
1980 - 1984	Keith Wright	17	9	5	3	30	16	53
1985 - 1988	Kevin Verity	12	7	2	3	23	15	58
1989 - 1996	Tony Jennings	19	10	4	5	27	18	53
1997	Ron Reid	2	0	1	1	0	2	-
1998 - 2002	John Owens	14	8	5	1	22	10	57
2002 -	Paul Fairclough	74	39	13	22	125	95	53

*Calculated for those who managed for 10 games or more.

the
FOOTBALL ASSOCIATION COMPETITIONS

FAC EP - Fearon (Liversedge) heads home the equaliser against Irlam.

FAC EP - Lever (Irlam) Walker (Liversedge).

FAC EP - Cassell (Irlam) Walton (Liversedge).

FAC EP - Walton (Liversedge) diving header against Irlam. Photos Keith Clayton.

2020-21

FAC P - VCD keeper Nick Blue clears from the onrushing Cray Valley's Francis Babalola. Photo Alan Coomes.

FAC P - Cleethorpes Town v AFC Mansfield - the AFC Mansfield player stoops to head the only goal of the tie. Photo Bill Wheatcroft.

FAC P - Cleethorpes Town v AFC Mansfield. Photo Bill Wheatcroft.

EXTRA PRELIMINARY ROUND - Tuesday 1 September 2020

	Home		Away	Score	Att
1	Penrith	v	Pickering Town	3-2	161
2	Northallerton Town	v	Billingham Town	1-4	194
3	Sunderland RCA	v	Durham City	3-1	170
4	Whickham	v	West Allotment Celtic	0-0	
	(West allotment Celtic won 4-2 on kicks from the penalty mark)				
5	Thornaby	v	Bridlington Town	2-0	260
6	Crook Town	v	Yorkshire Amateur (2/9)	1-1	199
	(Crook Town won 5-4 on kicks from the penalty mark)				
7	Guisborough Town	v	Newton Aycliffe (2/9)	1-0	236
8	Glasshoughton Welfare	v	Knaresborough Town	1-1	272
	(Knaresborough Town won 4-2 on kicks from the penalty mark)				
9	Hebburn Town	v	Hemsworth Miners Welfare	4-1	
10	Consett	v	Sunderland Ryhope CW	3-2	
11	Marske United	v	North Shields	3-0	255
12	Stockton Town	v	Shildon (2/9)	3-0	300
13	Garforth Town	v	Whitley Bay	0-3	226
14	Newcastle Benfield	v	Seaham Red Star	1-1	176
	(Newcastle Benfield won 4-3 on kicks from the penalty mark)				
15	Ashington	v	Goole	2-1	320
16	Heaton Stannington	v	West Auckland Town (2/9)	2-3	261
17	Bishop Auckland	v	Hall Road Rangers (2/9)	1-0	263
18	1874 Northwich	v	Warrington Rylands	1-6	300
19	St Helens Town	v	Cammell Laird 1907 (3/9)	1-1	182
	(St Helens Town won 5-4 on kicks from the penalty mark)				
20	Longridge Town	v	Winsford United	2-1	
21	Wythenshawe Amateurs	v	Shelley	1-1	
	(Wythenshawe Amateurs won 4-2 on kicks from the penalty mark)				
22	Avro	v	Bootle (2/9)	1-2	
23	Runcorn Town	v	Thackley	2-1	137
24	Litherland Remyca	v	Ashton Athletic (2/9)	3-0	135
25	Eccleshill United	v	Silsden	0-3	320
26	AFC Darwen	v	Barnoldswick Town	2-4	317
27	Northwich Victoria	v	Padiham	1-0	222
28	Skelmersdale United	v	Penistone Church	3-2	
29	Daisy Hill	v	Colne	0-2	
30	Campion	v	Albion Sports (2/9)	0-1	189
31	Athersley Recreation	v	Charnock Richard	1-4	
32	Irlam	v	Liversedge	2-1	165
33	Maine Road	v	Squires Gate	0-5	154
34	Congleton Town	v	Burscough	1-1	200
	(Congleton Town won 3-2 on kicks from the penalty mark)				
35	Hanley Town	v	Lye Town	3-1	300
36	Rugby Town	v	Worcester City	0-2	328
37	Sporting Khalsa	v	Boldmere St Michaels	2-1	
38	Highgate United	v	AFC Bridgnorth	0-3	
39	Stourport Swifts	v	Coventry United	1-3	160
40	Gresley Rovers	v	Wellington FC	2-0	243
41	Stone Old Alleynians	v	Tividale	0-0	
	(Tividale won 4-1 on kicks from the penalty mark)				
42	Bewdley Town	v	OJM Black Country	1-5	269
43	Romulus	v	Coventry Sphinx	0-0	199
	(Coventry Sphinx won 4-3 on kicks from the penalty mark)				
44	Chelmsley Town	v	Shifnal Town	0-3	318
45	Westfields	v	Brocton	2-0	
46	Heather St Johns	v	Walsall Wood	0-1	142
47	Whitchurch Alport	v	Haughmond	3-1	
48	Racing Club Warwick	v	AFC Wulfrunians	3-0	203
49	Anstey Nomads	v	Sleaford Town	3-0	195
50	Lutterworth Town	v	Staveley MW	2-0	184
51	Carlton Town	v	Loughborough University (2/9)	1-1	
	(Carlton Town won 4-2 on kicks from the penalty mark)				
52	Bottesford Town	v	Selston (2/9)	2-1	170
53	Radford	v	Shepshed Dynamo	1-1	
	(Shepshed Dynamo won 4-3 on kicks from the penalty mark)				
54	Spalding United	v	Barton Town	1-3	152
55	Quorn	v	Melton Town	2-0	
56	AFC Mansfield	v	Sherwood Colliery	2-1	
57	Holbeach United	v	Kirby Muxloe (2/9)	1-0	
58	Long Eaton United	v	Grimsby Borough	3-1	150
59	Newark	v	Deeping Rangers	4-0	250
60	Maltby Main	v	Handsworth	2-1	293
61	Blackstones	v	Boston Town (2/9)	2-3	
62	West Bridgford	v	Dunkirk	1-1	
	(West Bridgford won 5-3 on kicks from the penalty mark)				
63	Leicester Nirvana	v	GNG Oadby Town	1-3	145
64	Long Melford	v	Northampton On Chenecks	3-2	
65	Whitton United	v	Ipswich Wanderers	4-3	150
66	Newmarket Town	v	Walsham Le Willows		
	(walkover for Newmarket Town – Walsham Le Willows withdrawn)				
67	Hadleigh United	v	Mildenhall Town	3-4	126
68	Peterborough Northern Star	v	Potton United	0-1	97
69	Kirkley & Pakefield	v	Cogenhoe United	1-2	
70	Diss Town	v	Framlingham Town	1-0	166
71	Thetford Town	v	Wellingborough Town	2-0	137
72	Pinchbeck United	v	St Neots Town (2/9)	0-4	
73	Burton Park Wanderers	v	AFC Sudbury		
	(walkover for AFC Sudbury – Burton Park Wanderers withdrawn)				
74	Gorleston	v	Swaffham Town	5-0	205
75	Haverhill Rovers	v	Norwich United	2-1	212
76	Eynesbury Rovers	v	Desborough Town	7-3	132
77	Wellingborough Whitworth	v	Harborough Town	1-6	172
78	Woodbridge Town	v	Biggleswade United	2-2	
	(Biggleswade United won 7-6 on kicks from the penalty mark)				
79	Stowmarket Town	v	Rothwell Corinthians	2-1	
80	Wroxham	v	Arlesey Town	5-0	235
81	Godmanchester Rovers	v	Ely City (2/9)	1-1	
	(Ely City won 4-2 on kicks from the penalty mark)				
82	Redbridge	v	Harpenden Town	0-2	134
83	Park View	v	Hashtag United (2/9)	1-2	
84	Harlow Town	v	Enfield	5-1	260
85	Clapton	v	Sporting Bengal United	2-2	
	(Sporting Bengal United won 6-5 on kicks from the penalty mark)				
86	Hoddesdon Town	v	FC Clacton	1-2	129
	(at Ware FC)				
87	New Salamis	v	Colney Heath	1-0	236
88	Southend Manor	v	Ware	0-5	200
89	Walthamstow	v	London Lions	3-2	
90	Saffron Walden Town	v	Little Oakley	4-2	
91	Baldock Town	v	St Margaretsbury (2/9)	2-2	
	(St Margaretsbury won 4-2 on kicks from the penalty mark)				
92	Stansted	v	Takeley	3-2	143
93	Cockfosters	v	Stanway Rovers	4-2	221
94	Hullbridge Sports	v	Hadley	0-2	
95	Sawbridgeworth Town	v	Romford	2-1	
96	Brantham Athletic	v	Benfleet	1-1	
	(Brantham Athletic won 3-2 on kicks from the penalty mark)				
97	Woodford Town	v	London Colney (31/8)	3-1	247
98	West Essex	v	Crawley Green (2/9)	6-3	
	(at Redbridge FC)				
99	Ilford	v	Halstead Town (2/9)	1-3	
100	Oxhey Jets	v	Bishop's Cleeve	1-0	110
101	Clanfield 85	v	Long Crendon	0-1	183
102	Leverstock Green	v	Wembley	3-1	111
103	Tuffley Rovers	v	Harefield United	2-5	144

FAC P - Ade Yusuff slips the ball past VCD keeper Nick Blue to score for Cray Valley. Photo Alan Coomes.

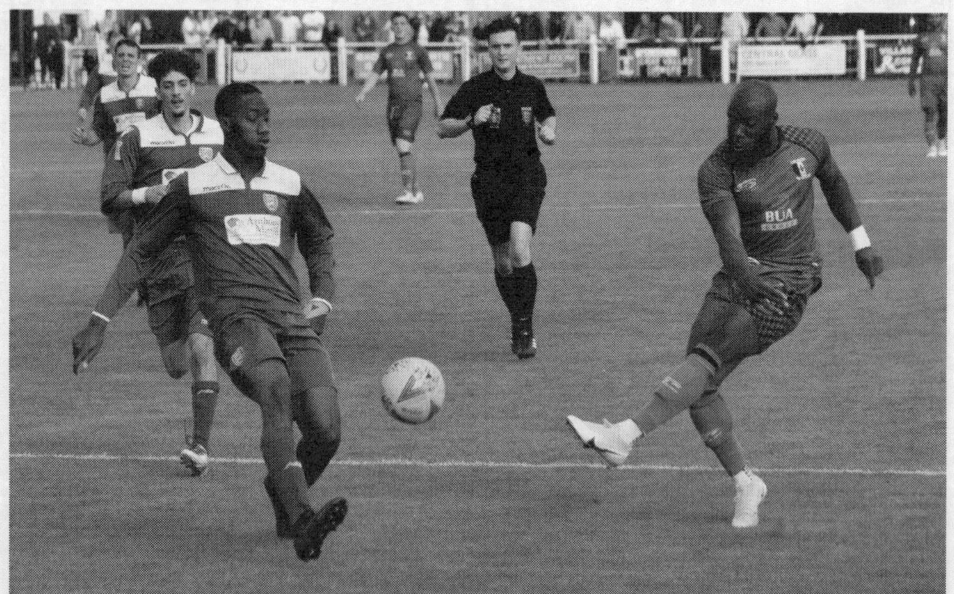

FAC P - Mohammed Oshilaja of VCD blocks this effort from Cray Valleys Francis Babalola. Photo Alan Coomes.jpg

EXTRA PRELIMINARY ROUND

No.	Home		Away	Score	Att
104	Holmer Green	v	Shrivenham	3-2	140
105	Winslow United	v	Newport Pagnell Town	2-1	285
106	Cribbs	v	Newent Town	3-1	
107	Easington Sports	v	Tring Athletic	2-0	90
108	Aylesbury Vale Dynamos	v	Windsor	1-2	143
109	Ardley United	v	Edgware Town	0-0	123
	(Edgware Town won 6-5 on kicks from the penalty mark)				
110	Lydney Town	v	Fairford Town	0-1	140
111	Risborough Rangers	v	Longlevens	4-1	190
112	Leighton Town	v	Abingdon United	3-0	121
113	AFC Dunstable	v	Hallen	4-0	48
114	Roman Glass St George	v	Flackwell Heath (2/9)	1-2	
115	Royal Wootton Bassett Town	v	Chipping Sodbury Town	2-2	181
	(Royal Wootoon Bassett town won 4-1 on kicks from the penalty mark)				
116	Burnham	v	Cheltenham Saracens	0-0	149
	(Burnham won 5-3 on kicks from the penalty mark)				
117	Dunstable Town	v	Thame Rangers (2/9)	1-1	137
	(Dunstable Town won 5-4 on kicks from the penalty mark)				
118	North Greenford United	v	Brimscombe & Thrupp	1-2	
119	CB Hounslow United	v	Banstead Athletic	6-1	77
120	East Preston	v	Chatham Town	0-2	132
121	Billingshurst	v	Westside	0-2	
122	Lordswood	v	Hanworth Villa	2-3	87
123	Molesey	v	Southall	0-7	
124	AFC Croydon Athletic	v	Sutton Common Rovers	0-3	174
125	Glebe	v	Whyteleafe	1-3	226
126	Broadbridge Heath	v	Raynes Park Vale	3-1	210
127	Alfold	v	Shoreham	9-1	194
128	Saltdean United	v	Eastbourne Town	1-3	232
129	Colliers Wood United	v	Hollands & Blair (2/9)	0-1	
130	Kennington	v	Erith & Belvedere	0-1	300
131	Langney Wanderers	v	Tower Hamlets	3-1	
132	Stansfeld	v	Punjab United (2/9)	3-3	282
	(Stansfeld won 4-3 on kicks from the penalty mark)				
133	Abbey Rangers	v	Welling Town	3-1	119
134	Oakwood	v	Cobham	0-2	110
135	Tunbridge Wells	v	Erith Town	1-0	
136	Newhaven	v	Lingfield	1-1	114
	(Newhaven won 4-2 on kicks from the penalty mark)				
137	Broadfields United	v	Loxwood	3-0	
138	Crowborough Athletic	v	Crawley Down Gatwick	3-4	116
139	Redhill	v	Egham Town		
	(walkover for Egham Town – Redhill withdrawn)				
140	Fisher	v	Horsham YMCA	2-0	85
141	Corinthian	v	Sheerwater	2-1	112
142	Guildford City	v	Canterbury City (2/9)	3-2	150
143	K Sports	v	Steyning Town Community	0-2	70
144	AFC Uckfield Town	v	Little Common	0-1	
145	Mile Oak	v	Beckenham Town (2/9)	0-4	273
146	Lancing	v	Phoenix Sports	3-3	204
	(Phoenix Sports won 11-10 on kicks from the penalty mark)				
147	Eastbourne United	v	Horley Town	0-1	185
148	Balham	v	Hassocks (2/9)	2-2	125
	(Hassocks won 5-3 on kicks from the penalty mark)				
149	Knaphill	v	Deal Town	0-4	
150	Bearsted	v	Peacehaven & Telescombe	3-5	
	(tie awarded to Bearsted – Peacehaven & Telscombe removed)				
151	Spelthorne Sports	v	Virginia Water	1-0	
152	Sheppey United	v	Sutton Athletic	1-0	189
153	Pagham	v	Fleet Town	2-1	159
154	Corsham Town	v	Farnham Town	2-2	204
	(Corsham Town won 4-2 on kicks from the penalty mark)				
155	Hamworthy United	v	Calne Town	3-0	
156	Badshot Lea	v	Amesbury Town	4-0	159
157	Hamble Club	v	Reading City	2-1	
	(at Romsey Town FC)				
158	Frimley Green	v	Fareham Town	1-0	
159	Bashley	v	Whitchurch United	8-2	
160	Brockenhurst	v	Lymington Town	0-1	300
161	Baffins Milton Rovers	v	AFC Stoneham (2/9)	1-2	
162	Cowes Sports	v	Totton & Eling	1-0	205
163	Basingstoke Town	v	Bournemouth	1-1	
	(Basingstoke Town won 5-4 on kicks from the penalty mark – at Reading City FC)				
164	Camberley Town	v	Blackfield & Langley	0-0	56
	(Camberley Town won 5-4 on kicks from the penalty mark)				
165	Shaftesbury	v	Fawley	2-2	164
	(Fawley won 6-5 on kicks from the penalty mark)				
166	Tadley Calleva	v	Alresford Town	1-0	142
167	Westbury United	v	Binfield	0-2	
93					
168	Bemerton Heath Harlequins	v	Horndean	2-1	
169	Christchurch	v	Ascot United	1-1	143
	(Christchurch won 7-6 on kicks from the penalty mark)				
170	AFC Portchester	v	Sandhurst Town	4-0	271
171	Keynsham Town	v	Exmouth Town	1-3	145
172	Tavistock	v	Bradford Town (2/9)	2-0	
173	Odd Down	v	Helston Athletic	1-4	117
174	Buckland Athletic	v	Bitton (7.30)	1-1	153
	(Bitton won 5-3 on kicks from the penalty mark)				
175	Wells City	v	Bovey Tracey	2-0	
176	Willand Rovers	v	Bridport (2/9)	2-1	
177	Shepton Mallet	v	Torrington	3-0	
178	Wellington AFC	v	Bodmin Town	2-2	62
	(Bodmin Town won 4-3 on kicks from the penalty mark – at Cullompton Rangers FC)				
179	Plymouth Parkway	v	Saltash United	1-1	
	(Saltash United won 5-4 on kicks from the penalty mark)				
180	Millbrook	v	Bridgwater Town	0-1	247
181	Portland United	v	Clevedon Town	0-1	
182	Sherborne Town	v	Street (2/9)	2-1	292
183	Brislington	v	Cadbury Heath	0-2	221
184	Newton Abbot Spurs	v	AFC St Austell	3-0	164

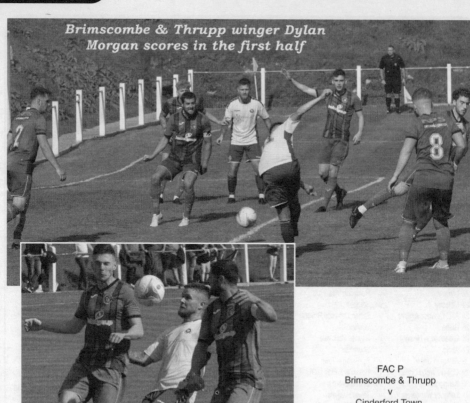

Brimscombe & Thrupp winger Dylan Morgan scores in the first half

FAC P
Brimscombe & Thrupp
v
Cinderford Town.
Photos Peter Barnes.

PRELIMINARY ROUND - Saturday 12 September 2020

1	Whitley Bay	v	Dunston		
	(walkover for Whitley Bay – Dunston withdrawn)				
2	Penrith	v	West Allotment Celtic	1-3	167
3	Kendal Town	v	Bishop Auckland	0-5	257
4	West Auckland Town	v	Ashington	3-3	
	(West Auckland Town won 3-0 on kicks from the penalty mark)				
5	Billingham Town	v	Stockton Town	1-2	
	(at Stockton Town FC)				
6	Knaresborough Town	v	Workington	1-3	255
7	Crook Town	v	Marske United	0-2	
8	Thornaby	v	Sunderland RCA	0-2	300
9	Frickley Athletic	v	Newcastle Benfield	3-1	222
10	Hebburn Town	v	Pontefract Collieries	2-2	300
	(Pontefract Collieries won 5-3 on kicks from the penalty mark)				
11	Guisborough Town	v	Tadcaster Albion	1-2	300
12	Consett	v	Ossett United	2-2	
	(Consett won 5-4 on kicks from the penalty mark)				
13	Congleton Town	v	Skelmersdale United	1-2	286
14	Glossop North End	v	City of Liverpool	0-3	350
15	Ramsbottom United	v	Irlam	4-1	
16	Ashton United	v	Squires Gate	2-0	236
17	Wythenshawe Amateurs	v	Trafford	1-4	
18	Runcorn Linnets	v	Albion Sports	2-0	384
19	Droylsden	v	Litherland Remyca		
	(walkover for Litherland Remyca – Droylsden withdrawn)				
20	Silsden	v	Bootle	2-5	211
21	Mossley	v	St Helens Town	3-0	
22	Stocksbridge Park Steels	v	Stalybridge Celtic (12.30)	1-3	361
	(Live on BBC Sport)				
23	Northwich Victoria	v	Charnock Richard	2-2	
	(Charnock Richard won 5-4 on kicks from the penalty mark)				
24	Colne	v	Prescot Cables	0-2	
25	Runcorn Town	v	Brighouse Town	1-1	
	(Runcorn Town won 5-4 on kicks from the penalty mark)				
26	Warrington Rylands	v	Clitheroe	1-0	275
27	Marine	v	Barnoldswick Town	2-1	323
28	Widnes	v	Longridge Town	2-3	153
29	Worcester City	v	Walsall Wood	2-1	
30	OJM Black Country	v	Matlock Town	0-1	
	(at Matlock Town FC)				
31	Coventry Sphinx	v	Coleshill Town	0-0	146
	(Coventry Sphinx won 4-3 on kicks from the penalty mark)				
32	Sutton Coldfield Town	v	Belper Town	0-1	
33	Kidsgrove Athletic	v	Chasetown	0-1	327
34	Leek Town	v	Sporting Khalsa	2-1	400
35	Westfields	v	Whitchurch Alport	2-0	227
36	Racing Club Warwick	v	Bedworth United	1-1	233
	(Bedworth United won 3-2 on kicks from the penalty mark)				
37	Market Drayton Town	v	Tividale	0-1	121
38	Newcastle Town	v	Halesowen Town	1-2	
39	Evesham United	v	Coventry United		
	(walkover for Evesham United – Coventry United withdrawn)				
40	Hanley Town	v	Gresley Rovers	5-1	320
41	Shifnal Town	v	AFC Bridgnorth	4-1	320
42	Cleethorpes Town	v	AFC Mansfield	0-1	
43	Boston Town	v	Coalville Town	0-3	
44	Anstey Nomads	v	Worksop Town	1-2	300
45	Holbeach United	v	Sheffield	0-4	
46	Quorn	v	Barton Town	2-0	
47	Maltby Main	v	Newark	0-4	241
48	West Bridgford	v	Lincoln United		
	(walkover for West Bridgford – Lincoln United withdrawn)				
49	Ilkeston Town	v	Shepshed Dynamo	3-0	363
50	Long Eaton United	v	Bottesford Town	1-1	123
	(Long Eaton United won 4-2 on kicks from the penalty mark)				
51	GNG Oadby Town	v	Carlton Town		
	(walkover for Carlton Town – GNG Oadby Town withdrawn)				
52	Lutterworth Town	v	Loughborough Dynamo	0-6	238
53	Wroxham	v	Gorleston	3-1	
54	Biggleswade	v	Histon	1-0	203
55	Cambridge City	v	Biggleswade United	4-0	293
56	Yaxley	v	Stowmarket Town	1-2	
57	Mildenhall Town	v	Corby Town	1-1	175
	(Mildenhall Town won 4-3 on kicks from the penalty mark)				
58	Ely City	v	Eynesbury Rovers	3-1	
59	Stamford	v	Diss Town	4-0	
60	Thetford Town	v	Potton United	0-2	138
61	Dereham Town	v	Whitton United	3-2	171
62	Daventry Town	v	Bedford Town	1-0	206
63	AFC Sudbury	v	Harborough Town	4-2	
64	Haverhill Rovers	v	Wisbech Town	4-3	170
65	Cogenhoe United	v	Bury Town	0-1	
66	Long Melford	v	Kempston Rovers	0-0	
	(Long Melford won 4-2 on kicks from the penalty mark)				
67	Soham Town Rangers	v	St Neots Town	3-2	203
68	Royston Town	v	Newmarket Town	6-0	310
69	Great Wakering Rovers	v	Brantham Athletic	0-1	125
70	Welwyn Garden City	v	Saffron Walden Town	2-0	181
71	Grays Athletic	v	Witham Town	1-0	
72	Coggeshall Town	v	Tilbury	2-0	
73	Walthamstow	v	Cockfosters	1-1	
	(Walthamstow won 3-2 on kicks from the penalty mark)				
74	Sawbridgeworth Town	v	St Margaretsbury	1-3	
75	FC Romania	v	Brentwood Town	0-1	76
76	Barking	v	Heybridge Swifts	2-0	129
77	FC Clacton	v	Hadley	1-1	
	(FC Clacton won 10-9 on kicks from the penalty mark)				
78	Hertford Town	v	Maldon & Tiptree	0-1	
79	Bowers & Pitsea	v	Barton Rovers	5-1	155
80	Stansted	v	Basildon United	2-0	171

FAC 1Q - AFC Mansfield v Gainsborough Trinity . Photo Bill Wheatcroft.

FAC 3Q - Ilkeston Town v Alvechurch. Photo Bill Wheatcroft.

PRELIMINARY ROUND

81	Harlow Town	v	Sporting Bengal United	3-0	157
82	Harpenden Town	v	Aveley	0-3	
83	Canvey Island	v	Ware	2-0	216
84	Leiston	v	Halstead Town	5-0	174
85	New Salamis	v	West Essex	5-1	315
86	Hashtag United	v	Felixstowe & Walton United (13/9)	1-1	
	(Hashtag United won 13-12 on kicks from the penalty mark)				
87	Waltham Abbey	v	Woodford Town	1-0	
88	Oxhey Jets	v	Chalfont St Peter	0-1	148
89	Aylesbury United	v	Long Crendon	3-0	197
90	Risborough Rangers	v	Winslow United	2-1	270
91	Flackwell Heath	v	Cirencester Town	0-3	95
92	Didcot Town	v	Royal Wootton Bassett Town	1-2	283
93	Holmer Green	v	Highworth Town	0-2	166
94	Dunstable Town	v	Easington Sports	1-1	138
	(Dunstable Town won 7-6 on kicks from the penalty mark)				
95	Kidlington	v	Thame United	1-0	152
96	Cribbs	v	Berkhamsted	2-0	
97	Harefield United	v	Leighton Town	1-2	250
98	Brimscombe & Thrupp	v	Cinderford Town	1-2	177
99	Fairford Town	v	Edgware Town	2-2	118
	(Fairford Town won 4-2 on kicks from the penalty mark)				
100	Northwood	v	Slimbridge	1-1	153
	(Northwood won 4-2 on kicks from the penalty mark)				
101	Wantage Town	v	Windsor	3-2	132
102	Marlow	v	North Leigh	2-0	
103	Thatcham Town	v	AFC Dunstable	1-5	
104	Leverstock Green	v	Burnham	1-4	137
105	Tunbridge Wells	v	Beckenham Town	1-1	
	(Tunbridge Wells won 4-1 on kicks from the penalty mark)				
106	Cray Valley (PM)	v	VCD Athletic	6-0	
107	Hanwell Town	v	Spelthorne Sports	4-1	175
108	Sevenoaks Town	v	CB Hounslow United	3-0	
	(tie awarded to Sevenoaks Town)				
109	Southall	v	Ashford Town (Middx)	2-1	
110	Chertsey Town	v	Abbey Rangers	2-0	
111	Staines Town	v	Guildford City	2-1	
112	East Grinstead Town	v	Phoenix Sports	3-2	208
113	Langney Wanderers	v	Harrow Borough (11.30)	1-1	
	(Harrow Borough won 3-2 on kicks from the penalty mark)				
114	Hastings United	v	Herne Bay	1-0	400
115	Ramsgate	v	Chipstead	0-3	400
116	Sutton Common Rovers	v	Broadfields United	4-0	
117	Carshalton Athletic	v	Whitstable Town	5-1	300
118	Bedfont Sports Club	v	Hassocks	3-1	71
119	Deal Town	v	Sittingbourne	4-1	287
120	Newhaven	v	Corinthian	1-2	
121	Erith & Belvedere	v	Alfold	1-1	
	(Erith & Belvedere won 4-3 on kicks from the penalty mark)				
122	Kingstonian	v	Horley Town	4-1	355
123	Westside	v	Chatham Town	0-2	156
124	Cobham	v	Three Bridges	1-1	
	(Cobham won 4-3 on kicks from the penalty mark)				
125	Whyteleafe	v	Bearsted	4-0	
126	Egham Town	v	Crawley Down Gatwick	1-3	79
127	Steyning Town Community	v	Hanworth Villa	2-1	
128	Broadbridge Heath	v	Haywards Heath Town		
	(walkover for Haywards Heath Town – Broadbridge Heath withdrawn)				
129	Sheppey United	v	Uxbridge	4-1	235
130	Hythe Town	v	South Park	1-2	
131	Tooting & Mitcham United	v	Fisher	2-2	398
	(Fisher won 3-1 on kicks from the penalty mark)				
132	Stansfeld	v	Little Common	2-3	246
133	Faversham Town	v	Eastbourne Town	1-1	
	(Faversham Town won 6-5 on kicks from the penalty mark)				
134	Ashford United	v	Whitehawk	2-0	
135	Burgess Hill Town	v	Hollands & Blair		
	(tie awarded to Burgess Hill Town – Hollands & Blair failed to fulfil fixture)				
136	Farnborough	v	Lymington Town	0-0	232
	(Farnborough won 4-3 on kicks from the penalty mark)				
137	Basingstoke Town	v	Chichester City (14/9)	2-2	255
	(Chichester City won 3-1 on kicks from the penalty mark)				
138	Hartley Wintney	v	Hamworthy United	1-0	
139	Bashley	v	Christchurch	0-2	
140	Westfield	v	Frimley Green	2-2	142
	(Frimley Green won 5-3 on kicks from the penalty mark)				
141	Fawley	v	Tadley Calleva (13/9)	0-1	231
142	Moneyfields	v	Camberley Town	4-2	164
143	Winchester City	v	Corsham Town	2-0	163
144	Cowes Sports	v	Hamble Club	1-0	188
145	Badshot Lea	v	Bracknell Town	0-2	
146	Binfield	v	AFC Totton	5-1	220
147	Bemerton Heath Harlequins	v	Sholing	0-1	101
148	Wimborne Town	v	AFC Portchester	3-0	
149	AFC Stoneham	v	Pagham	3-0	113
150	Frome Town	v	Bodmin Town	3-0	
151	Cadbury Heath	v	Bristol Manor Farm	1-5	172
152	Exmouth Town	v	Melksham Town	0-2	
153	Saltash United	v	Paulton Rovers	1-0	174
154	Shepton Mallet	v	Willand Rovers	1-0	224
155	Sherborne Town	v	Clevedon Town	1-2	
156	Newton Abbot Spurs	v	Larkhall Athletic	0-4	171
157	Bideford	v	Wells City	3-0	234
158	Bridgwater Town	v	Bitton	2-3	241
159	Barnstaple Town	v	Helston Athletic	2-0	
160	Tavistock	v	Mangotsfield United	2-1	

FAC 2Q - Gordon (Waltham Abbey) scores against Bury Town. Photo Keith Clayton.

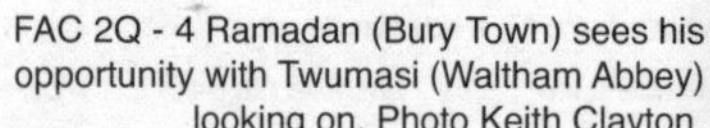

FAC 2Q - 4 Ramadan (Bury Town) sees his opportunity with Twumasi (Waltham Abbey) looking on. Photo Keith Clayton.

FAC 2Q - Edwards (Bury Town) sees his shot go over the Waltham Abbey crossbar. Photo Keith Clayton.

FIRST QUALIFYING ROUND - Tuesday 22 September 2020

1	Sunderland RCA	v	Prescot Cables	0-4	207
2	Lancaster City	v	Runcorn Town	0-0	273
	(Lancaster City won 4-3 on kicks from the penalty mark)				
3	Warrington Town	v	South Shields	0-0	426
	(South Shields won 6-5 on kicks from the penalty mark)				
4	Marske United	v	Trafford	1-0	300
5	Mossley	v	Ramsbottom United	2-1	371
6	West Allotment Celtic	v	Hyde United	0-5	145
7	Skelmersdale United	v	Bootle (8.00)	2-1	
8	West Auckland Town	v	Runcorn Linnets	0-0	
	(Runcorn Linnets won 3-2 on kicks from the penalty mark)				
9	Whitley Bay	v	Witton Albion	3-2	253
10	Radcliffe	v	Workington	5-3	309
11	Scarborough Athletic	v	Ashton United	0-2	
12	Frickley Athletic	v	Marine	0-1	
13	Whitby Town	v	Warrington Rylands	1-1	
	(Warrington Rylands won 4-3 on kicks from the penalty mark)				
14	City of Liverpool	v	Morpeth Town	0-3	
15	Atherton Collieries	v	Bamber Bridge		
	(walkover for Atherton Collieries – Bamber Bridge withdrawn)				
16	Longridge Town	v	Charnock Richard	2-0	
17	Stalybridge Celtic	v	Bishop Auckland	3-0	332
18	Consett	v	Stockton Town	1-0	
19	FC United of Manchester	v	Pontefract Collieries	6-2	
20	Tadcaster Albion	v	Litherland Remyca	7-2	191
21	Hednesford Town	v	Long Eaton United	3-2	342
22	Tamworth	v	Stourbridge	3-3	380
	(Tamworth won 5-4 on kicks from the penalty mark)				
23	Worcester City	v	Stafford Rangers (Wed 23 Sep 7.45)		
24	Quorn	v	Matlock Town	0-2	
25	Leek Town	v	Mickleover	1-2	400
26	Grantham Town	v	Rushall Olympic	2-2	153
	(Grantham Town won 3-1 on kicks from the penalty mark)				
27	Nuneaton Borough	v	Loughborough Dynamo	2-1	311
28	Westfields	v	Worksop Town	1-3	
29	West Bridgford	v	Halesowen Town	0-1	287
30	Coventry Sphinx	v	Ilkeston Town	0-2	247
31	Banbury United	v	Carlton Town	1-0	369
32	Chasetown	v	Basford United	2-1	
33	Tividale	v	Nantwich Town	2-4	
34	Barwell	v	Bedworth United	3-1	206
35	AFC Mansfield	v	Gainsborough Trinity	3-0	
36	Coalville Town	v	Sheffield	2-0	369
37	Buxton	v	Belper Town	7-0	317
38	Daventry Town	v	Evesham United	0-2	195
39	AFC Rushden & Diamonds	v	Newark	0-5	450
40	Shifnal Town	v	Alvechurch	0-2	320
41	Bromsgrove Sporting	v	Stratford Town	1-2	472
42	Hanley Town	v	Redditch United	3-2	320
43	Ely City	v	Biggleswade	1-2	
44	Haverhill Rovers	v	Maldon & Tiptree	0-3	298
45	Walthamstow	v	St Margaretsbury	0-0	
	(Walthamstow won 4-3 on kicks from the penalty mark)				
46	Bury Town	v	Brightlingsea Regent	2-1	400
47	Dereham Town	v	Canvey Island	0-2	
48	Kings Langley	v	FC Clacton	1-1	299
	(Kings Langley won 4-2 on kicks from the penalty mark)				
49	Stamford	v	AFC Sudbury	4-0	
50	Hitchin Town	v	Needham Market (21/9)	3-0	410
51	Bowers & Pitsea	v	Hornchurch	0-3	242
52	Grays Athletic	v	Potton United (Wed 23 Sep 7.45)		
53	Long Melford	v	Cheshunt	1-3	
54	Hashtag United	v	Soham Town Rangers (21/9)	1-1	
	(Hashtag United won 4-2 on kicks from the penalty mark – Live on BBC Sport)				
55	Leiston	v	Biggleswade Town	5-1	175
56	Cambridge City	v	Stowmarket Town	1-1	315
	(Cambridge City won 4-2 on kicks from the penalty mark)				
57	Lowestoft Town	v	Aveley (8.00)	2-3	275
58	Peterborough Sports	v	Enfield Town	2-2	233
	(Peterborough Sports won 5-4 on kicks from the penalty mark)				
59	Potters Bar Town	v	East Thurrock United	1-0	206
60	Harlow Town	v	Waltham Abbey	0-1	337
61	Royston Town	v	Wroxham	2-0	330
62	Leighton Town	v	Mildenhall Town	4-0	
63	Welwyn Garden City	v	Bishop's Stortford	1-1	210
	(Bishop's Stortford won 4-3 on kicks from the penalty mark)				
64	Coggeshall Town	v	Stansted	0-1	170
65	Barking	v	Dunstable Town	6-1	105
66	Brantham Athletic	v	St Ives Town	1-0	
67	New Salamis	v	Brentwood Town (21/9)	1-2	325
68	Burnham	v	Northwood	1-0	237
69	Horsham	v	Kingstonian	2-1	509
70	Corinthian	v	Sevenoaks Town	3-1	221
71	Hartley Wintney	v	Erith & Belvedere (7.30)	5-0	254
72	Whyteleafe	v	Binfield	2-0	253
73	Chipstead	v	Deal Town	1-1	157
	(Chipstead won 4-2 on kicks from the penalty mark)				
74	Staines Town	v	Walton Casuals	1-2	
75	Frimley Green	v	Marlow	1-1	
	(Marlow won 4-1 on kicks from the penalty mark)				
76	Little Common	v	Corinthian Casuals	0-3	149
77	Haringey Borough	v	Tunbridge Wells	5-1	
78	Haywards Heath Town	v	Hanwell Town	0-1	155
79	Sutton Common Rovers	v	Metropolitan Police (Wed 23 Sep 7.45)		
80	Cobham	v	Risborough Rangers	1-3	
81	Ashford United	v	Bracknell Town	1-4	
82	Bedfont Sports Club	v	Lewes	3-1	
83	Crawley Down Gatwick	v	Hendon (7.30)	1-2	180
84	Wingate & Finchley	v	Folkestone Invicta (Wed 23 Sep 7.45)		
85	Hastings United	v	Chesham United	0-0	384
	(Hastings United won 6-5 on kicks from the penalty mark)				
86	Cray Wanderers	v	Fisher (Wed 23 Sep 7.45)		
87	Steyning Town Community	v	Sheppey United	0-5	235
88	East Grinstead Town	v	Worthing (7.30)	3-3	273
	(East Grinstead Town won 4-3 on kicks from the penalty mark)				
89	South Park	v	Bognor Regis Town	2-2	202
	(Bognor Regis Town won 4-2 on kicks from the penalty mark)				
90	Merstham	v	AFC Dunstable	2-2	
	(AFC Dunstable won 7-6 on kicks from the penalty mark)				
91	Chertsey Town	v	Leatherhead	0-0	
	(Chertsey Town won 5-4 on kicks from the penalty mark)				
92	Cray Valley (PM)	v	Burgess Hill Town (Wed 23 Sep 7.45)		
93	Beaconsfield Town	v	Harrow Borough (21/9)	0-2	
94	Chatham Town	v	Southall	3-2	300
95	Chalfont St Peter	v	Farnborough	2-3	178
96	Margate	v	Hayes & Yeading United	1-2	
97	Carshalton Athletic	v	Faversham Town (21/9)	5-0	334
98	Tavistock	v	Gosport Borough (Wed 23 Sep 7.45)		
99	Fairford Town	v	Sholing	1-2	150
100	Cinderford Town	v	Royal Wootton Bassett Town	2-2	
	(Royal Wootton Bassett Town won 6-5 on kicks from the penalty mark)				
101	Chichester City	v	Cribbs	3-1	274
102	Cowes Sports	v	Weston Super Mare (7.30)	0-5	300
103	Kidlington	v	Salisbury (Wed 23 Sep 7.45)		
104	Aylesbury United	v	Moneyfields	2-2	112
	(Moneyfields won 4-3 on kicks from the penalty mark)				
105	Taunton Town	v	Wantage Town	5-0	349
106	Winchester City	v	Clevedon Town	3-2	218
107	Larkhall Athletic	v	Bitton (Wed 23 Sep 7.45)		
108	Tiverton Town	v	Bideford (Wed 23 Sep 7.45)		
109	Tadley Calleva	v	Truro City	0-1	297
110	Barnstaple Town	v	Wimborne Town	2-3	
111	Yate Town	v	Bristol Manor Farm	1-2	303
112	Highworth Town	v	Melksham Town (Wed 23 Sep 7.45)		
113	Merthyr Town	v	Poole Town		
	(walkover for Poole Town – Merthyr Town withdrawn)				
114	Frome Town	v	AFC Stoneham	4-1	
115	Christchurch	v	Dorchester Town	2-1	300
116	Swindon Supermarine	v	Shepton Mallet	3-0	
117	Saltash United	v	Cirencester Town	3-1	294

FAC 3Q
Weston-S-Mare
v
Larkhall Athletic
Photo Peter Barnes.

SECOND QUALIFYING ROUND - Saturday 3 October 2020

1	Guiseley	v	Atherton Collieries	4-0	
2	Mossley	v	Tadcaster Albion	1-1	400
	(Tadcaster Albion won 4-3 on kicks from the penalty mark)				
3	Chorley	v	Gateshead	2-1	
4	Southport	v	Morpeth Town	2-1	
5	Stalybridge Celtic	v	Longridge Town	2-3	
6	Whitley Bay	v	Blyth Spartans	2-4	176
7	Farsley Celtic	v	Radcliffe	2-1	
8	Runcorn Linnets	v	Marine	1-1	331
	(Marine won 4-3 on kicks from the penalty mark)				
9	Ashton United	v	South Shields	0-4	300
10	Curzon Ashton	v	FC United of Manchester	1-2	
11	Darlington	v	Prescot Cables	2-2	
	(Darlington won 5-4 on kicks from the penalty mark)				
12	Bradford (Park Avenue)	v	Spennymoor Town	1-3	
13	Warrington Rylands	v	York City	0-1	300
	(Live on BBC Sport)				
14	Hyde United	v	AFC Fylde	2-4	405
15	Marske United	v	Consett	6-0	361
16	Skelmersdale United	v	Lancaster City	2-1	
17	Boston United	v	AFC Mansfield	4-2	
	(at Gainsborough Trinity FC)				
18	Hednesford Town	v	Halesowen Town	0-0	
	(Halesowen Town won 5-3 on kicks from the penalty mark)				
19	Coalville Town	v	Alfreton Town	1-2	437
20	Tamworth	v	Evesham United	3-1	
21	Chasetown	v	AFC Telford United	1-1	369
	(AFC Telford United won 5-4 on kicks from the penalty mark)				
22	Alvechurch	v	Kidderminster Harriers	2-2	445
	(Alvechurch won 4-2 on kicks from the penalty mark)				
23	Nantwich Town	v	Barwell	1-0	225
24	Mickleover	v	Newark	4-1	
25	Buxton	v	Stafford Rangers	0-0	401
	(Stafford Rangers won 4-2 on kicks from the penalty mark)				
26	Grantham Town	v	Matlock Town	0-1	349
27	Leamington	v	Banbury United	0-1	
28	Worksop Town	v	Chester	2-2	293
	(Chester won 5-3 on kicks from the penalty mark)				
29	Nuneaton Borough	v	Stratford Town	2-1	
30	Ilkeston Town	v	Hanley Town	4-1	398
31	AFC Dunstable	v	Hemel Hempstead Town	1-2	214
32	Brackley Town	v	Billericay Town	2-2	
	(Brackley Town won 4-2 on kicks from the penalty mark)				
33	Maldon & Tiptree	v	Grays Athletic	2-2	251
	(Maldon & Tiptree won 5-4 on kicks from the penalty mark)				
34	Canvey Island	v	Biggleswade	2-2	289
	(Canvey Island won 4-3 on kicks from the penalty mark)				
35	Cheshunt	v	Cambridge City	1-2	
36	Royston Town	v	Stamford	2-2	
	(Royston Town won 4-2 on kicks from the penalty mark)				
37	Barking	v	Kings Langley	2-2	197
	(Barking won 3-2 on kicks from the penalty mark)				
38	Hashtag United	v	Braintree Town	1-1	
	(Braintree Town won 7-6 on kicks from the penalty mark)				
39	St Albans City	v	Hitchin Town	5-0	
40	Bishop's Stortford	v	Brentwood Town	1-0	314
41	Concord Rangers	v	Potters Bar Town (4/10)	2-1	148
	(at Potters Bar Town FC)				
42	Walthamstow	v	Hornchurch	0-2	300
43	Leighton Town	v	Leiston	1-2	
44	Brantham Athletic	v	Aveley	0-3	
45	Kettering Town	v	Chelmsford City	2-0	
46	Peterborough Sports	v	Stansted	4-2	
47	Bury Town	v	Waltham Abbey	4-1	400
48	Havant & Waterlooville	v	Horsham (4/10)	2-1	
	(at Bognor Regis Town FC)				
49	Hayes & Yeading United	v	Bognor Regis Town	5-0	301
50	Dartford	v	Slough Town	0-1	
51	Farnborough	v	Tonbridge Angels	0-1	382
52	Harrow Borough	v	Cray Valley (PM)	1-5	153
53	Chipstead	v	East Grinstead Town	1-0	
54	Chichester City	v	Risborough Rangers	2-1	343
55	Corinthian Casuals	v	Dulwich Hamlet	2-2	
	(Dulwich Hamlet won 3-1 on kicks from the penalty mark)				
56	Haringey Borough	v	Chertsey Town	2-0	
57	Folkestone Invicta	v	Chatham Town	0-3	
58	Hendon	v	Maidstone United	0-1	310
59	Hanwell Town	v	Hartley Wintney	3-5	280
60	Moneyfields	v	Cray Wanderers	2-6	
61	Ebbsfleet United	v	Hastings United	2-2	
	(Ebbsfleet United won 4-1 on kicks from the penalty mark)				
62	Sheppey United	v	Welling United	2-0	300
63	Corinthian	v	Hampton & Richmond Borough	0-1	221
64	Bedfont Sports Club	v	Carshalton Athletic	2-0	
65	Dorking Wanderers	v	Eastbourne Borough	3-3	
	(Eastbourne Borough won 4-3 on kicks from the penalty mark)				
66	Bracknell Town	v	Marlow	2-2	389
	(Bracknell Town won 4-3 on kicks from the penalty mark)				
67	Metropolitan Police	v	Walton Casuals	1-2	287
68	Burnham	v	Whyteleafe (5/10)	1-3	248
	(at Whyteleafe FC)				
69	Weston Super Mare	v	Swindon Supermarine	2-2	
	(Weston Super Mare won 4-2 on kicks from the penalty mark)				
70	Truro City	v	Hungerford Town	4-0	
71	Saltash United	v	Sholing	1-3	285
72	Frome Town	v	Larkhall Athletic	1-1	
	(Larkhall Athletic won 4-3 on kicks from the penalty mark)				
73	Christchurch	v	Gloucester City	1-1	265
	(Christchurch won 6-5 on kicks from the penalty mark)				
74	Tiverton Town	v	Taunton Town	3-5	560
75	Gosport Borough	v	Hereford	1-3	501
76	Bath City	v	Winchester City	3-2	
77	Wimborne Town	v	Melksham Town	0-0	
	(Wimborne Town won 5-4 on kicks from the penalty mark)				
78	Kidlington	v	Bristol Manor Farm	1-1	294
	(Bristol Manor Farm won 7-6 on kicks from the penalty mark)				
79	Royal Wootton Bassett Town	v	Oxford City	1-2	320
80	Chippenham Town	v	Poole Town	2-2	
	(Chippenham Town won 5-4 on kicks from the penalty mark)				

FAC 2P - Daggers Ogogo and Mansfield's Lapslie. Photo Bill Wheatcroft.

FAC 2P - Paul McCallum fires past Stech to give Dag & Red the lead. Photo Bill Wheatcroft.

FAC 2P - Mansfield Town v Dagenham & Redbridge. Photo Bill Wheatcroft.

THIRD QUALIFYING ROUND
Tuesday 13 October 2020

1	Southport	v	South Shields	1-1	
	(South Shields won 4-2 on kicks from the penalty mark)				
2	Longridge Town	v	Skelmersdale United	0-1	
3	Chester	v	Spennymoor Town	3-1	
4	Marske United	v	Blyth Spartans (14/10)	1-0	400
5	Farsley Celtic	v	AFC Fylde	1-3	
6	Darlington	v	Tadcaster Albion	6-1	
7	Marine	v	Nantwich Town	4-1	397
8	Chorley	v	York City	1-0	
9	Guiseley	v	Matlock Town	2-0	
10	FC United of Manchester	v	Alfreton Town		
	(walkover for FC United of Manchester – Alfreton Town withdrawn)				
11	St Albans City	v	Mickleover	1-1	
	(St Albans city won 4-3 on kicks from the penalty mark)				
12	Braintree Town	v	Maldon & Tiptree (7.30)	0-1	
13	Ilkeston Town	v	Alvechurch	1-0	400
14	Bishop's Stortford	v	Royston Town (14/10)	3-0	600
15	Stafford Rangers	v	Hereford	3-1	585
16	Peterborough Sports	v	Banbury United	1-1	478
	(Banbury United won 7-6 on kicks from the penalty mark)				
17	Leiston	v	AFC Telford United	0-0	334
	(Leiston won 9-8 on kicks from the penalty mark)				
18	Brackley Town	v	Kettering Town		
	(walkover for Brackley Town – Kettering Town withdrawn)				
19	Cambridge City	v	Halesowen Town	2-0	400
20	Oxford City	v	Tamworth	6-1	80
21	Bury Town	v	Nuneaton Borough	2-0	400
22	Boston United	v	Hemel Hempstead Town		
	(walkover for Hemel Hempstead Town – Boston United withdrawn)				
23	Haringey Borough	v	Bracknell Town	5-1	
24	Havant & Waterlooville	v	Chatham Town (14/10)	4-1	
25	Bedfont Sports Club	v	Canvey Island	0-2	237
26	Cray Valley (PM)	v	Aveley	2-0	
27	Hartley Wintney	v	Barking (7.30)	3-1	
28	Bristol Manor Farm	v	Cray Wanderers	3-3	392
	(Cray Wanderers won 4-2 on kicks from the penalty mark)				
29	Eastbourne Borough	v	Sheppey United	3-1	
30	Hayes & Yeading United	v	Chipstead	0-0	369
	(Hayes & Yeading United won 4-2 on kicks from the penalty mark)				
31	Slough Town	v	Bath City	0-1	
32	Taunton Town	v	Truro City	4-2	584
33	Christchurch	v	Dulwich Hamlet	1-1	300
	(Dulwich Hamlet won 3-1 on kicks from the penalty mark – live on bbc sport)				
34	Wimborne Town	v	Maidstone United (7.30)	2-2	
	(Wimborne Town won 3-1 on kicks from the penalty mark)				
35	Sholing	v	Walton Casuals (7.30)	5-2	341
36	Chichester City	v	Tonbridge Angels	1-2	400
37	Weston Super Mare	v	Larkhall Athletic	6-0	
38	Hampton & Richmond Boro	v	Hornchurch	2-2	
	(Hampton & Richmond Borough won 4-3 on kicks from the penalty mark)				
39	Whyteleafe	v	Concord Rangers	1-2	
40	Ebbsfleet United	v	Chippenham Town	1-1	
	(Chippenham Town won 9-8 on kicks from the penalty mark)				

FOURTH QUALIFYING ROUND
Saturday 24 October 2020

1	Darlington	v	Cambridge City	2-0	
2	Stafford Rangers	v	Skelmersdale United	1-4	
3	Solihull Moors	v	Wrexham	4-0	
4	Banbury United	v	Bury Town	2-1	600
5	South Shields	v	FC Halifax Town	2-0	300
6	Ilkeston Town	v	Hartlepool United	0-6	400
	(Live on BBC Sport)				
7	FC United of Manchester	v	Guiseley	2-1	
8	Brackley Town	v	Marske United	5-1	
9	King's Lynn Town	v	Notts County		
	(walkover for King's Lynn Town – Notts County withdrawn)				
10	Stockport County	v	Chesterfield (4/11)	4-0	
	(24/10 – TIE ORDERED TO BE REPLAYED)				
11	AFC Fylde	v	Altrincham (1.00)	2-1	
12	Chester	v	Marine	0-1	
13	Maidenhead United	v	Cray Valley (PM)	2-3	
14	Canvey Island	v	Cray Wanderers	3-2	400
15	Wealdstone	v	Hayes & Yeading United	0-2	
16	Sutton United	v	Bromley	0-1	
17	Tonbridge Angels	v	Taunton Town	5-0	
18	Hemel Hempstead Town	v	Hampton & Richmond Boro	0-1	
19	Aldershot Town	v	Woking	1-2	
20	Maldon & Tiptree	v	Haringey Borough	1-0	382
21	Dagenham & Redbridge	v	Hartley Wintney	1-0	
22	Leiston	v	Barnet	2-3	600
23	Weymouth	v	Oxford City	2-3	
24	Eastbourne Borough	v	Dulwich Hamlet	1-0	
25	Eastleigh	v	Weston Super Mare	3-1	
26	Sholing	v	Torquay United	0-2	400
27	Bath City	v	Havant & Waterlooville	0-3	
28	Boreham Wood	v	Wimborne Town	2-0	
29	Yeovil Town	v	Dover Athletic	3-3	
	(Yeovil Town won 7-6 on kicks from the penalty mark)				
30	Bishop's Stortford	v	St Albans City (26/10)	2-0	600
	(Live on BT Sport)				
31	Concord Rangers	v	Chippenham Town		2-1
	BYE – Chorley				

FIRST ROUND PROPER - Saturday 7 November 2020

1	LEYTON ORIENT	v	NEWPORT COUNTY	1-2
2	HAVANT & WATERLOOVILLE	v	CRAY VALLEY (PM) (8/11)	1-0
3	SUNDERLAND	v	MANSFIELD TOWN	0-1
4	BOLTON WANDERERS	v	CREWE ALEXANDRA	2-3
5	OXFORD UNITED	v	PETERBOROUGH UNITED	1-2
6	EXETER CITY	v	AFC FYLDE	2-1
7	TONBRIDGE ANGELS	v	BRADFORD CITY (12.30)	0-7
8	WALSALL	v	BRISTOL ROVERS	1-2
9	ROCHDALE	v	STOCKPORT COUNTY	1-2
10	SWINDON TOWN	v	DARLINGTON	1-2
11	BARNET	v	BURTON ALBION (8/11)	1-0
12	WIGAN ATHLETIC	v	CHORLEY (8/11)	2-3aet
13	TRANMERE ROVERS	v	ACCRINGTON STANLEY	2-1
14	OXFORD CITY	v	NORTHAMPTON TOWN (9/11)	2-1
	(Live on BT Sport 1)			
15	MALDON & TIPTREE	v	MORECAMBE (8/11)	0-1
16	BROMLEY	v	YEOVIL TOWN	0-1aet
17	TORQUAY UNITED	v	CRAWLEY TOWN (8/11)	5-6aet
18	EASTBOURNE BOROUGH	v	BLACKPOOL (8/11)	0-3
	(Live on BT Sport 1)			
19	CHELTENHAM TOWN	v	SOUTH SHIELDS	3-1
20	STEVENAGE	v	CONCORD RANGERS	2-2aet
	(Stevenage won 5-4 on kicks from the penalty mark)			
21	HARROGATE TOWN	v	SKELMERSDALE UNITED (6/11)	4-1
	(Live on BT Sport 1)			
22	GILLINGHAM	v	WOKING	3-2
23	CHARLTON ATHLETIC	v	PLYMOUTH ARGYLE	0-1
24	HAYES & YEADING UNITED	v	CARLISLE UNITED (8/11)	2-2aet
	(Carlisle United won 4-3 on kicks from the penalty mark)			
25	FC UNITED OF MANCHESTER	v	DONCASTER ROVERS (5.30)	1-5
	(Live on BBC Two)			
26	SALFORD CITY	v	HARTLEPOOL UNITED	2-0aet
27	SCUNTHORPE UNITED	v	SOLIHULL MOORS (8/11)	2-3
28	HULL CITY	v	FLEETWOOD TOWN	2-0
29	COLCHESTER UNITED	v	MARINE	1-1aet
	(Marine won 5-4 on kicks from the penalty mark)			
30	BARROW	v	AFC WIMBLEDON (26/11)	0-0aet
	(AFC Wimbledon won 4-2 on kicks from the penalty mark)			
31	DAGENHAM & REDBRIDGE	v	GRIMSBY TOWN	3-1
32	CAMBRIDGE UNITED	v	SHREWSBURY TOWN	0-2
33	BRACKLEY TOWN	v	BISHOP'S STORTFORD	3-3aet
	(Brackley Town won 3-2 on kicks from the penalty mark)			
34	EASTLEIGH	v	MILTON KEYNES DONS (8/11)	0-0aet
	(Milton Keynes Dons won 4-3 on kicks from the penalty mark)			
35	HAMPTON & RICHMOND	v	OLDHAM ATHLETIC (8/11)	2-3
36	BOREHAM WOOD	v	SOUTHEND UNITED	3-3aet
	(Boreham Wood won 4-3 on kicks from the penalty mark)			
37	IPSWICH TOWN	v	PORTSMOUTH	2-3aet
38	PORT VALE	v	KING'S LYNN TOWN	0-1
39	LINCOLN CITY	v	FOREST GREEN ROVERS	6-2
40	BANBURY UNITED	v	CANVEY ISLAND	1-2

SECOND ROUND PROPER - Saturday 28 November 2020

1	STEVENAGE	v	HULL CITY (29/11)	1-1aet
	(Stevenage won 6-5 on kicks from the penalty mark)			
2	HARROGATE TOWN	v	BLACKPOOL	0-4
3	TRANMERE ROVERS	v	BRACKLEY TOWN (27/11)	1-0
	(Live on BBC Two)			
4	AFC WIMBLEDON	v	CRAWLEY TOWN (29/11)	1-2
5	STOCKPORT COUNTY	v	YEOVIL TOWN (29/11)	3-2aet
6	PLYMOUTH ARGYLE	v	LINCOLN CITY	2-0
7	PORTSMOUTH	v	KING'S LYNN TOWN	6-1
8	CHELTENHAM TOWN	v	CREWE ALEXANDRA	2-1aet
9	PETERBOROUGH UNITED	v	CHORLEY (5.30)	1-2
	(Live on BT Sport 2)			
10	MORECAMBE	v	SOLIHULL MOORS (12.30)	4-2aet
11	SHREWSBURY TOWN	v	OXFORD CITY (29/11)	1-0aet
12	MANSFIELD TOWN	v	DAGENHAM & REDBRIDGE (29/11)	2-1aet
13	NEWPORT COUNTY	v	SALFORD CITY (1.00)	3-0
14	MARINE	v	HAVANT & WATERLOOVILLE (29/11)	1-0aet
	(Live on BT Sport 1)			
15	GILLINGHAM	v	EXETER CITY (1.00)	2-3
16	CANVEY ISLAND	v	BOREHAM WOOD (30/11)	0-3
	(Live on BT Sport 1)			
17	CARLISLE UNITED	v	DONCASTER ROVERS (29/11)	1-2
18	BARNET	v	MILTON KEYNES DONS (29/11)	0-1
19	BRISTOL ROVERS	v	DARLINGTON (29/11)	6-0
20	BRADFORD CITY	v	OLDHAM ATHLETIC	1-2

THIRD ROUND PROPER - Saturday 9 January 2021

1	HUDDERSFIELD TOWN	v	PLYMOUTH ARGYLE	2-3
2	SOUTHAMPTON	v	SHREWSBURY TOWN (19/1)	2-0
3	CHORLEY	v	DERBY COUNTY	2-0
	(Live on BT Sport 1)			
4	MARINE	v	TOTTENHAM HOTSPUR (10/1)	0-5
	(Live on BBC One)			
5	WOLVERHAMPTON W.	V	CRYSTAL PALACE (8/1)	1-0
6	STOCKPORT COUNTY	v	WEST HAM UNITED (11/1)	0-1
	(Live on BT Sport 1)			
7	OLDHAM ATHLETIC	v	AFC BOURNEMOUTH	1-4
	(At AFC Bournemouth)			
8	MANCHESTER UNITED	v	WATFORD	1-0
9	STEVENAGE	v	SWANSEA CITY	0-2
	(LIVE ON BBC DIGITAL PLATFORMS)			
10	EVERTON	v	ROTHERHAM UNITED	2-1aet
11	NOTTINGHAM FOREST	v	CARDIFF CITY	1-0
12	ARSENAL	v	NEWCASTLE UNITED	2-0aet
13	BARNSLEY	v	TRANMERE ROVERS (10/1)	2-0
14	BRISTOL ROVERS	v	SHEFFIELD UNITED	2-3
15	BOREHAM WOOD	v	MILLWALL	0-2
	(Live on BT Sport Extra 3)			
16	BLACKBURN ROVERS	v	DONCASTER ROVERS	0-1
17	STOKE CITY	v	LEICESTER CITY	0-4
18	WYCOMBE WANDERERS	v	PRESTON NORTH END	4-1
19	CRAWLEY TOWN	V	LEEDS UNITED (10/1)	3-0
20	BURNLEY	v	MILTON KEYNES DONS	1-1aet
	(Burnley won 4-3 on kicks from the penalty mark)			
21	BRISTOL CITY	v	PORTSMOUTH (10/1)	2-1
22	QUEENS PARK RANGERS	v	FULHAM	0-2aet
23	ASTON VILLA	v	LIVERPOOL (8/1)	1-4
24	BRENTFORD	v	MIDDLESBROUGH	2-1
25	MANCHESTER CITY	v	BIRMINGHAM CITY (10/1)	3-0
26	LUTON TOWN	v	READING	1-0
27	CHELSEA	v	MORECAMBE (10/1)	4-0
28	EXETER CITY	v	SHEFFIELD WEDNESDAY	0-2
29	NORWICH CITY	v	COVENTRY CITY	2-0
30	BLACKPOOL	v	WEST BROMWICH ALBION	2-2aet
	(Blackpool won 3-2 on kicks from the penalty mark)			
31	NEWPORT COUNTY	v	BRIGHTON & HOVE ALBION (10/1)	1-1aet
	(Brighton & Hove Albion won 4-3 on kicks from the penalty mark)			
32	CHELTENHAM TOWN	v	MANSFIELD TOWN (10/1)	2-1aet

FOURTH ROUND PROPER - Saturday 23 January 2021

1	CHELTENHAM TOWN	v	MANCHESTER CITY	1-3
2	AFC BOURNEMOUTH	v	CRAWLEY TOWN (26/1)	2-1
3	SWANSEA CITY	v	NOTTINGHAM FOREST	5-1
4	MANCHESTER UNITED	v	LIVERPOOL (24/1)	3-2
5	SOUTHAMPTON	v	ARSENAL	1-0
6	BARNSLEY	v	NORWICH CITY	1-0
7	CHORLEY (Live on BT Sport 1)	v	WOLVERHAMPTON W. (22/1)	0-1
8	MILLWALL	v	BRISTOL CITY	0-3
9	BRIGHTON & HOVE ALBION	v	BLACKPOOL	2-1
10	WYCOMBE WANDERERS	v	TOTTENHAM HOTSPUR (25/1)	1-4
11	FULHAM	v	BURNLEY (24/1)	0-3
12	SHEFFIELD UNITED	v	PLYMOUTH ARGYLE	2-1
13	CHELSEA	v	LUTON TOWN (24/1)	3-1
14	WEST HAM UNITED	v	DONCASTER ROVERS	4-0
15	BRENTFORD	v	LEICESTER CITY (24/1)	1-3
16	EVERTON	v	SHEFFIELD WEDNESDAY (24/1)	3-0

CHORLEY **MANAGER:** J Vermigilo

1 M. Urwin
4 A. Halls
5 S. Leather
2 A. Birch
6 L. Baines (S. Miller 84)
13 O. Shenton (A. Hanley 84)
12 W. Tomlinson
8 M. Calveley
9 H. Cardwell
11 E. Newby
27 C. Hall (H. Smith 87)

Unused subs: L. Birchall, O. Putnam, L. Roberts, L. Dutton, M. McKenzie, T. Garratt.

WOLVES **MANAGER:** Nuno Espirito Santo

21 J. Ruddy
15 W. Boly
16 C. Coady
32 L. Dendoncker
49 M. Kilman
2 K. Hoever
3 R. Aït Nouri
28 João Moutinho (Ruben Neves 68)
20 Vitinha (Pedro Neto 69)
23 P. Cutrone (Adama Traore 69)
17 Fábio Silva

Unused subs: N. Lonwijk, Nélson Semedo, T. Corbeanu, Rui Patrício, O. Otasowie, L. Richards.

FIFTH ROUND PROPER - Wednesday 10 February 2021

1	BURNLEY	V	AFC BOURNEMOUTH (9/2)	0-2
2	MANCHESTER UNITED	V	WEST HAM UNITED (9/2)	1-0aet
3	SHEFFIELD UNITED	V	BRISTOL CITY	1-0
4	WOLVERHAMPTON WANDERERS	V	SOUTHAMPTON (11/2)	0-2
5	BARNSLEY	V	CHELSEA (11/2)	0-1
6	EVERTON	V	TOTTENHAM HOTSPUR	5-4aet
7	SWANSEA CITY	V	MANCHESTER CITY	1-3
8	LEICESTER CITY	V	BRIGHTON & HOVE ALBION	1-0

QUARTER FINALS

1	EVERTON	V	MANCHESTER CITY (20/3)	0-2
2	AFC BOURNEMOUTH	V	SOUTHAMPTON (20/3)	0-3
3	LEICESTER CITY	V	MANCHESTER UNITED (21/3)	3-1
4	CHELSEA	V	SHEFFIELD UNITED (21/3)	2-0

SEMI FINALS (AT WEMBLEY STADIUM)

1	LEICESTER CITY	V	SOUTHAMPTON (18/4)	1-0	4000
2	CHELSEA	v	MANCHESTER CITY (17/4)	1-0	

THE FINAL
Saturday 15 May 2021

CHELSEA	0	1	**LEICESTER CITY** *Tielemans 63*

AT WEMBLEY STADIUM ~ ATTENDANCE: 21,000

FA CUP FINALS

1871-72	Wanderers	1-0	Royal Engineers	Kennington Oval	2,000
1872-73	Wanderers	2-0	Oxford University	Lillie Bridge	3,000
1873-74	Oxford University	2-0	Royal Engineers	Kennington Oval	2,000
1874-75	Royal Engineers	1-1*	Old Etonians	Kennington Oval	2,000
(R)	Royal Engineers	2-0	Old Etonians	Kennington Oval	3,000
1875-76	Wanderers	1-1*	Old Etonians	Kennington Oval	3,500
(R)	Wanderers	3-0	Old Etonians	Kennington Oval	1,500
1876-77	Wanderers	2-1*	Oxford University	Kennington Oval	3,000
1877-78	Wanderers	3-1	Royal Engineers	Kennington Oval	4,500
1878-79	Old Etonians	1-0	Clapham Rovers	Kennington Oval	5,000
1879-80	Clapham Rovers	1-0	Oxford University	Kennington Oval	6,000
1880-81	Old Carthusians	3-0	Old Etonians	Kennington Oval	4,000
1881-82	Old Etonians	1-0	Blackburn Rovers	Kennington Oval	6,500
1882-83	Blackburn Olympic	2-1*	Old Etonians	Kennington Oval	8,000
1883-84	Blackburn Rovers	2-1	Queen's Park	Kennington Oval	4,000
1884-85	Blackburn Rovers	2-0	Queen's Park	Kennington Oval	12,500
1885-86	Blackburn Rovers	0-0	W.B.A.	Kennington Oval	15,000
(R)	Blackburn Rovers	2-0	W.B.A.	Racecourse Ground	12,000
1886-87	Aston Villa	2-0	W.B.A.	Kennington Oval	15,500
1887-88	West Bromwich Albion	2-1	Preston North End	Kennington Oval	19,000
1888-89	Preston North End	3-0	Wolverhampton W.	Kennington Oval	22,000
1889-90	Blackburn Rovers	6-1	The Wednesday	Kennington Oval	20,000
1890-91	Blackburn Rovers	3-1	Notts County	Kennington Oval	23,000
1891-92	West Bromwich Albion	3-0	Aston Villa	Kennington Oval	32,810
1892-93	Wolverhampton W.	1-0	Everton	Fallowfield Stadium	45,000
1893-94	Notts County	4-1	Bolton Wanderers	Goodison Park	37,000
1894-95	Aston Villa	1-0	W.B.A.	Crystal Palace	42,560
1895-96	The Wednesday	2-1	Wolverhampton W.	Crystal Palace	48,836
1896-97	Aston Villa	3-2	Everton	Crystal Palace	65,891
1897-98	Nottingham Forest	3-1	Derby County	Crystal Palace	62,017
1898-99	Sheffield United	4-1	Derby County	Crystal Palace	73,833
1899-1900	Bury	4-0	Southampton	Crystal Palace	68,945
1900-01	Tottenham Hotspur	2-2	Sheffield United	Crystal Palace	110,820
(R)	Tottenham Hotspur	3-1	Sheffield United	Burnden Park	20,470
1901-02	Sheffield United	1-1	Southampton	Crystal Palace	76,914
(R)	Sheffield United	2-1	Southampton	Crystal Palace	33,068
1902-03	Bury	6-0	Derby County	Crystal Palace	63,102
1903-04	Manchester City	1-0	Bolton Wanderers	Crystal Palace	61,374
1904-05	Aston Villa	2-0	Newcastle United	Crystal Palace	101,117
1905-06	Everton	1-0	Newcastle United	Crystal Palace	75,609
1906-07	The Wednesday	2-1	Everton	Crystal Palace	84,594
1907-08	Wolverhampton W.	3-1	Newcastle United	Crystal Palace	74,697
1908-09	Manchester United	1-0	Bristol City	Crystal Palace	71,401
1909-10	Newcastle United	1-1	Barnsley	Crystal Palace	77,747
(R)	Newcastle United	2-0	Barnsley	Goodison Park	69,000
1910-11	Bradford City	0-0	Newcastle United	Crystal Palace	69,068
(R)	Bradford City	1-0	Newcastle United	Old Trafford	58,000
1911-12	Barnsley	0-0	West Bromwich Albion	Crystal Palace	54,556
(R)	Barnsley	1-0*	West Bromwich Albion	Bramall Lane	38,555
1912-13	Aston Villa	1-0	Sunderland	Crystal Palace	121,919
1913-14	Burnley	1-0	Liverpool	Crystal Palace	72,778
1914-15	Sheffield United	3-0	Chelsea	Old Trafford	49,557
1919-20	Aston Villa	1-0*	Huddersfield Town	Stamford Bridge	50,018
1920-21	Tottenham Hotspur	1-0	Wolverhampton W.	Stamford Bridge	72,805
1921-22	Huddersfield Town	1-0	Preston North End	Stamford Bridge	53,000
1922-23	Bolton Wanderers	2-0	West Ham United	Wembley Stadium	126,047
1923-24	Newcastle United	2-0	Aston Villa	Wembley Stadium	91,695
50th Final - 1924-25					
	Sheffield United	1-0	Cardiff City	Wembley Stadium	91,763
1925-26	Bolton Wanderers	1-0	Manchester City	Wembley Stadium	91,447
1926-27	Cardiff City	1-0	Arsenal	Wembley Stadium	91,206
1927-28	Blackburn Rovers	3-1	Huddersfield Town	Wembley Stadium	92,041
1928-29	Bolton Wanderers	2-0	Portsmouth	Wembley Stadium	92,576
1929-30	Arsenal	2-0	Huddersfield Town	Wembley Stadium	92,488
1930-31	West Bromwich Albion	2-1	Birmingham	Wembley Stadium	92,406
1931-32	Newcastle United	2-1	Arsenal	Wembley Stadium	92,298
1932-33	Everton	3-0	Manchester City	Wembley Stadium	92,950
1933-34	Manchester City	2-1	Portsmouth	Wembley Stadium	93,258
1934-35	Sheffield Wednesday	4-2	W.B.A.	Wembley Stadium	93,204
1935-36	Arsenal	1-0	Sheffield United	Wembley Stadium	93,384
1936-37	Sunderland	3-1	Preston North End	Wembley Stadium	93,495
1937-38	Preston North End	1-0*	Huddersfield Town	Wembley Stadium	93,497
1938-39	Portsmouth	4-1	Wolverhampton W.	Wembley Stadium	99,370
1945-46	Derby County	4-1*	Charlton Athletic	Wembley Stadium	98,000
1946-47	Charlton Athletic	1-0*	Burnley	Wembley Stadium	99,000
1947-48	Manchester United	4-2	Blackpool	Wembley Stadium	99,000
1948-49	Wolverhampton W.	3-1	Leicester City	Wembley Stadium	99,500
1949-50	Arsenal	2-0	Liverpool	Wembley Stadium	100,000
1950-51	Newcastle United	2-0	Blackpool	Wembley Stadium	100,000
1951-52	Newcastle United	1-0	Arsenal	Wembley Stadium	100,000
1952-53	Blackpool	4-3	Bolton Wanderers	Wembley Stadium	100,000
1953-54	West Bromwich Albion	3-2	Preston North End	Wembley Stadium	100,000
1954-55	Newcastle United	3-1	Manchester City	Wembley Stadium	100,000
1955-56	Manchester City	3-1	Birmingham City	Wembley Stadium	100,000
1956-57	Aston Villa	2-1	Manchester United	Wembley Stadium	100,000
1957-58	Bolton Wanderers	2-0	Manchester United	Wembley Stadium	100,000
1958-59	Nottingham Forest	2-1	Luton Town	Wembley Stadium	100,000
1959-60	Wolverhampton W.	3-0	Blackburn Rovers	Wembley Stadium	100,000
1960-61	Tottenham Hotspur	2-0	Leicester City	Wembley Stadium	100,000
1961-62	Tottenham Hotspur	3-1	Burnley	Wembley Stadium	100,000
1962-63	Manchester United	3-1	Leicester City	Wembley Stadium	100,000
1963-64	West Ham United	3-2	Preston North End	Wembley Stadium	100,000
1964-65	Liverpool	2-1*	Leeds United	Wembley Stadium	100,000
1965-66	Everton	3-2	Sheffield Wednesday	Wembley Stadium	100,000
1966-67	Tottenham Hotspur	2-1	Chelsea	Wembley Stadium	100,000
1967-68	West Bromwich Albion	1-0*	Everton	Wembley Stadium	100,000
1968-69	Manchester City	1-0	Leicester City	Wembley Stadium	100,000
1969-70	Chelsea	2-2*	Leeds United	Wembley Stadium	100,000
(R)	Chelsea	2-1*	Leeds United	Old Trafford	62,078
1970-71	Arsenal	2-1*	Liverpool	Wembley Stadium	100,000
1971-72	Leeds United	1-0	Arsenal	Wembley Stadium	100,000
1972-73	Sunderland	1-0	Leeds United	Wembley Stadium	100,000
1973-74	Liverpool	3-0	Newcastle United	Wembley Stadium	100,000
1974-75	West Ham United	2-0	Fulham	Wembley Stadium	100,000
1975-76	Southampton	1-0	Manchester United	Wembley Stadium	100,000
1976-77	Manchester United	2-1	Liverpool	Wembley Stadium	100,000
1977-78	Ipswich Town	1-0	Arsenal	Wembley Stadium	100,000
1978-79	Arsenal	3-2	Manchester United	Wembley Stadium	100,000
1979-80	West Ham United	1-0	Arsenal	Wembley Stadium	100,000
100th Final - 1980-81					
	Tottenham Hotspur	1-1*	Manchester City	Wembley Stadium	100,000
(R)	Tottenham Hotspur	3-2	Manchester City	Wembley Stadium	92,000
1981-82	Tottenham Hotspur	1-1*	Queens Park Rangers	Wembley Stadium	100,000
(R)	Tottenham Hotspur	1-0	Queens Park Rangers	Wembley Stadium	90,000
1982-83	Manchester United	2-2*	Brighton & H.A.	Wembley Stadium	100,000
(R)	Manchester United	4-0	Brighton & H.A.	Wembley Stadium	100,000
1983-84	Everton	2-0	Watford	Wembley Stadium	100,000
1984-85	Manchester United	1-0*	Everton	Wembley Stadium	100,000
1985-86	Liverpool	3-1	Everton	Wembley Stadium	98,000
1986-87	Coventry City	3-2*	Tottenham Hotspur	Wembley Stadium	98,000
1987-88	Wimbledon	1-0	Liverpool	Wembley Stadium	98,203
1988-89	Liverpool	3-2*	Everton	Wembley Stadium	82,500
1989-90	Manchester United	3-3*	Crystal Palace	Wembley Stadium	80,000
(R)	Manchester United	1-0	Crystal Palace	Wembley Stadium	80,000
1990-91	Tottenham Hotspur	2-1*	Nottingham Forest	Wembley Stadium	80,000
1991-92	Liverpool	2-0	Sunderland	Wembley Stadium	80,000
1992-93	Arsenal	1-1*	Sheffield Wednesday	Wembley Stadium	79,347
(R)	Arsenal	2-1*	Sheffield Wednesday	Wembley Stadium	62,267
1993-94	Manchester United	4-0	Chelsea	Wembley Stadium	79,634
1994-95	Everton	1-0	Manchester United	Wembley Stadium	79,592
1995-96	Manchester United	1-0	Liverpool	Wembley Stadium	79,007
1996-97	Chelsea	2-0	Middlesbrough	Wembley Stadium	79,160
1997-98	Arsenal	2-0	Newcastle United	Wembley Stadium	79,183
1998-99	Manchester United	2-0	Newcastle United	Wembley Stadium	79,101
1999-2000	Chelsea	1-0	Aston Villa	Wembley Stadium	78,217
2000-01	Liverpool	2-1	Arsenal	Millennium Stadium	72,500
2001-02	Arsenal	2-0	Chelsea	Millennium Stadium	73,963
2002-03	Arsenal	1-0	Southampton	Millennium Stadium	73,726
2003-04	Manchester United	3-0	Millwall	Millennium Stadium	71,350
2004-05	Arsenal	0-0* 5-4p	Manchester United	Millennium Stadium	71,876
2005-06	Liverpool	3-3* 3-1p	West Ham United	Millennium Stadium	71,140
2006-07	Chelsea	1-0*	Manchester United	Wembley Stadium	89,826
2007-08	Portsmouth	1-0	Cardiff City	Wembley Stadium	89,874
2008-09	Chelsea	2-1	Everton	Wembley Stadium	89,39
2009-10	Chelsea	1-0	Portsmouth	Wembley Stadium	88,335
2010-11	Manchester City	1-0	Stoke City	Wembley Stadium	88,643
2011-12	Chelsea	2-1	Liverpool	Wembley Stadium	89,041
2012-13	Wigan Athletic	1-0	Manchester City	Wembley Stadium	86,254
2013-14	Arsenal	3-2*	Hull City	Wembley Stadium	89,345
2014-15	Arsenal	4-0	Aston Villa	Wembley Stadium	89,283
2015-16	Manchester United	2-1*	Crystal Palace	Wembley Stadium	88,619
2016-17	Arsenal	2-1	Chelsea	Wembley Stadium	89,472
2017-18	Chelsea	1-0	Manchester United	Wembley Stadium	87,647
2018-19	Manchester City	6-0	Watford	Wembley Stadium	85,854
2019-20	Arsenal	2-1	Chelsea	Wembley Stadium	0
2020-21	Leicester City	1-0	Chelsea	Wembley Stadium	21,000

THE FA TROPHY
2019-20 Final

2019/20 F A Trophy Final played at Wembley Stadium on Monday 3rd May 2021, twelve months late on account of the Covid lockdown, in front of a very small number of officials and players' families.

Team	Score	Squad
CONCORD RANGERS (National South)	0	**SQUAD:** Chris Haigh, Joe Payne, Billy Roast (sub 83), Aron Pollock, Jack Cawley, James Blanchfield (sub 78), Sam Blackman, Lewis Simper, Ryan Charles (sub 60), Tyrone Sterling, Lamar Reynolds. Substitutes:- Archie Mcfadden, Alex Wall (78), Dan Wilks, Odel Martin (83), Ben Search, Alex Hernandez, Temi Babalola (60).
HARROGATE TOWN (League Two) *Falkingham 76*	1	**SQUAD:** Joe Cracknell, Dan Jones (61), Josh Falkingham, Will Smith, Warren Burrell, George Thomson, Jon Stead (sub 61), Lloyd Kerry, Jack Muldoon, Connor Hall, Josh McPake (sub 67). Substitutes James Belshaw, Ryan Fallowfield (61), Mark Beck (61), Brendan Kiernan (67), Edward Francis, Kevin Lokko, Jay Williams.

Referee:- Peter Banks, assisted by James Mainwaring and Tim Wood. 4th official – Marc Edwards

Without a baying crowd any stadium, let alone the spacious Wembley, is akin to Mars in lacking atmosphere. The cold easterly wind added to the funereal air experienced by the few spectators present. One pitied poor Emily who stood courageously alone to sing the National Anthem, baring her shoulders for her second performance of the afternoon. She deserved a medal, even though it would not have been presented to her but self-collected as were the trophies and medals for the day's two finals. At least she was spared the under the sponsors' arch champagne spraying, courtesy of the winning team's managerial and backroom staff, which Vase and Trophy winners underwent.

Following a lively Vase exchange this second final of the day, the Senior Competition, was to prove a disappointment as it lacked the inventiveness and unstructured freedom from fear of its junior predecessor. Concord and Harrogate, the latter being in the strange position of being now a Football League team following promotion at the end of the season when this final should have been held, were both dogged performers but understandably Harrogate throughout had a slight edge in organisation and skill but never dominated in the way one might have anticipated. They had, after all, been playing regular fixtures in Division Two while Rangers' season in National League South had been curtailed three months before, since when they had played no competitive fixture.

In fairness to both teams the cold wind by now had an even keener bite and the rain frequently arrowed challengingly. An early chance fell Harrogate's way when Dan Jones' long throw in caused concern in the Rangers' defence but no opposition player was able to produce the necessary forceful header. A low drive from George Thomson tested keeper Chris Haigh at his near post before, at the other end, Lamar Reynolds' low drive was securely held by Joe Cracknell as Jack Muldoon closed in for any possible rebound.

Harrogate were on the front foot again when Warren Burrell's accurate pass allowed Jon Stead a shot on goal before the same player headed over when reasonably placed. The Yorkshire men spurned further opportunities to take a half time lead when Thomson just failed to put the finishing touch to Connor Hall's cross and Jack Muldoon's shot was blocked. Another Jones' long throw caused consternation and Haigh yet again saved Concord, tipping over a fierce effort from Lloyd Kerry, before, at full stretch, turning aside Stead's skimmer. The first half ended with the only booking of the day, Harrogate's Jones the recipient. Unusual to watch 135 minutes of Football without the brandishing of a yellow card.

There was no let up for the Essex side as the second half opened, the first opportunity falling Harrogate's way when a Jones' drive cannoned off an opponent for a corner. However, with little significant action there was a rare moment of interest when the referee handed something small to the fourth official who placed it by the substitutes' board. Had a coin been thrown from the empty benches or had the toss up coin become too burdensome for the main official to continue carrying? Tongues wagged as imaginations were stirred but no solution appeared.

Back to the football action - when Concord mounted an attack, Jack Cawley despatched a half chance over Cracknell's bar. Haigh was still the busier keeper though and, despite his valiant efforts, the deadlock was broken with quarter of an hour to go. A Muldoon rocket ricocheted off the post and fell to Harrogate skipper Josh Falkingham who made no mistake in finding the back of the net.

Tempers flared for a brief moment when Cracknell just managed to push the ball aside before being flattened by two onrushing Concordians in their last ditch attempt to force an equaliser. Further forays saw Reynolds slip sub Alex Wall through on goal but Cracknell was quickly out to block before making an excellent save to deny the same player. Just before the final whistle Concord keeper Haigh, who had saved several penalties in earlier rounds, made yet another fine save to justify fully his selection as Man of the Match, despite his excessive use of the footballer's favourite adjective so clearly audible in the crowdless stadium.

Arthur Evans

Paulton Rovers striker Will Hailston sees his penalty kick saved by Alex Harris

FAT 1Q - Cirencester Town v Paulton Rovers. Photos Peter Barnes.

FIRST QUALIFYING ROUND 2020-21

SATURDAY 26 SEPTEMBER 2020

1	Tadcaster Albion	v	Marine	1-3	221
2	Ossett United	v	Ramsbottom United	0-2	346
3	Market Drayton Town	v	Bury Town	0-1	78
4	Cambridge City	v	Kidsgrove Athletic	2-3	
5	Soham Town Rangers	v	Corby Town	0-3	131
6	Evesham United	v	Biggleswade	2-1	271
7	South Park	v	Three Bridges	0-1	
8	Waltham Abbey	v	Staines Town	3-2	100
9	Hullbridge Sports	v	Ashford Town (Middx)	0-1	
10	Hythe Town	v	Chalfont St Peter	3-0	
11	AFC Sudbury	v	Barking	1-2	178
12	Felixstowe & Walton United	v	Great Wakering Rovers	2-1	202
13	Northwood	v	Basildon United	1-1	111
	(Northwood won 4-3 on kicks from the penalty mark)				
14	AFC Dunstable	v	Tooting & Mitcham United	1-2	97
15	Witham Town	v	Hanwell Town	0-2	
16	Melksham Town	v	North Leigh	3-3	259
	(North Leigh won 5-4 on kicks from the penalty mark)				
17	Cirencester Town	v	Paulton Rovers	1-1	100
	(Cirencester Town won 5-4 on kicks from the penalty mark)				

SECOND QUALIFYING ROUND

SATURDAY 17 October 2020

1	Pontefract Collieries	v	Workington	1-4	191
2	Prescot Cables	v	Frickley Athletic		
	(walkover for Frickley Athletic – Prescot Cables withdrawn)				
3	Worksop Town	v	Ramsbottom United	4-4	298
	(Worksop Town won 5-4 on kicks from the penalty mark)				
4	Pickering Town	v	Trafford	1-0	124
5	Kendal Town	v	Brighouse Town	1-0	210
	(tie awarded to Brighouse Town – Kendal Town removed)				
6	Marine	v	Mossley	5-0	260
7	Widnes	v	Colne	3-4	
8	Sheffield	v	Runcorn Linnets	2-3	
9	Dunston	v	Clitheroe	0-1	212
10	Stocksbridge Park Steels	v	Marske United	0-4	230
11	City of Liverpool	v	Cleethorpes Town		
	(walkover for City of Liverpool – Cleethorpes Town withdrawn)				
12	Droylsden	v	Glossop North End		
	(walkover for Glossop North End – Droylsden withdrawn)				
13	Sutton Coldfield Town	v	Dereham Town	2-3	283
14	Newcastle Town	v	Belper Town	2-2	
	(Newcastle Town won 5-4 on kicks from the penalty mark)				
15	Yaxley	v	Chasetown		
	(walkover for Yaxley – Chasetown withdrawn)				
16	Corby Town	v	Halesowen Town	1-0	
17	Daventry Town	v	Kidsgrove Athletic	0-2	95
18	Ilkeston Town	v	Kempston Rovers	2-1	370
19	Evesham United	v	Carlton Town	2-0	269
20	Histon	v	Leek Town	1-2	226
21	Loughborough Dynamo	v	Bury Town	1-0	
22	Spalding United	v	Bedford Town	0-1	224
23	Wisbech Town	v	Coleshill Town	1-2	164
24	Stamford	v	Lincoln United	2-1	
25	Bedworth United	v	St Neots Town	1-4	154
26	Hastings United	v	FC Romania	3-0	377
27	Northwood	v	Heybridge Swifts	3-3	151
	(Heybridge Swifts won 5-4 on kicks from the penalty mark)				
28	Sittingbourne	v	East Grinstead Town	1-0	175
29	Felixstowe & Walton United	v	Westfield	5-0	266
30	Phoenix Sports	v	Marlow	0-2	
31	Ashford Town (Middx)	v	Whitstable Town	1-0	
32	VCD Athletic	v	Herne Bay	1-2	128
33	Faversham Town	v	Hertford Town	4-1	
34	Barking	v	Harlow Town	1-0	107
35	Tooting & Mitcham United	v	Romford	2-0	400
36	Chertsey Town	v	Berkhamsted	1-2	
37	Whitehawk	v	Barton Rovers	2-1	400
38	Ramsgate	v	Canvey Island		
	(walkover for Ramsgate – Canvey Island withdrawn)				
39	Bedfont Sports Club	v	Coggeshall Town	0-0	
	(Coggeshall Town won 6-5 on kicks from the penalty mark)				
40	Whyteleafe	v	Cray Valley (PM)	0-0	227
	(Whyteleafe won 3-2 on kicks from the penalty mark)				
41	Maldon & Tiptree	v	Grays Athletic	4-1	
42	Brentwood Town	v	Chichester City	3-2	301
43	Chipstead	v	Three Bridges	1-2	132
44	Uxbridge	v	Waltham Abbey	2-1	137
45	Aylesbury United	v	Tilbury	2-2	197
	(Aylesbury United won 4-2 on kicks from the penalty mark)				
46	Bracknell Town	v	Sevenoaks Town	2-0	
47	Hythe Town	v	Ashford United	2-2	
	(Hythe Town won 7-6 on kicks from the penalty mark)				
48	Burgess Hill Town	v	Ware	2-0	250
49	Haywards Heath Town	v	Welwyn Garden City	1-4	163
50	Hanwell Town	v	Aveley	1-1	201
	(Aveley won 8-7 on kicks from the penalty mark)				
51	Thame United	v	Cirencester Town	4-1	160
52	Thatcham Town	v	North Leigh	2-4	186
53	AFC Totton	v	Frome Town	2-2	252
	(Frome Town won 6-5 on kicks from the penalty mark)				
54	Sholing	v	Wantage Town	0-2	174
55	Bideford	v	Slimbridge	3-2	200
56	Moneyfields	v	Basingstoke Town	2-1	198
57	Highworth Town	v	Winchester City	2-1	124
58	Larkhall Athletic	v	Barnstaple Town	5-0	120
59	Kidlington	v	Didcot Town	2-1	170
60	Willand Rovers	v	Bristol Manor Farm	2-1	
61	Mangotsfield United	v	Cinderford Town	1-2	154

FAT 2Q - Marlows Curtis Chapple blocks this cross from Phoenix Sports Lewis Clark. Photo Alan Coomes.

FAT 2Q - Marlows Devontae Romeo takes on a couple of Phoenix defenders. Photo Alan Coomes.

FAT 2Q - Phoenix Spots Kweku Ansah takes a tumble after a tackle by Marlows Curtis Chapple. Photo Alan Coomes.jpg

THIRD QUALIFYING ROUND - Saturday 31 October 2020

1	FC United of Manchester	v	Marske United	2-3	
2	Atherton Collieries	v	City of Liverpool (4/11)	0-3	
3	Hyde United	v	Frickley Athletic	2-1	273
4	Warrington Town	v	Lancaster City	1-1	
	(Warrington Town won 4-3 on kicks from the penalty mark)				
5	Brighouse Town	v	Buxton	0-2	
6	Ashton United	v	Clitheroe	1-0	
7	Radcliffe	v	Bamber Bridge	1-2	447
8	Scarborough Athletic	v	Witton Albion		
	(walkover for Witton Albion – Scarborough Athletic withdrawn)				
9	Pickering Town	v	Runcorn Linnets	1-4	166
10	Marine	v	Stalybridge Celtic	3-2	400
11	Glossop North End	v	Workington	0-1	313
12	South Shields	v	Colne	1-0	300
13	Morpeth Town	v	Whitby Town	3-1	300
14	Newcastle Town	v	Nuneaton Borough	0-2	
15	Evesham United	v	Leek Town	3-2	271
16	Redditch United	v	Nantwich Town	2-3	
17	Tamworth	v	Banbury United	2-1	355
18	Bromsgrove Sporting	v	Coleshill Town	0-1	482
19	AFC Rushden & Diamonds	v	Ilkeston Town		
	(walkover for AFC Rushden & Diamonds – Ilkeston Town withdrawn)				
20	Yaxley	v	Grantham Town	0-2	
21	Loughborough Dynamo	v	Bedford Town	1-3	169
22	Rushall Olympic	v	Barwell	4-1	308
23	Mickleover	v	Dereham Town	5-0	203
24	Coalville Town	v	Matlock Town (3/11)	3-3	362
	(Matlock Town won 4-2 on kicks from the penalty mark)				
25	Peterborough Sports	v	Gainsborough Trinity	4-2	
26	Stourbridge	v	Stamford	0-3	572
27	Basford United	v	Alvechurch	2-1	291
28	Corby Town	v	Hednesford Town	1-2	391
29	St Neots Town	v	Worksop Town	6-1	371
30	St Ives Town	v	Stafford Rangers	1-1	156
	(St Ives Town won 4-1 on kicks from the penalty mark)				
31	Stratford Town	v	Kidsgrove Athletic	1-3	
32	Maldon & Tiptree	v	Kingstonian	3-2	256
33	Hastings United	v	Ashford Town (Middx)	1-1	400
	(Hastings United won 4-2 on kicks from the penalty mark)				
34	Leiston	v	Worthing	4-4	134
	(Leiston won 4-2 on kicks from the penalty mark)				
35	Burgess Hill Town	v	Harrow Borough	4-1	
36	Marlow	v	Berkhamsted (3/11)	2-1	
37	Needham Market	v	Three Bridges	4-1	189
38	Bowers & Pitsea	v	Hornchurch	1-3	
39	Royston Town	v	Hythe Town	2-0	
40	East Thurrock United	v	Cheshunt	3-4	
41	Faversham Town	v	Haringey Borough	1-2	
42	Walton Casuals	v	Folkestone Invicta	2-1	
43	Merstham	v	Carshalton Athletic (4/11)	1-3	
44	Coggeshall Town	v	Wingate & Finchley	1-1	
	(Wingate & Finchley won 3-0 on kicks from the penalty mark)				
45	Kings Langley	v	Brightlingsea Regent	4-1	
46	Lowestoft Town	v	Lewes	3-1	236
47	Biggleswade Town	v	Heybridge Swifts	1-0	
48	Aveley	v	Beaconsfield Town	3-0	
49	Uxbridge	v	Hayes & Yeading United (3/11)	2-1	251
50	Enfield Town	v	Ramsgate	8-1	415
51	Barking	v	Sittingbourne	1-1	158
	(Barking FC won 4-3 on kicks from the penalty mark)				
52	Bishop's Stortford	v	Brentwood Town (4/11)	3-2	406
53	Hitchin Town	v	Herne Bay	3-1	
54	Bognor Regis Town	v	Tooting & Mitcham United	2-0	260
55	Whitehawk	v	Cray Wanderers	0-3	390
56	Aylesbury United	v	Margate (1/11)	2-4	243
57	Leatherhead	v	Potters Bar Town	3-1	258
58	Chesham United	v	Whyteleafe	2-2	315
	(Chesham United won 3-2 on kicks from the penalty mark)				
59	Horsham	v	Welwyn Garden City	1-1	473
	(Welwyn Garden City won 5-3 on kicks from the penalty mark)				
60	Felixstowe & Walton United	v	Metropolitan Police	3-1	
61	Corinthian Casuals	v	Hendon	5-4	407
62	Frome Town	v	Farnborough	3-0	253
63	Taunton Town	v	Truro City (3/11)	2-4	427
64	Bracknell Town	v	Cinderford Town		
	(walkover for Bracknell Town – Cinderford Town withdrawn)				
65	Dorchester Town	v	Gosport Borough	2-1	247
66	Moneyfields	v	Kidlington	3-2	128
67	Thame United	v	Wimborne Town		
	(walkover for Thame United – Wimborne Town withdrawn)				
68	Salisbury	v	Tiverton Town	6-0	519
69	Wantage Town	v	North Leigh (30/10)	1-4	398
70	Hartley Wintney	v	Poole Town	1-4	255
71	Weston Super Mare	v	Larkhall Athletic	2-1	
72	Highworth Town	v	Swindon Supermarine	2-3	302
73	Yate Town	v	Bideford		
	(walkover for Bideford – Yate Town withdrawn)				
BYE	– Willand Rovers (Bye awarded due to withdrawal of Merthyr Town)				

FIRST ROUND PROPER - TUESDAY 8 DECEMBER 2020

No.	Home		Away	Score	Att
1	Ashton United	v	South Shields	2-1	
2	Runcorn Linnets	v	Morpeth Town	2-2	270
	(Morpeth Town won 3-2 on kicks from the penalty mark)				
3	Witton Albion	v	Bamber Bridge (12/12)	2-0	300
4	Marske United	v	Warrington Town (7.00)	3-1	
5	Nantwich Town	v	Workington	3-1	272
6	Marine	v	Hyde United (12/12)	1-0	400
7	Buxton	v	City of Liverpool	1-2	
8	Royston Town	v	Tamworth (7.30)	3-1	179
9	Grantham Town	v	St Ives Town (10/12)	3-4	
10	Coleshill Town	v	Matlock Town	5-2	30
11	St Neots Town	v	Kings Langley	3-1	270
12	Hitchin Town	v	Mickleover	3-0	203
13	Marlow	v	Nuneaton Borough	1-4	135
14	Biggleswade Town	v	Bedford Town	0-0	201
	(Bedford Town won 5-3 on kicks from the penalty mark)				
15	AFC Rushden & Diamonds	v	Peterborough Sports	1-5	252
16	Kidsgrove Athletic	v	Stamford (12/12)	0-2	198
17	Basford United	v	Rushall Olympic (7.30)	5-0	
18	Welwyn Garden City	v	Hednesford Town	3-1	119
19	Aveley	v	Hastings United	1-0	
20	Carshalton Athletic	v	Barking	3-0	396
21	Lowestoft Town	v	Cheshunt	0-3	200
22	Haringey Borough	v	Bishop's Stortford	2-1	
23	Needham Market	v	Leiston (12/12)	2-1	230
24	Margate	v	Burgess Hill Town		
	(walkover for Burgess Hill Town – Margate withdrawn)				
25	Corinthian Casuals	v	Walton Casuals		
	(walkover for Corinthian Casuals – Walton Casuals withdrawn)				
26	Hornchurch	v	Wingate & Finchley	4-1	208
27	Uxbridge	v	Cray Wanderers	1-3	102
28	Leatherhead	v	Felixstowe & Walton United	0-1	223
29	Enfield Town	v	Maldon & Tiptree (9/12)	2-2	335
	(Maldon & Tiptree won 4-3 on kicks from the penalty mark)				
30	Salisbury	v	Bracknell Town (7.30)	0-1	402
31	North Leigh	v	Frome Town	0-1	
32	Moneyfields	v	Truro City (5/12)	1-5	237
33	Thame United	v	Bognor Regis Town	2-5	161
34	Evesham United	v	Bideford (5/12)	1-1	309
	(Evesham United won 5-4 on kicks from the penalty mark)				
35	Swindon Supermarine	v	Dorchester Town (5/12)	3-2	289
36	Poole Town	v	Willand Rovers	3-1	257
37	Weston Super Mare	v	Chesham United	1-3	

FAT 2Q - Phoenix Sports Ainsley Everett shields the ball from Issac Olorunfemi of Marlow. Photo Alan Coomes.

SECOND ROUND PROPER - TUESDAY 15 DECEMBER 2020

1	Spennymoor Town	v	Marske United	6-2	
2	Witton Albion	v	Nantwich Town	2-5	351
3	Chester	v	Bradford (Park Avenue)	3-1	552
4	Guiseley	v	Chorley	2-0	
5	Gateshead	v	Farsley Celtic	2-3	
6	Ashton United	v	York City	3-3	
	(Ashton United won 4-2 on kicks from the penalty mark)				
7	Curzon Ashton	v	AFC Fylde	1-4	
8	Darlington	v	City of Liverpool (16/12)	2-0	
9	Marine	v	Southport	0-1	400
10	Blyth Spartans	v	Morpeth Town		
	(walkover for Morpeth Town – Blyth Spartans withdrawn)				
11	Stamford	v	Kidderminster Harriers	1-0	
12	Brackley Town	v	Royston Town	3-2	159
13	Evesham United	v	Boston United (14/12)	0-3	370
14	Coleshill Town	v	AFC Telford United	1-10	30
15	Leamington	v	St Ives Town	5-0	
16	Alfreton Town	v	Bedford Town		
	(walkover for Alfreton Town – Bedford Town withdrawn)				
17	Hereford	v	St Neots Town	3-0	285
18	Kettering Town	v	Nuneaton Borough	5-1	
19	Hitchin Town	v	Peterborough Sports (12/12)	0-4	385
20	Basford United	v	Felixstowe & Walton United (12/12)	3-0	247
21	Gloucester City	v	Needham Market	4-2	
22	Slough Town	v	Dartford	2-2	
	(Dartford won 6-5 on kicks from the penalty mark)				
23	Dulwich Hamlet	v	Cheshunt	3-1	
24	Welling United	v	Oxford City	0-2	
25	Bracknell Town	v	Havant & Waterlooville (7.30)	2-3	324
26	Billericay Town	v	Braintree Town	1-1	302
	(Braintree Town won 4-2 on kicks from the penalty mark)				
27	Dorking Wanderers	v	Hungerford Town	2-0	
28	Maidstone United	v	Poole Town (19/12)	2-0	
29	Concord Rangers	v	Truro City (19/12)	1-2	
30	Aveley	v	Chesham United	1-3	
31	Corinthian Casuals	v	Hemel Hempstead Town (19/12)	0-0	
	(Hemel Hempstead Town won 4-2 on kicks from the penalty mark)				
32	Ebbsfleet United	v	Chippenham Town	1-1	
	(Ebbsfleet United won 4-2 on kicks from the penalty mark)				
33	Bath City	v	Chelmsford City	3-2	
34	Maldon & Tiptree	v	Bognor Regis Town	2-1	184
35	St Albans City	v	Cray Wanderers	3-0	174
36	Welwyn Garden City	v	Burgess Hill Town	2-1	216
37	Tonbridge Angels	v	Hornchurch	0-1	
38	Haringey Borough	v	Eastbourne Borough	3-1	
39	Swindon Supermarine	v	Carshalton Athletic (12/12)	0-0	281
	(Swindon Supermarine won 5-4 on kicks from the penalty mark)				
40	Frome Town	v	Hampton & Richmond Borough		
	(walkover for Frome Town – Hampton & Richmond Borough withdrawn)				

THIRD ROUND PROPER - SATURDAY 19 DECEMBER 2020

1	Darlington	v	AFC Telford United	2-2	
	(Darlington won 5-3 on kicks from the penalty mark)				
2	Peterborough Sports	v	Basford United	3-2	
3	FC Halifax Town	v	Hartlepool United	3-3	
	(FC Halifax Town won 4-2 on kicks from the penalty mark)				
4	Alfreton Town	v	King's Lynn Town (22/12)	1-3	
	(at Basford United FC)				
5	Solihull Moors	v	Farsley Celtic	4-0	
6	Wrexham	v	Leamington	0-0	
	(Leamington won 6-5 on kicks from the penalty mark)				
7	Altrincham	v	Chester	2-1	
	(at Chester FC)				
8	Stockport County	v	Guiseley	3-1	
9	Ashton United	v	Kettering Town	1-2	
10	Spennymoor Town	v	Southport	2-2	
	(Southport won 5-4 on kicks from the penalty mark)				
11	Morpeth Town	v	Notts County	0-3	
12	Nantwich Town	v	Hereford	0-1	433
13	Chesterfield	v	Brackley Town	0-0	
	(Chesterfield won 4-3 on kicks from the penalty mark)				
14	Boston United	v	AFC Fylde	1-1	
	(Boston United won 4-2 on kicks from the penalty mark)				
15	Dorking Wanderers	v	Barnet	3-1	
16	Weymouth	v	Maidenhead United	3-2	306
17	Oxford City	v	Truro City		
	(walkover for Oxford City – Truro City withdrawn)				
18	Chesham United	v	Torquay United	0-1	
19	Dagenham & Redbridge	v	Ebbsfleet United	5-2	
20	St Albans City	v	Sutton United	0-2	
21	Dulwich Hamlet	v	Hornchurch	1-2	
22	Welwyn Garden City	v	Aldershot Town	1-5	
23	Havant & Waterlooville	v	Braintree Town	1-0	
24	Bath City	v	Swindon Supermarine	4-0	
25	Dartford	v	Haringey Borough	0-1	
26	Bromley	v	Hemel Hempstead Town (22/12)	2-0	
27	Boreham Wood	v	Yeovil Town		
	(walkover for Boreham Wood – Yeovil Town withdrawn)				
28	Woking	v	Dover Athletic	2-1	
29	Maldon & Tiptree	v	Gloucester City (23/12)	1-7	
30	Maidstone United	v	Frome Town		
	(walkover for Maidstone United – Frome Town failed to fulfil fixture)				
31	Wealdstone	v	Eastleigh	4-3	

BYE – Stamford (Bye awarded due to the withdrawal of Macclesfield Town)

FOURTH ROUND PROPER

SATURDAY 16 JANUARY 2021

1	Kettering Town	v	Leamington (19/1)	0-3
	(at Leamington FC)			
2	FC Halifax Town	v	Southport (19/1)	1-2
3	Aldershot Town	v	Solihull Moors (19/1)	3-2
4	Weymouth	v	Darlington	0-1
5	Sutton United	v	Dagenham & Redbridge	3-1
6	Stockport County	v	Notts County	1-2
7	Maidstone United	v	Dorking Wanderers	2-1
8	Wealdstone	v	Gloucester City (18/1)	3-1
9	Boreham Wood	v	Torquay United (19/1)	0-4
10	Havant & Waterlooville	v	Altrincham	
	(walkover for Havant & Waterlooville – Altrincham withdrawn)			
11	Boston United	v	Chesterfield (20/1)	1-1
	(Chesterfield won 4-1 on kicks from the penalty mark)			
12	Stamford	v	Hereford (19/1)	0-2
13	Bath City	v	Peterborough Sports	0-1
14	Hornchurch	v	King's Lynn Town	1-1
	(Hornchurch won 3-0 on kicks from the penalty mark)			
15	Bromley	v	Woking (19/1)	1-1
	(Woking won 7-6 on kicks from the penalty mark)			
16	Oxford City	v	Haringey Borough	4-2

FIFTH ROUND PROPER

SATURDAY 8 February 2021

1	Sutton United	v	Woking	0-1
2	Aldershot Town	v	Chesterfield	
	(walkover for Aldershot Town – Chesterfield withdrawn)			
3	Darlington	v	Wealdstone	4-1
4	Hereford	v	Leamington	1-0
5	Havant & Waterlooville	v	Notts County (1.00)	2-2
	(Notts County won 4-2 on kicks from the penalty mark)			
6	Southport	v	Torquay United	0-2
7	Oxford City	v	Peterborough Sports	2-0
8	Hornchurch	v	Maidstone United	5-4

QUARTER FINALS

SATURDAY 27 FEBRUARY 2021

1	Notts County	v	Oxford City	3-1
2	Darlington	v	Hornchurch	1-2
3	Aldershot Town	v	Hereford	1-1
	(Hereford won 5-3 on kicks from the penalty mark)			
4	Woking	v	Torquay United	1-0

SEMI FINALS

SATURDAY 27 MARCH 2021

1	Notts County	v	Hornchurch	3-3
	(Hornchurch won 5-4 on kicks from the penalty mark)			
2	Hereford	v	Woking	1-0

FAT 2P - Gloucester City v Needham Market. Photo Peter Barnes.

THE FA TROPHY
2020-21 Final

HEREFORD (National North) *Owen-Evans 13*	**1-3** Att: 9.000	**HORNCHURCH** (Isthmian Premier) *Ruff 75 Nash 86 Brown 90+5*
SQUAD: Brandon Hall, Jared Hodgkiss, Luke Haines, Jamie Grimes, Chris Camwell (sub 74), Joey Butlin, Tom Owen-Evans, Kyle Finn (sub 88), Ryan Lloyd, Michael Bakare (sub 90), Lewis Butroid. Substitues:- Paul White, Ben Pollock, Kennedy Digie, James McQuilkin (74), Yan Klukowski (90), Dylan Jones, Maziar Kouhyar (88).		**SQUAD:** Joseph Wright, Mickey Parcell, Remi Sutton, Jordan Clark, Rickie Hayles, Oliver Muldoon, Joe Christou, Lewis Spence (59), Sam Higgins (59), Liam Nash (90), Ellis Brown. Substitues:- Finlay Thackway, Charlie Stimson (90), Ronnie Winn, Charlie Ruff (59), Sakariya Hassan, Christopher Dickson (59), Nathan Cooper.

Referee:- Tony Harrington (Durham), assisted by Ian Cooper (Kent) and Richard Wild (Lancashire). 4th Official Charles Breakspear (Surrey)

Unusually none of the National League's highest tier had made this final which contained surprising participants from much lower down the pyramid under the Hornchurch banner. Having not played a league game since the previous November and being two tiers below their opponents, Hornchurch were coming into this final the definite underdogs in most people's eyes. Yet, looking at the fact they had, in earlier rounds already beaten five teams from higher steps, forecasters should have been more wary, especially as the Hornchurch manager, Mark Stimson, had a string of Trophy Final successes already on his C V, twice with Grays Athletic, once with Stevenage and once as a player. His record will take some beating with another triumph added after this victory.

The final opened with Hornchurch firstly on the attack when a powerful effort from Liam Nash saw Bulls keeper Brandon Hall diving smartly to his left to save but it was Hereford who took an early lead when, taking 13th minute advantage of a short corner perhaps practised in training sessions, Tom Owen-Evans was able to shoot low and forcefully past Hornchurch custodian, Joseph Wright, who appeared to have his view temporarily blocked by a clutch of defenders. A couple more chances to increase the lead followed with Joey Butlin heading over when well placed and a seemingly casual lob from Michael Bakare just evading the crossbar. At the other end Hall was quick off his line to thwart Hornchurch midfielders' attempts to set up scoring opportunities for their forwards with balls over the top of retreating defenders. A free kick, caused by Remi Sutton who was duly booked for pulling back Joe Christou, saw Hereford captain Jared Hodgkiss bring out a fine save from Wright who diverted the effort for a corner.

There was a lively opening to the second half when Ellis Brown crossed into the Hereford penalty area where Christou was only able to half hit the ball and send it over from twelve yards. A second Hereford score seemed likely as an Owen-Evans' header needed to be diverted for a corner via a defending head, followed closely by Luke Haines' long throw in causing confusion in the Hornchurch area. However the appearance of Hornchurch substitute Charlie Ruff injected some life into their attack although his first sight of goal brought only a gentle lob into Hall's arms. Sutton shot over, Christou fired into the side netting and Hodgkiss had to boot off his own line as the Urchins pressed. With fifteen minutes left Hornchurch at last found the equaliser they had threatened. Following a long throw in, which caused a melee in the area, Ruff was at hand to force the ball over the line as it fell to him from the crossbar. Kyle Finn's shot for the Bulls was deflected for a corner from which Chris Camwell headed over but with only minutes to go Hornchurch took the lead, Ruff and Christopher Dickson combining to set Liam Nash up and his rasping shot found the target. Rubbing salt into Hereford's now gaping wound the Urchins claimed a third goal in added time when Ellis Brown raced into the penalty area and shot with sufficient force for the ball to roll over the line despite Hall's half parrying the low effort.

So Hereford joined the other Trophy victims mastered by their Greater London opponents, the comeback specialists who had battled through eight rounds to reach the final. On each previous occasion Hornchurch had come from behind to win. What a record. In the semi - final they had equalised three times against Notts County before going on to win on penalties. There was disappointment but no complaints from Hereford who, as manager Josh Gowling agreed, had missed several first half chances to take a firmer lead into the second half. There was no denying that the stronger team had carried the day.

Man of the Match:- Liam Nash (Hornchurch)

Arthur Evans

PAST FINALS

1970 **MACCLESFIELD TOWN** 2 (Lyons, B Fidler) — **TELFORD UNITED 0** — **Att: 28,000**
Northern Premier League — *Southern League*
Macclesfield: Cooke, Sievwright, Bennett, Beaumont, Collins, Roberts, Lyons, B Fidler,Young, Corfield, D Fidler.
Telford: Irvine, Harris, Croft, Flowers, Coton, Ray,Fudge, Hart, Bentley, Murray, Jagger. Ref: K Walker

1971 **TELFORD UTD** 3 (Owen, Bentley, Fudge) — **HILLINGDON BORO.** 2 (Reeve, Bishop) — **Att: 29,500**
Southern League — *Southern League*
Telford: Irvine, Harris, Croft, Ray, Coton, Carr, Fudge, Owen, Bentley, Jagger ,Murray.
Hillingdon B.: Lowe, Batt, Langley, Higginson, Newcombe, Moore, Fairchild,Bishop, Reeve, Carter, Knox. Ref: D Smith

1972 **STAFFORD RANGERS** 3 (Williams 2, Cullerton) — **BARNET 0** — **Att: 24,000**
Northern Premier League — *Southern League*
Stafford R.: Aleksic, Chadwick, Clayton, Sargeant, Aston, Machin, Cullerton, Chapman,Williams, Bayley, Jones.
Barnet: McClelland, Lye, Jenkins, Ward, Embrey, King, Powell, Ferry, Flatt, Easton, Plume . Ref: P Partridge

1973 **SCARBOROUGH** 2 (Leask, Thompson) — **WIGAN ATHLETIC** 1 (Rogers) aet — **Att:23,000**
Northern Premier League — *Northern Premier League*
Scarborough: Garrow, Appleton, Shoulder, Dunn, Siddle, Fagan, Donoghue, Franks,Leask (Barmby), Thompson, Hewitt.
Wigan: Reeves, Morris, Sutherland, Taylor,Jackson, Gillibrand, Clements, Oats (McCunnell), Rogers, King, Worswick. Ref: H Hackney

1974 **MORECAMBE** 2 (Richmond, Sutton) — **DARTFORD** 1 (Cunningham) — **Att: 19,000**
Northern Premier League — *Southern League*
Morecambe: Coates, Pearson, Bennett, Sutton, Street, Baldwin, Done, Webber,Roberts (Galley), Kershaw, Richmond.
Dartford: Morton, Read, Payne, Carr, Burns,Binks, Light, Glozier, Robinson (Hearne), Cunningham, Halleday. Ref: B Homewood

1975(1) **MATLOCK TOWN** 4 (Oxley, Dawson, T Fenoughty, N Fenoughty) — **SCARBOROUGH 0** — **Att: 21,000**
Northern Premier League — *Northern Premier League*
Matlock: Fell, McKay, Smith, Stuart, Dawson, Swan, Oxley, N Fenoughty, Scott, T Fenoughty, M Fenoughty.
Scarborough: Williams, Hewitt, Rettitt, Dunn, Marshall, Todd, Houghton, Woodall, Davidson, Barnby, Aveyard. Ref: K Styles

1976 **SCARBOROUGH** 3 (Woodall, Abbey, Marshall(p)) — **STAFFORD R.** 2 (Jones 2) aet — **Att: 21,000**
Northern Premier League — *Northern Premier League*
Scarborough: Barnard, Jackson, Marshall, H Dunn, Ayre (Donoghue), HA Dunn, Dale,Barmby, Woodall, Abbey, Hilley.
Stafford: Arnold, Ritchie, Richards, Sargeant,Seddon, Morris, Chapman, Lowe, Jones, Hutchinson, Chadwick. Ref: R Challis

1977 **SCARBOROUGH** 2 (Dunn(p), Abbey) — **DAGENHAM** 1 (Harris) — **Att: 21,500**
Northern Premier League — *Isthmian League*
Scarborough: Chapman, Smith, Marshall (Barmby), Dunn, Ayre, Deere, Aveyard,Donoghue, Woodall, Abbey, Dunn.
Dagenham: Hutley, Wellman, P Currie, Dunwell,Moore, W Currie, Harkins, Saul, Fox, Harris, Holder. Ref: G Courtney

1978 **ALTRINCHAM** 3 (King, Johnson, Rogers) — **LEATHERHEAD** 1 (Cook) — **Att: 20,000**
Northern Premier League — *Isthmian League*
Altrincham: Eales, Allan, Crossley, Bailey, Owens, King, Morris, Heathcote,Johnson, Rogers, Davidson (Flaherty).
Leatherhead: Swannell, Cooper, Eaton, Davies,Reid, Malley, Cook, Salkeld, Baker, Boyle (Bailey). Ref: A Grey

1979 **STAFFORD RANGERS** 2 (A Wood 2) — **KETTERING TOWN 0** — **Att: 32,000**
Northern Premier League — *Southern League*
Stafford: Arnold, F Wood, Willis, Sargeant, Seddon, Ritchie, Secker, Chapman, A Wood, Cullerton, Chadwick (Jones).
Kettering: Lane, Ashby, Lee, Eastell, Dixey,Suddards, Flannagan, Kellock, Phipps, Clayton, Evans (Hughes). Ref: D Richardson

1980(2) **DAGENHAM** 2 (Duck, Maycock) — **MOSSLEY** 1 (Smith) — **Att: 26,000**
Isthmian League — *Northern Premier League*
Dagenham: Huttley, Wellman, Scales, Dunwell, Moore, Durrell, Maycock, Horan,Duck, Kidd, Jones (Holder).
Mossley: Fitton, Brown, Vaughan, Gorman, Salter, Polliot, Smith, Moore, Skeete, O'Connor, Keelan (Wilson). Ref: K Baker

1981(3) **BISHOP'S STORTFORD** 1 (Sullivan) — **SUTTON UNITED 0** — **Att: 22,578**
Isthmian League — *Isthmian League*
Bishop's Stortford: Moore, Blackman, Brame, Smith (Worrell), Bradford, Abery, Sullivan,Knapman, Radford, Simmonds, Mitchell.
Sutton Utd.: Collyer, Rogers, Green, J Rains,T Rains, Stephens (Sunnucks), Waldon, Pritchard, Cornwell, Parsons, Dennis. Ref: J Worrall

1982 **ENFIELD** 1 (Taylor) — **ALTRINCHAM 0** — **Att: 18,678**
Alliane Premier League — *Alliane Premier League*
Enfield: Jacobs, Barrett, Tone, Jennings, Waite, Ironton, Ashford, Taylor,Holmes, Oliver (Flint), King. Ref: B Stevens
Altrincham: Connaughton, Crossley, Davison, Bailey, Cuddy, King (Whitbread), Allan, Heathcote, Johnson, Rogers, Howard.

Notes:
1 The only occasion three members of the same family played in the same FA Trophy Final team.
2 The first of the Amateurs from the Isthmian League to win the FA Trophy.
3 Goalkeeper Terry Moore had also won an Amateur Cup Winners Medal with Bishop's Stortford in 1974.
All games played at Wembley (old & new) unless stated.

1983 TELFORD UTD 2 (Mather 2) — **NORTHWICH VICTORIA 1 (Bennett)** — **Att: 22,071**
Alliane Premier League — *Alliane Premier League*
Telford: Charlton, Lewis, Turner, Mayman (Joseph), Walker, Easton, Barnett,Williams, Mather, Hogan, Alcock.
Northwich: Ryan, Fretwell, Murphy, Jones, Forshaw, Ward, Anderson, Abel (Bennett), Reid, Chesters, Wilson. Ref: B Hill

1984 NORTHWICH VICTORIA 1 (Chester) — **BANGOR CITY 1 (Whelan)** — **Att: 14,200**
Replay NORTHWICH VICTORIA 2 (Chesters(p), Anderson) — **BANGOR CITY 1 (Lunn)** — **Att: 5,805 (at Stoke)**
Alliane Premier League — *Alliane Premier League*
Northwich: Ryan, Fretwell, Dean, Jones, Forshaw (Power 65), Bennett, Anderson,Abel, Reid, Chesters, Wilson. Ref: J Martin
Bangor: Letheren, Cavanagh, Gray, Whelan, Banks,Lunn, Urqhart, Morris, Carter, Howat, Sutcliffe (Westwood 105) . Same in replay.

1985 WEALDSTONE 2 (Graham, Holmes) — **BOSTON UNITED 1 (Cook)** — **Att: 20,775**
Alliane Premier League — *Alliane Premier League*
Wealdstone: Iles, Perkins, Bowgett, Byatt, Davies, Greenaway, Holmes, Wainwright,Donnellan, Graham (N Cordice 89), A Cordice.
Boston: Blackwell, Casey, Ladd,Creane, O'Brien, Thommson, Laverick (Mallender 78), Simpsom, Gilbert, Lee, Cook. Ref: J Bray

1986 ALTRINCHAM 1 (Farrelly) — **RUNCORN 0** — **Att: 15,700**
Gola League — *Gola League*
Altrincham: Wealands, Gardner, Densmore, Johnson, Farrelly, Conning, Cuddy,Davison, Reid, Ellis, Anderson. Sub: Newton.
Runcorn: McBride, Lee, Roberts,Jones, Fraser, Smith, S Crompton (A Crompton), Imrie, Carter, Mather, Carrodus. Ref: A Ward

1987 KIDDERMINSTER HARRIERS 0 — **BURTON ALBION 0** — **Att: 23,617**
Replay KIDDERMINSTER HARRIERS 2 (Davies 2) — **BURTON ALBION 1 (Groves)** — **Att: 15,685 (at West Brom)**
Conferene — *Southern League*
Kidderminster: Arnold, Barton, Boxall, Brazier (sub Hazlewood in rep), Collins (sub Pearson 90 at Wembley), Woodall, McKenzie, O'Dowd, Tuohy, Casey, Davies. sub:Jones.
Burton: New, Essex, Kamara, Vaughan, Simms, Groves, Bancroft, Land, Dorsett, Redfern, (sub Wood in replay), Gauden.
Sub: Patterson. Ref: D Shaw

1988 ENFIELD 0 — **TELFORD UNITED 0** — **Att: 20,161**
Replay ENFIELD 3 (Furlong 2, Howell) — **TELFORD UNITED 2 (Biggins, Norris(p))** — **Att: 6,912 (at W Brom)**
Conferene — *Conferene*
Enfield: Pape, Cottington, Howell, Keen (sub Edmonds in rep), Sparrow (sub Hayzleden at Wembley), Lewis (sub Edmonds at Wembley), Harding, Cooper, King,Furlong, Francis.
Telford: Charlton, McGinty, Storton, Nelson, Wiggins, Mayman (sub Cunningham in rep (sub Hancock)), Sankey, Joseph, Stringer (sub Griffiths at Wembley, Griffiths in replay), Biggins, Norris. Ref: L Dilkes

1989 TELFORD UNITED 1 (Crawley) — **MACCLESFIELD TOWN 0** — **Att: 18,102**
Conferene — *Conferene*
Telford: Charlton, Lee, Brindley, Hancock, Wiggins, Mayman, Grainger, Joseph, Nelson, Lloyd, Stringer. Subs: Crawley, Griffiths.
Macclesfield: Zelem, Roberts, Tobin, Edwards, Hardman, Askey, Lake, Hanton, Imrie, Burr, Timmons. Subs: Devonshire, Kendall.

1990 BARROW 3 (Gordon 2, Cowperthwaite) — **LEEK TOWN 0** — **Att: 19,011**
Conferene — *Northern Premier League*
Barrow: McDonnell, Higgins, Chilton, Skivington, Gordon, Proctor, Doherty (Burgess), Farrell (Gilmore), Cowperthwaite, Lowe, Ferris.
Leek: Simpson, Elsby (Smith), Pearce, McMullen, Clowes, Coleman (Russell),Mellor, Somerville, Sutton, Millington, Norris Ref: T Simpson

1991 WYCOMBE W. 2 (Scott, West) — **KIDDERMINSTER HARRIERS 1 (Hadley)** — **Att: 34,842**
Conferene — *Conferene*
Wycombe: Granville, Crossley, Cash, Kerr, Creaser, Carroll, Ryan, Stapleton,West, Scott, Guppy (Hutchinson). Ref: J Watson
Kidderminster: Jones, Kurila, McGrath, Weir, Barnett, Forsyth, Joseph (Wilcox), Howell (Whitehouse), Hadley, Lilwall, Humphries

1992 COLCHESTER UTD* 3 (Masters, Smith, McGavin) — **WITTON ALBION 1 (Lutkevitch)** — **Att: 27,806**
Conferene — *Conferene*
Colchester: Barrett, Donald, Roberts, Knsella, English, Martin, Cook, Masters,McDonough (Bennett 65), McGavin, Smith. Ref: K P Barratt
Witton: Mason, Halliday, Coathup, McNeilis, Jim Connor, Anderson, Thomas, Rose, Alford, Grimshaw (Joe Connor), Lutkevitch (McCluskie)

1993 WYCOMBE W*. 4 (Cousins, Kerr, Thompson, Carroll) — **RUNCORN 1 (Shaughnessy)** — **Att: 32,968**
Conferene — *Conferene*
Wycombe: Hyde, Cousins, Cooper, Kerr, Crossley, Thompson (Hayrettin 65),Carroll, Ryan, Hutchinson, Scott, Guppy. Sub: Casey.
Runcorn: Williams, Bates, Robertson, Hill, Harold (Connor 62), Anderson, Brady (Parker 72), Brown, Shaughnessy, McKenna, Brabin

1994 WOKING 2 (D Brown, Hay) — **RUNCORN 1 (Shaw (pen))** — **Att: 15,818**
Conferene — *Conferene*
Woking: Batty, Tucker, L Wye, Berry, Brown, Clement, Brown (Rattray 32), Fielder, Steele, Hay (Puckett 46), Walker. Ref: Paul Durkin
Runcorn: Williams, Bates, Robertson, Shaw, Lee, Anderson, Thomas, Connor, McInerney (Hill 71), McKenna, Brabin. Sub: Parker

1995 WOKING 2 (Steele, Fielder) — **KIDDERMINSTER HARRIERS 1 aet (Davies)** — **Att: 17,815**
Conferene — *Conferene*
Woking: Batty, Tucker, L Wye, Fielder, Brown, Crumplin (Rattray 42), S Wye, Ellis, Steele, Hay (Newberry 112), Walker. (Sub: Read(gk)
Kidderminster: Rose, Hodson, Bancroft, Webb, Brindley (Cartwright 94), Forsyth, Deakin, Yates, Humphreys (Hughes 105), Davies, Purdie. Sub: Dearlove (gk) Ref: D J Gallagher

1996 **MACCLESFIELD TOWN** 3 (Payne, OG, Hemmings) *Conferene* — **NORTHWICH VICTORIA 1 (Williams)** *Conferene* — **Att: 8,672**

Macclesfield: Price, Edey, Gardiner, Payne, Howarth(C), Sorvel, Lyons, Wood (Hulme 83), Coates, Power, Hemmings (Cavell 88).
Northwich: Greygoose, Ward, Duffy, Burgess (Simpson 87), Abel (Steele), Walters, Williams, Butler (C), Cooke, Humphries, Vicary.
Ref: M Reed

1997 **WOKING** 1 (Hay 112) *Conferene* — **DAGENHAM & REDBRIDGE 0** *Isthmian League* — **Att: 24,376**

Woking: Batty, Brown, Howard, Foster, Taylor, S Wye, Thompson (sub Jones 115), Ellis, Steele (L Wye 108), Walker, Jackson (Hay 77).
Dagenham: Gothard, Culverhouse, Connor, Creaser, Jacques (sub Double 75), Davidson, Pratt (Naylor 81), Parratt, Broom, Rogers, Stimson (John 65). Ref: J Winter

1998 **CHELTENHAM TOWN** 1 (Eaton 74) *Conferene* — **SOUTHPORT 0** *Conferene* — **Att: 26,387**

Cheltenham: Book, Duff, Freeman, Banks, Victory, Knight (Smith 78), Howells, Bloomer, Walker (sub Milton 78), Eaton, Watkins. Sub: Wright.
Southport: Stewart, Horner, Futcher, Ryan, Farley, Kielty, Butler, Gamble, Formby (sub Whittaker 80), Thompson (sub Bollard 88), Ross. Sub: Mitten. Ref: G S Willard

1999 **KINGSTONIAN** 1 (Mustafa 49) *Conferene* — **FOREST GREEN ROVERS 0** *Conferene* — **Att: 20,037**

Kingstonian: Farrelly, Mustafa, Luckett, Crossley, Stewart, Harris, Patterson, Pitcher, Rattray, Leworthy (Francis 87), Akuamoah. Subs (not used): John, Corbett, Brown, Tranter
Forest Green Rovers: Shuttlewood, Hedges, Forbes, Bailey (Smart 76), Kilgour, Wigg (Cook 58), Honor (Winter 58), Drysdale, McGregor, Mehew, Sykes. Subs (not used): Perrin, Coupe Ref: A B Wilkie

2000 **KINGSTONIAN** 3 (Akuamoah 40, 69, Simba 75) *Conferene* — **KETTERING TOWN 2 (Vowden 55, Norman 64p)** *Conferene* — **Att: 20,034**

Kingstonian: Farelly, Mustafa, Luckett, Crossley, Stewart (Saunders 77), Harris, Kadi (Leworthy 83), Pitcher, Green (Basford 86), Smiba, Akuamoah. Subs (not used): Hurst, Allan
Kettering Town: Sollit, McNamara, Adams, Perkins, Vowden, Norman (Duik 76), Fisher, Brown, Shutt, Watkins (Hudson 46), Setchell (Hopkins 81). Subs (not used): Ridgway, Wilson Ref: S W Dunn

2001 **CANVEY ISLAND** 1 (Chenery) *Isthmian League* — **FOREST GREEN ROVERS 0** *Conferene* — **Att: 10,007 at Villa Park**

Forest Green Rovers: Perrin, Cousins, Lockwood, Foster, Clark, Burns, Daley, Drysdale (Bennett 46), Foster (Hunt 75), Meecham, Slater. Subs (not used): Hedges, Prince, Ghent
Canvey Island: Harrison, Duffy, Chenery, Bodley, Ward, Tilson, Stimson (Tanner 83), Gregory, Vaughan (Jones 76), Parmenter. Subs (not used): Bennett, Miller, Thompson. Ref: A G Wiley

2002 **YEOVIL TOWN** 2 (Alford, Stansfield) *Conferene* — **STEVENAGE BOROUGH 0** *Conferene* — **Att: 18,809 at Villa Park**

Yeovil Town: Weale, Lockwood, Tonkin, Skiverton, Pluck (White 51), Way, Stansfield, Johnson, Alford (Giles 86), Crittenden (Lindegaard 83), McIndoe. Subs (not used): O'Brien, Sheffield
Stevenage Borough: Wilkerson, Hamsher, Goodliffe, Trott, Fraser, Fisher, Wormull (Stirling 71), Evers (Williams 56), Jackson, Sigere (Campbell 74), Clarke. Subs (not used): Campbell, Greygoose Ref: N S Barry

2003 **BURSCOUGH** 2 (Martindale 25, 55) *Northern Premier* — **TAMWORTH 1 (Cooper 78)** *Southern Premier* — **Att: 14,265 at Villa Park**

Burscough: Taylor, Teale, Taylor, Macauley (White 77), Lawless, Bowen, Wright, Norman, Martindale (McHale 80), Byrne (Bluck 84), Burns. Subs (not used): McGuire (g/k) Molyneux.
Tamworth: Acton, Warner, Follett, Robinson, Walsh, Cooper, Colley, Evans (Turner 64), Rickards (Hatton 88), McGorry, Sale (Hallam 54). Subs (not used): Grocutt, Barnes (g/k). Ref: U D Rennie

2004 **HEDNESFORD TOWN** 3 (Maguire 28, Hines 53, Brindley 87) *Southern Premier* — **CANVEY ISLAND 2 (Boylan 46, Brindley 48 og)** *Isthmian Premier Champions* — **Att: 6,635 at Villa Park**

Hednesford Town: Young, Simkin, Hines, King, Brindley, Ryder (Barrow 59), Palmer, Anthrobus, Danks (Piearce 78), Maguire, Charie (Evans 55). Subs (not used): Evans (g/k) McGhee.
Canvey Island: Potter, Kennedy, Duffy, Chenery, Cowan, Gooden (Dobinson 89), Minton, Gregory (McDougald 80), Boylan, Midgley (Berquez 73), Ward. Subs (not used): Theobald, Harrison (g/k).
Ref: M L Dean

2005 **GRAYS ATHLETIC** 1 (Martin 65) Pens: 6 *Conferene South* — **HUCKNALL TOWN 1 (Ricketts 75) Pens: 5** *Conferene North* — **Att: 8,116 at Villa Park**

Grays Athletic: Bayes, Brennan, Nutter, Stuart, Matthews, Thurgood, Oli (Powell 80), Hopper (Carthy 120), Battersby (sub West 61), Martin, Cole. Subs (not used): Emberson, Bruce..
Hucknall Town: Smith, Asher, Barrick (Plummer 30), Hunter, Timons, Cooke, Smith (Ward 120), Palmer (Heathcote 94), Ricketts, Bacon, Todd. Subs (not used): Winder, Lindley. Ref: P Dowd

2006 **GRAYS ATHLETIC** 2 (Oli, Poole) *Conferene* — **WOKING 0** *Conferene* — **Att: 13,997 at Upton Park**

Grays Athletic: Bayes, Sambrook, Nutter, Stuart, Hanson, Kightly (Williamson 90), Thurgood, Martin, Poole, Oli, McLean. Subs (not used): Eyre (g/k), Hooper, Olayinka, Mawer.
Woking: Jalal, Jackson, MacDonald, Nethercott (Watson 60), Hutchinson, Murray, Smith (Cockerill 60), Evans (Blackman 85), Ferguson, McAllister, Justin Richards. Subs (not used): Davis (g/k), El-Salahi.
Ref: Howard Webb (Sheffield)

2007 STEVENAGE BOROUGH 3 (Cole, Dobson, Morrison) **KIDDERMINSTER HARRIERS 2 (Constable 2)** **Att: 53,262**
Conferene *Conferene* **(New Trophy record)**
Stevenage Borough: Julian, Fuller, Nutter, Oliver, Gaia, Miller, Cole, Morrison, Guppy (Dobson 63), Henry, Beard.
Subs not used: Potter, Slabber, Nurse, McMahon.
Kidderminster Harriers: Bevan, Kenna, Hurren, Creighton, Whitehead, Blackwood, Russell, Penn, Smikle (Reynolds 90), Christie (White 75) , Constable.
Subs not used: Taylor, Sedgemore, McGrath. Ref: Chris Foy (Merseyside)

2008 EBBSFLEET UNITED 1 (McPhee) **TORQUAY UNITED 0** **Att: 40,186**
Blue Square Premier *Blue Square Premier*
Ebbsfleet United: Cronin, Hawkins, McCarthy, Smith, Opinel, McPhee, Barrett, Bostwick, Long (MacDonald 84), Moore, Akinde.
Subs not used: Eribenne, Purcell, Ricketts, Mott.
Torquay United: Rice, Mansell, Todd, Woods, Nicholson, D'Sane (Benyon 66), Hargreaves, Adams, Zebroski, Sills (Hill 88), Phillips (Stevens 46). Subs not used: Hockley and Robertson. Ref: Martin Atkinson (West Riding)

2009 STEVENAGE BOROUGH 2 (Morison, Boylan) **YORK CITY 0** **Att: 27,102**
Blue Square Premier *Blue Square Premier*
Stevenage Borough: Day, Henry, Bostwick, Roberts, Wilson, Mills, Murphy, Drury, Vincenti (Anaclet 86), Boylan, Morison.
Subs not used: Bayes, Albrighton, Maamria and Willock.
York City:Ingham, Purkiss, McGurk, Parslow, Pejic, Mackin, Greaves(McWilliams 74), Rusk (Russell 80), Brodie, McBreen (Sodje 60), Boyes. Subs not used – Mimms and Robinson. Referee: Michael Jones.

2010 BARROW 2 (McEvilly 79, Walker 117) **STEVENAGE BOROUGH 1 (Drury 10)** **Att: 21,223**
Blue Square Premier *Blue Square Premier*
Barrow: Stuart Tomlinson, Simon Spender, Paul Jones, Phil Bolland, Paul Edwards, Simon Wiles (sub Carlos Logan 63rd min), Robin Hulbert, Andy Bond, Paul Rutherford (sub Mark Boyd 109th min), Jason Walker, Gregg Blundell (sub Lee McEvilly 73rd min).
Subs not used – Tim Deasy and Mike Pearson.
Stevenage Borough: Chris Day (sub Ashley Bayes 90th min), Ronnie Henry, Jon Ashton, Mark Roberts, Scott Laird, Joel Byrom (sub Lawrie Wilson 58th min), David Bridges, Michael Bostwick, Andy Drury, Chris Beardsley (sub Charlie Griffin 64th min), Yemi Odubade. Subs not used – Stacey Long and Peter Vincenti.
Man of the match - Paul Rutherford. Referee Lee Probert.

2011 DARLINGTON 1 (Senior 120) **MANSFIELD TOWN 0** **Att: 24,668**
Blue Square Premier *Blue Square Premier*
Darlington: Sam Russell, Paul Arnison, Ian Miller, Liam Hatch, Aaron Brown, Jamie Chandler, Chris Moore, Marc Bridge-Wilkinson (sub Paul Terry 100th min), Gary Smith (sub Arman Verma 38th min), John Campbell (sub Chris Senior 75th min), Tommy Wright.
Subs not used – Danzelle St Louis-Hamilton (gk) and Phil Gray.
Mansfield Town: Alan Marriott, Gary Silk, Stephen Foster, Tom Naylor, Dan Spence, Louis Briscoe, Tyrone Thompson, Kyle Nix, Adam Smith (sub Ashley Cain 95th min), Adam Murray (sub Danny Mitchley 108th min), Paul Connor
Subs not used – Paul Stonehouse and Neil Collett (gk)
Man of the match - Jamie Chandler. Referee Stuart Atwell

2012 YORK CITY 2 (Blair 61, Oyebanjo 68) **NEWPORT COUNTY 0** **Att: 19,844**
Blue Square Premier *Blue Square Premier*
York City: Michael Ingham, Jon Challinor, Chris Smith, Daniel Parslow, Ben Gibson, Matty Blair, Lanre Oyebanjo, Patrick McLaughlan (sub Jamal Fyfield 82nd min), James Meredith, Ashley Chambers (Adriano Moke (89th min), Jason Walker (Jamie Reed 90th min).
Subs not used – Paul Musselwhite (g/k), Michael Potts.
Newport County: Glyn Thompson, David Pipe, Ismail Yakubu, Gary Warren, Andrew Hughes, Sam Foley, Lee Evans, Nat Jarvis (sub Jake Harris 68th min), Max Porter (sub Darryl Knights 79th min), Romone Rose (sub Elliott Buchanan 68th min), Lee Minshull.
Subs not used – Matthew Swan (g/k), Paul Rodgers.
Man of the match - Lanre Oyebanjo. Referee Anthony Taylor

2013 WREXHAM 1 (Thornton 82 (pen)) **GRIMSBY TOWN 1 (Cook 71)** **Att: 35,226**
Wrexham won 4-1 on kicks from the penalty mark after extra time.
Blue Square Premier *Blue Square Premier*
Wrexham: Chris Maxwell, Stephen Wright, Martin Riley, Jay Harris, Danny Wright, Brett Ormerod (Robert Ogleby 77 min), Andy Morrell (Adrian Cieslewicz 61 min), Dean Keates, Johnny Hunt, Chris Westwood, Kevin Thornton (Joe Clarke 89 min).
Subs not used - Andy Coughlin (gk) Glen Little.
Grimsby Town: Sam Hatton, Aswad Thomas, Shaun Pearson, Ian Miller, Joe Colbeck, Craig Disley, Frankie Artus, Andy Cook, James McKeown, Ross Hannah (Andi Thanoj 55 min), Marcus Marshall (Richard Brodie 87 min).
Subs not used - Jamie Devitt, Bradley Wood, Lenell John-Lewis. Referee Jonathan Moss

2014 CAMBRIDGE UNITED 4 (Bird 38, Donaldson 50,59, Berry 78 (pen)) **GOSPORT BOROUGH 0** **Att: 18,120**
Conferene Premier *Conferene South*
Cambridge United: Will Norris, Greg Taylor, Jock Coulson (Tom Bonner 87 min), Ian Miller, Ryan Donaldson, Tom Champion, Richard Tait, Liam Hughes (Nathan Arnold 73 min), Luke Berry, Ryan Bird, Josh Gillies (Andy Pugh 61 min).
Subs not used - Kevin Roberts, Mitch Austin.
Gosport Borough: Nathan Ashmore, Lee Molyneaux, Andy Forbes, Jamie Brown (Rory Williams 57 min), Brett Poate, Sam Pearce, Josh Carmichael, Danny Smith, Tim Sills (Dan Woodward 57 min), Justin Bennett, Michael Gosney (Dan Wooden 72 min).
Subs not used - Ryan Scott, Adam Wilde.

Referee Craig Pawson

2015 NORTH FERRIBY UNITED 3 (King 76 (pen), Kendall 86, 111) **WREXHAM** 3 (Moult 11, 118, Harris 59) **Att: 14,548**
Conferene North *Conferene National*

North Ferriby United: Adam Nicklin, Sam Topliss, Danny Hone, Matt Wilson, Josh Wilde (Nathan Peat 90), Liam King, Adam Bolder (Nathan Jarman 62), Russell Fry (Ryan Kendall 80), Danny Clarke, Tom Denton, Jason St Juste.
Subs not used - Tom Nicholson and Mark Gray.
Wrexham: Andy Coughlin, Steve Tomassen, Manny Smith, Blaine Hudson, Neil Ashton, Jay Harris, Dean Keates (Robbie Evans 73), Joe Clarke (Andy Bishop 102), Kieron Morris (Wes York 87), Louis Moult, Connor Jennings.
Subs not used - Mark Carrington and Luke Waterfall. Referee Michael Oliver

2016 FC HALIFAX TOWN 1 (McManus 48) **GRIMSBY TOWN 0** **Att: 46,781** (Inaugural Non-League finals day)
Conferene National *Conferene National*

FC Halifax Town: Sam Johnson, Matty Brown, Hamza Bencherif, Kevin Roberts, James Bolton, Nicky Wroe, Jake Hibbs, Scott McManus (Kingsley James 73), Josh McDonald (Sam Walker 63), Jordan Burrow, Richard Peniket (Connor Hughes 86).
Subs not used - Jordan Porter and Shaquille McDonald.
Grimsby Town: James McKeown, Richard Tait (Danny East 81), Shaun Pearson, Aristote Nsiala, Gregor Robertson, Andy Monkhouse (Jon-Paul Pitman 68), Craig Disley, Craig Clay (Nathan Arnold 63), Jon Nolan, Omar Bogle, Padraig Amond.
Subs not used - Josh Gowling and Josh Venney. Referee Lee Mason

2017 YORK CITY 3 (Parkin 8, Oliver 22, Connolly 86) **MACCLESFIELD TOWN** 2 (Browne 13, Norburn 45+1)
Conferene National *Conferene National* **Att: 38,224** (Combined Trophy/Vase att.)

York City: Kyle Letheren, Asa Hall (Aidan Connolly 69), Yan Klukowski (Adriano Moke 46), Hamza Bencherif, Danny Holmes (Shaun Rooney 76) Amari Morgan-Smith, Simon Heslop, Sean Newton, Daniel Parslow, Jon Parkin, Vadaine Oliver.
Subs not used - Luke Simpson, Scott Fenwick.
Macclesfield Town: Scott Flinders, Andy Halls, David Fitzpatrick, Neill Byrne (John McCombe 68), George Pilkington, Rhys Browne, Chris Holroyd, Kingsley James, Ollie Norburn (Anthony Dudley 89), Mitch Hancox (Luke Summerfield 86), Danny Whitaker.
Subs not used - Craig Ross, Danny Whitehead. Referee Paul Tierney

2018 BRACKLEY TOWN 1, 5p (R Johnson 90+6 (og)) **BROMLEY** 1, 4p (Bugiel 19)
Conferene National North *Conferene National* **Att: 31,430** (Combined Trophy/Vase att.)

Brackley Town: Danny Lewis, Matt Lowe, Connor Franklin (Ellis Myles 77), Shane Byrne, Alex Gudger, Gareth Dean (c), Glenn Walker, James Armson, Lee Ndlovu (Andy Brown 53), Aaron Williams, Adam Walker..
Subs not used - Luke Graham, Theo Streete, Steve Diggin.
Bromley: David Gregory, Jack Holland (c), Raymond Raymond, Louis Dennis (Brandon Hanlan 68), Adam Mekki (Ben Chorley 72), Jordan Higgs, Tyrone Sterling, George Porter (Josh Rees 61), Roger Johnson, Frankie Sutherland, Omar Bugiel.
Subs not used - Alan Dunne, Dan Johnson. Referee Chris Kavanagh

2019 AFC FYLDE 1 (Rowe 60 (direct free-kick)) **LEYTON ORIENT 0**
Conferene National *Conferene National* **Att: 42,962** (Combined Trophy/Vase att.)

AFC Fylde: Jay Lynch, Arlen Birch (Tom Crawford 90), Neil Byrne (c) (Tom Brewitt 12), Jordan Tunnicliffe, Zaine Francis-Angol, Danny Philliskirk, Ryan Croasdale, Nick Haughton (Tim Odusina 74), Alex Reid, Andy Bond, Danny Rowe.
Subs not used - Russell Griffiths, James Hardy.
Leyton Orient: Dean Brill, Jamie Turley (Jordan Maguire-Drew 46), Marvin Ekpiteta, Josh Coulson, Daniel Happe (Matt Harrold 68), Joe Widdowson, Craig Clay, James Brophy, John McAnuff (c) (Charlie Lee 78), Josh Koroma, Macauley Bonne.
Subs not used - Sam Sargeant, Sam Ling. Referee Andrew Madley

FAT 3P - Alfreton Town v Kings Lynn Town.
Photos Bill Wheatcroft.

THE FA VASE
2019-20 Final

Played at Wembley Stadium on Monday 3rd May 2021, delayed for twelve months on account of Covid restrictions and, for the same reason, played in front of a small number of officials and players' families.

CONSETT AFC (Northern Lge D1)	2-3	HEBBURN TOWN (Northern Lge D1)
Alshabeeb 18, Pearson 42		*Purewal 19, Richardson 44, Martin 82*

SQUAD: Kyle Hayes, Jermaine Metz, Darren Holden (sub 87), Matthew Slocombe, Arjun Purewal, Ross Wilkinson, Jake Orrell (sub 29), Calvin Smith, Dale Pearson, Matthew Cornish (sub 61), Ali Alshabeeb. Substitutes:-Joshua Wilson, Luke Carr (61), Nicholas Allen (29), Daniel Marriott, Simon Jacab, Max Russell, Carl Lawson (87).

SQUAD: Mark Foden, Daniel Groves, Darren Lough, Robbie Spence, Louis Storey, Daniel Carson, Thomas Potter, Michael McKeown, Graeme Armstrong, Michael Richardson, Amar Purewal (77).
Substitutes:- Kieran Hunter, Oliver Martin (77), Jack Donaghy, Carl Taylor, Luke Hudson, Damen Mullen, Angelos Eleftheriadis.

Referee - Michael Salisbury. Assistants - George Byrne and Joe Clark. 4th official - Leigh Doughty

After suffering an excess of televised Football League dross, all too frequently sleep inducing, among the glut of matches televised during the Covid pandemic, this match, particularly the first half, was a wonderful reminder of how exhilarating and entertaining the game can be. Eschewing the constant tip tapping of the ball back, forth and sideways between midfielders and defenders here we witnessed two teams happy to take a risk by sending the ball speedily forward without the slightest hesitation. This, to many, is what true non-league football, or any football perhaps, is about – involving a distinct lack of over coached, negative, hesitant, safety first, plodding build up but, instead, some joyous freedom to press forward at every opportunity and take a risk.
As has become customary for the Vase, the Northern League was well represented, this time by not one but two clubs from that neck of the woods, where promotion in the Pyramid, with its additional travel costs and longer journeys, has proved a disincentive. In a very much shortened programme the two teams had not met each other during the league season but Hebburn were slight favourites since they had been league leaders when the season concluded abruptly.

Thank you, Hebburn and Consett, for a magnificent festival of attacking football, especially in the first forty five minutes. Sadly there had to be a loser and, after twice taking the lead, it fell to Consett to settle as runners up when Hebburn managed a late winner as both teams understandably tired when the Wembley turf, noted for its tendency to tire even the fittest professional, took its customary toll on energy.

Adding savour to the contest was the presence of twins, one on each side, striker Amar for Hebburn and Consett defender and captain, Arjun, the first British South Asian Sikhs to face each other at Wembley, a fantastic occasion for the Purewal family.

In winning this final Hebburn became the tenth Northern Leaguers to take the honour and, still going at that time in the quarter finals of the 20/21 Vase (later to lose out in the quarter finals, they thought they could, in nineteen days, be returning to contest a second Vase final in the same year.

From the off it was Consett who made the running, Ali Alshabeeb causing concern in the Hebburn defence and Darren Holden, with shot and cross, threatening Mark Foden's goal. After Michael Richardson had struck the Consett bar and Graeme Armstrong had seen his shot well blocked by Consett keeper Kyle Hayes it was the white shirted Consett who, in minute 18, took the lead through Alshabeeb when, slipped in by Matthew Cornish, he was left free to fire into the roof of the net. However, with barely another minute gone, it was all square as Amar Purewal was able to burst into the box to send a scorcher past Hayes.

There then followed an eight minute delay while careful treatment was given to Consett's Jake Orrell before he was placed in a neck brace and stretchered from the field to be replaced by Nicholas Allen. Calvin Smith shot over a chance to restore Consett's lead and chances followed at both ends before, with the half drawing to a close, Dale Pearson regained Consett's lead, his low shot finding the bottom corner. Two minutes later it was back to all square, Richardson restoring parity when left to tap home a rebound off Hayes who had blocked Louis Storey's shot. Hebburn were only denied a half time lead after Hayes, misjudging a Darren Lough cross, was lucky no opponent was near.

As soon as the second half opened Hebburn became dominant. After Arjan Purewal had unnecessarily given away a corner a Thomas Potter cross fell to Armstrong to tap home but somehow he put it wide. Another dangerous drive across goal by Potter failed to find a colleague. Consett retaliated with an inviting centre from Holden, a close range effort from Smith and a Wilkinson header before Potter and Richardson combined to present another tap in chance. For Hebburn both Smith and substitute Luke Carr sent long range efforts over the bar.

With time and energy running out Hebburn took an 84th minute lead, sub Oliver Martin guiding the ball just inside the post having been set up by Richardson. Consett had one last chance but Ross Wilkinson could not get enough power in his header and Foden was able to clutch comfortably as time ran out and victory went to the yellow and black kitted team. Man of Match – Michael Richardson, Hebburn Town.

Arthur Evans

FAV SF 19-20 - Corinthains Andres Tobon and George Snelling crowd out Hebburns Robbie Spence.

FAV SF 19-20 - Corinthians James Trueman holds off Hebburns Daniel Groves.
Photos Alan Coomes.

FAV 1Q - White (Boston Town) takes his penalty against Doran (Sleaford), only to see the 'keeper save it. Photos Keith Clayton.

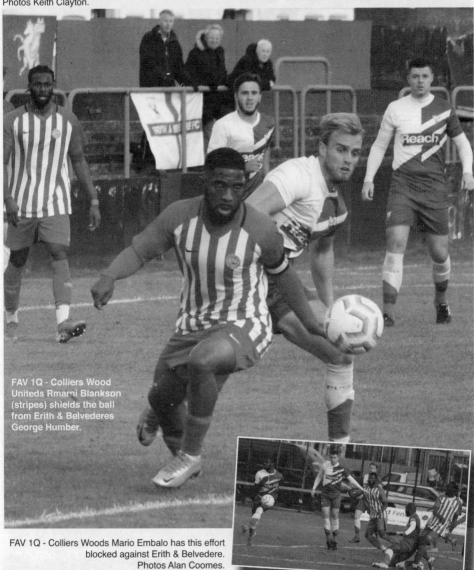

FAV 1Q - Colliers Wood Uniteds Rmarni Blankson (stripes) shields the ball from Erith & Belvederes George Humber.

FAV 1Q - Colliers Woods Mario Embalo has this effort blocked against Erith & Belvedere. Photos Alan Coomes.

FAV 1Q - Stansfelds Ryan Hassan (stripes) and Knaphills Connor Holland tussle for the ball.

FAV 1Q - Stansfelds Ollie Milton is tackled by Knaphills James Dinsdale.
Photos Alan Coomes.

FAV 1Q - Grigas (Boston Town) sees the ball into the Sleaford goal.

FAV 1Q - Below a header from Ford (Boston Town) beats Doran (Sleaford).
Photos Keith Clayton.

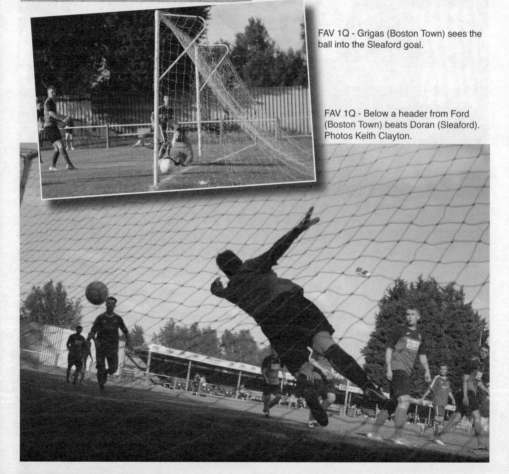

FIRST QUALIFYING ROUND 2020-21

SATURDAY 19 SEPTEMBER 2020

No	Home		Away	Score	Att
1	Bishop Auckland	v	Billingham Synthonia	1-5	237
2	Durham City	v	Thackley (18/9)	0-4	102
3	Bedlington Terriers	v	Heaton Stannington	1-2	96
4	Crook Town	v	Albion Sports	1-0	208
5	Garforth Town	v	Sunderland West End	5-1	97
6	Willington	v	Whickham	0-4	132
7	North Shields	v	Tow Law Town	3-0	268
8	Northallerton Town	v	Billingham Town	2-0	191
9	West Allotment Celtic	v	Penrith	3-3	70
	(Penrith won 7-6 on kicks from the penalty mark)				
10	Ryton & Crawcrook Albion	v	Ashington	2-4	140
11	Holker Old Boys	v	Eccleshill United	3-0	123
12	Shildon	v	Chester-Le-Street Town	2-1	180
13	Whitley Bay	v	Newcastle University	1-4	254
14	Guisborough Town	v	Washington	3-0	268
15	Newton Aycliffe	v	Barnoldswick Town	4-0	130
16	Birtley Town	v	Squires Gate	1-1	BCD
	(Birtley Town won 4-1 on kicks from the penalty mark)				
17	Harrogate Railway Athletic	v	Cleator Moor Celtic	1-1	99
	(Harrogate Railway Athletic won 9-8 on kicks from the penalty mark)				
18	Steeton	v	Jarrow	2-2	102
	(Jarrow won 9-8 on kicks from the penalty mark)				
19	Carlisle City	v	Nelson	3-5	121
20	AFC Blackpool	v	Knaresborough Town	1-0	102
21	Silsden	v	Garstang	3-1	115
22	Retford	v	Cammell Laird 1907	0-2	154
23	Staveley MW	v	AFC Darwen	0-0	110
	(AFC Darwen won 6-5 on kicks from the penalty mark – at Sheffield FC)				
24	Skelmersdale United	v	Stockport Town	1-2	169
25	Hemsworth Miners Welfare	v	Armthorpe Welfare	3-2	98
26	West Didsbury & Chorlton	v	Bury AFC	2-1	300
27	Hall Road Rangers	v	Barnton	2-4	53
28	Litherland Remyca	v	Selby Town	1-2	88
29	Penistone Church	v	Prestwich Heys	2-2	272
	(Penistone Church won 5-4 on kicks from the penalty mark)				
30	Goole	v	Cheadle Heath Nomads	7-3	78
	(at Cheadle Heath Nomads FC)				
31	Parkgate	v	Worsbrough Bridge Athletic	4-0	95
32	Charnock Richard	v	Barton Town	3-0	173
33	Rossington Main	v	Nostell MW	0-2	90
34	Brigg Town	v	Winterton Rangers	2-3	260
35	Emley	v	Irlam	1-1	169
	(Irlam won 5-3 on kicks from the penalty mark)				
36	St Helens Town	v	North Ferriby	0-2	242
	(at North Ferriby FC)				
37	Liversedge	v	Handsworth	3-1	159
38	Swallownest	v	Ashton Town	1-0	97
39	Daisy Hill	v	Warrington Rylands	2-5	66
40	Cheadle Town	v	Athersley Recreation	1-1	112
	(Cheadle Town won 4-3 on kicks from the penalty mark)				
41	Golcar United	v	Northwich Victoria	0-2	300
42	Pilkington	v	Bacup Borough	1-3	58
	(at Bacup Borough FC)				
43	Avro	v	Bottesford Town	1-0	110
44	FC Isle of Man	v	AFC Liverpool		
	(walkover for AFC Liverpool – FC Isle of Man withdrawn)				
45	Burscough	v	Hallam	1-1	300
	(Hallam won 4-3 on kicks from the penalty mark – at Hallam FC)				
46	Whitchurch Alport	v	Littleton	0-2	170
47	Hinckley	v	Studley (20/9)	0-2	242
48	Boldmere St Michaels	v	Brocton (26/9)	4-0	121
49	Highgate United	v	Wellington FC	3-3	52
	(Highgate United won 8-7 on kicks from the penalty mark)				
50	Darlaston Town (1874)	v	Heather St Johns	2-0	176
51	Dudley Sports	v	Wem Town	3-0	35
52	Wolverhampton SC	v	Bewdley Town	0-1	40
53	Heath Hayes	v	Dudley Town	1-2	143
54	Nuneaton Griff	v	Chelmsley Town	2-2	83
	(Chelmsley Town won 4-1 on kicks from the penalty mark)				
55	Romulus	v	Coventry Copsewood	3-1	81
56	Paget Rangers	v	Wolverhampton Casuals	3-1	109
57	Winsford United	v	Alsager Town	4-1	198
58	Sandbach United	v	Stapenhill	0-1	142
59	Leicester Road	v	Haughmond	0-0	79
	(Leicester Road won 3-0 on kicks from the penalty mark)				
60	St Martins	v	Pershore Town	1-4	105
61	Coventry Sphinx	v	Worcester Raiders	1-1	77
	(Coventry Sphinx won 3-1 on kicks from the penalty mark)				
62	Ellesmere Rangers	v	Cradley Town	3-1	65
63	Racing Club Warwick	v	Hereford Pegasus	2-1	65
	(at Hereford Pegasus FC)				
64	AFC Wulfrunians	v	Uttoxeter Town	0-3	87
65	AFC Bridgnorth	v	Wednesfield	3-3	97
	(AFC Bridgnorth won 5-4 on kicks from the penalty mark)				
66	Abbey Hulton United	v	Shawbury United	3-2	100
67	Rugby Town	v	Bilston Town	1-1	183
	(Rugby Town won 4-1 on kicks from the penalty mark)				
68	Stafford Town	v	Lichfield City	0-4	107
69	OJM Black Country	v	Rocester (18/9)	0-1	60
70	Sherwood Colliery	v	St Andrews	3-0	87
71	Harborough Town	v	Barrow Town	8-1	148
72	Hucknall Town	v	Anstey Nomads	1-2	247
73	Selston	v	Eastwood Community	3-3	172
	(Seslton won 4-3 on kicks from the penalty mark)				
74	Holbeach United	v	Loughborough University	1-5	90
75	Graham Street Prims	v	Leicester Nirvana	0-3	65
76	Teversal	v	Shirebrook Town	0-3	94
77	Dunkirk	v	Harrowby United	1-2	77
78	Deeping Rangers	v	GNG Oadby Town	10-1	80
79	Aylestone Park	v	Pinchbeck United	4-1	95
80	Boston Town	v	Sleaford Town	6-0	77
81	Ingles	v	Saffron Dynamo	2-0	82
82	Blackstones	v	Lutterworth Athletic	0-3	70
83	Clipstone	v	Radford	2-2	81
	(Radford won 3-2 on kicks from the penalty mark)				
84	Birstall United Social	v	Holwell Sports	2-0	90
85	Clifton All Whites	v	Quorn	0-2	56
86	Peterborough Northern Star	v	Mulbarton Wanderers	0-7	30
87	Sheringham	v	Newmarket Town	2-0	120
88	Huntingdon Town	v	Mildenhall Town	0-2	40
89	Diss Town	v	Fakenham Town	0-1	93
90	Lakenheath	v	Framlingham Town	7-1	83
91	Godmanchester Rovers	v	Norwich United	0-0	95
	(Norwich United won 4-2 on kicks from the penalty mark)				
92	Downham Town	v	Ely City	3-0	70
93	Barkingside	v	Coggeshall United (18/9)	1-3	103
94	Colney Heath	v	Wivenhoe Town	0-0	91
	(Colney Heath won 4-2 on kicks from the penalty mark)				
95	Brimsdown	v	Clapton	2-4	30
96	Little Oakley	v	Stotfold	2-1	106
97	Hackney Wick	v	Halstead Town (20/9)	0-1	93
98	Enfield Borough	v	Tower Hamlets	3-2	38
99	West Essex	v	Haverhill Borough (20/9)	8-1	71
100	St Margaretsbury	v	London Colney	1-1	83
	(London Colney won 6-5 on kicks from the penalty mark)				
101	Ipswich Wanderers	v	Brantham Athletic	5-3	94
102	Potton United	v	Biggleswade United	2-1	158
103	Redbridge	v	May & Baker Eastbrook Community	1-3	68
104	Ilford	v	Long Melford	5-3	80
105	Southend Manor	v	Cockfosters	0-1	46
106	Sporting Bengal United	v	Sawbridgeworth Town	3-3	39
	(Sporting Bengal United won 4-2 on kicks from the penalty mark – at Sawbridgeworth Town FC)				
107	Holland	v	Enfield (20/9)	2-0	150
108	Saffron Walden Town	v	Whitton United	3-3	210
	(Whitton United won 4-1 on kicks from the penalty mark)				
109	Harwich & Parkeston	v	Walthamstow	1-1	180
	(Walthamstow won 5-4 on kicks from the penalty mark)				
110	Frenford	v	Newbury Forest	2-4	51
111	Hashtag United	v	Takeley	3-1	145
112	Hoddesdon Town	v	Langford	3-2	69
113	Hadley	v	Hadleigh United	2-0	138
114	Athletic Newham	v	Wormley Rovers	0-1	20
115	Northampton Sileby Rangers	v	Bedfont & Feltham	4-3	84
116	Leverstock Green	v	AFC Hayes	0-3	67
117	Buckingham Athletic	v	Holmer Green	0-2	80
118	Ardley United	v	Easington Sports	0-2	70
119	Amersham Town	v	Cogenhoe United	1-4	33
120	London Tigers	v	Northampton On Chenecks (20/9)	0-5	60
121	Egham Town	v	Raunds Town	0-2	51
122	Winslow United	v	Risborough Rangers	0-3	182
123	Ampthill Town	v	Dunstable Town	4-1	171
124	Holyport	v	FC Deportivo Galicia	0-1	114

FAV 2Q
Brimscombe & Thrupp
v
AFC Aldermaston.
Photos Peter Barnes.

FIRST QUALIFYING ROUND 2020-21

125	British Airways	v	CB Hounslow United	1-1	66
	(CB Hounslow United won 6-5 on kicks from the penalty mark)				
126	North Greenford United	v	Chalvey Sports	5-1	83
127	Rushden & Higham United	v	Flackwell Heath	0-4	44
128	Harefield United	v	Tring Athletic	1-1	95
	(Tring Athletic won 6-5 on kicks from the penalty mark)				
129	Spelthorne Sports	v	Arlesey Town	2-4	79
130	Thame Rangers	v	Milton Keynes Irish (18/9)	0-6	75
131	Penn & Tylers Green	v	Burnham	1-0	147
132	Broadfields United	v	Aylesbury Vale Dynamos (18/9)	0-0	163
	(Broadfields United won 5-4 on kicks from the penalty mark)				
133	Rayners Lane	v	Hanworth Villa	2-4	130
134	Wembley	v	Wellingborough Whitworth	1-2	68
135	Edgware Town	v	Irchester United	3-1	48
136	Windsor	v	Long Buckby	0-3	141
137	Longlevens	v	Tytherington Rocks	3-3	78
	(Longlevens won 4-3 on kicks from the penalty mark)				
138	Tadley Calleva	v	Wallingford Town	4-1	126
139	Wokingham & Emmbrook	v	Cheltenham Saracens	3-0	155
140	Abingdon Town	v	Thornbury Town	0-3	53
141	Cove	v	Frimley Green	2-2	104
	(Frimley Green won 7-6 on kicks from the penalty mark)				
142	Fleet Town	v	Newent Town	3-1	109
143	Clanfield 85	v	Tuffley Rovers	2-0	58
144	Eversley & California	v	Long Crendon	1-3	40
145	Chipping Sodbury Town	v	Bishop's Cleeve	0-1	74
146	Shrivenham	v	Camberley Town	1-0	70
147	Abingdon United	v	Shortwood United	0-0	59
	(Abingdon United won 4-3 on kicks from the penalty mark)				
148	Fairford Town	v	Lydney Town	0-1	108
149	Virginia Water	v	Reading City (18/9)	0-1	91
150	Walton & Hersham	v	Meridian VP (7.45)	3-1	140
151	Seaford Town	v	Southwick		
	(walkover for Seaford Town – Southwick withdrawn)				
152	Fisher	v	Little Common	4-0	163
153	Colliers Wood United	v	Mile Oak	7-1	48
154	Raynes Park Vale	v	Rusthall	3-2	77
155	Forest Hill Park	v	Lingfield	2-3	60
	(at Lingfield FC)				
156	Holmesdale	v	Kent Football United	4-2	42
157	Crowborough Athletic	v	Molesey	1-1	137
	(Molesesy won 4-2 on kicks from the penalty mark)				
158	Worthing United	v	Greenways	5-4	108
159	Lydd Town	v	Broadbridge Heath	1-1	85
	(Lydd Town won 3-2 on kicks from the penalty mark)				
160	Redhill	v	Snodland Town	2-2	71
	(Redhill won 3-1 on kicks from the penalty mark)				
161	Horley Town	v	Hollands & Blair	4-2	106
162	Oakwood	v	East Preston	0-2	40
163	Lewisham Borough (Com)	v	Balham	0-2	50
164	Hailsham Town	v	AFC Varndeanians	0-3	94
165	Croydon	v	Sheppey United	1-2	167
	(at Glebe FC)				
166	Alfold	v	Chessington & Hook United	4-0	80
167	Sheerwater	v	Sporting Club Thamesmead	2-1	91
168	K Sports	v	Tunbridge Wells	2-1	115
169	Stansfeld	v	Knaphill	2-2	75
	(Stansfeld won 8-7 on kicks from the penalty mark)				
170	Hassocks	v	Peacehaven & Telscombe	0-3	219
171	Godalming Town	v	Shoreham	3-3	154
	(Shoreham won 5-4 on kicks from the penalty mark)				
172	Epsom & Ewell	v	Bridon Ropes (13/10)	2-1	68
	(20/9 – tie ordered to be replayed)				
173	Westside	v	Abbey Rangers (20/9)	1-3	73
174	Banstead Athletic	v	Guildford City	2-2	40
	(Guildford City won 4-2 on kicks from the penalty mark)				
175	Greenwich Borough	v	Cobham		
	(walkover for Cobham – Greenwich Borough withdrawn)				
176	Wick	v	AFC Croydon Athletic	2-1	35
177	Steyning Town Community	v	Bagshot	3-1	110
178	Storrington Community	v	Bexhill United	2-1	92
179	Langney Wanderers	v	Eastbourne United	4-2	157
180	Beckenham Town	v	Littlehampton Town	1-2	65
181	Punjab United	v	Bearsted	1-1	72
	(Punjab United won 5-3 on kicks from the penalty mark)				
182	Kennington	v	Erith Town (20/9)	1-0	190
183	Billingshurst	v	FC Elmstead	2-2	50
	(Billingshurst won 7-6 on kicks from the penalty mark)				
184	Erith & Belvedere	v	Loxwood	1-0	80
185	Horsham YMCA	v	Arundel	4-0	82
186	Blackfield & Langley	v	Folland Sports	1-0	71
187	Amesbury Town	v	Lymington Town	0-3	80
188	Cowes Sports	v	Devizes Town	2-2	184
	(Cowes Sports won 5-4 on kicks from the penalty mark)				
189	Farnham Town	v	Downton	4-2	111
190	AFC Portchester	v	Bemerton Heath Harlequins	3-2	167
191	East Cowes Victoria Athletic	v	Westbury United	1-2	72
192	Hythe & Dibden	v	Verwood Town	0-2	73
193	Newport (IW)	v	Calne Town (20/9)	2-2	151
	(Newport (IW) won 5-3 on kicks from the penalty mark)				
194	Portland United	v	Hamble Club	0-4	95
195	Alresford Town	v	AFC Stoneham	1-1	179
	(AFC Stoneham won 4-3 on kicks from the penalty mark)				
196	New Milton Town	v	Andover New Street	0-0	104
	(New Milton Town won 6-5 on kicks from the penalty mark)				
197	Shaftesbury	v	Badshot Lea	0-4	57
198	Fawley	v	Ringwood Town (18/9)	3-4	95
199	Baffins Milton Rovers	v	Bashley	2-2	200
	(Bashley won 4-3 on kicks from the penalty mark)				
200	Corsham Town	v	Brockenhurst	1-1	175
	(Brockenhurst won 6-5 on kicks from the penalty mark)				
201	Romsey Town	v	Selsey	4-0	257
202	Sidmouth Town	v	Cheddar	4-5	84
203	Elburton Villa	v	Saltash United	1-1	102
	(Elburton Villa won 10-9 on kicks from the penalty mark)				
204	Ilfracombe Town	v	Portishead Town	3-3	95
	(Ilfracombe Town won 5-3 on kicks from the penalty mark)				
205	Odd Down	v	Brislington	2-2	70
	(Brislington won 3-2 on kicks from the penalty mark)				
206	Exmouth Town	v	Mousehole	0-0	252
	(Exmouth Town won 5-3 on kicks from the penalty mark)				
207	Torpoint Athletic	v	Porthleven	3-2	94
208	Launceston	v	Axminster Town	0-4	66
209	Wellington AFC	v	Hengrove Athletic	2-2	75
	(Hengrove Athletic won 5-4 on kicks from the penalty mark)				
210	Newquay	v	Street	3-6	210
211	Bridport	v	AFC St Austell	4-3	134
212	St Blazey	v	Bishops Lydeard	4-2	101
213	Radstock Town	v	Longwell Green Sports	1-1	70
	(Longwell Green Sports won 5-3 on kicks from the penalty mark)				
214	Bodmin Town	v	Keynsham Town	2-3	90
215	Callington Town	v	Ivybridge Town	0-3	82
216	Welton Rovers	v	Cullompton Rangers	4-1	76
217	Shepton Mallet	v	Bishop Sutton	3-1	157
218	Wells City	v	Godolphin Atlantic	6-0	57
219	Brixham	v	Newton Abbot Spurs	2-4	88
220	Camelford	v	Almondsbury	5-1	73
221	Liskeard Athletic	v	Millbrook	0-3	54

FAV 1P - Buckby (Wellingborough) shoots over the Haverhill bar. Photo Keith Clayton.

FAV 1P - Davies (Haverhill) Long (Wellingborough). Photo Keith Clayton.

FAV 1P - Anderson (Haverhill) Wilson (Wellingborough). Photo Keith Clayton.

SECOND QUALIFYING ROUND - SATURDAY 10 OCTOBER 2020

No	Home		Away	Score	Att
1	Esh Winning	v	AFC Blackpool	1-2	91
2	Newcastle University	v	Thornaby	4-1	90
3	Holker Old Boys	v	Crook Town	2-1	147
4	Silsden	v	Guisborough Town	3-5	215
5	Thackley	v	Harrogate Railway Athletic	0-1	181
6	Redcar Athletic	v	Whickham	2-1	255
7	Heaton Stannington	v	Padiham	1-2	170
8	North Shields	v	Northallerton Town	3-2	150
9	Nelson	v	Ashington (17/10)	1-4	101
10	Newton Aycliffe	v	Billingham Synthonia	2-0	146
11	Brandon United	v	Penrith	1-2	50
12	Jarrow	v	Birtley Town	3-2	114
13	Sunderland RCA	v	Shildon	2-3	150
14	Campion	v	Sunderland Ryhope CW	0-4	90
15	Garforth Town	v	Seaham Red Star	1-1	218
	(Seaham Red Star won 6-5 on kicks from the penalty mark)				
16	Avro	v	Abbey Hey	0-3	266
17	Warrington Rylands	v	Goole	6-0	117
18	Penistone Church	v	Wythenshawe Amateurs	2-1	280
19	North Ferriby	v	Northwich Victoria	3-2	300
20	Hallam	v	Parkgate	3-1	300
21	Hemsworth MW	v	Nostell MW	3-0	108
	(at Nostell MW FC)				
22	Barnton	v	Swallownest (11/10)	4-0	203
23	West Didsbury & Chorlton	v	Charnock Richard	0-2	300
24	Bacup Borough	v	Stockport Town	1-1	92
	(Bacup Borough won 4-3 on kicks from the penalty mark)				
25	Cheadle Town	v	Dronfield Town	4-0	141
26	Glasshoughton Welfare	v	Irlam	1-3	86
27	1874 Northwich	v	Selby Town	3-0	180
28	Cammell Laird 1907	v	Maltby Main	0-3	96
29	AFC Liverpool	v	Maine Road (9/10)	3-2	119
30	Bootle	v	Shelley		
	(walkover for Bootle – Shelley withdrawn)				
31	Liversedge	v	Ashton Athletic (17/10)	3-1	221
32	New Mills	v	Winterton Rangers (17/10)	2-1	164
33	AFC Darwen	v	Runcorn Town	0-2	238
34	Chelmsley Town	v	Paget Rangers (11/10)	0-1	320
35	Romulus	v	Leicester Road (17/10)	0-0	92
	(Romulus won 7-6 on kicks from the penalty mark)				
36	Pershore Town	v	AFC Bridgnorth	0-1	127
37	Highgate United	v	Racing Club Warwick	1-5	115
38	Rugby Town	v	Ellesmere Rangers	6-1	240
39	Winsford United	v	Boldmere St Michaels	1-1	173
	(Boldmere St Michaels won 14-13 on kicks from the penalty mark)				
40	Uttoxeter Town	v	Stourport Swifts	1-3	120
41	Rocester	v	Bewdley Town (17/10)	1-3	159
42	Dudley Sports	v	Littleton	2-1	45
43	Studley	v	Darlaston Town (1874)	3-1	77
44	Coventry Sphinx	v	Shifnal Town	2-0	91
45	Eccleshall	v	Hanley Town (17/10)	0-7	176
46	Dudley Town	v	Stone Old Alleynians	0-2	95
47	GNP Sports	v	Gresley Rovers	1-2	277
	(at Gresley Rovers FC)				
48	Tividale	v	Stapenhill	0-2	129
49	Cadbury Athletic	v	Lichfield City	1-0	72
	(at Lichfield City FC)				
50	Abbey Hulton United	v	Ashby Ivanhoe	3-1	97
51	Anstey Nomads	v	Boston Town (17/10)	3-1	138
52	Rainworth MW	v	Gedling MW	3-3	77
	(Rainworth MW won 4-3 on kicks from the penalty mark)				
53	West Bridgford	v	Harrowby United	2-2	95
	(Harrowby United won 4-2 on kicks from the penalty mark)				
54	Sherwood Colliery	v	Aylestone Park	1-3	87
55	Melton Town	v	Birstall United Social	8-1	132
56	Long Eaton United	v	Selston	4-1	105
57	Quorn	v	Kirby Muxloe	5-2	130
58	Radford	v	Ollerton Town	3-3	115
	(Radford won 4-3 on kicks from the penalty mark)				
59	Harborough Town	v	Leicester Nirvana	3-5	162
60	Belper United	v	Kimberley Miners Welfare (11/10)	2-1	258
61	Lutterworth Athletic	v	Deeping Rangers	0-3	115
62	Bourne Town	v	Loughborough University	0-4	116
63	Shirebrook Town	v	Ingles	1-1	121
	(Shirebrook Town won 5-4 on kicks from the penalty mark)				
64	Borrowash Victoria	v	Skegness Town	0-3	196
65	Swaffham Town	v	Fakenham Town	2-2	102
	(Fakenham Town won 4-3 on kicks from the penalty mark)				
66	Lakenheath	v	Mildenhall Town	1-3	137
67	Whittlesey Athletic	v	Debenham LC	2-0	90
68	Thetford Town	v	Norwich United	1-2	109
69	Gorleston	v	Downham Town	3-2	168
70	Great Yarmouth Town	v	Mulbarton Wanderers	1-3	118
71	Sheringham	v	Walsham Le Willows	0-1	180
72	March Town United	v	Norwich CBS	2-2	100
	(Norwich CBS won 6-5 on kicks from the penalty mark)				
73	Ipswich Wanderers	v	London Colney	1-0	120
74	Coggeshall United	v	Sporting Bengal United (11/10)	3-2	70
75	Potton United	v	Clapton	1-3	78
76	Hashtag United	v	Wormley Rovers	5-0	300
77	Park View	v	Cockfosters	2-2	
	(Cockfosters won 4-2 on kicks from the penalty mark)				
78	West Essex	v	Haverhill Rovers (9/10)	3-4	91
79	Whitton United	v	White Ensign (17/10)	1-2	62
80	Hadley	v	Enfield Borough	1-1	145
	(Hadley won 8-7 on kicks from the penalty mark)				
81	Hoddesdon Town	v	Woodford Town	2-1	68
82	Baldock Town	v	Halstead Town (11/10)	3-2	128
83	New Salamis	v	Cornard United	3-0	45
84	Holland	v	Colney Heath (17/10)	0-0	
	(Colney Heath won 4-3 on kicks from the penalty mark)				
85	May & Baker Eastbrook C	v	Little Oakley (9/10)	2-2	105
	(May & Baker Eastbrook Community won 6-5 on kicks from the penalty mark)				
86	Newbury Forest	v	Burnham Ramblers	2-2	41
	(Newbury Forest won 4-3 on kicks from the penalty mark)				
87	Ilford	v	Benfleet	1-1	90
	(Ilford won 4-3 on kicks from the penalty mark)				
88	Walthamstow	v	London Lions	3-1	189
89	Crawley Green	v	Wellingborough Whitworth	6-4	BCD
90	Flackwell Heath	v	Desborough Town	3-0	84
91	CB Hounslow United	v	Easington Sports	2-2	70
	(CB Hounslow United won 4-2 on kicks from the penalty mark)				
92	Edgware Town	v	Tring Athletic (9/10)	4-1	146
93	AFC Hayes	v	Penn & Tylers Green	2-0	77
	(at Penn & Tylers Green FC)				
94	Burton Park Wanderers	v	Northampton On Chenecks (11/10)	2-2	126
	(Burton Park Wanderers won 6-5 on kicks from the penalty mark)				
95	Holmer Green	v	Bugbrooke St Michaels	1-4	52
96	Raunds Town	v	Risborough Rangers	1-4	78
97	Hanworth Villa	v	FC Deportivo Galicia	4-0	116
98	Arlesey Town	v	Northampton Sileby Rangers	2-3	92
99	Long Buckby	v	Ampthill Town	2-3	111
100	Broadfields United	v	Milton Keynes Irish	1-2	63
101	Oxhey Jets	v	North Greenford United	1-3	76
102	Rothwell Corinthians	v	St Panteleimon	3-0	72
103	Cogenhoe United	v	Harpenden Town	2-1	61
104	Brimscombe & Thrupp	v	AFC Aldermaston	5-0	109
105	Sandhurst Town	v	Long Crendon (9/10)	3-1	65
106	Stonehouse Town	v	Royal Wootton Bassett Town	0-1	124
107	Longlevens	v	Wokingham & Emmbrook	2-0	67

Jack Bartman scores for Brimscombe & Thrupp against Bridgwater Town

FAV 3P - Brimscombe & Thrupp v Bridgwater Town. Photos Peter Barnes.

FAV 4P - North Ferriby v West Auckland. Photo Bill Wheatcroft

SECOND QUALIFYING ROUND

No	Home		Away	Score	Att
108	Bishop's Cleeve	v	Malmesbury Victoria	1-0	129
109	Milton United	v	Lydney Town	3-1	91
110	Clanfield 85	v	Fleet Spurs	3-2	81
111	Tadley Calleva	v	Frimley Green	1-2	76
112	Thornbury Town	v	Abingdon United	1-4	149
113	Woodley United	v	Reading City	2-3	207
114	Fleet Town	v	Shrivenham	3-1	160
115	Rochester United	v	Sutton Athletic	0-4	68
116	Worthing United	v	Canterbury City	4-3	122
117	Steyning Town Community	v	Lingfield	3-1	105
118	Holmesdale	v	AFC Varndeanians	2-0	67
119	Tooting Bec	v	Lydd Town (11/10)	2-2	174
	(Tooting Bec won 4-2 on kicks from the penalty mark)				
120	Sheerwater	v	Horsham YMCA	2-1	97
121	Wick	v	Saltdean United	0-2	60
122	Erith & Belvedere	v	Colliers Wood United	3-0	146
123	Seaford Town	v	Storrington Community	2-2	111
	(Seaford Town won 6-5 on kicks from the penalty mark)				
124	Kennington	v	Shoreham (11/10)	7-0	192
125	East Preston	v	Fisher	0-2	114
126	Alfold	v	Stansfeld	2-4	61
127	Littlehampton Town	v	Lordswood	3-1	106
128	Walton & Hersham	v	K Sports	1-0	129
129	Peacehaven & Telscombe	v	Balham	2-2	208
	(Peacehaven & Telscombe won 4-3 on kicks from the penalty mark)				
130	Abbey Rangers	v	Guildford City	1-1	105
	(Guildford City won 4-3 on kicks from the penalty mark)				
131	Punjab United	v	Horley Town	2-3	62
132	Billingshurst	v	Jersey Bulls (1.30)	0-3	115
133	Epsom & Ewell	v	Langney Wanderers (18/10)	1-1	130
	(Epsom & Ewell won 3-2 on kicks from the penalty mark)				
134	Redhill	v	Raynes Park Vale	0-1	68
135	Crawley Down Gatwick	v	Cobham	1-1	116
	(Cobham won 5-3 on kicks from the penalty mark)				
136	Sheppey United	v	Molesey	6-0	300
137	New Milton Town	v	Totton & Eling	4-0	114
138	Fareham Town	v	Badshot Lea	3-3	172
	(Fareham Town won 3-0 on kicks from the penalty mark)				
139	Farnham Town	v	Petersfield Town	0-0	263
	(Petersfield Town won 6-5 on kicks from the penalty mark)				
140	Romsey Town	v	Ringwood Town	1-5	236
141	Bournemouth	v	Blackfield & Langley	2-2	152
	(Bournemouth won 5-4 on kicks from the penalty mark)				
142	Cowes Sports	v	Pagham	1-4	169
143	Horndean	v	Westbury United	0-1	90
144	Whitchurch United	v	Verwood Town	2-1	93
145	Newport (IW)	v	Alton	1-0	111
146	Lymington Town	v	Hamble Club	2-0	127
147	Ash United	v	Bashley	2-6	82
148	Brockenhurst	v	AFC Stoneham	3-2	173
149	United Services Portsmouth	v	AFC Portchester	2-1	300
	(at AFC Portchester)				
150	Street	v	Hengrove Athletic	2-0	105
151	Cheddar	v	Ivybridge Town	3-2	77
152	Bridport	v	Ilfracombe Town	1-3	149
153	Camelford	v	Wadebridge Town	0-0	133
	(Camelford won 6-5 on kicks from the penalty mark)				
154	Oldland Abbotonians	v	Keynsham Town	0-5	60
155	Axminster Town	v	Clevedon Town	0-2	107
156	Shepton Mallet	v	Torrington	5-1	160
157	Helston Athletic	v	Torpoint Athletic	1-0	73
158	Millbrook	v	Hallen	2-1	146
159	Sherborne Town	v	Exmouth Town		
	(walkover for Sherborne Town – Exmouth Town withdrawn)				
160	Cadbury Heath	v	Ashton & Backwell United		
	(walkover for Ashton & Backwell United – Cadbury Heath withdrawn)				
161	Welton Rovers	v	Elburton Villa	1-0	112
162	St Blazey	v	Brislington	3-0	203
163	Newton Abbot Spurs	v	Crediton United	3-2	126
164	Longwell Green Sports	v	Bovey Tracey	2-1	45
165	Wells City	v	Bristol Telephones	3-0	51

FIRST ROUND PROPER - SATURDAY 31 OCTOBER 2020

No	Home		Away	Score	Att
1	Redcar Athletic	v	Holker Old Boys	1-2	197
2	Penistone Church	v	AFC Liverpool	3-0	266
3	Abbey Hey	v	Hemsworth MW (5/12)	3-1	
4	Jarrow	v	Yorkshire Amateur	0-0	134
	(Jarrow won 3-0 on kicks from the penalty mark)				
5	Liversedge	v	Newcastle Benfield	5-2	300
6	Charnock Richard	v	Ashington		
	(walkover for Charnock Richard – Ashington withdrawn)				
7	Warrington Rylands	v	Padiham	2-0	152
8	Guisborough Town	v	Runcorn Town	2-0	187
9	Lower Breck	v	Newton Aycliffe	3-2	118
10	Maltby Main	v	Newcastle University	3-1	153
11	Wythenshawe Town	v	North Ferriby	2-2	182
	(North Ferriby won 5-4 on kicks from the penalty mark)				
12	Hallam	v	AFC Blackpool (5/12)	4-3	
13	Bridlington Town	v	North Shields	2-2	
	(North Shields won 5-4 on kicks from the penalty mark)				
14	Bootle	v	Shildon	0-2	196
15	Irlam	v	Seaham Red Star	0-2	127
16	Sunderland Ryhope CW	v	Penrith	3-0	59
17	Cheadle Town	v	New Mills	0-2	213
18	Barnton	v	Bacup Borough (6/12)	1-0	145
19	1874 Northwich	v	Harrogate Railway Athletic	2-1	210
20	Bewdley Town	v	Stapenhill	2-2	115
	(Bewdley Town won 4-3 on kicks from the penalty mark)				
21	Shepshed Dynamo	v	Melton Town	3-2	182
22	Coventry Sphinx	v	Heanor Town	6-1	101
23	Aylestone Park	v	Lye Town	3-3	106
	(Aylestone Park won 4-3 on kicks from the penalty mark)				
24	Grimsby Borough	v	Quorn	1-0	123
25	Hanley Town	v	Deeping Rangers		
	(walkover for Hanley Town – Deeping Rangers withdrawn)				
26	Harrowby United	v	AFC Bridgnorth	0-1	214
27	Racing Club Warwick	v	Abbey Hulton United	1-1	94
	(Abbey Hulton United won 4-2 on kicks from the penalty mark – at Abbey Hulton United FC)				
28	Paget Rangers	v	Radford	0-4	213
29	Shirebrook Town	v	Boldmere St Michaels	0-3	84
30	Dudley Sports	v	Rugby Town	2-1	127
31	Loughborough University	v	Cadbury Athletic	4-0	112
32	Rainworth MW	v	Belper United	3-2	142
33	Anstey Nomads	v	Leicester Nirvana (5/12)	1-0	
	(at Beaumont Park)				
34	Stourport Swifts	v	Skegness Town		
	(walkover for Stourport Swifts – Skegness Town withdrawn)				
35	Congleton Town	v	Gresley Rovers	5-0	300
36	Studley	v	Long Eaton United (3/11)	1-4	48
37	Malvern Town	v	Rothwell Corinthians	3-1	252
38	Westfields	v	Romulus	2-2	119
	(Westfields won 3-2 on kicks from the penalty mark)				
39	Stone Old Alleynians	v	AFC Mansfield	3-2	75
40	Gorleston	v	Baldock Town	4-2	149
41	Cockfosters	v	Cogenhoe United (3/11)	1-3	113
42	Ilford	v	FC Clacton	4-1	51
43	Bugbrooke St Michaels	v	Stanway Rovers	1-2	83
44	Ampthill Town	v	Walthamstow	1-1	280
	(Ampthill Town won 4-2 on kicks from the penalty mark)				
45	Wellingborough Town	v	Haverhill Rovers	2-0	91
46	Norwich United	v	White Ensign		
	(walkover for Norwich United – White Ensign withdrawn)				
47	Whittlesey Athletic	v	Mildenhall Town	0-6	90
48	Colney Heath	v	New Salamis	3-1	192
49	Fakenham Town	v	Crawley Green	2-1	145
50	Newbury Forest	v	May & Baker Eastbrook C (4/11)	0-4	50
	(at Barking FC)				
51	Norwich CBS	v	Ipswich Wanderers	3-2	59
52	Milton Keynes Irish	v	Stansted	2-0	106
53	Northampton Sileby Rangers	v	Burton Park Wanderers	2-2	125
	(Burton Park Wanderers won 5-4 on kicks from the penalty mark)				
54	Mulbarton Wanderers	v	Newport Pagnell Town	4-0	100
55	Coggeshall United	v	Hashtag United (1/11)	0-2	209
56	Walsham Le Willows	v	Hoddesdon Town	5-1	89

FAV 4P - North Ferriby v West Auckland.
Photos Bill Wheatcroft.

FAV 5P - Walsall Wood v Anstey Nomads.
Photos Bill Wheatcroft.

FAV 5P - Walsall Wood's Nelson fires the winning penalty past Nomads keeper Logan. Photo Bill Wheatcroft.

FIRST ROUND PROPER

No	Home		Away	Score	Att
57	Raynes Park Vale	v	Sheerwater (4/11)	1-0	95
58	Sandhurst Town	v	North Greenford United	2-6	45
59	Jersey Bulls	v	Cobham		
	(walkover for Cobham – Jersey Bulls withdrawn)				
60	Risborough Rangers	v	Erith & Belvedere (3/11)	0-0	138
	(Risborough Rangers won 4-2 on kicks from the penalty mark)				
61	Fleet Town	v	Littlehampton Town	0-2	185
62	Frimley Green	v	Flackwell Heath	0-2	90
63	Clapton	v	Petersfield Town	1-1	55
	(Petersfield Town won 3-0 on kicks from the penalty mark tie awarded to Clapton – Petersfield Town removed)				
64	Saltdean United	v	Epsom & Ewell	3-1	117
65	Eastbourne Town	v	Southall	0-3	300
66	Tooting Bec	v	Guildford City	2-3	114
67	Worthing United	v	Edgware Town (5/12)	3-1	121
	(31/10 – tie ordered to be replayed)				
68	Steyning Town Community	v	Seaford Town	9-1	168
69	Sutton Athletic	v	Sheppey United	0-2	170
70	Newhaven	v	Ascot United	4-1	152
71	Kennington	v	Fisher	1-1	300
	(Kennington won 5-4 on kicks from the penalty mark)				
72	Walton & Hersham	v	Peacehaven & Telscombe	3-0	227
73	Stansfeld	v	AFC Hayes (6/12)	2-2	223
	(Stansfeld won 4-3 on kicks from the penalty mark)				
74	Welling Town	v	Hanworth Villa	1-6	63
75	Hadley	v	Pagham	2-1	122
76	Holmesdale	v	AFC Uckfield Town	2-4	89
77	CB Hounslow United	v	Horley Town	1-5	68
	(at Horley Town FC)				
78	Reading City	v	Lancing	0-1	81
79	Cheddar	v	Ashton & Backwell United (5/12)	2-1	65
80	Bridgwater Town	v	Welton Rovers	5-0	173
81	Keynsham Town	v	Bashley	0-4	142
82	Bishop's Cleeve	v	Shepton Mallet (3/11)	6-3	99
83	Clevedon Town	v	Whitchurch United	2-1	143
84	Brockenhurst	v	Street (6/12)	2-2	113
	(Brockenhurst won 5-3 on kicks from the penalty mark)				
85	Fareham Town	v	Roman Glass St George (5/12)	4-1	240
86	St Blazey	v	Helston Athletic	2-2	271
	(Helston Athletic won 4-3 on kicks from the penalty mark)				
87	New Milton Town	v	Clanfield 85	1-1	135
	(New Milton Town won 4-1 on kicks from the penalty mark)				
88	Falmouth Town	v	Abingdon United	3-1	281
89	Millbrook	v	Sherborne Town (5/12)	3-1	97
90	Newton Abbot Spurs	v	Ringwood Town	3-1	171
91	Brimscombe & Thrupp	v	Longwell Green Sports (3/11)	4-2	78
92	Royal Wootton Bassett Town	v	Camelford	4-0	142
93	Cribbs	v	Newport (IW)	4-3	84
94	Hamworthy United	v	Ilfracombe Town	4-0	152
95	Wells City	v	Westbury United	2-2	113
	(Wells City won 4-3 on kicks from the penalty mark)				
96	United Services Portsmouth	v	Bournemouth (4/11)	3-1	184
	(at AFC Portchester)				
97	Milton United	v	Longlevens	2-2	113
	(Longlevens won 5-4 on kicks from the penalty mark)				
98	Lymington Town	v	Tavistock	1-2	131

SECOND ROUND PROPER - SATURDAY 5 DECEMBER 2020

No	Home		Away	Score	Att
1	Guisborough Town	v	Liversedge (1.30)	1-4	
2	Hebburn Town	v	North Shields (12/12)	3-2	150
3	New Mills	v	Congleton Town	2-2	191
	(Congleton Town won 5-4 on kicks from the penalty mark – at Congleton Town FC)				
4	Stockton Town	v	Charnock Richard	4-2	
5	Holker Old Boys	v	Vauxhall Motors	0-1	136
6	Consett	v	Maltby Main	5-0	
7	Jarrow	v	Warrington Rylands (12/12)	1-1	79
	(Warrington Rylands won 5-4 on kicks from the penalty mark)				
8	Longridge Town	v	Penistone Church (12/12)	1-1	
	(Longridge Town won 6-5 on kicks from the penalty mark - at Penistone Church FC)				
9	Sunderland Ryhope CW	v	Abbey Hey (12/12)	1-0	42
10	Barnton	v	Seaham Red Star (19/12)	0-4	247
11	Hallam	v	Shildon (12/12)	0-2	150
12	North Ferriby	v	Lower Breck	2-1	
13	1874 Northwich	v	West Auckland Town	1-4	281
14	Radford	v	Bewdley Town	3-1	
15	Long Eaton United	v	Stone Old Alleynians	3-2	
16	Atherstone Town	v	Malvern Town	0-1	
17	Lutterworth Town	v	Westfields	3-3	
	(Westfields won 5-4 on kicks from the penalty mark)				
18	Dudley Sports	v	Coventry Sphinx	1-1	
	(Coventry Sphinx won 3-2 on kicks from the penalty mark)				
19	Hanley Town	v	Loughborough University	2-1	
20	Walsall Wood	v	AFC Bridgnorth (9/12)	3-0	
21	Anstey Nomads	v	Rainworth MW (12/12)	1-0	60
	(at Beaumont Park)				
22	Stourport Swifts	v	Grimsby Borough (12/12)	3-1	173
23	Shepshed Dynamo	v	Worcester City	3-2	
24	Boldmere St Michaels	v	Newark	3-4	
25	Sporting Khalsa	v	Aylestone Park	4-1	
26	Coventry United	v	Abbey Hulton United	3-2	
27	Ilford	v	Colney Heath	2-4	105
28	Norwich United	v	Burton Park Wanderers		
	(walkover for Norwich United – Burton Park Wanderers withdrawn)				
29	Wroxham	v	Milton Keynes Irish	3-3	223
	(Milton Keynes Irish won 4-3 on kicks from the penalty mark)				
30	Mulbarton Wanderers	v	Cogenhoe United (12/12)	5-0	102
31	Gorleston	v	Kirkley & Pakefield		
	(walkover for Gorleston – Kirkley & Pakefield withdrawn)				
32	Fakenham Town	v	Hashtag United	0-0	300
	(Fakenham Town won 4-3 on kicks from the penalty mark)				
33	Wellingborough Town	v	Woodbridge Town	1-0	151
34	Stowmarket Town	v	Eynesbury Rovers	5-0	176
35	Stanway Rovers	v	Ampthill Town	1-1	124
	(Ampthill Town won 4-2 on kicks from the penalty mark)				
36	Norwich CBS	v	May & Baker Eastbrook C (12/12)	2-1	80
37	Mildenhall Town	v	Leighton Town		
	(walkover for Leighton Town – Mildenhall Town withdrawn)				
38	Hadley	v	Raynes Park Vale	4-1	179
39	Lancing	v	Worthing United (12/12)	3-0	300
40	North Greenford United	v	Walsham Le Willows	2-1	141
41	Hanworth Villa	v	Corinthian	2-2	135
	(Hanworth Villa won 6-5 on kicks from the penalty mark)				
42	Newhaven	v	Binfield	2-2	129
	(Binfield won 4-1 on kicks from the penalty mark)				
43	Saltdean United	v	Deal Town	2-2	113
	(Deal Town won 3-2 on kicks from the penalty mark)				
44	Horley Town	v	Chatham Town	3-5	98
45	Cobham	v	Risborough Rangers	1-0	84
46	Steyning Town Community	v	Walton & Hersham	1-6	105
47	Littlehampton Town	v	Sheppey United	3-3	204
	(Littlehampton won 5-4 on kicks from the penalty mark)				
48	Sutton Common Rovers	v	Southall (6/12)	4-0	102
49	Stansfeld	v	Flackwell Heath (12/12)	0-3	152
50	Glebe	v	Kennington	0-2	104
51	AFC Uckfield Town	v	Guildford City	2-4	116
52	Plymouth Parkway	v	Newton Abbot Spurs	3-1	272
53	Christchurch	v	Cribbs (12/12)	2-1	144
54	United Services Portsmouth	v	Brockenhurst (12/12)	2-1	104
55	Millbrook	v	Bashley (12/12)	2-0	107
56	Bradford Town	v	Brimscombe & Thrupp	2-3	161
57	Wells City	v	Buckland Athletic	1-2	71
58	New Milton Town	v	Longlevens (12/12)	2-0	143
59	Helston Athletic	v	Fareham Town (12/12)	0-2	119
60	Bridgwater Town	v	Royal Wootton Bassett Town	2-1	191
61	Clapton	v	Hamworthy United (1.00)	2-1	81
	(at Aveley FC)				
62	Tavistock	v	Cheddar (12/12)	6-1	160
63	Falmouth Town	v	Bishop's Cleeve (12/12)	2-1	300
64	Clevedon Town	v	Bitton	4-3	

FAV QF - Warrington Rylands v Hebburn Town a last minute scramble in the Rylands penalty area as Hebburn look for an equaliser.Photos Bill Wheatcroft.

THIRD ROUND PROPER

SATURDAY 19 DECEMBER 2020 (REVISED SATURDAY 10 APRIL 2021)

1	Longridge Town	v	Warrington Rylands	1-2	91
	(at Warrington Rylands FC)				
2	North Ferriby	v	Seaham Red Star (10/4)	1-0	
	(29/12 – North Ferriby won 7-6 on kicks from the penalty mark – tie ordered to be replayed)				
3	Sunderland Ryhope CW	v	Liversedge	0-0	
	(Liversedge won 4-3 on kicks from the penalty mark)				
4	Hebburn Town	v	Vauxhall Motors	2-2	
	(Hebburn Town won 5-4 on kicks from the penalty mark)				
5	Stockton Town	v	Shildon	1-3	150
6	Consett	v	West Auckland Town	1-2	
7	Stourport Swifts	v	Shepshed Dynamo	4-3	280
8	Long Eaton United	v	Hanley Town	2-0	92
9	Newark	v	Walsall Wood	1-1	150
	(Walsall Wood won 8-7 on kicks from the penalty mark)				
10	Radford	v	Westfields	0-5	95
11	Coventry Sphinx	v	Anstey Nomads	1-2	
12	Malvern Town	v	Sporting Khalsa	5-5	
	(Malvern Town won 6-5 on kicks from the penalty mark)				
13	Congleton Town	v	Coventry United	1-1	264
	(Congleton Town won 4-3 on kicks from the penalty mark)				
14	Fakenham Town	v	Milton Keynes Irish	2-2	
	(Fakenham Town won 4-2 on kicks from the penalty mark)				
15	Wellingborough Town	v	Norwich United	2-1	145
16	Leighton Town	v	Gorleston	4-2	159
17	Stowmarket Town	v	Norwich CBS	2-0	282
18	Mulbarton Wanderers	v	Ampthill Town	1-0	
19	Hadley	v	Colney Heath	0-0	150
	(Hadley won 4-1 on kicks from the penalty mark)				
20	Clapton	v	Cobham	0-5	
21	Guildford City	v	Walton & Hersham (10/4)	1-1	
	(Walton & Hersham won 4-2 on kicks from the penalty mark)				
22	Kennington	v	Sutton Common Rovers	1-1	
	(Sutton Common Rovers won 4-1 on kicks from the penalty mark)				
23	Deal Town	v	Binfield (10/4)	1- 4	
24	Littlehampton Town	v	Hanworth Villa	2-2	200
	(Hanworth Villa won 5-4 on kicks from the penalty mark)				
25	Chatham Town	v	Flackwell Heath	0-1	150
26	Lancing	v	North Greenford United	2-2	155
	(Lancing won 5-3 on kicks from the penalty mark)				
27	Christchurch	v	Falmouth Town (27/12)	1-1	263
	(Christchurch won 6-5 on kicks from the penalty mark)				
28	Clevedon Town	v	New Milton Town	2-0	171
29	United Services Portsmouth	v	Millbrook	3-2	
30	Buckland Athletic	v	Tavistock (26/12)	0-4	202
31	Plymouth Parkway	v	Fareham Town 10/4)	5-2	
	(at Devon FA)				
32	Brimscombe & Thrupp	v	Bridgwater Town (27/12)	2-2	141
	(Bridgwater Town won 5-4 on kicks from the penalty mark)				

FOURTH ROUND PROPER

SATURDAY 9 JANUARY 2021 (REVISED SATURDAY 17 APRIL 2021)

1	Shildon	v	Warrington Rylands (12.30)	0-0
	(Warrington Rylands won 5-4 on kicks from the penalty mark)			
2	North Ferriby	v	West Auckland Town (12.30)	4-0
	(tie awarded to West Auckland Town – North Ferriby removed)			
3	Hebburn Town	v	Liversedge (4.30)	2-1
4	Stourport Swifts	v	Walsall Wood (16/4)	1-2
5	Congleton Town	v	Malvern Town (5.00)	1-0
6	Long Eaton United	v	Westfields (4.30)	1-1
	(Long Eaton United won 5-4 on kicks from the penalty mark)			
7	Anstey Nomads	v	Wellingborough Town (12.45)	4-2
8	Mulbarton Wanderers	v	Hanworth Villa (4.15)	0-0
	(Hanworth Villa won 3-1 on kicks from the penalty mark)			
9	Leighton Town	v	Walton & Hersham (6.00)	2-1
10	Lancing	v	Flackwell Heath (12.30)	1-1
	(Flackwell Heath won 4-2 on kicks from the penalty mark)			
11	Fakenham Town	v	Binfield (12.30)	2-2
	(Binfield won 4-1 on kicks from the penalty mark)			
12	Stowmarket Town	v	Cobham	
	(walkover for Cobham – Stowmarket Town withdrawn)			
13	Sutton Common Rovers	v	Hadley (4.15)	1-3
14	Plymouth Parkway	v	Clevedon Town (4.30)	2-1
15	United Services Portsmouth	v	Christchurch (12.00)	1-1
	(United Services Portsmouth won 4-1 on kicks from the penalty mark)			
16	Bridgwater Town	v	Tavistock (16/4)	0-1

FIFTH ROUND PROPER

SATURDAY 24 APRIL 2021

1	Hebburn Town	v	Congleton Town	1-0
2	Warrington Rylands	v	West Auckland Town	1-1
	(Warrington Rylands won 3-1 on kicks from the penalty mark)			
3	Walsall Wood	v	Anstey Nomads	0-0
	(Walsall Wood won 5-4 on kicks from the penalty mark)			
4	Hanworth Villa	v	Long Eaton United	2-2
	(Long Eaton United won 5-3 on kicks from the penalty mark)			
5	Cobham	v	Leighton Town	0-1
6	Hadley	v	Binfield	0-0
	(Binfield won 5-4 on kicks from the penalty mark)			
7	Tavistock	v	United Services Portsmouth	1-3
8	Plymouth Parkway	v	Flackwell Heath	2-4

QUARTER FINALS

SATURDAY 1 MAY 2021

1	Warrington Rylands	v	Hebburn Town (8/5)	1-0
2	Leighton Town	v	Walsall Wood	1-2
3	Long Eaton United	v	Binfield	0-5
4	United Services Portsmouth	v	Flackwell Heath	2-0

SEMI FINALS

SATURDAY 8 MAY 2021

1	Warrington Rylands	v	Walsall Wood (15/5)	2-1
2	United Services Portsmouth	v	Binfield	1-1
	(Binfield won 4-3 on kicks from the penalty mark)			

THE FA VASE
2020-21 Final

BINFIELD (Hellenic Premier)	2-3	WARRINGTON RYLANDS (NWC Premier)
Ferdinand 42 67	Att: 9.000	*Nevitt 25 44 (pen) 59*

SQUAD: Chris Grace, David Hancock, Elliot Legg (sub 72nd min), Tom Willment, Liam Gavin, James McClurg, Sean Moore, George Short (sub 63rd min), Ollie Harris (sub 73rd min), Liam Ferdinand, Kensley Maloney.
Substitutes:- Jack Broome, Josh Howell (63), Jack Thomson-Wheeler (72), Josh Helmore, Phil Veal, Jemel Johnson, Asa Povey (73).

SQUAD: Graeme McCall, Warren Gerrard, Jack Tinning (sub 75th min), Gary Kenny, Charlie Doyle, Andrew Scarisbrick, Elliott Nevitt, Stephen Milne (sub 89th min), Kane Drummond, Richard Smith, Joseph Coveney (sub 62nd min).
Substitutes:- Michael Emery, Joseph Denman, Sam Sheen (62), Callum Lees, Paul Shanley, Freddie Potter (89), Thomas Freeman (75).

Referee - John Busby (Oxfordshire), assisted by Wade Smith (Manchester) and Hristo Karaivanov (Nottinghamshire). 4th Official – Sam Purkiss (London)

The week before this fixture, Rylands' Elliott Nevitt had scored the extra time winner for his side, Campfield, in the FA Sunday Cup final having the previous day scored the Rylands' winner in their Trophy semi-final triumph over Walsall Wood, repeating what he had done in their quarter final victory over the previous season's Vase victors, Hebburn Town. It was therefore no surprise to see his name on the scoresheet in this match but it was surely astonishing that he should net all three of his team's scores to close a season that will surely be the highlight of his footballing achievements. What a run Rylands have been on too in progressing through the pyramid in preceding seasons, during which they have climbed from Step 7 Cheshire League to achieve Step 4 Northern League status for next season, all under the ownership of Wayne Rooney's agent, Paul Stretford.

Rylands' opponents on the day had also enjoyed a successful season having earned promotion to the Isthmian South Central League and forcing their way through to this final despite having been drawn as the away side in each of their Vase ties en route to the final.

In the opening phases of the game it was red kitted Binfield making the early running, looking particularly strong on their left wing, where skipper Sean Moore, supported by Elliot Legg, was prominent. Stephen Milne broke through on the right for Rylands but his cross was too far ahead for any of his compatriots to reach. However, just after spurning a chance, it was Nevitt who put Rylands ahead in the 25th minute when his half hit shot fortuitously bounced over opposition keeper Chris Grace to find the net. Rylands' tails were up now. A cross from Warren Gerrard caused consternation in the Binfield defence and only a last ditch intervention prevented Milne from doubling the lead. Binfield retaliated with an Elliot Legg long range effort before they drew level when Liam Ferdinand found himself virtually on the goal line to bundle in an equaliser. The first half scoring was concluded with Rylands taking the lead for the second time through a Nevitt penalty after Liam Gavin had fouled Charlie Doyle. Even though Grace chose to dive the right way he could not prevent the score.

The second half was still in its infancy when Binfield's Legg was yellow carded for bringing down Kane Drummond. Rylands were certainly in the ascendancy now. Their supporters howled for a second penalty as Richard Smith was halted by Tom Willment in the act of shooting before, in the 59th minute, the blue shirted Rylands increased their lead. Milne's shot had been blocked by Gavin at the expense of a corner from which that man Nevitt rose to head home and put his side 3-1 up. Shortly after it was Milne threatening to add a fourth but despite his dribbling across the width of the penalty area he could not create a shooting chance.

Binfield, to their credit, were not surrendering and a crossfield ball from substitute Josh Howell was zipped into the net by Ferdinand to halve the deficit and lift his team's spirits. Another sub, Asa Povey, was only beaten by his own stumble as he engineered a shooting chance with the Moles pressing for the equaliser and the prospect of extra time. Rylands retaliated, racing to the other end where Grace blocked Drummond's shot with his feet. Binfield's Harris also forced his way into the other penalty area before losing control and the match ended with Nevitt racing towards the Binfield goal in pursuit of a fourth score before Grace was able to block with his feet at the expense of a corner. There was only one possible nomination for man of the match, duly assigned to hat trick hero Elliott Nevitt, who was in good company, it being apparently the first hat trick at Wembley since Harry Kane's against Montenegro two seasons before.

Arthur Evans

PAST FINALS

1975 HODDESDON TOWN 2 *(South Midlands)* — **EPSOM & EWELL 1** *(Surrey Senior)* — **Att: 9,500**
Sedgwick 2 — Wales — Ref: Mr R Toseland
Hoddesdon: Galvin, Green, Hickey, Maybury, Stevenson, Wilson, Bishop, Picking, Sedgwick, Nathan, Schofield
Epsom & Ewell: Page, Bennett, Webb, Wales, Worby, Jones, O'Connell, Walker, Tuite, Eales, Lee

1976 BILLERICAY TOWN 1 *(Essex Senior)* — **STAMFORD 0 (aet)** *(United Counties)* — **Att: 11,848**
Aslett — Ref: Mr A Robinson
Billericay: Griffiths, Payne, Foreman, Pullin, Bone, Coughlan, Geddes, Aslett, Clayden, Scott, Smith
Stamford: Johnson, Kwiatowski, Marchant, Crawford, Downs, Hird, Barnes, Walpole, Smith, Russell, Broadbent

1977 BILLERICAY TOWN 1 *(Essex Senior)* — **SHEFFIELD 1 (aet)** *(Yorkshire)* — **Att: 14,000**
Clayden — Coughlan og — Ref: Mr J Worrall
Billericay: Griffiths, Payne, Bone, Coughlan, Pullin, Scott, Wakefield, Aslett, Clayden,Woodhouse, McQueen. Sub: Whettell
Sheffield: Wing, Gilbody, Lodge, Hardisty, Watts, Skelton, Kay, Travis, Pugh, Thornhill,Haynes. Sub: Strutt
Replay BILLERICAY TOWN 2 — **SHEFFIELD 1** — **Att: 3,482**
Aslett, Woodhouse — Thornhill — at Nottingham Forest
Billericay: Griffiths, Payne, Pullin, Whettell, Bone, McQueen, Woodhouse, Aslett, Clayden, Scott, Wakefield
Sheffield: Wing, Gilbody, Lodge, Strutt, Watts, Skelton, Kay, Travis, Pugh, Thornhill, Haynes

1978 NEWCASTLE BLUE STAR 2 *(Wearside)* — **BARTON ROVERS 1** *(South Midlands)* — **Att: 16,858**
Dunn, Crumplin — Smith — Ref: Mr T Morris
Newcastle: Halbert, Feenan, Thompson, Davidson, S Dixon, Beynon, Storey, P Dixon, Crumplin, Callaghan, Dunn. Sub: Diamond
Barton Rovers: Blackwell, Stephens, Crossley, Evans, Harris, Dollimore, Dunn, Harnaman, Fossey, Turner, Smith. Sub: Cox

1979 BILLERICAY TOWN 4 *(Athenian)* — **ALMONDSBURY GREENWAY 1** *(Glos. Co)* — **Att: 17,500**
Young 3, Clayden — Price — Ref: Mr C Steel
Billericay: Norris, Blackaller, Bingham, Whettell, Bone, Reeves, Pullin, Scott, Clayden,Young, Groom. Sub: Carrigan
Almondsbury: Hamilton, Bowers, Scarrett, Sulllivan, Tudor, Wookey, Bowers, Shehean, Kerr, Butt, Price. Sub: Kilbaine

1980 STAMFORD 2 *(United Counties)* — **GUISBOROUGH TOWN 0** *(Northern Alliance)* — **Att: 11,500**
Alexander, McGowan — Ref: Neil Midgeley
Stamford: Johnson, Kwiatkowski, Ladd, McGowan, Bliszczak I, Mackin, Broadhurst, Hall,Czarnecki, Potter, Alexander. Sub: Bliszczak S
Guisborough: Cutter, Scott, Thornton, Angus, Maltby, Percy, Skelton, Coleman, McElvaney,Sills, Dilworth. Sub: Harrison

1981 WHICKHAM 3 *(Wearside)* — **WILLENHALL 2 (aet)** *(West Midlands)* — **Att: 12,000**
Scott, Williamson, Peck og — Smith, Stringer — Ref: Mr R Lewis
Whickham: Thompson, Scott, Knox, Williamson, Cook, Ward, Carroll, Diamond, Cawthra,Robertson, Turnbull. Sub: Alton
Willenhall: Newton, White, Darris, Woodall, Heath, Fox, Peck, Price, Matthews, Smith,Stringer. Sub: Trevor

1982 FOREST GREEN ROVERS 3 *(Hellenic)* — **RAINWORTH M.W 0** *(Notts Alliance)* — **Att: 12,500**
Leitch 2, Norman — Ref: Mr K Walmsey
Forest Green: Moss, Norman, Day, Turner, Higgins, Jenkins, Guest, Burns, Millard, Leitch, Doughty. Sub: Dangerfield
Rainworth M.W: Watson, Hallam, Hodgson, Slater, Sterland, Oliver, Knowles, Raine, Radzi, Reah, Comerford. Sub: Robinson

1983 V.S. RUGBY 1 *(West Midlands)* — **HALESOWEN TOWN 0** *(West Midlands)* — **Att: 13,700**
Crawley — Ref: Mr B Daniels
VS Rugby: Burton, McGinty, Harrison, Preston, Knox, Evans, ingram, Setchell, Owen,Beecham, Crawley. Sub: Haskins
Halesowen Town: Coldicott, Penn, Edmonds, Lacey, Randall, Shilvock, Hazelwood, Moss, Woodhouse,P Joinson, L Joinson. Sub: Smith

1984 STANSTED 3 *(Essex Senior)* — **STAMFORD 2** *(United Counties)* — **Att: 8,125**
Holt, Gillard, Reading — Waddicore, Allen — Ref: Mr T Bune
Stanstead: Coe, Williams, Hilton, Simpson, Cooper, Reading, Callanan, Holt, Reevs,Doyle, Gillard. Sub: Williams
Stamford: Parslow, Smitheringate, Blades, McIlwain, Lyon, Mackin, Genovese, Waddicore,Allen, Robson, Beech. Sub: Chapman

1985 HALESOWEN TOWN 3 *(West Midlands)* — **FLEETWOOD TOWN 1** *(N W Counties)* — **Att: 16,715**
L Joinson 2, Moss — Moran — Ref: Mr C Downey
Halesowen: Coldicott, Penn, Sherwood, Warner, Randle, Heath, Hazlewood, Moss (Smith),Woodhouse, P Joinson, L Joinson
Fleetwood Town: Dobson, Moran, Hadgraft, Strachan, Robinson, Milligan, Hall, Trainor, Taylor(Whitehouse), Cain, Kennerley

1986 HALESOWEN TOWN 3 *(West Midlands)* — **SOUTHALL 0** *(Isthmian 2 South)* — **Att: 18,340**
Moss 2, L Joinson — Ref: Mr D Scott
Halesowen: Pemberton, Moore, Lacey, Randle (Rhodes), Sherwood, Heath, Penn, Woodhouse, PJoinson, L Joinson, Moss
Southall: Mackenzie, James, McGovern, Croad, Holland, Powell (Richmond), Pierre,Richardson, Sweales, Ferdinand, Rowe

1987 ST. HELENS 3 *(N W Counties)* — **WARRINGTON TOWN 2** *(N W Counties)* — **Att: 4,254**
Layhe 2, Rigby — Reid, Cook — Ref: Mr T Mills
St Helens: Johnson, Benson, Lowe, Bendon, Wilson, McComb, Collins (Gledhill), O'Neill,Cummins, Lay, Rigby. Sub: Deakin
Warrington: O'Brien. Copeland, Hunter, Gratton, Whalley, Reid, Brownville (Woodyer), Cook,Kinsey, Looker (Hill), Hughes

1988 COLNE DYNAMOES 1 *(N W Counties)* — **EMLEY 0** *(Northern Counties East)* — **Att: 15,000**
Anderson — Ref: Mr A Seville
Colne Dynamoes: Mason, McFafyen, Westwell, Bentley, Dunn, Roscoe, Rodaway, Whitehead (Burke),Diamond, Anderson, Wood (Coates)
Emley: Dennis, Fielding, Mellor, Codd, Hirst (Burrows), Gartland (Cook), Carmody,Green, Bramald, Devine, Francis

1989 TAMWORTH 1 *(West Midlands)* — **SUDBURY TOWN 1 (aet)** *(Eastern)* — **Att: 26,487**
Devaney — Hubbick — Ref: Mr C Downey
Tamworth: Bedford, Lockett, Atkins, Cartwright, McCormack, Myers, Finn, Devaney, Moores,Gordon, Stanton. Subs: Rathbone, Heaton
Sudbury Town: Garnham, Henry, G Barker, Boyland, Thorpe, Klug, D Barker, Barton, Oldfield,Smith, Hubbick. Subs: Money, Hunt
Replay TAMWORTH 3 — **SUDBURY TOWN 0** — **Att: 11,201**
Stanton 2, Moores — at Peterborough
Tamworth: Bedford, Lockett, Atkins, Cartwright, Finn, Myers, George, Devaney, Moores,Gordon, Stanton. Sub: Heaton
Sudbury Town: Garnham, Henry, G Barker, Boyland, Thorpe, Klug, D Barker, Barton, Oldfield,Smith, Hubbick. Subs: Money, Hunt

1990 YEADING 0 *(Isthmian 2 South)* — **BRIDLINGTON TOWN 0 (aet)** *(N Co East)* — **Att: 7,932**
Ref: Mr R Groves
Yeading: Mackenzie, Wickens, Turner, Whiskey (McCarthy), Croad, Denton, Matthews, James(Charles), Sweates, Impey, Cordery
Bridlington: Taylor, Pugh, Freeman, McNeill, Warburton, Brentano, Wilkes (Hall), Noteman,Gauden, Whiteman, Brattan (Brown)
Replay YEADING 1 — **BRIDLINGTON TOWN 0** — **Att: 5,000**
Sweales — at Leeds Utd FC
Yeading: Mackenzie, Wickens, Turner, Whiskey, Croad (McCarthy), Schwartz, Matthews,James, Sweates, Impey (Welsh), Cordery
Bridlington: Taylor, Pugh, Freeman, McNeill, Warburton, Brentano, Wilkes (Brown), Noteman,Gauden (Downing), Whiteman, Brattan

1991 GRESLEY ROVERS 4 *(West Midlands)* — **GUISELEY 4 (aet)** *(Northern Co East)* — **Att: 11,314**
Rathbone, Smith 2, Stokes — Tennison 2, Walling, A Roberts — Ref: Mr C Trussell
Gresley: Aston, Barry, Elliott (Adcock), Denby, Land, Astley, Stokes, K Smith, Acklam,Rathbone, Lovell (Weston)
Guiseley: Maxted, Bottomley, Hogarth, Tetley, Morgan, McKenzie, Atkinson (Annan),Tennison, Walling, A Roberts, B Roberts
Replay GUISELEY 3 — **GRESLEY ROVERS 1** — **Att: 7,585**
Tennison, Walling, Atkinson — Astley — at Bramall Lane
Guiseley: Maxted, Annan, Hogarth, Tetley, Morgan, McKenzie (Bottomley), Atkinson,Tennison (Noteman), Walling, A Roberts, B Roberts
Gresley: Aston, Barry, Elliott, Denby, Land, Astley, Stokes (Weston), K Smith, Acklam, Rathbone, Lovell (Adcock)

1992 WIMBORNE TOWN 5 *(Wessex)* — **GUISELEY 3** *(Northern Premier Div 1)* — **Att: 10,772**
Richardson, Sturgess 2, Killick 2 — Noteman 2, Colville — Ref: Mr M J Bodenham
Wimborne: Leonard, Langdown, Wilkins, Beacham, Allan, Taplin, Ames, Richardson, Bridle,Killick, Sturgess (Lovell), Lynn
Guiseley: Maxted, Atkinson, Hogarth, Tetley (Wilson), Morgan, Brockie, A Roberts,Tennison, Noteman (Colville), Annan, W Roberts

1993 BRIDLINGTON TOWN 1 *(NPL Div 1)* — **TIVERTON TOWN 0** *(Western)* — **Att: 9,061**
Radford — Ref: Mr R A Hart
Bridlington: Taylor, Brentano, McKenzie, Harvey, Bottomley, Woodcock, Grocock, A Roberts, Jones, Radford (Tyrell), Parkinson. Sub: Swailes
Tiverton Town: Nott, J Smith, N Saunders, M Saunders, Short (Scott), Steele, Annunziata, KSmith, Everett, Daly, Hynds (Rogers)

1994 DISS TOWN 2 *(Eastern)* — **TAUNTON TOWN 1** *(Western)* — **Att: 13,450**
Gibbs (p), Mendham — Fowler — Ref: Mr K. Morton
Diss Town: Woodcock, Carter, Wolsey (Musgrave), Casey (Bugg), Hartle, Smith, Barth, Mendham, Miles, Warne, Gibbs
Taunton Town: Maloy, Morris, Walsh, Ewens, Graddon, Palfrey, West (Hendry), Fowler, Durham, Perrett (Ward), Jarvis

1995 ARLESEY TOWN 2 *(South Midlands)* — **OXFORD CITY 1** *(Ryman 2)* — **Att: 13,670**
Palma, Gyalog — S Fontaine — Ref: Mr G S Willard
Arlesey: Young, Cardines, Bambrick, Palma (Ward), Hull, Gonsalves, Gyalog, Cox, Kane,O'Keefe, Marshall (Nicholls). Sub: Dodwell
Oxford: Fleet, Brown (Fisher), Hume, Shepherd, Muttock, Hamilton (Kemp), Thomas, Spittle, Sherwood, S Fontaine, C Fontaine. Sub: Torres

1996 BRIGG TOWN 3 *(N Co East)* — **CLITHEROE 0** *(N W Counties)* — **Att: 7,340**
Stead 2, Roach — Ref: Mr S J Lodge
Brigg: Gawthorpe, Thompson, Rogers, Greaves (Clay), Buckley (Mail), Elston, C Stead, McLean, N Stead (McNally), Flounders, Roach
Clitheroe: Nash, Lampkin, Rowbotham (Otley), Baron, Westwell, Rovine, Butcher, Taylor (Smith), Grimshaw, Darbyshire, Hill (Dunn)

1997 WHITBY TOWN 3 *(Northern)* — **NORTH FERRIBY UTD. 0** *(N Co East)* — **Att: 11,098**
Williams, Logan, Toman — Ref: Graham Poll
North Ferriby: Sharp, Deacey, Smith, Brentano, Walmsley, M Smith, Harrison (Horne), Phillips (Milner), France (Newman), Flounders, Tennison
Whitby Town: Campbell, Williams, Logan, Goodchild, Pearson, Cook, Goodrick (Borthwick), Hodgson, Robinson, Toman (Pyle), Pitman (Hall)

1998 TIVERTON TOWN 1 *(Western)* — **TOW LAW TOWN 0** *(Northern Division 1)* **Att: 13,139**
Varley **Ref: M A Riley**
Tiverton Town: Edwards, Felton, Saunders, Tatterton, Smith J, Conning, Nancekivell (Rogers), Smith K (Varley), Everett, Daly, Leonard (Waters)
Tow Law Town: Dawson, Pickering, Darwent, Bailey, Hague, Moan, Johnson, Nelson, Suddick, Laidler (Bennett), Robinson.

1999 TIVERTON TOWN 1 *(Western)* — **BEDLINGTON TERRIERS 0** *(Northern)* **Att: 13, 878**
Rogers 88 **Ref: W. C. Burns**
Bedlington Terriers: O'Connor, Bowes, Pike, Boon (Renforth), Melrose, Teasdale, Cross, Middleton (Ludlow), Gibb, Milner, Bond. Subs: Pearson, Cameron, Gowans
Tiverton Town: Edwards, Fallon, Saunders, Tatterton, Tallon, Conning (Rogers), Nancekivell (Pears), Varley, Everett, Daly, Leonard. Subs: Tucker, Hynds, Grimshaw

2000 DEAL TOWN 1 *(Kent)* — **CHIPPENHAM TOWN 0** *(Western)* **Att: 20,000**
Graham 87 **Ref: D Laws**
Deal Town: Tucker, Kempster, Best, Ash, Martin, Seager, Monteith, Graham, Lovell, Marshall, Ribbens. Subs: Roberts, Warden, Turner
Chippenham Town: Jones, James, Andrews, Murphy, Burns, Woods, Brown, Charity, Tweddle, Collier, Godley. Subs: Tiley, Cutler

2001 TAUNTON TOWN 2 *(Western)* — **BERKHAMPSTED TOWN 1** *(Isthmian 2)* **(at Villa Park) Att: 8,439**
Fields 41, Laight 45 — **Lowe 71** **Ref: E. K. Wolstenholme**
Taunton Town: Draper, Down, Chapman, West, Hawkings, Kelly, Fields (Groves), Laight, Cann (Tallon), Bastow, Lynch (Hapgood). Subs: Ayres, Parker
Berkhampsted Town: O'Connor, Mullins, Lowe, Aldridge, Coleman, Brockett, Yates, Adebowale, Richardson, Smith, Nightingale. Subs: Ringsell, Hall, Knight, Franklin, Osborne

2002 WHITLEY BAY 1 *(Northern)* — **TIPTREE UNITED 0** *(Eastern)* **(at Villa Park) Att: 4742**
Chandler 97 **Ref: A Kaye**
Whitley Bay: Caffrey, Sunderland, Walmsley, Dixon (Neil), Anderson, Locker, Middleton, Bowes (Carr), Chandler, Walton, Fenwick (Cuggy). Subs: Cook, Livermore
Tiptree United: Haygreen, Battell, Wall, Houghton, Fish, Streetley (Gillespie), Wareham (Snow), Daly, Barefield, Aransibia (Parnell), Brady. Subs: Powell, Ford.

2003 BRIGG TOWN 2 *(Northern Co.East)* — **A.F.C SUDBURY 1** *(Eastern Counties)* **(at Upton Park) Att: 6,634**
Housham 2, Carter 68 — **Raynor 30** **Ref: M Fletcher**
Brigg Town:- Steer, Raspin, Rowland, Thompson, Blanchard, Stones, Stead (Thompson 41), Housham, Borman (Drayton 87), Roach, Carter. Subs (not used) Nevis, Gawthorpe.
AFC Sudbury:- Greygoose, Head (Norfolk 63), Spearing, Tracey, Bishop, Anderson (Owen 73), Rayner, Gardiner (Banya 79), Bennett, Claydon, Betson. Subs (not used) Taylor, Hyde.

2004 WINCHESTER CITY 2 *(Wessex)* — **A.F.C SUDBURY 0** *(Eastern Counties)* **(at St Andrews) Att: 5,080**
Forbes 19, Smith 73 (pen) **Ref: P Crossley**
Winchester City:- Arthur, Dyke (Tate 83), Bicknell, Redwood, Goss, Blake, Webber, Green, Mancey, Forbes (Rogers 70), Smith (Green 90). Subs (not used) - Lang and Rastall.
AFC Sudbury:- Greygoose, Head, Wardley, Girling, Tracey, Norfolk, Owen (Banya 62), Hyde (Calver 57), Bennett, Claydon, Betson (Francis 73n). Subs (not used) - Rayner, Nower.

2005 DIDCOT TOWN 3 *(Hellenic)* — **A.F.C SUDBURY 2** *(Eastern Counties)* **(at White Hart Lane) Att: 8,662**
Beavon (2), Wardley (og) — **Wardley, Calver (pen)** **Ref: R Beeby**
Didcot Town:- Webb, Goodall, Heapy, Campbell, Green, Parrott, Hannigan, Ward, Concannon (Jones 88), Beavon (Bianchini 90), Powell. Subs (not used) – Cooper, Allen, Spurrett.
AFC Sudbury:- Greygoose, Girling, Wardley, Bennett, Hyde (Hayes 78), Owen (Norfolk 65), Claydon (Banya 59), Head, Calver, Betson, Terry Rayner. Subs (not used) – Howlett, Nower.

2006 NANTWICH TOWN 3 *(NWC 1)* — **HILLINGDON BOROUGH 1** *(Spartan S.Mids P.)* **(at St Andrews) Att: 3,286**
Kinsey (2), Scheuber — **Nelson**
Nantwich Town:- Hackney, A.Taylor, T.Taylor, Smith, Davis, Donnelly, Beasley, Scheuber (Parkinson 69), Kinsey (Marrow 69), Blake (Scarlett 86) and Griggs. Subs (not used): O'Connor and Read.
Hillingdon Borough:- Brown, Rundell (Fenton 80),Kidson, Phillips, Croft, Lawrence, Duncan (Nelson 46), Tilbury, Hibbs, Wharton (Lyons 38). Subs (not used): O'Grady, White.

2007 TRURO 3 *(Western Division 1)* — **AFC TOTTON 1** *(Wessex Division 1)* **Att: 27,754 (New Vase record)**
Wills (2), Broad — **Potter** **Ref: P Joslin**
AFC Totton: Brunnschweiler, Reacord, Troon (Stevens 60), Potter (Gregory 82), Bottomley, Austen, Roden, Gosney, Hamodu (Goss 89), Osman, Byres. Subs not used: Zammit, McCormack.
Truro City: Stevenson, Ash, Power, Smith, Martin (Pope 84), Broad, Wills, Gosling, Yetton, Watkins, Walker (Ludlam 90). Subs not used: Butcher, Routledge, Reski.

2008 KIRKHAM & WESHAM 2 *(North West Co. Div.2)* — **LOWESTOFT TOWN 1** *(Eastern Co. Premier)* — **Att: 19,537**
Walwyn (2) — **Thompson (og)** — **Ref: A D'Urso**

Kirkham and Wesham: Summerfield, Jackson (Walwyn 79), Keefe (Allen 55), Thompson, Shaw, Eastwood, Clark, Blackwell, Wane, Paterson (Sheppard 90), Smith. Subs not used: Moffat and Abbott

Lowestoft Town: Reynolds, Poppy, Potter, Woodrow, Saunders, Plaskett (McGee 79), Godbold, Darren Cockrill (Dale Cockrill 46), Stock, Hough, King (Hunn 55). Subs not used: McKenna and Rix.

2009 WHITLEY BAY 2 *(Northern Division One)* — **GLOSSOP NORTH END 0** *(North West Co. Prem)* — **Att: 12,212**
Kerr, Chow — **Ref: K Friend**

Whitley Bay: Burke, Taylor, Picton, McFarlane (Fawcett 60), Coulson, Ryan, Moore, Robson, Kerr, Chow (Robinson 73), Johnston (Bell 60). Subs not used: McLean and Reay.

Glossop North End: Cooper, Young, Kay, Lugsden, Yates, Gorton, Bailey (Hind 57), Morris, Allen (Balfe 65), Hamilton (Bailey 72), Hodges. Subs not used: Whelan and Parker.

2010 WHITLEY BAY 6 *(Northern Division One)* — **WROXHAM 1** *(Eastern Counties Premier Division)* — **Att: 8,920**
Chow 21(sec), Easthaugh 16 (og), Kerr, Johnston, Robinson, Gillies — **Cook 12** — **Ref: A Taylor**

Whitley Bay: Terry Burke, Craig McFarlane, Callum Anderson, Richard Hodgson, (sub Lee Picton 69th min), Darren Timmons, Leon Ryan, Adam Johnston (sub Joshua Gillies 77th min), Damon Robson, Lee Kerr, Paul Chow (sub Phillip Bell 61st min), Paul Robinson.
Subs not used – Tom Kindley and Chris Reid.

Wroxham: Scott Howie, Gavin Pauling (sub Ross Durrant 57th min), Shaun Howes, Graham Challen, Martin McNeil (sub Josh Carus 46th min), Andy Easthaugh (sub Owen Paynter 69th min), Steve Spriggs, Gavin Lemmon, Paul Cook, Danny White, Gary Gilmore.
Subs not used – Danny Self and Gareth Simpson.

2011 WHITLEY BAY 3 *(Northern Division One)* — **COALVILLE TOWN 2** *(Midland Alliance)* — **Att: 8,778**
Chow 28, 90, Kerr 61 — **Moore 58, Goodby 80** — **Ref: S Mathieson**

Whitley Bay: Terry Burke, Craig McFarlane (sub Steve Gibson 90th min), Callum Anderson, Darren Timmons, Gareth Williams (sub David Coulson 68th min), Damon Robson, Lee Kerr, Paul Chow, Paul Robinson, David Pounder (sub Brian Smith 68th min), Gary Ormston.
Subs not used – Kyle Hayes (gk) and Brian Rowe. Coalville Town: Sean Bowles, Ashley Brown (sub Matthew Gardner 88th min), Cameron Stuart, Adam Goodby, Zach Costello, Lee Miveld,
Callum Woodward, Anthony Carney (sub Craig Attwood 90th min), Ryan Robbins (sub Ashley Wells 66th min), Matt Moore, Jerome Murdock.
Subs not used – Richard Williams (gk) and James Dodd.

2012 DUNSTON UTS 2 *(Northern Division One)* — **WEST AUCKLAND TOWN 0** *(Northern Division One)* — **Att: 5,126**
Bulford 32, 79 — **Ref: R East**

Dunston UTS: Liam Connell, Ben Cattenach, Terry Galbraith, Michael Robson, Chris Swailes, Kane Young, Steven Shaw, Michael Dixon, Stephen Goddard (sub Sreven Preen 84th min), Andrew Bulford (sub Danny Craggs 88th min), Lee McAndrew.
Subs not used – Andrew Clark (g/k), Ian Herron, Jack Burns.

West Auckland Town: Mark Bell, Neil Pattinson, Andrew Green, Jonny Gibson, John Parker, Mark Stephenson (sub Daniel Hindmarsh 76th min), Stuart Banks, Mark Hudson, Mattie Moffatt, Michael Rae, Adam Nicholls (sub Martin Young 60th min).
Subs not used – Daryll Hall, Ross Preston, Matthew Coad.

2013 SPENNYMOOR TOWN 2 *(Northern Division One)* — **TUNBRIDGE WELLS 1** *(Kent League)* — **Att: 16,751**
Cogdon 18, Graydon 80 — **Stanford 78** — **Ref: M Naylor**

Spennymoor Town: Robert Dean, Kallum Griffiths, Leon Ryan, Chris Mason, Stephen Capper, Keith Graydon, Lewis Dodds, Wayne Phillips (Anthony Peacock 64 min), Joe Walton (Andrew Stephenson 73 min), Mark Davison, (Michael Rae 76 min), Gavin Congdon.
Subs not used - David Knight (g/k), Steven Richardson.

Tunbridge Wells: Chris Oladogba, Jason Bourne, Scott Whibley, Perry Spackman, Lewis Mingle, Jon Pilbeam (Richard Sinden 85 min), Andy McMath, Joe Fuller (Tom Davey 58 min), Andy Irvine, Carl Connell (Jack Harris 58 min), Josh Stanford.
Subs not used - Michael Czanner (gk), Andy Boyle.

2014 SHOLING 1 *(Wessex Premier Division - 1st)* — **WEST AUCKLAND TOWN 0** *(Northern Division One - 5th)* — **Att: 5,432**
McLean 71 — **Ref: D Coote**

Sholing: Matt Brown, Mike Carter, Marc Diaper, Peter Castle (Dan Miller 53 min), Lee Bright, Tyronne Bowers (Kevin Brewster 75 min), Barry Mason, Lewis Fennemore (Alex Sawyer 78 min), Lee Wort, Byron Mason, Marvin McLean.
Subs not used - Ashley Jarvis, Nick Watts.

West Auckland Town: Jordan Nixon, Neil Pattinson, Andrew Green (Jonathan Gibson 63 min), Daryll Hall, Lewis Galpin, Brian Close, Shaun Vipond (Stuart Banks 76 min), Robert Briggs, Mattie Moffat (Steven Richardson 74 min). John Campbell, Dennis Knight.
Subs not used - Paul Garthwaite, Adam Wilkinson..

2015 NORTH SHIELDS 2 *(Northern Division One - 4th)* — **GLOSSOP NORTH END 1** *(North West Co. Premier - 1st)* — **Att: 9,674**
Bainbridge 80, Forster 96 — **Bailey 55** — **Ref: A Madley**

North Shields: Christopher Bannon, Stuart Donnison, John Parker, Kevin Hughes, John Grey, James Luccock (Ryan Carr 59), Ben Richardson, Mciahel McKeown, Dean Holmes (Adam Forster 69), Denver Morris, Gareth Bainbridge (Kieran Wrightson 107).
Subs not used - Curtis Coppen and Marc Lancaster.

Glossop North End: Greg Hall, Michael Bowler, Matthew Russell, Kevin Lugsden, Dave Young, Martin Parker, Lee Blackshaw (Samuel Grimshaw 69), Samuel Hare (Samuel Hind 82), Tom Bailey, Kieran Lugsden, Eddie Moran (Daniel White 60).
Subs not used - Benjamin Richardson and Richard Gresty.

2016 **MORPETH TOWN 4** *(Northern Division One - 4th)* **HEREFORD 1** *(Midland League - 1st)* **Att: 46,781**
Swailes 34, Carr 47, Taylor 59, Bell 92 **Purdie 2** (Inaugural Non-League finals day)
Ref: S Atwelly

Morpeth Town: Karl Dryden, Stephen Forster, James Novak, Ben Sayer, Chris Swailes, Michael Hall, Sean Taylor (sub Damien Mullen 78), Keith Graydon, Luke Carr (sub Shaun Bell 88), Michael Chilton (sub Steven Anderson 69), Jordan Fry.
Subs not used - Dale Pearson and Niall Harrison.
Hereford: Martin Horsell, Jimmy Oates, Joel Edwards, Rob Purdie, Ryan Green, Aaron Birch, Pablo Haysham, Mike Symons, Jamie Willets (sub John Mills 70), Joe Tumelty (sub Mustapha Bundu 55), Sirdic Grant.
Subs not used - Nathan Summers, Dylan Bonella and Ross Staley.

2017 **SOUTH SHIELDS 4** *(Northern Division One - 1st)* **CLEETHORPES TOWN 0** *(Northern Counties East Premier - 1st)* **Att: 38,224**
Finnigan 43 (pen), Morse 80, Foley 86, 89 (Combined FA Trophy/Vase att.)
Ref: D England

South Shields: Liam Connell, Alex Nicholson, Darren Lough, Jon Shaw, Dillon Morse, Julio Arca, Andrew Stephenson (sub Robert Briggs 56), Wayne Phillips (sub Barrie Smith 82), Gavin Congdon, Carl Finnigan (sub Michael Richardson 71), David Foley.
Subs not used - Louis Storey and Darren Holden.
Cleethorpes Town: Liam Higton, Tim Lowe, Peter Winn, Liam Dickens, Matt Bloomer, Matty Coleman (sub Luke Mascall 70), Liam Davis (sub Jack Richardson 73), Alex Flett, Marc Cooper (Andy Taylor 61), Brody Richardson, Jon Oglesby.
Subs not used - Gary King and Kieran Wressell.

2018 **THATCHAM TOWN 1** *(Hellenic Premier - 1st)* **STOCKTON TOWN 0** *(Northern League D1 - 6th)* **Att: 31,430**
Cooper-Clark 23 (pen) (Combined FA Trophy/Vase att.)
Ref: J Brooks

Thatcham Town: Chris Rackley, Lewis Brownhill, Curtis Angell, Tom Melledew (c) (Ashliegh James 81), Baboucarr Jarra, Tom Moran, Harrison Bayley, Shane Cooper-Clark (Rose Cook 89), Gavin James, Ekow Elliott, Jordan Brown (Jemel Johnson 70).
Subs not used - Harry Grant, Gareth Thomas.
Stockton Town: Michael Arthur, Joe Carter (Matthew Garbutt 61), James Ward (Adam Nicholson 79), Nathan Mulligan, Dale Mulligan, Tom Coulthard (c), Kevin Hayes, Fred Woodhouse, Jamie Owens, James Risbrough, Chris Stockton (Sonni Coleman 67).
Subs not used - Alan Cossavella, Chris Dunwell.

2019 **CHERTSEY TOWN 3** *(Combined Counties Prem - 1st)* **CRAY VALLEY (PM) 1** *(Southern Counties East Prem - 1st)* **Att: 42,962**
Flegg 38, Baxter 105 (pen), Rowe 117 **Tomlin 36** (Combined FA Trophy/Vase att.)
Ref: R Joyce

Chertsey Town: Nick Jupp, Sam Flegg, Michael Peacock, Quincy Rowe, Mason Welch-Turner, Kevin Maclaren (Dave Taylor 79), Lubomir Guentchev, Sam Murphy, Lewis Driver (Andy Crossley 83), Dale Binns (Lewis Jackson 97), Jake Baxter (John Pomroy 118).
Subs not used - Lewis Gallifent, Michael Kinsella, Danny Bennell.
Cray Valley (PM): Andy Walker, Denzel Gayle, Cem Tumkaya (Brad Potter 106), Ashley Sains (Calum Willock 112), Liam Hickey, Danny Smith, Ryan Flack (Josh James 72), Paul Semakula, Anthony Edgar, Gavin Tomlin, Kevin Lisbie (Francis Babalola 100).
Subs not used - Deren Ibrahim, Tyler Myers, Lea Dawson.

All Finals at Wembley unless otherwise stated.

FAV QF - Warrington Rylands v Hebburn Town. Photos Bill Wheatcroft.

FAV QF - Leighton Town v Walsall Wood. Photos Bill Wheatcroft.

PRELIMINARY ROUND

No	Home		Away	Score	Att
1	Stockton Town	v	Carlisle City (8/9)	4-0	123
2	Consett	v	South Shields (10/9)	1-4	
3	Guisborough Town	v	Morpeth Town (10/9)	0-8	82
4	Workington	v	Scarborough Athletic (13/9)	3-1	
5	Durham City	v	Spennymoor Town		
	(walkover for Spennymoor Town – Durham City withdrawn)				
6	Pickering Town	v	Cleator Moor Celtic (6/9)	3-2	147
	(tie awarded to Cleator Moor Celtic - Pickering Town removed)				
7	Newcastle Benfield	v	Hebburn Town (7/9)	3-3	143
	(Hebburn Town won 5-4 on kicks from the penalty mark)				
8	Buxton	v	Ashton Town (10/9)	4-2	64
9	Sandbach United	v	Cheadle Town (7/9)	1-3	
10	Prestwich Heys	v	Stalybridge Celtic (9/9)	11-1	
11	Mossley	v	Litherland Remyca (9/9)	0-4	20
12	Prescot Cables	v	City Of Liverpool (11/9)	1-5	
13	Irlam	v	Curzon Ashton (8/9)	2-1	137
14	Chester	v	Abbey Hey (9/9)	2-0	
	(at Runcorn Linnets FC)				
15	Stockport Town	v	Ashton Athletic (7/9)	3-1	55
16	Hyde United	v	Runcorn Linnets (11/9)	3-1	103
17	Wythenshawe Amateurs	v	Nantwich Town (8/9)	1-1	218
	(Wythenshawe Amateurs won 4-1 on kicks from the penalty mark)				
18	St Helens Town	v	AFC Liverpool (13/9)	5-0	146
19	Bootle	v	Southport (15/9)	0-3	
	(8/9 – tie abandoned due to serious injury to player after 81 mins, 2-1)				
20	Skelmersdale United	v	Runcorn Town (8/9)	6-0	
21	Marine	v	Lancaster City (9/9)	2-1	121
22	Clitheroe	v	Trafford (9/9)	3-1	59
23	Tadcaster Albion	v	York City (11/9)	1-4	
24	Sheffield	v	Staveley MW (7/9)	8-1	118
25	Garforth Town	v	Stocksbridge Park Steels		
	(walkover for Stocksbridge Park Steels – Garforth Town withdrawn)				
26	Frickley Athletic	v	Guiseley		
	(walkover for Guiseley – Frickley Athletic withdrawn)				
27	Brigg Town	v	Emley (9/9)	0-10	
28	North Ferriby	v	Bottesford Town (8/9)	3-1	91
29	Shelley	v	Farsley Celtic (7/9)	0-6	
30	Harrogate Railway Athletic	v	Grimsby Borough (7/9)	3-3	129
	(Harrogate Railway Athletic won 3-0 on kicks from the penalty mark)				
31	Silsden	v	Pontefract Collieries		
	(walkover for Pontefract Collieries – Silsden withdrawn)				
32	Eccleshill United	v	Retford (9/9)	6-0	90
33	Steeton	v	Hall Road Rangers		
	(walkover for Hall Road Rangers – Steeton withdrawn)				
34	Gresley Rovers	v	Heather St Johns (9/9)	1-2	107
35	Long Eaton United	v	Kirby Muxloe (10/9)	1-1	74
	(Kirby Muxloe won 5-4 on kicks from the penalty mark)				
36	Borrowash Victoria	v	Mickleover (10/9)	1-3	95
37	Grantham Town	v	Dunkirk (10/9)	5-1	115
38	Holbeach United	v	Harborough Town (7/9)	8-0	90
39	Ilkeston Town	v	Stamford (10/9)	3-2	
40	Alfreton Town	v	Basford United (10/9)	1-7	
	(at Hucknall Town FC)				
41	Nuneaton Borough	v	Kidsgrove Athletic (9/9)	4-2	
42	Worcester City	v	Lichfield City (7/9)	4-1	
43	Newcastle Town	v	Racing Club Warwick (8/9)	2-1	94
44	Bilston Town	v	Stratford Town		
	(walkover for Stratford Town – Bilston Town withdrawn)				
45	Stourbridge	v	Redditch United (7/9)	4-1	192
46	Shawbury United	v	Stourport Swifts (8/9)	7-0	
47	Alvechurch	v	Evesham United (10/9)	2-2	51
	(Evesham United won 4-2 on kicks from the penalty mark)				
48	Rugby Town	v	Sutton Coldfield Town (9/9)	10-1	120
49	Malvern Town	v	Paget Rangers (7/9)	0-2	
50	Lye Town	v	Haughmond (7/9)	2-3	67
51	Chelmsley Town	v	Rushall Olympic (7/9)	0-5	122
52	Stafford Rangers	v	AFC Telford United (7/9)	1-0	212
53	Halesowen Town	v	Bedworth United (10/9)	2-3	84
54	Leamington	v	Boldmere St Michaels (9/9)	3-2	69
55	Wellingborough Whitworth	v	Stotfold (10/9)	4-2	
56	Royston Town	v	Godmanchester Rovers (10/9)	3-1	123
57	Cogenhoe United	v	St Ives Town (10/9)	2-2	
	(Cogenhoe United won 5-4 on kicks from the penalty mark)				
58	Baldock Town	v	Corby Town (9/9)	8-0	76
59	Crawley Green	v	Winslow United (9/9)	2-3	20
60	Barton Rovers	v	Biggleswade Town (11/9)	1-5	101
61	Eynesbury Rovers	v	Bugbrooke St Michaels (10/9)	0-8	90
62	Kettering Town	v	Leighton Town (10/9)	2-1	70
63	Rothwell Corinthians	v	Peterborough Sports (7/9)	3-2	33
64	Brackley Town	v	Newport Pagnell Town		
	(walkover for Newport Pagnell Town – Brackley Town withdrawn)				
65	Wellingborough Town	v	Arlesey Town (10/9)	2-1	90
66	Haverhill Rovers	v	Histon (10/9)	1-3	
67	Walsham Le Willows	v	Whitton United (10/9)	2-2	53
	(Walsham Le Willows won 4-3 on kicks from the penalty mark)				
68	Long Melford	v	AFC Sudbury (10/9)	0-6	32
69	Brantham Athletic	v	Newmarket Town (7/9)	3-4	
70	Whittlesey Athletic	v	Needham Market (7/9)	0-9	
71	Mildenhall Town	v	Swaffham Town (10/9)	3-1	
72	Ipswich Wanderers	v	Fakenham Town (10/9)	2-0	
73	Cambridge City	v	Stowmarket Town (7/9)	0-0	38
	(Cambridge City won 5-4 on kicks from the penalty mark – at Huntingdon Town FC)				
74	Dereham Town	v	Lowestoft Town (10/9)	3-2	94
75	Cornard United	v	Woodbridge Town (10/9)	0-1	
76	Hadleigh United	v	Leiston (10/9)	0-3	81
77	FC Clacton	v	Ware (11/9)	0-6	69
78	St Albans City	v	Hadley (9/9)	4-0	83
79	Barking	v	Colney Heath (7/9)	2-1	79
80	Brightlingsea Regent	v	Billericay Town		
	(walkover for Billericay Town – Brightlingsea Regent withdrawn)				
81	Bowers & Pitsea	v	Bishop's Stortford		
	(walkover for Bowers & Pitsea – Bishop's Stortford withdrawn)				
82	Hoddesdon Town	v	Brentwood Town		
	(walkover for Brentwood Town – Hoddesdon Town withdrawn)				
83	Romford	v	Barkingside (9/9)	4-2	
84	Redbridge	v	Sawbridgeworth Town (7/9)	4-2	84
85	Hullbridge Sports	v	Concord Rangers (10/9)	1-7	
86	Harpenden Town	v	Woodford Town (8/9)	1-2	83
87	Cockfosters	v	Tilbury (10/9)	2-1	126
88	Takeley	v	Wingate & Finchley		
	(walkover for Wingate & Finchley – Takeley withdrawn)				
89	Potters Bar Town	v	Enfield Town (9/9)	3-3	125
	(Potters Bar Town won 4-3 on kicks from the penalty mark)				
90	Chelmsford City	v	Haringey Borough (7/9)	4-0	
91	Braintree Town	v	Aveley (8/9)	1-2	100
92	Hackney Wick	v	Ilford (9/9)	2-4	
93	Hertford Town	v	May & Baker Eastbrook (9/9)	9-0	
94	Chesham United	v	Hanworth Villa (8/9)	1-2	104
95	Ashford Town (Middx)	v	Brimsdown (7/9)	0-2	64
96	Harefield United	v	Hampton & Richmond Borough (8/9)	3-5	98
97	Windsor	v	Northwood (7/9)	2-1	
98	London Tigers	v	Leverstock Green (10/9)	0-7	
99	CB Hounslow United	v	Bedfont Sports Club (7/9)	1-2	
	(at Bedfont & Feltham FC)				
100	Edgware Town	v	Spelthorne Sports (9/9)	0-8	
101	Beaconsfield Town	v	Chalfont St Peter (7/9)	2-2	
	(Chalfont St Peter won 7-6 on kicks from the penalty mark)				
102	K Sports	v	Glebe (10/9)	5-3	65
103	Hastings United	v	Lewisham Borough (Community)		
	(walkover for Hastings United – Lewisham Borough (Community) withdrawn)				
104	Tower Hamlets	v	Margate (8/9)	0-1	
105	Erith Town	v	Sevenoaks Town (9/9)	2-2	280
	(Erith Town won 4-2 on kicks from the penalty mark)				
106	Ramsgate	v	Meridian VP (8/9)	2-5	75
107	Dulwich Hamlet	v	East Grinstead Town (11/9)	3-0	
108	Ashford United	v	Tooting & Mitcham United		
	(walkover for Tooting & Mitcham United – Ashford United withdrawn)				
109	Punjab United	v	Tonbridge Angels (7/9)	0-2	82
110	Bexhill United	v	Maidstone United (8/9)	1-1	85
	(Maidstone United won 4-3 on kicks from the penalty mark)				
111	Greenwich Borough	v	AFC Croydon Athletic		
	(walkover for AFC Croydon Athletic – Greenwich Borough withdrawn)				
112	Cray Wanderers	v	Carshalton Athletic (9/9)	0-4	62
113	Croydon	v	Whitstable Town (10/9)	3-1	35
	(at Glebe FC)				
114	Faversham Town	v	Chatham Town (8/9)	1-1	
	(Faversham Town won 4-2 on kicks from the penalty mark)				
115	Folkestone Invicta	v	Corinthian (9/9)	1-1	
	(Folkestone Invicta won 5-3 on kicks from the penalty mark)				
116	Newhaven	v	South Park (10/9)	2-6	39
117	Dorking Wanderers	v	Walton & Hersham (8/9)	3-0	100

No	Home		Away	Score	Att
118	Alfold	v	Abbey Rangers (10/9)	1-0	65
119	Eastbourne Town	v	Broadbridge Heath (7/9)	1-3	
120	Three Bridges	v	Shoreham (7/9)	4-1	63
121	Lancing	v	Loxwood		
	(walkover for Lancing – Loxwood withdrawn)				
122	Burgess Hill Town	v	Horsham (7/9)	1-0	126
123	Arundel	v	Worthing United (9/9)	3-2	
124	Saltdean United	v	Mile Oak (9/9)	1-3	
125	Lewes	v	East Preston (10/9)	3-1	94
	(at East Preston FC)				
126	Worthing	v	Guildford City (10/9)	4-2	
127	Sutton Common Rovers	v	Virginia Water (11/9)	5-0	
128	Kingstonian	v	Chertsey Town (10/9)	2-2	
	(Kingstonian won 3-2 on kicks from the penalty mark)				
129	Metropolitan Police	v	Corinthian Casuals (10/9)	18-0	
130	Westfield	v	Westfield (13/9)	1-1	
	(Westfield won 3-2 on kicks from the penalty mark)				
131	Godalming Town	v	Walton Casuals (7/9)	8-2	
132	Chessington & Hook United	v	Badshot Lea (9/9)	3-0	109
133	Billingshurst	v	Chipstead (9/9)	0-7	
134	Bognor Regis Town	v	Knaphill (10/9)	1-4	70
	(at Arundel FC)				
135	Bracknell Town	v	Fleet Town (9/9)	2-2	27
	(Fleet Town won 5-4 on kicks from the penalty mark)				
136	Thame United	v	Hungerford Town (10/9)	0-0	51
	(Thame United won 5-4 on kicks from the penalty mark)				
137	Farnborough	v	Cove		
	(walkover for Cove – Farnborough withdrawn)				
138	Oxford City	v	Easington Sports (8/9)	4-0	45
139	North Leigh	v	Clanfield 85 (7/9)	1-1	123
	(Clanfield 85 won 4-2 on kicks from the penalty mark)				
140	Fleet Spurs	v	Wokingham & Emmbrook (10/9)	1-1	
	(Wokingham & Emmbrook win 5-4 on kicks from the penalty mark)				
141	Hartley Wintney	v	Shrivenham (9/9)	1-1	70
	(Shrivenham won 4-2 on kicks from the penalty mark)				
142	Hamworthy United	v	Gosport Borough (13/9)	6-0	
143	Dorchester Town	v	Poole Town (9/9)	1-4	119
144	Hamble Club	v	Bemerton Heath Harlequins (7/9)	1-2	
145	Sholing	v	AFC Stoneham (9/9)	2-2	110
	(AFC Stoneham won 5-4 on kicks from the penalty mark)				
146	Alton	v	AFC Portchester (10/9)	0-4	107
147	United Services Portsmouth	v	Bournemouth (9/9)	5-1	93
148	Bitton	v	Tuffley Rovers (10/9)	3-6	
149	Bishop's Cleeve	v	Bristol Manor Farm (10/9)	4-0	
150	Yate Town	v	Malmesbury Victoria (9/9)	2-0	62
151	Odd Down	v	Cribbs (7/9)	4-0	51
152	Gloucester City	v	Cirencester Town (10/9)	2-1	
153	Chippenham Town	v	Newent Town (7/9)	8-1	28
154	Wells City	v	Paulton Rovers (9/9)	3-1	
155	Truro City	v	Clevedon Town (9/9)	3-2	
156	Barnstaple Town	v	Bridgwater Town		
	(walkover for Bridgwater Town – Barnstaple Town withdrawn)				
157	Weston Super Mare	v	Bishop Sutton (10/9)	6-1	
	(at Bishop Sutton FC)				
158	Frome Town	v	Street (8/9)	0-4	

FIRST ROUND QUALIFYING

No	Home		Away	Score	Att
1	Seaham Red Star	v	Penrith		
	(walkover for Seaham Red Star – Penrith withdrawn)				
2	Chester-Le-Street Town	v	Spennymoor Town (24/9)	0-17	
3	Hebburn Town	v	Workington (24/9)	2-1	96
4	Morpeth Town	v	Blyth Spartans (2/10)	4-0	
	(at Blyth Spartans FC)				
5	Stockton Town	v	Gateshead (23/9)	0-1	108
6	Cleator Moor Celtic	v	Darlington (27/9)	2-7	
7	North Shields	v	South Shields		
	(walkover for South Shields – North Shields withdrawn)				
8	Litherland Remyca	v	Cheadle Town (23/9)	5-0	78
9	FC United of Manchester	v	West Didsbury & Chorlton (25/9)	2-0	387
10	AFC Fylde	v	Stockport Town (23/9)	2-2	
	(AFC Fylde won 4-3 on kicks from the penalty mark)				
11	Marine	v	Irlam (23/9)	3-5	82
12	Clitheroe	v	Chorley (21/9)	2-1	
13	Hyde United	v	Southport (25/9)	3-0	128
14	Wythenshawe Amateurs	v	Skelmersdale United (23/9)	1-2	242
15	Bamber Bridge	v	Prestwich Heys		
	(walkover for Prestwich Heys – Bamber Bridge withdrawn)				
16	St Helens Town	v	Witton Albion		
	(walkover of St Helens Town – Witton Albion withdrawn)				
17	Buxton	v	City Of Liverpool (24/9)	0-3	50
18	Chester	v	Vauxhall Motors (25/9)	11-0	
	(at Vauxhall Motors FC)				
19	Cleethorpes Town	v	York City (25/9)	0-5	103
20	Ossett United	v	Pontefract Collieries (24/9)	4-2	121
21	Guiseley	v	Emley (23/9)	5-0	175
22	Eccleshill United	v	Handsworth		
	(walkover for Eccleshill United – Handsworth withdrawn)				
23	Swallownest	v	Harrogate Railway Athletic (21/9)	1-2	101
24	Dronfield Town	v	Stocksbridge Park Steels (24/9)	0-2	
25	Farsley Celtic	v	Worsbrough Bridge Athletic (23/9)	2-5	
26	Hall Road Rangers	v	North Ferriby		
	(walkover for North Ferriby – Hall Road Rangers withdrawn)				
27	Sheffield	v	Bradford (P A) Com (23/9)	2-0	
28	Leicester Nirvana	v	Heather St Johns (24/9)	0-6	
29	West Bridgford	v	Boston United (24/9)	1-3	
30	Grantham Town	v	Holbeach United (24/9)	6-0	128
31	Bourne Town	v	Lincoln United (23/9)	1-8	90
32	Loughborough Dynamo	v	Aylestone Park (24/9)	0-1	
33	Eastwood Community	v	Mickleover (23/9)	0-4	
34	Basford United	v	Lutterworth Athletic (24/9)	5-1	
35	Deeping Rangers	v	Ilkeston Town (24/9)	2-4	114
36	Kirby Muxloe	v	Matlock Town (24/9)	7-1	
	(at Barwell FC)				
37	Stratford Town	v	Worcester City (21/9)	0-2	107
38	Pershore Town	v	Kidderminster Harriers (24/9)	1-1	
	(Pershore Town won 5-4 on kicks from the penalty mark)				
39	Tamworth	v	Rugby Town (25/9)	0-2	
40	Leamington	v	Shawbury United (23/9)	1-1	75
	(Shawbury United won 5-4 on kicks from the penalty mark)				
41	Coleshill Town	v	Walsall Wood (25/9)	4-1	73
42	Paget Rangers	v	Stafford Rangers (25/9)	2-3	75
43	Haughmond	v	Bedworth United (24/9)	2-1	40
44	Hereford	v	Newcastle Town		
	(walkover for Newcastle Town – Hereford withdrawn)				
45	Rushall Olympic	v	Romulus (22/9)	2-3	
46	Nuneaton Borough	v	Stourbridge (23/9)	0-8	128
47	Evesham United	v	Coventry Sphinx (21/9)	1-2	84
48	Kempston Rovers	v	Wellingborough Whitworth (24/9)	1-6	82
49	Northampton On Chenecks	v	Rothwell Corinthians		
	(walkover for Rothwell Corinthians – Northampton On Chenecks withdrawn)				
50	Baldock Town	v	Winslow United (23/9)	1-2	79
51	Newport Pagnell Town	v	Hitchin Town (24/9)	5-2	92
	(tie awarded to Hitchin Town – Newport Pagnell Town removed)				
52	St Neots Town	v	Kettering Town (23/9)	0-3	102
53	AFC Dunstable	v	Cogenhoe United (24/9)	3-2	
54	Bugbrooke St Michaels	v	Yaxley (24/9)	4-1	75
55	Wellingborough Town	v	Biggleswade Town (24/9)	3-1	115
56	Royston Town	v	AFC Rushden & Diamonds (24/9)	2-1	
57	Framlingham Town	v	Woodbridge Town (24/9)	4-3	
58	Leiston	v	Mildenhall Town (24/9)	6-0	44
59	Ely City	v	Newmarket Town (24/9)	0-6	
60	Walsham Le Willows	v	Cambridge City (24/9)	0-1	46
61	Felixstowe & Walton United	v	Wroxham (24/9)	0-3	84
62	Bury Town	v	March Town United (24/9)	4-0	
63	AFC Sudbury	v	Ipswich Wanderers (23/9)	8-0	
64	Needham Market	v	Dereham Town (24/9)	3-4	
65	Saffron Walden Town	v	Gorleston (24/9)	8-1	
66	Histon	v	Lakenheath (24/9)	4-0	81
67	Brentwood Town	v	Grays Athletic (23/9)	2-2	67
	(Grays Athletic won 3-2 on kicks from the penalty mark)				
68	Chelmsford City	v	Walthamstow (21/9)	9-2	327
69	Ilford	v	London Lions (27/9)	0-2	
70	Potters Bar Town	v	Hertford Town (23/9)	2-3	
71	Ware	v	Wingate & Finchley (23/9)	3-2	88
72	Concord Rangers	v	Aveley (23/9)	6-1	212
73	Cockfosters	v	Hornchurch (24/9)	1-0	127
74	Little Oakley	v	St Margaretsbury (24/9)	1-2	56
75	Heybridge Swifts	v	Romford (25/9)	1-1	
	(Heybridge Swifts won 6-5 on kicks from the penalty mark)				
76	Billericay Town	v	Barking (24/9)	5-0	84
77	Bowers & Pitsea	v	Cheshunt (23/9)	3-4	84
78	Stanway Rovers	v	St Albans City (25/9)	2-2	

No	Home		Away	Score	Att
	(St Albans City won 4-2 on kicks from the penalty mark)				
79	Redbridge	v	Woodford Town (21/9)	6-0	94
80	Balham	v	Hanworth Villa (24/9)	0-4	
81	Uxbridge	v	Burnham (21/9)	9-0	
82	Windsor	v	Leverstock Green (21/9)	1-5	
83	Berkhamsted	v	Hanwell Town (24/9)	5-2	103
84	Hayes & Yeading United	v	Chalfont St Peter (24/9)	0-3	70
85	Kings Langley	v	Hampton & Richmond Borough (23/9)	4-1	75
86	Spelthorne Sports	v	Hendon (22/9)	8-2	
87	Hemel Hempstead Town	v	Bedfont Sports Club (23/9)	1-3	
88	Brimsdown	v	North Greenford United (18/9)	1-0	50
89	Erith Town	v	Hastings United (23/9)	2-1	
90	Crowborough Athletic	v	Whyteleafe		
	(walkover for Whyteleafe – Crowborough Athletic withdrawn)				
91	VCD Athletic	v	Tonbridge Angels		
	(walkover for Tonbridge Angels – VCD Athletic withdrawn)				
92	Folkestone Invicta	v	Dulwich Hamlet (24/9)	1-2	
93	Dartford	v	Lingfield		
	(walkover for Dartford – Lingfield withdrawn)				
94	Maidstone United	v	Croydon (22/9)	2-3	115
95	AFC Croydon Athletic	v	Faversham Town (21/9)	0-1	
96	Welling Town	v	Margate (24/9)	1-3	44
	(at Meridian VP FC)				
97	Carshalton Athletic	v	Phoenix Sports (23/9)	3-0	68
98	K Sports	v	Meridian VP (24/9)	3-1	54
99	Tooting & Mitcham United	v	Ebbsfleet United (23/9)	3-1	
100	Pagham	v	Westfield (24/9)	3-3	105
	(Pagham won 4-3 on kicks from the penalty mark)				
101	Godalming Town	v	Broadbridge Heath (21/9)	3-2	91
102	Arundel	v	Kingstonian (23/9)	0-10	72
103	South Park	v	Worthing (21/9)	5-4	64
104	Lancing	v	Raynes Park Vale (22/9)	0-3	
105	Steyning Town Community	v	Leatherhead (24/9)	1-4	11
106	Redhill	v	Metropolitan Police (21/9)	0-4	
107	Chessington & Hook United	v	Mile Oak (23/9)	6-1	109
108	Lewes	v	Alfold (24/9)	3-0	102
109	Three Bridges	v	Oakwood (21/9)	3-2	107
110	Chichester City	v	Sutton Common Rovers (24/9)	1-4	60
111	Chipstead	v	Burgess Hill Town (23/9)	7-0	71
112	Eastbourne Borough	v	Knaphill (22/9)	2-1	57
113	Whitehawk	v	Dorking Wanderers (21/9)	1-1	60
	(Dorking Wanderers won 3-1 on kicks from the penalty mark)				
114	Camberley Town	v	Shrivenham (24/9)	7-1	145
115	Aylesbury Vale Dynamos	v	Holmer Green (24/9)	0-1	
116	Fleet Town	v	Clanfield 85 (21/9)	3-0	62
117	Oxford City	v	Ascot United (22/9)	0-1	
118	Thatcham Town	v	Kidlington (22/9)	2-3	
119	Wokingham & Emmbrook	v	Cove (24/9)	6-2	
120	Didcot Town	v	Thame United (21/9)	6-0	
121	Binfield	v	Reading City (23/9)	0-4	
122	Moneyfields	v	Basingstoke Town (24/9)	3-2	
123	Brockenhurst	v	AFC Portchester (24/9)	5-0	131
124	Wimborne Town	v	AFC Stoneham (24/9)	6-3	
125	Bemerton Heath Harlequins	v	Totton & Eling (21/9)	2-4	46
126	Hamworthy United	v	Havant & Waterlooville (22/9)	3-1	158
127	United Services Portsmouth	v	Fareham Town (22/9)	9-0	
128	Winchester City	v	Poole Town (25/9)	2-2	
	(Poole Town won 4-2 on kicks from the penalty mark)				
129	Keynsham Town	v	Mangotsfield United (21/9)	0-8	122
130	Oldland Abbotonians	v	Gloucester City (21/9)	0-3	
131	Cinderford Town	v	Odd Down (24/9)	2-3	56
132	Yate Town	v	Bradford Town (24/9)	5-1	110
133	Tuffley Rovers	v	Bath City (24/9)	4-1	147
134	Chippenham Town	v	Slimbridge (21/9)	1-0	
135	Corsham Town	v	Bishop's Cleeve (22/9)	2-3	84
136	Street	v	Bishops Lydeard (24/9)	5-0	66
137	Wells City	v	Weston Super Mare (22/9)	1-2	
138	Bridgwater Town	v	Radstock Town (24/9)	2-0	130
	(tie awarded to Radstock Town – Bridgwater Town removed)				
139	Welton Rovers	v	Elburton Villa (23/9)	1-2	51
140	Portishead Town	v	Truro City (24/9)	0-5	

SECOND ROUND QUALIFYING

No	Home		Away	Score	Att
1	Hartlepool United	v	Hebburn Town (7/10)	0-1	
2	Darlington	v	South Shields (7/10)	0-6	
3	Morpeth Town	v	Spennymoor Town (5/10)	1-1	
	(Spennymoor Town won 5-4 on kicks from the penalty mark – at Bedlington Terriers FC)				
4	Seaham Red Star	v	Gateshead (9/10)	0-3	94
5	St Helens Town	v	Chester (11/10)	0-4	
6	Altrincham	v	City of Liverpool (9/10)	2-0	
7	Stockport County	v	Hyde United (9/10)	1-2	
	(at Hyde United FC)				
8	Irlam	v	Newcastle Town (8/10)	2-1	95
9	Skelmersdale United	v	Prestwich Heys (8/10)	4-4	
	(Skelmersdale United won 3-0 on kicks from the penalty mark – at Prestwich Heys FC)				
10	Clitheroe	v	AFC Fylde (7/10)	1-7	165
11	Wrexham	v	Litherland Remyca		
	(walkover for Litherland Remyca – Wrexham withdrawn)				
12	FC United of Manchester	v	Macclesfield Town		
	(walkover for FC United of Manchester – Macclesfield Town withdrawn)				
13	Sheffield	v	Guiseley (7/10)	0-5	111
14	Eccleshill United	v	Harrogate Railway Athletic	7-1	117
15	Ossett United	v	Worsbrough Bridge Athletic (5/10)	4-3	154
16	Stocksbridge Park Steels	v	York City (7/10)	1-3	115
17	FC Halifax Town	v	North Ferriby (7/10)	6-0	
18	Boston United	v	Grantham Town (8/10)	3-0	215
	(at Grantham Town FC)				
19	Chesterfield	v	Notts County (7/10)	0-2	
20	Heather St Johns	v	Rugby Town (7/10)	2-5	69
21	Lincoln United	v	Kirby Muxloe (8/10)	3-2	
22	Ilkeston Town	v	Aylestone Park (7/10)	2-3	131
23	Basford United	v	Mickleover (8/10)	1-1	
	(Basford United won 3-0 on kicks from the penalty mark)				
24	Solihull Moors	v	Coleshill Town (8/10)	0-0	55
	(Solihull Moors won 5-3 on kicks from the penalty mark)				
25	Stourbridge	v	Romulus (5/10)	2-2	112
	(Romulus won 4-3 on kicks from the penalty mark)				
26	Worcester City	v	Stafford Rangers (5/10)	3-0	
27	Coventry Sphinx	v	Pershore Town (8/10)	4-2	72
28	Shawbury United	v	Haughmond (5/10)	2-1	
29	Wellingborough Town	v	Bugbrooke St Michaels (8/10)	2-4	
30	Wellingborough Whitworth	v	Kettering Town (8/10)	2-4	161
31	Holmer Green	v	Royston Town (8/10)	0-8	55
32	AFC Dunstable	v	Hitchin Town (15/10)	0-2	
33	Winslow United	v	Rothwell Corinthians (8/10)	6-1	90
34	Dereham Town	v	AFC Sudbury (9/10)	2-4	191
35	Leiston	v	Saffron Walden Town (8/10)	6-1	56
36	Bury Town	v	St Margaretsbury (15/10)	10-0	45
37	Histon	v	Framlingham Town (8/10)	2-1	103
38	King's Lynn Town	v	Cambridge City (6/10)	3-0	
39	Newmarket Town	v	Wroxham (6/10)	3-2	
40	Cheshunt	v	Billericay Town (8/10)	0-4	
41	Hertford Town	v	Grays Athletic (7/10)	5-2	
42	Cockfosters	v	Concord Rangers (8/10)	1-3	103
43	St Albans City	v	Dagenham & Redbridge (8/10)	6-0	116
44	Heybridge Swifts	v	Redbridge (9/10)	1-3	
45	London Lions	v	Chelmsford City (7/10)	3-6	121
46	Bedfont Sports Club	v	Brimsdown (5/10)	4-1	35
47	Spelthorne Sports	v	Ware (6/10)	0-5	
48	Leverstock Green	v	Wealdstone (8/10)	2-2	84
	(Wealdstone won 8-7 on kicks from the penalty mark)				
49	Boreham Wood	v	Berkhamsted (9/10)	1-3	
50	Uxbridge	v	Barnet (5/10)	7-0	137
51	Chalfont St Peter	v	Kings Langley (8/10)	1-4	167
52	Dartford	v	Tooting & Mitcham United (7/10)	5-1	290
53	Erith Town	v	K Sports (5/10)	0-1	272
54	Tonbridge Angels	v	Whyteleafe (7/10)	2-1	
55	Hanworth Villa	v	Dover Athletic (5/10)	0-2	
56	Bromley	v	Faversham Town (9/10)	3-1	184
57	Dulwich Hamlet	v	Croydon (7/10)	2-2	
	(Dulwich Hamlet won 4-1 on kicks from the penalty mark)				
58	Carshalton Athletic	v	Margate (5/10)	3-2	40
59	Woking	v	Three Bridges (5/10)	7-0	109
60	Chipstead	v	Metropolitan Police (5/10)	1-3	76
61	Godalming Town	v	Lewes (5/10)	1-2	90
62	Sutton Common Rovers	v	South Park (9/10)	1-0	
63	Sutton United	v	Raynes Park Vale (5/10)	2-0	137
64	Eastbourne Borough	v	Kingstonian (8/10)	4-2	76
65	Dorking Wanderers	v	Chessington & Hook United (6/10)	1-1	110
	(Dorking Wanderers won 7-6 on kicks from the penalty mark)				
66	Pagham	v	Leatherhead (8/10)	0-14	129
67	Camberley Town	v	Maidenhead United (8/10)	5-0	80

68	Reading City	v	Fleet Town (8/10)	7-1	46
69	Didcot Town	v	Ascot United (5/10)	1-0	257
70	Wokingham & Emmbrook	v	Kidlington (8/10)	0-3	
71	Poole Town	v	Brockenhurst (9/10)	0-1	162
72	United Services Portsmouth	v	Weymouth (6/10)	3-0	47
73	Totton & Eling	v	Wimborne Town (14/10)	1-6	
74	Moneyfields	v	Aldershot Town (8/10)	2-4	
75	Eastleigh	v	Hamworthy United (8/10)	4-2	251
76	Gloucester City	v	Truro City (8/10)	1-2	
77	Torquay United (at South Devon College)	v	Elburton Villa (9/10)	2-1	72
78	Bishop's Cleeve	v	Yeovil Town (8/10)	0-6	
79	Tuffley Rovers	v	Radstock Town (8/10)	6-2	109
80	Mangotsfield United	v	Yate Town (7/10)	10-0	174
81	Weston Super Mare	v	Street (5/10)	1-1	
	(Weston Super Mare won 4-3 on kicks from the penalty mark)				
82	Odd Down	v	Chippenham Town (8/10)	0-1	62

THIRD ROUND QUALIFYING

1	Gateshead	v	Eccleshill United (21/10)	3-5	
2	Hyde United	v	Skelmersdale United (23/10)	8-1	185
3	Spennymoor Town	v	Ossett United (20/10)	1-1	
	(Ossett United won 2-1 on kicks from the penalty mark)				
4	Litherland Remyca	v	FC United of Manchester		
	(walkover for FC United of Manchester – Litherland Remyca withdrawn)				
5	Hebburn Town	v	AFC Fylde (20/10)	1-8	88
6	Guiseley	v	FC Halifax Town (21/10)	3-0	263
7	Altrincham	v	South Shields (22/10)	2-2	
	(Altrincham won 4-2 on kicks from the penalty mark)				
8	York City	v	Chester (21/10)	1-2	
9	Irlam	v	Romulus (20/10)	3-0	75
10	Lincoln United	v	Basford United (21/10)	2-2	
	(Basford United won 4-1 on kicks from the penalty mark)				
11	Worcester City	v	Rugby Town (23/10)	3-1	
12	Winslow United	v	Hitchin Town (22/10)	4-3	152
13	Aylestone Park	v	Bugbrooke St Michaels (19/10)	2-3	
14	Kettering Town	v	Solihull Moors (22/10)	1-3	
15	Coventry Sphinx	v	Shawbury United (22/10))	2-1	139
16	Boston United	v	Notts County (22/10)	0-1	125
17	Redbridge	v	AFC Sudbury (19/10)	2-3	69
18	Billericay Town	v	Newmarket Town (21/10)	1-1	143
	(Newmarket Town won 3-0 on kicks from the penalty mark)				
19	St Albans City	v	Histon (21/10)	4-3	150
20	King's Lynn Town	v	Bury Town (28/10)	1-2	196
21	Chelmsford City	v	Concord Rangers (19/10)	2-1	
22	Hertford Town	v	Leiston (21/10)	3-1	
23	Dorking Wanderers	v	Royston Town (20/10)	3-2	
24	Dover Athletic	v	Lewes (20/10)	1-0	
25	Woking	v	Sutton Common Rovers (19/10)	1-0	147
26	Leatherhead	v	Ware (22/10)	6-3	
27	Carshalton Athletic	v	Eastbourne Borough (23/10)	1-3	
28	Sutton United	v	Kings Langley (19/10)	3-0	118
29	Wealdstone	v	Bromley (28/10)	0-6	
30	K Sports	v	Uxbridge (22/10)	2-0	115
31	Dulwich Hamlet	v	Metropolitan Police (21/10)	0-4	
32	Berkhamsted	v	Bedfont Sports Club (22/10)	2-6	
33	Dartford	v	Tonbridge Angels (21/10)	4-1	357
34	Torquay United (at South Devon College)	v	Tuffley Rovers (19/10)	2-4	
35	Truro City	v	Aldershot Town (21/10)	1-1	119
	(Truro City won 4-2 on kicks from the penalty mark)				
36	Mangotsfield United	v	Eastleigh (21/10)	1-2	172
37	Didcot Town	v	United Services Portsmouth (19/10)	1-1	291
	(Didcot Town won 5-4 on kicks from the penalty mark)				
38	Brockenhurst	v	Kidlington (20/10)	3-1	217
39	Camberley Town	v	Weston Super Mare (22/10)	1-1	110
	(Camberley Town won 4-2 on kicks from the penalty mark)				
40	Chippenham Town	v	Reading City (29/10)	1-1	
	(Chippenham Town won 4-3 on kicks from the penalty mark)				
41	Yeovil Town	v	Wimborne Town (20/10)	3-4	217

FIRST ROUND PROPER

1	Morecambe	v	AFC Fylde (6/11)	1-4	
2	Blackpool	v	Bradford City (28/10)	2-3	
3	Eccleshill United	v	Altrincham (4/11)	1-3	61
4	Bolton Wanderers	v	Guiseley (28/10)	1-2aet	
5	Wigan Athletic	v	Harrogate Town (3/11)	5-0	
6	Tranmere Rovers	v	Hyde United (9/12)	0-0	261
	(Tranmere Rovers won 8-7 on kicks from the penalty mark)				
7	Salford City	v	Rochdale (4/11)	3-2	
8	Oldham Athletic	v	FC United of Manchester (28/10)	6-0	
9	Ossett United	v	Sunderland (3/11)	1-8	400
10	Carlisle United	v	Chester (4/11)	3-2	
11	Fleetwood Town	v	Accrington Stanley (4/11)	1-0	
12	Coventry Sphinx	v	Doncaster Rovers (4/11)	1-2	157
13	Solihull Moors	v	Lincoln City (4/11)	0-3	
14	Bugbrooke St Michaels	v	Mansfield Town (10/12)	0-3	300
15	Irlam	v	Notts County(11/12)	0-6	38
16	Grimsby Town	v	Scunthorpe United (27/10)	2-0	
17	Port Vale	v	Basford United (4/11)	1-4	
18	Burton Albion	v	Worcester City (8/12)	4-1	
19	Crewe Alexandra	v	Hull City (4/11)	0-2	
20	Shrewsbury Town	v	Walsall (4/11)	0-4	
21	Milton Keynes Dons	v	Hertford Town (4/11)	8-1	
22	Bury Town	v	AFC Sudbury (7/12)	0-7	240
23	Newmarket Town	v	Peterborough United (4/11)	2-7aet	
24	Chelmsford City	v	St Albans City (2/11)	3-1	
25	Ipswich Town	v	Southend United (3/11)	4-1	
26	Stevenage	v	Colchester United (4/11)	1-4	
27	Northampton Town	v	Cambridge United (4/11)	1-1aet	
	(Cambridge United won 11-10 on kicks from the penalty mark – at Wellingborough Town FC)				
28	Dartford	v	Metropolitan Police (3/11)	1-3	
29	Oxford United (at Thame United FC)	v	AFC Wimbledon (11/11)	1-2	
30	Bromley	v	Bedfont Sports Club (11/12)	2-1	
31	Crawley Town	v	Sutton United		
	(walkover for Sutton United – Crawley Town withdrawn)				
32	Leyton Orient (at Haringey Borough FC)	v	Woking (9/11)	2-3	
33	Winslow United	v	Charlton Athletic (4/11)	0-5	263
34	Dorking Wanderers	v	Dover Athletic (3/11)	1-0	36
35	Gillingham	v	Leatherhead (3/11)	7-1	
36	Eastbourne Borough	v	K Sports (11/12)	1-0	202
37	Plymouth Argyle	v	Exeter City (4/11)	2-3aet	
38	Wimborne Town	v	Newport County (4/11)	0-1	174
39	Swindon Town	v	Forest Green Rovers (4/11)	2-2aet	
	(Swindon Town won 8-7 on kicks from the penalty mark)				
40	Brockenhurst	v	Truro City (4/11)	2-1	300
41	Cheltenham Town	v	Tuffley Rovers (2/11)	4-0	
42	Eastleigh	v	Chippenham Town (4/11)	3-4aet	
43	Bristol Rovers	v	Camberley Town (9/12)	2-3	
44	Portsmouth	v	Didcot Town (3/11)	4-2	

SECOND ROUND PROPER

1	Oldham Athletic	v	Lincoln City (18/11)	0-1	
2	Altrincham	v	Peterborough United (20/11)	1-2	
3	Burton Albion	v	Mansfield Town (21/12)	3-2	
4	Cambridge United	v	Guiseley (17/11)	4-0	
5	Hull City	v	Doncaster Rovers (18/11)	2-3	
6	Wigan Athletic	v	Notts County (18/12)	3-2	
7	Fleetwood Town	v	Walsall (13/11)	3-0	
8	Carlisle United	v	Bradford City (19/11)	3-1	
9	Salford City	v	Tranmere Rovers (18/12)	2-1	
10	AFC Fylde	v	Sunderland (20/11)	3-1	
11	Basford United	v	Grimsby Town (21/12)	1-0	300
12	Milton Keynes Dons	v	Eastbourne Borough (19/12)	3-0	
13	Metropolitan Police	v	Swindon Town (21/12)	1-2aet	
14	Portsmouth	v	Bromley (16/12)	1-2	123
15	Chelmsford City	v	Ipswich Town (23/11)	0-5	
16	Chippenham Town	v	Woking (18/11)	0-7	
17	Dorking Wanderers	v	Colchester United (18/11)	0-2	
18	Exeter City	v	Cheltenham Town (11/11)	3-2aet	
19	AFC Sudbury	v	AFC Wimbledon (23/12)	1-2	203
20	Sutton United	v	Camberley Town (21/12)	6-0	
21	Newport County (at Spytty Stadium)	v	Brockenhurst (19/12)	3-2aet	
22	Gillingham	v	Charlton Athletic (17/11)	1-1aet	
	(Charlton Athletic won 9-8 on kicks from the penalty mark – at Chatham Town FC)				

THIRD ROUND PROPER

1	Watford (at St Albans City FC)	v	Colchester United (9/12)	2-0
2	Swansea City (at Landore Training Ground)	v	Queens Park Rangers (8/12)	2-1
3	Nottingham Forest	v	Bristol City (7/12)	1-2
4	Middlesbrough (at Bishop Auckland FC)	v	Millwall (4/12)	4-0
5	**Brighton & Hove Albion (at AMEX Training Ground)**	v	**Woking (7/12)**	**5-1**
6	Stoke City (at Clayton Wood Training Ground)	v	Burton Albion (12/3)	2-3aet
7	Huddersfield Town (Newcastle United won 5-3 on kicks from the penalty mark)	v	Newcastle United (15/12)	1-1aet
8	**Cambridge United (at Newmarket Town FC)**	v	**AFC Fylde (17/3)**	**2-3**
9	AFC Wimbledon	v	Burnley (18/3)	1-0
10	Everton (at Southport FC)	v	Wigan Athletic (17/3)	4-2aet
11	Carlisle United	v	Blackburn Rovers (8/12)	0-1
12	Derby County	v	Cardiff City (4/12)	2-3aet
13	Rotherham United	v	Arsenal (15/12)	1-2
14	Chelsea (at Kingsmeadow)	v	Barnsley (28/11)	8-1
15	Reading	v	Aston Villa (11/12)	3-4
16	**Liverpool (at LFC Academy)**	v	**Sutton United (16/3)**	**6-0**
17	**Basford United**	v	**West Bromwich Albion (17/3)**	**0-4**
18	Lincoln City (at Preston North End FC)	v	Preston North End (6/1)	1-0
19	Manchester City (at Academy Stadium)	v	Birmingham City (12/3)	6-1
20	Wolverhampton Wanderers (at St George's Park)	v	Norwich City (18/12)	2-4
21	Salford City	v	Manchester United (10/3)	0-2
22	**Swindon Town**	v	**Bromley (12/1)**	**3-0**
23	Charlton Athletic (at Dartford FC)	v	Sheffield United (17/3)	0-2
24	Leeds United (at York City FC)	v	Milton Keynes Dons (17/3)	8-2
25	Tottenham Hotspur (at Tottenham Hotspur Training Centre)	v	Newport County (12/1)	6-2
26	Ipswich Town	v	Fulham (7/12)	3-2
27	Leicester City (at LCFC Academy)	v	Sheffield Wednesday (5/3)	5-0
28	Luton Town (West Ham United won 4-2 on kicks from the penalty mark)	v	West Ham United (3/12)	3-3aet
29	Peterborough United	v	Doncaster Rovers (19/3)	2-1
30	Exeter City	v	AFC Bournemouth (2/12)	3-1
31	Southampton	v	Coventry City (5/12)	3-0
32	Fleetwood Town	v	Crystal Palace (11/12)	2-1

FOURTH ROUND PROPER

1	Exeter City	v	Leicester City (23/3)	1-2aet
2	Ipswich Town	v	Swindon Town (27/3)	3-1
3	Peterborough United (at Sheffield United FC)	v	Sheffield United (3/4)	0-2
4	Newcastle United (at Whitley Park)	v	Leeds United (3/4)	4-1
5	Southampton	v	Burton Albion (23/3)	0-1
6	Manchester City (at Academy Stadium)	v	Everton (3/4)	0-1
7	Fleetwood Town (Bristol City won 4-2 on kicks from the penalty mark)	v	Bristol City (22/3)	1-1aet
8	Blackburn Rovers (at BRFC Academy)	v	Arsenal (20/3)	1-4
9	AFC Wimbledon	v	Tottenham Hotspur (31/3)	0-3aet
10	Manchester United (at Leigh Sports Village)	v	Liverpool (3/4)	0-1
11	West Bromwich Albion	v	Cardiff City (31/3)	2-1
12	**Chelsea (at Kingsmeadow)**	v	**AFC Fylde (2/4)**	**2-0**
13	Norwich City	v	West Ham United (22/3)	0-5
14	Lincoln City	v	Watford (19/3)	2-3aet
15	Swansea City (at Landore Training Ground)	v	Middlesbrough (2/4)	0-1
16	Aston Villa	v	Brighton & Hove Albion (24/3)	3-0

FIFTH ROUND PROPER

1	Newcastle United	v	Watford (11/4)	3-2aet
2	Aston Villa	v	Burton Albion (14/4)	9-0
3	West Ham United (at Rush Green Training Ground)	v	Arsenal (16/4)	1-3
4	Sheffield United	v	Bristol City (17/4)	3-1
5	Leicester City (at LCFC Training Ground)	v	Liverpool (16/4)	1-5
6	Chelsea (at Kingsmeadow)	v	Everton (15/4)	1-2
7	Tottenham Hotspur (at THFC Training Centre)	v	West Bromwich Albion (13/4)	0-5
8	Middlesbrough (at Bishop Auckland FC)	v	Ipswich Town (10/4)	0-1

QUARTER FINALS

1	Newcastle United	v	Aston Villa (27/4)	1-6
2	Liverpool	v	Arsenal (30/4)	3-1
3	Ipswich Town	v	Sheffield United (30/4)	3-2aet
4	West Bromwich Albion	v	Everton (27/4)	2-1

SEMI FINALS

1	Ipswich Town (Live on BT Sport 1)	v	Liverpool (12/5)	1-2
2	Aston Villa (Live on BT Sport 1)	v	West Bromwich Albion (14/5)	4-1

THE FINAL

1	Aston Villa (Live on BT Sport 1)	v	Liverpool	2-1	4406

PREVIOUS TEN FINALS

				Aggregate Score
2020	Manchester City	v	Chelsea	3-2
2019	Liverpool	v	Manchester City	1-1, 5-3p
2018	Chelsea	v	Arsenal	7-1
2017	Chelsea	v	Manchester City	6-2
2016	Chelsea	v	Manchester City	4-2
2015	Chelsea	v	Manchester City	5-2
2014	Chelsea	v	Fulham	7-6
2013	Norwich City	v	Chelsea	4-2
2012	Chelsea	v	Blackburn Rovers	4-1
2011	Manchester Utd	v	Sheffield United	4-1

CONCLUSION OF THE 2019-20 COMPETITION

QUARTER FINALS

1 Brighton & Hove Albion v Birmingham City (27/9) 2-2
(Birmingham City won 4-2 on kick from the penalty mark - at Crawley Town)
2 Everton v Chelsea (27/9) 2-1
(at Goodison Park)
3 Arsenal v Tottenham Hotspur (26/9) 4-0
(at Boreham Wood)
4 Leicester City v Manchester City (27/9) 1-2
(at Quorn)

SEMI FINALS

1 Birmingham City v Everton (30/09) 0-3
(at Solihull Moors)
2 Manchester City v Arsenal (1/10) 2-1
(at Academy Stadium)

THE FINAL - Saturday 1 November - @ Wembley Stadium

Everton v Manchester City 1-3aet

2020-21 COMPETITION

EXTRA PRELIMINARY ROUND

1 Boro Rangers v Workington Reds Ladies 0-1
(at M Foundation)
2 Birtley Town Ladies v Bishop Auckland Ladies 0-3 60
(at Birtley Sports Complex)
3 Stanwix v South Shields Ladies 0-6
(at Gilford Park)
4 Wallsend BC Women v Hartlepool United Ladies 6-1 75
(at Kirkley Park)
5 Gateshead Leam Rangers v CLS Amazons Women 1-3
(at Gateshead Leam Rangers)
6 Appleby Frodingham v South Cave Sporting Club Ladies 4-3
(at Brumby Hall Social Club)
7 Harworth Colliery Ladies v Silsden A Ladies 6-1
(at Jones & Co Recreational Ground)
8 Wakefield Trinity Ladies v Hepworth United Ladies 5-0
(at Hemsworth MW)
9 Harrogate Town Ladies v Farsley Celtic Women 3-1
(at Farsley Celtic)
10 Yorkshire Amateurs v Altofts Ladies
(walkover for Altofts – Yorkshire Amateur A Ladies withdrawn)
11 Rotherham United Women v Oughtibridge War Memorial Ladies 3-3
(Rotherham United won 3-0 on kicks from the penalty mark – at Roundwood Pavilion)
12 Crewe Alexandra Women v West Didsbury & Chorlton 1-0
(at Cumberland Arena)
13 Tranmere Rovers Ladies v Fleetwood Town Wrens 2-3
(at Ellesmere Port Sports Village)
14 Cheadle Town Stingers W v Chester Ladies 5-1 43
(at Cheadle Town)
15 Curzon Ashton Women v Haslingden Girls & Ladies 7-2
(at Curzon Ashton)
16 Merseyrail Ladies v Mossley A Women 5-0
(at Admiral Park)
17 Didsbury Ladies v Northwich Vixens 1-2
(at Didsbury Sports Ground)
18 United Of Manchester Women v West Kirby Ladies 13-0 66
(at Broadhurst Park)
19 Mossley Hill Ladies v Ashton United Women's (13/9)12-0
(at Tiber Football Centre)
20 A Darwen Ladies v Nelson Ladies 9-0 100
(at A Darwen)
21 Grimsby Borough v Pride Park
(walkover for Grimsby Borough – Pride Park withdrawn)
22 Notts County Women v Lincoln United 4-4 152
(Lincoln United won 3-2 on kicks from the penalty mark - at Basford United)
23 A Leicester Girls & Ladies v Woodlands Ladies 0-5
(at Wreake Valley Academy)
24 Sherwood Women v HBW United
(walkover for Sherwood Women – HBW United Ladies withdrawn)
25 Rise Park Ladies v Asfordby Amateurs Ladies 3-0
(at Calverton MW)
26 Dronfield Town v Arnold Eagles Women 2-1
(at Dronfield Town)
27 Arnold Town Ladies v Allexton & New Parks
(walkover for Allexton & New Parks – Arnold Town withdrawn)
28 Beaumont Park Ladies v Groby Women 6-2
(at Beaumont Park)
29 Coalville Town Ladies v Oadby & Wigston Women 2-7
(at Coalville Town)
30 Darlaston Town (1874) Ladies v Shifnal Town Ladies 2-6
(at The Paycare Ground)
31 Kingfisher v Knowle Ladies 0-3
(at Dickens Heath Sports Club)
32 Sutton Coldfield Town v Coventrians Ladies 5-0 80
(at Sutton Coldfield Town)
33 Westfields v Leamington Lions Ladies 2-1 97
(at Westfields)
34 Shrewsbury Juniors Ladies v Lye Town Ladies 0-5
(at Greenfields Sports Ground)
35 Coventry Sphinx Ladies v Sandwell Ladies 3-0
(at Coventry Sphinx)
36 Tamworth v Doveridge 8-0
(at Tamworth)
37 Solihull Sporting v Kidderminster Harriers 1-4
(at Chelmsley Town)
38 Cookley Sports v Coundon Court Ladies 2-1 64
(at Stourport Swifts)
39 Hereford Pegasus Ladies v Rugby Borough 1-0 65
(at Hereford Pegasus)
40 Stourbridge Ladies v Port Vale Ladies (3.00) 8-0 225
(at Stourbridge)
41 Walsall Wood Ladies v Redditch United 0-6 232
(at Walsall Wood)
42 Tamworth Academy Women v Worcester City 0-15 40
(at Austrey Playing Fields)
43 Balls To Cancer Ladies v Stockingford AA Pavilion Ladies 1-9
(at Hadley Stadium)
44 Rugby Town Women v Sedgley & Gornal United Women 2-6
(at Rugby Town)
45 St Ives Town Ladies v Hartham United Ladies 12-0
(at St Ives Town)
46 Newmarket Town Ladies v Wymondham Town 3-3
(Newmarket Town Ladies won 4-2 on kicks from the penalty mark - at Newmarket Town)
47 Whittlesey Athletic Ladies v Peterborough United 1-3
(at Whittlesey Athletic)
48 Wroxham Women v Kettering Town W 10-091
(at Wroxham)
49 Bedford Ladies & Girls v Corby Town 12-0
(at Bedford Town)
50 Henley Athletic Ladies v March Town Ladies 4-4
(March Town Ladies won 5-4 on kicks from the penalty mark - at Henley Community Centre)

51 Northampton Town Women v Haverhill Rovers 5-0
(at Harpole)

52 Aylesford v Ashford Ladies 1-3 80
(at Kings Hill Sports Park)

53 Herne Bay v Whyteleafe Women (2.30) 5-1 121
(at Herne Bay)

54 Dulwich Hamlet Women's v Margate 6-1
(at Dulwich Hamlet)

55 New London Lionesses v Parkwood Ladies 4-2
(at Rayners Lane)

56 Hastings United v Hackney Women's 0-2 300
(at Hastings United)

57 Tunbridge Wells Foresters v Ramsgate Women (2.15) 1-1 30
(Ramsgate Women won 5-4 on kicks from the penalty mark - at St Greggs)

58 Runwell Sports Ladies v Harlow Town Ladies 0-6
(at Runwell Sports Social Club)

59 Rayleigh Town Ladies v Hoddesdon Town Ladies
(walkover for Rayleigh Town – Hoddesdon Town withdrawn)

60 Chelmsford City Ladies v Frontiers Ladies 3-2 23
(at Chelmsford City)

61 Colney Heath Ladies v Herts Vipers 2-1
(at Colney Heath)

62 Hemel Hempstead Ladies v Garston Ladies 1-3
(at Bushey Sports Club)

63 Abingdon Town v Abingdon United 0-4
(at Abingdon Town)

64 Banbury United Women's v Swindon Supermarine Women 1-2
(at Banbury United)

65 Woodley United v Wargrave Women 5-2 50
(at Bishopswood Sports Ground)

66 Royal Wootton Bassett Town v Brentford W 1-1
(Brentford W won 7-6 on kicks from the penalty mark - at Royal Wootton Bassett Town)

67 Wycombe Wanderers Ladies v Oxford City Women 4-0
(at Amersham & Wycombe College)

68 Eastbourne United A Women v Pagham Ladies 1-0 60
(at Eastbourne United A)

69 Badshot Lea v Oakwood Ladies 7-3
(at Badshot Lea)

70 Walton Casuals Ladies v A Littlehampton Ladies (3.00) 4-0
(at Walton Casuals)

71 Mole Valley Women v A Acorns Ladies 0-11
(at Stable Meadow)

72 Roffey Women v Chichester City Women 1-4 60
(at Bartholomew Way)

73 Seaford Town v Newhaven 1-1 105
(Seaford Town won 3-1 on kicks from the penalty mark - at Seaford Town)

74 Burgess Hill Town Women v Saltdean United Women 0-10 100
(at Burgess Hill Town)

75 A Stoneham Ladies v Merley Cobham Sports Ladies 10-0
(at Stoneham Lane Complex)

76 Eastleigh In The Community v A Bournemouth Women 1-10 230
(at Eastleigh)

77 Bournemouth Sports Ladies v Redlands 21-0
(at Chapel Gate)

78 Alton Ladies v Meon Milton Ladies 13-0 36
(at Alton)

79 Longwell Green Ladies v Paulton Rovers Ladies 2-2
(Paulton Rovers won 6-5 on kicks from the penalty mark - at Longwell Green Community Centre)

80 Chippenham Ladies v Oldland Abbotonians 0-6
(at Stanley Park)

81 Bristol Ladies Union v Middlezoy Rovers Ladies (12.15) 1-1
(Middlezoy Rovers won 4-2 on kicks from the penalty mark - Coombe Dingle Sports Complex)

82 Downend Flyers Ladies v AEK-Boco 1-2
(at Hanham Athletic)

83 Bristol Rovers Women's v Bristol & West 6-0 100
(at Lockleaze Sports Centre)

84 Banwell v Ilminster Town 0-10
(at Banwell)

85 St Agnes A Ladies v Saltash United Women 0-1
(at Enys Parc)

86 Marine Academy Plymouth v Ottery St Mary A Ladies 21-0
(at Ivybridge Town)

87 A St Austell Ladies v Feniton Women's 7-0
(at A St Austell)

PRELIMINARY ROUND

1 Lumley Ladies v Spennymoor Town Ladies 0-1
(at New Ferens Park)

2 South Shields Ladies v Gateshead Rutherford Ladies 3-1
(at Harton Westoe MW)

3 Blyth Town Ladies v Guisborough Town Ladies (27/9)7-1
(at South Newsham Pavilion)

4 Washington L v Alnwick Town Ladies 0-7
(at Northumbria Centre)

5 Sunderland West End Ladies v Carlisle United Ladies 7-0
(at Herrington Recreation Park)

6 Durham United L v Workington Reds Ladies 3-4 50
(at Ushaw Moor Cricket & Football Cub)

7 CLS Amazons Women v Penrith A Ladies 1-2
(at Riverside Sports Complex)

8 Hartlepool Pools Youth L v Wallsend BC Women 0-9 53
(at John Howard Park)

9 Redcar Town Ladies v Bishop Auckland Ladies 6-1
(at Redcar Town)

10 Thackley A Ladies v Ripon City Ladies 3-3 78
(Ripon City won 4-3 on kicks from the penalty mark – at Thackley A)

11 Hull United Ladies v Millmoor Juniors L 2-1 60
(at Steve Prescott Centre)

12 Bradford Park Avenue Ladies v Ossett United Ladies 1-4
(at Bradford (Park Avenue))

13 Sheffield Wednesday Ladies v Harworth Colliery Ladies 3-2
(at SHU Sports Park)

14 Farsley Celtic Juniors Ladies A v Harrogate Town L 2-2
(Farsley Celtic Juniors won 3-1 on kicks from the penalty mark – at Bramley Park)

15 Brighouse Sports L v Appleby Frodingham L 6-1
(at Brighouse Sports & Social Club)

16 York City Ladies v Rotherham United Women 4-0
(at York St John's University Sports Park)

17 Altofts Ladies v Wakefield Trinity Ladies 3-4 70
(at Altofts Community Sports)

18 Curzon Ashton Women v Blackburn Community SC L 2-5
(at Curzon Ashton)

19 Morecambe Ladies v Salford City Lionesses L 3-0
(at Slyne with Hest)

20 Rylands L v Fleetwood Town Wrens L 0-14
(at Rylands Recreational Club)

21 A Darwen Ladies v Sir Tom Finney L 6-4
(at A Darwen)

22 United of Manchester Women v Ashton Town Ladies 9-0
(at United of Manchester)

23 Altrincham Ladies v Northwich Vixens L 0-5 197
(at Altrincham)

24 Mossley Hill Ladies v Wythenshawe Amateurs L 1-2
(at Mossley Hill Athletic Club)

25 Merseyrail Ladies v Cheadle Town Stingers W 7-3
(at Admiral Park)
26 SK Vipers L v Warrington Wolves Foundation W 0-8
(at Silverlands Stadium)
27 Crewe Alexandra Women v Accrington Stanley Community L14-1
(at Cumberland Arena)
28 Leicester City Ladies v Oakham United Women 7-1
(at Linwood Playing Fields)
29 Woodlands Ladies v Oadby & Wigston Women 0-2
(at Borrowash Victoria A)
30 St Joseph's Rockware of Worksop v Lincoln Moorlands Railway L 1-1
(Lincoln Moorlands Railway won 3-1 on kicks from the penalty mark – at Rockware)
31 Grimsby Town Women's v Ollerton Town Ladies 5-1 60
(at Bradley Football Development Centre)
32 Cleethorpes Town Ladies v Dronfield Town L 1-2 77
(at Cleethorpes Town)
33 Beaumont Park Ladies v Grimsby Borough L 2-1
(at Beaumont Park)
34 Rise Park Ladies v Allexton & New Parks L
(walkover for Rise Park Ladies – Allexton & New Parks Ladies withdrawn)
35 Belper Town Ladies v Sherwood Women (1.30) 0-3
(at Alton Manor)
36 Nottingham Trent University W v Lincoln United L 1-2
(at Nottingham Trent University)
37 Westfields L v Worcester City L 1-2
(at Westfields)
38 Stockingford AA Pavilion Ladies v Droitwich Spa Ladies 0-3 73
(at Stockingford Pavilion)
39 A Telford United Ladies v Knowle Ladies 2-3
(at A Telford United)
40 Cookley Sports L v Sedgley & Gornal United W 2-1 78
(at Lea Lane)
41 Tamworth L v Solihull Ladies United 3-2
(at Tamworth)
42 Hereford Pegasus Ladies v Coventry Sphinx Ladies 0-7
(at Hereford Pegasus)
43 Kidderminster Harriers L v Crusaders Ladies 0-1
(at Lea Castle)
44 Lye Town Ladies v Sutton Coldfield Town L 1-4
(at Lye Town)
45 Stourbridge Ladies v Wyrley Ladies 8-1 135
(at War Memorial Athletic Ground)
46 Shifnal Town Ladies v Redditch United L 3-3
(Redditch United won 5-3 on kicks from the penalty mark – at Shifnal Town)
47 Desborough Ladies v Netherton United Ladies 0-10
(at Wellingborough Old Grammarians)
48 Peterborough United L v Royston Town L 2-2
(Royston Town won 4-2 on kicks from the penalty mark – at Mick George Training Ground)
49 Waveney Ladies v Brett Vale L 2-2 69
(Brett Vale won 5-4 on kicks from the penalty mark – at Saturn Close)
50 A Sudbury Ladies v Needham Market L 3-1
(at A Sudbury)
51 Peterborough Northern Star L v March Town Ladies 13-1
(at Peterborough Northern Star)
52 Histon Ladies v St Ives Town Ladies 2-4 75
(at Histon)
53 Bedford Ladies & Girls v Northampton Town W 1-3
(at Bedford Town)
54 King's Lynn Town Ladies v Wroxham Women 3-7
(at Wroxham)
55 Bungay Town L v Newmarket Town L 0-5
(at Maltings Pavilion)
56 Bexhill United L v Sutton United Women 0-0
(Sutton United won 4-1 on kicks from the penalty mark – at Bexhill United)
57 Regents Park Rangers L v Phoenix Sports L 2-1
(at Barn Elms Sports Ground)
58 Haringey Borough Women's v Fulham Women (2.30) 1-2
(at Haringey Borough)
59 Comets W v Herne Bay L 1-1
(Comets won 4-3 on kicks from the penalty mark – at Barn Elms Sports Ground)
60 Millwall Lionesses L v New London Lionesses L 0-8
(at St Paul's Sports Ground)
61 Islington Borough Ladies v Ashford Ladies 1-4
(at St Aloysius Playing Fields)
62 Dartford Women v Ramsgate Women 8-0
(at Dartford)
63 Hackney Women's v Dulwich Hamlet Women's 2-6
(at Hackney Marshes)
64 Southend United Community SC L v Houghton Athletic L 1-1
(Southend United Community won 3-1 on kicks from the penalty mark – at Garon Park)
65 Wodson Park Ladies v Watford Ladies Development 1-2 51
(at Wodson Park Sports Centre)
66 Chelmsford City Ladies v Leigh Ramblers Ladies 1-2
(at Chelmsford City)
67 Rayleigh Town Ladies v Luton Town Ladies 1-9 110
(at Rayleigh Town Sports & Social Club)
68 Bowers & Pitsea Ladies v Garston Ladies (3.00) 5-0
(at Bowers & Pitsea)
69 Colney Heath Ladies v Harlow Town Ladies 3-4
(at Colney Heath)
70 Denham United Ladies v Queens Park Rangers Women 2-2
(Denham United won 5-3 on kicks from the penalty mark – at Oxford Road)
71 Ascot United L v Swindon Supermarine Women 6-0 123
(at Ascot United)
72 Brentford W v Ashford Town (Middx) W (3.00)1-6
(at Bedfont Sports Club)
73 Wycombe Wanderers Ladies v Eversley & California L 2-1
(at Amersham & Wycombe College)
74 Tilehurst Panthers L v Slough Town L 7-1
(at The Rivermoor Stadium)
75 Abingdon United L v Newbury Ladies 6-0
(at Abingdon United)
76 Woodley United L v Milton United L 5-3
(at UofR Bulmershe Pavilion)
77 Steyning Town Community L v Worthing Women 1-8
(at The Shooting Field)
78 Seaford Town L v Badshot Lea L 1-2
(at Seaford Town)
79 A Acorns Ladies v Lancing L 2-2
(Lancing won 5-4 on kicks from the penalty mark – at Copthorne Jubilee Pavilion)
80 Chichester City Women v Eastbourne Town L 0-3
(at Chichester City)
81 Woking Ladies v Godalming Town Ladies
(walkover for Woking Ladies – Godalming Town Ladies withdrawn)
82 Eastbourne United A Women v Dorking Wanderers Ladies 0-2 65
(at Eastbourne United A)
83 Walton Casuals Ladies v Saltdean United W 3-5
(at Walton Casuals)
84 Sherborne Town Ladies v Bournemouth Sports Ladies 3-0
(at Sherborne Town)
85 Alton Ladies v A Stoneham Ladies 2-5
(at Alton)
86 Shanklin Ladies v Moneyfields Women 0-8 50
(at Shanklin)
87 New Milton Town Ladies v Winchester City Flyers L 0-5
(at New Milton Town)

88 United Services Portsmouth W v A Bournemouth Women (27/9) 0-9
(at Burnaby Road Sports Ground)
89 Pen Mill Ladies v Ilminster Town L
(walkover for Ilminster Town – Pen Mill withdrawn)
90 Weston Super Mare L v Portishead Town Ladies 2-3
(at Weston Super Mare)
91 Middlezoy Rovers Ladies v Bishops Lydeard Ladies 4-3
(at Middlezoy Rovers)
92 Oldland Abbotonians L v Almondsbury Ladies 2-0
(at Oldland Abbotonians)
93 Chipping Sodbury Town Women's v Bristol Rovers Women's 2-4
(at Chipping Sodbury Town)
94 AEK-Boco L v Paulton Rovers L 4-3
(at AEK-Boco)
95 Helston Athletic Women v Saltash United W 5-4 113
(at Helston Athletic)
96 Callington Town L v Bideford Ladies 2-1
(at Callington Town)
97 Torquay United W v RNAS Culdrose Ladies 4-0
(at South Devon College Sports Centre)
98 A St Austell Ladies v Marine Academy Plymouth L 1-6
(at Poltair Park)

FIRST QUALIFYING ROUND

1 Penrith A Ladies v South Shields Ladies 1-2
(at Penrith A)
2 United of Manchester Women v Wakefield Trinity Ladies 4-1
(at United of Manchester)
3 Fleetwood Town Wrens L v A Darwen Ladies 1-1
(Fleetwood Town Wrens won 5-4 on kicks from the penalty mark – at Poolfoot Sports Complex)
4 Brighouse Sports L v Blyth Town Ladies 2-3
(at Brighouse Sports Club)
5 Hull United Ladies v Sunderland West End Ladies 1-2
(at Steve Prescott Centre)
6 Farsley Celtic Juniors Ladies A v Warrington Wolves Foundation (11/10) 1-2
(at Leeds Modernians Sports & Social Club)
7 Morecambe Ladies v Workington Reds Ladies 5-2
(at Slyne With Hest)
8 Blackburn Community SC L v Alnwick Town Ladies (11/10) 3-2
(at Harrison Playing Fields)
9 Wallsend BC Women v York City Ladies 2-1
(at Kirkley Park)
10 Spennymoor Town Ladies v Wythenshawe Amateurs L 3-3
(Spennymoor Town won 4-3 on kicks from the penalty mark – at Consett A)
11 Redcar Town Ladies v Ossett United Ladies 0-4
(at Redcar Town)
12 Ripon City Ladies v Merseyrail Ladies 1-4
(at Mallorie Park)
13 Sutton Coldfield Town L v Lincoln United L 1-0
(at Sutton Coldfield Town)
14 Worcester City L v Droitwich Spa Ladies (11/10) 4-1 202
(at Worcester City)
15 Lincoln Moorlands Railway L v Beaumont Park Ladies 2-3 64
(at Lincoln Moorlands Railway)
16 Oadby & Wigston Women v Rise Park Ladies 5-2
(at Oadby & Wigston)
17 Crusaders Ladies v Cookley Sports L 4-0
(at Rowheath Pavilion)
18 Tamworth L v Dronfield Town L 1-2
(at Tamworth)
19 Leicester City Ladies v Grimsby Town Women's 0-9
(at Linwood Playing Fields)
20 Sheffield Wednesday Ladies v Northwich Vixens L 1-1 50
(Northwich Vixens won 5-4 on kicks from the penalty mark – at SHU Sports Park)
21 Crewe Alexandra Women v Coventry Sphinx Ladies 1-4
(at Cumberland Arena)
22 Knowle Ladies v Stourbridge Ladies 0-6
(at Knowle)
23 Redditch United L v Sherwood Women 4-0
(at Redditch United)
24 Netherton United Ladies v Leigh Ramblers Ladies 5-4
(at Netherton United)
25 Northampton Town W v St Ives Town Ladies 0-1
(at Harpole)
26 Bowers & Pitsea Ladies v Harlow Town Ladies 0-1
(at Bowers & Pitsea)
27 Royston Town L v Brett Vale L (11/10) 8-0 70
(at Royston Town)
28 Peterborough Northern Star L v Southend United Community L 10-0
(at Peterborough Northern Star)
29 Luton Town Ladies v Wroxham Women (11/10) 5-0
(at 61)
30 A Sudbury Ladies v Newmarket Town L 3-3
(Newmarket Town won 4-2 on kicks from the penalty mark – at A Sudbury)
31 Dartford Women v Winchester City Flyers L (2.30)7-1
(at Dartford)
32 Ascot United L v Denham United Ladies 0-3
(at Ascot United)
33 Moneyfields Women v A Bournemouth Women (11/10)1-1
(A Bournemouth won 4-3 on kicks from the penalty mark - at Moneyfields)
34 Lancing L v Dulwich Hamlet Women's 0-1
(at Lancing)
35 Watford Ladies Development v Ashford Ladies (11/10) 1-9
(at Bovingdon)
36 Eastbourne Town L v Tilehurst Panthers L 2-0
(at Eastbourne Town)
37 Badshot Lea L v Saltdean United W (11/10) 1-6
(at Badshot Lea)
38 Comets W v Wycombe Wanderers Ladies (11/10) 0-1
(at Barn Elms Playing Fields)
39 Worthing Women v Sutton United Women (11/10)6-0
(at Wick)
40 Woking Ladies v Abingdon United L 1-2
(at Woking College)
41 Regents Park Rangers L v New London Lionesses L (11/10)0-5
(at Barn Elms Playing Fields)
42 Dorking Wanderers Ladiesv Ashford Town (Middx) W 1-7
(at Dorking Wanderers)
43 Fulham Women v Woodley United L 5-0
(at Metropolitan Police)
44 Callington Town L v Ilminster Town L (11/10) 1-2
(at Ginsters Marsh)
45 Bristol Rovers Women's v AEK-Boco L 1-1
(AEK Boco won 4-3 on kicks from the penalty mark – at Lockleaze Sports Centre)
46 Torquay United W v Portishead Town Ladies 0-12
(at SDCSC)
47 Sherborne Town Ladies v Oldland Abbotonians L (11/10)2-1
(at Sherborne Town)
48 Marine Academy Plymouth L v Helston Athletic Women (11/10) 3-5
(at Ivybridge Town)
49 Middlezoy Rovers Ladies v A Stoneham Ladies (11/10) 2-2
(A Stoneham won 3-1 on kicks from the penalty mark at Middlezoy Rovers)

SECOND QUALIFYING ROUND

1 Merseyrail Ladies v Bolton Ladies 3-2
(at Admiral Park)

2 Stockport County v Leeds United Women (25/10) 0-2
(at Stockport Sports Village)

3 Ossett United Ladies v Liverpool Feds 0-5
(at Ossett United)

4 Brighouse Town Women v Spennymoor Town Ladies 6-0 198
(at Brighouse Town)

5 Warrington Wolves Foundation W v Durham Cestria 2-3
(at Tetley Walker Sports Club)

6 Blyth Town Ladies v Barnsley Women's 0-5
(at South Newsham Pavilion)

7 Norton & Stockton Ancients v United of Manchester Women 2-5 100
(at Station Road)

8 Chorley Women v Wallsend BC Women
(walkover for Chorley Women – Wallsend BC Women withdrawn)

9 Chester-Le-Street Town Ladies v South Shields Ladies 9-0 50
(at Chester-Le-Street Town)

10 Bradford City Women's v Sunderland West End Ladies 0-2
(at Eccleshill United)

11 Morecambe Ladies v Fleetwood Town Wrens 1-2
(at Slyne with Hest)

12 Newcastle United Women v Blackburn Community SC 11-0 68
(at Druid Park)

13 Dronfield Town v Coventry Sphinx Ladies 1-2
(at Dronfield Town)

14 Worcester City v Stourbridge Ladies 0-5
(at Worcester City)

15 Sporting Khalsa Women v Leafield Athletic 4-2
(at Sporting Khalsa)

16 Sutton Coldfield Town v Wolverhampton Wanderers W 0-2 201
(at Sutton Coldfield Town)

17 Lincoln City Women v Burton Albion 10-1
(at Active Nation Yarborough)

18 Oadby & Wigston Women v Crusaders Ladies 2-3
(at Oadby & Wigston)

19 Beaumont Park Ladies v Boldmere St Michaels Women 1-2
(at Beaumont Park)

20 Solihull Moors Women v Bedworth United (3.00) 2-2
(Solihull Moors Women won 3-2 on kicks from the penalty mark – at Solihull Moors)

21 Holwell Sports Women v Grimsby Town Women's 7-2
(at Holwell Sports)

22 Redditch United v Doncaster Rovers Belles 1-1 156
(Redditch United won 4-1 on kicks from the penalty mark – at Redditch United)

23 Long Eaton United v Netherton United Ladies 7-1
(at Long Eaton United)

24 Northwich Vixens v Wem Town Ladies 1-2
(at Lostock Gralam)

25 Harlow Town Ladies v St Ives Town Ladies (3.00) 5-1
(at Harlow Town)

26 Newmarket Town v Norwich City Women (3.00) 1-5
(at Newmarket Town)

27 Billericay Town v Cambridge United Women 4-1
(at Billericay Town)

28 Luton Town Ladies v Cambridge City 1-0
(at 61)

29 Hashtag United Women v Enfield Town 0-2
(at Canvey Island)

30 Stevenage Women v Royston Town 3-3 120
(Royston Town won 5-3 on kicks from the penalty mark – at Hertford Town)

31 Ipswich Town v Peterborough Northern Star 10-0
(at Felixstowe & Walton United)

32 A Wimbledon Ladies v Ashford Ladies 6-0
(at The War Memorial Ground)

33 Actonians v Saltdean United W 6-2
(at Rectory Park)

34 New London Lionesses v Worthing Women 1-1
(Worthing Women won 4-3 on kicks from the penalty mark – at Barn Elms Playing Fields)

35 Dartford Women v Eastbourne Town 1-1
(Eastbourne Town won 3-2 on kicks from the penalty mark – at Dartford)

36 Dulwich Hamlet Women's v Leyton Orient W 0-1
(at Dulwich Hamlet)

37 Fulham Women v Wycombe Wanderers Ladies 1-0
(at Metropolitan Police)

38 Maidenhead United v Denham United Ladies 1-0
(at Maidenhead United)

39 Abingdon United v Chesham United 1-3
(at Abingdon United)

40 Ashford Town (Middx) Women's v Kent Football United 2-2
(Kent Football United won 5-4 on kicks from the penalty mark – at Ashford Town (Middx))

41 AEK-Boco v Larkhall Athletic 4-3
(at LA Clark Pavilion)

42 Portishead Town Ladies v Sherborne Town Ladies 2-0
(at Portishead Town)

43 Cheltenham Town v Brislington 3-0
(at Cheltenham Saracens)

44 Exeter City Women v Swindon Town 2-1
(at Cullompton Rangers)

45 A Stoneham Ladies v Buckland Athletic 1-6
(at A Stoneham)

46 Ilminster Town v Poole Town 4-1
(at Ilminster Town)

47 Helston Athletic Women v Southampton Women (1.00) 0-11 292
(at Helston Athletic)

48 Southampton Women's v A Bournemouth Women 1-3
(at Alresford Town)

THIRD QUALIFYING ROUND

1 Fleetwood Town Wrens v Liverpool Feds (6/12) 0-3
(at Poolfoot Sports Village)

2 United of Manchester Women v Chorley Women 2-1 134
(at United of Manchester)

3 Barnsley Women's v Leeds United Women (2.00) 4-1
(at Oakwell Academy)

4 Brighouse Town Women v Merseyrail Ladies 3-0
(at Brighouse Town)

5 Newcastle United Women v Sunderland West End Ladies (2.00) 4-1 129
(at Druid Park)

6 Chester-Le-Street Town Ladies v Durham Cestria 3-2 50
(at Chester-Le-Street Town)

7 Solihull Moors Women v Sporting Khalsa Women (3.00) 3-0
(at Solihull Moors)

8 Holwell Sports Women v Lincoln City Women 0-2 36
(at Holwell Sports)

9 Stourbridge Ladies v Crusaders Ladies (2.00) 3-0 258
(at Stourbridge)

10 Wem Town Ladies v Coventry Sphinx Ladies (2.00) 4-3
(at Wem Town)

11 Long Eaton United v Wolverhampton Wanderers W 0-1
(at Long Eaton United)

12 Redditch United v Boldmere St Michaels Women 1-2 150
(at Redditch United)

13 Luton Town Ladies v Enfield Town (6/12) 1-2
(at 61)

14 Harlow Town Ladies v Royston Town (2.00) 3-3
(Harlow Town won 4-2 on kicks from the penalty mark - at Harlow Town)
15 Billericay Town v Chesham United 2-1
(at Billericay Town)
16 Norwich City Women v Ipswich Town 1-3 300
(at The Nest)
17 Actonians v Worthing Women (2.00) 4-0
(at Rectory Park)
18 Fulham Women v Maidenhead United (2.00) 1-2 101
(at Corinthian Casuals)
19 Kent Football United v A Wimbledon Ladies (13/12) 2-1
(at The Efes Stadium)
20 Eastbourne Town v Leyton Orient W (6/12) 1-4
(at Eastbourne Town)
21 Exeter City Women v AEK-Boco 7-0
(at Exwick Sports Hub)
22 Cheltenham Town v Portishead Town Ladies 3-1
(at Tewkesbury School)
23 A Bournemouth Women v Buckland Athletic 3-1
(at Verwood Town)
24 Ilminster Town v Southampton Women 0-4
(at Ilminster Town)

FIRST ROUND

1 United of Manchester Women v Liverpool Feds 1-2 121
(at United of Manchester)
2 Chester-Le-Street Town Ladies v Brighouse Town Women 0-3
(at Chester-Le-Street Town)
3 Newcastle United Women v Barnsley Women's (2.00) 3-1
(at Druid Park)
4 Wolverhampton Wanderers W v Stourbridge Ladies (3.00) 3-0
(at Wolverhampton Wanderers Academy)
5 Lincoln City Women v Solihull Moors Women 3-1
(at Active Nation Yarborough)
6 Wem Town Ladies v Boldmere St Michaels Women (20/12) 4-3
(at Wem Town)
7 Harlow Town Ladies v Ipswich Town (2.00) 2-9
(at Harlow Town)
8 Kent Football United v Enfield Town (31/3) 1-1aet
(Kent Football United won 4-3 on kicks from the penalty mark – at The Efes Stadium)
9 Billericay Town v Maidenhead United 4-0
(at Billericay Town)
10 Leyton Orient W v Actonians (2.00) 2-1
(at Hornchurch)
11 A Bournemouth Women v Southampton Women 0-5
(at Verwood Town)
12 Exeter City Women v Cheltenham Town 1-1aet
(Cheltenham Town won 4-3 on kicks from the penalty mark – at Exwick Sports Hub)

SECOND ROUND

1 Sunderland AFC Ladies v Sheffield Women (1.00) 5-1
(at Academy of Light)
2 Liverpool Feds v Huddersfield Town W (3/1) 2-3aet
(at Jericho Lane)
3 Brighouse Town Women v Newcastle United Women (1.00)3-0aet
(at Brighouse Town)
4 Middlesbrough Women v Hull City Ladies 3-1
(at Billingham Town)
5 Burnley Women v Fylde Ladies 1-0aet
(at Padiham)
6 Wolverhampton Wanderers W v Nottingham Forest Women 2-2aet
(Wolverhampton Wanderers won 6-5 on kicks from the penalty mark – at A Wulfrunians)
7 West Bromwich Albion Women v Lincoln City Women (1.00) 5-2
(at Sutton Coldfield Town)
8 Loughborough Foxes Women v Derby County Women 0-6
(at Loughborough University)
9 Stoke City v Wem Town Ladies
(walkover for Wem Town – Stoke City withdrawn)
10 Crawley Wasps v Gillingham Ladies 2-3
(at Horley Town)
11 Billericay Town v Ipswich Town 2-1
(at Billericay Town)
12 Hounslow Women v Leyton Orient W 0-4
(at Tithe Farm Sports & Social)
13 Watford Women v MK Dons Women (3.00) 3-1
(at Kings Langley)
14 Chichester & Selsey Ladies v Kent Football United (1.00) 3-1
(at Selsey)
15 Portsmouth Women v Cheltenham Town 2-0aet
(tie awarded to Cheltenham Town – Portsmouth removed)
16 Southampton Women v Plymouth Argyle (3.00) 3-0
(at A Totton)
17 Keynsham Town v Yeovil United Women (1.00) 0-1
(at Keynsham Town)
18 Cardiff City v Oxford United Women 0-1
(at Centre of Sporting Excellence)

THIRD ROUND

1 Huddersfield Town W v Brighouse Town Women 1-1aet
(Huddersfield Town won 5-3 on kicks from the penalty mark - at Shelley)
2 Middlesbrough Women v Wem Town Ladies 4-0
(at Billingham Town)
3 Burnley Women v Sunderland A Ladies 0-0aet
(Burnley won 3-1 on kicks from the penalty mark - at Padiham)
4 Oxford United Women v Billericay Town Women 3-1
(at Oxford City)
5 West Bromwich Albion Women v Derby County Women 1-4
(at Sutton Coldfield Town)
6 Watford Women v Wolverhampton W W (3. 1-4
(at Kings Langley)
7 Cheltenham Town v Gillingham Ladies 1-2aet
(at Cheltenham Town)
8 Southampton Women v Yeovil United Women 3-0
(at A Totton)
9 Leyton Orient W v Chichester & Selsey Ladies 1-2
(at Leyton Orient)

FOURTH ROUND

1 Leicester City Women v Liverpool Women 1-0
(at Quorn)
2 Middlesbrough Women v Sheffield United Women 0-9
(at Billingham Town)
3 Birmingham City Women v Coventry United W (12.30) 5-1
(at Solihull Moors – Live on BBC Red Button)
4 Burnley Women v Manchester United Women 0-6
(at Lancashire FA)
5 Everton Women v Durham Women 2-1
(at Walton Hall Park)
6 Manchester City Women v Aston Villa Women (17/4) 8-0
(at Academy Stadium)
7 Wolverhampton W W v Blackburn Rovers (3.00) 2-5
(at A Telford United)
8 Huddersfield Town W v Derby County Women 3-2
(at Shelley)

9	Reading Women (at Reading)	v	Tottenham Hotspur Women	2-3aet
10	Oxford United Women (at Oxford City)	v	Charlton Athletic Women	1-2aet
11	Arsenal Women (at Boreham Wood)	v	Gillingham Ladies	10-0
12	Chelsea Women (at Kingsmeadow)	v	London City Lionesses (16/4)	5-0
13	Lewes Women (at Lewes)	v	Southampton Women	1-2
14	Brighton & Hove Albion Women (at Crawley Town)	v	Bristol City Women	1-0
15	West Ham United Women (at Dagenham & Redbridge)	v	Chichester & Selsey Ladies (1.00)	11-0
16	Crystal Palace (at Bromley)	v	London Bees W	3-0

FIFTH ROUND

1	Birmingham City Women (at Solihull Moors)	v	Southampton Women	3-2
2	Brighton & Hove Albion Women (at Crawley Town)	v	Huddersfield Town W	6-0
3	Arsenal Women (at Boreham Wood)	v	Crystal Palace (3.00)	9-0
4	Blackburn Rovers (at Lancashire FA)	v	Charlton Athletic Women	0-1
5	Manchester City Women (at Academy Stadium)	v	West Ham United Women	5-1
6	Chelsea Women (at Kingsmeadow – Live on BBC Red Button)	v	Everton Women (20/5)	3-0
7	Manchester United Women (at Leigh Sports Village)	v	Leicester City Women	2-3
8	Tottenham Hotspur Women (at Barnet FC)	v	Sheffield United Women	2-1aet

QUARTER FINALS

1	Manchester City (at Academy Stadium)	v	Leicester City	29/9
2	Birmingham City (at St Andrews)	v	Chelsea	29/9
3	Arsenal (at Boreham Wood FC)	v	Tottenham Hotspur	29/9
4	Brighton & Hove Albion (at Crawley Town)	v	Charlton Athletic	29/9

SEMI FINALS

1		v		31/10
2		v		31/10

THE FINAL - Saturday 5 December - @ Wembley Stadium

v

The FA DISABILITY CUP

POWERCHAIR FINAL
Aspire PFC **0 - 2** WBA PFC

CEREBRAL PALSY FINAL
North East & Yorkshire **5 - 2** CP North West

PARTIALLY SIGHTED FINAL
Scorpian Futsal Club **1 - 3** Birmingham Futsall

AMPUTEE FINAL
Peterborough United **0-0 6-5p** Portsmouth

BLIND FINAL
RNC Hereford **1-1 2-1p** Merseyside Blind & VC

July 2021 - St George's Park Photos by: Keith Clayton

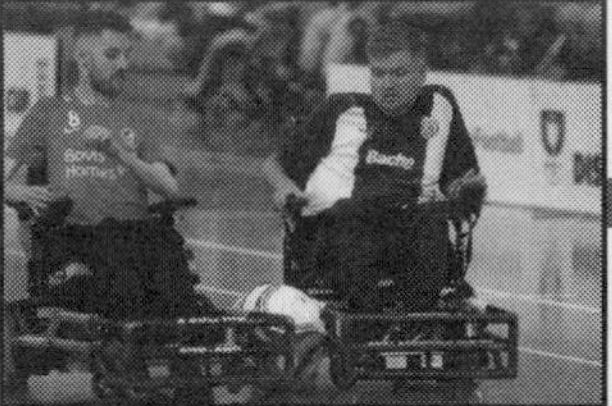

Bolding (Aspire) blocks Gordon (WBA).

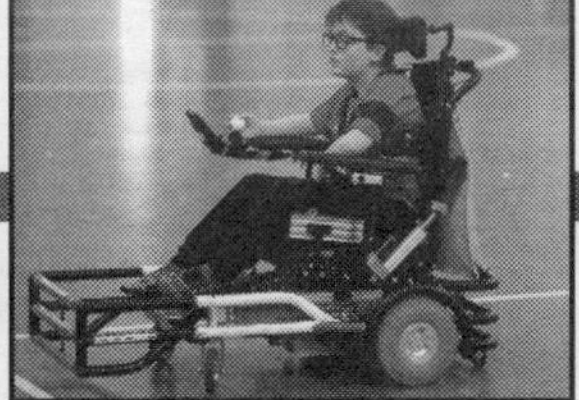

Dan McLellan (Aspire) just 12 years old.

Aspire Powerchair Team.

Fox Hockney (NE Yorks) DeSouza (North West).

Tupman (North West) just fails to connect with a corner.

CP North West FC.

MacDougal (Brum) Pack (Scorpions).

Price (Scorpions) Pugh (Brum).

Scorpions Futsal.

Houghton (Peterboro) Whitehouse (Portsmouth).

Lambourne (Peterboro) saves the penalty from Whitehouse (Portsmouth),

and Harry Ash (Peterboro) steps up to beat Atkinson (Portsmouth) to win the cup.

English (Hereford) Coleman (Merseyside).

Christople (Hereford) blocks Williams (Merseyside) effort on the line.

Merseyside.

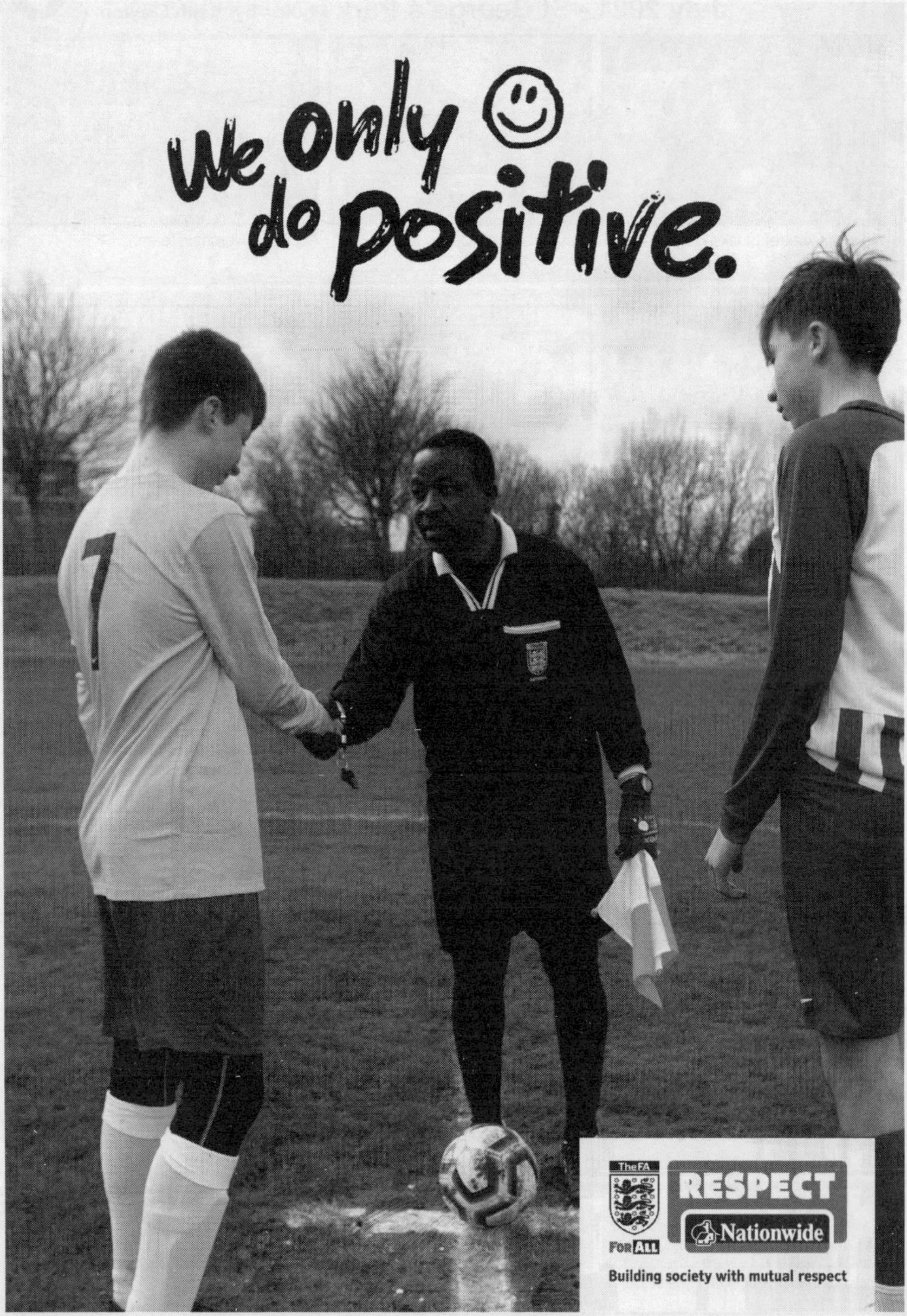
We only do positive.
TheFA
FOR ALL
RESPECT
Nationwide
Building society with mutual respect

THE NON-LEAGUE CLUB DIRECTORY 2021-22

FA National League System Club Allocations - Steps 1 - 6

(Correct at the time of going to press 31/07/2021)

STEP 1

NATIONAL LEAGUE 482

STEP 2

NATIONAL NORTH 494
NATIONAL SOUTH 505

STEP 3 & 4

ISTHMIAN LEAGUE

PREMIER 516
NORTH 527
SOUTH CENTRAL 537
SOUTH EAST 547

NORTHERN PREMIER LEAGUE

PREMIER 558
EAST 570
MIDLANDS 580
WEST 590

SOUTHERN LEAGUE

PREMIER CENTRAL 602
PREMIER SOUTH 613
DIVISION ONE CENTRAL 624
DIVISION ONE SOUTH 634

STEP 5/6

COMBINED COUNTIES LEAGUE

PREMIER NORTH 644
PREMIER SOUTH 650
DIVISION ONE 657

EASTERN COUNTIES

PREMIER 663
DIVISION ONE NORTH 670
DIVISION ONE SOUTH 674

ESSEX SENIOR LEAGUE 679

HELLENIC LEAGUE

PREMIER 686
DIVISION ONE 693

MIDLAND FOOTBALL LEAGUE

PREMIER 698
DIVISION ONE 705

NORTH WEST COUNTIES

PREMIER 710
DIVISION ONE NORTH 717
DIVISION ONE SOUTH 721

NORTHERN COUNTIES EAST

PREMIER 727
DIVISION ONE 734

NORTHERN LEAGUE

DIVISION ONE 740
DIVISION TWO 747

SOUTH WEST PENINSULA LEAGUE

PREMIER EAST 753
PREMIER WEST 758

SOUTHERN COMBINATION

PREMIER 763
DIVISION ONE 770

SOUTHERN COUNTIES EAST

PREMIER 775
DIVISION ONE 782

SPARTAN SOUTH MIDLANDS LEAGUE

PREMIER 787
DIVISION ONE 794

UNITED COUNTIES LEAGUE

PREMIER NORTH 799
PREMIER SOUTH 806
DIVISION ONE 815

WESSEX LEAGUE

PREMIER 819
DIVISION ONE 826

WESTERN LEAGUE

PREMIER 831
DIVISION ONE 838

ALDERSHOT TOWN

National League

The Shots **Founded** 1992 **Club Colours** Red & blue

Club Contact Details 01252 320 211 admin@theshots.co.uk

Previous Names: None

Previous Leagues: Isthmian 1992-2003. Conference 2003-2008. Football League 2008-13.

2020-21 Season
Nat 15
FAC 4Q
FAT QF
Record
P 47 W 18 D 8 L 21
Top Goalscorer
Rees (13)

11-12		12-13		13-14		14-15		15-16		16-17		17-18		18-19		19-20ppg	
FL 2	11	FL 2	24	Conf	19	Conf	18	Nat	15	Nat	5	Nat	5	Nat	21	Nat	18
FAC	2P	FAC	4P	FAC	4Qr	FAC	2Pr	FAC	1Pr	FAC	4Q	FAC	1P	FAC	1Pr	FAC	4Q
FLC	4P	FLC	1P	FAT	QF	FAT	1P	FAT	1P	FAT	1Pr	FAT	1P	FAT	1Pr	FAT	1P

LEAGUE HONOURS:
Isthmian League Division Three 1992-93, Division One 97-98, Premier Division 2002-03.
Conference 2007-08.

COUNTY FA HONOURS: Hampshire Senior Cup 1998-99, 99-2000, 01-02, 02-03, 06-07.

CLUB RECORDS

FA Cup (As a non-League side) Third Round Proper - 2006-07. (Football League side) Fourth Round Proper - 2012-13.
FA Trophy Semi-Finals 2003-04, 07-08. **FA Vase** Quarter-Finals 1993-94.
Victory: 8-0 v Bishop's Stortford (A) Isthmian Premier 05/09/1998
Defeat: 0-6 v Worthing (A) Isthmian League Cup 02/03/99
Goalscorer: Mark Butler - 155 (1992-98)
Appearances: Jason Chewings - 489 (August 1994 - May 2004)
Additional: Paid an undisclosed record fee to Woking for Marvin Morgan (05/2008)
Received £130,000 from Crewe Alexandra for Joel Grant (11/2008)

GROUND: EBB Stadium, High street, Aldershot, GU11 1TW
Ground Capacity: 7,025 **Seats:** 2,676 **Covered:** 5,975 **Clubhouse:** Yes **Shop:** Yes
Previous Grounds: None
Record Attendance: 7,500 v Brighton & Hove Albion, FA Cup 1st Round, 18/11/2000

ALTRINCHAM

National League

The Robins **Founded** 1891 **Club Colours** Red & white stripes

Club Contact Details 0161 928 1045 office@altrinchamfootballclub.co.uk

Previous Names: Rigby Memorial Club 1891-93. Merged with the 'Grapplers' to form Broadheath FC 1893-1903.

Previous Leagues: Manchester (Founder members) 1893-1911. Lancashire Combination 1911-19. Cheshire County (FM) 1919-68. Northern Premier (FM) 1968-79, 97-99, 00-04, 17-18. Alliance/Conference/National (FM) 1979-97, 99-00, 04-17.

2020-21 Season
Nat 17
FAC 4Q
FAT 3P
Record
P 45 W 14 D 11 L 20
Top Goalscorer
Hancock (12)

11-12		12-13		13-14		14-15		15-16		16-17		17-18		18-19		19-20ppg	
FLCh	8	Conf N	4	Conf N	3	Conf	17	Nat	22	Nat N	22	NP P	1	Nat N	5	Nat N	5
FAC	2Q	FAC	1Pr	FAC	2Q	FAC	1P	FAC	2P	FAC	1P	FAC	3Q	FAC	4Q	FAC	1P
FAT	3Q	FAT	1P	FAT	1P	FAT	3P	FAT	2P	FAT	1Pr	FAT	1Pr	FAT	1P	FAT	1Pr

LEAGUE HONOURS:
Manchester 1904-05, 06-07. Cheshire 1965-66, 66-67. Football Alliance 1979-80, 80-81.
Northern Premier League Premier Division 1998-99, 2017-18.

COUNTY FA HONOURS: Cheshire Amateur Cup 1903-04.
Cheshire Senior Cup Winners 1904-05, 33-34, 66-67, 81-82, 98-99, 04-05, 08-09.

CLUB RECORDS

FA Cup Fourth Round Proper 1985-86
FA Trophy Winners 1977-78, 85-86
Victory: 14-2 v Sale Holmfield, Cheshire Amateur Cup, 05/12/1903
Defeat: 1-13 v Stretford (H) - 04.11.1893
Goalscorer: Jack Swindells - 252 (1965-71)
Appearances: John Davison - 677 (1971-86)
Additional: Transfer fee paid - £15k to Blackpool for Keith Russell. Received - £50k from Leicester for Kevin Ellison

GROUND: The J Davidson Stadium, Moss Lane, Altrincham, Cheshire WA15 8AP
Ground Capacity: 6,085 **Seats:** 1,323 **Covered:** Yes **Clubhouse:** Yes **Shop:** Yes
Previous Grounds: Pollitts Field 1903-10.
Record Attendance: 10,275 - Altrincham Boys v Sunderland Boys English Schools Shield 28/02/1925.
Nearest Railway Station Altrincham - Approx. 10min walk from the ground
Bus Route Arriva 263 & Stagecoach X41

BARNET

National League

The Bees **Founded** 1885 **Club Colours** Amber and black

Club Contact Details 020 8381 3800 tellus@thehivelondon.com

2020-21 Season
Nat 22
FAC 2P
FAT 3P

Record
P 47 W 10 D 7 L 30

Top Goalscorer
Petrasso (10)

Previous Names: New Barnet 1885-88. Barnet 1888-1902 (folded). Barnet Alston 1904-19.

Previous Leagues: Post 1945 - Athenian 1945-65. Southern 1965-79. Conference 1979-91, 2001-05, 13-15. Football League 1991-2001, 05-13.

11-12		12-13		13-14		14-15		15-16		16-17		17-18		18-19		19-20ppg	
FL 2	22	FL 2	23	Conf	8	Conf	1	FL 2	15	FL 2	15	FL 2	24	Nat	12	Nat	7
FAC	2P	FAC	1P	FAC	1P	FAC	1P	FAC	2P	FAC	1P	FAC	1P	FAC	4Pr	FAC	1P
FLC	2P	FLC	1P	FAT	2P	FAT	1Pr	FLC	2P	FLC	1P	FLC	2P	FAT	4P	FAT	4P

LEAGUE HONOURS:
Athenian League 1931-32, 32-33, 46-47, 58-59, 63-64, 64-65. Southern League Division One 1965-66, Division One South 1977-78. Football Conference 1990-91, 2004-05, 2014-15.

COUNTY FA HONOURS: Herts Senior Cup 1985-86, 90-91, 91-92, 92-93, 95-96, 2006-07, 10-11.

CLUB RECORDS

FA Cup (As a non-League side) 4th Rnd Proper Replay - 2018-19. (FL) 4th Rnd Proper - 2006-07, 07-08.
FA Am Cup Winners 1945-46
FA Trophy Finalists 1971-72
Victory: 7-0 v Blackpool Division 3 11/11/2000
Defeat: 1-9 v Peterborough Division 3 05/09/1998
Goalscorer: Arthur Morris - 403 (1927-36)
Appearances: Les Eason - 648 (1965-74, 77-78)

GROUND: The Hive, Camrose Avenue, Edgware, Middlesex, HA8 6AG
Ground Capacity: 6,500 **Seats:** 3,434 **Covered:** 5,176 **Clubhouse:** Yes **Shop:** Yes
Previous Grounds: Underhill 1907-2013
Record Attendance: 11,026 v Wycombe Wanderers FA Amateur Cup 01/01/1953
Nearest Railway Station Canons Park Underground (Jubilee line) is a 5 min walk away.
Bus Route 340, 186 & 79 from Edgware to Canons Park.

BOREHAM WOOD

National League

The Wood **Founded** 1948 **Club Colours** White & black

Club Contact Details 0208 953 5097 ddelldell@aol.com

2020-21 Season
Nat 14
FAC 3P
FAT 4P

Record
P 48 W 15 D 18 L 15

Top Goalscorer
Tshimanga (22)

Previous Names: Boreham Wood Rovers and Royal Retournez amalgamated in 1948 to form today's club

Previous Leagues: Mid Herts 1948-52, Parthenon 1952-57, Spartan 1957-66, Athenian 1966-74, Isthmian 1974-2004, Southern 2004-10

11-12		12-13		13-14		14-15		15-16		16-17		17-18		18-19		19-20ppg	
Conf S	8	Conf S	9	Conf S	13	Conf S	2	Nat	19	Nat	11	Nat	4	Nat	20	Nat	5
FAC	2Q	FAC	1P	FAC	1Pr	FAC	4Q	FAC	1Pr	FAC	1Pr	FAC	2P	FAC	1P	FAC	4Q
FAT	1P	FAT	1Pr	FAT	3Q	FAT	3Q	FAT	1P	FAT	QF	FAT	2Pr	FAT	2P	FAT	1P

LEAGUE HONOURS:
Athenian League Division Two 1968-69, Division One 73-74. Isthmian League Division Two 1976-77, Division One 1994-95, 2000-01. Southern Division One East 2005-06.

COUNTY FA HONOURS: Herts Senior cup 1971-72, 98-99, 2001-02, 07-08, 13-14, 18-19.
Herts Charity Cup 1980-81, 83-84, 85-86, 88-89, 89-90. London Challenge Cup 1997-98.

CLUB RECORDS

FA Cup Third Round Proper - 2020-21
FA Trophy Semi-Finals - 2005-06
Goalscorer: Mickey Jackson
Appearances: Dave Hatchett - 714

GROUND: Meadow Park, Broughinge Road, Boreham Wood WD6 5AL
Ground Capacity: 4,502 **Seats:** 1,700 **Covered:** 2,800 **Clubhouse:** Yes **Shop:** Yes
Previous Grounds: Eldon Avenue 1948-63
Record Attendance: 4,030 v Arsenal - Friendly 13/07/2001
Nearest Railway Station Elstree & Boreham Wood.

BROMLEY

National League

The Ravens or The Lillywhites **Founded** 1892 **Club Colours** White

Club Contact Details 020 8460 5291 info@bromleyfc.net

Previous Names: None

Previous Leagues: South London, Southern, London, West Kent, South Surburban, Kent, Spartan 1907-08, Isthmian 1908-11, 52-2007, Athenian 1919-1952

2020-21 Season
Nat 7
FAC 1P
FAT 4P

Record
P 48 W 22 D 13 L 13

Top Goalscorer
Cheek (25)

11-12		12-13		13-14		14-15		15-16		16-17		17-18		18-19		19-20ppg	
Conf S	17	Conf S	15	Conf S	3	Conf S	1	Nat	14	Nat	10	Nat	9	Nat	11	Nat	13
FAC	1P	FAC	1P	FAC	3Q	FAC	1P	FAC	4Q	FAC	4Q	FAC	1P	FAC	1P	FAC	1Pr
FAT	3Q	FAT	3P	FAT	3Q	FAT	2P	FAT	1P	FAT	2P	FAT	F	FAT	1P	FAT	1P

LEAGUE HONOURS:
Spartan 1907-08. Isthmian League 1908-09, 09-10, 53-54, 60-61. Athenian League 1922-23, 48-49, 50-51. Conference South 2014-15.

COUNTY FA HONOURS: Kent Senior Cup 1949/50, 76-77, 91-92, 96-97, 2005-06, 06-07. Kent Amateur Cup x12. London Senior Cup 1909-10, 45-46, 50-51, 2002-03, 12-13.

CLUB RECORDS

FA Cup Second Round Proper 1937-38, 45-46
FA Trophy Fourth Round Proper 2020-21
Victory: 13-1 v Redhill - Athenian League 1945-46
Defeat: 1-11 v Barking - Athenian League 1933-34
Goalscorer: George Brown - 570 (1938-61)
Appearances: George Brown
Additional: Received £50,000 from Millwall for John Goodman

GROUND: The Stadium, Hayes Lane, Bromley, Kent BR2 9EF
Ground Capacity: 5,000 **Seats:** 1,300 **Covered:** 2,500 **Clubhouse:** Yes **Shop:** Yes
Previous Grounds: White Hart Field. Widmore Road. Plaistow Cricket Ground.
Record Attendance: 10,798 v Nigeria - 1950

CHESTERFIELD

National League

The Spireites **Founded** 1866 **Club Colours** Blue & white

Club Contact Details 01246 269 300 reception@chesterfield-fc.co.uk

Previous Names: Chesterfield Town 1891-1915, Chesterfield Municipal 1915-20.

Previous Leagues: Sheffield & District 1892-96. Midland 1896-99, 1909-15, 19-20. Football League 1899-1909, 1921-2018.

2020-21 Season
Nat 6
FAC 4Q
FAT 4P

Record
P 47 W 21 D 9 L 17

Top Goalscorer
Asante (10)

11-12		12-13		13-14		14-15		15-16		16-17		17-18		18-19		19-20ppg	
FL 1	22	FL 2	8	FL 2	1	FL 1	6	FL 1	18	FL 1	24	FL 2	23	Nat	14	Nat	20
FAC	1P	FAC	2P	FAC	2P	FAC	4P	FAC	2Pr	FAC	2P	FAC	1P	FAC	2P	FAC	4Qr
FLC	1P	FLC	1P	FLC	1P	FLC	1P	FLC	1P	FLC	1P	FLC	1P	FAT	3P	FAT	1P

LEAGUE HONOURS:
Midland 1909-10, 19-20. League Division Three North 1930-31, 35-36, Division Four/League Two 69-70, 84-85, 2010-11, 13-14.

COUNTY FA HONOURS: Derbyshire Senior Cup 1898-99, 1920-21, 21-22, 24-25, 32-33, 36-37, 2017-18.

CLUB RECORDS

FA Cup (As a non-League side) Second Round Proper - 2018-19. (Football League side) Semi-Finals 1996-97 (r).
FA Trophy Third Round Proper 2018-19.
Appearances: Mark Allott - 385 (League) 2001-12.
Goalscorer: Jack Lester - 92 (League) 2007-13.
Victory: 8-1 v Barrow 13/11/1926 and v Gateshead 25/04/1931.

GROUND: Technique Stadium, 1866 Sheffield Road, Whittington Moor, Chesterfield S41 8NZ
Ground Capacity: 10,000 **Seats:** 10,000 **Covered:** Yes **Clubhouse:** Yes **Shop:** Yes
Previous Grounds: Athletic Ground 1866-72. Saltergate (Recreation Ground) 1872-2010.
Record Attendance: 30,561 (Saltergate) v Tottenham, 12/02/1938. 10,089 (1866 Sheffield Rd) v Rotherham United.
Nearest Railway Station Chesterfield

DAGENHAM & REDBRIDGE

National League

The Daggers **Founded** 1992 **Club Colours** Red & blue

Club Contact Details 0208 592 1549 info@daggers.co.uk

2020-21 Season
Nat 12
FAC 2P
FAT 4P
Record
P 48 W 21 D 9 L 18
Top Goalscorer
McCallum (18)

Previous Names: Formed by the merger of Dagenham and Redbridge Forest

Previous Leagues: Football Conference 1992-96, 2000-2007. Isthmian 1996-2000. Football League 2007-16.

11-12		12-13		13-14		14-15		15-16		16-17		17-18		18-19		19-20ppg	
FL 2	19	FL 2	22	FL 2	9	FL 2	14	FL 2	23	Nat	4	Nat	11	Nat	18	Nat	17
FAC	3Pr	FAC	1P	FAC	1P	FAC	1Pr	FAC	3P	FAC	1Pr	FAC	4Qr	FAC	4Q	FAC	4Q
FLC	1P	FLC	1P	FLC	1P	FLC	1P	FLC	1P	FAT	1P	FAT	1P	FAT	2P	FAT	1P

LEAGUE HONOURS:
Isthmian League Premier Division 1999-2000. Football Conference 2006-07.

COUNTY FA HONOURS: Essex Senior Cup 1997-98, 2000-01.

CLUB RECORDS

FA Cup Fourth Round Proper 2002-03.
FA Trophy Finalists 1996-97.
Victory: 8-1 v Woking, Football Conference, 19.04.94
Defeat: 0-9 v Hereford United, Football Conference, 27.02.04.
Goalscorer: Danny Shipp - 105
Appearances: Tony Roberts - 507
Additional: Transfer fee received: £470,000 Dwight Gayle to Peterborough United

GROUND: Chigwell Construction Stadium, Victoria Road, Dagenham, Essex RM10 7XL
Ground Capacity: 6,078 **Seats:** 2,200 **Covered:** Yes **Clubhouse:** Yes **Shop:** Yes
Previous Grounds: None
Record Attendance: 5,949 v Ipswich Town (05/01/2002) FA Cup Third Round Proper
Nearest Railway Station Dagenham East Underground (District line), exit left and take fifth turning on the left 400 metres away.
Bus Route The 103 runs from Romford Station and stops outside the ground.

DOVER ATHLETIC

National League

The Whites **Founded** 1983 **Club Colours** White & black

Club Contact Details 01304 822 373 enquiries@doverathletic.com

2020-21 Season
Nat Exp
FAC 4Q
FAT 3P
Record
P 17 W 3 D 2 L 12
Top Goalscorer
N/A

Previous Names: Dover F.C. until club folded in 1983

Previous Leagues: Southern 1983-93, 2002-04, Conference 1993-2002, Isthmian 2004-2009

11-12		12-13		13-14		14-15		15-16		16-17		17-18		18-19		19-20ppg	
Conf S	7	Conf S	3	Conf S	5	Conf	8	Nat	5	Nat	6	Nat	8	Nat	13	Nat	11
FAC	4Q	FAC	3Qr	FAC	2P	FAC	3P	FAC	1P	FAC	1Pr	FAC	4Qr	FAC	1P	FAC	2P
FAT	3Q	FAT	3Qr	FAT	3P	FAT	QFr	FAT	QF	FAT	1Pr	FAT	3P	FAT	2P	FAT	1P

LEAGUE HONOURS:
Southern League Southern Division 1987-88, Premier Division 1989-90, 92-93.
Isthmian League Division One South 2007-08, Premier Division 2008-09.

COUNTY FA HONOURS: Kent Senior Cup 1990-91, 2016-17.

CLUB RECORDS

FA Cup Third Round Proper 2010-11, 14-15.
FA Trophy Semi-Finals 1997-98.
Victory: 7-0 v Weymouth - 03/04/1990
Defeat: 1-7 v Poole Town
Goalscorer: Lennie Lee - 160
Appearances: Jason Bartlett - 520+
Additional: Paid £50,000 to Farnborough Town for David Lewworthy August 1993
Received £50,000 from Brentford for Ricky Reina 1997

GROUND: Crabble Athletic Ground, Lewisham Road, Dover, Kent CT17 0JB
Ground Capacity: 6,500 **Seats:** 1,010 **Covered:** 4,900 **Clubhouse:** Yes **Shop:** Yes
Previous Grounds: None
Record Attendance: 4,186 v Oxford United - FA Cup 1st Round Proper November 2002
Nearest Railway Station Main line - Dover Priory 2 miles away. Kearsney Station is a 10-15 minute walk from the ground.

EASTLEIGH

National League

The Spitfires **Founded** 1946 **Club Colours** Blue

Club Contact Details 02380 613 361 admin@eastleighfc.com

Previous Names: Swaythling Athletic 1946-59, Swaythling 1973-80

Previous Leagues: Southampton Junior & Senior 1946-59, Hampshire 1950-86, Wessex 1986-2003, Southern 2003-04, Isthmian 2004-05

2020-21 Season
Nat 9
FAC 1P
FAT 3P

Record
P 46 W 19 D 13 L 14

Top Goalscorer
Barnett (13)

11-12		12-13		13-14		14-15		15-16		16-17		17-18		18-19		19-20ppg	
Conf S	12	Conf S	4	Conf S	1	Conf	4	Nat	7	Nat	15	Nat	14	Nat	7	Nat	16
FAC	3Q	FAC	3Q	FAC	3Q	FAC	2P	FAC	3Pr	FAC	3P	FAC	4Q	FAC	4Q	FAC	2Pr
FAT	3Q	FAT	3Q	FAT	QF	FAT	1P	FAT	2P	FAT	1P	FAT	1P	FAT	1P	FAT	3P

LEAGUE HONOURS:
Southampton Senior (West) 1949-50. Hampshire Division Three 1950-51, 53-54, Division Two 1967-68. Wessex Division One 2002-03. Conference South 2013-14.

COUNTY FA HONOURS: Hampshire Intermediate Cup 1950-51, Senior Cup 2011-12.

CLUB RECORDS

FA Cup Third Round Proper 2015-16 (r), 16-17.
FA Trophy Quarter Finals 2013-14.
FA Vase Fourth Round 1982-83, 90-91, 94-95.
Victory: 12-1 v Hythe & Dibden (H) - 11/12/1948
Defeat: 0-11 v Austin Sports (A) - 01.01.1947
Goalscorer: Johnnie Williams - 177
Appearances: Ian Knight - 611
Additional: Paid £10,000 to Newport (I.O.W.) for Colin Matthews

GROUND: The Silverlake Stadium 'Ten Acres', Stoneham Lane, Eastleigh SO50 9HT
Ground Capacity: 3,000 **Seats:** 2,700 **Covered:** Yes **Clubhouse:** Yes **Shop:** Yes
Previous Grounds: Southampton Common. Walnut Avenue >1957.
Record Attendance: 5,250 v Bolton Wanderers, FA Cup Third Round 09/01/2016
Nearest Railway Station Eastleigh or Southampton Airport Parkway - both about 20 mins walk.

FC HALIFAX TOWN

National League

The Shaymen **Founded** 1911 **Club Colours** Blue and white trim

Club Contact Details 01422 341 222 tonyallen@fchalifaxtown.com

Previous Names: Halifax Town 1911-2008 then reformed as F.C. Halifax Town

Previous Leagues: Yorkshire Combination 1911-12, Midland 1912-21, Football League (FM Division Three North)1921-93, 98-2002, Conference 1993-98, 2002-08

2020-21 Season
Nat 10
FAC 4Q
FAT 4P

Record
P 45 W 19 D 9 L 17

Top Goalscorer
Hyde (12)

11-12		12-13		13-14		14-15		15-16		16-17		17-18		18-19		19-20ppg	
Conf N	3	Conf N	5	Conf	5	Conf	9	Nat	21	Nat N	3	Nat	16	Nat	15	Nat	6
FAC	1P	FAC	4Qr	FAC	1P	FAC	1P	FAC	1P	FAC	2Pr	FAC	4Q	FAC	2P	FAC	4Q
FAT	3Qr	FAT	QFr	FAT	1P	FAT	QF	FAT	F	FAT	3Qr	FAT	2P	FAT	2Pr	FAT	3P

LEAGUE HONOURS:
Conference 1997-98. Northern Premier League Division One North 2009-10, Premier Division 2010-11.

COUNTY FA HONOURS: West Riding County Cup 2012-13.

CLUB RECORDS

FA Cup Fifth Round Proper 1932-33, 52-53 as Halifax Town. Second Round Proper 2016-17 (r) as FC Halifax Town.
FA Trophy Winners 2015-16
Victory: 12-0 v West Vale Ramblers - FA Cup 1st Qualifying Road 1913-14
Defeat: 0-13 v Stockport County - Division 3 North 1933-34
Goalscorer: Ernie Dixon - 132 (1922-30)
Appearances: John Pickering - 402 (1965-74)
Additional: Recorded a 30 game unbeaten run at The Shay between 18/04/2009 - 20/11/2010 (W 24 D 6 F 79 A 20). Fee paid - £150,000 for Chris Tate, July 1999. Fee Received - £350,000 for Geoff Horsfield, October 1998.

GROUND: The Shay Stadium, Shay Syke, Halifax HX1 2YS
Ground Capacity: 10,401 **Seats:** 5,830 **Covered:** Yes **Clubhouse:** Yes **Shop:** Yes
Previous Grounds: Sandhall Lane 1911-15, Exley 1919-21.
Record Attendance: 36,885 v Tottenham Hotspur - FA Cup 5th Round 14/02/1953
Nearest Railway Station Halifax - 5-10min walk from the ground.

GRIMSBY TOWN

National League

The Mariners **Founded** 1878 **Club Colours** Black & white

Club Contact Details 01472 605 050 enquiries@gtfc.co.uk

Previous Names: Grimsby Pelham 1878-79

Previous Leagues: Football League 1892-2010, 16-21. Conference/National League 2010-16.

2020-21 Season
FL 2 24
FAC 1P
FLC 1P

Record
P 51 W 10 D 14 L 27

Top Goalscorer
Green & John-Lewis (4)

11-12		12-13		13-14		14-15		15-16		16-17		17-18		18-19		19-20	
Conf	11	Conf	4	Conf	4	Conf	3	Nat	4	FL 2	14	FL 2	18	FL 2	17	FL 2	13
FAC	2Pr	FAC	4Q	FAC	3P	FAC	1P	FAC	2Pr	FAC	1P	FAC	1P	FAC	3P	FAC	1Pr
FAT	QF	FAT	F	FAT	SF	FAT	2Pr	FAT	F	FLC	1P	FLC	1P	FLC	1P	FLC	3P

LEAGUE HONOURS:
Football League Division 2 1900-01, 33-34, Division 3 North 1925-26, 55-56, Division 3 1979-80, Division 4 1971-72.

COUNTY FA HONOURS: Lincolnshire Senior Cup x38 - First time 1885-86 and most recently 2012-13.

CLUB RECORDS

FA Cup Semi-final 1935-36, 38-39
FA Trophy Runners-up 2012-13, 15-16
Football League Cup: Quarter-finals 1965-66(r), 79-80(rx2), 84-85
Football League Trophy: Winners 1997-98
Victory: 8-0 v Tranmere Rovers, League, 04/09/1925
Defeat: 1-9 v Arsenal - Division 1 28/01/1931
Goalscorer: Pat Glover - 180 (1930-39)
Appearances: John McDermott - 754 (1987-2007)

GROUND: Blundell Park, Cleethorpes, North East Lincolnshire DN35 7PY
Ground Capacity: 9,031 **Seats:** Yes **Covered:** Yes **Clubhouse:** Yes **Shop:** Yes
Previous Grounds: Clee Park, Abbey Park
Record Attendance: 31,651 v Wolverhampton Wanderers - FA Cup 5th Round 20/02/1937
Nearest Railway Station Cleethorpes - just over 20mins walk.
Bus Route Stagecoach Nos. 9, 13 and 46 operate along Grimsby Road and stop near the ground.

KING'S LYNN TOWN

National League

The Linnets **Founded** 2010 **Club Colours** Yellow & blue

Club Contact Details 01553 760 060 office@kltown.co.uk

Previous Names: King's Lynn Town formed in 2010 after King's Lynn FC folded.

Previous Leagues: United Counties 2010-12. Northern Premier 2012-15. Southern 2015-19.

2020-21 Season
Nat 21
FAC 2P
FAT 4P

Record
P 47 W 10 D 11 L 26

Top Goalscorer
Marriott & Mitchell (8)

11-12		12-13		13-14		14-15		15-16		16-17		17-18		18-19		19-20ppg	
UCL P	2	NP1S	1	NP P	11	NP P	18	SthP	9	SthP	13	SthP	2	SthPC	2	Nat N	1
FAC	4Q	FAC	1Qr	FAC	1Q	FAC	4Q	FAC	3Q	FAC	3Q	FAC	2Q	FAC	3Q	FAC	4Q
FAV	2P	FAT	3P	FAT	1Q	FAT	3Q	FAT	2Q	FAV	1P	FAT	1Q	FAT	1Qr	FAT	2P

LEAGUE HONOURS:
Northern Premier Division One South 2012-13.
National North 2019-20 (Based on PPG).

COUNTY FA HONOURS: Norfolk Senior Cup 2016-17.

CLUB RECORDS

FA Cup Second Round Proper 2020-21.
FA Trophy Fourth Round Proper 2020-21.
FA Vase Semi-finals 2010-11.
Victory: 7-1 v Gosport Borough (A), Southern Premier, 06/02/2018

GROUND: The Walks Stadium, Tennyson Road, King's Lynn PE30 5PB
Ground Capacity: 8,200 **Seats:** 1,400 **Covered:** 5,000 **Clubhouse:** Yes **Shop:** Yes
Previous Grounds: None
Record Attendance:
Nearest Railway Station King's Lynn - 5min walk away.
Bus Route Serviced by Eastern Counties & Norfolk Green

MAIDENHEAD UNITED

National League

Magpies **Founded** 1870 **Club Colours** Black & white

Club Contact Details 01628 636 314 social@maidenheadunitedfc.org

Previous Names: After WWI Maidenhead F.C and Maidenhead Norfolkians merged to form Maidenhead Town >1920.

Previous Leagues: Southern (FM) 1894-1902, 2006-07, West Berkshire 1902-04, Gr. West Suburban 04-22, Spartan 1922-39, Gr. West Comb. 1939-45, Corinthian 45-63, Athenian 63-73, Isthmian 73-2004, Conference 04-06.

2020-21 Season
Nat 13
FAC 4Q
FAT 3P
Record
P 44 W 15 D 11 L 18
Top Goalscorer
Orsi-Dadamo (21)

11-12		12-13		13-14		14-15		15-16		16-17		17-18		18-19		19-20ppg	
Conf S	20	Conf S	19	Conf S	18	Conf S	18	Nat S	7	Nat S	1	Nat	12	Nat	19	Nat	21
FAC	1Pr	FAC	3Q	FAC	2Q	FAC	3Qr	FAC	1Pr	FAC	2Q	FAC	1P	FAC	1P	FAC	1P
FAT	1Pr	FAT	1P	FAT	3P	FAT	2Pr	FAT	2P	FAT	3Q	FAT	3Pr	FAT	1P	FAT	2Pr

LEAGUE HONOURS:
West Berkshire 1902-03. Spartan 1926-27, 31-32, 33-34. Corinthian 1957-58, 60-61, 61-62.
National South 2016-17.

COUNTY FA HONOURS: Berks & Bucks Senior Cup 1894-95, 95-96, 1911-12, 27-28, 29-30, 30-31, 31-32, 38-39, 45-46, 55-56, 56-57, 60-61, 62-63, 65-66, 69-70, 97-98, 98-99, 2001-02, 02-03, 09-10, 14-15, 16-17. Wycombe Senior Cup

CLUB RECORDS

FA Cup As United - First Round Proper 1960-61, 62-63, 63-64, 71-72, 2006-07, 07-08, 11-12 (r), 15-16 (r), 18-19.
FA Trophy Quarter-finals 2003-04 **FA Vase** Second Round Proper 1989-90
Victory: 14-1 v Buckingham Town - FA Amateur Cup 06/09/1952
Defeat: 0-14 v Chesham United (A) - Spartan League 31/03/1923
Goalscorer: George Copas - 270 (1924-35). Most goals in a season: Jack Palethorpe - 65 in 39 apps (1929-30).
Appearances: Bert Randall - 532 (1950-64)
Additional: Received £5,000 from Norwich City for Alan Cordice 1979

GROUND: York Road, Maidenhead, Berkshire SL6 1SF
Ground Capacity: 4,500 **Seats:** 550 **Covered:** 2,000 **Clubhouse:** Yes **Shop:** Yes
Previous Grounds: Kidwells Park (Norfolkians)
Record Attendance: 7,989 v Southall - FA Amateur Cup Quarter final 07/03/1936
Nearest Railway Station Maidenhead - 200 yards from the ground.

NOTTS COUNTY

National League

The Magpies **Founded** 1862 **Club Colours** Black & white

Club Contact Details 0115 952 9000 office@nottscountyfc.co.uk

Previous Names: None

Previous Leagues: Football League (FM) 1888-2019

2020-21 Season
Nat 5
FAC 4Q
FAT SF
Record
P 51 W 24 D 12 L 15
Top Goalscorer
Wootton (19)

11-12		12-13		13-14		14-15		15-16		16-17		17-18		18-19		19-20ppg	
FL 1	7	FL 1	12	FL 1	20	FL 1	21	FL 2	7	FL 2	16	FL 2	5	FL 2	23	Nat	3
FAC	4P	FAC	2Pr	FAC	1P	FAC	1Pr	FAC	1P	FAC	2Pr	FAC	4Pr	FAC	1P	FAC	2P
FLC	1P	FLC	1P	FLC	2P	FLC	1P	FLC	2P	FLC	1P	FLC	1P	FLC	1P	FAT	SF

LEAGUE HONOURS:
Football League Division Two 1896-97, 1913-14, 22-23, Division Three South 1930-31, 49-50, Division Four 1970-71, Division Three 1997-98, League Two 2009-10.

COUNTY FA HONOURS: None

CLUB RECORDS

FA Cup Winners 1893-94.
FA Trophy Semi Finals 2019-20, 20-21
Victory: (League) 11-1 v Newport County, Division Three South, 15/01/1949
Victory: (Cup) 15-0 v Rotherham Town, FA Cup 1st Round Proper, 24/10/1885
Goalscorer: (League) Les Bradd - 125 (1967-78). In a season: Tom Keetley - 39 (1930-31)
Appearances: (League) Albert Iremonger - 564 (1904-26)

GROUND: Meadow Lane Stadium, Meadow Lane, Nottingham NG2 3HJ
Ground Capacity: 19,841 **Seats:** 19,841 **Covered:** Yes **Clubhouse:** Yes **Shop:** Yes
Previous Grounds: 1862-63 Park Hollow, 63-73 Meadows Cket Gd, 73-77, 94-1910 Trent Bridge, 77-78 Beeston Cket Gd, 80-94 Castle Gd
Record Attendance: 47,310 v York City, FA Cup Six Round, 12/03/1955
Nearest Railway Station The ground is 10min walk from Nottingham train station.
Bus Route None directly to the ground only to Nottingham's coach station on Station Street, the ground is a short walk from there.

SOLIHULL MOORS

National League

Moors **Founded** 2007 **Club Colours** Blue with yellow

Club Contact Details 0121 705 6770 info@solihullmoorsfc.co.uk

2020-21 Season
Nat 11
FAC 2P
FAT 4P

Record
P 48 W 23 D 7 L 18

Top Goalscorer
Hudlin (12)

Previous Names: Today's club was formed after the amalgamation of Solihull Borough and Moor Green in 2007.

Previous Leagues: None

11-12		12-13		13-14		14-15		15-16		16-17		17-18		18-19		19-20ppg	
Conf N	19	Conf N	9	Conf N	8	Conf N	12	Nat N	1	Nat	16	Nat	18	Nat	2	Nat	9
FAC	4Q	FAC	3Q	FAC	4Q	FAC	2Q	FAC	3Q	FAC	2P	FAC	1P	FAC	2Pr	FAC	2P
FAT	1P	FAT	2P	FAT	3Q	FAT	1P	FAT	1P	FAT	1P	FAT	2P	FAT	4P	FAT	1Pr

LEAGUE HONOURS:
National North 2015-16.

COUNTY FA HONOURS: Birmingham Senior Cup 2015-16.

CLUB RECORDS

FA Cup Second Round Proper 2016-17(r) 18-19(r) 19-20, 20-21
FA Trophy Fourth Round Proper 2018-19, 20-21
Victory: 7-2 v Corby Town, Conference North, 12/02/2011
Defeat: 0-9 v Tranmere Rovers, National, 08/04/2017
Appearances: Carl Motteram - 71 (2007-08)

GROUND: The SportNation.bet Stadium, Damson Park, Damson Parkway, Solihull B91 2PP (satnav B92 9EJ)
Ground Capacity: 4,510 **Seats:** 2,131 **Covered:** Yes **Clubhouse:** Yes **Shop:** Yes
Previous Grounds: None
Record Attendance: 3,681 v Leyton Orient, National, 22/04/2019.
Nearest Railway Station Solihull & Birmingham within 3 miles away.
Bus Route Nos. X12 or 966 from Town Centre.

SOUTHEND UNITED

National League

The Shrimpers or Sesiders **Founded** 1906 **Club Colours** Blue & white

Club Contact Details 01702 304 050 info@southend-united.co.uk

2020-21 Season
FL 2 23
FAC 1P
FLC 1P

Record
P 51 W 10 D 15 L 26

Top Goalscorer
Clifford and Dieng (3)

Previous Names: None

Previous Leagues: Southern 1906-20. Football League 1920-2021.

11-12		12-13		13-14		14-15		15-16		16-17		17-18		18-19		19-20	
FL 2	4	FL 2	11	FL 2	5	FL 2	5	FL 1	14	FL 1	7	FL 1	10	FL 1	19	FL 1	22
FAC	2Pr	FAC	3Pr	FAC	4P	FAC	1P	FAC	1P	FAC	1P	FAC	1P	FAC	2P	FAC	1P
FLC	1P	FLC	1P	FLC	1P	FLC	1P	FLC	1P	FLC	1P	FLC	1P	FLC	1P	FLC	2P

LEAGUE HONOURS:
Southern Division Two 1906-07, 07-08.
Division Four/League Two 1980-81, Division Three/League Two 2005-06.

COUNTY FA HONOURS: Essex Professional Cup 1949-50, 52-53,53-54,54-55, 56-57, 61-62, 64-65, 66-67, 71-72, 72-73.
Essex Senior Cup 1982-83, 90-91, 96-97, 2007-08.

CLUB RECORDS

FA Cup Fifth Round Proper 1925-26, 51-52, 75-76, 92-93.
Football League Cup: Quarter-final 2006-07.
Football League Trophy: Runners-up 2003-04, 04-05, 12-13
Victory: 10-1 v Golders Green, FAC, 1934-35, v Brentwood, FAC, 68-69 and v Aldershot, FLT, 90-91.
Defeat: 1-9 v Brighton & HA, Division 3, 27/11/1965.
Goalscorer: Roy Hollis - 135 (1954-60). **Goals in a Season:** Sammy McCrorry - 31, D3S, 1957-58.
Appearances: Alan Moody - 504 (1972-84)
Additional: Paid a record £750,000 to Crystal Palace for Stan Collymore (Nov 1992) and then sold him for a record £3,570,000 to Nottingham Forest (June 1993).

GROUND: Roots Hall, Victoria Avenue, Southend-on-Sea, Essex SS2 6NQ
Ground Capacity: 12,492 **Seats:** Yes **Covered:** Yes **Clubhouse:** Yes **Shop:** Yes
Previous Grounds: Roots Hall 1906-19. Kursaal 19-34. Southend Stadium 34-55. New Writtle Street (Chelmsford City FC) 39-41.
Record Attendance: 31,090 v Liverpool, FA Cup Third Round Proper, 10/01/1979
Nearest Railway Station Prittlewell (Abellio Greater Anglia) 5 mins walk.

STOCKPORT COUNTY

National League

County or Hatters **Founded** 1883 **Club Colours** Blue and white

Club Contact Details 0161 286 8888

Previous Names: Heaton Norris Rovers 1883-88, Heaton Norris 1888-90.

Previous Leagues: Lancashire 1863-1900. Football League 1900-2011.

2020-21 Season
Nat 3
FAC 3P
FAT 4P

Record
P 51 W 26 D 15 L 10

Top Goalscorer
Reid & Rooney (21)

11-12		12-13		13-14		14-15		15-16		16-17		17-18		18-19		19-20ppg	
Conf	16	Conf	21	Conf N	14	Conf N	11	Nat N	9	Nat N	8	Nat N	5	Nat N	1	Nat	8
FAC	4Q	FAC	1P	FAC	3Q	FAC	4Q	FAC	2Q	FAC	1P	FAC	3Qr	FAC	2P	FAC	4Q
FAT	1Pr	FAT	2Pr	FAT	3Qr	FAT	2Pr	FAT	3Q	FAT	2Pr	FAT	4Pr	FAT	SF	FAT	2Pr

LEAGUE HONOURS:
Lancashire 1899-1900.
League Division Three North 1921-22, 36-37, Division Four 1966-67. National North 2018-19.

COUNTY FA HONOURS: Manchester S.C. 1897-98,98-99, 1914-15,22-23. Cheshire Medal 1922-23,24-25,28-29,29-30,30-31. Ches' Bowl 1933-34,48-49, 52-53,55-56,56-57,58-59,60-61,62-63. Ches' S.C.1905-06,46-47,48-49,65-66,2015-16. Ches' Prem. Cup 1969-70,70-71, 2010-11.

CLUB RECORDS

FA Cup Fifth Round Proper 1934-35, 49-50, 2000-01.
FA Trophy Semi-finals 2018-19.
Victory: 13-0 v Halifax Town, Division Three North 06/01/1934.
Defeat: 0-9 v Everton Reserves, Lancashire League, 09/12/1893.
Goalscorer: (League) Jack Connor - 132, 1951-56.
Appearances: (League) Andy Thorpe - 555, 1978-86, 88-92.
Additional: Paid, £800,000 for Ian Moore from Nottingham Forest, 07/1998.
Received, £1,600,000 for Alun Armstrong from Middlesbrough, 02/1998.

GROUND: Edgeley Park, Hardcastle Road, Stockport SK3 9DD
Ground Capacity: 10,800 **Seats:** 10,800 **Covered:** Yes **Clubhouse:** Yes **Shop:** Yes
Previous Grounds: Heaton Norris Recreation Ground & other various locations 1883-89. Green Lane 1889-1902.
Record Attendance: 27,833 v Liverpool, FA Cup 5th Round 11/02/1950. 10,273 (all seated) v Leeds United, 28/12/2008.
Nearest Railway Station Stockport - Approx. half a mile from the ground.

TORQUAY UNITED

National League

The Gulls **Founded** 1899 **Club Colours** Yellow & blue

Club Contact Details 01803 328 666 reception@torquayunited.com

Previous Names: Torquay United & Ellacombe merged to form Torquay Town 1910, then merged with Babbacombe to form Torquay United in 1921

Previous Leagues: Western 1921-27. Football League 1927-2007, 09-14. Conference 2007-09.

2020-21 Season
Nat 2
FAC 1P
FAT QF

Record
P 51 W 29 D 12 L 10

Top Goalscorer
Hall (15)

11-12		12-13		13-14		14-15		15-16		16-17		17-18		18-19		19-20ppg	
FL 2	5	FL 2	19	FL 2	24	Conf	13	Nat	18	Nat	17	Nat	22	Nat S	1	Nat	14
FAC	2P	FAC	1P	FAC	1P	FAC	4Q	FAC	4Q	FAC	4Qr	FAC	4Q	FAC	1P	FAC	1P
FLC	1P	FLC	1P	FLC	1P	FAT	SF	FAT	QF	FAT	1P	FAT	1P	FAT	1P	FAT	2P

LEAGUE HONOURS:
Torquay & District 1909-09. Plymouth & District 1911-12. Southern Western Section 1926-27.
National South 2018-19.

COUNTY FA HONOURS: Devon Senior Cup 1910-11, 21-22. Devon Bowl/Devon St Luke's Bowl 1933-34, 34-35, 36-37,45-46, 47-48, 48-49, 54-55 (shared), 57-58, 60-61, 69-70, 70-71, 71-72, 95-96 (shared), 97-98, 2006-07.

CLUB RECORDS

FA Cup Fourth Round Proper 1948-49, 54-55, 70-71, 82-83, 89-90, 2008-09, 10-11.
FA Trophy Finalists 2007-08
Victory: 9-0 v Swindon Town, Division Three South, 08/03/1952
Defeat: 2-10 v Fulham, Division Three South, 07/09/1931
Goalscorer: Sammy Collins - 219 in 379 games (1948-58) Scored 40 during the 1955-56 season.
Appearances: Dennis Lewis - 443 (1947-59)
Additional: Paid £75,000 for Leon Constantine from Peterborough United, December 2004.
Received £650,000 from Crewe for Rodney Jack, July 1998.

GROUND: Plainmoor, Torquay, Devon TQ1 3PS
Ground Capacity: 6,500 **Seats:** 2,950 **Covered:** Yes **Clubhouse:** Yes **Shop:** Yes
Previous Grounds: Recreation Ground. Cricketfield Road > 1910.
Record Attendance: 21,908 v Huddersfield Town, FA Cup 4th Rnd, 29/01/1955.
Nearest Railway Station Torre, 25 mins away. Main Torquay 2+ miles away.

WEALDSTONE

National League

The Stones **Founded** 1899 **Club Colours** Blue & white

Club Contact Details 07790 038 095 wealdstonefc@btinternet.com

2020-21 Season
Nat 19
FAC 4Q
FAT 5P
Record
P 46 W 12 D 7 L 27
Top Goalscorer
Mendy (10)

Previous Names: None

Previous Leagues: Willesden & District 1899-1906, 08-13, London 1911-22, Middlesex 1913-22, Spartan 1922-28, Athenian 1928-64, Isthmian 1964-71, 95-2006, 2007-14. Southern 1971-79, 81-82, 88-95, Conference 1979-81, 82-88

11-12		12-13		13-14		14-15		15-16		16-17		17-18		18-19		19-20ppg	
Isth P	4	Isth P	3	Isth P	1	Conf S	12	Nat S	13	Nat S	8	Nat S	11	Nat S	7	Nat S	1
FAC	1Q	FAC	2Q	FAC	3Q	FAC	2Qr	FAC	1P	FAC	4Q	FAC	3Q	FAC	4Q	FAC	4Qr
FAT	SF	FAT	3Qr	FAT	2Qr	FAT	2P	FAT	1P	FAT	3P	FAT	SF	FAT	1P	FAT	3Q

LEAGUE HONOURS:
Athenian 1951-52. Southern Division One South 1973-74, Southern Division 1981-82. Conference 1984-85. Isthmian Division Three 1996-97, Premier 2013-14. National South 2019-20.

COUNTY FA HONOURS: Middlesex Junior Cup 1912-13. Senior 1929-30, 37-38, 40-41, 41-42, 42-43, 45-46, 58-59, 62-63, 63-64, 67-68, 84-85. Charity Cup 1929-30, 30-31, 37-38, 38-39, 49-50, 63-64, 68-68, 03-04, 10-11 Prem Cup 2003-04, 07-08, 08-09, 10-11. London Senior 1961-62.

CLUB RECORDS

FA Cup Third Round Proper 1977-78.
FA Vase Third Round Proper 1997-98.
FA Trophy Winners 1984-85.
FA Am Cup Winners 1965-66.
Victory: 22-0 v The 12th London Regiment (The Rangers) - FA Amateur Cup 13/10/1923
Defeat: 0-14 v Edgware Town (A) - London Senior Cup 09/12/1944
Goalscorer: George Duck - 251
Appearances: Charlie Townsend - 514
Additional: Became the first club to win the 'Non-League Double' when they won the Conference and FA Trophy in 1984-85.
Paid £15,000 to Barnet for David Gipp. Received £70,000 from Leeds United for Jermaine Beckford.

GROUND: Grosvenor Vale, Ruislip, Middlesex HA4 6JQ
Ground Capacity: 3,607 **Seats:** 329 **Covered:** 1,166 **Clubhouse:** Yes **Shop:** No
Previous Grounds: Locket Road, Belmont Road, Lower Mead Stadium 1922-91, Watford FC, Yeading FC, Edgware Town, Northwood FC
Record Attendance: 13,504 v Leytonstone - FA Amateur Cup 4th Round replay 05/03/1949 (at Lower Mead)
Nearest Railway Station Ruislip and Ruislip Gardens both walking distance.
Bus Route E7

WEYMOUTH

National League

The Terras **Founded** 1890 **Club Colours** Claret & blue

Club Contact Details 01305 785 558 info@theterras.co.uk

2020-21 Season
Nat 18
FAC 4Q
FAT 4P
Record
P 45 W 12 D 6 L 27
Top Goalscorer
Dallas (12)

Previous Names: None

Previous Leagues: Dorset, Western 1907-23, 28-49, Southern 1923-28, 49-79, 89-2005, Alliance/Conference 1979-89, 2005-10.

11-12		12-13		13-14		14-15		15-16		16-17		17-18		18-19		19-20ppg	
SthP	17	SthP	9	SthP	12	SthP	7	SthP	7	SthP	10	SthP	5	SthPS	1	Nat S	3
FAC	3Q	FAC	2Q	FAC	4Q	FAC	4Qr	FAC	1Q	FAC	4Q	FAC	3Q	FAC	1Qr	FAC	4Q
FAT	2P	FAT	2Q	FAT	2Q	FAT	1Pr	FAT	3Q	FAT	1Pr	FAT	1Q	FAT	2Pr	FAT	1P

LEAGUE HONOURS:
Dorset 1897-98, 1913-14, Division One 1921-22. Western Division One 1922-23, 36-37, 37-38, Division Two 33-34.Southern 1964-65, 65-66, Southern Division 1997-98, Southern Premier South 2018-19. Conference South 2005-06.

COUNTY FA HONOURS: Dorset Senior Cup x12 - Firstly in 1985-86 and most recently in 2016-17.

CLUB RECORDS

FA Cup Fourth Round Proper 1961-62.
FA Trophy Quarter-finals 1973-74, 76-77(r).
Goalscorer: W 'Farmer' Haynes - 275
Appearances: Tony Hobsons - 1,076
Additional: Paid £15,000 to Northwich Victoria for Shaun Teale
Received £100,000 from Tottenham Hotspur for Peter Guthrie 1988
Defeat: 0-9 v Rushden & Diamonds, Conference South, 21/02/2009 - this was a game which, due to an administration issue, the club had to field their U18 team.

GROUND: Bob Lucas Stadium, Radipole Lane, Weymouth DT4 9XJ
Ground Capacity: 6,600 **Seats:** 900 **Covered:** Yes **Clubhouse:** Yes **Shop:** Yes
Previous Grounds: Recreation Ground > 1987.
Record Attendance: 4,995 v Manchester United - Ground opening 21/10/97
Nearest Railway Station Weymouth - 2.2km
Bus Route 3 & X53 stop outside the ground

WOKING

National League

The Cards | **Founded** 1887 | **Club Colours** Red, white & black

Club Contact Details 01483 772 470 admin@wokingfc.co.uk

Previous Names: None

Previous Leagues: West Surrey 1895-1911. Isthmian 1911-92.

2020-21 Season
Nat 20
FAC 1P
FAT SF

Record
P 50 W 13 D 10 L 27

Top Goalscorer
Kretzshmar (10)

11-12		12-13		13-14		14-15		15-16		16-17		17-18		18-19		19-20ppg	
Conf S	1	Conf	12	Conf	9	Conf	7	Nat	12	Nat	18	Nat	21	Nat S	2	Nat	10
FAC	3Q	FAC	4Q	FAC	4Q	FAC	1P	FAC	4Q	FAC	2P	FAC	2Pr	FAC	3P	FAC	4Qr
FAT	3Q	FAT	2P	FAT	2P	FAT	3Pr	FAT	QF	FAT	1Pr	FAT	1P	FAT	1Pr	FAT	1P

LEAGUE HONOURS:
West Surrey 1895-96. Isthmian League Division Two South 1986-87, Premier Division 1991-92.
Conference South 2011-12.

COUNTY FA HONOURS: Surrey Senior Cup 1912-13, 26-27, 55-56, 56-57, 71-72, 90-91, 93-94, 95-96, 99-00, 03-04, 2011-12, 13-14, 16-17.

CLUB RECORDS

FA Cup Fourth Round Proper 1990-91.
FA Am Cup Winners 1957-58.
FA Trophy Winners 1993-94, 94-95, 96-97
Victory: 17-4 v Farnham - 1912-13
Defeat: 0-16 v New Crusaders - 1905-06
Goalscorer: Charlie Mortimore - 331 (1953-65)
Appearances: Brian Finn - 564 (1962-74)
Additional: Paid £60,000 to Crystal Palace for Chris Sharpling
Received £150,000 from Bristol Rovers for Steve Foster

GROUND: The Laithwaite Community Stadium, Kingfield Road, Woking, Surrey GU22 9AA
Ground Capacity: 6,000 **Seats:** 2,500 **Covered:** 3,900 **Clubhouse:** Yes **Shop:** Yes
Previous Grounds: Wheatsheaf, Ive Lane (pre 1923)
Record Attendance: 6,000 v Swansea City - FA Cup 1978-79 and v Coventry City - FA Cup 1996-97
Nearest Railway Station Woking - about 15 mins from the ground.
Bus Route 34 & 462

WREXHAM

National League

The Robins | **Founded** 1864 | **Club Colours** Red & white

Club Contact Details 01978 891 864 info@wrexhamfc.tv

Previous Names: Wrexham Athletic for the 1882-83 season only

Previous Leagues: The Combination 1890-94, 1896-1906, Welsh League 1894-96, Birmingham & District 1906-21, Football League 1921-2008

2020-21 Season
Nat 8
FAC 4Q
FAT 3P

Record
P 45 W 20 D 12 L 13

Top Goalscorer
Young (12)

11-12		12-13		13-14		14-15		15-16		16-17		17-18		18-19		19-20ppg	
Conf	2	Conf	5	Conf	17	Conf	11	Nat	8	Nat	13	Nat	10	Nat	4	Nat	19
FAC	3Pr	FAC	1P	FAC	2P	FAC	3P	FAC	4Q	FAC	4Qr	FAC	4Q	FAC	2Pr	FAC	1Pr
FAT	1P	FAT	F	FAT	2P	FAT	F	FAT	2P	FAT	1P	FAT	1P	FAT	2P	FAT	1P

LEAGUE HONOURS:
Welsh Senior League 1894-95, 95-96. Combination 1900-01, 01-02, 02-03, 04-05.
Football League Division Three 1977-78.

COUNTY FA HONOURS: Denbighshire & Flintshire (Soames) Charity Cup 1894-95, 98-99, 1902-03, 04-05, 05-06, 08-09.

CLUB RECORDS

FA Cup Quarter-Finals 1973-74, 77-78, 96-97
FA Trophy Winners 2012-13
Victory: 10-1 v Hartlepool United - Division Four 03/03/62
Defeat: 0-9 v v Brentford - Division Three
Goalscorer: Tommy Bamford - 201 (1928-34)
Appearances: Arfon Griffiths - 591 (1959-61 & 62-79)
Additional: Paid £800,000 to Birmingham City for Bryan Hughes March 1997
Received £212,000 from Liverpool for Joey Jones October 1978

GROUND: Racecourse Ground, Mold road, Wrexham LL11 2AH
Ground Capacity: 10,771 **Seats:** 10,771 **Covered:** Yes **Clubhouse:** Yes **Shop:** Yes
Previous Grounds: Rhosddu Recreation Ground during the 1881-82 and 1882-83 seasons.
Record Attendance: 34,445 v Manchester United - FA Cup 4th Round 26/01/57
Nearest Railway Station Wrexham General is right next to the ground.

YEOVIL TOWN F.C. ACHIEVE BY UNITY

YEOVIL TOWN

National League

The Glovers **Founded** 1895 **Club Colours** Green & white

Club Contact Details 01935 423 662 info@ytfc.net

2020-21 Season
Nat 16
FAC 2P
FAT 3P

Record
P 46 W 17 D 8 L 21

Top Goalscorer
Murphy (15)

Previous Names: Yeovil Casuals 1895-1907. Yeovil Town & Petters United >1946.

Previous Leagues: Somerset Senior. Dorset District. Bristol Charity. Western. Southern 1946-79. Alliance 1979-85. Isthmian 1985-88, 95-97. Conference 1988-95, 97-2002. Football League 2002-19.

11-12		12-13		13-14		14-15		15-16		16-17		17-18		18-19		19-20ppg	
FL 1	7	FL 1	4	FLCh	24	FL 1	24	FL 2	20	FL 2	20	FL 2	19	FL 2	24	Nat	4
FAC	2Pr	FAC	4P	FAC	4P	FAC	3P	FAC	3Pr	FAC	1Pr	FAC	4P	FAC	1P	FAC	1P
FLC	1P	FLC	2P	FLC	2P	FLC	1P	FLC	1P	FLC	2P	FLC	1P	FLC	1P	FAT	3P

LEAGUE HONOURS:
Somerset Sen 1896-97, 1901-02, 12-13, 20-21. Dorset Dist 08-09. Bristol Charity 21-22.
Western 21-22, 24-25, 29-30, 34-35. Southern Western Div. 23-24, 31-32, 34-35, Premier 54-55, 63-64, 70-71. Isthmian Premier Division 1987-88, 96-97. Conference 2002-03. Football League 2 2004-05.

COUNTY FA HONOURS: Somerset Professional/Premier Cup x25 firstly in 1912-13 and most recently in 2004-05.

CLUB RECORDS

FA Cup Fifth Round Proper 1948-49
FA Trophy Winners 2001-02
Goalscorer: Johnny Hayward - 548 (1906-28). Most league goals Dave Taylor - 284 (1960-69).
Appearances: Len Harris - 691 (1958-72)

GROUND: Huish Park, Lufton Way, Yeovil BA22 8YF
Ground Capacity: 9,565 **Seats:** 5,212 **Covered:** Yes **Clubhouse:** Yes **Shop:** Yes
Previous Grounds: Pen Mill Athletic Ground. Huish > 1990.
Record Attendance: 9,527 v Leeds United, League One, 25/04/2008
Nearest Railway Station Pen Mill Junction and Yeovil Junction - taxi ride away from the ground.
Bus Route No.68 from the above stations takes you to the town centre where you can get the First traveller No.1 to near the

Notts County 2020-21. Photo Bill Wheatcroft.

AFC FYLDE

National North

The Coasters **Founded** 1988 **Club Colours** White

Club Contact Details 01772 682 593 info@afcfylde.co.uk

Previous Names: Wesham FC and Kirkham Town amalgamated in 1988 to form Kirkham & Wesham > 2008.

Previous Leagues: West Lancashire > 2007. North West Counties 2007-09. Northern Premier 2009-14.

11-12	12-13	13-14	14-15	15-16	16-17	17-18	18-19	19-20ppg	20-21
NP1N 1	NP P 5	NP P 2	Conf N 2	Nat N 3	Nat N 1	Nat 7	Nat 5	Nat 23	Nat N n&v
FAC 2Qr	FAC 1P	FAC 2Q	FAC 1P	FAC 1P	FAC 2Q	FAC 2Pr	FAC 4Q	FAC 3P	FAC 1P
FAT 1Q	FAT 3Q	FAT 3Q	FAT 3P	FAT 3P	FAT 1Pr	FAT 1P	FAT F	FAT 4P	FAT 3P

LEAGUE HONOURS:
West Lancashire League 1999-2000, 00-01, 01-02, 03-04, 04-05, 05-06, 06-07.
North West Counties League 2008-09. Northern Premier Division One North 2011-12.
National North 2016-17.

COUNTY FA HONOURS: Lancashire FA Challenge Trophy 2010-11, 12-13, 13-14. Lancashire Amateur Shield 2000-01, 03-04, 04-05, 05-06. Northern Inter Counties Cup 2004-05, 05-06, 06-07.

CLUB RECORDS

FA Cup Third Round Proper 2019-20, 20-21

FA Vase Winners 2007-08

FA Trophy Winners 2018-19

Victory: 10-0 v Droylsden (A), Northern Premier League Premier Division, 29/10/2013

Goalscorer: Danny Rowe - 192 - August 2014 - 16/01/2020 (293 apps). Bradley Barnes scored five in the club's record 10-0 win over Droylsden

GROUND: Mill Farm, Coronation Way, Wesham, Preston PR4 3JZ

Ground Capacity: 6,000 **Seats:** 6,000 **Covered:** Yes **Clubhouse:** Yes **Shop:** Yes

Previous Grounds: Coronation Road > 2006. Kellamergh Park 2006-2016.

Record Attendance: 3,858 v Chorley, National League North, 26/12/2016.

Nearest Railway Station Kirkham & Wesham half a mile away.

Bus Route No. 61

AFC TELFORD UNITED

National North

The Bucks **Founded** 1892 **Club Colours** White and navy

Club Contact Details 01952 640 064 enquiries@afctu.co.uk

Previous Names: Wellington Town 1892-1969.
AFC Telford United was formed when Telford United folded in May 2004

Previous Leagues: Shropshire 1892-98. Birmingham & District 1898-1901, 02-06, 08-38, 39-45. The Combination 1901-02. Cheshire County 1938-39, 45-58. Southern 1958-79. Alliance/Conference 1979-2004. Northern Premier 2004-06.

11-12	12-13	13-14	14-15	15-16	16-17	17-18	18-19	19-20ppg	20-21
Conf 20	Conf 24	Conf N 1	Conf 22	Nat N 18	Nat N 17	Nat N 14	Nat N 8	Nat N 14	Nat N n&v
FAC 1P	FAC 4Qr	FAC 2Q	FAC 2P	FAC 2Q	FAC 2Qr	FAC 1P	FAC 3Q	FAC 2Q	FAC 3Q
FAT 2P	FAT 2P	FAT 1Pr	FAT 2P	FAT 1P	FAT 1P	FAT 1P	FAT SF	FAT 1P	FAT 3P

LEAGUE HONOURS:
Birmingham & District 1920-21, 34-35, 35-36, 39-40. Cheshire County 1945-46, 46-47, 51-52.
National North 2013-14.

COUNTY FA HONOURS: Birmingham Senior Cup 1946-47. Walsall Senior Cup 1946-47. Shropshire Senior Cup 2008-09, 13-14, 16-17.

CLUB RECORDS

FA Cup Fifth Round Proper 1984-85. As AFC Telford United - Second Round Proper 2014-15.

FA Trophy Winners 1970-71, 82-83. As AFC Telford United - Semi-Finals 2008-09, 18-19.

Victory: 7-0 v Runcorn (A) - Northern Premier League Division One, 17/04/06.

Defeat: 1-6 v Guiseley (A) - Conference North, 01/04/14.

Goalscorer: Andy Brown - 56 (2008-12)

Appearances: Ryan Young - 367 (2007-14)

Additional: Paid £5,000 to Tamworth for Lee Moore 08/12/06
Received £25,000 from Burnley for Duane Courtney 31/08/05

GROUND: New Bucks Head Stadium, Watling Street, Wellington, Telford TF1 2TU

Ground Capacity: 6,380 **Seats:** 2,200 **Covered:** 4,800 **Clubhouse:** Yes **Shop:** Yes

Previous Grounds: None - Renovation of the old Bucks Head started in 2000 and was completed in 2003.

Record Attendance: 5,710 vs Burscough 28/04/2007

Nearest Railway Station Wellington (Shropshire) - 20min walk to ground.

Bus Route 44 - every 10 mins from Town centre.

ALFRETON TOWN

National North

The Reds **Founded** 1959 **Club Colours** All red

Club Contact Details 01773 830 277

Previous Names: Formed when Alfreton Miners Welfare and Alfreton United merged.

Previous Leagues: Central Alliance 1959-61. Midland 1961-82. Northern Counties East 1982-87, 99-02. Northern Premier 1987-99, 02-04.

11-12		12-13		13-14		14-15		15-16		16-17		17-18		18-19		19-20ppg		20-21	
Conf	15	Conf	13	Conf	11	Conf	21	Nat N	10	Nat N	18	Nat N	17	Nat N	15	Nat N	13	Nat N	n&v
FAC	1P	FAC	2P	FAC	1P	FAC	4Qr	FAC	4Q	FAC	1Pr	FAC	3Q	FAC	1P	FAC	2Qr	FAC	2Q
FAT	3P	FAT	1P	FAT	1P	FAT	2P	FAT	3Q	FAT	2P	FAT	3Q	FAT	3Q	FAT	3Qr	FAT	3P

LEAGUE HONOURS:
Midland 1969-70, 73-74, 76-77. Northern Counties East 1986-87, 2001-02
Northern Premier League Division One 2002-03. Conference North 2010-11

COUNTY FA HONOURS: Derbyshire Senior Cup 1960-61, 69-70, 72-73, 73-74, 81-82, 94-95, 2001-02, 02-03, 15-16, 18-19

CLUB RECORDS

FA Cup Second Round Proper 2008-09, 12-13
FA Vase Fifth Round Proper 1999-00
FA Trophy Fourth Round Proper 2002-03 (r), 2004-05
Victory: 15-0 v Loughbrough Midland League 1969-70
Defeat: 1-9 v Solihull - FAT 1997. 0-8 v Bridlington - 1992
Goalscorer: John Harrison - 303
Appearances: John Harrison - 561
Additional: Paid £2,000 to Worksop Town for Mick Goddard
Received £150,000 from Swindon Town for Aden Flint, January 2011

GROUND: The Impact Arena, North Street, Alfreton, Derbyshire DE55 7FZ
Ground Capacity: 3,600 **Seats:** 1,500 **Covered:** 2,600 **Clubhouse:** Yes **Shop:** Yes
Previous Grounds: None
Record Attendance: 5,023 v Matlock Town - Central Alliance 1960
Nearest Railway Station Alfreton - Approx. 15min walk from the ground
Bus Route 150, 55 , 9.1, 9.3, Rainbow One

BLYTH SPARTANS

National North

Spartans **Founded** 1899 **Club Colours** Green and white

Club Contact Details 01670 352 373 generalmanager@blythspartans.com

Previous Names: None

Previous Leagues: Northumberland 1901-07, Northern All. 1907-13, 46-47, North Eastern 1913-39, Northern Com. 1945-46, Midland 1958-60, Northern Counties 1960-62, Northern 1962-94, NPL 1994-2006, 13-17. Conference 2006-13.

11-12		12-13		13-14		14-15		15-16		16-17		17-18		18-19		19-20ppg		20-21	
Conf N	21	NP P	16	NP P	8	NP P	6	NP P	2	NP P	1	Nat N	10	Nat N	6	Nat N	21	Nat N	n&v
FAC	1P	FAC	2Qr	FAC	1Q	FAC	3P	FAC	1Q	FAC	2Q	FAC	2Q	FAC	4Q	FAC	3Q	FAC	3Q
FAT	3Q	FAT	1Q	FAT	2Q	FAT	2Qr	FAT	3Q	FAT	3Qr	FAT	2P	FAT	3P	FAT	1P		

LEAGUE HONOURS:
North Eastern 1935-36. Northern 1972-73, 74-75, 75-76, 79-80, 80-81, 81-82, 82-83, 83-84, 86-87, 87-88.
Northern Division 1 1994-95. Northern Premier Premier Division 2005-06, 16-17.

COUNTY FA HONOURS: Northumberland Senior Cup 2014-15, 16-17.

CLUB RECORDS

FA Cup Fifth Round Proper 1977-78(r).
FA Trophy Quarter-finals 1979-80(r), 82-83(r), 2010-11.
Victory: 18-0 v Gateshead Town - Northern Alliance 28/12/1907
Defeat: 0-10 v Darlington - North Eastern League 12/12/1914
Appearances: Robbie Dale (pictured) became Blyth's record appearance holder during the 2018-19 season.
Additional: Received £30,000 from Hull City for Les Mutrie
Goalscorer: Jeff Hunter scored 63 during the 1946-47 season, revised to 58 after his five against Prudhoe East Park were chalked off when their record was expunged having failed to finish the season.

GROUND: Croft Park, Blyth, Northumberland NE24 3JE
Ground Capacity: 4,435 **Seats:** 563 **Covered:** 1,000 **Clubhouse:** Yes **Shop:** Yes
Previous Grounds: None
Record Attendance: 10,186 v Hartlepool United - FA Cup 08/12/1956
Nearest Railway Station Cramlington five miles from the ground - the X9 bus runs from Cramlington to Blyth.
Bus Route X9 from Cramlington. 308 from Whitley Bay.

BOSTON UNITED

National North

The Pilgrims **Founded** 1933 **Club Colours** Amber and black

Club Contact Details 01205 364 406 admin@bufc.co.uk

Previous Names: Reformed as Boston United when Boston Town folded in 1933

Previous Leagues: Midland 1933-58, 62-64, Southern 1958-62, 98-2000, United Counties 1965-66, West Midlands 1966-68, NPL 1968-79, 93-98, 2008-10, Alliance/Conference 1979-93, 2000-02, 07-08, Football League 2002-07.

11-12		12-13		13-14		14-15		15-16		16-17		17-18		18-19		19-20ppg		20-21	
Conf N	11	Conf N	16	Conf N	6	Conf N	3	Nat N	5	Nat N	15	Nat N	9	Nat N	11	Nat N	3	Nat N	n&v
FAC	2Qr	FAC	4Q	FAC	3Q	FAC	3Q	FAC	2Q	FAC	3Q	FAC	4Qr	FAC	2Q	FAC	2Pr	FAC	2Q
FAT	2P	FAT	1Pr	FAT	2P	FAT	1Pr	FAT	3Q	FAT	3Q	FAT	3Qr	FAT	1P	FAT	3Q	FAT	4P

LEAGUE HONOURS:
Central Alliance League 1961-62. United Counties League 1965-66. West Midlands League 1966-67, 67-68.
Northern Premier League 1972-73, 73-74, 76-77, 77-78. Southern League 1999-2000. Conference 2001-02.

COUNTY FA HONOURS: Lincolnshire Senior Cup 1934-35, 36-37, 37-38, 45-46, 49-50, 54-55, 55-56, 56-57, 59-60, 76-77, 78-79, 85-86, 87-88, 88-89, 05-06. East Anglian Cup 1960-61.

CLUB RECORDS

FA Cup Third Round Proper 1971-72, 73-74 (r), 2004-05 (r)
FA Trophy Final 1984-85
Victory: 12-0 v Spilsby Town - Grace Swan Cup 1992-93
Defeat: 2-9 v AFC Fylde - (A) National North, 19/11/2017
Goalscorer: Chris Cook - 181
Appearances: Billy Howells - 500+
Additional: Paid £30,000 to Scarborough for Paul Ellender, 08/2001
Received £50,000 from Bolton Wanderers for David Norris 2000

GROUND: Jakemans Community Stadium, Pilgrim Way, Wyberton, Boston PE21 7NH
Ground Capacity: 5,000 **Seats:** Yes **Covered:** Yes **Clubhouse:** Yes **Shop:** Yes
Previous Grounds: Jakemans Stadium, York Street 1933-2020.
Record Attendance: 11,000 v Derby County, FA Cup Third Round Proper Replay, 09/01/1974
Nearest Railway Station Boston
Bus Route B13 to Tytton Lane West

BRACKLEY TOWN

National North

Saints **Founded** 1890 **Club Colours** Red and white

Club Contact Details 01280 704 077 janenebutters@brackleytownfc.co.uk

Previous Names: N/A

Previous Leagues: Oxfordshire Senior. North Bucks & District. Banbury & District. Hellenic 1977-83, 94-97, 99-2004. United Counties 1983-84. Southern 1997-99.

11-12		12-13		13-14		14-15		15-16		16-17		17-18		18-19		19-20ppg		20-21	
SthP	1	Conf N	3	Conf N	7	Conf N	18	Nat N	19	Nat N	7	Nat N	3	Nat N	3	Nat N	4	Nat N	n&v
FAC	1Q	FAC	3Q	FAC	2P	FAC	3Q	FAC	1Pr	FAC	2P	FAC	4Qr	FAC	3Q	FAC	4Q	FAC	2P
FAT	1P	FAT	1P	FAT	3Qr	FAT	3Q	FAT	3Q	FAT	QF	FAT	F	FAT	4P	FAT	3Q	FAT	3P

LEAGUE HONOURS:
United Counties Division One 1983-84. Hellenic Premier Division 1996-97, 2003-04.
Southern Division One Midlands 2006-07, Premier Division 2011-12.

COUNTY FA HONOURS: Northamptonshire Senior Cup 2010-11, 11-12, 14-15.

CLUB RECORDS

FA Cup Second Round Proper 2013-14, 16-17, 20-21 **FA Vase** Third Round Proper 1987-88.
FA Trophy Winners 2017-18
Goalscorer: Paul Warrington - 320
Appearances: Terry Muckelberg - 350
Additional: Received £2,000 from Oxford City for Phil Mason 1998

GROUND: St James Park, Churchill Way, Brackley NN13 7EJ
Ground Capacity: 3,500 **Seats:** 600 **Covered:** 1,500 **Clubhouse:** Yes **Shop:** Yes
Previous Grounds: Manor Road 1890-1968. Buckingham Road 1968-74.
Record Attendance: 2,604 v FC Halifax Town, Conference North Play-off final, 12/05/13.
Nearest Railway Station Banbury - Approx. 10 miles from the ground.
Bus Route Stagecoach No. 500 from Banbury.

BRADFORD (PARK AVENUE)

National North

Avenue **Founded** 1863 **Club Colours** Green and white

Club Contact Details 01274 674 584 info@bpafc.com

Previous Names: Bradford FC. 1863-1907. Reformed as a Sunday club in 1974, then as a Saturday club in 1988.

Previous Leagues: West York. 1895-98. Yorkshire 98-99. Southern 1907-08. Football Lge 08-70. NPL 70-74, 95-04, 05-12. Bradford Am Sun. 74-76. Bradford Sun.All. 76-92. W. Riding Co. Am. 88-89. Cen Mids 89-90. NWC 90-95. Conf 2004-05

11-12		12-13		13-14		14-15		15-16		16-17		17-18		18-19		19-20ppg		20-21	
NP P	4	Conf N	7	Conf N	10	Conf N	13	Nat N	14	Nat N	16	Nat N	7	Nat N	7	Nat N	22	Nat N	n&v
FAC	1P	FAC	1P	FAC	4Qr	FAC	2Qr	FAC	3Qr	FAC	2Q	FAC	3Qr	FAC	3Q	FAC	2Q	FAC	2Q
FAT	1Qr	FAT	3Q	FAT	2P	FAT	1P	FAT	2Pr	FAT	3Q	FAT	3Qr	FAT	3Q	FAT	1Pr	FAT	2P

LEAGUE HONOURS:
West Yorkshire 1895-96 (Shared). Football League Division Three North 1927-28.
North West Counties Div.One 1994-95
Northern Premier Division One 2000-01, Division One North 2007-08.

COUNTY FA HONOURS: West Riding Senior Cup x9. West Riding County Cup 1990-91, 2014-15, 15-16.

CLUB RECORDS

FA Cup Quarter-finals 1912-13, 19-20, 45-46.

FA Vase Second Round Proper 1994-95.

FA Trophy Fourth Round Proper 1998-99.

Victory: 11-0 v Derby Dale - FA Cup 1908

Defeat: 0-7 v Barnsley - 1911

Goalscorer: Len Shackleton - 171 (1940-46)

Appearances: Tommy Farr - 542 (1934-50)

Additional: Paid £24,500 to Derby County for Leon Leuty 1950
Received £34,000 from Derby County for Kevin Hector 1966

GROUND: Horsfall Stadium, Cemetery Road, Bradford, West Yorkshire BD6 2NG

Ground Capacity: 3,500 **Seats:** 1,800 **Covered:** 2,000 **Clubhouse:** Yes **Shop:** Yes

Previous Grounds: Park Ave 1907-73,87-88, Valley Parade 1973-74, Bingley Road, Hope Ave, Ave Rd, Bramley, Mount Pleasant

Record Attendance: 2,100 v Bristol City - FA Cup 1st Round 2003

Nearest Railway Station Bradford Foster Square or Bradford Interchange

Bus Route From Interchange - 681 (682 Eve & Sun)

CHESTER

National North

The Blues **Founded** 2010 **Club Colours** Blue & white

Club Contact Details 01244 371 376 info@chesterfc.com

Previous Names: Formed after the demise of Chester City, which itself was formed in 1983 after the original Chester of 1885 folded.

Previous Leagues: Northern Premier League 2010-12.

11-12		12-13		13-14		14-15		15-16		16-17		17-18		18-19		19-20ppg		20-21	
NP P	1	Conf N	1	Conf	21	Conf	12	Nat	17	Nat	19	Nat	23	Nat N	9	Nat N	6	Nat	n&v
		FAC	3Qr	FAC	4Q	FAC	2Pr	FAC	4Q	FAC	4Q	FAC	4Q	FAC	3Q	FAC	2Qr	FAC	4Q
FAT	2P	FAT	3Qr	FAT	1P	FAT	1Pr	FAT	3P	FAT	2P	FAT	2P	FAT	3Qr	FAT	2P	FAT	3P

LEAGUE HONOURS:
Northern Premier League Division One North 2010-11, Premier Division 2011-12. Conference North 2012-13.

COUNTY FA HONOURS: Cheshire Senior Cup 2012-13.

CLUB RECORDS

FA Cup Fourth Qualifying Round 2013-14, 15-16, 16-17, 17-18, 20-21

FA Trophy Third Round Proper 2015-16, 20-21

Goalscorer: League - Michael Wilde - 41 (2010-12)

Appearances: League - Craig Mahon - 187 (2013-)

GROUND: Deva Stadium, Bumpers Lane, Chester CH1 4LT

Ground Capacity: 5,376 **Seats:** 4,170 **Covered:** Yes **Clubhouse:** Yes **Shop:** Yes

Previous Grounds: None

Record Attendance: 5,009 v Northwich Victoria, April 2012

Nearest Railway Station Chester - 2.5 miles away.

Bus Route No.10A from City Centre Bus Exchange.

CHORLEY

National North

Magpies **Founded** 1875 **Club Colours** Black and white

Club Contact Details 01257 230 007 commercial@chorleyfc.com

Previous Names: Founded as a Rugby Union side in 1875 then switched to football in 1883.

Previous Leagues: Lancashire Jr 1889-90. Lancashire All 1890-94. Lancashire 1894-1903. Lancashire Comb 1903-68, 69-70. NPL (FM) 1968-69, 70-72, 82-88, 90-2014. Cheshire Co 1972-82. Conference 1988-90.

11-12		12-13		13-14		14-15		15-16		16-17		17-18		18-19		19-20ppg		20-21	
NP P	3	NP P	8	NP P	1	Conf N	4	Nat N	8	Nat N	6	Nat N	6	Nat N	2	Nat	24	Nat N	n&v
FAC	1Qr	FAC	2Q	FAC	2Q	FAC	4Qr	FAC	4Qr	FAC	3Q	FAC	1P	FAC	1Pr	FAC	1P	FAC	4P
FAT	1Q	FAT	1Q	FAT	3P	FAT	2Pr	FAT	3Qr	FAT	1P	FAT	1P	FAT	3Q	FAT	1P	FAT	2P

LEAGUE HONOURS:
Lancashire Alliance 1892-93. Lancashire 1896-97, 98-99. Lancashire Combination 1919-20, 22-23, 27-28, 28-29, 32-33, 33-34, 39-40, 45-46, 59-60, 60-61, 63-64. Cheshire County 1975-76, 76-77, 81-82.
Northern Premier League Premier 1987-88, 2013-14.

COUNTY FA HONOURS: Lancashire FA Trophy (Record 18 times) 1893-94, 1908-09, 23-24, 39-40, 45-46, 57-58, 58-59, 60-61, 63-64, 64-65, 75-76, 79-80, 81-82, 82-83, 2011-12, 14-15, 15-16, 17-18.

CLUB RECORDS

FA Cup Fourth Round Proper 2020-21
FA Trophy Semi-finals 1995-96
Victory: 14-1 v Morecambe, April 1946.
Goalscorer: Peter Watson - 372 (1958-66).
Additional: Received £30,000 from Newcastle United for David Eatock 1996.

GROUND: Victory Park Stadium, Duke Street, Chorley, Lancashire PR7 3DU
Ground Capacity: 3,550 **Seats:** 900 **Covered:** 2,800 **Clubhouse:** Yes **Shop:** Yes
Previous Grounds: Dole Lane 1883-1901, Rangletts Park 1901-05, St George's Park 1905-20.
Record Attendance: 9,679 v Darwen, FA Cup Fourth Qualifying Round, 15/11/1932.
Nearest Railway Station Chorley - half a mile from the ground.
Bus Route Bus station half a mile from the ground.

CURZON ASHTON

National North

The Nash **Founded** 1963 **Club Colours** Royal blue and

Club Contact Details 07713 252 310 rob@curzon-ashton.co.uk

Previous Names: Club formed when Curzon Road Methodists and Ashton Amateurs merged, and were initially known as Curzon Amateurs.

Previous Leagues: Manchester Amateur. Manchester > 1978. Cheshire (FM of Div.2) 1978-82. North West Counties (FM) 1983-87, 98-2007. Northern Premier (FM) 1987-97, 2007-15. Northern Counties East 1997-98.

11-12		12-13		13-14		14-15		15-16		16-17		17-18		18-19		19-20ppg		20-21	
NP1N	2	NP1N	7	NP1N	1	NP P	4	Nat N	11	Nat N	14	Nat N	18	Nat N	18	Nat N	20	Nat N	n&v
FAC	Pr	FAC	2Q	FAC	3Q	FAC	3Q	FAC	2Q	FAC	1Pr	FAC	2Q	FAC	3Q	FAC	2Qr	FAC	2Q
FAT	3Q	FAT	1Q	FAT	1P	FAT	2Q	FAT	2P	FAT	2P	FAT	3Q	FAT	3Q	FAT	1P	FAT	2P

LEAGUE HONOURS:
Manchester Amateur Division One 1963-64, 65-66. Manchester Premier Division 1977-78.
Northern Premier Division One North 2013-14, Premier Division Play-off 2014-15.

COUNTY FA HONOURS: Manchester Premier Cup 1981-82, 83-84, 85-86, 87-87, 89-90.

CLUB RECORDS

FA Cup Second Round Proper 2008-09
FA Vase Semi-finals 1979-80, 2006-07
FA Trophy Second Round Proper 2015-16, 16-17, 20-21
Victory: 10-1 v Wakefield, 2012-13
Defeat: 0-8 v Bamber Bridge
Goalscorer: Rod Lawton - 376
Appearances: Alan Sykes

GROUND: Tameside Stadium, Richmond Street, Ashton-u-Lyme OL7 9HG
Ground Capacity: 4,000 **Seats:** 527 **Covered:** 1,100 **Clubhouse:** Yes **Shop:** Yes
Previous Grounds: National Park 1963-2004. Stalybridge Celtic FC 2004-05.
Record Attendance: 3,210 v FC United of Manchester, North West Counties Challenge Cup Final, 03/05/07.
Nearest Railway Station Ashton-under-Lyne - Approx. one mile from ground.
Bus Route Also 5mins from Ashton West Metrolink.

DARLINGTON 1883

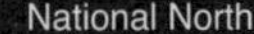

National North

The Quakers **Founded** 1883 **Club Colours** Black and white

Club Contact Details 01325 363 777 Dave.watson@darlingtonfc.org

Previous Names: Darlington FC 1883-2012

Previous Leagues: Northern League 1883-1908, 2012-13, North Eastern 1908-21, Football League 1921-89, 91-2010, Conference 1989-90, 10-12.

11-12	12-13	13-14	14-15	15-16	16-17	17-18	18-19	19-20ppg	20-21
Conf 22	NL 1 1	NP1N 2	NP1N 2	NP P 1	Nat N 5	Nat N 12	Nat N 18	Nat N 10	Nat N n&v
FAC 4Qr			FAC 1Qr	FAC 1Q	FAC 2Q	FAC 2Q	FAC 2Q	FAC 1Pr	FAC 2p
FAT 1P		FAT 1Qr	FAT 2Q	FAT 2Q	FAT 3Qr	FAT 3Q	FAT 3Q	FAT 2P	FAT QF

LEAGUE HONOURS:
Northern 1895-96, 99-1900, 2012-13. North Eastern 1912-13, 20-21. Football League Division Three North 1924-25, Division Four 1990-91. Conference 1989-90. Northern Premier League Premier Division 2015-16.

COUNTY FA HONOURS: Durham Challenge Cup 1884-85, 90-91, 92-93, 96-97, 1919-20, 99-2000.

CLUB RECORDS

FA Cup Fifth Round Proper 1910-11, 57-58
FA Trophy Winners 2010-11
Victory: 13-1 v Scarborough, FA Cup, 24/10/1891
Defeat: 0-10 v Doncaster Rovers - Division 4 25/01/1964
Goalscorer: Alan Walsh - 100, Jerry Best - 80
Appearances: Ron Greener - 490, John Peverell - 465, Brian Henderson - 463
Additional: Paid £95,000 to Motherwell for Nick Cusack January 1992.
Received £400,000 from Dundee United for Jason Devos October 1998

GROUND: Blackwell Meadows, Grange Road, Darlington DL1 5NR
Ground Capacity: 3299 **Seats:** 588 **Covered:** Yes **Clubhouse:** Yes **Shop:**
Previous Grounds: Feethams 1883-2003. Darlington Arena 2003-12. Bishop Auckland 2012-16.
Record Attendance: 21,023 v Bolton Wanderers - League Cup 3rd Round 14/11/1960
Nearest Railway Station Darlington - 1.5 miles away
Bus Route 13B

FARSLEY CELTIC

National North

The Celt Army **Founded** 2010 **Club Colours** Green & white

Club Contact Details 07736 037 604 office@farsleyceltic.com

Previous Names: Farsley AFC 2010-15.

Previous Leagues: Northern Counties East 2010-11. Northern Premier 2011-19.

11-12	12-13	13-14	14-15	15-16	16-17	17-18	18-19	19-20ppg	20-21
NP1N 4	NP1N 14	NP1N 7	NP1N 12	NP1N 9	NP1N 2	NP P 5	NP P 1	Nat N 11	Nat N n&v
	FAC 1Qr	FAC P	FAC 2Q	FAC 1Q	FAC 3Q	FAC 1Q	FAC 2Q	FAC 3Q	FAC 3Q
FAT 1Qr	FAT Pr	FAT P	FAT 1Q	FAT 1Q	FAT 1P	FAT 1Qr	FAT 1P	FAT 2Pr	FAT 3P

LEAGUE HONOURS:
Northern Counties East Premier Division 2010-11.
Northern Premier League Premier Division 2018-19.

COUNTY FA HONOURS: West Riding County Cup 2016-17.

CLUB RECORDS

FA Cup Third Qualifying Round 2016-17
FA Trophy Third Round Proper 2020-21
Victory: 8-0 v Arnold Town (H) Northern Counties East Premier 2010-11.
Defeat: 5-1 v Tadcaster Albion, President's Cup Final 27/04/11.

GROUND: The Citadel, Newlands, Pudsey, Leeds, LS28 5BE
Ground Capacity: 4,000 **Seats:** 300 **Covered:** 1,500 **Clubhouse:** Yes **Shop:** Yes
Previous Grounds: None
Record Attendance: 11,000 v Tranmere Rovers, FA Cup First Round Proepr, 1974-75 (at Elland Road)
Nearest Railway Station New Pudsey - 1km
Bus Route Town Street - stop 500m away

GATESHEAD

National North

Tynesiders, The Heed **Founded** 1930 **Club Colours** White & black

Club Contact Details 01914 783 883 info@gateshead-fc.com

Previous Names: Gateshead AFC (formerly South Shields)1930-73. Gateshead Town 1973-74. Gateshead Utd (formerly South Shields) 1974-77.

Previous Leagues: Football League 1930-60, NCE 60-62, North Regional 62-68, Northern Prem 68-70, 73-83, 85-86, 87-90, Wearside 70-71, Midland 71-72, Northern Comb 73-74. Alliance/Conf 1983-85, 86-87, 90-98.

11-12		12-13		13-14		14-15		15-16		16-17		17-18		18-19		19-20ppg		20-21	
Conf	8	Conf	17	Conf	3	Conf	10	Nat	9	Nat	8	Nat	17	Nat	17	Nat N	7	Nat N	n&v
FAC	2P	FAC	4Q	FAC	1Pr	FAC	3P	FAC	4Q	FAC	4Qr	FAC	2P	FAC	1P	FAC	1P	FAC	2Q
FAT	QF	FAT	3P	FAT	2P	FAT	3Pr	FAT	QFr	FAT	2P	FAT	SF	FAT	1P	FAT	3Q	FAT	2P

LEAGUE HONOURS:
Northern Regional 1963-64. Northern Premier League 1982-83, 85-86.

COUNTY FA HONOURS: Durham Senior Professional Cup 1930-31, 48-49, 501-51, 54-55, 58-59. Durham Challenge Cup 2010-11 (Reserve

CLUB RECORDS

FA Cup Quarter Finals 1952-53 as a League club. Third Round Proper 2014-15 as a Non-League Club.
FA Trophy Semi-Finals 2010-11
Victory: 8-0 v Netherfield - Northern Premier League
Defeat: 0-9 v Sutton United - Conference 22/09/90
Goalscorer: Paul Thompson - 130
Appearances: James Curtis - 506 (2003-present)
Additional: Record transfer fee paid; £9,000 - Paul Cavell, Dagenham & Redbridge 1994
Record transfer fee received; £150,000 Lee Novak, Huddersfield Town 2009

GROUND: The International Stadium, Neilson Road, Gateshead NE10 0EF
Ground Capacity: 11,795 **Seats:** 11,795 **Covered:** 7,271 **Clubhouse:** Yes **Shop:** Yes
Previous Grounds: Redheugh Park 1930-71
Record Attendance: 11,750 v Newcastle United - Friendly 07/08/95
Nearest Railway Station Gateshead Stadium Metro stop 5min walk away.
Bus Route 27, 93, 94

GLOUCESTER CITY

National North

The Tigers **Founded** 1883 **Club Colours** Red & amber

Club Contact Details info@gcafc.co.uk

Previous Names: Gloucester 1883-86,1889-1901, Gloucester Nomads 1888-89, Gloucester YMCA 1910-25, Gloucester City 1902-10,1925 to date

Previous Leagues: Bristol & District (now Western) 1893-96, Gloucester & Dist. 1897-1907, North Gloucestershire 1907-10, Gloucestershire Northern Senior (FM) 1920-34, Birmingham Comb 1934-39, Southern 1939-2000

11-12		12-13		13-14		14-15		15-16		16-17		17-18		18-19		19-20ppg		20-21	
Conf N	14	Conf N	11	Conf N	17	Conf N	14	Nat N	15	Nat N	10	Nat S	14	Nat S	17	Nat N	17	Nat N	n&v
FAC	4Qr	FAC	1P	FAC	1P	FAC	4Q	FAC	4Q	FAC	3Qr	FAC	2Q	FAC	4Q	FAC	3Qr	FAC	2Q
FAT	3Qr	FAT	3Q	FAT	1P	FAT	3Qr	FAT	3Qr	FAT	3Q	FAT	3Q	FAT	3Q	FAT	3Q	FAT	4P

LEAGUE HONOURS:
Gloucester & District Division One 1897-98, 99-1900, 03-04. North Gloucestershire Division One 1907-08, 08-09 Gloucestershire Northern Senior 1933-34. Southern League Midland Division 1988-89.

COUNTY FA HONOURS: Glos Junior Cup 1902-03. Glos Senior Amateur Cup 1931-32. Glos Senior Cup 1937-38, 49-50, 50-51, 52-53, 54-55, 55-56, 57-58, 65-66, 68-69, 70-71, 74-75, 78-79, 79-80, 81-82, 82-83, 83-84, 90-91, 92-93.

CLUB RECORDS

FA Cup Second Round Proper 1989-90 (r)
Welsh Cup Quarter-finals 1958-59 (r).
FA Trophy Semi-finals 1996-97 (r)
Victory: 12-1 v Bristol Saint George, April 1934
Defeat: 0-14 v Brimscombe FC, January 1923
Goalscorer: Jerry Causon - 206 (1930-36)
Appearances: Tom Webb - 675+ (2001 to date)
Additional: Paid £25,000 to Worcester City for Steve Ferguson 1990-91
Received £25,000 from AFC Bournemouth for Ian Hedges 1990

GROUND: Meadow Park, Sudmeadow Road, Hempsted, Gloucester GL2 5HS
Ground Capacity: 3,208 **Seats:** 700 **Covered:** Yes **Clubhouse:** Yes **Shop:** Yes
Previous Grounds: Longlevens 1934-64. Horton Rd 64-86. Meadow Pk 86-2007. FGR 07-08. Cirencester T. 08-10. Cheltenham 10-17. Evesham United 17-20.
Record Attendance: Longlevens: 10,500 v Spurs (F) 1952. Meadow Park: 4,500 v Dagenham & Red. - FAT 3rd Q Rnd 12/04/97
Nearest Railway Station Gloucester - six min walk to Station Road (see below)
Bus Route Station Road (Stop Q) No.8 to Sainsbury's Supermarket - 5min walk from there.

GUISELEY

National North

The Lions **Founded** 1909 **Club Colours** White and navy

Club Contact Details 01943 873 223 (Office) 872 872 (Club) admin@guiseleyafc.co.uk

Previous Names: None

Previous Leagues: Wharfedale, Leeds, West Riding Counties, West Yorkshire, Yorkshire 1968-82, Northern Counties East 1982-91, Northern Premier 1991-2010

11-12		12-13		13-14		14-15		15-16		16-17		17-18		18-19		19-20ppg		20-21	
Conf N	2	Conf N	2	Conf N	5	Conf N	5	Nat	20	Nat	20	Nat	24	Nat N	19	Nat N	9	Nat N	n&v
FAC	3Q	FAC	1Pr	FAC	2Q	FAC	4Q	FAC	4Qr	FAC	4Qr	FAC	2P	FAC	2P	FAC	3Q	FAC	4Q
FAT	3P	FAT	2P	FAT	3P	FAT	1P	FAT	3Pr	FAT	2P	FAT	1P	FAT	3Qr	FAT	3Q	FAT	3P

LEAGUE HONOURS:
Wharfedale 1912-13. Yorkshire Division Two 1975-76. Northern Counties East 1990-91.
Northern Premier League Division One 1993-94, Premier Division 2009-10.

COUNTY FA HONOURS: West Riding County Cup 1978-79, 79-80, 80-81, 93-94, 95-96, 2004-05, 10-11, 11-12.

CLUB RECORDS

FA Cup First Round Proper 1991-92, 94-95, 99-00, 02-03, 10-11, 12-13(r) **FA Vase** Winners 1990-91(r), Runners-up 91-92.

FA Trophy Semi-Finals 1993-94.

Misc: Highest points total gained - 93 - Northern Premier League Division One (1st) 1993-94 and Premier (3rd) 1994-95.

GROUND: Nethermoor Park, Otley Road, Guiseley, Leeds LS20 8BT

Ground Capacity: 4,200 **Seats:** 500 **Covered:** 1,040 **Clubhouse:** Yes **Shop:** Yes

Previous Grounds: None

Record Attendance: 2,486 v Bridlington Town - FA Vase Semi-final 1st Leg 1989-90

Nearest Railway Station Nethermoor is about 5 min walk away.

Bus Route There are two bus stops directly outside.

HEREFORD

National North

The Bulls **Founded** 2015 **Club Colours** White and black

Club Contact Details 01432 268 257 info@herefordfc.co.uk

Previous Names: Formed in 2015 after the demise of Hereford United who folded during the 2014-15 season.

Previous Leagues: Midland 2015-16. Southern 2016-18.

11-12		12-13		13-14		14-15		15-16		16-17		17-18		18-19		19-20ppg		20-21	
								MidL	1	Sthsw	1	SthP	1	Nat N	17	Nat N	16	Nat N	n&v
										FAC	3Q	FAC	2P	FAC	3Q	FAC	3Qr	FAC	3Q
								FAV	F	FAT	P	FAT	1P	FAT	2P	FAT	3Qr	FAT	F

LEAGUE HONOURS:
Midland League 2015-16. Southern Division One South & West 2016-17, Premier Division 17-18.

COUNTY FA HONOURS: Herefordshire County Cup 2015-16, 17-18

CLUB RECORDS

FA Cup Second Round Proper 2017-18 **FA Vase** Runners-up 2015-16

FA Trophy Runners-up 2020-21

Victory: 8-0 v Heanor Town - Midland League 23/04/16 & v Godalming Town (H), FAC 1Q, 02/09/2017.

Defeat: 4-5 v Coleshill Town - Midland League 2015-16.

Goalscorer: John Mills

GROUND: Edgar Street, Hereford HR4 9JU

Ground Capacity: 8,843 **Seats:** 2,761 **Covered:** 6,082 **Clubhouse:** Yes **Shop:** Yes

Previous Grounds: None

Record Attendance: 4,712 v AFC Telford United, FA Cup 1P, 04/11/2017.

Nearest Railway Station Hereford - 0.6km

Bus Route 476 & 492

KETTERING TOWN

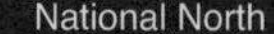

National North

The Poppies **Founded** 1872 **Club Colours** Red & black

Club Contact Details 01536 217 006 info@ketteringtownfc.com

Previous Names: Kettering > 1924

Previous Leagues: Midland 1892-1900, also had a team in United Counties 1896-99, Southern 1900-30, 1950-79, 2001-02, 12-19. Birmingham 1930-50, Alliance/Conference 1979-2001, 02-03, 04-12. Isthmian 2003-04.

11-12		12-13		13-14		14-15		15-16		16-17		17-18		18-19		19-20ppg		20-21	
Conf	24	SthP	22	SthC	3	SthC	1	SthP	6	SthP	9	SthP	4	SthPC	1	Nat N	19	Nat N	n&v
FAC	1P	FAC	2Q	FAC	P	FAC	2Q	FAC	3Qr	FAC	4Q	FAC	4Qr	FAC	4Q	FAC	2Qr	FAC	2Q
FAT	1P	FAT	1Q	FAT	1Q	FAT	1Q	FAT	2Q	FAT	2Q	FAT	1Q	FAT	2Q	FAT	1P	FAT	4P

LEAGUE HONOURS:
Midland 1895-96, 99-1900. United Counties 1904-05, 38-39. Southern 1927-28, 56-57, 72-73, 2001-02, Division One Central 2014-15, Premier Central 2018-19. National North 2007-08.

COUNTY FA HONOURS: Northamptionshire Senior Cup 2016-17, 17-18.

CLUB RECORDS

FA Cup Fourth Round Proper 1988-89, 2008-09
FA Trophy Runners-up 1978-79, 1999-2000
Victory: 16-0 v Higham YMCI - FA Cup 1909
Defeat: 0-13 v Mardy - Southern League Division Two 1911-12
Goalscorer: Roy Clayton - 171 (1972-81)
Appearances: Roger Ashby
Additional: Paid £25,000 to Macclesfield for Carl Alford 1994.
Recieved £150,000 from Newcastle United for Andy Hunt

GROUND: Latimer Park, Burton Latimer, Kettering NN15 5PS
Ground Capacity: 2,500 **Seats:** 332 **Covered:** Yes **Clubhouse:** Yes **Shop:** Yes
Previous Grounds: North Park, Green Lane, Rockingham Road > 2011. Nene Park 2011-13.
Record Attendance: 11,536 v Peterborough - FA Cup 1st Round replay 1958-59
Nearest Railway Station Kettering - 4.1km
Bus Route Station Road - stop 150m away

KIDDERMINSTER HARRIERS

National North

Harriers **Founded** 1886 **Club Colours** Red and white

Club Contact Details 01562 823 931 info@harriers.co.uk

Previous Names: Kidderminster Harriers and Football Club 1886-90. Kidderminster FC 1890-1891.

Previous Leagues: B'ham & Dist (FM) 1889-90, 91-1939, 47-48, 60-62. Midland 1890-91. Southern 1939-45, 48-60, 72-83. B'ham Comb 1945-47. West Mids (Reg) 1962-72. Conference 1983-2000. Football Lg 2000-05.

11-12		12-13		13-14		14-15		15-16		16-17		17-18		18-19		19-20ppg		20-21	
Conf	6	Conf	2	Conf	7	Conf	16	Nat	23	Nat N	2	Nat N	4	Nat N	10	Nat N	15	Nat N	n&v
FAC	4Qr	FAC	1P	FAC	4P	FAC	4Q	FAC	4Q	FAC	1P	FAC	1P	FAC	3Q	FAC	2Qr	FAC	2Q
FAT	3P	FAT	2P	FAT	1P	FAT	2P	FAT	1P	FAT	3Q	FAT	2Pr	FAT	3Q	FAT	3Q	FAT	2P

LEAGUE HONOURS:
Birmingham & District 1937-38. West Midlands (Regional) 1964-65, 68-69, 69-70, 70-71.
Conference 1993-94, 1999-2000.

COUNTY FA HONOURS: Worcestershire Senior Cup (27 times) Firstly in 1895-96 and most recently 2016-17. Birmingham Senior Cup (7x) Firstly in 1933-34 and most recently in 1966-67. Staffordshire Senior Cup (4x) Firstly in 1980-81 and most recently in 1984-85.

CLUB RECORDS

FA Cup Fifth Round Proper 1993-94 **Welsh Cup** Finalists 1985-86, 1988-89
FA Trophy Winners 1986-87 (Runners-up 1990-91, 94-95, 2006-07)
Victory: 25-0 v Hereford (H), Birmingham Senior Cup First Round, 12/10/1889
Defeat: 0-13 v Darwen (A), FA Cup First Round Proper, 24/01/1891
Goalscorer: Peter Wassell - 448 (1963-74)
Appearances: Brendan Wassell - 686 (1962-74)
Additional: Paid £80,000 to Nuneaton Borough for Andy Ducros July 2000
Recieved £380,000 from W.B.A. for Lee Hughes July 1997

GROUND: Aggborough Stadium, Hoo Road, Kidderminster DY10 1NB
Ground Capacity: 6,444 **Seats:** 3,140 **Covered:** 3,062 **Clubhouse:** Yes **Shop:** Yes
Previous Grounds: Chester Road 1886-87.
Record Attendance: 9,155 v Hereford United, FA Cup First Round Proper, 27/11/48
Nearest Railway Station Kidderminster - half a mile from the ground.
Bus Route 192 & 42

LEAMINGTON

National North

The Brakes **Founded** 1892 **Club Colours** Gold and black

Club Contact Details 01926 430 406 info@leamingtonfc.co.uk

Previous Names: Leamington Town 1892-1937, Lockheed Borg & Beck 1944-46 , Lockheed Leamington 1946-73, AP Leamington 1973-88

Previous Leagues: B'ham Comb, B'ham & Dist, West Mids (Reg), Midland Counties, Southern, Midland Combination, Midland Alliance 2005-07. Southern 2007-13, 15-17. Football Conference 2013-15.

11-12		12-13		13-14		14-15		15-16		16-17		17-18		18-19		19-20ppg		20-21	
SthP	7	SthP	1	Conf N	13	Conf N	21	SthP	3	SthP	2	Nat N	19	Nat N	13	Nat N	18	Nat N	n&v
FAC	2Q	FAC	2Q	FAC	2Qr	FAC	3Qr	FAC	1Qr	FAC	1Q	FAC	3Qr	FAC	2Q	FAC	3Q	FAC	2Q
FAT	1Q	FAT	1Qr	FAT	2P	FAT	3Q	FAT	1Pr	FAT	1Q	FAT	1P	FAT	2P	FAT	3P	FAT	5P

LEAGUE HONOURS:
Birmingham & Dist 1961-62. West Mids Regional 1962-63. Midland Co 1964-65. Southern League 1982-83, 2012-13, Division One Midlands 2008-09. Midland Comb Div Two 2000-01, Premier Div 2004-05. Midland All 2006-07.

COUNTY FA HONOURS: Birmingham Senior Cup 2016-17, 18-19.

CLUB RECORDS

FA Cup First Round Proper 2005-06
FA Vase Quarter-finals 2006-07
FA Trophy Fifth Round Proper 2020-21
Goalscorer: Josh Blake - 187
Appearances: Josh Blake - 406

GROUND: Your Co-Op Community Stadium, Harbury Lane, Whitmarsh, Leamington CV33 9QB
Ground Capacity: 2,300 **Seats:** 294 **Covered:** 720 **Clubhouse:** Yes **Shop:** Yes
Previous Grounds: Old Windmill Ground
Record Attendance: 1,380 v Retford United - 17/02/2007
Nearest Railway Station Leamington Spa - 3 miles away
Bus Route Nos. 65 & 66

SOUTHPORT

National North

The Sandgrounders **Founded** 1881 **Club Colours** Yellow & black

Club Contact Details 01704 533 422 mark.lockyear@southportfc.net

Previous Names: Southport Central 1888-1918, Southport Vulcan 1918-21.

Previous Leagues: Preston & District, Lancashire 1889-1903, Lancashire Combination 1903-11, Central 1911-21, Football League 1921-78, Northern Premier 1978-93, 2003-04, Conference 1993-2003.

11-12		12-13		13-14		14-15		15-16		16-17		17-18		18-19		19-20ppg		20-21	
Conf	7	Conf	20	Conf	18	Conf	19	Nat	16	Nat	23	Nat N	15	Nat N	14	Nat N	12	Nat N	n&v
FAC	1P	FAC	4Q	FAC	1P	FAC	3P	FAC	4Q	FAC	1Pr	FAC	2Q	FAC	2Pr	FAC	4Q	FAC	3Q
FAT	1P	FAT	QF	FAT	1P	FAT	1Pr	FAT	2P	FAT	2P	FAT	3Qr	FAT	1P	FAT	2P	FAT	5P

LEAGUE HONOURS:
Football League Division Four 1972-73. Northern Premier League Premier Division 1992-93.
Conference North 2004-05, 2009-10.

COUNTY FA HONOURS: Lancs Senior Cup 1904-05. Lancs Junior Cup 1919-20, 92-93, 96-97, 97-98, 2001-01, 05-06, 07-08, 09-10. Liverpool Senior Cup 1930-31, 31-32, 43-44, 62-63, 74-75, 90-91, 92-93, 98-99, 2011-12.

CLUB RECORDS

FA Cup Quarter-Finals 1930-31. As a Non-League side - Third Round Proper 1998-99, 2014-15.
FA Trophy Runners-up 1998-98
Victory: 8-1 v Nelson - 01/01/31
Defeat: 0-11 v Oldham Athletic - 26/12/62
Goalscorer: Alan Spence - 98
Appearances: Arthur Peat - 401 (1962-72)
Additional: Paid £20,000 to Macclesfield Town for Martin McDonald

GROUND: Merseyrail Community Stadium, Haig Avenue, Southport, Merseyside PR8 6JZ
Ground Capacity: 6,008 **Seats:** 1,660 **Covered:** 2,760 **Clubhouse:** Yes **Shop:** Yes
Previous Grounds: Sussex Road Sports Ground, Scarisbrick New Road 1886-1905, Ash Lane (later named Haig Ave)
Record Attendance: 20,010 v Newcastle United - FA Cup 1932
Nearest Railway Station Meols Cop - 1mile away. Southport - 1.5miles away.
Bus Route 44 Arriva from the Southport Station.

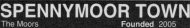

SPENNYMOOR TOWN

National North

The Moors **Founded** 2005 **Club Colours** Black and white

Club Contact Details 01388 813 255

Previous Names: Evenwood Town and Spennymoor United merged to form today's club in 2005.

Previous Leagues: Northern League 2005-14. Northern Premier 2014-17.

11-12		12-13		13-14		14-15		15-16		16-17		17-18		18-19		19-20ppg		20-21	
NL 1	1	NL 1	2	NL 1	1	NP1N	5	NP1N	2	NP P	2	Nat N	8	Nat N	4	Nat N	8	Nat N	n&v
FAC	3Q	FAC	2Q	FAC	1Q	FAC	4Qr	FAC	2Q	FAC	1P	FAC	2Q	FAC	2Q	FAC	4Q	FAC	3Q
FAV	3P	FAV	F	FAV	5P	FAT	1P	FAT	3Q	FAT	1Q	FAT	4Pr	FAT	3P	FAT	3Q	FAT	3P

LEAGUE HONOURS:
Northern League Division One 2009-10, 2010-11, 2011-12, 2013-14, Division Two 2006-07.

COUNTY FA HONOURS: Durham Challange Cup 2011-12.

CLUB RECORDS

FA Cup First Round Proper 1956-57, 2016-17 **FA Vase** Winners 2012-13.
FA Trophy Third Round Proper 2020-21
Victory: 10-0 v Billingham Town (H), Northern League Division One, 18/03/2014
Defeat: 2-8 v Clitheroe (A), FA Cup 2nd Qualifying Round, 29/09/2007
Goalscorer: Gavin Cogdon - 103
Appearances: Lewis Dodds - 227
Additional: Northern League record points tally of 109 during 2012-13.

GROUND: The Brewery Field, Durham Road, Spennymoor DL16 6JN
Ground Capacity: 3,000 **Seats:** 224 **Covered:** 800 **Clubhouse:** Yes **Shop:** Yes
Previous Grounds: None
Record Attendance: 2,670 v Darlington, Northern League 2012-13.
Nearest Railway Station Durham
Bus Route No.6 from Durham Bus Station in Durham Town Centre (15min journey)

YORK CITY

National North

Minstermen **Founded** 1922 **Club Colours** Red and navy blue

Club Contact Details 01904 624 447 / 559 500 enquiries@yorkcityfootballclub.co.uk

Previous Names: None

Previous Leagues: Midland 1922-29. Football League 1929-2004, 2012-16. Conference 2004-12.

11-12		12-13		13-14		14-15		15-16		16-17		17-18		18-19		19-20ppg		20-21	
Conf	4	FL 2	17	FL 2	7	FL 2	18	FL 2	24	Nat	21	Nat N	11	Nat N	12	Nat N	2	Nat N	n&v
FAC	4Q	FAC	1Pr	FAC	1Pr	FAC	1Pr	FAC	1P	FAC	4Qr	FAC	3Q	FAC	1P	FAC	1P	FAC	3Q
FAT	F	FLC	1P	FLC	1P	FLC	1P	FLC	2P	FAT	F	FAT	1P	FAT	1P	FAT	3Q	FAT	2P

LEAGUE HONOURS:
Football League Division Four 1983-84, Third Division Play-offs 1992-93.
Conference Premier Play-offs 2011-12.

COUNTY FA HONOURS: North Riding Senior Cup 1949-50, 56-57, 69-70, 79-80, 87-88. 88-89, 95-96, 98-99, 99-00, 05-06, 09-10.

CLUB RECORDS

FA Cup Semi-Finals 1954-55.
FA Trophy Winners 2011-12, 16-17. Runners-up 08-09.
Victory: 9-1 v Southport - Division Three North 1957
Defeat: 0-12 v Chester City - Division Three North 1936
Goalscorer: Norman Wilkinson - 143 (1954-66)
Appearances: Barry Jackson - 539 (1958-70)
Additional: Paid £140,000 to Burnley for Adrian Randall December 1995
Received £950,000 from Sheffield Wednesday for Richard Cresswell 25/03/1999

GROUND: LNER Community Stadium, Kathryn Avenue, Monks Cross Drive, Huntington, York YO32 9AF
Ground Capacity: 8,500 **Seats:** Yes **Covered:** Yes **Clubhouse:** Yes **Shop:** Yes
Previous Grounds: Fulfordgate 1922-32. Bootham Crescent 1932-2021.
Record Attendance: 28,123 v Huddersfield Town - FA Cup Sixth Round Proper 1938
Nearest Railway Station York - 20 min walk away.
Bus Route 2 & 5A

NOTE: At the time of going to press the club were unsure if they would be moving into their new 8,000 all seater stadium at Monks Cross for 2020/21.

BATH CITY

National South

The Romans **Founded** 1889 **Club Colours** Black & white

Club Contact Details 01225 423 087 info@bathcityfootballclub.co.uk

Previous Names: Bath AFC 1889-92. Bath Railway FC 1902-05. Bath Amateurs 1913-23 (Reserve side)

Previous Leagues: Western 1908-21. Southern 1921-79, 88-90, 97-2007. Football League Division Two North 1939-45. Alliance/Conference 1979-88, 90-97.

11-12	12-13	13-14	14-15	15-16	16-17	17-18	18-19	19-20ppg	20-21
Conf 23	Conf S 11	Conf S 7	Conf S 14	Nat S 14	Nat S 9	Nat S 9	Nat S 5	Nat S 4	Nat S n&v
FAC 1Pr	FAC 3Qr	FAC 4Q	FAC 4Q	FAC 3Qr	FAC 4Q	FAC 4Qr	FAC 4Q	FAC 3Q	FAC 4Q
FAT 3P	FAT 1P	FAT 3Q	FAT SF	FAT 3Q	FAT 1P	FAT 1P	FAT 1P	FAT 2Pr	FAT 4P

LEAGUE HONOURS:
Western Division Two 1928-29, Premier 1933-34. Southern Premier Division 1959-60, 77-78, 2006-07.

COUNTY FA HONOURS: Somerset Premier Cup 1929-30, 33-34, 35-36, 51-52, 52-53, 57-58, 59-60, 65-66, 67-68, 69-70, 77-78, 80-81, 81-82, 83-84, 84-85, 85-86, 88-89, 89-90, 93-94, 94-95, 2007-08.

CLUB RECORDS

FA Cup Third Round Proper 1963-64 (r), 93-94 (r).
FA Trophy Semi-Finals 2014-15.
Victory: 8-0 v Boston United - 1998-99
Defeat: 0-9 v Yeovil Town - 1946-47
Goalscorer: Paul Randall - 106
Appearances: David Mogg - 530
Additional: Paid £15,000 to Bristol City for Micky Tanner.
Received £80,000 from Southampton for Jason Dodd.

GROUND: Twerton Park, Twerton, Bath, Somerset BA2 1DB
Ground Capacity: 8,880 **Seats:** 1,006 **Covered:** 4,800 **Clubhouse:** Yes **Shop:** Yes
Previous Grounds: The Belvoir Ground 1889-92 & 1902-15. Lambridge Show Ground 1919-32.
Record Attendance: 18,020 v Brighton & Hove Albion - FA Cup 1960
Nearest Railway Station Bath Spa - 2 miles from ground or Avon Street - 1 mile
Bus Route No.5 - every 12mins from Town Centre.

BILLERICAY TOWN

National South

Town or Blues **Founded** 1880 **Club Colours** All blue

Club Contact Details 01277 286 474 info@billericaytownfc.co.uk

Previous Names: Billericay FC.

Previous Leagues: Romford & Dist 1890-1914, Mid Essex 1918-47, South Essex Comb 1947-66, Essex Olympian 1966-71, Essex Senior 1971-77, Athenian 1977-79. Isthmian 1979-2012. Conference 2012-13.

11-12	12-13	13-14	14-15	15-16	16-17	17-18	18-19	19-20ppg	20-21
Isth P 1	Conf S 21	Isth P 10	Isth P 8	Isth P 9	Isth P 8	Isth P 1	Nat S 8	Nat S 17	Nat S n&v
FAC 3Q	FAC 3Qr	FAC 2Q	FAC 3Q	FAC 1Qr	FAC 4Q	FAC 1Pr	FAC 1Pr	FAC 1P	FAC 2Q
FAT 3Q	FAT 1P	FAT 2Qr	FAT 1Q	FAT 1Q	FAT 2Q	FAT 4P	FAT 1P	FAT 3Q	FAT 2P

LEAGUE HONOURS:
Chelmsford & District Division Three 1932-33. Essex Olympian 1969-70, 70-71.
Essex Senior 1972-73, 74-75, 75-76. Athenian 1977-78, 78-79.
Isthmian Division Two 1979-80, Premier Division 2011-12.

COUNTY FA HONOURS: Essex Senior Cup 1975-76, 2010-11, 17-18. Essex Senior Trophy 1977-78, 79-80, 2017-18.

CLUB RECORDS

FA Cup First Round Proper 1997-98, 2004-05, 07-08, 18-19(r), 19-20. **FA Vase** Winners 1975-76, 76-77, 78-79.
FA Trophy Fifth Round Proper 2000-01.
Victory: 11-0 v Stansted (A) - Essex Senior League 05/05/1976
Defeat: 3-10 v Chelmsford City (A) - Essex Senior Cup 04/01/1993
Goalscorer: Freddie Claydon - 273
Appearances: J Pullen - 418
Additional: Leon Gutzmore scored 51 goals during the 1997-98 season.
Received £22,500+ from West Ham United for Steve Jones November 1992

GROUND: New Lodge, Blunts Wall Road, Billericay CM12 9SA
Ground Capacity: 3,500 **Seats:** 424 **Covered:** 2,000 **Clubhouse:** Yes **Shop:** Yes
Previous Grounds: None
Record Attendance: 3,841 v West Ham United - Opening of Floodlights 1977
Nearest Railway Station Billericay - 1.4km
Bus Route London Road - stop 300m away

BRAINTREE TOWN

National South

The Iron **Founded** 1898 **Club Colours** Orange & white

Club Contact Details 01376 345 617 braintreeTFC@aol.com

Previous Names: Manor Works 1898-1921, Crittall Athletic 1921-68, Braintree and Crittall Athletic 1968-81, Braintree 1981-83.

Previous Leagues: N.Essex 1898-1925, Essex & Suffolk B 1925-29, 55-64, Spartan 28-35, Eastern Co. 35-37, 38-39, 52-55, 70-91, Essex Co. 37-38, London 45-52, Gt London 64-66, Met 66-70, Southern 91-96, Isthmian 96-2006

11-12		12-13		13-14		14-15		15-16		16-17		17-18		18-19		19-20ppg		20-21	
Conf	12	Conf	9	Conf	6	Conf	14	Nat	3	Nat	22	Nat S	6	Nat	23	Nat S	21	Nat S	n&v
FAC	4Q	FAC	1P	FAC	1Pr	FAC	1P	FAC	1Pr	FAC	2P	FAC	3Q	FAC	4Q	FAC	2Q	FAC	3Q
FAT	2Pr	FAT	1Pr	FAT	2P	FAT	3Pr	FAT	2P	FAT	3Pr	FAT	1Pr	FAT	1P	FAT	3Q	FAT	3P

LEAGUE HONOURS:
North Essex 1905-06, 10-11, 11-12. Eastern Counties League 1936-37, 83-84, 84-85.
Essex & Suffolk Border 1959-60. Isthmian League Premier Division 2005-06. Conference South 2010-11.

COUNTY FA HONOURS: Essex Senior Cup 1995-96. Essex Senior Trophy 1986-87.

CLUB RECORDS

FA Cup Second Round Proper 2016-17
FA Trophy Fifth Round Proper 2001-02 (r) **FA Vase** Fifth Round Proper 1984-85 (r)
Victory: 12-0 v Thetford - Eastern Counties League 1935-36
Defeat: 0-14 v Chelmsford City (A) - North Essex League 1923
Goalscorer: Chris Guy - 211 (1963-90). Gary Bennett scored 57 goals during season 1997-98
Appearances: Paul Young - 524 (1966-77)
Additional: Received £10,000 from Brentford for Matt Metcalf and from Colchester United for John Cheesewright

GROUND: Cressing Road Stadium, off Clockhouse Way, Braintree CM7 3DE
Ground Capacity: 4,222 **Seats:** 553 **Covered:** 1,288 **Clubhouse:** Yes **Shop:** Yes
Previous Grounds: The Fiar Field 1898-1903, Spalding Meadow 1903-23.
Record Attendance: 4,000 v Tottenham Hotspur - Testimonial May 1952
Nearest Railway Station Braintree - less than a mile from the ground.
Bus Route 133, 38A & 70

CHELMSFORD CITY

National South

City or Clarets **Founded** 1878 **Club Colours** Claret and white

Club Contact Details 01245 290 959

Previous Names: Chelmsford FC 1878-1938.

Previous Leagues: North Essex (FM) 1895-1900. South Essex 1900-13. Athenian (FM) 1912-22. Middlesex Co 1922-38. Essex & Suffolk Border 1923-24. London 1924-35. Eastern Co (FM) 1935-38. Southern 1938-2004. Isthmian 2004-08

11-12		12-13		13-14		14-15		15-16		16-17		17-18		18-19		19-20ppg		20-21	
Conf S	6	Conf S	5	Conf S	17	Conf S	10	Nat S	15	Nat S	4	Nat S	3	Nat S	4	Nat S	10	Nat S	n&v
FAC	2Pr	FAC	2P	FAC	2Q	FAC	4Qr	FAC	3Q	FAC	2Q	FAC	1P	FAC	2Q	FAC	2Q	FAC	2Q
FAT	1P	FAT	3P	FAT	3Q	FAT	3Q	FAT	1P	FAT	3Pr	FAT	3Qr	FAT	3Q	FAT	3P	FAT	2P

LEAGUE HONOURS:
Middlesex County 1923-24. London League 1930-31. Southern League 1930-40 (joint), 45-46, 67-68, 71-72, Division One South 88 -89. Isthmian League Premier Division 2007-08.

COUNTY FA HONOURS: Essex Senior Cup 1892-93, 1901-02, 85-86, 88-89, 92-93, 2002-03, 08-09 16-17. East Anglian Cup 1924-25, 26-27, 28-29. Essex Professional Cup 1957-58, 69-70, 70-71, 73-74, 74-75.

CLUB RECORDS

FA Cup Fourth Round Proper 1938-39.
FA Trophy Semi-Finals 1969-70.
Victory: 10-1 v Bashley (H) - Southern League 26/04/2000
Defeat: 1-10 v Barking (A) - FA Trophy 11/11/1978
Goalscorer: Tony Butcher - 286 (1956-71)
Appearances: Tony Butcher - 560 (1956-71)
Additional: Paid £10,000 to Dover Athletic for Tony Rogers, 1992 and to Heybridge Swifts for Kris Lee ,2001
Received £50,000 from Peterborough United for David Morrison, 1994

GROUND: Melbourne Community Stadium, Salerno Way, Chelmsford CM1 2EH
Ground Capacity: 3,000 **Seats:** 1,300 **Covered:** 1,300 **Clubhouse:** Yes **Shop:** Yes
Previous Grounds: New Writtle Street 1938-97, Maldon Town 1997-98, Billericay Town 1998-2005
Record Attendance: 3,201 v AFC Wimbledon, 15/03/2008.
Nearest Railway Station Chelmsford - take bus or taxi to ground.
Bus Route No. 54 and 56 opposite the train station.

CHIPPENHAM TOWN

National South

The Bluebirds **Founded** 1873 **Club Colours** All royal blue

Club Contact Details 01249 650 400

Previous Names: None

Previous Leagues: Western 1904-06, 30-65, 73-2001. Wiltshire Senior. Wiltshire Premier. Hellenic 1968-73. Southern 2001-17.

11-12	12-13	13-14	14-15	15-16	16-17	17-18	18-19	19-20ppg	20-21
SthP 11	SthP 15	SthP 18	SthP 11	SthP 8	SthP 1	Nat S 1	Nat S 13	Nat S 14	Nat S n&v
FAC 1Q	FAC 4Q	FAC 1Q	FAC 3Q	FAC 4Q	FAC 3Q	FAC 2Q	FAC 4Qr	FAC 1P	FAC 4Q
FAT 1P	FAT 2Q	FAT 2Q	FAT 2Q	FAT 1Q	FAT 2Q	FAT 3Q	FAT 3Qr	FAT 3Qr	FAT 2P

LEAGUE HONOURS:
Western League 1951-52.
Southern League Premier Division 2016-17.

COUNTY FA HONOURS: Wiltshire Senior Cup. Wiltshire Senior Shield x4.

CLUB RECORDS

FA Cup First Round Proper 1951-52, 2005-06(r), 19-20
FA Vase Runners-up 1999-2000.
FA Trophy Second Round Proper 2002-03, 09-10, 20-21
Victory: 9-0 v Dawlish Town (H) - Western League
Defeat: 0-10 v Tiverton Town (A) - Western League
Goalscorer: Dave Ferris
Appearances: Ian Monnery

GROUND: Hardenhuish Park, Bristol Road, Chippenham SN14 6LR
Ground Capacity: 3,000 **Seats:** 300 **Covered:** 1,000 **Clubhouse:** Yes **Shop:** Yes
Previous Grounds: Played at four different locations before moving in to Hardenhuish on 24/09/1919.
Record Attendance: 4,800 v Chippenham United - Western League 1951
Nearest Railway Station Chippenham - 1km
Bus Route Bus stops within 200m of the ground.

CONCORD RANGERS

National South

Beach Boys **Founded** 1967 **Club Colours** Yellow and blue

Club Contact Details 01268 515 750 media@concordrangers.co.uk

Previous Names: None

Previous Leagues: Thundermite Boys League 1967-73. Vange & District 1973-79. Mid-Essex 1979-88. Essex Intermediate 1988-91. Essex Senior 1991-2008. Isthmian 2008-13.

11-12	12-13	13-14	14-15	15-16	16-17	17-18	18-19	19-20ppg	20-21
Isth P 14	Isth P 4	Conf S 9	Conf S 7	Nat S 10	Nat S 18	Nat S 17	Nat S 6	Nat S 16	Nat S n&v
FAC 2Qr	FAC 2Qr	FAC 4Q	FAC 1Pr	FAC 2Q	FAC 3Q	FAC 4Qr	FAC 4Q	FAC 2Q	FAC 4Q
FAT 1Q	FAT 2Q	FAT 1P	FAT 2P	FAT 3Q	FAT 3Q	FAT 3Q	FAT 3Q	FAT F	FAT 2P

LEAGUE HONOURS:
Essex Intermediate League Division 2 1990-91. Essex Senior League 1997-98, 2003-04, 07-08.

COUNTY FA HONOURS: Essex Senior Cup 2013-14, 14-15, 15-16.

CLUB RECORDS

FA Cup First Round Proper 2014-15
FA Vase Quarter-Finals 2007-08
FA Trophy Runners-up 2019-20 (Played a year late - 03/05/21 - when Harrogate Town were a League Two club)
Goalscorer: Tony Stokes - 120
Appearances: Steve King - 312 (2013-16)

GROUND: Aspect Arena, Thames Road, Canvey Island, Essex SS8 0HH
Ground Capacity: 3,250 **Seats:** 375 **Covered:** Yes **Clubhouse:** Yes **Shop:**
Previous Grounds: Waterside 70s-85
Record Attendance: 1,537 v Mansfield Town, FA Cup First Round Replay, 25/11/2014.
Nearest Railway Station Benfleet - Approx. 3 miles from the ground.
Bus Route First Buses operate a regular service to Thorney Bay Road, 5-10min walk from there

DARTFORD

National South

The Darts **Founded** 1888 **Club Colours** White and black

Club Contact Details 01322 299 991 operations@dartfordfc.com

Previous Names: None

Previous Leagues: Kent League (FM) 1894-96, 97-98, 99-1902, 09-14, 21-26, 93-96, Southern (FM) 1896-97, 1926-81, 82-84, 86-92, 96-2006. West Kent 1902-09. Alliance 1981-82, 84-86.

11-12		12-13		13-14		14-15		15-16		16-17		17-18		18-19		19-20ppg		20-21	
Conf S	2	Conf	8	Conf	22	Conf	23	Nat S	8	Nat S	3	Nat S	2	Nat S	10	Nat S	6	Nat S	n&v
FAC	4Q	FAC	4Qr	FAC	1P	FAC	2P	FAC	2Q	FAC	1P	FAC	1P	FAC	3Q	FAC	4Q	FAC	2Q
FAT	3Pr	FAT	SF	FAT	1Pr	FAT	3Pr	FAT	3Q	FAT	2P	FAT	1Pr	FAT	3Qr	FAT	3Qr	FAT	3P

LEAGUE HONOURS:
Southern League Division 2 1896-97, Eastern Section 1930-31, 31-32, Southern Championship 30-31, 31-32, 73-74, 83-84, Southern Division 1980-81. West Kent 1908-09. Isthmian League Division One North 2007-08, Premier Division 2009-10.

COUNTY FA HONOURS: Kent Senior Cup 1930-31, 31-32, 32-33, 34-35, 46-47, 69-70, 72-73, 86-87, 87-88, 2010-11, 15-16. Kent Senior

CLUB RECORDS

FA Cup Third Round Proper 1935-36, 36-37. **FA Vase** First Round Proper 1994-95.
FA Trophy Runners-up 1973-74.
Appearances: Steve Robinson - 692
Additional: Paid £6,000 to Chelmsford City for John Bartley
Received £25,000 from Redbridge Forest for Andy Hessenthaler

GROUND: Princes Park Stadium, Grassbanks, Darenth Road, Dartford DA1 1RT
Ground Capacity: 4,097 **Seats:** 642 **Covered:** Yes **Clubhouse:** Yes **Shop:** Yes
Previous Grounds: The Brent/Westgate House, Potters Meadow, Engleys Meadow, Summers Meadow, Watling Street
Record Attendance: 4,097 v Horsham YMCA - Isth Div 1 South 11/11/2006 and v Crystal Palace - Fr 20/07/07
Nearest Railway Station Dartford - bus ride away from the ground.
Bus Route Fasttrack B towards Bluewater/Dartford.

DORKING WANDERERS

National South

Wanderers **Founded** 1999 **Club Colours** Red & white stripes

Club Contact Details info@dorkingwanderers.com

Previous Names: None

Previous Leagues: Crawley & District 1999-2000. West Sussex 2000-2007. Sussex County 2007-2015. Isthmian 2015-19.

11-12		12-13		13-14		14-15		15-16		16-17		17-18		18-19		19-20ppg		20-21	
SxC2	3	SxC1	20	SxC1	8	SxC1	2	Isth1S	2	Isth1S	2	Isth P	14	Isth P	1	Nat S	7	Nat S	n&v
				FAC	Pr	FAC	2Qr	FAC	1Q	FAC	1Q	FAC	3Q	FAC	3Qr	FAC	2Q	FAC	2Q
		FAV	2Q	FAV	2Qr	FAV	2Q	FAT	1Qr	FAT	P	FAT	3Q	FAT	1P	FAT	3P	FAT	4P

LEAGUE HONOURS:
West Sussex Division Four North 2000-01, Division Two North 2003-04, Premier Division 2006-07.
Sussex County Division Three 2010-11. Isthmian Premier Division 2018-19.

COUNTY FA HONOURS: None

CLUB RECORDS

FA Cup Third Qualifying Round 2018-19(r) **FA Vase** Second Qualifying Round 2012-13, 13-14(r), 14-15.
FA Trophy Fourth Round Proper 2020-21

GROUND: Meadowbank Stadium, Mill Lane, Dorking RH4 1DX
Ground Capacity: 3,000 **Seats:** 522 **Covered:** Yes **Clubhouse:** Yes **Shop:**
Previous Grounds: Big Field Brockham 1999-2007. West Humble Playing Fields 2007-18.
Record Attendance: Not known
Nearest Railway Station Dorking West and Dorking Deepdene
Bus Route 21 & 465

DULWICH HAMLET

National South

Hamlet **Founded** 1893 **Club Colours** Navy and pink

Club Contact Details 020 7274 8707

Previous Names: None

Previous Leagues: Camberwell 1894-97. Southern Suburban 1897-1900, 01-07. Dulwich 1900-01. Spartan 1907-08. Isthmian 1907-2018.

11-12		12-13		13-14		14-15		15-16		16-17		17-18		18-19		19-20ppg		20-21	
Isth1S	3	Isth1S	1	Isth P	6	Isth P	4	Isth P	5	Isth P	3	Isth P	2	Nat S	14	Nat S	19	Nat S	n&v
FAC	2Q	FAC	2Q	FAC	3Q	FAC	1Q	FAC	2Q	FAC	2Q	FAC	2Q	FAC	3Q	FAC	1P	FAC	4Q
FAT	1Q	FAT	P	FAT	3Qr	FAT	2Q	FAT	2P	FAT	QFr	FAT	2Q	FAT	1P	FAT	1P	FAT	3P

LEAGUE HONOURS:
Dulwich 1899-00, 1900-01.
Isthmian League Premier Division 1919-20, 25-26, 32-33, 48-49, Division One 1977-78, Division One South 2012-13.

COUNTY FA HONOURS: Surrey Senior Cup x16, firstly in 1904-05 and most recently 74-75.
London Senior Cup x5, firstly in 1924-25 and most recently in 2003-04. London Challenge Cup 1998-99.

CLUB RECORDS
FA Cup First Round Proper 1925-26, 26-27, 27-28, 28-29, 29-30, 30-31(r), 32-33, 33-34(r), 34-35, 35-36, 36-37, 37-38, 48-49, 98-99, 2019-20.
FA Trophy Quarter-Finals 1979-80(r), 2016-17(r).
FA Am Cup Winners 1919-20, 31-32, 36-37.
Victory: 13-0 v Walton-on-Thames, Surrey Senior Cup, 1936-37
Defeat: 1-10 v Hendon, Isthmian league, 1963-64
Goalscorer: Edgar Kail - 427 (1919-33)
Appearances: Reg Merritt - 576 (1950-66)
Additional: Received £35,000 from Charlton Athletic for Chris Dickson 2007

GROUND: Champion Hill, Dog Kennell Hill, Edgar Kail Way SE22 8BD
Ground Capacity: 3,000 **Seats:** 500 **Covered:** 1,000 **Clubhouse:** Yes **Shop:** Yes
Previous Grounds: Woodwarde Rd 1893-95,College Farm 95-96,Sunray Ave 1896-02,Freeman's Gd,Champ Hill 02-12, Champ Hill (old grd)12-92. Champion Hill 92-2018. T&M FC 18.
Record Attendance: 3,104 v Bath City, National South, 05/01/2019
Nearest Railway Station East Dulwich 200 yards. Denmark Hill 10 min walk. Herne Hill then bus 37 stops near ground. Mitcham Tram.
Bus Route Buses 40 & 176 from Elephant & Castle, 185 from Victoria.

EASTBOURNE BOROUGH

National South

Borough **Founded** 1964 **Club Colours** All red

Club Contact Details 01323 766 265 info@ebfc.co.uk

Previous Names: Langney FC 1964-68. Langney Sports 1968-2001.

Previous Leagues: Eastbourne & Dist 1964-73. Eastbourne & Hastings 1973-83. Sussex County 1983-2000. Southern 2000-2004.

11-12		12-13		13-14		14-15		15-16		16-17		17-18		18-19		19-20ppg		20-21	
Conf S	18	Conf S	12	Conf S	10	Conf S	11	Nat S	17	Nat S	11	Nat S		Nat S	18	Nat S	18	Nat S	n&v
FAC	4Q	FAC	3Qr	FAC	3Q	FAC	4Qr	FAC	4Q	FAC	1P	FAC	3Q	FAC	4Q	FAC	3Q	FAC	1P
FAT	3Qr	FAT	3Q	FAT	3Q	FAT	3Q	FAT	2P	FAT	3Qr	FAT	1P	FAT	1P	FAT	1Pr	FAT	2P

LEAGUE HONOURS:
Eastbourne & Hastings Premier Division 1981-82.
Sussex County League Division Three 1986-87, Division Two 1987-88, Division One 1999-2000, 02-03.

COUNTY FA HONOURS: Sussex Senior Challenge Cup 2001-02, 08-09, 15-16.

CLUB RECORDS
FA Cup First Round Proper 2005-06, 07-08, 08-09(r), 16-17, 20-21
FA Vase Second Round Proper 1990-91, 91-92, 97-98
FA Trophy Third Round Proper 2001-02, 02-03, 04-05, 10-11
Victory: 11-1 v Crowborough, Sussex Senior Cup Quarter-final, 13/01/2009
Defeat: 0-8 v Sheppey United (A) - FA Vase 09/10/93 and v Peachaven & Tels (A) - Sussex Co. Div.1 09/11/93
Goalscorer: Nigel Hole - 146
Appearances: Darren Baker - 952 (1992-2013)
Additional: Paid £1,800 to Yeovil Town for Yemi Odoubade.
Received £25,000 from Oxford United for Yemi Odoubade.

GROUND: Langney Sports Club, Priory Lane, Eastbourne BN23 7QH
Ground Capacity: 4,151 **Seats:** 542 **Covered:** 2,500 **Clubhouse:** Yes **Shop:** Yes
Previous Grounds: Local Recreation Grounds. Princes Park >1983.
Record Attendance: 3,770 v Oxford United - FA Cup 1st Round 05/11/05
Nearest Railway Station Pevensey & Westham - 15-20 mins walk.
Bus Route The LOOP Bus from the town centre.

EBBSFLEET UNITED

National South

The Fleet **Founded** 1946 **Club Colours** Red & white

Club Contact Details 01474 533 796 info@eufc.co.uk

Previous Names: Gravesend United and Northfleet United merged in 1946 to form Gravesend and Northfleet > 2007

Previous Leagues: Southern 1946-79, 82-97. Alliance (FM) 1979-82. Isthmian 1997-2002.

11-12		12-13		13-14		14-15		15-16		16-17		17-18		18-19		19-20ppg		20-21	
Conf	14	Conf	23	Conf S	4	Conf S	8	Nat S	2	Nat S	2	Nat	6	Nat	8	Nat	22	Nat S	n&v
FAC	4Q	FAC	1P	FAC	4Qr	FAC	3Q	FAC	2Qr	FAC	4Q	FAC	1P	FAC	1Pr	FAC	1P	FAC	3Q
FAT	3P	FAT	1P	FAT	3P	FAT	QF	FAT	1P	FAT	2P	FAT	2Pr	FAT	1P	FAT	3P	FAT	3P

LEAGUE HONOURS:
Southern League 1957-58, Division One South 1974-75, Southern Division 1993-94.
Isthmian League Premier 2001-02.

COUNTY FA HONOURS: Kent Senior Cup 1948-49, 52-53, 80-81, 99-00, 00-01, 01-02, 07-08, 13-14

CLUB RECORDS

FA Cup Fourth Round Proper 1962-63
FA Trophy Winners 2007-08
Victory: 8-1 v Clacton Town - Southern League 1962-63
Defeat: 0-9 v Trowbridge Town - Southern League Premier DIvision 1991-92
Goalscorer: Steve Portway - 152 (1992-94, 97-2001)
Appearances: Ken Burrett - 537
Additional: Paid £8,000 to Wokingham Town for Richard Newbery 1996 and to Tonbridge for Craig Williams 1997
Received £35,000 from West Ham United for Jimmy Bullard 1998

GROUND: Stonebridge Road, Northfleet, Kent DA11 9GN
Ground Capacity: 4,184 **Seats:** 2,300 **Covered:** 3,000 **Clubhouse:** Yes **Shop:** Yes
Previous Grounds: Gravesend United: Central Avenue
Record Attendance: 12,036 v Sunderland - FA Cup 4th Round 12/02/1963
Nearest Railway Station Northfleet - 300 yards from the ground.
Bus Route 480/490 or FASTRACK 'B' Service

HAMPTON & RICHMOND BOROUGH

National South

Beavers or Borough **Founded** 1921 **Club Colours** Red & blue

Club Contact Details 0208 979 2456

Previous Names: Hampton 1921-99

Previous Leagues: Kingston & District 1921-33. South West Middlesex 1933-59. Surrey Senior 1959-64. Spartan 1964-71. Athenian 1971-73. Isthmian 1973-2007, 12-16. Conference 2007-12.

11-12		12-13		13-14		14-15		15-16		16-17		17-18		18-19		19-20ppg		20-21	
Conf S	21	Isth P	13	Isth P	12	Isth P	15	Isth P	1	Nat S	7	Nat S	4	Nat S	15	Nat S	8	Nat S	n&v
FAC	3Q	FAC	3Q	FAC	4Q	FAC	1Q	FAC	1Q	FAC	3Q	FAC	4Q	FAC	1P	FAC	3Q	FAC	4Q
FAT	3P	FAT	1Pr	FAT	3Q	FAT	1Q	FAT	3Q	FAT	3Qr	FAT	1Pr	FAT	3Q	FAT	2P	FAT	1P

LEAGUE HONOURS:

Surrey Senior 1963-64. Spartan 1964-65, 65-66, 66-67, 69-70. Isthmian Premier Division 2006-07, 2015-16.

COUNTY FA HONOURS: Middlesex Charity Cup 1969-70, 95-96, 97-98, 98-99. Middlesex Super Cup 1999-00, 06-07.
Middlesex Senior Cup 2005-06, 07-08, 11-12, 13-14, 16-17.

CLUB RECORDS

FA Cup First Round Proper 2000-01, 07-08.
FA Trophy Third Round Proper 2011-12.
Victory: 11-1 v Eastbourne United - Isthmian League Division 2 South 1990-91
Defeat: 0-13 v Hounslow Town - Middlesex Senior Cup 1962-63
Goalscorer: Peter Allen - 176 (1964-73)
Appearances: Tim Hollands - 750 (1977-95)
Additional: Paid £3,000 to Chesham United for Matt Flitter June 2000
Received £40,000 from Queens Park Rangers for Leroy Phillips

GROUND: Beveree Stadium, Beaver Close, Station Road, Hampton TW12 2BX
Ground Capacity: 3,500 **Seats:** 644 **Covered:** 800 **Clubhouse:** Yes **Shop:** Yes
Previous Grounds: Moved to the Beveree Stadium in 1959
Record Attendance: 3,500 v Hayes & Yeading United, Conference South Play-off Final, 2008-09
Nearest Railway Station Hampton - less than half a mile from the ground.
Bus Route 111 & 216

HAVANT AND WATERLOOVILLE

National South

The Hawks **Founded** 1998 **Club Colours** White & blue

Club Contact Details 02392 787 822 generalmanager@havantandwaterloovillefc.co.uk

Previous Names: Havant Town and Waterlooville merged in 1998

Previous Leagues: Southern 1998-2004. Conference/National 2004-16. Isthmian 2016-17.

11-12		12-13		13-14		14-15		15-16		16-17		17-18		18-19		19-20ppg		20-21	
Conf S	19	Conf S	10	Conf S	6	Conf S	5	Nat S	20	Isth P	1	Nat S	1	Nat	22	Nat S	2	Nat S	n&v
FAC	3Q	FAC	2Q	FAC	2Qr	FAC	1P	FAC	4Qr	FAC	3Q	FAC	4Q	FAC	4Q	FAC	4Q	FAC	2P
FAT	3Qr	FAT	2P	FAT	SF	FAT	2P	FAT	3P	FAT	3Q	FAT	1P	FAT	1Pr	FAT	1P	FAT	5P

LEAGUE HONOURS:
Southern League Southern Division 1998-99. Isthmian League Premier Division 2016-17.
National South 2017-18.

COUNTY FA HONOURS: Hampshire Senior Cup 2015-16, 17-18.

CLUB RECORDS

FA Cup Fourth Round Proper 2007-08 (Eventually going out to Liverpool at Anfield 5-2)
FA Trophy Semi-finals 2013-14
Victory: 9-0 v Moneyfields - Hampshire Senior Cup 23/10/2001
Defeat: 0-5 v Worcester City - Southern Premier 20/03/2004
Goalscorer: James Taylor - 138
Appearances: James Taylor - 297
Additional: Paid £5,000 to Bashley for John Wilson
Received £15,000 from Peterborough United for Gary McDonald

GROUND: Westleigh Park, Martin Road, West Leigh, Havant PO9 5TH
Ground Capacity: 5,300 **Seats:** 710 **Covered:** Yes **Clubhouse:** Yes **Shop:** Yes
Previous Grounds: None
Record Attendance: 4,400 v Swansea City - FA Cup 3rd Round 05/01/2008
Nearest Railway Station Havant - within 2 miles of the ground.
Bus Route 20 & 21

HEMEL HEMPSTEAD TOWN

National South

The Tudors **Founded** 1885 **Club Colours** All red

Club Contact Details 01442 259 777 secretary@hemelfc.com

Previous Names: Apsley End 1885-99. Hemel Hempstead 1899-1955, 72-99. Hemel Hempstead Town 1955-72. Merged with Hemel Hempstead United 1972.

Previous Leagues: West Herts 1885-99. Herts County 1899-1922. Spartan 1922-52. Delphian 1952-63. Athenian 1963-77. Isthmian 1977-2004. Southern 2004-14.

11-12		12-13		13-14		14-15		15-16		16-17		17-18		18-19		19-20ppg		20-21	
SthP	19	SthP	4	SthP	1	Conf S	9	Nat S	6	Nat S	12	Nat S	5	Nat S	16	Nat S	11	Nat S	n&v
FAC	2Q	FAC	1Q	FAC	4Qr	FAC	1P	FAC	3Qr	FAC	4Qr	FAC	3Q	FAC	4Qr	FAC	2Q	FAC	4Q
FAT	2Q	FAT	1Qr	FAT	3Q	FAT	3P	FAT	1P	FAT	3Qr	FAT	3Qr	FAT	3P	FAT	1P	FAT	3P

LEAGUE HONOURS:
West Herts 1894-95, 97-98, 1904-05. Herts County 1899-1900. Spartan Division One 1933-34.
Isthmian League Division Three 1997-98, Division Two 1999-2000. Southern Premier Division 2013-14.

COUNTY FA HONOURS: Herts Senior Cup 1905-06, 07-08, 08-09, 25-26, 2012-13, 14-15.
Herts Charity Shield 1925-26, 34-35, 51-52, 63-64, 76-77, 83-84. Herts Charity Cup 2004-05, 08-09, 09-10.

CLUB RECORDS

FA Cup First Round Proper 2014-15 **FA Vase** Third Round Proper 1999-00, 00-01
FA Trophy Third Round Proper 2018-19, 20-21
Victory: 13-0 v RAF Uxbridge (A), Spartan Division One, 1933-34. and v Chipperfield Corinthians (H), St Mary's Cup QF, 2014-15.
Defeat: 1-13 v Luton Town, FA Cup First Qualifying Round, 05/10/1901.
Goalscorer: Dai Price
Appearances: John Wallace - 1012

GROUND: Vauxhall Road, Adeyfield Road, Hemel Hempstead HP2 4HW
Ground Capacity: 3,152 **Seats:** 300 **Covered:** 900 **Clubhouse:** Yes **Shop:** Yes
Previous Grounds: Salmon Meadow 1885-1928. Gees Meadow 1928-29. Crabtree Lane (Wood Lane Ground) 1929-72.
Record Attendance: 3,500 v Tooting & Mitcham - Amateur Cup 1962 (Crabtree Lane)
Nearest Railway Station Hemel Hempstead - Taxi ride away from the ground
Bus Route 320 from Stop 'A' outside the station

HUNGERFORD TOWN

National South

The Crusaders **Founded** 1886 **Club Colours** White & black

Club Contact Details 07585 770 148 nmatthews@rhsystems.co.uk

Previous Names: None

Previous Leagues: Hungerford League. Newbury League (FM) 1909-39. Newbury & District. Swindon & District. Hellenic 1958-78, 2003-09. Isthmian 1978-2003. Southern 2009-16.

11-12		12-13		13-14		14-15		15-16		16-17		17-18		18-19		19-20ppg		20-21	
Sthsw	5	Sthsw	2	SthP	6	SthP	4	SthP	5	Nat S	6	Nat S	19	Nat S	19	Nat S	22	Nat S	n&v
FAC	2Qr	FAC	2Qr	FAC	3Q	FAC	1Q	FAC	1Qr	FAC	3Q	FAC	3Qr	FAC	3Q	FAC	2Q	FAC	2Q
FAT	P	FAT	P	FAT	3P	FAT	1Qr	FAT	2P	FAT	3Q	FAT	3Q	FAT	3Q	FAT	3Q	FAT	2P

LEAGUE HONOURS:
Newbury League 1912-13, 13-14, 19-20, 21-22.
Hellenic Division One 1970-71, Premier Division 2008-09.

COUNTY FA HONOURS: Berks & Bucks Senior Cup 1981-82. Basingstoke Senior Cup 2012-13, 14-15.

CLUB RECORDS

FA Cup First Round Proper 1979-80
FA Vase Semi-Finals 1977-78, 79-80, 88-89
FA Trophy Third Round Proper 2014-15
Goalscorer: Ian Farr - 268
Appearances: Dean Bailey and Tim North - 400+
Additional: Paid £4,000 to Yeovil Town for Joe Scott. Received £3,800 from Barnstaple Town for Joe Scott. Isthmian representatives in Anglo Italian Cup 1981.

GROUND: Bulpitt Lane, Hungerford RG17 0AY
Ground Capacity: 2,500 **Seats:** 400 **Covered:** 400 **Clubhouse:** Yes **Shop:** Yes
Previous Grounds: Hungerford Marsh Field.
Record Attendance: 1,684 v Sudbury Town - FA Vase Semi-final 1988-89
Nearest Railway Station Hungerford - Approx. one mile from the ground.
Bus Route Priory Close stop - 120m away

MAIDSTONE UNITED

National South

The Stones **Founded** 1992 **Club Colours** Amber & black

Club Contact Details 01622 753 817 info@maidstoneunited.co.uk

Previous Names: Maidstone Invicta > 1997

Previous Leagues: Kent County 1993-2001, Kent 2001-06. Isthmian 2006-15.

11-12		12-13		13-14		14-15		15-16		16-17		17-18		18-19		19-20ppg		20-21	
Isth1S	6	Isth1S	2	Isth P	7	Isth P	1	Nat S	3	Nat	14	Nat	19	Nat	24	Nat S	9	Nat S	n&v
FAC	2Q	FAC	3Q	FAC	3Q	FAC	2P	FAC	1P	FAC	1Pr	FAC	2P	FAC	2P	FAC	2P	FAC	3Q
FAT	P	FAT	2P	FAT	3Q	FAT	2Q	FAT	1P	FAT	1P	FAT	3Pr	FAT	4Pr	FAT	1P	FAT	5P

LEAGUE HONOURS:
Kent County Division Four 1993-94, Division Two 1994-95, Division One 1998-99, Premier 2001-02.
Kent 2000-02, 05-06. Isthmian Division One South 2006-07, Premier 2014-15.

COUNTY FA HONOURS: Kent Junior Cup 1994-95, Weald of Kent Charity Cup 1999-00, 00-01, Kent Senior Trophy 2002-03. Kent Senior Cup 2017-18, 18-19.

CLUB RECORDS

FA Cup Second Round Proper 2014-15, 18-19, 19-20
FA Vase Third Round Proper 2005-06(r)
FA Trophy Fifth Round Proper 2020-21
Victory: 12-1 v Aylesford - Kent League 1993-94
Defeat: 2-8 v Scott Sports - 1995-96
Goalscorer: Richard Sinden - 98
Appearances: Tom Mills
Additional: Paid £2,000 for Steve Jones - 2000

GROUND: The Gallagher Stadium, James Whatman Way, Maidstone, Kent ME14 1LQ
Ground Capacity: 4,200 **Seats:** 792 **Covered:** 1,850 **Clubhouse:** Yes **Shop:** Yes
Previous Grounds: London Rd 1993-01, Central Pk 01-02 & Bourne Pk 02-09 (S'bourne), 11-12, The Homelands (A'ford) 09-11.
Record Attendance: 3,560 v Oldham Athletic, FA Cup 2nd Round, 1 December 2018
Nearest Railway Station Maidstone East & Maidstone Barracks a walk away
Bus Route Nos. 101 or 155 from the Mall Bus Station

OXFORD CITY

National South

The Hoops **Founded** 1990 **Club Colours** Blue & white

Club Contact Details 01865 750 906 club@oxcityfc.co.uk

Previous Names: The original club, founded in 1882, folded in 1988 when they were evicted from their White House ground and did not reform until 1990.

Previous Leagues: South Midlands 1990-93. Isthmian 1993-2004. Southern 2004-05, 06-12. Spartan South Midlands 2005-06.

11-12		12-13		13-14		14-15		15-16		16-17		17-18		18-19		19-20ppg		20-21	
SthP	2	Conf N	10	Conf N	20	Conf N	6	Nat S	12	Nat S	14	Nat S	16	Nat S	12	Nat S	13	Nat S	n&v
FAC	1Pr	FAC	2Q	FAC	4Q	FAC	2Q	FAC	3Q	FAC	2Qr	FAC	2P	FAC	1Pr	FAC	1P	FAC	2P
FAT	1Q	FAT	2P	FAT	3Q	FAT	2Pr	FAT	3P	FAT	3Q	FAT	3Q	FAT	2P	FAT	3Qr	FAT	QF

LEAGUE HONOURS:

Spartan South Midlands Premier Division 1992-93, 2005-06.
Isthmian Division One 1995-96.

COUNTY FA HONOURS: Oxford Senior Cup 1996-97, 98-99, 99-00, 02-03, 17-18.

CLUB RECORDS

FA Cup Second Round Proper 2017-18, 20-21
FA Vase Runners-up 1994-95
FA Trophy Quarter-final 2020-21

GROUND: Court Place Farm, Marsh Lane, Marston, Oxford OX3 0NQ

Ground Capacity: 3,500 **Seats:** 520 **Covered:** 400 **Clubhouse:** Yes **Shop:** Yes
Previous Grounds: Cuttleslowe Park 1990-91, Pressed Steel 1991-93.
Record Attendance: 2,276 v Oxford United, pre-season friendly, 08/07/2017
Nearest Railway Station Oxford - three miles from the ground.
Bus Route 14A from the Station to the ground.

SLOUGH TOWN

National South

The Rebels **Founded** 1890 **Club Colours** Yellow & blue

Club Contact Details 07792 126 124 gensec@sloughtownfc.net

Previous Names: Slough FC. Slough United.

Previous Leagues: Southern All 1892-93, Berks & Bucks 1901-05, Gt Western Suburban 09-19, Spartan 20-39, Herts & Middx 40-45, Corinthian 46-63, Athenian 63-73, Isthmian 73-90, 94-95, 98-2007, Conf 90-94, 95-98, Southern 2007-2018.

11-12		12-13		13-14		14-15		15-16		16-17		17-18		18-19		19-20ppg		20-21	
SthC	2	SthC	6	SthC	5	SthP	16	SthP	17	SthP	5	SthP	3	Nat S	11	Nat S	5	Nat S	n&v
FAC	3Qr	FAC	1Pr	FAC	Pr	FAC	1Q	FAC	2Q	FAC	3Q	FAC	2P	FAC	2P	FAC	3Qr	FAC	3Q
FAT	P	FAT	1Qr	FAT	1Q	FAT	2Qr	FAT	2Q	FAT	3Q	FAT	3Qr	FAT	3Q	FAT	3Qr	FAT	2P

LEAGUE HONOURS:

Isthmian League 1980-81, 89-90. Athenian League x3.

COUNTY FA HONOURS: Berks & Bucks Senior Cup 1902-03, 19-20, 23-24, 26-27, 35-36, 54-55, 70-71, 71-72, 76-77, 80-81, 2018-19

CLUB RECORDS

FA Cup Second Round Proper 1970-71, 79-80, 82-83, 85-86(r), 86-87, 2004-05, 17-18, 18-19.
FA Trophy Semi-finals 1976-77, 97-98
FA Am Cup Runners-up 1972-73
Victory: 17-0 v Railway Clearing House - 1921-22
Defeat: 1-11 v Chesham Town - 1909-10
Goalscorer: Ted Norris - 343 in 226 appearances. Scored 84 during the 1925-26 season.
Appearances: Terry Reardon - 475 (1964-81)
Additional: Paid £18,000 to Farnborough Town for Colin Fielder
Received £22,000 from Wycombe Wanderers for Steve Thompson

GROUND: Arbour Park, Stoke Road, Slough SL2 5AY

Ground Capacity: 2,000 **Seats:** 250 **Covered:** Yes **Clubhouse:** Yes **Shop:** Yes
Previous Grounds: Dolphin Stad 1890-1936. Wrexham Park >2003. Stag Meadow W & Eton 03-07. Holloways Park B'field SYCOB 07-16.
Record Attendance: 1,401 v Hayes & Yeading United, Southern Premier, 29/08/2016
Nearest Railway Station Slough
Bus Route First Group 1, 13, 12, 14, 353.

ST ALBANS CITY

National South

The Saints **Founded** 1908 **Club Colours** Yellow & blue

Club Contact Details 01727 848 914

Previous Names: None

Previous Leagues: Herts County 1908-10. Spartan 1908-20. Athenian 1920-23. Isthmian 1923-2004. Conference 2004-11. Southern 2011-14.

11-12		12-13		13-14		14-15		15-16		16-17		17-18		18-19		19-20ppg		20-21	
SthP	8	SthP	11	SthP	4	Conf S	13	Nat S	18	Nat S	10	Nat S	8	Nat S	9	Nat S	20	Nat S	n&v
FAC	2Qr	FAC	3Q	FAC	1P	FAC	4Q	FAC	1P	FAC	1P	FAC	4Q	FAC	3Q	FAC	3Q	FAC	4Q
FAT	1Q	FAT	1Q	FAT	2P	FAT	3Qr	FAT	3Q	FAT	3Qr	FAT	2Pr	FAT	3Qr	FAT	3Q	FAT	3P

LEAGUE HONOURS:
Herts County Western Division 1909-09, Western & Championship 09-10.
Spartan B Division 1909-10, Spartan 11-12. Athenian League 1920-21, 21-22.
Isthmian League 1923-24, 26-27, 27-28, Division One 1985-86.

COUNTY FA HONOURS: London Senior Cup 1970-71.

CLUB RECORDS

FA Cup Second Round Proper 1968-69 (r), 80-81 (r), 96-97.
FA Trophy Semi-final 1998-99.
Victory: 14-0 v Aylesbury United (H) - Spartan League 19/10/1912
Defeat: 0-11 v Wimbledon (H) - Isthmian League 1946
Goalscorer: Wilfred Minter - 356 in 362 apps. (Top scorer for 12 consecutive seasons from 1920-32)
Appearances: Phil Wood - 900 (1962-85)
Additional: Wilfred Minter scored seven goals in an 8-7 defeat by Dulwich Hamlet, the highest tally by a player on the losing side of an FAC tie. Paid £6,000 to Yeovil Town for Paul Turner 1957. Received £92,759 from Southend United for Dean Austin 1990.

GROUND: Clarence Park, York Road, St. Albans, Herts AL1 4PL
Ground Capacity: 5,007 **Seats:** 667 **Covered:** 1,900 **Clubhouse:** Yes **Shop:** Yes
Previous Grounds: N/A
Record Attendance: 9,757 v Ferryhill Athletic - FA Amateur Cup 1926
Nearest Railway Station St. Albans City - 5-10 minute walk from the ground.
Bus Route 302, 321, 602 & 84

TONBRIDGE ANGELS

National South

Angels **Founded** 1947 **Club Colours** Blue and white

Club Contact Details 01732 352 417 charlie.cole@tonbridgeangels.co.uk

Previous Names: Tonbridge FC 1947-94.

Previous Leagues: Southern 1948-80, 93-2004, Kent 1989-93, Isthmian 2004-11, 14-19, Conference 2011-14.

11-12		12-13		13-14		14-15		15-16		16-17		17-18		18-19		19-20ppg		20-21	
Conf S	9	Conf S	16	Conf S	21	Isth P	20	Isth P	4	Isth P	6	Isth P	11	Isth P	4	Nat S	15	Nat S	n&v
FAC	2Q	FAC	2Q	FAC	3Q	FAC	2Q	FAC	2Q	FAC	4Q	FAC	1Q	FAC	2Q	FAC	2Q	FAC	1P
FAT	3Qr	FAT	2P	FAT	1Pr	FAT	3Qr	FAT	2Q	FAT	2Qr	FAT	1Qr	FAT	2Q	FAT	1Pr	FAT	2P

LEAGUE HONOURS:
Kent 1992-93.

COUNTY FA HONOURS: Kent Senior Cup 1964-65, 74-75. Kent Senior Shield 1951-52, 55-56, 57-58, 58-59, 63-64.

CLUB RECORDS

FA Cup First Round Proper 1967-68, 72-73, 2020-21 **FA Vase** Third Round Proper 1993-94.
FA Trophy Third Round Proper 2004-05(r).
Victory: 11-1 v Worthing - FA Cup 1951
Defeat: 2-11 v Folkstone - Kent Senior Cup 1949
Goalscorer: Jon Main scored 44 goals in one season including seven hat-tricks
Appearances: Mark Giham

GROUND: Longmead Stadium, Darenth Avenue, Tonbridge, Kent TN10 3JF
Ground Capacity: 3,000 **Seats:** 760+ **Covered:** 1,500 **Clubhouse:** Yes **Shop:** Yes
Previous Grounds: The Angel 1948-80
Record Attendance: 8,236 v Aldershot - FA Cup 1951 at The Angel.
Nearest Railway Station Tonbridge - 3.1km
Bus Route Heather Walk - stop 250m away

WELLING UNITED

National South

The Wings **Founded** 1963 **Club Colours** Red & white

Club Contact Details 0208 301 1196 info@wellingunited.com

Previous Names: None

Previous Leagues: Eltham & District Sunday 1963-71, Metropolitan 1971-75, London Spartan 1975-78, Athenian 1978-81, Southern 1981-86, 2000-04, Conference 1986-2000

11-12		12-13		13-14		14-15		15-16		16-17		17-18		18-19		19-20ppg		20-21	
Conf S	3	Conf S	1	Conf	16	Conf	20	Nat	24	Nat S	16	Nat S	10	Nat S	3	Nat S	12	Nat S	n&v
FAC	2Q	FAC	4Q	FAC	2P	FAC	4Q	FAC	2P	FAC	4Q	FAC	2Q	FAC	4Q	FAC	4Qr	FAC	2Q
FAT	1P	FAT	3P	FAT	1P	FAT	1Pr	FAT	2P	FAT	3P	FAT	3Q	FAT	3Qr	FAT	1P	FAT	2P

LEAGUE HONOURS:
Southern League Premier Division 1985-86. Conference South 2012-13.

COUNTY FA HONOURS: Kent Senior Cup 1985-86, 98-99, 2008-09. London Senior Cup 1989-90. London Challenge Cup 1991-92.

CLUB RECORDS

FA Cup Third Round Proper 1988-89

FA Vase Third Round Proper 1979-80

FA Trophy Quarter-finals 1988-89, 2006-07

Victory: 7-1 v Dorking - 1985-86

Defeat: 0-7 v Welwyn Garden City - 1972-73

Additional: Paid £30,000 to Enfield for Gary Abbott
Received £95,000 from Birmingham City for Steve Finnan 1995

GROUND: Park View Road Ground, Welling, Kent DA16 1SY

Ground Capacity: 4,000 **Seats:** 1,070 **Covered:** 1,500 **Clubhouse:** Yes **Shop:** Yes

Previous Grounds: Butterfly Lane, Eltham 1963-77.

Record Attendance: 4,100 v Gillingham - FA Cup First Round Proper, 22nd November 1989

Nearest Railway Station Welling - 15-20 minute walk from the ground.

Bus Route Numbers 89, 486 and B16.

BISHOP'S STORTFORD

Isthmian Premier

Founded 1874 **Nickname:** Blues or Bishops **Club Colours:** Blue and white

Club Contact Details

01279 306 456 fredplume@hotmail.co.uk

Previous Names: None

Previous Leagues: East Herts 1896-97, 1902-06, 19-21, Stansted & Dist. 1906-19, Herts Co. 1921-25, 26-29, Herts & Essex Border 1925-26, Spartan 1929-51, Delphian (FM) 1951-63, Athenian 1963-71, Isthmian 1971-2004, Conference 2004-17, Southern 2017-18.

11-12		12-13		13-14		14-15		15-16		16-17		17-18		18-19		19-20		20-21	
Conf N	10	Conf N	17	Conf S	15	Conf S	16	Nat S	11	Nat S	21	SthP	18	Isth P	7	Isth P	n&v	Isth P	n&v
FAC	4Q	FAC	1P	FAC	1P	FAC	2Qr	FAC	2Q	FAC	3Q	FAC	1Q	FAC	1Q	FAC	2Q	FAC	1P
FAT	1P	FAT	1P	FAT	3Q	FAT	1P	FAT	3Q	FAT	3Q	FAT	2Q	FAT	2Q	FAT	1Qr	FAT	1P

HONOURS / RECORDS

FA Comps: FA Amateur Cup 1973-74. FA Trophy 1980-81.

League: Stansted & District 1910-11, 12-13, 19-20. Spartan Division Two East 1931-32. Delphian 1954-55.
Athenian Division One 1965-66, Premier 69-70. Isthmian Division One 1980-81, 93-94.

County FA: Herts Senior Cup 1932-33, 58-59, 59-60, 63-64, 70-71, 72-73, 73-74, 75-76, 86-87, 2005-06, 09-10, 11-12.
London Senior Cup 1973-74.

Victory: 11-0 v Nettleswell & Buntwill - Herts Junior Cup 1911

Defeat: 0-13 v Cheshunt (H) - Herts Senior Cup 1926

Goalscorer: Post 1929 Jimmy Badcock - 123

Appearances: Phil Hopkins - 543

GROUND: A&D Advisors Uk Stadium, Woodside Park, Dunmow Road, Bishop's Stortford CM23 5RG

Ground Capacity: 4,000 **Seats:** 525 **Covered:** 700 **Clubhouse:** Yes **Shop:** Yes

Previous Grounds: Silver Leys 1874-97. Hadham Rd 97-1900. Havers Lane 00-03. Laundry Field 03-19. Brazier's Field 1919-97.Shared>99

Record Attendance: 6,000 v Peterborough Utd - FAC 2nd Rnd 1972-73 and v Middlesbrough - FA Cup 3rd Rnd replay 1982-83

Nearest Railway Station Bishop's Stortford - 20 minute walk from ground.

Bus Route 508, 7 & 7A

BOGNOR REGIS TOWN

Isthmian Premier

Founded 1883 **Nickname:** The Rocks **Club Colours:** White & green

Club Contact Details

01243 822 325 sajcook2@aol.com

Previous Names: None

Previous Leagues: West Sussex 1896-1926, Brighton & Hove District 1926-27, Sussex County 1927-72, Southern League 1972-81, Isthmian 1982-2004, 2009-17, Conference 2004-09, 17-18.

11-12		12-13		13-14		14-15		15-16		16-17		17-18		18-19		19-20		20-21	
Isth1S	2	Isth P	14	Isth P	3	Isth P	14	Isth P	2	Isth P	2	Nat S	22	Isth P	14	Isth P	n&v	Isth P	n&v
FAC	3Q	FAC	2Q	FAC	2Qr	FAC	1Qr	FAC	4Q	FAC	2Q	FAC	4Q	FAC	2Qr	FAC	2Q	FAC	2Q
FAT	P	FAT	3Q	FAT	3Q	FAT	1Qr	FAT	SF	FAT	1Q	FAT	2P	FAT	2Qr	FAT	3Q	FAT	2P

HONOURS / RECORDS

FA Comps: None

League: West Sussex 1920-21, 21-22, 22-23, 23-24, 24-25.
Sussex County Division One 1948-49 71-72, Division Two 70-71.

County FA: Sussex Professional Cup 1973-74.
Sussex Senior Cup 1954-55, 55-56, 79-80, 80-81, 81-82, 82083, 83084, 86-87, 2018-19.

Victory: 24-0 v Littlehampton - West Sussex League 1913-14

Defeat: 0-19 v Shoreham - West Sussex League 1906-07

Goalscorer: Kevin Clements - 216 (1978-89). On 16/12/14 Jason Prior scored his 100th goal for the club making it the fastest century of goals.

Appearances: Mick Pullen - 967 (20 seasons)

GROUND: Nyewood Lane, Bognor Regis PO21 2TY

Ground Capacity: 4,100 **Seats:** 350 **Covered:** 2,600 **Clubhouse:** Yes **Shop:** Yes

Previous Grounds: None

Record Attendance: 3,642 v Swnsea City - FA Cup 1st Round replay 1984

Nearest Railway Station Bognor is within walking distance to the ground.

Bus Route 600 & 700

BOWERS & PITSEA

Isthmian Premier

Founded 1946 **Nickname:** Bowers **Club Colours:** Red & white

Club Contact Details
01268 452 068 lee-stevens@sky.com

Previous Names: Bowers United 1946-2004.
Previous Leagues: Thurrock & Thameside Combination. Olympian. Essex Senior >2016.

11-12		12-13		13-14		14-15		15-16		16-17		17-18		18-19		19-20		20-21	
ESen	15	ESen	19	ESen	14	ESen	2	ESen	1	Isth1N	6	Isth1N	3	IsthN	1	Isth P	n&v	Isth P	n&v
FAC	EP	FAC	EP	FAC	EP	FAC	1Q	FAC	EP	FAC	Pr	FAC	P	FAC	2Q	FAC	4Q	FAC	1Q
FAV	2Q	FAV	1Q	FAV	1P	FAV	1P	FAV	SF	FAT	1Q	FAT	1Qr	FAT	EP	FAT	1Q	FAT	3Q

HONOURS / RECORDS
FA Comps: None
League: Thurrock & Thameside Combination 1958-59. Essex Senior 1980-81, 98-99, 2015-16.
Isthmian North Division 2018-19.
County FA: None

Victory: 14-1 v Stansted, 2006-07
Defeat: 0-8 v Ford United, 1996-97
Goalscorer: David Hope scored 50 during the 1998-99 season.

GROUND: Len Salmon Stadium, Crown Avenue, Pitsea, Basildon SS13 2BE
Ground Capacity: 2,000 **Seats:** 200 **Covered:** 1,000 **Clubhouse:** Yes **Shop:** Yes
Previous Grounds: Pitsea Market. Gun Meadow.
Record Attendance: 1,800 v Billericay Town, FA Vase.

Nearest Railway Station Pitsea - 1.7km
Bus Route Wilsner - stop 200m award

BRIGHTLINGSEA REGENT

Isthmian Premier

Founded 1928 **Nickname:** The Rs **Club Colours:** Red & black

Club Contact Details
01206 304 119 tony_osborne59@hotmail.com

Previous Names: Brightlingsea Athletic & Brightlingsea Town merged to form Brightlingsea United 1928-2005. Merged with Regent Park Rangers.
Previous Leagues: Essex Senior 1972-91. Eastern Counties 1990-02, 2011-14. Essex & Suffolk Border 2002-2011.

11-12		12-13		13-14		14-15		15-16		16-17		17-18		18-19		19-20		20-21	
EC1	5	EC1	3	ECP	2	Isth1N	6	Isth1N	8	Isth1N	1	Isth P	20	Isth P	13	Isth P	n&v	Isth P	n&v
				FAC	EPr	FAC	1Q	FAC	Pr	FAC	1Q	FAC	1Q	FAC	3Q	FAC	1Q	FAC	1Q
FAV	1Q	FAV	3P	FAV	5P	FAT	1Q	FAT	Pr	FAT	2Qr	FAT	1Q	FAT	3Qr	FAT	1Q	FAT	3Q

HONOURS / RECORDS
FA Comps: None
League: Essex & Suffolk Border Division One 1946-47, 60-61, Division Two 2005-06, Premier 10-11. Essex Senior 1988-89, 89-90.
Isthmian Division One North 2016-17.
County FA: None

Best FA Cup Third Qualifying Round 2018-19.
FA Trophy Third Qualifying Round 2018-19(r).
FA Vase Fifth Round Proper 2013-14.

GROUND: Tydal Stadium, North Road, Brightlingsea, Essex CO7 0PL
Ground Capacity: 2,500 **Seats:** 254 **Covered:** 1864 **Clubhouse:** Yes **Shop:**
Previous Grounds: Bell Green (Bellfield Close). Recreation Ground (Regent Road) > 1920.
Record Attendance: 1,200 v Colchester United, friendly, 1988.

Nearest Railway Station Alresford - 4.8km
Bus Route Spring Chase - stop 300m away

CARSHALTON ATHLETIC

Isthmian Premier

Founded 1905 **Nickname:** Robins **Club Colours:** All red

Club Contact Details

020 8642 2551 secretary@carshaltonathletic.co.uk

Previous Names: Mill Lane Mission 1905-07.

Previous Leagues: Croydon & District 1905-10. Southern Suburban 1910-22. Surrey Senior (Founding Members) 1922-23. London 1923-46. Corinthian 1946-56. Athenian 1956-73. Isthmian 1973-2004. Conference 2004-06.

11-12		12-13		13-14		14-15		15-16		16-17		17-18		18-19		19-20		20-21	
Isth P	16	Isth P	20	Isth P	23	Isth1S	20	Isth1S	10	Isth1S	6	Isth1S	1	Isth P	2	Isth P	n&v	Isth P	n&v
FAC	2Q	FAC	2Q	FAC	1Q	FAC	1Q	FAC	2Q	FAC	1Qr	FAC	2Q	FAC	P	FAC	4Q	FAC	2Q
FAT	3P	FAT	2Q	FAT	3Q	FAT	P	FAT	P	FAT	Pr	FAT	P	FAT	3Pr	FAT	1Pr	FAT	2P

HONOURS / RECORDS

FA Comps: None

League: Corinthian 1952-53, 53-54. Isthmian Division One South 2002-03, 17-18.

County FA: Surrey Intermediate Cup 1921-22, 31-32. Surrey Senior Shield 1975-76. Surrey Senior Cup 1988-89, 89-90, 91-92. London Challenge Cup 1991-92.

Victory: 13-0 v Worthing - Isthmian League Cup 28/01/1991

Defeat: 0-11 v Southall - Athenian League March 1963

Goalscorer: Jimmy Bolton - 242 during seven seasons

Appearances: Jon Warden - 504

Additional: Paid £15,000 to Enfield for Curtis Warmington. Received £30,000 from Crystal Palace for Ian Cox 1994

GROUND: War Memorial Sports Ground, Colston Avenue, Carshalton SM5 2PN

Ground Capacity: 8,000 **Seats:** 240 **Covered:** 4,500 **Clubhouse:** Yes **Shop:** Yes

Previous Grounds: Various before moving to Colston Avenue during the 1920-21 season.

Record Attendance: 7,800 v Wimbledon - London Senior Cup, Jan 1959.

Nearest Railway Station Carshalton - 0.3km

Bus Route 127, 157 & S1

CHESHUNT

Isthmian Premier

Founded 1946 **Nickname:** Ambers **Club Colours:** Amber & black

Club Contact Details

01992 625 793 info@cheshuntfc.com

Previous Names: None

Previous Leagues: London 1946-51, 55-59, Delphian 1951-55, Aetolian 1959-62, Spartan 1962-64, 88-93, Athenian 1964-77, Isthmian 1977-87, 94-2005, Southern 2006-08

11-12		12-13		13-14		14-15		15-16		16-17		17-18		18-19		19-20		20-21	
Isth1N	18	Isth1N	11	Isth1N	15	Isth1N	18	Isth1N	6	Isth1N	10	Isth1N	19	IsthSC	3	Isth P	n&v	Isth P	n&v
FAC	Pr	FAC	Pr	FAC	P	FAC	P	FAC	P	FAC	1Q	FAC	2Q	FAC	1Qr	FAC	2Q	FAC	2Q
FAT	P	FAT	P	FAT	1Q	FAT	P	FAT	2Q	FAT	1Q	FAT	1Q	FAT	EPr	FAT	1Q	FAT	2P

HONOURS / RECORDS

FA Comps: None

League: London Division One 1947-48, 48-49, Premier 49-50, Division One 1948, 49. Spartan 1962-63. Athenian 1967-68, 75-76. Isthmian Division Two 2002-03.

County FA: London Charity Cup 1974. East Anglian Cup 1975. Herts Charity Cup 2006, 2008.

Defeat: 0-10 v Eton Manor - London League 17/04/1956

Goalscorer: Darrell Cox - 152 (1997-2005, 07-08, 2010)

Appearances: John Poole - 526 (1970-76, 79-83)

Additional: Received £10,000 from Peterborough United for Lloyd Opara

GROUND: Cheshunt Stadium, Theobalds Lane, Cheshunt, Herts EN8 8RU

Ground Capacity: 3,500 **Seats:** 424 **Covered:** 600 **Clubhouse:** Yes **Shop:** No

Previous Grounds: Gothic Sports Ground 1946-47. College Road 1947-50. Brookfield Lane 1950-52, 53-58.

Record Attendance: 5,000 v Bromley - FA Amateur Cup 2nd Round 28/01/1950

Nearest Railway Station Theobalds Grove - 0.6km

Bus Route 217, 242, 279, 310 & 66

CORINTHIAN-CASUALS

Isthmian Premier

Founded 1939 **Nickname:** Casuals **Club Colours:** Chocolate and pink

Club Contact Details
020 8397 3368 secretary@ccfcltd.co.uk

Previous Names: Casuals and Corinthians merged in 1939
Previous Leagues: Isthmian 1939-84, Spartan 1984-96, Combined Counties 1996-97

11-12		12-13		13-14		14-15		15-16		16-17		17-18		18-19		19-20		20-21	
Isth1S	13	Isth1S	14	Isth1S	17	Isth1S	13	Isth1S	6	Isth1S	4	Isth1S	5	Isth P	17	Isth P	n&v	Isth P	n&v
FAC	P	FAC	P	FAC	1Q	FAC	P	FAC	P	FAC	1Q	FAC	1Q	FAC	2Qr	FAC	3Q	FAC	2Q
FAT	P	FAT	P	FAT	P	FAT	Pr	FAT	1P	FAT	1Q	FAT	2Q	FAT	1Q	FAT	1Q	FAT	2P

HONOURS / RECORDS
FA Comps: None

League: London Spartan Senior Division 1985-86.

County FA: Surrey Senior Cup 1953-54, 2010-11.

Goalscorer: Cliff West - 215
Appearances: Simon Shergold - 526
Best FA Cup First Round Proper 1965-66, 83-84.
FA Amateur C Runners-up 1955-56. **FA Trophy:** Second Round Proper 2002-03.
FA Vase First Round Proper 1983-84.

GROUND: King George's Field, Queen Mary Close, Hook Rise South, KT6 7NA
Ground Capacity: 2,000 **Seats:** 161 **Covered:** 700 **Clubhouse:** Yes **Shop:** Yes
Previous Grounds: Kingstonian's Richmond Road 1939-46. Polytechnic Ground in Chiswick 46-50. Oval 50-63. Dulwich Hamlet's Champion Hill 63-68, Tooting & Mitcham United's Sandy Lane 68-83, Molesey's Walton Road 83-84, 86-88. Wimbledon Park Athletics Stadium 84-86.
Record Attendance:

Nearest Railway Station Tolworth - 10-15 min walk
Bus Route K1 from new Malden, 265 from Putney, K2 from Hook or Kingston Hospital, 406 & 408 from Kingston and Epsom, 418 from Kingston

CRAY WANDERERS

Isthmian Premier

Founded 1860 **Nickname:** Wanderers or Wands **Club Colours:** Amber & black

Club Contact Details
020 8460 5291 martin.hodson25@ntlworld.com

Previous Names: Cray Old Boys (immediately after WW1); Sidcup & Footscray (start of WW2).
Previous Leagues: Kent 1894-1903, 06-07, 09-14, 34-38, 78-2004; West Kent & Sth Suburban (before WW1); London 20-34, 51-59; Kent Am 38-39, 46-51; South London All 43-46; Aetolian 59-64; Gr London 64-66; Metropolitan 66-71; Met. London 71-15; London Spartan 75-78.

11-12		12-13		13-14		14-15		15-16		16-17		17-18		18-19		19-20		20-21	
Isth P	9	Isth P	17	Isth P	24	Isth1N	16	Isth1N	4	Isth1S	11	Isth1S	3	IsthSE	1	Isth P	n&v	Isth P	n&v
FAC	3Q	FAC	3Q	FAC	1Q	FAC	1Q	FAC	1Q	FAC	1Q	FAC	P	FAC	1Q	FAC	3Q	FAC	4Q
FAT	1Q	FAT	3Q	FAT	1Q	FAT	3Q	FAT	P	FAT	2Q	FAT	3Q	FAT	P	FAT	1Q	FAT	2P

HONOURS / RECORDS
FA Comps: None
League: Kent 1901-02, 80-81, 2002-03, 03-04. London 1956-57, 57-58. Aetolian 1962-63. Greater London 1965-66. Metropolitan London 1974-75; London Spartan 1976-77, 77-78. Isthmian South East Division 2018-19.
County FA: Kent Amateur Cup 1930-31, 62-63, 63-64, 64-65. Kent Senior Trophy 1992-93, 2003-04.

Victory: 15-0 v Sevenoaks - 1894-95.
Defeat: 2-15 (H) and 0-14 (A) v Callenders Athletic - Kent Amateur League, 1947-48.
Goalscorer: Ken Collishaw 274 (1954-1965)
Appearances: John Dorey - 454 (1961-72).
Additional: Unbeaten for 28 Ryman League games in 2007-2008.

GROUND: Bromley FC, Hayes Lane, Bromley, Kent BR2 9EF
Ground Capacity: 5,000 **Seats:** 1,300 **Covered:** 2,500 **Clubhouse:** Yes **Shop:** Yes
Previous Grounds: Northfield Farm (1950-51), Tothills (aka Fordcroft, 1951-1955), Grassmeade (1955-1973), Oxford Road (1973-1998).
Record Attendance: Grassmeade - 2,160 v Leytonstone,FAAm.R3, 1968-69; Oxford Road - 1,523 v Stamford, FAV QF 1979-80; Hayes Lane - 1,082 v AFC Wimbledon, 2004-05
Nearest Railway Station Bromley South - 1km
Bus Route Hayes Road - stop 160m away

EAST THURROCK UNITED

Isthmian Premier

Founded 1969 **Nickname:** The Rocks **Club Colours:** Amber & black

Club Contact Details

01375 644 166 eastthurrockfc@gmail.com

Previous Names: Corringham Social > 1969 (Sunday side)

Previous Leagues: South Essex Comb 1969-70. Greater London 1970-72. Metropolitan London 1972-75. London Spartan 1975-79. Essex Senior 1979-92. Isthmian 1992-2004, 05-16. Southern 2004-05. National 16-19.

11-12		12-13		13-14		14-15		15-16		16-17		17-18		18-19		19-20		20-21	
Isth P	10	Isth P	5	Isth P	20	Isth P	13	Isth P	3	Nat S	13	Nat S	15	Nat S	21	Isth P	n&v	Isth P	n&v
FAC	1P	FAC	4Qr	FAC	1Qr	FAC	1P	FAC	3Q	FAC	2Q	FAC	4Qr	FAC	2Q	FAC	1Qr	FAC	1Q
FAT	2Pr	FAT	2Qr	FAT	1Pr	FAT	3Q	FAT	1P	FAT	2P	FAT	3Pr	FAT	3Q	FAT	2Q	FAT	3Q

HONOURS / RECORDS

FA Comps: None

League: Metropolitan London Division Two 1972-73.
Isthmian League Division Three 1999-2000, Division One North 2010-11.

County FA: East Anglian Cup 2002-03.

Victory: 7-0 v Coggeshall (H) - Essex Senior League 1984
Defeat: 0-9 v Eton Manor (A) - Essex Senior League 1982
Goalscorer: Graham Stewart - 102
Appearances: Glen Case - 600+
Additional: £22,000 from Leyton Orient for Greg Berry 1990

GROUND: Rookery Hill, Corringham, Essex SS17 9LB

Ground Capacity: 3,500 **Seats:** 160 **Covered:** 1,000 **Clubhouse:** Yes **Shop:** Yes
Previous Grounds: Billet, Stanford-le-Hope 1970-73, 74-76, Grays Ath 73-74, TilburyFC 77-82, New Thames Club 82-84.
Record Attendance: 1,661 vs Dulwich Hamlet, Isthmian League Premier Division Play-off final, 2016

Nearest Railway Station Stanford-le-Hope or Basildon.
Bus Route 100 - Stops 100 metres from the ground.

ENFIELD TOWN

Isthmian Premier

Founded 2001 **Nickname:** ET's or Towners **Club Colours:** White & blue

Club Contact Details

07787 875 650 jd1403@hotmail.co.uk

Previous Names: Broke away from Enfield F.C. in 2001

Previous Leagues: Essex Senior 2001-2005. Southern 2005-2006.

11-12		12-13		13-14		14-15		15-16		16-17		17-18		18-19		19-20		20-21	
Isth1N	2	Isth P	16	Isth P	19	Isth P	7	Isth P	6	Isth P	4	Isth P	17	Isth P	10	Isth P	n&v	Isth P	n&v
FAC	P	FAC	2Q	FAC	2Qr	FAC	2Qr	FAC	4Q	FAC	1Q	FAC	4Qr	FAC	1Q	FAC	3Q	FAC	1Q
FAT	1Q	FAT	3Q	FAT	2Q	FAT	1Q	FAT	2Q	FAV	2Q	FAT	1Q	FAT	2Q	FAT	1P	FAT	1P

HONOURS / RECORDS

FA Comps: None

League: Essex Senior 2002-03, 04-05.

County FA: Middlesex Charity Cup 2001-02, 07-08.

Victory: 7-0 v Ilford (A) - 29/04/2003
Goalscorer: Liam Hope - 108 (2009-15)
Appearances: Rudi Hall

GROUND: Queen Elizabeth II Stadium, Donkey Lane, Enfield EN1 3PL

Ground Capacity: 2,500 **Seats:** Yes **Covered:** Yes **Clubhouse:** Yes **Shop:** No
Previous Grounds: Brimsdown Rovers FC 2001-2010
Record Attendance: 969 v Tottenham Hotspur, friendly, November 2011.

Nearest Railway Station Southbury - 1.2km
Bus Route 191 towards Brimsdown from Enfield stops outside the ground.

FOLKESTONE INVICTA

Isthmian Premier

Founded 1936 **Nickname:** The Seasiders **Club Colours:** Yellow & black

Club Contact Details

01303 257 461 richardmurrill@gmail.com

Previous Names: None

Previous Leagues: East Kent Amateur. Kent County Eastern Section. Kent 1990-98, Southern 1998-2004

11-12		12-13		13-14		14-15		15-16		16-17		17-18		18-19		19-20		20-21	
Isth1S	4	Isth1S	5	Isth1S	2	Isth1S	2	Isth1S	1	Isth P	16	Isth P	4	Isth P	6	Isth P	n&v	Isth P	n&v
FAC	1Q	FAC	1Q	FAC	2Q	FAC	1Qr	FAC	1Qr	FAC	3Q	FAC	4Q	FAC	1Q	FAC	2Q	FAC	2Q
FAT	3Q	FAT	Pr	FAT	2Qr	FAT	2Qr	FAT	Pr	FAT	2Q	FAT	1Qr	FAT	3Q	FAT	1Q	FAT	3Q

HONOURS / RECORDS

FA Comps: None

League: Kent County Eastern Division One 1969-70, Premier 78-79. Kent Division Two 1991-92.
Isthmian Division One South 2015-16.

County FA: Kent Intermediate Shield 1991-92.

Victory: 13-0 v Faversham Town - Kent League Division One, May 1995.

Defeat: 1-7 v Crockenhill - Kent League Division One, February 1993 & v Welling United, Kent Senior Cup, February 2009.

Goalscorer: James Dryden - 141

Appearances: Michael Everitt - 631

GROUND: The BuildKent Stadium, Cheriton Road CT19 5JU

Ground Capacity: 4,000 **Seats:** 900 **Covered:** Yes **Clubhouse:** Yes **Shop:** Yes

Previous Grounds: South Road Hythe > 1991, County League matches on council pitches

Record Attendance: 2,332 v West Ham United, benefit match, 1996-97.

Nearest Railway Station Folkestone West - 0.4km

Bus Route 71, 72, 73 & 17 from the Town Centre

HARINGEY BOROUGH

Isthmian Premier

Founded 1973 **Nickname:** Borough **Club Colours:** Yellow & blue

Club Contact Details

0208 888 9933 baconjw@hotmail.com

Previous Names: Edmonton & Haringey 1973-76. Haringey Borough 1976-95. Tufnell Park 1995-96.

Previous Leagues: Athenian 1973-84. Isthmian 1984-89. Spartan South Midlands 1989-2013. Essex Senior 2013-15.

11-12		12-13		13-14		14-15		15-16		16-17		17-18		18-19		19-20		20-21	
SSM P	5	SSM P	9	ESen	2	ESen	1	Isth1N	15	Isth1N	5	Isth1N	4	Isth P	3	Isth P	n&v	Isth P	n&v
FAC	P	FAC	EP	FAC	2Q	FAC	EP	FAC	1Q	FAC	1Q	FAC	4Q	FAC	4Q	FAC	4Q	FAC	4Q
FAV	3P	FAV	2Q	FAV	3P	FAV	1Pr	FAT	2Qr	FAT	P	FAT	1P	FAT	1Qr	FAT	3Q	FAT	4P

HONOURS / RECORDS

FA Comps: None

League: Essex Senior 2014-15.

County FA: London Senior Cup 1990-91

Best FA Cup First Round Proper 2018-19.

FA Trophy First Round Proper 2017-18.

FA Vase Quarter Finals 1977-78.

GROUND: Coles Park, White Hart Lane, Tottenham, London N17 7JP

Ground Capacity: 2,500 **Seats:** 280 **Covered:** yes **Clubhouse:** Yes **Shop:** No

Previous Grounds: None

Record Attendance: 2,710 v AFC Wimbledon, FA Cup First Round Proper, 09/11/2018.

Nearest Railway Station White Hart Lane - 1.5km. Wood Green (UG) - 1.5km

Bus Route W3 stops outside the ground.

HORNCHURCH

Isthmian Premier

Founded 2005 **Nickname:** The Urchins **Club Colours:** Red and white

Club Contact Details
01708 220 080 normpos@aol.com

Previous Names: Formed in 2005 after Hornchurch F.C. folded. AFC Hornchurch 2005-18.
Previous Leagues: Essex Senior 2005-06. Isthmian 2006-12. Conference 2012-13.

11-12		12-13		13-14		14-15		15-16		16-17		17-18		18-19		19-20		20-21	
Isth P	2	Conf S	20	Isth P	5	Isth P	23	Isth1N	5	Isth1N	4	Isth1N	1	Isth P	15	Isth P	n&v	Isth P	n&v
FAC	1Q	FAC	2Q	FAC	4Q	FAC	1Qr	FAC	4Q	FAC	1Q	FAC	3Q	FAC	3Q	FAC	2Q	FAC	3Q
FAT	2P	FAT	3Q	FAT	1Q	FAT	3Q	FAT	1Q	FAT	P	FAT	Pr	FAT	2Q	FAT	2P	FAT	F

HONOURS / RECORDS
FA Comps: FA Trophy 2020-21.
League: Essex Senior 2005-06. Isthmian League Division One North 2006-07, 17-18.

County FA: Essex Senior Cup 2012-13.

Misc: Won the Essex League with a record 64 points in 2005-06
Best FA Cup First Round Proper 2008-09
FA Trophy Winners 2020-21
FA Vase Second Round Proper 2005-06

GROUND: The Stadium, Bridge Avenue, Upminster, Essex RM14 2LX
Ground Capacity: 3,500 **Seats:** 800 **Covered:** 1,400 **Clubhouse:** Yes **Shop:** Yes
Previous Grounds: None
Record Attendance: Not known

Nearest Railway Station Upminster Bridge Underground - 0.4km
Bus Route 248 & 370

HORSHAM

Isthmian Premier

Founded 1881 **Nickname:** Hornets **Club Colours:** Yellow & green

Club Contact Details
01403 458 854 jeff.barrett@btinternet.com

Previous Names: None
Previous Leagues: West Sussex Senior, Sussex Co 1926-51, Metropolitan 1951-57, Corinthian 1957-63, Athenian 1963-73, Isthmian 1973-2015. Southern Combination 2015-16,

11-12		12-13		13-14		14-15		15-16		16-17		17-18		18-19		19-20		20-21	
Isth P	22	Isth1S	15	Isth1S	16	Isth1S	24	SCom	1	Isth1S	16	Isth1S	15	IsthSE	2	Isth P	n&v	Isth P	n&v
FAC	2Qr	FAC	2Q	FAC	3Q	FAC	1Q	FAC	Pr	FAC	P	FAC	2Q	FAC	3Qr	FAC	2Q	FAC	2Q
FAT	1Q	FAT	P	FAT	1Q	FAT	3Q	FAV	1P	FAT	1Q	FAT	P	FAT	3Q	FAT	1Q	FAT	3Q

HONOURS / RECORDS
FA Comps: None
League: West Sussex Senior 1899-00, 1900-01, 01-02, 25-26. Sussex County 1931-32, 32-33, 34-35, 36-37, 37-38, 46-47. Metropolitan 1951-52. Athenian Division Two 1969-70, Division One 72-73. Isthmian Division Three 1995-96. Southern Combination 2015-16.
County FA: Sussex Senior Cup 1933-34, 38-39, 49-50, 53-54, 71-72, 73-74, 75-76.

Victory: 16-1 v Southwick - Sussex County League 1945-46
Defeat: 1-11 v Worthing - Sussex Senior Cup 1913-14
Goalscorer: Mick Browning
Appearances: Mark Stepney
Additional: Paid £2,500 to Lewes for Lee Farrell, July 2007. Received £10,000 from Tonbridge Angels for Carl Rook, Dec 2008.

GROUND: Hop Oast, Worthing Road, Horsham RH13 0AX
Ground Capacity: **Seats:** Yes **Covered:** Yes **Clubhouse:** Yes **Shop:** Yes
Previous Grounds: Queens Street 1904-2008. Worthing FC 08-09. Horsham YMCA 2009-17. Culver Road (Sussex FA) 2017-19.
Record Attendance: 7,134 v Swindon - FA Cup First Round Proper, November 1966

Nearest Railway Station Horsham from which you can catch a bus to the stadium.
Bus Route No.98 from Roffey, Southwater and Horsham Railway and Bus Stations. No.23 can be taken from Crawley & Worthing.

KINGSTONIAN

Isthmian Premier

Founded 1885 **Nickname:** The K's **Club Colours:** Red and white hoops

Club Contact Details
020 8330 6869 secretary@kingstonian.com

Previous Names: Kingston & Suburban YMCA 1885-87, Saxons 1887-90, Kingston Wanderers 1893-1904, Old Kingstonians 1908-19
Previous Leagues: Kingston & District, West Surrey, Southern Suburban, Athenian 1919-29, Isthmian 1929-98, Conference 1998-2001

11-12		12-13		13-14		14-15		15-16		16-17		17-18		18-19		19-20		20-21	
Isth P	11	Isth P	11	Isth P	2	Isth P	11	Isth P	7	Isth P	17	Isth P	13	Isth P	18	Isth P	n&v	Isth P	n&v
FAC	1Q	FAC	2Q	FAC	1Q	FAC	3Q	FAC	2Q	FAC	1Q	FAC	2Q	FAC	1Q	FAC	4Q	FAC	1Q
FAT	1Q	FAT	1P	FAT	1Q	FAT	1Q	FAT	3Q	FAT	3Q	FAT	3Qr	FAT	1Qr	FAT	2Pr	FAT	3Q

HONOURS / RECORDS

FA Comps: FA Amateur Cup 1932-33. FA Trophy 1998-99, 99-2000.

League: Athenian League 1923-24, 25-26. Isthmian 1933-34, 36-37, 97-98, Division One South 2008-09.

County FA: Surrey Senior Cup 1910-11, 13-14, 25-26, 30-31, 31-32, 34-35, 38-39, 51-52, 62-63, 63-64, 66-67, 97-98, 2005-06. London Senior Cup 1962-63, 64-65, 86-87.

Victory: 15-1 v Delft - 1951
Defeat: 0-11 v Ilford - Isthmian League 13/02/1937
Goalscorer: Johnnie Whing - 295 (1948-62)
Appearances: Micky Preston - 555 (1967-85)
Additional: Paid £18,000 to Rushden & Diamonds for David Leworthy 1997 Received £150,000 from West Ham for Gavin Holligan 1999

GROUND: Corinthian-Casuals FC, King George's Field, Queen Mary Close, Hook Rise South, KT6 7NA
Ground Capacity: 3,400 **Seats:** 125 **Covered:** Yes **Clubhouse:** Yes **Shop:** Yes
Previous Grounds: Several > 1921, Richmond Road 1921-89. Kingsmeadow 1989-2017. Leatherhead FC 2017-18.
Record Attendance: 8,760 v Dulwich Hamlet at Richmond Road 1933.

Nearest Railway Station Tolworth - 10-15 min walk
Bus Route K1 from new Malden, 265 from Putney, K2 from Hook or Kingston Hospital, 406 & 408 from Kingston and Epsom, 418 from Kingston

LEATHERHEAD

Isthmian Premier

Founded 1946 **Nickname:** The Tanners **Club Colours:** Green & white

Club Contact Details
01372 360 151 jeremysmith.lfc@gmail.com

Previous Names: Club was formed when Leatherhead Rose and Leatherhead United merged in 1946.
Previous Leagues: Surrey Senior 1946-50, Metropolitan 1950-51, Delphian 1951-58, Corinthian 1958-63, Athenian 1963-72

11-12		12-13		13-14		14-15		15-16		16-17		17-18		18-19		19-20		20-21	
Isth P	19	Isth1S	6	Isth1S	3	Isth P	10	Isth P	11	Isth P	13	Isth P	6	Isth P	8	Isth P	n&v	Isth P	n&v
FAC	4Qr	FAC	2Q	FAC	3Q	FAC	1Q	FAC	1Qr	FAC	1Q	FAC	2P	FAC	4Qr	FAC	1Qr	FAC	1Q
FAT	1Q	FAT	3Qr	FAT	2Q	FAT	3Q	FAT	1Q	FAT	1Q	FAT	2Q	FAT	1Q	FAT	3Q	FAT	1P

HONOURS / RECORDS

FA Comps: None

League: Surrey Senior 1946-47, 47-48, 48-49, 49-50. Corinthian 1962-63. Athenian Division One 1963-64.

County FA: Surrey Senior Cup 1968-69. Surrey Senior Shield 1968-69. Surrey Intermediate Cup 1968-69.

Victory: 13-1 v Leyland Motors - Surrey Senior League 1946-47
Defeat: 1-11 v Sutton United
Goalscorer: Steve Lunn scored 46 goals during 1996-97
Appearances: P Caswell - 200
Additional: Paid £1,500 to Croydon for B Salkeld. Received £1,500 from Croydon for B Salkeld.

GROUND: Fetcham Grove, Guildford Road, Leatherhead, Surrey KT22 9AS
Ground Capacity: 3,400 **Seats:** 125 **Covered:** Yes **Clubhouse:** Yes **Shop:** Yes
Previous Grounds: None
Record Attendance: 5,500 v Wimbledon - 1976

Nearest Railway Station Leatherhead - half a mile away
Bus Route 21, 465 & 479

LEWES

Isthmian Premier

Founded 1885 **Nickname:** Rooks **Club Colours:** Red & black

Club Contact Details
01273 470 820 john@lewesfc.com

Previous Names: None
Previous Leagues: Mid Sussex 1886-1920, Sussex County 1920-65, Athenian 1965-77, Isthmian 1977-2004, Conference 2004-11.

11-12	12-13	13-14	14-15	15-16	16-17	17-18	18-19	19-20	20-21
Isth P 6	Isth P 19	Isth P 16	Isth P 19	Isth P 23	Isth1S 9	Isth1S 2	Isth P 11	Isth P n&v	Isth P n&v
FAC 1Q	FAC 2Q	FAC 3Q	FAC 2Q	FAC 1Q	FAC 1Qr	FAC 1Q	FAC 3Q	FAC 2Q	FAC 1Q
FAT 2Q	FAT 2Qr	FAT 1Q	FAT 3Q	FAT 1Qr	FAT 1Q	FAT 3Q	FAT 3Qr	FAT 1Q	FAT 3Q

HONOURS / RECORDS
FA Comps: None
League: Mid Sussex 1910-11, 13-14. Sussex County 1964-65. Athenian Division Two 1967-68, Division One 1969-70. Isthmian Division Two 2001-02, Division One South 2003-04. Conference South 2007-08.
County FA: Sussex Senior Cup 1964-65, 70-71, 84-85, 2000-01, 05-06.

Goalscorer: 'Pip' Parris - 350
Appearances: Terry Parris - 662
Additional: Paid £2,000 for Matt Allen
Received £2,500 from Brighton & Hove Albion for Grant Horscroft

GROUND: The Dripping Pan, Mountfield Road, Lewes, East Sussex BN7 2XA
Ground Capacity: 3,000 **Seats:** 600 **Covered:** 1,400 **Clubhouse:** Yes **Shop:** Yes
Previous Grounds: Played at Convent Field for two seasons before WWI
Record Attendance: 2,500 v Newhaven - Sussex County League 26/12/1947

Nearest Railway Station Lewes - 0.3km
Bus Route Priory School - stop 100m away

MARGATE

Isthmian Premier

Founded 1896 **Nickname:** The Gate **Club Colours:** Blue & white

Club Contact Details
01843 221 769 secretary@margate-fc.com

Previous Names: Margate Town 1896-1929. Thanet United 1981-89.
Previous Leagues: Kent 1911-23, 24-28, 29-33, 37-38, 46-59. Southern 1933-37, 59-2001, Conference 2001-05, 15-17. Isthmian 2005-15.

11-12	12-13	13-14	14-15	15-16	16-17	17-18	18-19	19-20	20-21
Isth P 15	Isth P 9	Isth P 11	Isth P 2	Nat S 19	Nat S 22	Isth P 7	Isth P 12	Isth P n&v	Isth P n&v
FAC 3Q	FAC 3Q	FAC 2Q	FAC 2Q	FAC 4Q	FAC 4Qr	FAC 4Q	FAC 2Q	FAC 4Q	FAC 1Q
FAT 2Qr	FAT 1Q	FAT 3Q	FAT 1Q	FAT 3Q	FAT 3Qr	FAT 3Q	FAT 1Q	FAT 2Q	FAT 1P

HONOURS / RECORDS
FA Comps: None
League: Kent 1932-33, 37-38, 46-47, 47-48. Southern League Eastern Section & Championship 1935-36, Division One 1962-63, Division One South 1977-78, Premier Division 2000-01.
County FA: Kent Senior Cup 1935-36, 36-37, 73-74, 93-94, 97-98, 2002-03, 03-04, 04-05.

Victory: 12-1 v Deal Cinque Ports, FA Cup 1Q, 1919-20 and v Erith & Belvedere, Kent League, 1927-28.
Defeat: 0-11 v AFC Bournemouth (A), FA Cup, 20/11/1971.
Goalscorer: Martin Buglione - 158
Appearances: Bob Harrop - 564
Additional: Paid £5,000 to Dover Athletic for Steve Cuggy

GROUND: Hartsdown Park, Hartsdown Road, Margate, Kent CT9 5QZ
Ground Capacity: 3,000 **Seats:** 400 **Covered:** 1,750 **Clubhouse:** Yes **Shop:** Yes
Previous Grounds: At least six before moving to Hartsdown in 1929. Shared with Dover Ath. 2002-03 and Ashford Town 04-05.
Record Attendance: 14,169 v Tottenham Hotspur - FA Cup 3rd Round 1973

Nearest Railway Station Margate - 0.7 miles from the ground.
Bus Route 8 & 8X

MERSTHAM

Isthmian Premier

Founded 1892 **Nickname:** The Moatsiders **Club Colours:** Yellow & black

Club Contact Details
01737 644 046 mike@monair.co.uk

Previous Names: None
Previous Leagues: Redhill & District. Surrey Intermediate. Surrey Senior 1965-78. London Spartan 1978-84. Combined Counties 1984-2008.

11-12		12-13		13-14		14-15		15-16		16-17		17-18		18-19		19-20		20-21	
Isth1S	9	Isth1S	12	Isth1S	7	Isth1S	4	Isth P	10	Isth P	20	Isth P	18	Isth P	5	Isth P	n&v	Isth P	n&v
FAC	2Q	FAC	P	FAC	2Q	FAC	2Q	FAC	1Q	FAC	1P	FAC	1Q	FAC	1Qr	FAC	1Q	FAC	1Q
FAT	1Q	FAT	2Q	FAT	Pr	FAT	2Q	FAT	1Qr	FAT	2Q	FAT	1Qr	FAT	2Q	FAT	1Q	FAT	3Q

HONOURS / RECORDS
FA Comps: None

League: Redhill & District 1934-35, 35-36, 49-50, 50-51. Surrey Intermediate 1952-53. Surrey Senior 1971-72. Combined Counties Premier Division 2007-08.

County FA: East Surrey Junior Cup 1929-30. Surrey Senior Charity Cup 1976-77. East Surrey Charities Senior Cup 1979-80, 80-81. East Surrey Charity Cup 1998-99, 2004-05, 06-07. Surrey Senior Cup 2007-08, 15-16, 17-18.

Defeat: 1-8 v Aldershot Town, FA First Qualifying Round, 1996-97.
Best FA Cup First Round Proper 2016-17.
FA Trophy Second Qualifying Round 2009-10, 12-13, 16-17, 18-19.
FA Vase Quarter Finals 2007-08.

GROUND: Moatside Stadium, Weldon Way, Merstham, Surrey RH1 3QB
Ground Capacity: 2,500 **Seats:** 174 **Covered:** 100 **Clubhouse:** Yes **Shop:** No
Previous Grounds: None
Record Attendance: 1,920 v Oxford United, FAC First Round Proper, 05/11/2016

Nearest Railway Station Merstham - 0.7km
Bus Route 405, 430 & 435

POTTERS BAR TOWN

Isthmian Premier

Founded 1960 **Nickname:** Grace or Scholars **Club Colours:** Maroon & white

Club Contact Details
01707 654 833 jeff@jeffbarnes.co.uk

Previous Names: Mount Grace Old Scholars 1960-84. Mount Grace 1984-91.
Previous Leagues: Barnet & District 1960-65, North London Combination 1965-68, Herts Senior County 1968-91, Spartan South Midlands 1991-2005, Southern 2005-06, 13-17. Isthmian 2006-13.

11-12		12-13		13-14		14-15		15-16		16-17		17-18		18-19		19-20		20-21	
Isth1N	12	Isth1N	10	SthC	15	SthC	14	SthC	12	SthC	9	Isth1N	2	Isth P	16	Isth P	n&v	Isth P	n&v
FAC	P	FAC	1Qr	FAC	P	FAC	P	FAC	2Q	FAC	4Q	FAC	2Qr	FAC	1Q	FAC	4Qr	FAC	2Q
FAT	2Q	FAT	1Q	FAT	1Qr	FAT	Pr	FAT	Pr	FAT	P	FAT	2Qr	FAT	2Q	FAT	2Q	FAT	3Q

HONOURS / RECORDS
FA Comps: None

League: North London Combination Premier Division 1967-68. Herst Senior county Premier Division 1990-91. Spartan South Midlands Premier Division 1996-97, 2004-05.

County FA: None

Goalscorer: Micky Gray scored 51 during a single season. Richard Howard has come closest to that record having scored 49 goals during seasons 2004-05 and 2006-07 respectively.

Best FA Cup Fourth Qualifying Round 2006-07, 16-17.
FA Trophy Second Round Qualifying 2011-12, 17-18(r).
FA Vase Sixth Round Proper 1997-98.

GROUND: LA Construction Stadium, Parkfield, Watkins Rise, Potters Bar EN6 1QB
Ground Capacity: 2,000 **Seats:** 150 **Covered:** 250 **Clubhouse:** Yes **Shop:** Yes
Previous Grounds: None
Record Attendance: 2011 v Barnet - FA Cup Fourth Qualifying Round 2019-20 (4,000 watched a charity match in 1997)

Nearest Railway Station Potters Bar - 0.9km
Bus Route 298, 313 & 84

WINGATE & FINCHLEY

Isthmian Premier

Founded 1991 **Nickname:** Blues **Club Colours:** Blue & black

Club Contact Details

0208 446 2217 mark@wingatefinchley.com

Previous Names: Wingate (founded 1946) and Finchley (founded late 1800s) merged in 1991

Previous Leagues: South Midlands 1991-95, Isthmian 1995-2004, Southern 2004-2006

11-12		12-13		13-14		14-15		15-16		16-17		17-18		18-19		19-20		20-21	
Isth P	13	Isth P	18	Isth P	21	Isth P	12	Isth P	13	Isth P	5	Isth P	9	Isth P	19	Isth P	n&v	Isth P	n&v
FAC	1Q	FAC	2Q	FAC	1Qr	FAC	3Q	FAC	3Q	FAC	2Q	FAC	2Qr	FAC	1Q	FAC	2Q	FAC	1Q
FAT	1Q	FAT	2Qr	FAT	2Qr	FAT	1Q	FAT	1Q	FAT	1Pr	FAT	1P	FAT	2P	FAT	1Qr	FAT	1P

HONOURS / RECORDS

FA Comps: None

League: None

County FA: London Senior Cup 2010-11.

Victory: 9-1 v Winslow, South Midlands League, 23/11/1991

Defeat: 0-9 v Edgware, Isthmian Division Two, 15/01/2000

Goalscorer: Marc Morris 650 (including with Wingate FC)

Appearances: Marc Morris 720 (including with Wingate FC)

GROUND: Maurice Rebak Stadium, Summers Lane, Finchley N12 0PD

Ground Capacity: 1,500 **Seats:** 500 **Covered:** 500 **Clubhouse:** Yes **Shop:** No

Previous Grounds: None

Record Attendance: 528 v Brentwood Town (Division One North Play-Off) 2010/11

Nearest Railway Station New Southgate - 2.3km

Bus Route 134, 263 & 382

WORTHING

Isthmian Premier

Founded 1886 **Nickname:** Rebels **Club Colours:** All red

Club Contact Details

01903 233 444 secretary@worthingfc.com

Previous Names: None

Previous Leagues: West Sussex 1896-1904, 1905-14, 19-20, Brighton Hove & District 1919-20, Sussex County 1920-48, Corinthian 1948-63, Athenian 1963-77

11-12		12-13		13-14		14-15		15-16		16-17		17-18		18-19		19-20		20-21	
Isth1S	7	Isth1S	10	Isth1S	15	Isth1S	6	Isth1S	3	Isth P	15	Isth P	16	Isth P	9	Isth P	n&v	Isth P	n&v
FAC	3Q	FAC	1Q	FAC	P	FAC	2Q	FAC	3Q	FAC	3Q	FAC	1Q	FAC	4Q	FAC	2Qr	FAC	1Q
FAT	2Q	FAT	P	FAT	P	FAT	2Q	FAT	1Q	FAT	2Pr	FAT	2Q	FAT	3Q	FAT	2Q	FAT	3Q

HONOURS / RECORDS

FA Comps: None

League: Sussex League 1920-21, 21-22, 26-27, 28-29, 30-31, 33-34, 38-39, 39-40. Sussex League West 1945-46. Isthmian League Division Two 1981-82, 92-93, Division One 1982-83.

County FA: Sussex Senior Cup x21.

Victory: 25-0 v Littlehampton (H) - Sussex League 1911-12

Defeat: 0-14 v Southwick (A) - Sussex County League 1946-47

Goalscorer: Mick Edmonds - 276

Appearances: Mark Knee - 414

Additional: Received £7,500 from Woking for Tim Read 1990

GROUND: Woodside Road, Worthing, West Sussex BN14 7HQ

Ground Capacity: 3,650 **Seats:** 500 **Covered:** 1,500 **Clubhouse:** Yes **Shop:** No

Previous Grounds: None

Record Attendance: 3,600 v Wimbledon - FA Cup 14/11/1936

Nearest Railway Station Worthing - 0.6km

Bus Route 23, 7, & 700

AFC SUDBURY

Isthmian North

Founded 1999 **Nickname:** Yellows or The Suds **Club Colours:** Yellow & blue

Club Contact Details

01787 376 213 secretary@afcsudbury.co.uk

Previous Names: Sudbury Town (1874) and Sudbury Wanderers (1958) merged in 1999

Previous Leagues: Eastern Counties 1999-2006, Isthmian 2006-08, Southern 2008-10.

11-12		12-13		13-14		14-15		15-16		16-17		17-18		18-19		19-20		20-21	
Isth1N	8	Isth1N	17	Isth1N	10	Isth1N	3	Isth1N	1	Isth P	23	Isth1N	12	IsthN	8	IsthN	n&v	IsthN	n&v
FAC	3Q	FAC	1Q	FAC	3Q	FAC	1Q	FAC	2Q	FAC	2Q	FAC	3Q	FAC	3Q	FAC	1Q	FAC	1Q
FAT	1Q	FAT	P	FAT	3Qr	FAT	1P	FAT	2Q	FAT	2P	FAT	1Q	FAT	EP	FAT	3Q	FAT	1Q

HONOURS / RECORDS

FA Comps: None

League: Eastern Counties League 2000-01, 01-02, 02-03, 03-04, 04-05. Isthmian League Division One North 2015-16.

County FA: Suffolk Premier Cup 2001-02, 02-03, 03-04.

Goalscorer: Gary Bennett - 172

Appearances: Paul Betson - 376

Best FA Cup First Round Proper 2000-01.

FA Trophy First Round Proper 2006-07, 08-09, 10-11, 14-15.

GROUND: The Mel Group Stadium, Brundon Lane, Sudbury CO10 7HN

Ground Capacity: 2,500 **Seats:** 200 **Covered:** 1,500 **Clubhouse:** Yes **Shop:** Yes

Previous Grounds: The Priory Stadium

Record Attendance: 1,800

Nearest Railway Station Sudbury - 1.5km

Bus Route Bulmer Road - stop 100m away

AVELEY

Isthmian North

Founded 1927 **Nickname:** The Millers **Club Colours:** White & blue

Club Contact Details

01708 863 342 craigjohnson.aveleyfc@gmail.com

Previous Names: Lodge Meadow 1927-51.

Previous Leagues: Thurrock Combination 1946-49, London 1949-57, Delphian 1957-63, Athenian 1963-73, Isthmian 1973-2004, Southern 2004-06

11-12		12-13		13-14		14-15		15-16		16-17		17-18		18-19		19-20		20-21	
Isth P	20	Isth P	5	Isth1N	13	Isth1N	9	Isth1N	12	Isth1N	7	Isth1N	14	IsthN	2	IsthN	n&v	IsthN	n&v
FAC	2Q	FAC	2Q	FAC	1Q	FAC	3Q	FAC	3Q	FAC	P	FAC	P	FAC	P	FAC	P	FAC	3Q
FAT	1Q	FAT	P	FAT	P	FAT	P	FAT	P	FAT	P	FAT	1Q	FAT	2Q	FAT	4P	FAT	2P

HONOURS / RECORDS

FA Comps: None

League: London Division One 1950-51, Premier Division 54-55. Athenian 1970-71. Isthmian Division One North 2008-09.

County FA: Essex Thameside Trophy 1979-80, 2004-05, 06-07.

Victory: 11-1 v Histon - 24/08/1963

Defeat: 0-8 v Orient, Essex Thameside Trophy

Goalscorer: Jotty Wilks - 214

Appearances: Ken Riley - 422

GROUND: Parkside, Belhus Park Lane, Aveley RM15 4PX

Ground Capacity: 3,500 **Seats:** 424 **Covered:** Yes **Clubhouse:** Yes **Shop:** No

Previous Grounds: Lodge Meadow 1927-52. Mill Field 1952-2018.

Record Attendance: 3,741 v Slough Town - FA Amateur Cup 27/02/1971

Nearest Railway Station Purfleet

Bus Route 372 (Hornchurch to Lakeside) passes the ground.

BARKING

Isthmian North

Founded 1880 **Nickname:** The Blues **Club Colours:** All blue

Club Contact Details
0203 244 0069 secretary@barking-fc.co.uk

Previous Names: Barking Rov. Barking Woodville. Barking Working Lads Institute, Barking Institute. Barking T. Barking & East Ham United.
Previous Leagues: South Essex, London 1896-98, 1909-26. Athenian 1923-52. Isthmian. Southern. Essex Senior >2017.

11-12		12-13		13-14		14-15		15-16		16-17		17-18		18-19		19-20		20-21	
ESen	7	ESen	6	ESen	12	ESen	3	ESen	4	ESen	1	Isth1N	10	IsthN	12	IsthSC	n&v	IsthSC	n&v
FAC	EPr	FAC	EPr	FAC	Pr	FAC	EP	FAC	Pr	FAC	Pr	FAC	2Q	FAC	P	FAC	1Q	FAC	3Q
FAV	1P	FAV	1P	FAV	2P	FAV	1Q	FAV	2P	FAV	1P	FAT	1Q	FAT	P	FAT	1Qr	FAT	1P

HONOURS / RECORDS
FA Comps: None

League: South Essex Division One 1898-99, 1911-12, Division Two 1900-01. Division Two 1901-02. London Division One A 1909-10, Premier 1920-21. Athenian 1934-35. Isthmian Premier 1978-79. Essex Senior 2016-17.

County FA: Essex Senior Cup 1893-94, 95-96, 1919-20, 45-46, 62-63, 69-70, 89-90. London Senior Cup 1911-12, 20-21, 26-27, 78-79.

Goalscorer: Neville Fox - 242 (1965-73).
Appearances: Bob Makin - 569.
Victory: 14-0 v Sheppey United, Mithras Cup, 02/12/1969
Best FA Cup Second Round Proper replay 1981-82. **FA Amateur Cup:** Finalists 1926-27.
FA Trophy Second Round Proper 1979-80. **FA Vase:** Fifth Round Proper 1996-97.

GROUND: Mayesbrook Park, Lodge Avenue, Dagenham RM8 2JR
Ground Capacity: 2,500 **Seats:** 200 **Covered:** 600 **Clubhouse:** Yes **Shop:** Yes
Previous Grounds: Barking Park Recreation Ground. Vicarage Field 1884-1973.
Record Attendance: 1,972 v Aldershot, FA Cup Second Round Proper, 1978.

Nearest Railway Station Upney (District Line), 2 miles
Bus Route 368 (50 yards) 5, 145, 364 (400 yards)

BASILDON UNITED

Isthmian North

Founded 1963 **Nickname:** The Bees **Club Colours:** Yellow & black

Club Contact Details
01268 521 278 richard.barrett.bufc@gmail.com

Previous Names: Armada Sports.
Previous Leagues: Grays & Thurrock. Greater London. Essex Senior. Athenian. Isthmian. Essex Senior >2018.

11-12		12-13		13-14		14-15		15-16		16-17		17-18		18-19		19-20		20-21	
ESen	18	ESen	13	ESen	8	ESen	12	ESen	2	ESen	9	ESen	2	IsthN	17	IsthN	n&v	IsthN	n&v
FAC	EP	FAC	1Q	FAC	P	FAC	P	FAC	1Q	FAC	P	FAC	P	FAC	1Q	FAC	2Q	FAC	P
FAV	1P	FAV	1Q	FAV	1Q	FAV	1Q	FAV	3P	FAV	3P	FAV	1P	FAT	P	FAT	2Q	FAT	1Q

HONOURS / RECORDS
FA Comps: None

League: Essex Senior 1976-77, 77-78, 78-79, 79-80, 93-94. Isthmian Division Two 1983-84.

County FA: Essex Senior Trophy 1978-79.

Best FA Cup Third Qualifying Round 1983-84, 98-99.
FA Trophy Second Qualifying Round 1985-86.
FA Vase Quarter Finals 1980-81.

GROUND: Gardiners Close, Basildon SS14 3AW
Ground Capacity: 2,000 **Seats:** 400 **Covered:** 1,000 **Clubhouse:** Yes **Shop:** No
Previous Grounds: Gloucester Park Bowl 1963-70.
Record Attendance: 4,000 v West Ham, ground opening 11/08/1970 (4,999 watched a West Ham XI open Gloucester Park Bowl)

Nearest Railway Station Basildon (C2C), 2 miles
Bus Route 5 (First), 400 metres from ground

BRENTWOOD TOWN

Isthmian North

Founded 1954 **Nickname:** Blues **Club Colours:** Sky blue & white

Club Contact Details

07939 544 364 brentwoodtownsec@gmail.com

Previous Names: Manor Athletic, Brentwood Athletic, Brentwood F.C.

Previous Leagues: Romford & District, South Essex Combination, London & Essex Border, Olympian, Essex Senior

11-12		12-13		13-14		14-15		15-16		16-17		17-18		18-19		19-20		20-21	
Isth1N	9	Isth1N	9	Isth1N	19	Isth1N	4	Isth P	22	Isth1N	14	Isth1N	21	IsthN	13	IsthN	n&v	IsthN	n&v
FAC	1Qr	FAC	3Q	FAC	1Qr	FAC	2Q	FAC	4Q	FAC	P	FAC	P	FAC	1Q	FAC	1Q	FAC	2Q
FAV	1Q	FAV	3Qr	FAV	P	FAV	1Qr	FAV	2Q	FAV	P	FAT	3Q	FAT	2Qr	FAT	P	FAT	3Q

HONOURS / RECORDS

FA Comps: None

League: Essex Senior 2000-01, 2006-07.

County FA: None

Best FA Cup Third Round Proper 1969-70.

FA Trophy First Round Proper 1969-70.

FA Vase First Round 2004-05, 06-07.

GROUND: The Arena, Brentwood Centre, Doddinghurst Road, Brentwood CM15 9NN

Ground Capacity: 1,000 **Seats:** 150 **Covered:** 250 **Clubhouse:** Yes **Shop:** No

Previous Grounds: King George's Playing Fields (Hartswood), Larkins Playing Fields 1957-93

Record Attendance: 763 v Cheshunt, Isthmian Division One North, 23/04/2011.

Nearest Railway Station Shenfield - 2.1km

Bus Route Leisure Centre - stop 150m away

BURY TOWN

Isthmian North

Founded 1872 **Nickname:** The Blues **Club Colours:** Blue & white

Club Contact Details

01284 754 721 wendy@burytownfc.co.uk

Previous Names: Bury St Edmunds 1872-1885, 1895-1908. Bury Town 1885-95. Bury United 1908-23.

Previous Leagues: Norfolk & Suffolk Border, Essex & Suffolk Border, Eastern Counties 1935-64, 76-87, 97-2006, Metropolitan 1964-71, Southern 1971-76, 87-97

11-12		12-13		13-14		14-15		15-16		16-17		17-18		18-19		19-20		20-21	
Isth P	5	Isth P	7	Isth P	15	Isth P	24	Isth1N	13	Isth1N	11	Isth1N	9	IsthN	6	IsthN	n&v	IsthN	n&v
FAC	2Q	FAC	4Q	FAC	1Q	FAC	1Q	FAC	2Q	FAC	P	FAC	P	FAC	1Q	FAC	P	FAC	4Q
FAT	3Qr	FAT	1Qr	FAT	1P	FAT	1Q	FAT	1P	FAT	1Q	FAT	2Q	FAT	EP	FAT	P	FAT	2Q

HONOURS / RECORDS

FA Comps: None

League: Metropolitan 1965-66, 68-69. Eastern Counties1963-64. Southern Division One Central 2009-10

County FA: Suffolk Senior Cup 1936-37, 37-38, 38-39, 44-45, 84-85.
Suffolk Premier Cup x12 - Firstly in 1958-59 and most recently in 2013-14.

Goalscorer: Doug Tooley - 251 in nine seasons

Appearances: Dick Rayner - 610 over 12 seasons

Additional: Paid £1,500 to Chelmsford City for Mel Springett. Received £5,500 from Ipswich Town for Simon Milton

GROUND: Ram Meadow, Cotton Lane, Bury St Edmunds IP33 1XP

Ground Capacity: 3,500 **Seats:** 300 **Covered:** 1,500 **Clubhouse:** Yes **Shop:** Yes

Previous Grounds: Kings Road 1888-1976. Temporary Ground 1976-77.

Record Attendance: 2,500 v Enfield - FA Cup Fourth Qualifying Round 1986

Nearest Railway Station Bury St Edmunds - 0.7km

Bus Route 11, 15, 16, 385, 753 & 84

CANVEY ISLAND

Isthmian North

Founded 1926 **Nickname:** The Gulls **Club Colours:** Yellow & blue

Club Contact Details
01268 682 991 g.sutton@sky.com

Previous Names: None
Previous Leagues: Southend & District, Thurrock & Thames Combination, Parthenon, Metropolitan, Greater London 1964-71, Essex Senior 1971-95, Isthmian 1995-2004, Conference 2004-06

11-12		12-13		13-14		14-15		15-16		16-17		17-18		18-19		19-20		20-21	
Isth P	8	Isth P	8	Isth P	13	Isth P	17	Isth P	14	Isth P	22	Isth1N	6	IsthN	9	IsthN	n&v	IsthN	n&v
FAC	2Q	FAC	1Q	FAC	4Q	FAC	4Qr	FAC	1Q	FAC	2Qr	FAC	P	FAC	P	FAC	3Qr	FAC	2P
FAT	3Q	FAT	3Qr	FAT	2Q	FAT	1Qr	FAT	2Q	FAT	1Q	FAT	P	FAT	1Q	FAT	2Q	FAT	1Q

HONOURS / RECORDS
FA Comps: FA Trophy 2000-01.

League: Thurrock Combination 1955-56. Greater London Division One 1967-68, 68-69. Essex Senior 1986-87, 92-93. Isthmian Division Two 1995-96, 97-98, Division One 1998-99, Premier Division 2003-04.
County FA: Essex Senior Cup 1998-99, 99-00, 01-02, 11-12.

Goalscorer: Andy Jones
Appearances: Steve Ward
Additional: Paid £5,000 to Northwich Victoria for Chris Duffy
Received £4,500 from Farnborough Town for Brian Horne

GROUND: Park Lane, Canvey Island, Essex SS8 7PX
Ground Capacity: 4,100 **Seats:** 500 **Covered:** 827 **Clubhouse:** Yes **Shop:** Yes
Previous Grounds: None
Record Attendance: 3,553 v Aldershot Town - Isthmian League 2002-03

Nearest Railway Station Leigh-on-Sea - 3.2km
Bus Route Transport Museum - stop 100m away

COGGESHALL TOWN

Isthmian North

Founded 1878 **Nickname:** Seed Growers **Club Colours:** Red & black

Club Contact Details
01376 562 843 secretary@coggeshalltownfc.co.uk

Previous Names: None
Previous Leagues: North Essex 1899-1909. Colchester & District/Essex & Suffolk Border 1909-39, 58-72, 90-96, 2000-2016. North Essex. Braintree & Dist. Colchester & E Essex 1950-58. Essex Senior 1972-90. Essex Inter. 1996-98, 99-00. Eastern Co 2016-18.

11-12		12-13		13-14		14-15		15-16		16-17		17-18		18-19		19-20		20-21	
EsSu1	5	EsSu1	2	EsSuP	7	EsSuP	6	EsSuP	1	EC1	2	ECP	1	IsthN	4	IsthN	n&v	IsthN	n&v
														FAC	3Q	FAC	EP	FAC	1Q
												FAV	2Q	FAT	EP	FAT	EP	FAT	3Q

HONOURS / RECORDS
FA Comps: None

League: North Essex x4. Essex & Suffolk Border Division II B 1909-10, 10-11, Division One 1962-63, Premier Division 1966-67, 67-68, 69-70, 2015-16. Eastern Counties Premier 2017-18.
County FA: Essex Intermediate Cup 1970-71.

Best FA Cup Third Qualifying Round 2018-19.
FA Trophy Extra Preliminary Round 2018-19, 19-20.
FA Vase Second Qualifying Round 2017-18.

GROUND: West Street, Coggeshall CO6 1NT
Ground Capacity: **Seats:** Yes **Covered:** Yes **Clubhouse:** Yes **Shop:** Online
Previous Grounds: Mynheer Park. Barnard Field 1880-81. Highfields Farm Park 1881-90, 95-1960. Fabians Field 1890-95.
Record Attendance: 1,124 v Tiptree United, Essex & Suffolk Border League, 1967-68.

Nearest Railway Station Kelvedon - 3.6km
Bus Route 70

DEREHAM TOWN

Isthmian North

Founded 1884 **Nickname:** Magpies **Club Colours:** Black & white

Club Contact Details

01362 690 460 secdtfc@gmail.com

Previous Names: Dereham and Dereham Hobbies.

Previous Leagues: Norwich District. Dereham & District. Norfolk & Suffolk. Anglian Comb. Eastern Counties > 2013.

11-12		12-13		13-14		14-15		15-16		16-17		17-18		18-19		19-20		20-21	
ECP	10	ECP	1	Isth1N	7	Isth1N	7	Isth1N	9	Isth1N	18	Isth1N	8	IsthN	14	IsthN	n&v	IsthN	n&v
FAC	EP	FAC	3Qr	FAC	1Q	FAC	2Q	FAC	P	FAC	2Q	FAC	2Q	FAC	P	FAC	1Qr	FAC	1Q
FAV	1P	FAV	2P	FAT	1Q	FAT	2Q	FAT	P	FAT	P	FAT	Pr	FAT	P	FAT	EP	FAT	3Q

HONOURS / RECORDS

FA Comps: None

League: Anglian Combination Division One 1989-90, Premier Division 97-98. Eastern Counties Premier Division 2012-13.

County FA: Norfolk Senior Cup 2005-06, 06-07, 15-16.

Best FA Cup Third Qualifying Round replay 2012-13.
FA Trophy Second Qualifying Round 2014-15.
FA Vase Fifth Round Proper 2008-09.

GROUND: Aldiss Park, Norwich Road, Dereham, Norfolk NR20 3PX

Ground Capacity: 2,500 **Seats:** 150 **Covered:** 500 **Clubhouse:** Yes **Shop:** Yes

Previous Grounds: Bayfields Meadow. Recreation Ground >1996.

Record Attendance: 3000 v Norwich City, Friendly, 07/2001.

Nearest Railway Station Peterborough - take B excel bus towards Norwich City Centre, alight at Hornbeam Drive

Bus Route 8 & X1

FELIXSTOWE & WALTON UNITED

Isthmian North

Founded 2000 **Nickname:** Seasiders **Club Colours:** Red & white

Club Contact Details

01394 282 627 secretary@felixstowefootball.co.uk

Previous Names: Felixstowe Port & Town and Walton United merged in July 2000.

Previous Leagues: Eastern Counties 2000-18.

11-12		12-13		13-14		14-15		15-16		16-17		17-18		18-19		19-20		20-21	
ECP	18	ECP	14	ECP	3	ECP	5	ECP	4	ECP	2	ECP	2	IsthN	11	IsthN	n&v	IsthN	n&v
FAC	P	FAC	Pr	FAC	P	FAC	1Q	FAC	EPr	FAC	3Q	FAC	EP	FAC	P	FAC	P	FAC	P
FAV	2P	FAV	2Q	FAV	1Q	FAV	1P	FAV	1Q	FAV	2P	FAV	1P	FAT	EP	FAT	EP	FAT	2P

HONOURS / RECORDS

FA Comps: None

League: None

County FA: None

Best FA Cup Third Qualifying Round 2016-17.
FA Vase Second Round Proper 2011-12, 16-17.
FA Trophy Extra Preliminary Round 2018-19.

GROUND: Dellwood Avenue, Felixstowe IP11 9HT

Ground Capacity: 2,000 **Seats:** 200 **Covered:** 200 **Clubhouse:** Yes **Shop:** Yes

Previous Grounds: None

Record Attendance: 1,541 v Coggeshall Town, Eastern Counties Premier Division, 01/05/2018

Nearest Railway Station Felixstowe - 0.3km

Bus Route X7 - alight at Great eastern Square - ground is a 5min walk

GRAYS ATHLETIC

Isthmian North

Founded 1890 **Nickname:** The Blues **Club Colours:** All royal blue

Club Contact Details

07913 566 706 graysathleticfc@hotmail.co.uk

Previous Names: Grays Juniors 1890.

Previous Leagues: Grays & District. South Essex. Athenian 1912-14, 58-83. London 1914-24, 26-39,.Kent 1924-26. Corinthian 1945-58. Isthmian 1983-2004. Conference 2004-10

11-12	12-13	13-14	14-15	15-16	16-17	17-18	18-19	19-20	20-21
Isth1N 5	Isth1N 1	Isth P 14	Isth P 6	Isth P 15	Isth P 24	Isth1N 16	IsthN 7	IsthN n&v	IsthN n&v
FAC 1Q	FAC 2Q	FAC 3Q	FAC 3Qr	FAC 4Qr	FAC 1Q	FAC 1Qr	FAC P	FAC 1Q	FAC 2Q
FAT 2Q	FAT 2Qr	FAT 3Q	FAT 2Q	FAT 3Qr	FAT 1Qr	FAT 1Qr	FAT P	FAT P	FAT 2Q

HONOURS / RECORDS

FA Comps: FA Trophy 2004-05, 05-06.

League: South Essex Division Two B 1908-09. Corinthian 1945-46. London Prmier (Amateur) 1914-15, Premier 1921-22, 26-27, 29-30. Isthmian Division Two South 1984-85, Division One North 2012-13. Conference South 2004-05.

County FA: Essex Senior Cup 1914-15, 20-21, 22-23, 44-45, 56-57, 87-88, 93-94, 94-95. East Anglian Cup 1944-45.

Victory: 12-0 v Tooting & Mitcham United - London League 24/02/1923

Defeat: 0-12 v Enfield (A) - Athenian League 20/04/1963

Goalscorer: Harry Brand - 269 (1944-52)

Appearances: Phil Sammons - 673 (1982-97)

Additional: Paid £12,000 to Welling United for Danny Kedwell. Received £150,000 from Peterborough United for Aaron McLean.

GROUND: Aveley FC, Parkside, Park Lane, Aveley RM15 4PX

Ground Capacity: 3,500 **Seats:** 424 **Covered:** Yes **Clubhouse:** Yes **Shop:** No

Previous Grounds: Recreation Ground Bridge Road. Rookery Hill (East Thurrock Utd). Rush Green Road. Mill Field (Aveley FC).

Record Attendance: 9,500 v Chelmsford City - FA Cup 4th Qualifying Round 1959

Nearest Railway Station Purfleet

Bus Route 372 (Hornchurch to Lakeside) passes the ground.

GREAT WAKERING ROVERS

Isthmian North

Founded 1919 **Nickname:** Rovers **Club Colours:** Green & white

Club Contact Details

01702 217 812 info@gwrovers.com

Previous Names: None

Previous Leagues: Southend & District 1919-81, Southend Alliance 1981-89, Essex Intermediate 1989-92, Essex Senior 1992-99, 2012-14, Isthmian 1999-2004, 14-17, Southern 2004-05.

11-12	12-13	13-14	14-15	15-16	16-17	17-18	18-19	19-20	20-21
Isth1N 22	ESen 4	ESen 1	Isth1N 15	Isth1N 18	Isth1N 24	ESen 1	IsthN 15	IsthN n&v	IsthN n&v
FAC Pr	FAC P	FAC P	FAC P	FAC P	FAC P	FAC EP	FAC 2Q	FAC P	FAC P
FAT P	FAV 1P	FAV 3P	FAT P	FAT P	FAT P	FAV 3P	FAT P	FAT P	FAT 1Q

HONOURS / RECORDS

FA Comps: None

League: Essex Intermediate Division Three 1990-91, Division Two 91-92. Essex Senior 1994-95, 2013-14, 17-18.

County FA: None

Victory: 9-0 v Eton Manor - 27/12/1931

Defeat: 1-7 v Bowers United - Essex Senior League 01/04/1998

Appearances: John Heffer - 511

Best FA Cup Second Qualifying Round 1998-99, 2006-07, 18-19.

FA Trophy First Round Proper 2002-03, 04-05. **FA Vase:** Fifth Round 1997-98, 2001-02.

GROUND: Burroughs Park, Little Wakering Hall Lane, Great Wakering SS3 0HH

Ground Capacity: 3,000 **Seats:** 250 **Covered:** Yes **Clubhouse:** Yes **Shop:**

Previous Grounds: Great Wakering Rec

Record Attendance: 1,150 v Southend United - Friendly 19/07/2006

Nearest Railway Station Shoeburyness - 3.2km

Bus Route Barrow Hall Rd (Little Wakering Rd) - 631m

HASHTAG UNITED

Isthmian North

Founded 2016 **Nickname:** The Tags **Club Colours:** Blue & yellow

Club Contact Details
01268 452 068 secretary@hashtagunited.co.uk

Previous Names: Spencer FC.
Previous Leagues: Eastern Counties 2018-19. Essex Senior 2019-21.

11-12	12-13	13-14	14-15	15-16	16-17	17-18	18-19	19-20	20-21
							EC1S 1	ESen n&v	ESen n&v
									FAC 2Q
								FAV 2Q	FAV 2P

HONOURS / RECORDS
FA Comps: None
League: Eastern Counties Division One South 2018-19

County FA: None

Best FA Cup Second Qualifying Round 2020-21.
FA Vase Second Round Proper 2020-21.

GROUND: Bowers & Pitsea FC, Len Salmon Stadium, Crown Avenue, Pitsea, Basildon SS13 2BE
Ground Capacity: 2,000 **Seats:** 200 **Covered:** 1,000 **Clubhouse:** **Shop:**
Previous Grounds: Coles Park (Haringey B) 2018-19. Chadfields (Tilbury FC) 19-20.
Record Attendance:

Nearest Railway Station Pitsea - 1.7km
Bus Route Wilsner - stop 200m away

HEYBRIDGE SWIFTS

Isthmian North

Founded 1880 **Nickname:** Swifts **Club Colours:** Black & white

Club Contact Details
01621 852 978 secretaryhsfc@btinternet.com

Previous Names: Heybridge FC.
Previous Leagues: Essex & Suffolk Border, North Essex, South Essex, Essex Senior 1971-84

11-12	12-13	13-14	14-15	15-16	16-17	17-18	18-19	19-20	20-21
Isth1N 16	Isth1N 6	Isth1N 3	Isth1N 12	Isth1N 20	Isth1N 21	Isth1N 5	IsthN 5	IsthN n&v	IsthN n&v
FAC 1Q	FAC 2Q	FAC 4Q	FAC P	FAC 1Q	FAC 1Qr	FAC 1P	FAC 2Q	FAC P	FAC P
FAT P	FAT P	FAT 1Q	FAT 1Q	FAT 2Qr	FAT 1Q	FAT 2P	FAT EP	FAT 1Q	FAT 3Q

HONOURS / RECORDS
FA Comps: None
League: Essex & Suffolk Border Division Two (West) 1920-21, Division One 30-31. Essex Senior 1981-82, 82-83, 83-84.
Isthmian Division Two North 1989-90.
County FA: Essex Junior Cup 1931-32. East Anglian Cup 1993-94, 94-95.

Goalscorer: Arthur 'Stumpy' Moss - 193 (1948-60)
Appearances: John Pollard - 543
Additional: Paid £1,000 for Dave Rainford and for Lee Kersey
Received £35,000 from Southend United for Simon Royce

GROUND: Scraley Road, Heybridge, Maldon, Essex CM9 8JA
Ground Capacity: 3,000 **Seats:** 550 **Covered:** 1,200 **Clubhouse:** Yes **Shop:** Yes
Previous Grounds: Bentall's Sports Ground 1890-1964. Sadd's Athletic ground share 1964-66.
Record Attendance: 2,477 v Woking - FA Trophy Quarter-finals 1997.

Bus Route Scylla Close - stop 1km away

HULLBRIDGE SPORTS

Isthmian North

Founded 1945 **Nickname:** The Bridge or Sports **Club Colours:** Blue & white

Club Contact Details

01702 230 420 jason@hullbridgesports.co.uk

Previous Names: None

Previous Leagues: Southend & District. Southend Alliance.

11-12		12-13		13-14		14-15		15-16		16-17		17-18		18-19		19-20		20-21	
ESen	11	ESen	15	ESen	9	ESen	4	ESen	11	ESen	11	ESen	15	ESen	1	IsthN	n&v	IsthN	n&v
FAC	EP	FAC	EP	FAC	P	FAC	EP	FAC	2Q	FAC	P	FAC	Pr	FAC	P	FAC	EP	FAC	EP
FAV	1P	FAV	1P	FAV	4P	FAV	4P	FAV	4P	FAV	2P	FAV	4P	FAV	2P	FAT	EP	FAT	1Q

HONOURS / RECORDS

FA Comps: None

League: Southend & District Division Two 1951-52, Division Three 1956-57, Division One 1965-66. Essex Senior 2018-19.

County FA: None

Best FA Cup Second Qualifying Round 2015-16.
FA Vase Fourth Round Proper 2014-14, 14-15, 15-16, 17-18.
FA Trophy Extra Preliminary Round 2019-20.

GROUND: Lower Road, Hullbridge, Hockley Essex SS5 6BJ

Ground Capacity: 1,500 **Seats:** 60 **Covered:** 60 **Clubhouse:** Yes **Shop:** No

Previous Grounds: Originally played on land on the junction of Pooles Lane and Long Lane until 1980.

Record Attendance: 800 v Blackburn Rovers, FA Youth Cup 1999-00.

Nearest Railway Station Rayleigh, approx. 3 miles

Bus Route 20, bottom of the hill

MALDON & TIPTREE

Isthmian North

Founded 1946 **Nickname:** The Jammers **Club Colours:** Blue & red

Club Contact Details

01621 853 762 ron.dangerfield@maldontiptreefc.co.uk

Previous Names: Maldon Town were rebranded in 2010.

Previous Leagues: Chelmsford & Mid-Essex. North Essex. Essex & Suffolk Border. Eastern Counties 1966-72. Essex Senior 1972-2004. Southern 2004-05.

11-12		12-13		13-14		14-15		15-16		16-17		17-18		18-19		19-20		20-21	
Isth1N	11	Isth1N	2	Isth1N	9	Isth1N	19	Isth1N	7	Isth1N	2	Isth1N	7	IsthN	3	IsthN	n&v	IsthN	n&v
FAC	3Q	FAC	2Qr	FAC	1Q	FAC	P	FAC	P	FAC	1Q	FAC	1Qr	FAC	P	FAC	2P	FAC	1P
FAT	3Q	FAT	P	FAT	1Q	FAT	P	FAT	P	FAT	1Q	FAT	2Q	FAT	1Q	FAT	3Q	FAT	3P

HONOURS / RECORDS

FA Comps: None

League: Mid-Essex Premier Division 1949-50, 50-51. Essex & Suffolk Border Premier Division 1965-66. Essex Senior 1984-85.

County FA: Essex Intermediate Cup 1951-52.

Best FA Cup Second Round Proper 2019-20.
FA Trophy Third Round Proper 2020-21.
FA Vase Semi Finals 2002-03.

GROUND: Park Drive, Maldon CM9 5JQ

Ground Capacity: 2,800 **Seats:** 530 **Covered:** Yes **Clubhouse:** Yes **Shop:**

Previous Grounds: Sadd's Ground 1946-47. Promenade 1947-50. Farmbridge Road 1950-1994.

Record Attendance: 1,163 v AFC Sudbury, FA Vase semi-final 2003.

Nearest Railway Station Witham (6 miles) take a taxi. Chelmsford (11 miles) catch either the 31B or 31X bus

Bus Route 31B or 31X

ROMFORD

Isthmian North

Founded 1876 **Nickname:** Boro **Club Colours:** Yellow & blue

Club Contact Details
07973 717 074 romfordfc@aol.com

Previous Names: Original club founded in 1876 folded during WW1, Reformed in 1929 folded again in 1978 and reformed in 1992
Previous Leagues: Essex Senior 1992-96, 2002-09. Isthmian 1997-2002.

11-12		12-13		13-14		14-15		15-16		16-17		17-18		18-19		19-20		20-21	
Isth1N	13	Isth1N	8	Isth1N	11	Isth1N	20	Isth1N	16	Isth1N	16	Isth1N	23	IsthN	19	IsthN	n&v	IsthN	n&v
FAC	1Q	FAC	P	FAC	1Q	FAC	2Qr	FAC	Pr	FAC	1Q	FAC	1Q	FAC	1Q	FAC	1Q	FAC	EP
FAT	P	FAT	1Q	FAT	P	FAT	Pr	FAT	1Q	FAT	2Q	FAT	P	FAT	EP	FAT	P	FAT	2Q

HONOURS / RECORDS
FA Comps: None
League: Essex Senior 1995-96, 2008-09. Isthmian Division Two 1996-97.

County FA: East Anglian Cup 1997-98.

Goalscorer: Danny Benstock. Vinny John scored 45 goals during season 1997-98.
Appearances: Paul Clayton - 396 (2006-15)
Victory: 9-0 v Hullbridge Sports, Essex Senior, 21/10/1995.
Misc: Mark Lord became the oldest player to play for the club aged 48yrs 90 days on 03/03/2015.

GROUND: Barking FC, Mayesbrook Park, Lodge Avenue, Dagenham RM8 2JR
Ground Capacity: 2,500 **Seats:** 200 **Covered:** 600 **Clubhouse:** Yes **Shop:** Yes
Previous Grounds: Hornchurch 1992-95. Rush Green 1995-96. Sungate 1996-2001. The Mill Field (Aveley FC). Thurrock FC. E.Thurrock. Brentwood FC.
Record Attendance: 820 v Leatherhead - Isthmian Division Two

Nearest Railway Station Upney (District Line) 2 miles
Bus Route 368 (50 yards) 5, 145, 364 (400 yards)

STOWMARKET TOWN

Isthmian North

Founded 1883 **Nickname:** Old Gold and Blacks **Club Colours:** Old Gold & black

Club Contact Details
01449 612 533 davidwalker545@gmail.com

Previous Names: Stowuplands Corinthians. Stowmarket Corinthians. Stowmarket FC
Previous Leagues: Ipswich & District 1896-1925. Essex & Suffolk Border 1925-52. Eastern Counties 1952-2021.

11-12		12-13		13-14		14-15		15-16		16-17		17-18		18-19		19-20		20-21	
EC1	15	EC1	17	EC1	14	EC1	11	EC1	14	EC1	1	ECP	3	ECP	4	ECP	n&v	ECP	n&v
FAC	EP											FAC	Pr	FAC	EP	FAC	P	FAC	1Q
FAV	2Q	FAV	1Q	FAV	2Q	FAV	2Q	FAV	2Q	FAV	1Q	FAV	2Q	FAV	4P	FAV	5P	FAV	4P

HONOURS / RECORDS
FA Comps: None
League: Ipswich & District/Suffolk & Ipwich 1896-97, 97-98, 99-1900, 21-22. Essex & Suffolk Border 1950-51. Eastern Counties Division One 2016-17.
County FA: Suffolk Senior Cup 1930-31, 32-33, 33-34, 50-51, 51-52, 57-58 61-62, 64-65, 2006-07. Suffolk Premier Cup 1962-63, 76-77, 86-86, 90-91.
Victory: 13-0 v Cornard United (A), Eastern Counties Division One, 11/12/2010.
Best FA Cup Third Qualifying Round 2001-02.
FA Trophy First Qualifying Round 1974-75(r), 77-78(r).
FA Vase Fifth Round Proper 2019-20.

GROUND: Stowmarket Community S & S Club, Greens Meadow, Bury Road, Stowmarket, Suffolk IP14 1JQ
Ground Capacity: **Seats:** Yes **Covered:** Yes **Clubhouse:** Yes **Shop:** Online
Previous Grounds: Cricket Meadow.
Record Attendance: 3,338 v Romford, FA Amateur Cup, 1951-52 (Cricket Meadow).

Nearest Railway Station Stowmarket - 1km
Bus Route 88

TILBURY

Isthmian North

Founded 1895 **Nickname:** The Dockers **Club Colours:** Black & white

Club Contact Details

01375 843 093 amercer67@googlemail.com

Previous Names: None

Previous Leagues: Grays & District/South Essex, Kent 1927-31, London 1931-39, 46-50, 57-62, South Essex Combination (Wartime), Corinthian 1950-57, Delphian 1962-63, Athenian 1963-73, Isthmian 1973-2004, Essex Senior 2004-05

11-12		12-13		13-14		14-15		15-16		16-17		17-18		18-19		19-20		20-21	
Isth1N	3	Isth1N	16	Isth1N	16	Isth1N	14	Isth1N	11	Isth1N	12	Isth1N	17	IsthN	10	IsthN	n&v	IsthN	n&v
FAC	1Q	FAC	1Q	FAC	2Q	FAC	1Q	FAC	1Q	FAC	1Q	FAC	1Q	FAC	P	FAC	1Q	FAC	P
FAT	P	FAT	P	FAT	1Q	FAT	Pr	FAT	1P	FAT	Pr	FAT	P	FAT	P	FAT	1Q	FAT	2Q

HONOURS / RECORDS

FA Comps: None

League: London 1958-59, 59-60, 60-61, 61-62. Athenian Division One 1968-69. Isthmian Division Two 1975-76.

County FA: Essex Senior Cup x4. East Anglian Cup 2008-09.

Goalscorer: Ross Livermore - 282 in 305 games

Appearances: Nicky Smith - 424 (1975-85)

Additional: Received £2,000 from Grays Athletic for Tony Macklin 1990 and from Dartford for Steve Connor 1985

Best FA Cup Third Round Proper 1977-78 **FA Amateur Cup:** Quarter Finals 1946-47

FA Trophy Third Round Proper 1982-83 **FA Vase:** Fourth Round Proper 1988-89, 99-00

GROUND: Chadfields, St Chads Road, Tilbury, Essex RM18 8NL

Ground Capacity: 4,000 **Seats:** 350 **Covered:** 1,000 **Clubhouse:** Yes **Shop:**

Previous Grounds: Orient Field 1895-46.

Record Attendance: 5,500 v Gorleston - FA Cup 1949

Nearest Railway Station Tilbury Town - 1.1km

Bus Route Raphael Avenue - stop 75m away

WITHAM TOWN

Isthmian North

Founded 1947 **Nickname:** Town **Club Colours:** White & blue

Club Contact Details

01376 511 198 withamtownfc@gmail.com

Previous Names: Witham Town Football Clubs did exist before both World Wars with both folding due to the conflicts.

Previous Leagues: Mid-Essex 1947-52. South Essex 1952-58. Essex & Suffolk Border 1958-71. Essex Senior 1971-87, 2009-12. Isthmian 1987-2009.

11-12		12-13		13-14		14-15		15-16		16-17		17-18		18-19		19-20		20-21	
ESen	1	Isth1N	4	Isth1N	2	Isth P	22	Isth1N	19	Isth1N	13	Isth1N	11	IsthN	18	IsthN	n&v	IsthN	n&v
FAC	P	FAC	1Q	FAC	2Qr	FAC	4Q	FAC	2Q	FAC	2Q	FAC	1Q	FAC	Pr	FAC	1Q	FAC	P
FAV	3P	FAT	P	FAT	1Q	FAT	2Q	FAT	P	FAT	1Q	FAT	1Q	FAT	1Q	FAT	Pr	FAT	1Q

HONOURS / RECORDS

FA Comps: None

League: Braintree & District 1920-21, 24-25. Mid-Essex Division Three 1935-36, 47-48, Division Two 48-49. South Essex 1955-56. Essex & Suffolk Border 1964-65, 70-71. Essex Senior 1970-71, 85-86, 2011-12.

County FA: Essex Senior Trophy 1985-86.

Goalscorer: Colin Mitchell.

Appearances: Keith Dent.

GROUND: Spa Road, Witham CM8 1UN

Ground Capacity: 2,500 **Seats:** 157 **Covered:** 780 **Clubhouse:** Yes **Shop:** No

Previous Grounds: Crittall Windows works ground 1949-75.

Record Attendance: 800 v Billericay Town, Essex Senior League, May 1976.

Nearest Railway Station Witham - 1.1km

Bus Route Cuppers Close - stop 200m away

ASHFORD TOWN (MIDDX)

Isthmian League South Central

Founded 1958 **Nickname:** Ash Trees **Club Colours:** Tangerine, white & black

Club Contact Details

01784 245 908 yellowdot1@gmail.com

Previous Names: Ashford Albion 1958-64.

Previous Leagues: Hounslow & District 1964-68, Surrey Intermediate 1968-82, Surrey Premier 1982-90, Combind Counties 1990-2000, 14-16, Isthmian 20 00-04, 06-10, Southern 2004-06, 10-14, 16-18.

11-12		12-13		13-14		14-15		15-16		16-17		17-18		18-19		19-20		20-21	
SthC	9	SthC	10	SthC	22	CCP	3	CCP	2	SthC	10	Sth1E	12	IsthSC	11	IsthSC	n&v	IsthSC	n&v
FAC	P	FAC	2Q	FAC	1Q	FAC	Pr	FAC	1Q	FAC	1Q	FAC	3Q	FAC	P	FAC	P	FAC	P
FAT	2Q	FAT	1Qr	FAT	P	FAV	1P	FAV	1Pr	FAT	1Qr	FAT	2Qr	FAT	1Q	FAT	Pr	FAT	3Q

HONOURS / RECORDS

FA Comps: None

League: Surrey Intermediate (Western) Prmeier Division A 1974-75. Surrey Premier 1982-90.
Combined Counties 1994-95, 95-96, 96-97, 97-98, 99-00.

County FA: Middlesex Senior Charity Cup 1999-00, 11-12, 16-17. Aldershot Senior Cup 2002-03, 11-12.
Middlesex Premier Cup 2006-07. Surrey Senior Cup 2008-09.

Goalscorer: Andy Smith

Appearances: Alan Constable - 650

Additional: Received £10,000 from Wycombe Wanderers for Dannie Bulman 1997

GROUND: Robert Parker Stadium, Stanwell, Staines TW19 7BH

Ground Capacity: 2,550 **Seats:** 250 **Covered:** 250 **Clubhouse:** Yes **Shop:** No

Previous Grounds: Clockhouse Lane Recreation 1958-85.

Record Attendance: 992 v AFC Wimbledon - Isthmian League Premier Division 26/09/2006

Nearest Railway Station Heathrow Terminal 4 Underground - 1.5km

Bus Route Genesis Close - stop 400m away

BASINGSTOKE TOWN

Isthmian League South Central

Founded 1896 **Nickname:** Dragons **Club Colours:** Yellow & blue

Club Contact Details

07751 179 022 secretary@btfc.co.uk

Previous Names: The club was formed by the merger of Aldworth United and Basingstoke Albion in 1896.

Previous Leagues: Hampshire 1900-40, 45-71. Southern 1971-87, 16-21. Isthmian 1987-2004. Conference 2004-16.

11-12		12-13		13-14		14-15		15-16		16-17		17-18		18-19		19-20		20-21	
Conf S	5	Conf S	14	Conf S	14	Conf S	3	Nat S	22	SthP	12	SthP	10	SthPS	20	SthS	n&v	SthS	n&v
FAC	1P	FAC	3Q	FAC	2Q	FAC	1Pr	FAC	1P	FAC	2Q	FAC	1Qr	FAC	2Q	FAC	P	FAC	P
FAT	2P	FAT	3Q	FAT	1Pr	FAT	1Pr	FAT	3Q	FAT	3Q	FAT	1Q	FAT	3Q	FAT	1Q	FAT	2Q

HONOURS / RECORDS

FA Comps: None

League: Hampshire North Division 1911-12, 19-20, Division One 1967-68, 69-70, 70-71.
Southern Southern Division 1984-85.

County FA: Hampshire Senior Cup 1970-71, 89-90, 95-96, 96-97, 2007-08, 13-14, 16-17.

Victory: 10-1 v Chichester City (H) - FA Cup 1st Qualifying Round 1976

Defeat: 0-8 v Aylesbury United - Southern League April 1979

Goalscorer: Paul Coombs - 159 (1991-99)

Appearances: Billy Coomb

Additional: Paid £4,750 to Gosport Borough for Steve Ingham

GROUND: Hampshire FA, Winklebury Football Complex, Winklebury Way, Basingstoke RG23 8BF

Ground Capacity: **Seats:** Yes **Covered:** Yes **Clubhouse:** Yes **Shop:** Online

Previous Grounds: Castlefields 1896-1945. Winchester Road/Lord Camrose 1945-2019. Winchester FC 2019-20.

Record Attendance: 5,085 v Wycombe Wanderers - FA Cup 1st Round replay 1997-98

Nearest Railway Station Basingstoke

Bus Route No.6 bus from rail station to Winklebury, alight at Hampton Court stop, ground is opposite this stop.

BEDFONT SPORTS

Isthmian League South Central

Founded 2000 **Nickname:** The Eagles **Club Colours:** Red & black

Club Contact Details
0208 831 9067 or 07967 370 109 bedfontsports@yahoo.co.uk

Previous Names: Bedfont Sunday became Bedfont Sports in 2002 - Bedfont Eagles (1978) merged with the club shortly afterwards.
Previous Leagues: Hounslow & District 2003-04. Middlesex County 2004-09.

11-12		12-13		13-14		14-15		15-16		16-17		17-18		18-19		19-20		20-21	
CC1	2	CCP	13	CCP	17	CCP	16	CCP	13	CCP	8	CCP	2	IsthSC	12	IsthSC	n&v	IsthSC	n&v
FAC	Pr	FAC	EP	FAC	P	FAC	EP	FAC	P	FAC	P	FAC	EP	FAC	P	FAC	1Q	FAC	3Q
FAV	1P	FAV	2Q	FAV	2Q	FAV	1P	FAV	1P	FAV	3Pr	FAV	1Q	FAT	P	FAT	2Q	FAT	2Q

HONOURS / RECORDS
FA Comps: None

League: Hounslow & District League Division One 2003-04

County FA: Middlesex County Premier Cup 2009-10

Best FA Cup First Qualifying Round 2019-20
FA Vase Third Round Proper 2016-17(r)
FA Trophy Second Qualifying Round 2019-20

GROUND: Bedfont Sports Club, Hatton Road, Bedfont TW14 9QT
Ground Capacity: 3,000 **Seats:** Yes **Covered:** 200 **Clubhouse:** Yes **Shop:**
Previous Grounds: N/A
Record Attendance: Not known

Nearest Railway Station Hatton Cross or Feltham BR
Bus Route London Transport 203, H25, H26

BINFIELD

Isthmian League South Central

Founded 1892 **Nickname:** Moles **Club Colours:** Red

Club Contact Details
07515 336 989 robchallis@binfieldfc.com

Previous Names: None.
Previous Leagues: Ascot & District. Great Western Combination 1946-51. Reading & Dist 1951-89. Chiltonian 1989-2000. Hellenic 2000-21.

11-12		12-13		13-14		14-15		15-16		16-17		17-18		18-19		19-20		20-21	
Hel P	8	Hel P	3	Hel P	5	Hel P	6	Hel P	8	Hel P	8	Hel P	7	Hel P	9	Hel P	n&v	Hel P	n&v
FAC	P	FAC	EP	FAC	2Q	FAC	EP	FAC	P	FAC	EP	FAC	P	FAC	2Q	FAC	1Q	FAC	1Q
FAV	4P	FAV	3P	FAV	3P	FAV	2Q	FAV	1Qr	FAV	2Q	FAV	2Q	FAV	2Q	FAV	4Pr	FAV	F

HONOURS / RECORDS
FA Comps: None
League: Great Western Combination 1946-47. Reading & District Division One 1975-76, 87-88, Division Two 86-87. Chiltonian Division One 1989-90, Premier 95-96. Hellenic Division One East 2008-09.
County FA: Berks & Bucks Senior Trophy 2011-12.

Best FA Cup Second Qualifying Round 2013-14.
FA Vase Finalists 2020-21.

GROUND: Hill Farm Lane, Binfield RG42 5NR
Ground Capacity: 1,500 **Seats:** Yes **Covered:** Yes **Clubhouse:** Yes **Shop:**
Previous Grounds: Forest Road >1980.
Record Attendance: 1000+ Great Western Combination.

Nearest Railway Station Bracknell - 3.9km
Bus Route Church Lane North stop - 628m

BRACKNELL TOWN

Isthmian League South Central

Founded 1896 **Nickname:** The Robins **Club Colours:** Red & white

Club Contact Details
01344 412 305 ricky@thesbgroup.co.uk

Previous Names: Old Bracknell Wanderers 1896-1962.

Previous Leagues: Ascot & District. Reading & District 1949-58. Great Western Comb. 1958-63, Surrey Senior 1963-70, Spartan 1970-75, London Spartan 1975-84, Isthmian 1984-2004, Southern 2004-10, Hellenic 2010-18.

11-12		12-13		13-14		14-15		15-16		16-17		17-18		18-19		19-20		20-21	
Hel P	21	Hel1E	5	Hel P	13	Hel P	9	Hel P	14	Hel P	2	Hel P	2	IsthSC	2	IsthSC	n&v	IsthSC	n&v
FAC	EP	FAC	1Q	FAC	P	FAC	EP	FAC	1Q	FAC	P	FAC	P	FAT	1Qr	FAC	1Q	FAC	3Q
FAV	2Q	FAV	2Q	FAV	2Q	FAV	2Q	FAV	2Qr	FAV	1P	FAV	QF			FAT	P	FAT	2P

HONOURS / RECORDS

FA Comps: None

League: Ascot & District 1911-12, 32-33, Division Two 13-14. Surrey Senior 1969-70. Spartan Senior Division 1980-81, Premier 1982-83. Isthmian Division Three 1993-94.

County FA: Berks & Bucks Senior Trophy 2016-17

Goalscorer: Justin Day
Goalscorer: James Woodcock
Best FA Cup First Round Proper 2000-01
FA Trophy First Round Proper 2002-03, 03-04, 04-05
FA Vase Quarter Finals 2017-18

GROUND: Larges Lane, Bracknell RG12 9AN

Ground Capacity: 2,500 **Seats:** 150 **Covered:** 500 **Clubhouse:** Yes **Shop:** Online

Previous Grounds: Field next to Downshire Arms. Station Field > 1933

Record Attendance: 2,500 v Newquay - FA Amateur Cup 1971

Nearest Railway Station Bracknell - 0.5km

Bus Route Larges Bridge Drive stop - 282m away

CHALFONT ST PETER

Isthmian League South Central

Founded 1926 **Nickname:** Saints **Club Colours:** Red

Club Contact Details
01753 886 477 doors.cspafc@gmail.com

Previous Names: None

Previous Leagues: G W Comb 1948-58. Parthernon 1958-60. London 1960-62. Spartan 1962-75. London Spartan 1975-76. Athenian 1976-84. Isthmian 1984-2006. Spartan South Midlands 2006-11. Southern 2011-19.

11-12		12-13		13-14		14-15		15-16		16-17		17-18		18-19		19-20		20-21	
SthC	12	SthC	16	SthC	14	SthC	16	SthC	6	SthC	18	Sth1E	9	IsthSC	14	IsthSC	n&v	IsthSC	n&v
FAC	1Q	FAC	3Qr	FAC	2Q	FAC	3Q	FAC	P	FAC	1Q	FAC	Pr	FAC	1Qr	FAC	1Q	FAC	1Q
FAT	1Q	FAT	1Q	FAT	Pr	FAT	1Q	FAT	1Q	FAV	2Qr	FAT	1Qr	FAT	P	FAT	EP	FAT	1Q

HONOURS / RECORDS

FA Comps: None

League: Spartan Division Two 1975-76. Isthmian Division Two 1987-88. Spartan South Midlands Premier Division 2010-11.

County FA: Berks & Bucks Intermediate Cup 1952-53, 84-85.

Victory: 10-1 v Kentish Town (away) Spartan League Premier Division 23 Dec 2008
Defeat: 0-13 v Lewes (away) Isthmian Division 3, 7 Nov 2000
Appearances: Colin Davies

GROUND: Mill Meadow, Gravel Hill, Amersham Road, Chalfont St Peter SL9 9QX

Ground Capacity: 4,500 **Seats:** 220 **Covered:** 120 **Clubhouse:** Yes **Shop:** Yes

Previous Grounds: Gold Hill Common 1926-49.

Record Attendance: 2,550 v Watford benefit match 1985

Nearest Railway Station Gerrards Cross - 2.3km

Bus Route The Waggon & Horses Pub - stop 250m away

CHERTSEY TOWN

Isthmian League South Central

Founded 1890 **Nickname:** Curfews **Club Colours:** Royal blue & white stripes

Club Contact Details
01932 561 774 chrisegay@googlemail.com

Previous Names: Chertsey 1890-1950.

Previous Leagues: West Surrey. Surrey Inter 1919-39. Surrey Senior 46-63. Metropolitan 63-66. Greater London 66-67. Spartan 67-75. London Spartan 75-76. Athenian 76-84. Isthmian 84-85, 86-2006. Combined Counties 85-86, 2006-11, 14-19. Southern 2011-14.

11-12		12-13		13-14		14-15		15-16		16-17		17-18		18-19		19-20		20-21	
SthC	17	SthC	20	SthC	21	CCP	20	CCP	18	CCP	19	CCP	15	CCP	1	IsthSC	n&v	IsthSC	n&v
FAC	2Q	FAC	P	FAC	2Q	FAC	EPr	FAC	P	FAC	1Q	FAC	P	FAC	EP	FAC	3Q	FAC	2Q
FAT	3Q	FAT	1Q	FAT	1Q	FAV	1P	FAV	2Q	FAV	1Q	FAV	1Q	FAV	F	FAT	P	FAT	2Q

HONOURS / RECORDS

FA Comps: FA Vase 2018-19

League: Surrey Senior 1958-59, 60-61, 61-62. Combined Counties Premier 2018-19

County FA: Surrey Junior Cup 1896-97.

Goalscorer: Alan Brown (54) 1962-63.
FA Cup Third Qualifying Round 1994-95
FA Trophy Third Qualifying Round 2011-12
FA Vase Finalists 2018-19

GROUND: Alwyns Lane, Chertsey, Surrey KT16 9DW

Ground Capacity: 2,500 **Seats:** 240 **Covered:** 760 **Clubhouse:** Yes **Shop:** Yes
Previous Grounds: Pre 1929 - Willow Walk, Free Prae Road, Staines Lane and Chilsey Green.
Record Attendance: 2150 v Aldershot Town, Isthmian Div.2 04/12/93.

Nearest Railway Station Chertsey
Bus Route Abellio 446, 451, 461, 557

CHIPSTEAD

Isthmian League South Central

Founded 1906 **Nickname:** Chips **Club Colours:** Green, white & black

Club Contact Details
01737 553 250 secretary.chipsteadfc@gmail.com

Previous Names: None

Previous Leagues: Surrey Intermediate 1962-82, Surrey Premier 1982-86, Combined Counties 1986-2007

11-12		12-13		13-14		14-15		15-16		16-17		17-18		18-19		19-20		20-21	
Isth1S	12	Isth1S	20	Isth1S	13	Isth1S	15	Isth1S	21	Isth1S	20	Isth1S	20	IsthSC	13	IsthSC	n&v	IsthSC	n&v
FAC	2Q	FAC	1Q	FAC	3Q	FAC	1Qr	FAC	P	FAC	1Q	FAC	2Q	FAC	P	FAC	2Q	FAC	3Q
FAT	1Q	FAT	P	FAT	P	FAT	P	FAT	1Q	FAT	Pr	FAT	Pr	FAT	2Qr	FAT	1Qr	FAT	2Q

HONOURS / RECORDS

FA Comps: None

League: Combined Counties Premier 1989-90, 2006-07.

County FA: East Surrey Charity Cup 1960-61.

Goalscorer: Mick Nolan - 124
Best FA Cup Fourth Qualifying Round 2008-09
FA Trophy Second Qualifying Round 2009-10, 18-19(r)
FA Vase Third Round Proper 1997-98, 98-99

GROUND: High Road, Chipstead, Surrey CR5 3SF

Ground Capacity: 2,000 **Seats:** 150 **Covered:** 200 **Clubhouse:** Yes **Shop:** Yes
Previous Grounds: None
Record Attendance: 1,170

Nearest Railway Station Coulsdon South from where a Taxi can be taken to the ground. Chipstead a dangerous 1.25m walk away
Bus Route 405 to Star Lane, Hooley. Ground is a further 20min walk from there

GUERNSEY

Isthmian League South Central

Founded 2011 **Nickname:** Green Lions **Club Colours:** Green & white

Club Contact Details
01481 747 279 mark.letissier@guernseyfc.com

Previous Names: None
Previous Leagues: Combined Counties 2011-13.

11-12	12-13	13-14	14-15	15-16	16-17	17-18	18-19	19-20	20-21
CC1 1	CCP 2	Isth1S 4	Isth1S 10	Isth1S 13	Isth1S 21	Isth1S 18	IsthSE 18	IsthSE n&v	IsthSE n&v
		FAC 2Q	FAC P	FAC Pr	FAC Pr	FAC Pr	FAC Pr		
	FAV SF	FAT 1Q	FAT 1Q	FAT P	FAT P	FAT P		FAT P	

HONOURS / RECORDS
FA Comps: None
League: Combined Counties Division One 2011-12.

County FA: None

Victory: 11-0 v Crawley Down Gatwick, Isthmian Division One South, 01/01/2014
Defeat: 0-8 v Merstham, Isthmian Division One South, 18/11/2014
Goalscorer: Ross Allen - 239 in 226 appearances. (Scored 57 in all competitions during 2011-12)
FA Cup Second Qualifying Round 2013-14 **FA Trophy** First Qualifying Round 2013-14 14-15
FA Vase Semi Finals 2012-13

GROUND: Footes Lane Stadium, St Peter Port, Guernsey GY1 2UL
Ground Capacity: 5,000 **Seats:** 720 **Covered:** Yes **Clubhouse:** Yes **Shop:** No
Previous Grounds: None
Record Attendance: 4,290 v. Spennymoor Town, FA Vase semi-final first leg, 23/03/2013

Nearest Railway Station N/A
Bus Route Bus stops outside the ground

HANWELL TOWN

Isthmian League South Central

Founded 1920 **Nickname:** Magpies **Club Colours:** Black & white

Club Contact Details
020 8998 1701 clivecooke2@sky.com

Previous Names: None
Previous Leagues: London 1924-27. Dauntless. Wembley & District. Middlesex County 1970-83. London Spartan/Spartan 1983-97. Spartan South Midlands (FM) 1997-2006, 2007-14. Southern 2006-07, 14-18.

11-12	12-13	13-14	14-15	15-16	16-17	17-18	18-19	19-20	20-21
SSM P 21	SSM P 6	SSM P 1	SthC 7	SthC 20	SthC 11	Sth1E 18	IsthSC 8	IsthSC n&v	IsthSC n&v
FAC EP	FAC EP	FAC EPr	FAC P	FAC 3Q	FAC 2Qr	FAC 1Q	FAC 3Qr	FAC 1Q	FAC 2Q
FAV 1P	FAV 1Pr	FAV 5P	FAT P	FAT P	FAT 2Q	FAT 1Q	FAT P	FAT P	FAT 2Q

HONOURS / RECORDS
FA Comps: None
League: London Spartan Senior Division 1983-84. Spartan South Midlands Premier 2013-14.

County FA: London Senior Cup 1991-92, 92-93.

Goalscorer: Keith Rowlands
Appearances: Phil Player 617 (20 seasons)
Best FA Cup Third Qualifying Round 2015-16, 18-19(r)
FA Trophy Second Qualifying Round 2006-07, 16-17(r)
FA Vase Fifth Round Proper 2013-14

GROUND: Preivale Lane, Perivale, Greenford, UB6 8TL
Ground Capacity: 1,250 **Seats:** 175 **Covered:** 600 **Clubhouse:** Yes **Shop:** No
Previous Grounds: Moved to Reynolds Field in 1981.
Record Attendance: 600 v Spurs, floodlight switch on, 1989.

Nearest Railway Station Perivale Underground - 0.6km
Bus Route Perivale Lane - stop 200m away

MARLOW

Isthmian League South Central

Founded 1870 **Nickname:** The Blues **Club Colours:** Blue & white

Club Contact Details
01628 483 970 terry.staines@ntlworld.com

Previous Names: Great Marlow
Previous Leagues: Reading & District, Spartan 1908-10, 28-65, Gt Western Suburban, Athenian 1965-84, Isthmian 1984-2004. Southern 2004-12, 13-18. Hellenic 2012-13.

11-12		12-13		13-14		14-15		15-16		16-17		17-18		18-19		19-20		20-21	
SthC	22	Hel P	1	SthC	17	SthC	11	Sthsw	13	SthC	4	Sth1E	14	IsthSC	4	IsthSC	n&v	IsthSC	n&v
FAC	1Q	FAC	1Q	FAC	P	FAC	P	FAC	Pr	FAC	Pr	FAC	2Q	FAC	2Q	FAC	P	FAC	2Q
FAT	1Qr	FAV	2P	FAT	3Q	FAT	P	FAT	3Q	FAT	1Q	FAT	Pr	FAT	P	FAT	1Qr	FAT	1P

HONOURS / RECORDS
FA Comps: None

League: Spartan 1937-38, Division Two West 1929-30. Isthmian Division One 1987-88. Hellenic Premier Division 2012-13.

County FA: Berks & Bucks Senior Cup x11

Goalscorer: Kevin Stone
Appearances: Mick McKeown - 500+
Additional: Paid £5,000 to Sutton United for Richard Evans
Received £8,000 from Slough Town for David Lay

GROUND: Alfred Davies Memorial Ground, Oak tree Road, Marlow SL7 3ED
Ground Capacity: 3,000 **Seats:** 250 **Covered:** 600 **Clubhouse:** Yes **Shop:** No
Previous Grounds: Crown ground 1870-1919, Star Meadow 1919-24
Record Attendance: 3,000 v Oxford United - FA Cup 1st Round 1994

Nearest Railway Station Marlow - 1km
Bus Route Oak Tree Road - stop 100m away

NORTHWOOD

Isthmian League South Central

Founded 1926 **Nickname:** Woods **Club Colours:** All red

Club Contact Details
01923 827 148 enquiries@northwoodfc.com

Previous Names: Northwood United 1926-1945.
Previous Leagues: Harrow & Wembley 1932-69, Middlesex 1969-78, Hellenic 1979-84, London Spartan 1984-93, Isthmian 1993-2005, 2007-10, Southern 2005-07, 10-18.

11-12		12-13		13-14		14-15		15-16		16-17		17-18		18-19		19-20		20-21	
SthC	7	SthC	13	SthC	9	SthC	10	SthC	7	SthC	20	Sth1E	17	IsthSC	10	IsthSC	n&v	IsthSC	n&v
FAC	P	FAC	3Q	FAC	P	FAC	1Qr	FAC	2Q	FAC	P	FAC	P	FAC	1Qr	FAC	P	FAC	1Q
FAT	Pr	FAT	P	FAT	P	FAT	2Q	FAT	1Q	FAT	1Qr	FAT	P	FAT	P	FAT	P	FAT	2Q

HONOURS / RECORDS
FA Comps: None
League: Harrow, Wembley & District Premier 1932-33, 33-34, 34-35, 35-36, 36-37, 47-48, 48-49. Middlesex Premier 1977-78. Hellenic Division One 1978-79. Spartan Premier 1991-92. Isthmian Division One North 2002-03.
County FA: Middlesex Intermediate Cup 1978-79. Middlesex Senior Cup 2006-07, 15-16.

Victory: 15-0 v Dateline (H) - Middlesex Intermediate Cup 1973
Defeat: 0-8 v Bedfont - Middlesex League 1975
Goalscorer: Lawrence Yaku scored 61 goals during season 1999-2000
Appearances: Chris Gell - 493+

GROUND: Northwood Park, Chestnut Avenue, Northwood, Middlesex HA6 1HR
Ground Capacity: 3,075 **Seats:** 308 **Covered:** 932 **Clubhouse:** Yes **Shop:** No
Previous Grounds: Northwood Recreation Ground 1926-1928. Northwood Playing Fields 1928-1971.
Record Attendance: 1,642 v Chlesea - Friendly July 1997

Nearest Railway Station Northwood Hills Underground - 0.5m
Bus Route 282 & H11 to Northwood Hills

SOUTH PARK

Isthmian League South Central

Founded 1897 **Nickname:** The Sparks **Club Colours:** Red & green

Club Contact Details
01737 245 963 spfc1897@hotmail.com

Previous Names: South Park & Reigate Town 2001-03.
Previous Leagues: Redhill & District. Crawley & District > 2006. Combined Counties 2006-14.

11-12		12-13		13-14		14-15		15-16		16-17		17-18		18-19		19-20		20-21	
CCP	8	CCP	4	CCP	1	Isth1S	14	Isth1S	11	Isth1S	8	Isth1S	13	IsthSC	17	IsthSC	n&v	IsthSC	n&v
FAC	P	FAC	4Q	FAC	1Qr	FAC	1Qr	FAC	2Q	FAC	2Q	FAC	P	FAC	P	FAC	1Q	FAC	1Q
FAV	4P	FAV	3P	FAV	3P	FAT	1Q	FAT	1Q	FAT	2P	FAT	Pr	FAT	P	FAT	P	FAT	1Q

HONOURS / RECORDS
FA Comps: None
League: Combined Counties Premier Division 2013-14.

County FA: Surrey Premier Cup 2010-11.

Best FA Cup Fourth Qualifying Round 2012-13
FA Vase Fourth Round Proper 2011-12
FA Trophy Second Round Proper 2016-17

GROUND: King George's Field, Whitehall Lane, South Park RH2 8LG
Ground Capacity: 2,000 **Seats:** 113 **Covered:** Yes **Clubhouse:** Yes **Shop:** Yes
Previous Grounds: Crescent Road. Church Road.
Record Attendance: 643 v Metropolitan Police, 20/10/2012

Nearest Railway Station Reigate - 2km
Bus Route Sandcross Lane - stop 200m away

STAINES TOWN

Isthmian League South Central

Founded 1892 **Nickname:** The Swans **Club Colours:** Yellow and blue

Club Contact Details
01784 469 240 steve@stainestownfootballclub.co.uk

Previous Names: Staines Albany & St Peters Institute merged in 1895. Staines 1905-18, Staines Lagonda 1918-25, Staines Vale (WWII)
Previous Leagues: Great Western Suburban, Hounslow & District 1919-20, Spartan 1924-35, 58-71, Middlesex Senior 1943-52, Parthenon 1952-53, Hellenic 1953-58, Athenian 1971-73, Isthmian 1973-2009, 15-18. Conference 2009-15. Southern 2018-19.

11-12		12-13		13-14		14-15		15-16		16-17		17-18		18-19		19-20		20-21	
Conf S	15	Conf S	18	Conf S	8	Conf S	21	Isth P	16	Isth P	12	Isth P	8	SthPS	22	IsthSC	n&v	IsthSC	n&v
FAC	4Q	FAC	2Q	FAC	1P	FAC	3Qr	FAC	1P	FAC	3Q	FAC	1Q	FAC	1Q	FAC	2Q	FAC	1Q
FAT	2P	FAT	3Qr	FAT	1Pr	FAT	3Qr	FAT	1Q	FAT	1Q	FAT	1Q	FAT	1Q	FAT	P	FAT	1Q

HONOURS / RECORDS
FA Comps: None
League: Spartan League 1959-60. Athenian League Division Two 1971-72, Division One 1974-75, 88-89.

County FA: Middlesex Senior cup 1975-76, 76-77, 77-78, 88-89, 90-91, 94-95, 97-98, 2009-10, 12-13. Barassi Cup 1975-76.

Victory: 14-0 v Croydon (A) - Isthmian Division 1 19/03/1994
Defeat: 1-18 - Wycombe Wanderers (A) - Great Western Suburban League 27/12/1909
Goalscorer: Alan Gregory - 122
Appearances: Dickie Watmore - 840

GROUND: Wheatsheaf Park, Wheatsheaf Lane, Staines TW18 2PD
Ground Capacity: 3,000 **Seats:** 300 **Covered:** 850 **Clubhouse:** Yes **Shop:** Yes
Previous Grounds: Groundshared with Walton & Hersham and Egham Town whilst new Wheatsheaf stadium was built 2001-03.
Record Attendance: 2,860 v Stokcport County, FAC, 2007

Nearest Railway Station Staines - 1.3km
Bus Route Penton Hook Road - stop 100m away

SUTTON COMMON ROVERS

Isthmian League South Central

Founded 1978 **Nickname:** Commoners **Club Colours:** All yellow

Club Contact Details

020 8644 4440 scrfcsecretary@outlook.com

Previous Names: Inrad FC. Centre 21 FC . SCR Plough, SCR Grapes, SRC Litten Tree, SCR Kingfisher, Mole Valley SCR >2015.
Previous Leagues: South Eastern Combination >2007. Middlesex County 2007-08. Combined Counties 2008-21.

11-12		12-13		13-14		14-15		15-16		16-17		17-18		18-19		19-20		20-21	
CCP	21	CC1	2	CCP	18	CCP	18	CCP	19	CCP	12	CCP	3	CCP	2	CCP	n&v	CCP	n&v
FAC	EP	FAC	EPr	FAC	EP	FAC	P	FAC	EP	FAC	EPr	FAC	P	FAC	EP	FAC	1Q	FAC	1Q
FAV	2Q	FAV	2Q	FAV	2Q	FAV	1Q	FAV	4P	FAV	3P	FAV	1Q	FAV	2P	FAV	5P	FAV	4P

HONOURS / RECORDS

FA Comps: None

League: Combined Counties League Division One 2009-10.

County FA: None

Best FA Cup First Qualifying Round 2019-20, 20-21.
FA Vase Fifth Round Proper 2019-20.

GROUND: Sutton United FC, Gander Green Lane, Sutton. Surrey SM1 2EY

Ground Capacity: 5,013 **Seats:** 765 **Covered:** 1,250 **Clubhouse:** Yes **Shop:** Yes
Previous Grounds: Several
Record Attendance: Not known.

Nearest Railway Station West Sutton a few minutes walk from the ground.
Bus Route 413

THATCHAM TOWN

Isthmian League South Central

Founded 1895 **Nickname:** Kingfishers **Club Colours:** Blue and white

Club Contact Details

01635 862 016 stuartbailey1972@hotmail.com

Previous Names: Thatcham 1895-1974.
Previous Leagues: Reading Temperance 1896-1953. Hellenic (founder member) 1953-82, 2014-18. Athenian 1982-84, London Spartan 1984-86, Wessex 1986-2006. Southern 2006-14, 18-21.

11-12		12-13		13-14		14-15		15-16		16-17		17-18		18-19		19-20		20-21	
Sthsw	8	SthC	17	Sthsw	19	Hel P	12	Hel P	2	Hel P	4	Hel P	1	SthS	11	SthS	n&v	SthS	n&v
FAC	P	FAC	2Q	FAC	P	FAC	EPr	FAC	1Q	FAC	EP	FAC	2Q	FAC	Pr	FAC	1Q	FAC	P
FAT	2Qr	FAT	P	FAT	P	FAV	1P	FAV	2Q	FAV	3P	FAV	F	FAT	1Q	FAT	2Q	FAT	2Q

HONOURS / RECORDS

FA Comps: FA Vase 2017-18.

League: Reading Temperance Division Two 1905-06. Hellenic Division One 1958-59, 64-65, 72-73, Premier 1974-75, 2017-18. Wessex 1995-96.

County FA: Berks & Bucks Junior Cup 1935-36, Senior Cup 74-75, Senior Trophy 2004-05. Basingstoke Senior Cup 2008-09, 10-11, 11-12.

Best FA Cup Fourth Qualifying Round 1996-97
FA Trophy Second Qualifying Round 2008-09, 09-10, 11-12(r)
FA Vase Winners 2017-18

GROUND: Waterside Park, Crookham Hill, Thatcham, Berks RG19 4PA

Ground Capacity: 2,500 **Seats:** 300 **Covered:** 300 **Clubhouse:** Yes **Shop:** Yes
Previous Grounds: Station Road 1946-52, Lancaster Close 1952-92
Record Attendance: 1,400 v Aldershot - FA Vase

Nearest Railway Station Thatcham - 1.6km
Bus Route Vincent Road stop - 287m away

TOOTING & MITCHAM UNITED

Isthmian League South Central

Founded 1932 **Nickname:** The Terrors **Club Colours:** Black and white stripes

Club Contact Details
020 8685 6193 steve.adkins@tmsportsandleisure.co.uk

Previous Names: Tooting Town (Founded in 1887) and Mitcham Wanderers (1912) merged in 1932 to form Tooting & Mitcham FC.
Previous Leagues: London 1932-37, Athenian 1937-56

11-12		12-13		13-14		14-15		15-16		16-17		17-18		18-19		19-20		20-21	
Isth P	21	Isth1S	16	Isth1S	11	Isth1S	11	Isth1S	17	Isth1S	1	Isth P	24	IsthSC	6	IsthSC	n&v	IsthSC	n&v
FAC	1Q	FAC	1Q	FAC	P	FAC	3Q	FAC	2Q	FAC	P	FAC	2Q	FAC	2Q	FAC	3Q	FAC	P
FAT	1Q	FAT	1Q	FAT	P	FAT	P	FAT	1Q	FAT	1Q	FAT	1Q	FAT	EP	FAT	3Q	FAT	3Q

HONOURS / RECORDS
FA Comps: None

League: Athenian 1949-50, 54-55. Isthmian 1975-76, 59-60, Division Two 2000-01, Division One South 2016-17.

County FA: London Senior Cup 1942-43, 48-49, 58-59, 59-60, 2006-07, 07-08, 15-16. Surrey Senior cup 1937-38, 43-44, 44-45, 52-53, 59-60, 75-76, 76-77, 77-78, 2007-07. Surrey Senior Shield 1951-52, 60-61, 61-62, 65-66.

Victory: 11-0 v Welton Rovers - FA Amateur Cup 1962-63
Defeat: 1-8 v Kingstonian - Surrey Senior Cup 1966-67
Goalscorer: Alan Ives - 92
Appearances: Danny Godwin - 470
Additional: Paid £9,000 to Enfield for David Flint. Received £10,000 from Luton Town for Herbie Smith.

GROUND: Imperial Fields, Bishopsford Road, Morden, Surrey SM4 6BF
Ground Capacity: 3,500 **Seats:** 612 **Covered:** 1,200 **Clubhouse:** Yes **Shop:** Yes
Previous Grounds: Sandy Lane, Mitcham
Record Attendance: 17,500 v Queens Park Rangers - FA Cup 2nd Round 1956-57 (At Sandy Lane)

Nearest Railway Station Mitcham Tram Stop - 0.5km
Bus Route 280

UXBRIDGE

Isthmian League South Central

Founded 1871 **Nickname:** The Reds **Club Colours:** Red & white

Club Contact Details
01895 443 557 sec@uxbridgefc.co.uk

Previous Names: Uxbridge Town 1923-45
Previous Leagues: Southern 1894-99, Gt Western Suburban 1906-19, 20-23, Athenian 1919-20, 24-37, 63-82, Spartan 1937-38, London 1938-46, Great Western Comb. 1939-45, Corinthian 1946-63, Athenian 1963-82. Isthmian 1982-2004. Southern 2004-18.

11-12		12-13		13-14		14-15		15-16		16-17		17-18		18-19		19-20		20-21	
SthC	4	SthC	11	SthC	10	SthC	12	SthC	15	SthC	17	Sth1E	15	IsthSC	15	IsthSC	n&v	IsthSC	n&v
FAC	P	FAC	1Q	FAC	1Q	FAC	2Q	FAC	3Q	FAC	2Q	FAC	P	FAC	P	FAC	P	FAC	P
FAT	1P	FAT	2Qr	FAT	P	FAT	2Q	FAT	P	FAT	1Q	FAT	P	FAT	EPr	FAT	1Q	FAT	1P

HONOURS / RECORDS
FA Comps: None

League: Corinthian 1959-60.

County FA: Middlesex Senior Cup 1893-94, 95-96, 1950-51, 2000-01, Charity Cup 1907-08, 12-13, 35-36, 81-82, 2012-13, 13-14. London Challenge Cup 1993-94, 96-97, 98-99.

Goalscorer: Phil Duff - 153
Appearances: Roger Nicholls - 1,054
Best FA Cup Second Round Proper 1873-74 **FA Amateur Cup:** Finalists 1897-98
FA Trophy Second Round Proper 1998-99, 99-2000, 00-01, 08-09
FA Vase Fourth Round Proper 1983-84

GROUND: Honeycroft, Horton Road, West Drayton, Middlesex UB7 8HX
Ground Capacity: 3,770 **Seats:** 339 **Covered:** 760 **Clubhouse:** Yes **Shop:**
Previous Grounds: RAF Stadium 1923-48, Cleveland Road 1948-78
Record Attendance: 1,000 v Arsenal - Opening of the floodlights 1981

Nearest Railway Station West Drayton - 1km
Bus Route 350 & A10

WESTFIELD

Isthmian League South Central

Founded 1953 **Nickname:** The Field **Club Colours:** Amber & black

Club Contact Details

01483 771 106 david.robson12@ntlworld.com

Previous Names: None

Previous Leagues: Woking & District. Surrey Intermediate > 1962. Parthenon 1962-63. Surrey Senior 1963-78. Combined Counties (FM) 1978-2018

11-12		12-13		13-14		14-15		15-16		16-17		17-18		18-19		19-20		20-21	
CC1	8	CC1	3	CCP	4	CCP	14	CCP	9	CCP	2	CCP	1	IsthSC	5	IsthSC	n&v	IsthSC	n&v
FAC	EP	FAC	EP	FAC	1Qr	FAC	P	FAC	EPr	FAC	EP	FAC	2Q	FAC	P	FAC	1Q	FAC	P
FAV	2Q	FAV	1Q	FAV	1P	FAV	2P	FAV	2Q	FAV	2Q	FAV	3P	FAT	Pr	FAT	2Qr	FAT	2Q

HONOURS / RECORDS

FA Comps: None

League: Surrey Senior League 1972-73, 73-74. Combined Counties Premier 2017-18.

County FA: Surrey County Junior Charity Cup 1954-55

Best FA Cup Second Qualifying Round 2017-18

FA Vase Fourth Round Proper 2000-01

FA Trophy Second Qualifyig Round 2019-20(r)

GROUND: Woking Park, off Elmbridge Lane, Kingfield, Woking GU22 9BA

Ground Capacity: 1000 **Seats:** Yes **Covered:** Yes **Clubhouse:** Yes **Shop:**

Previous Grounds: Moved to Woking Park in 1960

Record Attendance: 325 v Guernsey, Combined Counties Division One, 2011-12

Nearest Railway Station Woking

Bus Route Arriva 34, 35

ASHFORD UNITED

Isthmian South East

Founded 1930 **Nickname:** The Nuts & Bolts **Club Colours:** Green & white

Club Contact Details
01233 611 838 aufootballclub@yahoo.com

Previous Names: Ashford Town 1930-2010.
Previous Leagues: Kent 1930-59. Southern 1959-2004. Isthmian 2004-10. Kent Invicta 2011-2013. Southern Counties East 2013-17.

11-12		12-13		13-14		14-15		15-16		16-17		17-18		18-19		19-20		20-21	
K_lv	5	K_lv	3	SCEP	2	SCEP	2	SCEP	3	SCEP	1	Isth1S	21	IsthSE	4	IsthSE	n&v	IsthSE	n&v
		FAC	P	FAC	P	FAC	P	FAC	EP	FAC	1Q	FAC	1Q	FAC	P	FAC	1Q	FAC	1Q
FAV	1Qr	FAV	2Q	FAV	4P	FAV	4P	FAV	QF	FAV	2P	FAT	P	FAT	EPr	FAT	1Q	FAT	2Q

HONOURS / RECORDS
FA Comps: None
League: Kent 1948-49. Southern Counties East 2016-17.

County FA: Kent Senior Cup 1958-59, 62-63, 92-93, 95-96. Kent Senior Trophy 2016-17.

Victory: 15-0 v Erith & Belvedere, Kent League, 28/04/1937.
Defeat: 3-14 v Folkestone Reserves, Kent League, 1933-34.
Goalscorer: Dave Arter - 197. Shaun Welford scored 48 goals during the 2016-17 season. Stuart Zanone scored 7 v Lingfield (A), Southern Counties East, 24/03/2015.
Appearances: Peter McRobert - 765

GROUND: The Homelands, Ashford Road TN26 1NJ
Ground Capacity: 3,200 **Seats:** 500 **Covered:** Yes **Clubhouse:** Yes **Shop:**
Previous Grounds: Essella Park 1931-1987.
Record Attendance: At Essella Park - 6,525 v Crystal Palace, FAC 1st Rnd, 1959-60. At Homelands - 3,363 v Fulham, FAC 1st , 1994-95.

Nearest Railway Station Ham Street - 4.2km
Bus Route Smithfields Crossroads - stop 600m away

BURGESS HILL TOWN

Isthmian South East

Founded 1882 **Nickname:** Hillians **Club Colours:** Green & black

Club Contact Details
01444 254 832 timspencer57@hotmail.com

Previous Names: Burgess Hill 1882-1969.
Previous Leagues: Mid Sussex >1958, Sussex County 1958-2003, Southern 2003-04

11-12		12-13		13-14		14-15		15-16		16-17		17-18		18-19		19-20		20-21	
Isth1S	20	Isth1S	8	Isth1S	6	Isth1S	1	Isth P	21	Isth P	20	Isth P	23	Isth P	21	IsthSE	n&v	IsthSE	n&v
FAC	P	FAC	P	FAC	2Q	FAC	4Q	FAC	1Q	FAC	4Qr	FAC	4Q	FAC	2Q	FAC	P	FAC	1Q
FAT	1Q	FAT	Pr	FAT	Pr	FAT	2P	FAT	1Q	FAT	3Q	FAT	2Q	FAT	1Qr	FAT	P	FAT	2P

HONOURS / RECORDS
FA Comps: None
League: Mid-Sussex 1900-01, 03-04, 39-40, 56-57. Sussex County Division Two 1974-75, Division One 75-76, 96-97, 98-99, 2001-02, 02-03. Isthmian Division One South 2014-15.
County FA: Sussex Senior Cup 1883-84, 84-85, 85-86.

Goalscorer: Ashley Carr - 208
Appearances: Paul Williams - 499
Best FA Cup Fourth Qualifying Round 1999-2000, 08-09, 14-15, 16-17(r), 17-18.
FA Trophy Second Round Proper 2003-04, 04-05, 14-15.
FA Vase Quarter Finals 2001-02.

GROUND: Green Elephant Stadium, Leylands Park, Maple Drive, Burgess Hill, West Sussex RH15 8DL
Ground Capacity: 2,500 **Seats:** 408 **Covered:** Yes **Clubhouse:** Yes **Shop:** Yes
Previous Grounds: Moved to Leylands Park in 1969.
Record Attendance: 2,005 v AFC Wimbledon - Isthmian League Division One 2004-05

Nearest Railway Station Wivelsfield - 0.3m
Bus Route 270, 271 & 272

CHICHESTER CITY

Isthmian South East

Founded 2000 **Nickname:** Lillywhites **Club Colours:** White & green

Club Contact Details

01243 533 368 secretary@chichestercityfc.co.uk

Previous Names: Chichester FC (pre 1948), Chichester City 1948-2000. Merged with Portfield in 2000, Chicester City United 2000-09
Previous Leagues: Sussex County/Southern Combination >2019

11-12		12-13		13-14		14-15		15-16		16-17		17-18		18-19		19-20		20-21	
SxC1	20	SxC1	19	SxC1	11	SxC1	14	SCP	5	SCP	3	SCP	6	SCP	1	IsthSE	n&v	IsthSE	n&v
FAC	EPr	FAC	EP	FAC	EP	FAC	EP	FAC	P	FAC	EP	FAC	EP	FAC	EP	FAC	2P	FAC	3Q
FAV	2P	FAV	2Q	FAV	1Q	FAV	1Q	FAV	1Q	FAV	4P	FAV	5P	FAV	2P	FAT	P	FAT	2Q

HONOURS / RECORDS
FA Comps: None

League: Sussex County Division One 2003-04. Southern Combination Premier 2018-19.

County FA: Sussex RUR Cup 2006-07

FA Cup Second Round Proper 2019-20 (Due to Bury folding, the club were the lucky ones to get a bye to the Second Round.)
FA Vase Fifth Round Proper 2017-18
FA Trophy Preliminary Round 2019-20

GROUND: Oaklands Park, Chichester, W Sussex PO19 6AR
Ground Capacity: 2,000 **Seats:** none **Covered:** 200 **Clubhouse:** Yes **Shop:** Yes
Previous Grounds: Church Road (Portfield) 2000-08.
Record Attendance: Not known

Nearest Railway Station Chichester - 1.2km
Bus Route University - stop 182m away

CORINTHIAN

Isthmian South East

Founded 1972 **Nickname:** The Hoops **Club Colours:** Green & white hoops

Club Contact Details

01474 573 116 corinthians@billingsgroup.com

Previous Names: Welling United Reserves > 2009.
Previous Leagues: Southern 1985-91. Kent/Southern Counties East >2021.

11-12		12-13		13-14		14-15		15-16		16-17		17-18		18-19		19-20		20-21	
Kent P	7	Kent P	4	SCE	5	SCE	6	SCE	6	SCEP	10	SCEP	9	SCEP	2	SCEP	n&v	SCEP	n&v
FAC	P	FAC	P	FAC	P	FAC	EP	FAC	P	FAC	EP	FAC	EPr	FAC	1Qr	FAC	EP	FAC	2Q
FAV	2Q	FAV	1Q	FAV	1P	FAV	1P	FAV	1P	FAV	4P	FAV	2P	FAV	2P	FAV	SF	FAV	2P

HONOURS / RECORDS
FA Comps: None
League: Southern Counties East 2003-04.

County FA: None

Best FA Cup Second Qualifying Round 1993094, 2020-21
FA Vase Semi-final 2019-20.

GROUND: Gay Dawn Farm, Valley Road, Longfield DA3 8LY
Ground Capacity: **Seats:** Yes **Covered:** Yes **Clubhouse:** Yes **Shop:**
Previous Grounds: None
Record Attendance: Not known

Nearest Railway Station Longfield - 1.5 miles away

CRAY VALLEY PAPER MILLS

Isthmian South East

Founded 1919 **Nickname:** Millers **Club Colours:** Green & black

Club Contact Details
07838 344 451 jason.taylor@nexusschool.org.uk

Previous Names: None
Previous Leagues: Sidcup & Kent 1919. Kent County Amateur >55. South London Alliance 55-91. Spartan 1991-97, Spartan South Midlands 1997-98, London Intermediate 1998-01, Kent County 2001-11, Kent/Southern Co East 2011-19.

11-12		12-13		13-14		14-15		15-16		16-17		17-18		18-19		19-20		20-21	
Kent P	11	Kent P	8	SCE	7	SCE	7	SCE	10	SCEP	4	SCEP	6	SCEP	1	IsthSE	n&v	IsthSE	n&v
				FAC	P	FAC	EP	FAC	P	FAC	P	FAC	1Q	FAC	2Q	FAC	P	FAC	1P
		FAV	1Q	FAV	2Pr	FAV	2Q	FAV	1P	FAV	1Q	FAV	1P	FAV	F	FAT	P	FAT	2Q

HONOURS / RECORDS
FA Comps: None
League: Sidcup & Kent Division Two 1919-20. South Kent County Division Three (Western) 1933-37, Division One West 2002-03, Premier Division 2004-05. London Alliance Premier Division 1980-81. Southern Counties Premier 2018-19.
County FA: Kent Junior Cup 1921-22, 77-78, 80-81. Kent Intermediate Shield 2004-05. London Intermediate Cup 2002-03, 03-04, 09-10. London Senior Cup 2016-17.
FA Cup First Round Proper 2020-21
FA Vase Runners-up 2018-19
FA Trophy Second Qualifying Round 2020-21

GROUND: Badgers Sports Ground, Middle Park Avenue, Eltham SE9 5HT
Ground Capacity: 1,000 **Seats:** 100 **Covered:** Yes **Clubhouse:** Yes **Shop:**
Previous Grounds: St Paul's Cray paper mills sports ground 1919-81. Played at many grounds until permanent move to Badgers.
Record Attendance: 663 v Canterbury City, FA Vase semi-final, 17/03/2019

Nearest Railway Station Mottingham - 30min walk from ground.
Bus Route 160 stops outside the ground.

EAST GRINSTEAD TOWN

Isthmian South East

Founded 1890 **Nickname:** The Wasps **Club Colours:** Amber & black

Club Contact Details
01342 325 885 brian.mcc@egtfc.co.uk

Previous Names: East Grinstead 1890-1997.
Previous Leagues: Mid Sussex, Sussex County, Souhern Amateur 1928-35. Sussex County 1935-2014.

11-12		12-13		13-14		14-15		15-16		16-17		17-18		18-19		19-20		20-21	
SxC1	9	SxC1	8	SxC1	2	Isth1S	22	Isth1S	20	Isth1S	18	Isth1S	22	IsthSE	13	IsthSE	n&v	IsthSE	n&v
				FAC	EP	FAC	Pr	FAC	P	FAC	P	FAC	1Q	FAC	2Q	FAC	P	FAC	2Q
		FAV	1Qr	FAV	2P	FAT	Pr	FAT	1Q	FAT	1Q	FAT	P	FAT	1Q	FAT	P	FAT	2Q

HONOURS / RECORDS
FA Comps: None
League: Mid-Sussex 1901-02, 36-37. Southern Amateur DivisioN Three 1931-32. Sussex County Division Two 2007-08.

County FA: Sussex RUR Cup 2003-04.

Appearances: Guy Hill
Best FA Cup Second Qualifying Round 1947-48, 50-51, 52-53, 71-72, 2018-19, 20-21
FA Trophy Second Qualifying Round 2020-21
FA Vase Third Round Proper 1974-75

GROUND: College Lane, East Court, East Grinstead RH19 3LS
Ground Capacity: 3,000 **Seats:** Yes **Covered:** Yes **Clubhouse:** Yes **Shop:** No
Previous Grounds: West Ground 1890-1962. King George's Field 1962-67.
Record Attendance: 2,006 v Lancing F A Am Cup, November 1947

Nearest Railway Station East Grinstead - 1.1km
Bus Route East Court - stop 100m away

FAVERSHAM TOWN

Isthmian South East

Founded 1884 **Nickname:** Lillywhites **Club Colours:** White & black

Club Contact Details

01795 591 000 wendy-walker@hotmail.co.uk

Previous Names: Faversham Invicta, Faversham Services, Faversham Railway and Faversham Rangers pre War.

Previous Leagues: Kent 1884-1900, 1904-12, 24-34, 37-59, 66-71, 76-2003. Kent County 1934-37. Aetolian 1959-63. Greater London 1964-66. Metropolitan London 1971-73. Athenian 1973-76. Kent County 2005-10.

11-12		12-13		13-14		14-15		15-16		16-17		17-18		18-19		19-20		20-21	
Isth1S	17	Isth1S	3	Isth1S	10	Isth1S	3	Isth1S	5	Isth1S	10	Isth1S	19	IsthSE	17	IsthSE	n&v	IsthSE	n&v
FAC	1Q	FAC	1Qr	FAC	2Q	FAC	2Q	FAC	1Qr	FAC	3Qr	FAC	2Q	FAC	1Q	FAC	P	FAC	1Q
FAT	2Q	FAT	1Q	FAT	P	FAT	1Q	FAT	P	FAT	1Q	FAT	P	FAT	P	FAT	P	FAT	3Q

HONOURS / RECORDS

FA Comps: None

League: Kent 1969-70, 70-71, 77-78, 89-90, Division Two 1895-96. Kent County 2009-10.

County FA: Kent Amateur Cup 1956-57, 58-59, 71-72, 72-73, 73-74. Kent Senior Trophy 1976-77, 77-78.

Best FA Cup Third Qualifying Round 2016-17
FA Trophy Third Qualifying Round 2020-21
FA Vase Third Round Proper 1991-92

GROUND: The Aquatherm Stadium, Salters Lane, Faversham Kent ME13 8ND

Ground Capacity: 2,000 **Seats:** 200 **Covered:** 1,800 **Clubhouse:** Yes **Shop:** No

Previous Grounds: Moved in to Salters Lane in 1948.

Record Attendance:

Nearest Railway Station Faversham - 0.5m

Bus Route 3 & 666

HASTINGS UNITED

Isthmian South East

Founded 1894 **Nickname:** The U's or The Arrows **Club Colours:** All white

Club Contact Details

01424 444 635 dane.martin@hastingsunited.com

Previous Names: Rock-a-Nore 1894-1921. Hastings and St Leonards Amateurs 1921-79. Hastings Town 1979-2002.

Previous Leagues: South Eastern 1904-05, Southern 1905-10, Sussex County 1921-27, 52-85, Southern Amateur 1927-46, Corinthian 1946-48

11-12		12-13		13-14		14-15		15-16		16-17		17-18		18-19		19-20		20-21	
Isth P	18	Isth P	22	Isth1S	5	Isth1S	19	Isth1S	7	Isth1S	5	Isth1S	9	IsthSE	3	IsthSE	n&v	IsthSE	n&v
FAC	1Q	FAC	3P	FAC	1Q	FAC	2Q	FAC	3Q	FAC	3Qr	FAC	1Q	FAC	3Q	FAC	1Qr	FAC	2Q
FAT	1Qr	FAT	1Q	FAT	2Q	FAT	P	FAT	2Q	FAT	2Qr	FAT	1Q	FAT	P	FAT	3Q	FAT	1P

HONOURS / RECORDS

FA Comps: None

League: Southern Division Two B 1909-10, Southern Division 1991-92, Eastern Division 2001-01.
Sussex County Division Two 1979-80.

County FA: Sussex Senior Cup 1935-36, 37-38, 95-96, 97-98.

Goalscorer: Terry White scored 33 during 1999-2000

Additional: Paid £8,000 to Ashford Town for Nicky Dent
Received £50,000 from Nottingham Forest for Paul Smith

GROUND: The Pilot Field, Elphinstone Road, Hastings TN34 2AX

Ground Capacity: 4,050 **Seats:** 800 **Covered:** 1,750 **Clubhouse:** Yes **Shop:** Yes

Previous Grounds: Bulverhythe Recreation > 1976

Record Attendance: 4,888 v Nottingham Forest - Friendly 23/06/1996

Nearest Railway Station Ore - 0.9km. Hastings - 1.9km.

Bus Route 2 & 21A

HAYWARDS HEATH TOWN

Isthmian South East

Founded 1888 **Nickname:** The Blues **Club Colours:** Blue & white

Club Contact Details

07385 744 630 rea.john@mail.com

Previous Names: Haywards Heath Juniors 1888-94. Haywards Heath Excelsior 1894-95. Haywards Heath 1895-1989.

Previous Leagues: Mid-Sussex 1888-1926. Brighton, Hove & Dist. 1926-27. Sussex County/Southern Combination 1927-52, 61-2018. Metropolitan 1952-61.

11-12	12-13	13-14	14-15	15-16	16-17	17-18	18-19	19-20	20-21
SxC3 15	SxC3 2	SxC2 5	SxC2 9	SC1 1	SCP 2	SCP 1	IsthSE 5	IsthSE n&v	IsthSE n&v
			FAC EP		FAC P	FAC 1Qr	FAC EP	FAC 1Q	FAC 1Q
FAV 1Qr		FAV 2Q	FAV 1Q	FAV 2P	FAV 2P	FAV 2P	FAT P	FAT 2Q	FAT 2Q

HONOURS / RECORDS

FA Comps: None

League: Mid-Sussex Division Two 1911-12, Premier 19-20, 22-23, 23-24, 24-25. Brighton, Hove & Dist 1926-27. Sussex County/Southern Combination 1949-50, 69-70, 2017-18, Eastern Division 45-46/ Division One 2015-16.

County FA: Sussex Senior Cup 1941-42, 57-58. Sussex RUR Cup 1943-44, 66-67, 74-75, 75-76. Sussex Intermediate Cup 2012-13

Best FA Cup Fourth Qualifying Round 1945-46

FA Vase Third Round Proper 1990-91

FA Trophy Second Qualifying Round 2019-20, 20-21

GROUND: Thank You NHS Stadium, Hanbury Park, Haywards Heath RH16 3PT

Ground Capacity: 2,000 **Seats:** Yes **Covered:** Yes **Clubhouse:** Yes **Shop:**

Previous Grounds: South Road/Victoria Park >1952.

Record Attendance: Not known

Nearest Railway Station Haywards Heath - 1.9km

Bus Route Market Square - stop 84m away

HERNE BAY

Isthmian South East

Founded 1886 **Nickname:** The Bay **Club Colours:** Blue & white

Club Contact Details

01227 374 156 mjsexton@btinternet.com

Previous Names: None.

Previous Leagues: East Kent. Faversham & Dist. Cantebury & Dist. Kent Am. Aetolian 1959-64. Athenian 1964-74.

11-12	12-13	13-14	14-15	15-16	16-17	17-18	18-19	19-20	20-21
Kent P 1	Isth1S 19	Isth1S 18	Isth1S 9	Isth1S 8	Isth1S 17	Isth1S 12	IsthSE 15	IsthSE n&v	IsthSE n&v
FAC 1Q	FAC P	FAC Pr	FAC 1Q	FAC 2Qr	FAC 2Qr	FAC 3Q	FAC 1Q	FAC 1Q	FAC P
FAV SF	FAT P	FAT 1Qr	FAT P	FAT 2Qr	FAT 1Qr	FAT P	FAT 2Q	FAT P	FAT 3Q

HONOURS / RECORDS

FA Comps: None

League: East Kent 1902-03, 03-04, 04-05, 05-06. Athenian Division Two 1970-71. Kent 1991-92, 93-94, 96-97, 97-98, 2011-12, Division Two 1954-55.

County FA: Kent Amateur Cup 1957-58. Kent Senior Trophy 1978-79, 1996-97.

Victory: 19-3 v Hythe Wanderers - Feb 1900.

Defeat: 0-11 v 7th Dragon Guards - Oct 1907.

Misc: Most League Victories in a Season: 34 - 1996-97.

GROUND: Winch's Field, Stanley Gardens, Herne Bay CT6 5SG

Ground Capacity: 3,000 **Seats:** 200 **Covered:** 1,500 **Clubhouse:** Yes **Shop:** Yes

Previous Grounds: Mitchell's Athletic Ground. Herne Bay Memorial Park.

Record Attendance: 2,303 v Margate, FA Cup 4th Qual. 1970-71.

Nearest Railway Station Herne Bay - 0.8km

Bus Route Triangle - alighting at Spenser Road East

HYTHE TOWN

Isthmian South East

Founded 1910 **Nickname:** The Cannons **Club Colours:** Red & white

Club Contact Details

01303 264 932 / 238 256 martinandsuegiles@gmail.com

Previous Names: Hythe Town 1910-1992, Hythe United 1992-2001

Previous Leagues: Kent Amateur League, Kent League, Southern League, Kent County League, Kent League.

11-12		12-13		13-14		14-15		15-16		16-17		17-18		18-19		19-20		20-21	
Isth1S	8	Isth1S	4	Isth1S	8	Isth1S	16	Isth1S	4	Isth1S	7	Isth1S	7	IsthSE	7	IsthSE	n&v	IsthSE	n&v
FAC	2Q	FAC	P	FAC	P	FAC	2Q	FAC	P	FAC	2Q	FAC	Pr	FAC	1Q	FAC	P	FAC	P
FAT	2Q	FAT	1Qr	FAT	2Qr	FAT	1Q	FAT	P	FAT	1P	FAT	1Q	FAT	1Q	FAT	P	FAT	3Q

HONOURS / RECORDS

FA Comps: None

League: Kent County Eastern Division Two 1936-37, Division One 71-72, Premier Division 73-74, 74-75, 75-76.
Kent League 1988-89, 2010-11.

County FA: Kent Senior Cup 2011-12.
Kent Senior Trophy 1990-91.

Victory: 10-1 v Sporting Bengal, 2008-09

Defeat: 1-10 v Swanley Furness, 1997-98

Goalscorer: Dave Cook - 130

Appearances: John Walker - 354, Jason Brazier - 349, Dave Cook - 346, Lee Winfield - 344

GROUND: Reachfields Stadium, Fort Road, Hythe CT21 6JS

Ground Capacity: 3,000 **Seats:** 350 **Covered:** 2,400 **Clubhouse:** Yes **Shop:** Yes

Previous Grounds: South Road 1910-77.

Record Attendance: 2,147 v Yeading, FA Vase Semi-Final, 1990.

Nearest Railway Station Hythe - 0.5km

Bus Route 10, 102, 104 & 16

LANCING

Isthmian South East

Founded 1941 **Nickname:** The Lancers **Club Colours:** Yellow and blue

Club Contact Details

01903 755 251 secretary@lancingfc.com

Previous Names: Lancing Athletic 1941-57

Previous Leagues: Brighton & Hove & District 1946-48. Sussex County/Southern Combination >2021.

11-12		12-13		13-14		14-15		15-16		16-17		17-18		18-19		19-20		20-21	
SxC1	2	SxC1	13	SxC1	18	SxC1	8	SCP	4	SCP	12	SCP	10	SCP	13	SCP	n&v	SCP	n&v
FAC	P	FAC	P	FAC	EPr	FAC	EP	FAC	EP	FAC	EPr	FAC	EPr	FAC	2Q	FAC	EPr	FAC	EP
FAV	3P	FAV	1P	FAV	2Q	FAV	2Q	FAV	1P	FAV	2P	FAV	2Q	FAV	1Q	FAV	3Pr	FAV	4P

HONOURS / RECORDS

FA Comps: None

League: Brighton 1946-47, 47-48. Sussex County Division Two 1957-58, 69-70.

County FA: Sussex RUR Cup 1965-66.

Best FA Cup Fourth Qualifying Round 1952-53

FA Vase Fourth Round Proper 2010-11, 20-21

GROUND: Culver Road, Lancing, West Sussex BN15 9AX

Ground Capacity: 2,000 **Seats:** 350 **Covered:** Yes **Clubhouse:** Yes **Shop:**

Previous Grounds: Croshaw Recreation Ground 1941-52.

Record Attendance: Not known

Nearest Railway Station Lancing - 0.2km

Bus Route North Road Post Office - stop 123m away

PHOENIX SPORTS

Isthmian South East

Founded 1935 **Nickname:** None **Club Colours:** Green & black

Club Contact Details
07795 182 927 alf_levy@sky.com

Previous Names: St Johns Welling. Lakeside. Phoenix.
Previous Leagues: Spartan League. Kent County > 2011. Kent Invicta 2011-13. Southern Counties East 2013-15.

11-12	12-13	13-14	14-15	15-16	16-17	17-18	18-19	19-20	20-21
K_Iv 2	K_Iv 1	SCE 6	SCE 1	Isth1N 14	Isth1N 8	Isth1N 11	IsthSE 9	IsthSE n&v	IsthSE n&v
			FAC EPr	FAC 2Q	FAC P	FAC 3Q	FAC 1Qr	FAC P	FAC P
		FAV 1P	FAV 5P	FAT 1Qr	FAT 2Q	FAT P	FAT Pr	FAT 1Q	FAT 2Q

HONOURS / RECORDS
FA Comps: None

League: Kent County Division One West 1999-2000, 2007-08, Division Two West 2004-05. Kent Invicta 2012-13. Southern Counties East 2014-15.
County FA: London Senior Trophy 2017-18

Best FA Cup Third Qualifying Round 2017-18
FA Trophy Second Qualifying Round 2016-17, 20-21
FA Vase Fifth Round Proper 2014-15

GROUND: Mayplace Ground, Mayplace Road East, Barnehurst, Kent DA7 6JT
Ground Capacity: 2,000 **Seats:** 439 **Covered:** Yes **Clubhouse:** Yes **Shop:** No
Previous Grounds: Danson Park >1950.
Record Attendance: Not known

Nearest Railway Station Barnehurst - 1.1km
Bus Route 492 stops at the ground

RAMSGATE

Isthmian South East

Founded 1945 **Nickname:** The Rams **Club Colours:** All red

Club Contact Details
01843 591 662 secretary@ramsgate-fc.co.uk

Previous Names: Ramsgate Athletic > 1972
Previous Leagues: Kent 1945-59, 1976-2005, Southern 1959-76

11-12	12-13	13-14	14-15	15-16	16-17	17-18	18-19	19-20	20-21
Isth1S 10	Isth1S 7	Isth1S 12	Isth1S 21	Isth1S 12	Isth1S 12	Isth1S 16	IsthSE 11	IsthSE n&v	IsthSE n&v
FAC Pr	FAC P	FAC P	FAC 1Q	FAC P	FAC 1Q	FAC 2Q	FAC 3Q	FAC 2Q	FAC P
FAT P	FAT 3Q	FAT 3Q	FAT P	FAT 1Q	FAT P	FAT P	FAT 1Q	FAT EPr	FAT 3Q

HONOURS / RECORDS
FA Comps: None
League: Kent Division One 1949-50, 55-56, 56-57, Premier 1998-99, 2004-05. Isthmian Division One 2005-06.

County FA: Kent Senior Shield 1960-61, 67-68, 68-69. Kent Senior Cup 1963-64. Kent Senior Trophy 1987-88, 88-89, 98-99.

Victory: 11-0 & 12-1 v Canterbury City - Kent League 2000-01
Goalscorer: Mick Willimson
Best FA Cup First Round Proper 1955-56, 2005-06
FA Trophy Third Qualifying Round 1969-70, 75-76, 2008-09, 09-10, 12-13, 13-14, 20-21
FA Vase Quarter Finals 1999-2000

GROUND: Southwood Stadium, Prices Avenue, Ramsgate, Kent CT11 0AN
Ground Capacity: 2,500 **Seats:** 400 **Covered:** 600 **Clubhouse:** Yes **Shop:** Yes
Previous Grounds: None
Record Attendance: 5,038 v Margate - 1956-57

Nearest Railway Station Ramsgate - 1km
Bus Route The Loop towards Ramsgate - alight at South Eastern Road

SEVENOAKS TOWN

Isthmian South East

Founded 1883 **Nickname:** Town **Club Colours:** Blue & black

Club Contact Details

07876 444 274 secretary@sevenoakstownfc.co.uk

Previous Names: None.

Previous Leagues: Sevenoaks League. Kent Amateur/County. Kent/Southern Counties East >2018.

11-12		12-13		13-14		14-15		15-16		16-17		17-18		18-19		19-20		20-21	
Kent P	14	Kent P	17	SCE	16	SCE	8	SCE	5	SCEP	3	SCEP	1	IsthSE	10	IsthSE	n&v	IsthSE	n&v
FAC	P	FAC	EP	FAC	EP	FAC	EP	FAC	EPr	FAC	2Qr	FAC	1Q	FAC	1Qr	FAC	1Q	FAC	1Q
FAV	2Q	FAV	1P	FAV	1P	FAV	1Q	FAV	2Q	FAV	2Q	FAV	3P	FAT	1Q	FAT	P	FAT	2Q

HONOURS / RECORDS

FA Comps: None

League: Kent County 1984-85, 95-96, 2002-03. Southern Counties East Premier 2017-18.

County FA:

Best FA Cup Second Qualifying Round 2016-17(r)

FA Vase Third Round Proper 2017-18

FA Trophy Second Qualifying Round 2020-21

GROUND: Greatness Park, Mill Lane, Sevenoaks TN14 5BX

Ground Capacity: 2,000 **Seats:** 150 **Covered:** 200 **Clubhouse:** Yes **Shop:**

Previous Grounds: None

Record Attendance: Not known

Nearest Railway Station Bat & Ball - 0.4km

Bus Route 308 & 402

SITTINGBOURNE

Isthmian South East

Founded 1886 **Nickname:** Brickies **Club Colours:** Red & black

Club Contact Details

01795 410 777 sittingbournefc.secretary@gmail.com

Previous Names: Sittingbourne United 1881-86

Previous Leagues: Kent 1894-1905, 1909-27, 30-39, 46-59, 68-91, South Eastern 1905-09, Southern 1927-30, 59-67

11-12		12-13		13-14		14-15		15-16		16-17		17-18		18-19		19-20		20-21	
Isth1S	19	Isth1S	9	Isth1S	14	Isth1S	12	Isth1S	18	Isth1S	15	Isth1S	14	IsthSE	16	IsthSE	n&v	IsthSE	n&v
FAC	1Q	FAC	1Q	FAC	3Q	FAC	P	FAC	2Q	FAC	Pr	FAC	Pr	FAC	1Q	FAC	1Q	FAC	P
FAT	1Q	FAT	1Q	FAT	P	FAT	P	FAT	P	FAT	P	FAT	2Qr	FAT	1Q	FAT	P	FAT	3Q

HONOURS / RECORDS

FA Comps: None

League: Kent 1902-03, 57-58, 58-59, 75-76, 83-84, 90-91. Southern Southern Division 1992-93, 95-96.

County FA: Kent Senior Cup 1901-02, 28-29, 29-30, 57-58.

Victory: 15-0 v Orpington, Kent League 1922-23)

Defeat: 0-10 v Wimbledon, SL Cup 1965-66)

Additional: Paid £20,000 to Ashford Town for Lee McRobert 1993
Received £210,000 from Millwall for Neil Emblem and Michael Harle 1993

GROUND: Woodstock Park, Broadoak Road, Sittingbourne ME9 8AG

Ground Capacity: 3,000 **Seats:** 300 **Covered:** 600 **Clubhouse:** Yes **Shop:** Yes

Previous Grounds: Sittingbourne Rec. 1881-90, Gore Court 1890-92, The Bull Ground 1892-1990. Central Park 1990-2001

Record Attendance: 5,951 v Tottenham Hotspur - Friendly 26/01/1993

Nearest Railway Station Sittingbourne - 3.1km

Bus Route Kent Science Park - stop 500m away

THREE BRIDGES

Isthmian South East

Founded 1901 **Nickname:** Bridges **Club Colours:** Yellow & black

Club Contact Details

01293 442 000 secretary@threebridgesfc.co.uk

Previous Names: Three Bridges Worth 1936-52. Three Bridges United 1953-64.

Previous Leagues: Mid Sussex, E Grinstead, Redhill & Dist 36-52. Sussex County/Southern Combintion >2012, 2017-18. Isthmian 2012-17.

11-12	12-13	13-14	14-15	15-16	16-17	17-18	18-19	19-20	20-21
SxC1 1	Isth1S 21	Isth1S 19	Isth1S 7	Isth1S 14	Isth1S 23	SCP 2	IsthSE 14	IsthSE n&v	IsthSE n&v
FAC EP	FAC P	FAC 1Q	FAC Pr	FAC P	FAC P	FAC P	FAC P	FAC P	FAC P
FAV 4Pr	FAT 2Q	FAT 2Q	FAT 1Q	FAT P	FAT P	FAV 1P	FAT P	FAT EP	FAT 3Q

HONOURS / RECORDS

FA Comps: None

League: Sussex County Division One 1953-54, 2011-12.

County FA: Sussex RUR Charity Cup 1982-83, 87-88, 2007-08

Appearances: John Malthouse

Best FA Cup Second Qualifying Round 1982-83, 83-84, 2002-03

FA Vase Fifth Round Proper 1981-82

FA Trophy Third Qualifying Round 2020-21

GROUND: Jubilee Walk, Three Bridges Road, Crawley, RH10 1LQ

Ground Capacity: 3,500 **Seats:** 120 **Covered:** 600 **Clubhouse:** Yes **Shop:**

Previous Grounds: None

Record Attendance: 2,000 v Horsham 1948

Nearest Railway Station Three Bridges - 0.4km

Bus Route Jubilee Walk - stop 71m away

VCD ATHLETIC

Isthmian South East

Founded 1916 **Nickname:** The Vickers **Club Colours:** Green & white

Club Contact Details

01322 524 262 davejoyo@yahoo.co.uk

Previous Names: Vickers (Erith). Vickers (Crayford) Now Vickers Crayford Dartford Athletic.

Previous Leagues: Dartford & District. Kent County 1997-2009, 2010-13. Isthmian 2009-10.

11-12	12-13	13-14	14-15	15-16	16-17	17-18	18-19	19-20	20-21
Kent P 3	Kent P 2	Isth1N 1	Isth P 18	Isth P 24	Isth1N 15	Isth1S 17	IsthSE 6	IsthSE n&v	IsthSE n&v
FAC 2Qr	FAC 1Q	FAC P	FAC 2Q	FAC 1Qr	FAC 2Q	FAC P	FAC P	FAC 1Q	FAC P
FAV 3Pr	FAV 1Pr	FAT Pr	FAT 1Q	FAT 2Q	FAT 1Q	FAT P	FAT 1Q	FAT P	FAT 2Q

HONOURS / RECORDS

FA Comps: None

League: Kent County 1952-53, 63-64, 96-97. Kent 2008-09. Isthmian Division One North 2013-14.

County FA: Kent Junior Cup 1926-27. Kent Amateur Cup 1961-62, 63-64. Kent Intermediate Cup 1995-96.
Kent Senior Trophy 2005-06, 08-09.

Best FA Cup Second Qualifying Round 2002-03, 08-09, 11-12(r), 14-15, 16-17

FA Trophy Second Qualifying Round 2015-16, 20-21

FA Vase Fifth Round Proper 2005-06, 06-07

GROUND: Oakwood, Old Road, Crayford DA1 4DN

Ground Capacity: 1,180 **Seats:** Yes **Covered:** Yes **Clubhouse:** Yes **Shop:** No

Previous Grounds: Groundshared with Thamesmead (5 seasons), Lordswood (2) and Greenwich Boro' (1) whilst waiting for planning at Oakwood.

Record Attendance: 13,500 Away v Maidstone, 1919.

Nearest Railway Station Crayford - 0.9km

Bus Route 492 & 96

WHITEHAWK

Isthmian South East

Founded 1945 **Nickname:** Hawks **Club Colours:** Red and white

Club Contact Details
01273 601 244 johnrosenblatt@whitehawkfc.com

Previous Names: Whitehawk & Manor Farm Old Boys untill 1960.
Previous Leagues: Brighton & Hove District >1952. Sussex County 1952-2010. Isthmian 2010-13. Conference/National 2013-18.

11-12	12-13	13-14	14-15	15-16	16-17	17-18	18-19	19-20	20-21
Isth1S 1	Isth P 1	Conf S 19	Conf S 4	Nat S 5	Nat S 17	Nat S 21	Isth P 20	IsthSE n&v	IsthSE n&v
FAC 2Qr	FAC 2Qr	FAC 2Q	FAC 3Qr	FAC 2Pr	FAC 1Pr	FAC 2Q	FAC 3Q	FAC 1Q	FAC P
FAT 1Q	FAT 3Q	FAT 2Pr	FAT 3Q	FAT 1P	FAT 2P	FAT 1P	FAT 1Q	FAT P	FAT 3Q

HONOURS / RECORDS
FA Comps: None

League: Sussex County League Division One 1961-62, 63-64, 83-84, 2009-10, Division Two 1967-68, 80-81.
Isthmian League Division One South 2011-12, Premier Division 2012-13.
County FA: Sussex Senior Cup 1950-51, 61-62, 2011-12, 14-15. Sussex RUR Charity Cup 1954-55, 58-59, 90-91.

Goalscorer: Billy Ford
Appearances: Ken Powell - 1,103
Victory: 14-0 v Southdown (H), Sussex Junior Cup Second Round, 27/03/1948.
Defeat: 2-13 v St Luke's Terrace Old Boys (A), Brighton & Hove District Division Two, 02/11/1946.
Misc: Scored 127 goals in 32 matches during the 1961-62 season.

GROUND: East Brighton Park, Wilson Avenue, Brighton BN2 5TS
Ground Capacity: 3,000 **Seats:** 800 **Covered:** Yes **Clubhouse:** Yes **Shop:** No
Previous Grounds: N/A
Record Attendance: 2,174 v Dagenham & Redbridge, FA Cup Second Round Proper replay, 6th December 2015.

Nearest Railway Station Brighton Central - two & half miles from the ground.
Bus Route B&H Bus No.7 or 27

WHITSTABLE TOWN

Isthmian South East

Founded 1886 **Nickname:** Oystermen or Natives **Club Colours:** Red & white

Club Contact Details
01227 266 012 secretary@whitstabletownfc.com

Previous Names: None
Previous Leagues: East Kent 1897-1909, Kent 1909-59, 67-2007, Aetolian 1959-60, 63-64, Kent Amateur 1960-62, 64-67, South East Anglian 1962-63, Isthmian 2007-16. Southern Counties East 2016-18.

11-12	12-13	13-14	14-15	15-16	16-17	17-18	18-19	19-20	20-21
Isth1S 18	Isth1S 17	Isth1S 20	Isth1S 8	Isth1S 23	SCEP 5	SCEP 2	IsthSE 12	IsthSE n&v	IsthSE n&v
FAC P	FAC P	FAC Pr	FAC 1Q	FAC 1Qr	FAC Pr	FAC EP	FAC 1Q	FAC 1Q	FAC P
FAT P	FAT 2Q	FAT 2P	FAT P	FAT P	FAV 1Qr	FAV 3P	FAT 1Q	FAT P	FAT 2Q

HONOURS / RECORDS
FA Comps: None

League: Kent Division Two (Mid Kent) 1927-28, Division Two 33-34, 49-50, Premier Division 2006-07.
Kent Amateur Eastern Division 1960-61
County FA:

Goalscorer: Barry Godfrey
Appearances: Frank Cox - 429 (1950-60)
Best FA Cup Third Qualifying Round 1957-58, 88-89, 89-90
FA Trophy Second Round Proper 2013-14
FA Vase Fifth Round Proper 1996-97

GROUND: The Belmont Ground, Belmont Road, Belmont, Whitstable CT5 4LN
Ground Capacity: 3,000 **Seats:** 500 **Covered:** 1,000 **Clubhouse:** Yes **Shop:** Yes
Previous Grounds: None
Record Attendance: 2,500 v Gravesend & Northfleet - FA Cup 19/10/1987.

Nearest Railway Station Whitstable 400 yards away
Bus Route 4, 638 & Triangle

ASHTON UNITED

NPL Premier Division

Founded 1878 **Nickname:** Robins **Club Colours:** Red and white

Club Contact Details
0161 339 4158

Previous Names: Hurst 1878-1947
Previous Leagues: Manchester, Lancashire Combination 1912-33, 48-64, 66-68, Midland 1964-66, Cheshire County 1923-48, 68-82, North West Counties 1982-92. NPL 92-2018. National 2018-19.

11-12		12-13		13-14		14-15		15-16		16-17		17-18		18-19		19-20		20-21	
NP P	12	NP P	10	NP P	5	NP P	3	NP P	3	NP P	11	NP P	2	Nat N	20	NP P	n&v	NP P	n&v
FAC	2Q	FAC	2Q	FAC	3Q	FAC	3Q	FAC	3Q	FAC	1Q	FAC	2Q	FAC	4Q	FAC	3Q	FAC	2Q
FAT	1Q	FAT	1Q	FAT	1Q	FAT	1Q	FAV	1P	FAT	1Q	FAT	2Pr	FAT	3Q	FAT	2Q	FAT	3P

HONOURS / RECORDS
FA Comps: None
League: Manchester League 1911-12. Lancashire Combination 1916-17.
North West Counties Division Two 1987-88, Division One 1991-92.
County FA: Manchester Senior Cup 1894-95, 1913-14, 75-76, 77-78.
Manchester Premier Cup 1979-80, 82-83, 91-92, 2000-01, 01-02, 02-03. Manchester Challenge Shield 1992-93.
Victory: 11-3 v Stalybridge Celtic - Manchester Intermediate Cup 1955
Defeat: 1-11 v Wellington Town - Cheshire League 1946-47
Appearances: Micky Boyle - 462
Additional: Paid £9,000 to Netherfield for Andy Whittaker 1994
Received £15,000 from Rotherham United for Karl Marginson 1993

GROUND: Hurst Cross, Surrey Street, Ashton-u-Lyne OL6 8DY
Ground Capacity: 4,500 **Seats:** 250 **Covered:** 750 **Clubhouse:** Yes **Shop:** Yes
Previous Grounds: Rose Hill 1878-1912
Record Attendance: 11,000 v Halifax Town - FA Cup 1st Round 1952

Nearest Railway Station Ashton-under-Lyne - 1.4km
Bus Route Kings Road - stop 50m away

ATHERTON COLLIERIES

NPL Premier Division

Founded 1916 **Nickname:** Colls **Club Colours:** Black & white

Club Contact Details
07968 548 056

Previous Names: None
Previous Leagues: Bolton Combination 1918-21, 52-71. Lancashire Alliance 1921. Manchester 1945-48. West Lancashire 1948-50. Lancashire Combination 1950-52, 71-78. Cheshire Co 1978-82. North West Co 1982-2017.

11-12		12-13		13-14		14-15		15-16		16-17		17-18		18-19		19-20		20-21	
NWC1	4	NWC1	4	NWC1	5	NWC1	1	NWCP	3	NWCP	1	NP1N	10	NP1W	1	NP P	n&v	NP P	n&v
FAC	P	FAC	1Q	FAC	Pr	FAC	Pr	FAC	Pr	FAC	P	FAC	2Q	FAC	1Q	FAC	1Qr	FAC	2Q
FAV	2Q	FAV	1Q	FAV	1Q	FAV	2P	FAV	3P	FAV	5P	FAT	2Q	FAT	Pr	FAT	1Pr	FAT	3Q

HONOURS / RECORDS
FA Comps: None
League: Bolton Combination 1919-20, 36-37, 37-38, 38-39, 40-41, 44-45, 56-57, 58-59, 60-61, 64-65.
North West Counties Division Three 1986-87, Division One 2014-15, Premier 2016-17. NPL Division One West 2018-19.
County FA: Lancashire County FA Shield 1919-20, 22-23, 41-42, 45-46, 56-57, 64-65.

Best FA Cup Third Qualifying Round 1994-95
FA Vase Fifth Round 2016-17
FA Trophy First Round Proper 2019-20

GROUND: Alder Street, Atherton, Greater Manchester M46 9EY
Ground Capacity: 2,500 **Seats:** Yes **Covered:** Yes **Clubhouse:** Yes **Shop:** No
Previous Grounds: None
Record Attendance: 3,300 in the Bolton Combination 1920's.

Nearest Railway Station Atherton - 0.7km
Bus Route High Street - stop 100m away

BAMBER BRIDGE

NPL Premier Division

Founded 1952 **Nickname:** Brig **Club Colours:** White & black

Club Contact Details
01772 909 690 admin@bamberbridgefc.com

Previous Names: None
Previous Leagues: Preston & District 1952-90, North West Counties 1990-93

11-12		12-13		13-14		14-15		15-16		16-17		17-18		18-19		19-20		20-21	
NP1N	10	NP1N	9	NP1N	4	NP1N	3	NP1N	12	NP1N	11	NP1N	4	NP P	16	NP P	n&v	NP P	n&v
FAC	1Q	FAC	2Q	FAC	1Qr	FAC	3Q	FAC	4Q	FAC	P	FAC	1Q	FAC	2Qr	FAC	1Q	FAC	1Q
FAT	1Q	FAT	P	FAT	P	FAT	1Q	FAT	P	FAT	1Q	FAT	1Q	FAT	1Q	FAT	1Q	FAT	1P

HONOURS / RECORDS
FA Comps: None
League: Preston & District Premier Division 1980-81, 85-86, 86-87, 89-90. North West Counties Division Two 1991-92. Northern Premier Premier Division 1995-96.
County FA: Lancashire FA Amateur Shield 1981-82, Trophy 1994-95.

Victory: 8-0 v Curzon Ashton - North West Counties 1994-95
Additional: Paid £10,000 to Horwich RMI for Mark Edwards
Received £15,000 from Wigan Athletic for Tony Black 1995

GROUND: Sir Tom Finney Stadium, Brownedge Road, Bamber Bridge PR5 6UX
Ground Capacity: 3,000 **Seats:** 554 **Covered:** 800 **Clubhouse:** Yes **Shop:** Yes
Previous Grounds: King George V, Higher Wallton 1952-86
Record Attendance: 2,300 v Czech Republic - Pre Euro '96 friendly

Nearest Railway Station Lostock Hall - 0.9km. Bamber Bridge - 0.9km
Bus Route Irongate - stop 100m away

BASFORD UNITED

NPL Premier Division

Founded 1900 **Nickname:** Community **Club Colours:** All amber

Club Contact Details
0115 924 4491

Previous Names: None
Previous Leagues: Notts Alliance 1905-39, 1946-2004. Notts Amateur League 1939-46. Notts Amateur Alliance 2004-06. Notts Senior 2006-11. Central Midlands 2011-12. East Midlands Counties 2012-13. Northern Counties East 2013-14. Midland League 2014-15.

11-12		12-13		13-14		14-15		15-16		16-17		17-18		18-19		19-20		20-21	
CMSth	1	EMC	1	NCEP	5	MFLP	1	NP1S	4	NP1S	6	NP1S	1	NP P	7	NP P	n&v	NP P	n&v
				FAC	1Q	FAC	Pr	FAC	2Q	FAC	P	FAC	3Q	FAC	1Q	FAC	1Q	FAC	1Q
		FAV	2P	FAV	2Q	FAV	2Q	FAT	2Q	FAT	P	FAT	1Q	FAT	1P	FAT	2Q	FAT	3P

HONOURS / RECORDS
FA Comps: None
League: Notts Alliance 1905-06, 07-08, 19-20, Division One 1997-98. Central Midlands Southern 2011-12. East Midland Counties 2012-13. Midland Football Premier Division 2014-15. Northern Premier Division One South 2017-18.
County FA: Notts Senior Cup 1946-47, 87-88, 2014-15, 15-16, 17-18, Intermediate Cup 2005-06.

Misc: Former club secretary, Wallace Brownlow, who took up the post when 19 in 1907, remained in the position until his death in 1970 - a world record of 63 years.
Best FA Cup Third Qualifying Round 2017-18
FA Amateur C Third Round 1911-12
FA Trophy Third Round Proper 2020-21
FA Vase Second Round Proper 2012-13

GROUND: Mill Street Playing Field, Greenwich Avenue, off Bagnall Road, Basford, Nottingham NG6 0LD
Ground Capacity: 2,200 **Seats:** Yes **Covered:** Yes **Clubhouse:** Yes **Shop:**
Previous Grounds: Old Peer Tree Inn, Dolly Tub > 1903, Catchems Corner 1903-30, Vernon Avenue 1930-34, Mill Street 1934-91.
Record Attendance: 3,500 v Grantham United, FACup 1937.

Nearest Railway Station Highbury Vale Tram Stop - 400m
Bus Route Christina Avenue - stop 150m away

BUXTON

NPL Premier Division

Founded 1877 **Nickname:** The Bucks **Club Colours:** Blue & white

Club Contact Details

01298 23197

Previous Names: None

Previous Leagues: Combination 1891-99. Manchester 1899-1932. Cheshire County 1932-40, 46-73. Northern Premier 1973-98, 2006- Northern Counties East 1998-2006.

11-12		12-13		13-14		14-15		15-16		16-17		17-18		18-19		19-20		20-21	
NP P	13	NP P	7	NP P	13	NP P	10	NP P	11	NP P	7	NP P	8	NP P	5	NP P	n&v	NP P	n&v
FAC	2Q	FAC	4Q	FAC	2Q	FAC	3Q	FAC	3Qr	FAC	1Q	FAC	4Q	FAC	2Qr	FAC	3Q	FAC	2Q
FAT	2Q	FAT	1Pr	FAT	2Q	FAT	2Q	FAT	3Q	FAT	2Q	FAT	1Q	FAT	2Qr	FAT	2Q	FAT	1P

HONOURS / RECORDS

FA Comps: None

League: Manchester 1931-32. Cheshire County 1972-73.
Northern Counties East 2005-06. Northern Premier Division One 2006-07.

County FA: Derbyshire Senior Cup 1938-39, 45-46, 56-57, 59-60, 71-72, 80-81, 85-86, 86-87, 2008-09, 11-12.

Goalscorer: Mark Reed - 251 (469 appearances)

Appearances: David Bainbridge - 642

Additional: Paid £5,000 to Hyde United for Gary Walker 1989
Received £16,500 from Rotherham for Ally Pickering 1989

GROUND: The Silverlands, Buxton, Derbyshire SK17 6QH

Ground Capacity: 5,200 **Seats:** 490 **Covered:** 2,500 **Clubhouse:** Yes **Shop:** Yes

Previous Grounds: The Park (Cricket Club) 1877-78. Fields at Cote Heath and Green Lane 1878-84.

Record Attendance: 6,000 v Barrow - FA Cup 1st Round 1962-63

Nearest Railway Station Higher Buxton - walking distance from the ground.

FC UNITED OF MANCHESTER

NPL Premier Division

Founded 2005 **Nickname:** F.C. **Club Colours:** Red/white/black

Club Contact Details

0161 769 2005 office@fc-utd.co.uk

Previous Names: None

Previous Leagues: North West Counties 2005-07. Northern Premier 2007-15. National 2015-19.

11-12		12-13		13-14		14-15		15-16		16-17		17-18		18-19		19-20		20-21	
NP P	6	NP P	3	NP P	2	NP P	1	Nat N	13	Nat N	13	Nat N	16	Nat N	21	NP P	n&v	NP P	n&v
FAC	2Q	FAC	4Q	FAC	1Q	FAC	2Q	FAC	1P	FAC	3Qr	FAC	4Q	FAC	3Q	FAC	2Q	FAC	1P
FAT	1P	FAT	2Q	FAT	1Qr	FAT	QF	FAT	3Q	FAT	3Q	FAT	3Q	FAT	3Q	FAT	2P	FAT	3Q

HONOURS / RECORDS

FA Comps: None

League: North West Counties League Division Two 2005-06, Division One 2006-07.
Northern Premier League Division One North Play-off 2007-08, Premier Division 2014-15.

County FA: Manchester Premier Cup 2016-17, 17-18.

Victory: 10-2 v Castleton Gabriels 10/12/2005. 8-0 v Squires Gate 14/10/06, Glossop N.E. 28/10/06 & Nelson 05/09/10

Defeat: 0-5 v Harrogate Town, 20 February 2016

Goalscorer: Rory Patterson - 99 (2005-08). Simon Carden scored 5 goals against Castleton Gabriels 10/12/2005.

Appearances: Jerome Wright - 400

Additional: Longest unbeaten run (League): 22 games 03/12/2006 - 18/08/2007.

GROUND: Broadhurst Park, 310 Lightbowne Road, Moston, Manchester, M40 0FJ

Ground Capacity: 4,400 **Seats:** 696 **Covered:** Yes **Clubhouse:** Yes **Shop:** Yes

Previous Grounds: Gigg Lane(Bury FC) 2005-14. Bower Fold (Stalybridge C) Aug-Dec'14. Tameside Stad (Curzon A)

Record Attendance: 6,731 v Brighton & Hove Albion, FA Cup 2nd Round 08/12/2010 (Gigg Lane)

Nearest Railway Station Moston - 11min walk from the ground.

Bus Route Matchday Special and Shuttle Bus

GAINSBOROUGH TRINITY

NPL Premier Division

Founded 1873 **Nickname:** The Blues **Club Colours:** All blue

Club Contact Details
07500 838 068

Previous Names: Trinity Recreationists
Previous Leagues: Midland (FM) 1889-96, 1912-60, 61-68. Football League 1896-1912. Yorkshire 1960-61. Northern Premier (FM) 1968-2004.

11-12		12-13		13-14		14-15		15-16		16-17		17-18		18-19		19-20		20-21	
Conf N	4	Conf N	8	Conf N	16	Conf N	17	Nat N	18	Nat N	19	Nat N	20	NP P	6	NP P	n&v	NP P	n&v
FAC	4Q	FAC	2Qr	FAC	2Q	FAC	4Q	FAC	1P	FAC	2Q	FAC	1P	FAC	3Q	FAC	2Q	FAC	1Q
FAT	3Q	FAT	SF	FAT	3Q	FAT	1P	FAT	3Qr	FAT	3Qr	FAT	1P	FAT	1Qr	FAT	1P	FAT	3Q

HONOURS / RECORDS
FA Comps: None

League: Midland 1890-91, 1927-28, 48-49, 66-67.

County FA: Lincolnshire County Senior Cup 1889-90, 92-93, 94-95, 97-98, 1903-04, 04-05, 06-07, 10-11, 46-47, 47-48, 48-49, 50-51, 51-52, 57-58, 58-59, 63-64, 70-71, 2002-03, 15-16, 17-18. Lincolnshire Shield 2007-08.

Victory: 7-0 v Fleetwood Town and v Great Harwood Town
Defeat: 1-7 v Stalybridge Celtic - Northern Premier 2000-01 and v Brentford - FA Cup 03-04.
Additional: Paid £3,000 to Buxton for Stuart Lowe
Received £30,000 from Lincoln City for Tony James

GROUND: The Martin & Co Arena, Gainsborough, Lincolnshire DN21 2QW
Ground Capacity: 4,340 **Seats:** 504 **Covered:** 2,500 **Clubhouse:** Yes **Shop:** Yes
Previous Grounds: Played at Bowling Green Ground and Sincil Bank when Northolme was being used for cricket.
Record Attendance: 9,760 v Scunthorpe United - Midland League 1948

Nearest Railway Station Gainsborough Central - less than half a mile away.
Bus Route 100 & 97

GRANTHAM TOWN

NPL Premier Division

Founded 1874 **Nickname:** Gingerbreads **Club Colours:** Black & white stripes

Club Contact Details
01476 591 818

Previous Names: Grantham FC 1874-1987.
Previous Leagues: Midland Amateur Alliance, Central Alliance 1911-25, 59-61, Midland Counties 1925-59, 61-72, Southern 1972-79, 85-2006, Northern Premier 1979-85

11-12		12-13		13-14		14-15		15-16		16-17		17-18		18-19		19-20		20-21	
NP1S	1	NP P	19	NP P	15	NP P	12	NP P	18	NP P	8	NP P	4	NP P	18	NP P	n&v	NP P	n&v
FAC	3Q	FAC	2Q	FAC	1Qr	FAC	3Q	FAC	1Q	FAC	1Qr	FAC	2Q	FAC	2Qr	FAC	1Q	FAC	2Q
FAT	1Q	FAT	1Q	FAT	1Qr	FAT	1Q	FAT	1Q	FAT	2Q	FAT	3Q	FAT	1Q	FAT	2Q	FAT	1P

HONOURS / RECORDS
FA Comps: None

League: Midland Amateur 1910-11. Central Alliance 1924-25. Midland 1963-64, 70-71, 71-72. Southern Division One North 1972-73, 78-79, Midland Division 97-98. Northern Premier Division One South 2011-12.
County FA: Lincolnshire Senior Cup 1884-85, 1971-72, 82-83, County Senior Cup 1936-37, Senior Cup 'A' 1953-54, 60-61, 61-62, County Shield 2003-04, 04-05.
Victory: 13-0 v Rufford Colliery (H) - FA Cup 15/09/1934
Defeat: 0-16 v Notts County Rovers (A) - Midland Amateur Alliance 22/10/1892
Goalscorer: Jack McCartney - 416
Appearances: Chris Gardner - 664
Additional: Received £20,000 from Nottingham Forest for Gary Crosby

GROUND: South Kesteven Sports Stadium, Trent Road, Gratham NG31 7XQ
Ground Capacity: 7,500 **Seats:** 750 **Covered:** 1,950 **Clubhouse:** Yes **Shop:** Yes
Previous Grounds: London Road >1990-91. Spalding United FC 1990-91.
Record Attendance: 6,578 v Middlesbrough, FA Cup Third Round Proper, 1973-74.

Nearest Railway Station Grantham - 1.5km
Bus Route Meres Leisure Centre - stop 100m away

HYDE UNITED

NPL Premier Division

Founded 1919 **Nickname:** The Tigers **Club Colours:** Red & navy

Club Contact Details
0161 367 7273

Previous Names: Hyde United 1919-2010, Hyde F.C. 2010-15.

Previous Leagues: Lancashire & Cheshire 1919-21, Manchester 1921-30, Cheshire County 1930-68, 1970-82, Northern Premier 1968-70, 1983-2004. Football Conference 2004-15.

11-12		12-13		13-14		14-15		15-16		16-17		17-18		18-19		19-20		20-21	
Conf N	1	Conf	18	Conf	24	Conf N	22	NP P	22	NP1N	10	NP1N	3	NP P	10	NP P	n&v	NP P	n&v
FAC	3Q	FAC	4Qr	FAC	4Q	FAC	2Q	FAC	2Qr	FAC	2Q	FAC	1P	FAC	1Q	FAC	1Q	FAC	2Q
FAT	1P	FAT	1Pr	FAT	1P	FAT	2P	FAT	1Qr	FAT	P	FAT	P	FAT	2Q	FAT	1Q	FAT	1P

HONOURS / RECORDS

FA Comps: None

League: Manchester 1920-21, 21-22, 22-23, 28-29, 29-30. Cheshire 1954-55, 55-56, 81-82.
Northern Premier Division One North 2003-04, Premier Division 2004-05. Conference North 2011-12.

County FA: Cheshire Senior Cup 1945-46, 62-63, 69-70, 80-81, 89-90, 96-97. Manchester Senior Cup 1974-75, Premier Cup 1993-94, 94-95, 95-96, 98-99.

Victory: 13-1 v Eccles United, 1921-22.

Goalscorer: Pete O'Brien - 247. Ernest Gillibrand 86 goals during the 1929-30 season, including 7 against New Mills.

Appearances: Steve Johnson - 623 (1975-1988)

Additional: Paid £8,000 to Mossley for Jim McCluskie 1989
Received £50,000 from Crewe Alexandra for Colin Little 1995

GROUND: Ewen Fields, Walker Lane, Hyde SK14 5PL

Ground Capacity: 4,250 **Seats:** 530 **Covered:** 4,073 **Clubhouse:** Yes **Shop:** Yes

Previous Grounds: None

Record Attendance: 7,600 v Nelson - FA Cup 1952

Nearest Railway Station Newton for Hyde - 0.8km

Bus Route Walker Lane - stop 110m away

LANCASTER CITY

NPL Premier Division

Founded 1911 **Nickname:** Dolly Blues **Club Colours:** Blue & white

Club Contact Details
01524 382 238 secretary@lancastercityfc.com

Previous Names: Lancaster Town 1911-37

Previous Leagues: Lancashire Combination 1911-70, Northern Premier League 1970-82, 87-2004, North West Counties 1982-87, Conference 2004-07

11-12		12-13		13-14		14-15		15-16		16-17		17-18		18-19		19-20		20-21	
NP1N	6	NP1N	13	NP1N	6	NP1N	11	NP1N	6	NP1N	1	NP P	17	NP P	12	NP P	n&v	NP P	n&v
FAC	3Q	FAC	1Q	FAC	2Qr	FAC	3Q	FAC	2Q	FAC	3Q	FAC	3Q	FAC	1Q	FAC	2Q	FAC	2Q
FAT	P	FAT	P	FAT	1Q	FAT	Pr	FAT	Pr	FAT	1Q	FAT	1P	FAT	1P	FAT	2Qr	FAT	3Q

HONOURS / RECORDS

FA Comps: None

League: Northern Premier Division One 1995-96, Division One North 2016-17.

County FA: Lancashire Junior Cup (ATS Challenge Trophy) 1927-28, 28-29, 30-31, 33-34, 51-52, 74-75.

Victory: 17-2 v Appleby, FA Cup, 1915.

Defeat: 0-10 v Matlock Town - Northern Premier League Division 1 1973-74

Goalscorer: David Barnes - 130, 1979-84, 88-91. Jordan Connerton scored 38 during the 2009-10 season.

Appearances: Edgar J Parkinson - 591, 1949-64.

Additional: Paid £6,000 to Droylsden for Jamie Tandy. Received £25,000 from Birmingham City for Chris Ward.

GROUND: Giant Axe, West Road, Lancaster LA1 5PE

Ground Capacity: 3,500 **Seats:** 513 **Covered:** 900 **Clubhouse:** Yes **Shop:** Yes

Previous Grounds: None

Record Attendance: 7,506 v Carlisle United - FA Cup Fourth Qualifying Round, 17/11/1927

Nearest Railway Station Lancaster - 3min walk

Bus Route 41, 42 & 89

MATLOCK TOWN

NPL Premier Division

Founded 1885 **Nickname:** The Gladiators **Club Colours:** Blue & white

Club Contact Details

01629 583 866

Previous Names: None

Previous Leagues: Midland Combination 1894-96, Matlock and District, Derbyshire Senior, Central Alliance 1924-25, 47-61, Central Combination 1934-35, Chesterfield & District 1946-47, Midland Counties 1961-69

11-12		12-13		13-14		14-15		15-16		16-17		17-18		18-19		19-20		20-21	
NP P	14	NP P	17	NP P	12	NP P	14	NP P	17	NP P	9	NP P	14	NP P	15	NP P	n&v	NP P	n&v
FAC	2Q	FAC	1Qr	FAC	2Q	FAC	1Q	FAC	1Qr	FAC	4Q	FAC	2Q	FAC	1Q	FAC	2Q	FAC	3Q
FAT	3Q	FAT	2P	FAT	3Q	FAT	1Q	FAT	1P	FAT	2P	FAT	1Q	FAT	1Q	FAT	2P	FAT	1P

HONOURS / RECORDS

FA Comps: FA Trophy 1974-75. Anglo Italian Non-League Cup 1979.

League: Central Alliance North Division 1959-60, 60-61. Midland Counties 1961-62, 68-69.

County FA: Derbyshire Senior Cup 1974-75, 76-77, 77-78, 83-84, 84-85, 91-92, 2003-04, 09-10, 14-15, 16-17.

Victory: 10-0 v Lancaster City (A) - 1974
Defeat: 0-8 v Chorley (A) - 1971
Goalscorer: Peter Scott
Appearances: Mick Fenoughty
Additional: Paid £2,000 for Kenny Clark 1996. Received £10,000 from York City for Ian Helliwell.

GROUND: Causeway Lane, Matlock, Derbyshire DE4 3AR

Ground Capacity: 2,757 **Seats:** 560 **Covered:** 1,200 **Clubhouse:** Yes **Shop:** Yes
Previous Grounds: None
Record Attendance: 5,123 v Burton Albion - FA Trophy Semi-final, 1975

Nearest Railway Station Matlock - 0.3km
Bus Route Causeway Lane - stop 100m away

MICKLEOVER

NPL Premier Division

Founded 1948 **Nickname:** Sports **Club Colours:** Red & black

Club Contact Details

01332 512 826

Previous Names: Mickleover Old Boys 1948-93. Mickleover Sports 1993-20.

Previous Leagues: Derby & District Senior 1948-93. Central Midlands 1993-99, Northern Counties East 1999-2009

11-12		12-13		13-14		14-15		15-16		16-17		17-18		18-19		19-20		20-21	
NP P	21	NP1S	21	NP1S	5	NP1S	1	NP P	20	NP P	16	NP P	12	NP P	19	NP P	n&v	NP P	n&v
FAC	2Q	FAC	Pr	FAC	2Qr	FAC	3Q	FAC	1Q	FAC	2Q	FAC	3Q	FAC	3Q	FAC	1Q	FAC	3Q
FAT	1Q	FAT	P	FAT	2Q	FAT	3Q	FAT	1Q	FAT	3Qr	FAT	1Q	FAT	2Qr	FAT	1Q	FAT	1P

HONOURS / RECORDS

FA Comps: None

League: Central Midlands Supreme Division 1998-99. Northern Counties East Division One 2002-03, Premier Division 2008-09. Northern Premier League Division One South 2009-10, 14-15.

County FA: None

Misc: Won 16 consecutive League matches in 2009-10 - a Northern Premier League record ay the time.
Best FA Cup Third Qualifying Round 2010-11, 14-15, 17-18, 18-19, 20-21
FA Trophy First Round Proper 2020-21
FA Vase Fourth Round Proper 2000-01

GROUND: Mickleover Sports Club, Station Road, Mickleover Derby DE3 9FE

Ground Capacity: 1,500 **Seats:** 280 **Covered:** 500 **Clubhouse:** Yes **Shop:** Yes
Previous Grounds: None
Record Attendance: 1,074 v FC United of Manchester, Northern Premier League Premier Division, 02/10/10.

Nearest Railway Station Peartree - 5.1km
Bus Route Buxton Drive - stop 100m away

MORPETH TOWN

NPL Premier Division

Founded 1909 **Nickname:** Highwaymen **Club Colours:** Amber & black

Club Contact Details
07882 991 356

Previous Names: None
Previous Leagues: Northern Alliance 1936-1994. Northern League 1994-2018.

11-12		12-13		13-14		14-15		15-16		16-17		17-18		18-19		19-20		20-21	
NL 2	4	NL 2	3	NL 2	17	NL 1	8	NL 1	4	NL 1	2	NL 1	2	NP1E	1	NP P	n&v	NP P	n&v
		FAC	EP	FAC	1Q	FAC	EP	FAC	P	FAC	3Q	FAC	EP	FAC	1Qr	FAC	3Q	FAC	2Q
FAV	1Q	FAV	2P	FAV	5P	FAV	2P	FAV	F	FAV	4P	FAV	2P	FAT	P	FAT	2Q	FAT	3P

HONOURS / RECORDS
FA Comps: FA Vase 2015-16.
League: Northern Alliance 1983-84, 93-94. Northern Division Two 1995-96.

County FA: Northumberland Benevolent Bowl 1978-79, 85-86. Northumberland Senior Cup 2006-07.

Best FA Cup Fourth Qualifying Round 1998-99
FA Trophy Third Round Proper 2020-21
FA Vase Winners 2015-16

GROUND: Craik Park, Morpeth Common, Morpeth, Northumberland NE61 2YX
Ground Capacity: 1,000 **Seats:** 100 **Covered:** Yes **Clubhouse:** Yes **Shop:**
Previous Grounds: Stobhill Cricket Hill. Storey Park 1954-94.
Record Attendance:

Nearest Railway Station Morpeth - 1.9km
Bus Route Whalton Road - stop 670m away

NANTWICH TOWN

NPL Premier Division

Founded 1884 **Nickname:** The Dabbers **Club Colours:** All green

Club Contact Details
01270 621 771 secretary@nantwichtownfc.com

Previous Names: Nantwich
Previous Leagues: Shropshire & Dist. 1891-92, Combination 1892-94, 1901-10, Cheshire Junior 1894-95, Crewe & Dist. 1895-97, North Staffs & Dist. 1897-1900, Cheshire 1900-01, Manchester 1910-12, 65-68, Lancs. Com. 1912-14, Cheshire Co. 1919-38, 68-82, Crewe & Dist. 1938-39, 47-48, Crewe Am. Comb. 1946-47, Mid-Cheshire 1948-65, North West Co. 1982-2007

11-12		12-13		13-14		14-15		15-16		16-17		17-18		18-19		19-20		20-21	
NP P	10	NP P	14	NP P	19	NP P	15	NP P	8	NP P	5	NP P	15	NP P	4	NP P	n&v	NP P	n&v
FAC	1P	FAC	1Q	FAC	1Q	FAC	1Q	FAC	1Q	FAC	4Q	FAC	1P	FAC	2Qr	FAC	4Q	FAC	3Q
FAT	1Q	FAT	2Qr	FAT	3Q	FAT	2Q	FAT	SF	FAT	1P	FAT	1Q	FAT	1Q	FAT	2Q	FAT	3P

HONOURS / RECORDS
FA Comps: FA Vase 2005-06.
League: Mid-Cheshire 1963-64. Cheshire County 1980-81.

County FA: Crew Amateur Combination 1946-47. Cheshire Amateur Cup 1895-96, 1963-64.
Cheshire Senior Cup 1932-33, 75-76, 2007-08, 11-12, 17-18, 18-19.
Victory: 20-0 v Whitchurch Alexandra (home) 1900/01 Cheshire League Division 1, 5 April 1901
Defeat: 2-16 v Stalybridge Celtic (away) 1932/33 Cheshire County League, 22 Oct 1932
Goalscorer: John Scarlett 161 goals (1992/3 to 2005/6).
Bobby Jones scored 60 goals during season 1946-47, Gerry Duffy scored 42 during season 1961-62
Additional: Received £20,000 from Crewe Alexandra for Kelvin Mellor - Feb 2008

GROUND: Weaver Stadium, Water Lode, Kingsley Fields, Nantwich, CW5 5UP
Ground Capacity: 3,500 **Seats:** 350 **Covered:** 495 **Clubhouse:** Yes **Shop:** Yes
Previous Grounds: London Road/Jackson Avenue (1884-2007)
Record Attendance: 5,121 v Winsford United - Cheshire Senior Cup 2nd Round 1920-21

Nearest Railway Station Nantwich - 1.1km
Bus Route Malbank School - stop 150m away

Pre-season action - Photos Keith Clayton.

Bourne (Nantwich) clears off the line after a save from Hall.

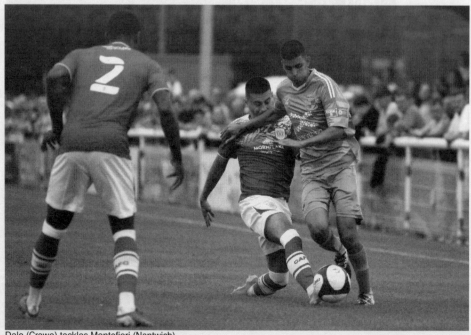

Dale (Crewe) tackles Montefiori (Nantwich).

RADCLIFFE

NPL Premier Division

Founded 1949 **Nickname:** The Boro **Club Colours:** Blue

Club Contact Details
0161 724 8346 secretary@radcliffefc.com

Previous Names: Radcliffe Borough >2018
Previous Leagues: South East Lancashire, Manchester 1953-63, Lancashire Combination 1963-71, Cheshire County 1971-82, North West Counties 1982-97

11-12		12-13		13-14		14-15		15-16		16-17		17-18		18-19		19-20		20-21	
NP1N	15	NP1N	15	NP1N	18	NP1N	19	NP1N	18	NP1N	20	NP1N	20	NP1W	2	NP P	n&v	NP P	n&v
FAC	3Q	FAC	Pr	FAC	1Q	FAC	1Q	FAC	P	FAC	1Q	FAC	1Q	FAC	2Q	FAC	Pr	FAC	2Q
FAT	2Qr	FAT	1Q	FAT	1Q	FAT	P	FAT	2Q	FAT	P	FAT	P	FAT	P	FAT	1Q	FAT	3Q

HONOURS / RECORDS
FA Comps: None
League: South Lancashire Division Two 1950-51, Division One 51-52, Premier 80-81. North West Counties Division Two 1982-83, Division One 84-85. Northern Premier Division One 1996-97.
County FA: Manchester Premier Cup 2007-08.

Goalscorer: Ian Lunt - 147. Jody Banim scored 46 during a single season.
Appearances: Simon Kelly - 502
Additional: Paid £5,000 to Buxton for Gary Walker 1991
Received £20,000 from Shrewsbury Town for Jody Banim 2003

GROUND: Stainton Park, Pilkington Road, Radcliffe, Lancashire M26 3PE
Ground Capacity: 4,000 **Seats:** 350 **Covered:** 1,000 **Clubhouse:** Yes **Shop:** Yes
Previous Grounds: Ashworth Street. Bright Street > 1970.
Record Attendance: 2,495 v York City - FA Cup 1st Round 2000-01

Nearest Railway Station Radcliffe - 1.3km
Bus Route Lowe Street - 100m away

SCARBOROUGH ATHLETIC

NPL Premier Division

Founded 2007 **Nickname:** The Seadogs **Club Colours:** Red & white

Club Contact Details
07538 903 723 club.secretary@scarboroughathletic.com

Previous Names: Formed after Scarborough F.C. folded in 2007.
Previous Leagues: Northern Counties East 2007-13.

11-12		12-13		13-14		14-15		15-16		16-17		17-18		18-19		19-20		20-21	
NCEP	3	NCEP	1	NP1S	7	NP1N	6	NP1N	20	NP1N	3	NP1N	2	NP P	8	NP P	n&v	NP P	n&v
FAC	1Q	FAC	EP	FAC	2Q	FAC	2Q	FAC	P	FAC	P	FAC	4Q	FAC	1Qr	FAC	2Q	FAC	1Q
FAV	1P	FAV	1P	FAT	3Q	FAT	1Q	FAT	P	FAT	P	FAT	P	FAT	1Q	FAT	1Q	FAT	3Q

HONOURS / RECORDS
FA Comps: None
League: Northern Counties East Division One 2008-09, Premier 2012-13.

County FA: None

Victory: 13-0 v Brodsworth, Northern Counties East, 2009-10.
Defeat: 0-6 v Thackley 16/04/2013 and AFC Telford United 16/11/2013.
Goalscorer: Ryan Blott - 231, including 42 scored during the 2008-09 season and 5 each against Yorkshire Amateur's (08/11/08) and Armthorpe Welfare (14/04/12).
Appearances: Ryan Blott - 376 (20/10/07 - 29/04/16).

GROUND: Scarborough Leisure Village, Ashburn Road YO11 2JW
Ground Capacity: 2,000 **Seats:** 250 **Covered:** Yes **Clubhouse:** Yes **Shop:** No
Previous Grounds: Queensgate - Bridlington FC >2017.
Record Attendance: 2,038 v Sheffield United, Opening of the new ground friendly, 15/07/2017.

Nearest Railway Station Scarborough - 1km
Bus Route 128, 7A & 843

SOUTH SHIELDS

NPL Premier Division

Founded 1974 **Nickname:** Mariners **Club Colours:** Claret & white

Club Contact Details
0191 454 7800

Previous Names: South Shields Mariners.
Previous Leagues: Northern Alliance 1974-76, Wearside 1976-95.

11-12		12-13		13-14		14-15		15-16		16-17		17-18		18-19		19-20		20-21	
NL 1	13	NL 1	23	NL 2	17	NL 2	15	NL 2	1	NL 1	1	NP1N	1	NP P	2	NP P	n&v	NP P	n&v
FAC	Pr	FAC	1Q	FAC	Pr					FAC	EP	FAC	4Q	FAC	2Q	FAC	1Qr	FAC	1P
FAV	1P	FAV	1P	FAV	1P	FAV	2Q	FAV	3P	FAV	F	FAT	2Q	FAT	3Q	FAT	1Pr	FAT	1P

HONOURS / RECORDS
FA Comps: FA Vase 2016-17.

League: Northern Alliance 1975-76. Wearside 1976-77, 92-93, 94-95. Northern Division Two 2015-16, Division One 2016-17.

County FA: Monkwearmouth Charity Cup 1986-87. Durham Senior Challenge Cup 2016-17.

Best FA Cup First Round Proper 2020-21
FA Trophy First Round Proper 2020-21
FA Vase Winners 2016-17

GROUND: Mariners Park, Shaftesbury Avenue, Jarrow, Tyne & Wear NE32 3UP
Ground Capacity: 3,500 **Seats:** Yes **Covered:** Yes **Clubhouse:** Yes **Shop:** No
Previous Grounds: Filtrona Park (renamed Mariners Park in 2015) 1992-2013. Eden Lane 2013-15.
Record Attendance: 3,464 v Coleshill Town, FA Vase semi-final, 2016-17.

Nearest Railway Station Bede - 0.2km
Bus Route Taunton Avenue - stop 200m away

STAFFORD RANGERS

NPL Premier Division

Founded 1876 **Nickname:** Rangers **Club Colours:** Black & white

Club Contact Details
01785 602 430 secretary@staffordrangersfc.co.uk

Previous Names: None
Previous Leagues: Shropshire 1891-93, Birmingham 1893-96, N. Staffs. 1896-1900, Cheshire 1900-01, Birmingham Combination 1900-12, 46-52, Cheshire County 1952-69, N.P.L. 1969-79, 83-85, Alliance 1979-83, Conf. 1985-95, 2005-11. Southern >2005.

11-12		12-13		13-14		14-15		15-16		16-17		17-18		18-19		19-20		20-21	
NP P	16	NP P	15	NP P	22	NP1S	6	NP1S	1	NP P	13	NP P	13	NP P	14	NP P	n&v	NP P	n&v
FAC	2Q	FAC	2Q	FAC	2Q	FAC	1Qr	FAC	P	FAC	1Q	FAC	4Q	FAC	2Q	FAC	3Q	FAC	4Q
FAT	2Q	FAT	1P	FAT	1Q	FAT	1Q	FAT	1Qr	FAV	3Q	FAT	3Q	FAT	2Q	FAT	1Q	FAT	3Q

HONOURS / RECORDS
FA Comps: FA Trophy 1971-72.

League: Birmingham Combination 1912-13. Cheshire County 1968-69. Northern Premier 1971-72, 84-85, Division One South 2015-16. Southern Premeir Division 2002-03. Coference North 2005-06.
County FA: Staffordshire Senior Cup 1954-55, 56-57, 62-63, 71-72, 77-78, 86-87, 91-92, 2002-03, 04-05, 14-15, 17-18.

Victory: 15-0 v Kidsgrove Athletic - Staffordshire Senior Cup 2003
Defeat: 0-12 v Burton Town - Birmingham League 1930
Goalscorer: M. Cullerton - 176. Les Box scored seven against Dudley Town, FA Cup, 06/09/1958.
Appearances: Jim Sargent
Additional: Paid £13,000 to VS rugby for S. Butterworth. Received £100,000 from Crystal Palace for Stan Collymore.

GROUND: Marston Road, Stafford ST16 3UF
Ground Capacity: 4,000 **Seats:** 530 **Covered:** Yes **Clubhouse:** Yes **Shop:** Yes
Previous Grounds: None
Record Attendance: 8,536 v Rotherham United - FA Cup 3rd Round 1975

Nearest Railway Station Stafford - 1.8km
Bus Route Co-operative Strret - stop 200m away

STALYBRIDGE CELTIC

NPL Premier Division

Founded 1909 **Nickname:** Celtic **Club Colours:** Royal blue & white

Club Contact Details
0161 338 2828 secretary@stalybridgeceltic.co.uk

Previous Names: None
Previous Leagues: Lancs & Cheshire Am. 1909-11. Lancashire Comb 1911-12, Central 1912-14, 15-21, Southern 1914-15, Football Lge 1921-23, Cheshire Co. 1923-82, North West Co. 1982-87, N.P.L. 1987-92, 98-2001, 02-04, Conference 1992-98, 01-02, 04-17.

11-12		12-13		13-14		14-15		15-16		16-17		17-18		18-19		19-20		20-21	
Conf N	6	Conf N	13	Conf N	19	Conf N	19	Nat N	12	Nat N	21	NP P	22	NP P	17	NP P	n&v	NP P	n&v
FAC	2Q	FAC	4Q	FAC	2Q	FAC	2Q	FAC	1P	FAC	3Q	FAC	3Q	FAC	1Q	FAC	1Q	FAC	2Q
FAT	2P	FAT	3Q	FAT	1P	FAT	3Qr	FAT	3Q	FAT	3Qr	FAT	3Q	FAT	3Q	FAT	1Q	FAT	3Q

HONOURS / RECORDS
FA Comps: None
League: Lancashire Combination Division Two 1911-12. Cheshire County 1979-80. North West Counties 1983-84, 86-87.
Northern Premier League Premier Division 1991-92, 2000-01.
County FA: Manchester Senior Cup 1922-23.
Cheshire Senior Cup 1952-53, 2000-01.
Victory: 16-2 v Manchester NE - 01/05/1926 and v Nantwich - 22/10/1932
Defeat: 1-10 v Wellington Town - 09/03/1946
Goalscorer: Harry Dennison - 215. Cecil Smith scored 77 goals during the 1931-32 season
Appearances: Kevan Keelan - 395
Additional: Paid £15,000 to Kettering Town for Ian Arnold 1995. Received £16,000 from Southport for Lee Trundle.

GROUND: Bower Fold, Mottram Road, Stalybridge, Cheshire SK15 2RT
Ground Capacity: 6,500 **Seats:** 1,300 **Covered:** 2,400 **Clubhouse:** Yes **Shop:** Yes
Previous Grounds: None
Record Attendance: 9,753 v West Bromwich Albion - FA Cup replay 1922-23

Nearest Railway Station Stalybridge - 1.5 miles from the ground.
Bus Route 236 & 237

WARRINGTON TOWN

NPL Premier Division

Founded 1949 **Nickname:** The Wire **Club Colours:** Yellow & blue

Club Contact Details
01925 653 044

Previous Names: Stockton Heath Albion 1949-61
Previous Leagues: Warrington & District 1949-52, Mid Cheshire 1952-78, Cheshire County 1978-82, North West Counties 1982-90 Northern Premier 1990-97

11-12		12-13		13-14		14-15		15-16		16-17		17-18		18-19		19-20		20-21	
NP1N	11	NP1N	10	NP1N	3	NP1N	9	NP1N	1	NP P	10	NP P	3	NP P	3	NP P	n&v	NP P	n&v
FAC	2Q	FAC	2Q	FAC	2Qr	FAC	2P	FAC	P	FAC	1Q	FAC	3Qr	FAC	4Qr	FAC	3Q	FAC	1Q
FAT	Pr	FAT	P	FAT	P	FAT	P	FAT	3Q	FAT	1Q	FAT	3P	FAT	1Q	FAT	1Q	FAT	1P

HONOURS / RECORDS
FA Comps: None
League: Mld-Cheshire 1960-61. North West Counties 1989-90, Division Two 2000-01.
Northern Premier Division One North 2015-16.
County FA: None

Goalscorer: Steve Hughes - 167
Appearances: Neil Whalley
Additional: Paid £50,000 to Preston North End for Liam Watson Received £60,000 from P.N.E. for Liam Watson
Players to progress - Roger Hunt, Liverpool legend and 1966 World Cup winner.

GROUND: Cantilever Park, Loushers Lane, Warrington WA4 2RS
Ground Capacity: 2,500 **Seats:** 350 **Covered:** 650 **Clubhouse:** Yes **Shop:** Yes
Previous Grounds: Stockton Lane 1949-50, 55-56. London Road 1950-53. Loushers Lane 1953-55.
Record Attendance: 2,600 v Halesowen Town - FA Vase Semi-final 1st leg 1985-86

Nearest Railway Station Warrington Central - 2.3km
Bus Route Fairfield Gardens - stop 200m away

Pre-season action - Photos Keith Clayton.

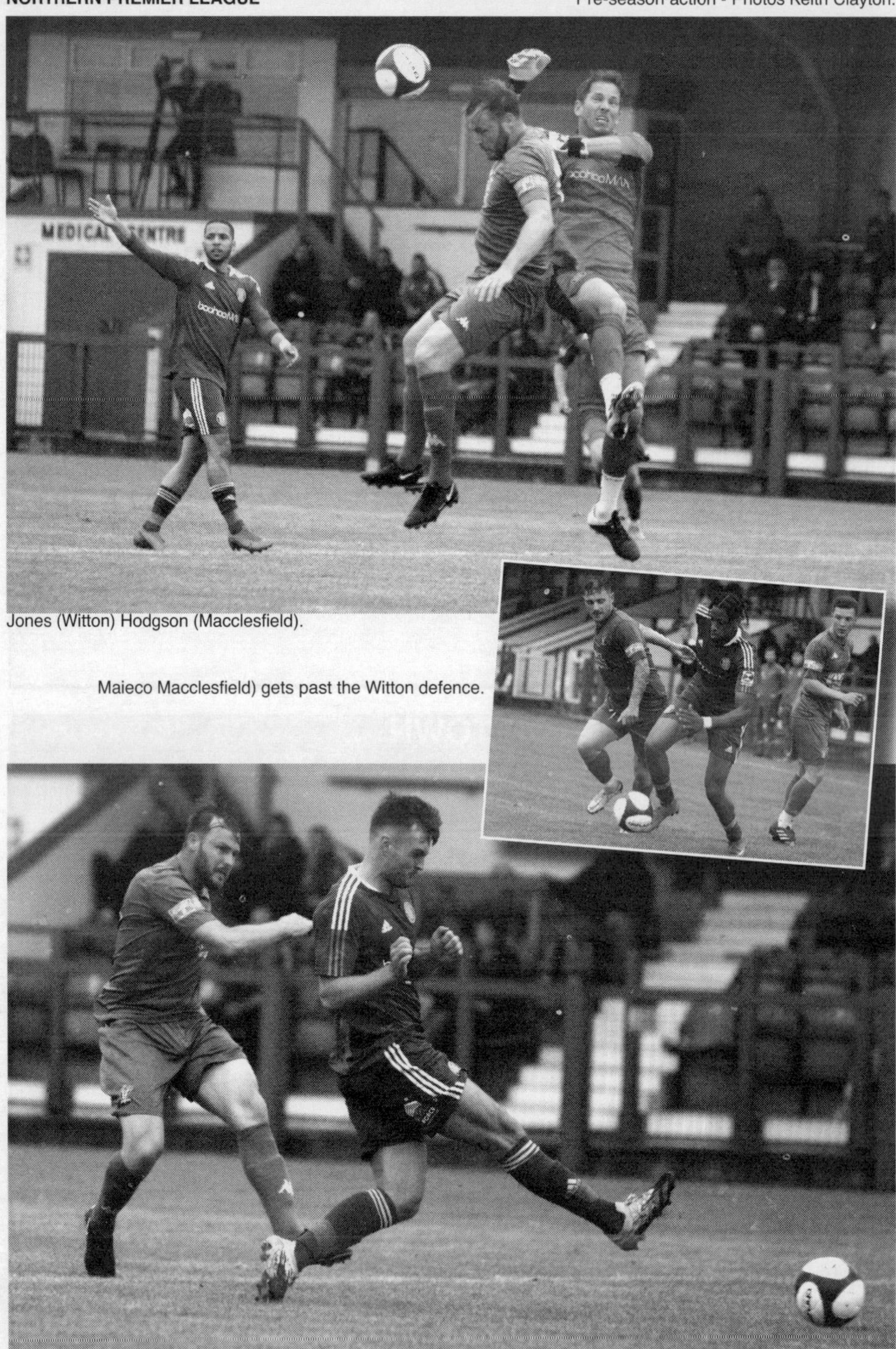

Jones (Witton) Hodgson (Macclesfield).

Maieco Macclesfield) gets past the Witton defence.

Jones (Witton) gets his shot in under pressure from Stead (Macclesfield).

WHITBY TOWN

NPL Premier Division

Founded 1926 **Nickname:** Seasiders **Club Colours:** All royal blue

Club Contact Details
Office: 01947 604 847

Previous Names: Whitby Whitehall Swifts and Whitby Town merged in 1926 to form Whitby United. Name changed to Whitby Town in 1949.
Previous Leagues: Northern 1926-97

11-12		12-13		13-14		14-15		15-16		16-17		17-18		18-19		19-20		20-21	
NP P	17	NP P	13	NP P	9	NP P	13	NP P	19	NP P	6	NP P	21	NP P	11	NP P	n&v	NP P	n&v
FAC	3Q	FAC	3Q	FAC	1Qr	FAC	1Qr	FAC	1Qr	FAC	2Q	FAC	2Q	FAC	1Q	FAC	4Qr	FAC	1Q
FAT	1Q	FAT	3Q	FAT	1Q	FAT	1Q	FAT	2Q	FAT	2Q	FAT	1Q	FAT	1Q	FAT	2Q	FAT	3Q

HONOURS / RECORDS
FA Comps: FA Vase 1996-97.
League: Northern 1992-93, 96-97.
Northern Premier Division One 1997-98.
County FA: North Riding Senior Cup 1964-65, 67-68, 82-83, 89-90, 2004-05, 16-17.

Victory: 11-2 v Cargo Fleet Works - 1950
Defeat: 3-13 v Willington - 24/03/1928
Goalscorer: Paul Pitman - 382
Appearances: Paul Pitman - 468
Additional: Paid £2,500 to Newcastle Blue Star for John Grady 1990. Received £5,000 from Gateshead for Graham Robinson 1997

GROUND: Turnbull Ground, Upgang Lane, Whitby, North Yorks YO21 3HZ
Ground Capacity: 3,500 **Seats:** 622 **Covered:** 1,372 **Clubhouse:** Yes **Shop:** Yes
Previous Grounds: None
Record Attendance: 4,000 v Scarborough - North Riding Cup 18/04/1965

Nearest Railway Station Whitby - 1km
Bus Route Argyle Road - 120m away

WITTON ALBION

NPL Premier Division

Founded 1887 **Nickname:** The Albion **Club Colours:** Red & white stripes

Club Contact Details
01606 430 08

Previous Names: None
Previous Leagues: Lancashire Combination, Cheshire County > 1979, Northern Premier 1979-91, Conference 1991-94

11-12		12-13		13-14		14-15		15-16		16-17		17-18		18-19		19-20		20-21	
NP1N	3	NP P	4	NP P	16	NP P	22	NP1N	11	NP1S	2	NP P	7	NP P	9	NP P	n&v	NP P	n&v
FAC	4Q	FAC	2Q	FAC	1Q	FAC	1Q	FAC	2Q	FAC	2Qr	FAC	1Q	FAC	4Q	FAC	2Qr	FAC	1Q
FAT	3Q	FAT	2Q	FAT	2Q	FAT	2Qr	FAT	1Q	FAT	1Pr	FAT	1Q	FAT	3Q	FAT	1Q	FAT	2P

HONOURS / RECORDS
FA Comps: None
League: Cheshire County 1948-49, 49-50, 53-54. Northern Premier Premier Division 1990-91.

County FA: Cheshire Senior Cup x7.

Victory: 13-0 v Middlewich (H)
Defeat: 0-9 v Macclesfield Town (A) - 18/09/1965
Goalscorer: Frank Fidler - 175 (1947-50)
Appearances: Brian Pritchard - 729
Additional: Paid £12,500 to Hyde United for Jim McCluskie 1991. Received £11,500 from Chester City for Peter Henderson.

GROUND: Wincham Park, Chapel Street, Wincham, CW9 6DA
Ground Capacity: 4,813 **Seats:** 600 **Covered:** 2,300 **Clubhouse:** Yes **Shop:** Yes
Previous Grounds: Central Ground (1910-1989)
Record Attendance: 3,940 v Kidderminster Harries - FA Trophy Semi-final 13/04/1991

Nearest Railway Station Northwich - 1.2km
Bus Route 89 & CAT9

BRIDLINGTON TOWN

NPL East

Founde 1918 **Nickname:** Seasiders **Club Colours:** All red

Club Contact Details

01262 606 879 admin@bridtownafc.com

Previous Names: Original Bridlington Town folded in 1994. Greyhound FC changed to Bridlington Town.

Previous Leagues: Yorkshire 1924-39, 59-82, NCEL 1982-90, 99-2003, 08-21. Northern Premier 1990-94, 2003-08.

11-12		12-13		13-14		14-15		15-16		16-17		17-18		18-19		19-20		20-21	
NCEP	2	NCEP	3	NCEP	12	NCEP	8	NCEP	5	NCEP	3	NCEP	9	NCEP	3	NCEP	n&v	NCEP	n&v
FAC	P	FAC	EP	FAC	Pr	FAC	1Q	FAC	EP	FAC	2Qr	FAC	P	FAC	P	FAC	P	FAC	EP
FAV	3P	FAV	1P	FAV	3P	FAV	1Q	FAV	2Q	FAV	1P	FAV	1P	FAV	1P	FAV	3P	FAV	3P

HONOURS / RECORDS

FA Comps: FA Vase 1992-93

League: Yorkshire League 1974-75. Northern Counties East 1989-90, 2001-02, 09-10, NPL Division One 1992-93.

County FA: ERCFA Senior Cup 19-20-21,21-22,22-23,30-31,52-53,56-57,60-61,64-65,66-67,69-70,71-72,88-89,92-93,2004-05, 11-12,14-15, 15-16, 16-17.

Goalscorer: Neil Grimson. **Apps:** Neil Grimson - 200+ (1987-97).

Best FA Cup First Round Proper 1960-61, 91-92

FA Trophy Second Round Proper 2004-05(r)

FA Vase Winners 1992-93

GROUND: The Hudgell Solicitor Stadium, Queensgate, Bridlington YO16 7LN

Ground Capacity: 3,000 **Seats:** 500 **Covered:** 500 **Clubhouse:** Yes **Shop:** Yes

Previous Grounds:

Record Attendance: 1,006 v FC Utd of Manchester, NPLD1N, 03.11.07. **Goalscorer:**

Nearest Railway Station Bridlington 3/4 miles

Bus Route 12 & 45

BRIGHOUSE TOWN

NPL East

Founde 1963 **Nickname:** Town **Club Colours:** Orange & black

Club Contact Details

07483 119 054

Previous Names: Blakeborough

Previous Leagues: Huddersfield Works 1963-75. West Riding County Amateur 1975-08.

11-12		12-13		13-14		14-15		15-16		16-17		17-18		18-19		19-20		20-21	
NCEP	4	NCEP	2	NCEP	1	NP1N	14	NP1N	14	NP1N	9	NP1N	17	NP1E	3	NPNW	n&v	NPNW	n&v
FAC	EP	FAC	P	FAC	2Q	FAC	1Q	FAC	1Q	FAC	1Q	FAC	P	FAC	P	FAC	P	FAC	P
FAV	1Q	FAV	4P	FAV	3Pr	FAT	P	FAT	1Q	FAT	P	FAT	P	FAT	1Q	FAT	P	FAT	1Q

HONOURS / RECORDS

FA Comps: None

League: Hudersfield Works 1966-67, 68-69, 73-74, 74-75. West Riding County Amateur Premier Division 1990-91, 94-95, 95-96, 2000-01, 01-02, Division One 88-89. Northern Counties East Premier 2013-14.

County FA: West Riding county Cup 1991-92.

Best FA Cup Second Qualifying Round 2013-14

FA Trophy First Qualifying Round 2015-16, 18-19, 20-21

FA Vase Fourth Round Proper 2012-13

GROUND: St Giles Road, Hove Edge, Brighouse, HD6 3PL

Ground Capacity: 1,000 **Seats:** 100 **Covered:** 200 **Clubhouse:** Yes **Shop:** No

Previous Grounds: Woodhouse Recreation Ground. Green Lane.

Record Attendance: 1,059 v Scarborough Athletic, Northern Counties East Premier Division, 13/04/2013.

Nearest Railway Station Brighouse - 2.5km

Bus Route 314

CLEETHORPES TOWN

NPL East

Founde 1998 **Nickname:** The Owls **Club Colours:** Blue & black

Club Contact Details
01472 693 601

Previous Names: Lincolnshire Soccer School Lucarlys 1998-2008.
Previous Leagues: Lincolnshire 2003-05, 10-12. Central Midlands 2005-06. Humber Premier 2006-09. Northern Counties East 2012-17.

11-12		12-13		13-14		14-15		15-16		16-17		17-18		18-19		19-20		20-21	
Lincs	1	NCE1	4	NCE1	1	NCEP	4	NCEP	3	NCEP	1	NP1S	10	NP1E	7	NPSE	n&v	NPSE	n&v
						FAC	2Q	FAC	P	FAC	P	FAC	1Q	FAC	3Qr	FAC	1Q	FAC	P
				FAV	2P	FAV	2P	FAV	5P	FAV	F	FAT	3Q	FAT	1Q	FAT	1Q	FAT	2Q

HONOURS / RECORDS
FA Comps: None
League: Lincolnshire 2011-12. Northern Counties East Division One 2013-14, Premier 2016-17.

County FA: Lincolnshire Senior Trophy 2016-17.

Best FA Cup Second Qualifying Round 2014-15
FA Vase Runners-up 2016-17
FA Trophy Third Qualifying Round 2017-18

GROUND: The Linden Club, Clee Road, Grimsby DN32 8QL
Ground Capacity: 1,875 **Seats:** 190 **Covered:** Yes **Clubhouse:** Yes **Shop:**
Previous Grounds: None
Record Attendance: 1,154 v Bromsgrove Sporting, FA Vase Semi-Final second leg, 18/03/2017.

Nearest Railway Station Grimsby - then a 5 min walk to main bus station (see below).
Bus Route From the bus station, take either No.14 or No.13 bus.

DUNSTON

NPL East

Founde 1975 **Nickname:** The Fed **Club Colours:** All blue

Club Contact Details
0191 493 2935

Previous Names: Whickham Sports 1975-82. Dunston Mechanics 82-87. Dunston Fed Brewery 87-2007. Dunston Fed 07-09. Dunston UTS 09-19
Previous Leagues: Newcastle City Amateur. Northern Amateur. Northern Combination 1980-87. Wearside 1987-91. Northern 91-2019.

11-12		12-13		13-14		14-15		15-16		16-17		17-18		18-19		19-20		20-21	
NL 1	3	NL 1	5	NL 1	7	NL 1	6	NL 1	11	NL 1	15	NL 1	10	NL 1	1	NPNW	n&v	NPNW	n&v
FAC	1Q	FAC	1Qr	FAC	P	FAC	2Q	FAC	1Q	FAC	2Q	FAC	P	FAC	4Q	FAC	4Q	FAC	P
FAV	F	FAV	4P	FAV	QF	FAV	5Pr	FAV	5Pr	FAV	3P	FAV	2P	FAV	2P	FAT	1Q	FAT	2Q

HONOURS / RECORDS
FA Comps: FA Vase 2011-12.
League: Northern Amateur 1977-78. Northern Combination 1986-87. Wearside 1988-89, 89-90.
Northern Division Two 1992-93, Division One 2003-04, 04-05, 18-19.
County FA: None

Goalscorer: Paul King
Appearances: Paul Dixon
Best FA Cup Fourth Qualifying Round 2018-19 19-20
FA Vase Winners 2011-12
FA Trophy Second Qualifying Round 2020-21

GROUND: UTS Stadium, Wellington Road, Dunston, Gateshead NE11 9JL
Ground Capacity: 2,000 **Seats:** 150 **Covered:** 400 **Clubhouse:** Yes **Shop:** No
Previous Grounds:
Record Attendance: 2,520 v Gateshead, FA Cup Fourth Qualifying Round, 20/10/2018

Nearest Railway Station Metrocentre - 0.9km. Dunston - 1km.
Bus Route Wellington Road - stop 24m away

FRICKLEY ATHLETIC

NPL East

Founde 1910 **Nickname:** The Blues **Club Colours:** All royal blue

Club Contact Details
01977 642 460

Previous Names: Frickley Colliery
Previous Leagues: Sheffield, Yorkshire 1922-24, Midland Counties 1924-33, 34-60, 70-76, Cheshire County 1960-70, Northern Premier 1976-80, Conference 1980-87

11-12	12-13	13-14	14-15	15-16	16-17	17-18	18-19	19-20	20-21
NP P 19	NP P 18	NP P 21	NP P 19	NP P 7	NP P 22	NP1S 3	NP1E 12	NPSE n&v	NPSE n&v
FAC 3Q	FAC 3Q	FAC 2Q	FAC 1Q	FAC 2Q	FAC 1Q	FAC 1Q	FAC 2Q	FAC P	FAC 1Q
FAT 1Q	FAT 1Q	FAT 1Q	FAT 1Q	FAT 1Q	FAT 1Q	FAT 1Q	FAT 1Q	FAT EP	FAT 3Q

HONOURS / RECORDS
FA Comps: None

League: None

County FA: Sheffield & Hallamshire Senior Cup x14 - Firstly in 1927-28 and most recently in 2015-16.

Goalscorer: K Whiteley
Additional: Received £12,500 from Boston United for Paul Shirtliff and from Northampton Town for Russ Wilcox

GROUND: Westfield Lane, South Elmsall, Pontefract WF9 2EQ
Ground Capacity: 2,087 **Seats:** 490 **Covered:** 700 **Clubhouse:** Yes **Shop:** Yes
Previous Grounds: None
Record Attendance: 5,800 v Rotherham United - FA Cup 1st Round 1971

Nearest Railway Station South Elmsall - 0.7km. Moorthorpe - 0.9km
Bus Route Westfield Lane - stop 100m away

HEBBURN TOWN

NPL East

Founde 1912 **Nickname:** Hornets **Club Colours:** Yellow & black

Club Contact Details
0191 483 5101

Previous Names: Reyrolles 1912-86, Hebburn Reyrolles 1986-88, Hebburn 1988-2000.
Previous Leagues: Jarrow & District. South Shields Combination. Tyneside Combination 1923-27. Tyneside 1927-41. Northern Combination 1941-44, 45-59. North Eastern 1944-45, 59-60. Wearside 1960-89.

11-12	12-13	13-14	14-15	15-16	16-17	17-18	18-19	19-20	20-21
NL 2 3	NL 1 18	NL 1 22	NL 2 5	NL 2 10	NL 2 11	NL 2 2	NL 1 2	NL 1 n&v	NL 1 n&v
FAC 4Q	FAC P	FAC P	FAC EPr	FAC EP			FAC EP	FAC Pr	FAC P
FAV 1P	FAV 2Q	FAV 1Q	FAV 1Q	FAV 1P	FAV 1Q	FAV 2Q	FAV 5P	FAV F	FAV QF

HONOURS / RECORDS
FA Comps: FA Vase 2019-20 (Final played on 03/05/21 due to COVID19)

League: Tyneside1938-39. Northern Combination 1943-44. Wearside 1966-67. Northern 1967-2021.

County FA: Durham Challenge Cup 1942-43, 91-92

Best FA Cup Fourth Qualifying Round 2011-12
FA Trophy Second Qualifying Round 1994-95(r)
FA Vase Winners 2019-20
Victory: 13-0 v Birtley Town, Northern League League Cup, 01/10/2019
Defeat: 3-10

GROUND: Hebburn Sports & Social, Victoria Rd West, Hebburn, Tyne & Wear NE31 1UN
Ground Capacity: **Seats:** Yes **Covered:** Yes **Clubhouse:** Yes **Shop:**
Previous Grounds: 1,705 v Plymouth Parkway, FA Vase Quarter final, 29/02/2019
Record Attendance: 503 v Darwen FA Cup Prelim replay 07/09/1991

Nearest Railway Station Hebburn - 1km
Bus Route Victoria Road West - stop 74m away

LINCOLN UNITED

NPL East

Founde 1938 **Nickname:** United **Club Colours:** White & red

Club Contact Details
01522 609 674

Previous Names: Lincoln Amateurs > 1954
Previous Leagues: Lincolnshire 1945-46, 60-67, Lincoln 1946-60, Yorkshire 1967-82, Northern Counties East 1982-86, 92-95, Central Midlands 1982-92

11-12		12-13		13-14		14-15		15-16		16-17		17-18		18-19		19-20		20-21	
NP1S	18	NP1S	20	NP1S	17	NP1S	9	NP1S	5	NP1S	8	NP1S	8	NP1E	14	NPSE	n&v	NPSE	n&v
FAC	P	FAC	P	FAC	P	FAC	1Q	FAC	2Q	FAC	4Q	FAC	1Q	FAC	P	FAC	P	FAC	P
FAT	1Q	FAT	1Q	FAT	P	FAT	P	FAT	2Q	FAT	3Q	FAT	P	FAT	P	FAT	EP	FAT	2Q

HONOURS / RECORDS
FA Comps: None
League: Yorkshire Division Two 1967-68, Division One 70-71, 73-74. Central Midlands Supreme Division 1991-92. Northern Counties East Division One (South) 82-83, Division Two 1985-86, Division One 92-93, Premier Division 1994-95.
County FA: Lincolnshire Senior Cup 2016-17.

Victory: 12-0 v Pontefract Colliery - 1995
Defeat: 0-7 v Huddersfield Town - FA Cup 1st Round 16/11/1991
Goalscorer: Tony Simmons - 215
Appearances: Steve Carter - 447
Additional: Paid £1,000 to Hucknall Town for Paul Tomlinson Dec 2000. Received £3,000 from Charlton for Dean Dye July 1991.

GROUND: Ashby Avenue, Hartsholme, Lincoln LN6 0DY
Ground Capacity: 2,200 **Seats:** 400 **Covered:** 1,084 **Clubhouse:** Yes **Shop:** Yes
Previous Grounds: Skew Bridge 1940s, Co-op Sports Ground > 1960s, Hartsholme Cricket Club > 1982
Record Attendance: 2,000 v Crook Town - FA Amateur Cup 1st Round 1968

Nearest Railway Station Hkeham - 2.1km
Bus Route Eccleshare Court - stop 75m away

LIVERSEDGE

NPL East

Founde 1910 **Nickname:** Sedge **Club Colours:** Sky blue

Club Contact Details
01274 862 108

Previous Names: None
Previous Leagues: Bradford 1919-22. West Riding Co. Amateur 1922-27, 49-72. Spen Valley 1947-49. Yorkshire 1972-82. Northern Counties East 1982-2021.

11-12		12-13		13-14		14-15		15-16		16-17		17-18		18-19		19-20		20-21	
NCEP	14	NCEP	15	NCEP	20	NCEP	18	NCEP	14	NCEP	11	NCEP	11	NCEP	13	NCEP	n&v	NCEP	n&v
FAC	Pr	FAC	EP	FAC	EP	FAC	EP	FAC	EP	FAC	EP	FAC	1Qr	FAC	P	FAC	1Q	FAC	EP
FAV	2Q	FAV	2Q	FAV	1P	FAV	2Q	FAV	1Q	FAV	2Q	FAV	1P	FAV	1Q	FAV	2Q	FAV	4P

HONOURS / RECORDS
FA Comps: None
League: West Riding County Amateur 1923-24, 25-26, 26-27, 64-65, 65-66, 68-69. Spen Valley 1948-49.
County FA: West Riding County Challenge Cup 1948-49, 51-52, 69-70. West Riding County Cup 1989-90.

Goalscorer: Dennis Charlesworth
Appearances: Barry Palmer

GROUND: Clayborn Ground, Quaker Lane, Hightown Road, Cleckheaton WF15 8DF
Ground Capacity: 2,000 **Seats:** 250 **Covered:** 750 **Clubhouse:** Yes **Shop:** Yes
Previous Grounds: None
Record Attendance: 986 v Thackley

Nearest Railway Station Low Moor - 4.5km
Bus Route Hightown Road - stop 142m away

MARSKE UNITED

NPL East

Founde 1956 **Nickname:** The Seasiders **Club Colours:** Yellow & navy

Club Contact Details
07803 248 709 admin@marskeunitedfc.com

Previous Names: None
Previous Leagues: Local leagues 1956-76. Teeside 1976- 85. Wearside 1985-97. Northern League 1997-2018.

11-12		12-13		13-14		14-15		15-16		16-17		17-18		18-19		19-20		20-21	
NL 1	18	NL 1	19	NL 1	16	NL 1	1	NL 1	2	NL 1	5	NL 1	1	NP1E	10	NPNW	n&v	NPNW	n&v
FAC	P	FAC	P	FAC	4Q	FAC	1Qr	FAC	Pr	FAC	1Q	FAC	Pr	FAC	P	FAC	1Qr	FAC	4Q
FAV	2Q	FAV	1Qr	FAV	1P	FAV	3P	FAV	4P	FAV	2P	FAV	SF	FAT	3Q	FAT	EP	FAT	2P

HONOURS / RECORDS
FA Comps: None
League: Teesside 1980-81, 84-85. Wearside 1995-96. Northern Division One 2014-15, 17-18.

County FA: None

Defeat: 3-9
Goalscorer: Chris Morgan 169.
Appearances: Mike Kinnair 583.
Victory: 16-0

GROUND: Mount Pleasant Avenue, Marske by the Sea, Redcar TS11 7BW
Ground Capacity: 2,500 **Seats:** Yes **Covered:** Yes **Clubhouse:** Yes **Shop:**
Previous Grounds: None
Record Attendance: 1,359 v Bedlington Terriers FA Vase.

Nearest Railway Station Marske - 0.4km
Bus Route Windy Hill Lane - stop 84m away

OSSETT UNITED

NPL East

Founde 2018 **Nickname:** United **Club Colours:** Blue

Club Contact Details
01924 272 960 secretary@ossettunited.com

Previous Names: Formed after the merger of Ossett Albion (1944) and Ossett Town (1936).
Previous Leagues: None

11-12		12-13		13-14		14-15		15-16		16-17		17-18		18-19		19-20		20-21	
														NP1E	5	NPNW	n&v	NPNW	n&v
														FAC	Pr	FAC	2Qr	FAC	P
														FAT	2Q	FAT	P	FAT	1Q

HONOURS / RECORDS
FA Comps: None
League: None

County FA: West Riding County Cup 2018-19.

Best FA Cup Second Qualifying Round 2019-20(r)
FA Trophy Second Qualifying Round 2018-19

GROUND: Ingfield Stadium, Prospect Road, Ossett WF5 9HA
Ground Capacity: 1,950 **Seats:** 360 **Covered:** 1,000 **Clubhouse:** Yes **Shop:** Yes
Previous Grounds: None
Record Attendance: 1,118 v AFC Guiseley, West Riding County Cup Final, 9/04/2019

Nearest Railway Station Dewsbury - 3.9km
Bus Route Prospect Road - stop 50m away

PICKERING TOWN

NPL East

Founde 1888 **Nickname:** Pikes **Club Colours:** All blue

Club Contact Details
01751 473 317

Previous Names: None
Previous Leagues: Beckett, York & District, Scarborough & District, Yorkshire 1972-82. Northern Counties East 1982-2018.

11-12		12-13		13-14		14-15		15-16		16-17		17-18		18-19		19-20		20-21	
NCEP	12	NCEP	5	NCEP	7	NCEP	11	NCEP	6	NCEP	2	NCEP	2	NP1E	16	NPNW	n&v	NPNW	n&v
FAC	1Qr	FAC	EPr	FAC	EP	FAC	EP	FAC	P	FAC	Pr	FAC	P	FAC	P	FAC	1Q	FAC	EP
FAV	2Q	FAV	2P	FAV	2Q	FAV	2Q	FAV	1Q	FAV	2P	FAV	1P	FAT	3Qr	FAT	1Qr	FAT	3Q

HONOURS / RECORDS
FA Comps: None
League: Scarborough & District Division One 1930-31, 50-51. York Division Two 1953-54, Division One 55-56, 66-67, 69-70. Yorkshire Division Three 1973-74. Northern Counties East Division Two 1987-88.
County FA: North Riding Cup 1990-91. North Riding Senior Cup 2012-13.

Best FA Cup Second Qualifying Round 1999-2000, 01-02, 03-04
FA Vase Quarter Finals 2005-06
FA Trophy Third Qualifying Round 2018-19(r), 20-21

GROUND: Recreation Club, off Mill Lane, Malton Road, Pickering YO18 7DB
Ground Capacity: 2,000 **Seats:** 200 **Covered:** 500 **Clubhouse:** Yes **Shop:** Yes
Previous Grounds: Not known
Record Attendance: 1,412 v Notts County (friendly) in August 1991

Nearest Railway Station Pickering - 650m
Bus Route Millfield Close - stop 62m away

PONTEFRACT COLLIERIES

NPL East

Founde 1958 **Nickname:** Colls **Club Colours:** All blue

Club Contact Details
01977 600 818

Previous Names: None
Previous Leagues: West Yorkshire 1958-79. Yorkshire 1979-82. Northern Counties East 1982-2018.

11-12		12-13		13-14		14-15		15-16		16-17		17-18		18-19		19-20		20-21	
NCE1	5	NCE1	5	NCE1	9	NCE1	2	NCEP	20	NCE1	2	NCEP	1	NP1E	2	NPNW	n&v	NPNW	n&v
FAC	P	FAC	EPr	FAC	EP	FAC	EP	FAC	P	FAC	1Q	FAC	P	FAC	P	FAC	2Q	FAC	1Q
FAV	1P	FAV	2Q	FAV	2Q	FAV	1Q	FAV	1Q	FAV	1Q	FAV	4P	FAT	P	FAT	1Q	FAT	2Q

HONOURS / RECORDS
FA Comps: None
League: Yorkshire Division Three 1981-82.
Northern Counties East Division One North 1983-84, Premier Division 2017-18.
County FA: Castleford & District FA Embleton Cup 1982-83, 86-87, 95-96, 99-2000, 05-06, 06-07, 07-08.

Best FA Cup Second Qualifying Round 2019-20
FA Vase Second Round Proper 2002-03
FA Trophy Second Qualifying Round 2020-21

GROUND: Beechnut Lane, Pontefract, WF8 4QE
Ground Capacity: 1,200 **Seats:** 300 **Covered:** 400 **Clubhouse:** Yes **Shop:** Yes
Previous Grounds: Not known
Record Attendance: 1,000 v Hull City, floodlight opening 1987.

Nearest Railway Station pontefract Tanshelf - ¼ mile
Bus Route 113, 148, 149, 184, 28, 410

SHEFFIELD

NPL East

Founde 1857 **Nickname:** The Club **Club Colours:** Red & black

Club Contact Details
0114 362 7016

Previous Names: None
Previous Leagues: Yorkshire 1949-82

11-12		12-13		13-14		14-15		15-16		16-17		17-18		18-19		19-20		20-21	
NP1S	4	NP1S	9	NP1S	16	NP1S	15	NP1S	17	NP1S	15	NP1S	15	NP1E	4	NPSE	n&v	NPSE	n&v
FAC	P	FAC	P	FAC	1Q	FAC	2Qr	FAC	Pr	FAC	1Q	FAC	P	FAC	P	FAC	1Q	FAC	1Q
FAT	3Q	FAT	P	FAT	3Q	FAT	1Q	FAT	1Q	FAT	P	FAT	P	FAT	EPr	FAT	EP	FAT	2Q

HONOURS / RECORDS
FA Comps: FA Amateur Cup 1902-03.
League: Northern Counties East Division One 1988-89, 90-91.

County FA: Sheffield and Hallamshire Senior Cup 1993-94, 2004-05, 05-06, 07-08, 09-10.

Misc: Oldest Football Club in the World.
Paid £1,000 to Arnold Town for David Wilkins. Received £1,000 from Alfreton for Mick Godber 2002.

Best FA Cup Fourth Round Proper 1877-78, 79-80.
FA Trophy Third Qualifying Round 2007-08, 11-12, 13-14
FA Vase Finalists 1976-77

GROUND: The Home of Football Stadium, Sheffield Road, Dronfield S18 2GD
Ground Capacity: 2,089 **Seats:** 250 **Covered:** 500 **Clubhouse:** Yes **Shop:** Yes
Previous Grounds: Abbeydale Park, Dore 1956-89, Sheffield Amateur Sports Stadium, Hillsborough Park 1989-91, Don Valley Stadium 1991-97
Record Attendance: 2,000 v Barton Rovers - FA Vase Semi-final 1976-77

Nearest Railway Station Dronfield - 1.1km
Bus Route 43

SHILDON

NPL East

Founde 1890 **Nickname:** Railwaymen **Club Colours:** Red

Club Contact Details
01388 773 877

Previous Names: Shildon Athletic 1903-1923.
Previous Leagues: Auckland & Dist 1892-86. Wear Valley 1896-97. Northern 1903-07, 33-2021. North Eastern 1907-33.

11-12		12-13		13-14		14-15		15-16		16-17		17-18		18-19		19-20		20-21	
NL 1	10	NL 1	8	NL 1	3	NL 1	2	NL 1	1	NL 1	4	NL 1	3	NL 1	6	NL 1	n&v	NL 1	n&v
FAC	1Qr	FAC	2Q	FAC	P	FAC	4Qr	FAC	EPr	FAC	2Q	FAC	4Q	FAC	P	FAC	EP	FAC	EP
FAV	1P	FAV	SF	FAV	2P	FAV	3P	FAV	1P	FAV	4P	FAV	2P	FAV	3P	FAV	2P	FAV	4P

HONOURS / RECORDS
FA Comps: None
League: Northern 1933-34, 34-35, 35-36,36-37, 39-40, 2015-16, Division Two 2001-02.

County FA: Durham Challenge Cup 2013-14, 14-15, 18-19.

Goalscorer: Jack Downing 61 (1936-7)
Appearances: Bryan Dale

GROUND: Dean Street, Shildon, Co. Durham DL4 1HA
Ground Capacity: 4,000 **Seats:** 480 **Covered:** 1000 **Clubhouse:** Yes **Shop:**
Previous Grounds: None
Record Attendance: 11,000 v Ferryhill Athletic, Durham Senior Cup 1922

Nearest Railway Station Shildon - 1.2km
Bus Route St. Johns Church - stop 149m away

STOCKSBRIDGE PARK STEELS

NPL East

Founde 1986 **Nickname:** Steels **Club Colours:** Yellow & royal blue

Club Contact Details
0114 288 8305 (Match days)

Previous Names: Stocksbridge Works and Oxley Park merged in 1986
Previous Leagues: Northern Counties East 1986-96

11-12		12-13		13-14		14-15		15-16		16-17		17-18		18-19		19-20		20-21	
NP P	18	NP P	20	NP P	23	NP1S	17	NP1S	6	NP1S	4	NP1S	11	NP1E	13	NPSE	n&v	NPSE	n&v
FAC	3Q	FAC	1Q	FAC	1Qr	FAC	P	FAC	Pr	FAC	P	FAC	P	FAC	P	FAC	P	FAC	P
FAT	1Qr	FAT	1P	FAT	1Q	FAT	P	FAT	1P	FAT	1P	FAT	P	FAT	P	FAT	P	FAT	2Q

HONOURS / RECORDS
FA Comps: None
League: Northern Counties East Division One 1991-92, Premier Division 1993-94.

County FA: Sheffield Senior Cup 1951-52, 92-93, 95-96, 98-99, 2006-07, 08-09.

Victory: 17-1 v Oldham Town - FA Cup 2002-03
Defeat: 0-6 v Shildon
Goalscorer: Trevor Jones - 145
Appearances: Paul Jackson scored 10 v Oldham Town in the 2002-03 FA Cup - a FA Cup record
Received £15,000 from Wolverhampton Wanderers for Lee Mills

GROUND: Bracken Moor Lane, Stocksbridge, Sheffield S36 2AN
Ground Capacity: 3,500 **Seats:** 450 **Covered:** 1,500 **Clubhouse:** Yes **Shop:** Yes
Previous Grounds: Stonemoor 1949-51, 52-53
Record Attendance: 2,050 v Sheffield Wednesday - opening of floodlights October 1991

Nearest Railway Station Tram - Meadowhall Interchange to Middlewood, then catch the SL1 alighting at Victoria Road.
Bus Route 201, 23 & SL1

STOCKTON TOWN

NPL East

Founde 1979 **Nickname:** The Anchors **Club Colours:** Yellow and blue

Club Contact Details
01642 604 915

Previous Names: Hartburn Juniors 1979-2003.
Previous Leagues: Teeside 2009-10. Wearside 2010-2016. Northern 2016-21.

11-12		12-13		13-14		14-15		15-16		16-17		17-18		18-19		19-20		20-21	
Wear	3	Wear	1	Wear	1	Wear	1	Wear	1	NL 2	1	NL 1	6	NL 1	7	NL 1	n&v	NL 1	n&v
												FAC	EP	FAC	EPr	FAC	2Q	FAC	1Q
										FAV	2P	FAV	F	FAV	3P	FAV	4P	FAV	3P

HONOURS / RECORDS
FA Comps: None
League: Wearside 2012-13, 13-14, 14-15,15-16. Northern Division Two 2016-17.

County FA: None

Best FA Cup Second Qualifying Round 2019-20
FA Vase Runners up 2017-18

GROUND: Bishopton Road West, Stockton-on-Tees TS19 0QD
Ground Capacity: 1,800 **Seats:** 200 **Covered:** Yes **Clubhouse:** Yes **Shop:**
Previous Grounds: Moved to Bishopton Road West in 2015.
Record Attendance: Not known

Nearest Railway Station Stockton - 1.4km
Bus Route Whitehouse Drive - stop 101m away

TADCASTER ALBION

NPL East

Founde 1892 **Nickname:** The Brewers / Taddy **Club Colours:** White & blue

Club Contact Details
01904 606 000

Previous Names: John Smith's FC > 1923.
Previous Leagues: York, Harrogate, Yorkshire 1973-82. Northern Counties East 1982-2016.

11-12		12-13		13-14		14-15		15-16		16-17		17-18		18-19		19-20		20-21	
NCEP	8	NCEP	6	NCEP	2	NCEP	3	NCEP	1	NP1N	19	NP1N	7	NP1E		NPNW	n&v	NPNW	n&v
FAC	2Q	FAC	3Q	FAC	EPr	FAC	P	FAC	P	FAC	2Q	FAC	P	FAC	1Q	FAC	1Qr	FAC	3Q
FAV	2P	FAV	1Q	FAV	1Q	FAV	QFr	FAV	3P	FAT	P	FAT	P	FAT	Pr	FAT	1Q	FAT	1Q

HONOURS / RECORDS
FA Comps: None
League: York Division One 1909-10, 23-24, 32-33, Premier 47-48.
Northern Counties East Division One 2009-10, Premier Division 2015-16.
County FA: None

Victory: 13-0 v Blidworth Welfare, NCEL Division One, 1997-98
Defeat: 10-2 v Thackley, 1984-85

GROUND: Ings Lane, Tadcaster LS24 9AY
Ground Capacity: 2,000 **Seats:** 159 **Covered:** 259 **Clubhouse:** Yes **Shop:** No
Previous Grounds: None
Record Attendance: 1,307 v Highworth Town, FA Vase, 2014-15.

Nearest Railway Station Ulleskelf - 4.3km
Bus Route John Smith's Brewery - stop 300m away

WORKSOP TOWN

NPL East

Founde 1861 **Nickname:** Tigers **Club Colours:** Yellow & black

Club Contact Details
07952 365 224

Previous Names: None
Previous Leagues: Sheffield Association. Midland 1949-60, 61-68, 69-74, Northern Premier 1968-69, 74-2004, 2007-14, Conf. 2004-07. Northern Counties East 2014-19.

11-12		12-13		13-14		14-15		15-16		16-17		17-18		18-19		19-20		20-21	
NP P	15	NP P	9	NP P	4	NCEP	2	NCEP	4	NCEP	13	NCEP	18	NCEP	1	NPSE	n&v	NPSE	n&v
FAC	1Q	FAC	1Q	FAC	3Q	FAC	EP	FAC	EP	FAC	Pr	FAC	EP	FAC	1Q	FAC	EP	FAC	2Q
FAT	2P	FAT	1P	FAT	1Q	FAV	4P	FAV	2P	FAV	2P	FAV	3P	FAV	2Q	FAT	1Q	FAT	3Q

HONOURS / RECORDS
FA Comps: None
League: Sheffield Association 1898-99 (joint), 47-48, 48-49. Midland 1921-22, 65-66, 72-73. Northern Counties east Premier 2018-19.

County FA: Sheffield & Hallamshire Senior Cup 1923-24, 52-53, 54-55, 65-66, 69-70, 72-73, 81-82, 84-85, 94-95, 96-97, 2002-03, 11-12
Victory: 20-0 v Staveley - 01/09/1984
Defeat: 1-11 v Hull City Reserves - 1955-56
Goalscorer: Kenny Clark - 287
Appearances: Kenny Clark - 347
Additional: Paid £5,000 to Grantham Town for Kirk Jackson. Received £47,000 from Sunderland for Jon Kennedy 2000.

GROUND: Babbage Way, Worksop S80 1UJ
Ground Capacity: 2,500 **Seats:** 200 **Covered:** 750 **Clubhouse:** Yes **Shop:** Yes
Previous Grounds: Central Avenue, Sandy Lane, shared with Ilkeston Town (New Manor Ground)
Record Attendance: 8,171 v Chesterfield - FA Cup 1925 (Central Avenue)

Nearest Railway Station Worksop - 0.5km
Bus Route Grafton Street - stop 114m away

YORKSHIRE AMATEUR

NPL East

Founde 1918 **Nickname:** Ammers **Club Colours:** White & blue

Club Contact Details
0113 289 2886

Previous Names: None
Previous Leagues: Yorkshire (FM) 1920-24, 30-82. Northern Counties East 1982-2021.

11-12	12-13	13-14	14-15	15-16	16-17	17-18	18-19	19-20	20-21
NCE1 19	NCE1 21	NCE1 19	NCE1 10	NCE1 11	NCE1 13	NCE1 2	NCEP 5	NCEP n&v	NCEP n&v
FAC EP				FAC EP				FAC EP	FAC EP
FAV 1P	FAV 2Q	FAV 1Q	FAV 1P	FAV 2Q	FAV 1Q		FAV 1Q	FAV 3P	FAV 1P

HONOURS / RECORDS
FA Comps: None
League: Yorkshire 1931-32, Division Two 1958-59, Division Three 1977-78.

County FA: West Riding Challenge Cup 1930-31, 33-34, 44-45. West Riding County Cup 1953-54, 60-61, 71-72.

Best FA Cup First Round Proper 1931-32, 44-46
FA Amateur C Semi-final 1931-32
FA Trophy Preliminary Round 1974-75
FA Vase Third Round Proper 1993-94

GROUND: Bracken Edge, Roxholme Road, Leeds, LS8 4DZ (Sat. Nav. LS7 4JG)
Ground Capacity: 1,550 **Seats:** 200 **Covered:** 160 **Clubhouse:** Yes **Shop:** Yes
Previous Grounds: Elland Road 1919-20. Shared a number of grounds, including Harrogate Town's, before moving to Bracken Edge in 1922.
Record Attendance: 3,569 v Wimbledon, FA Amateur Cup quarter finals, 1932.

Nearest Railway Station Leeds - 3.5km
Bus Route Harehills Ln Roxholme Ave - stop 168m away

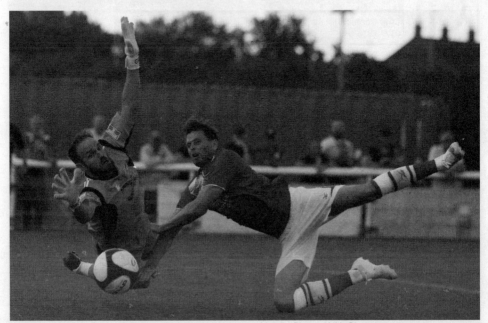

Hall (Nantwich) has Porter (Crewe) well covered - pre-season friendly. Photos Keith Clayton.

BEDWORTH UNITED

NPL Midlands

Founde 1895 **Nickname:** Greenbacks **Club Colours:** All green

Club Contact Details
07927 686 792 secretary@bedworthunitedfc.co.uk

Previous Names: Bedworth Town 1947-68
Previous Leagues: Birmingham Combination 1947-54, Birmingham/West Midlands 1954-72. Southern 1972-2013, 14-16, 18-21. Northern Premier 2013-14, 16-18.

11-12		12-13		13-14		14-15		15-16		16-17		17-18		18-19		19-20		20-21	
SthC	3	SthP	21	NP1S	20	SthC	4	SthP	21	NP1S	11	NP1S	4	SthPC	22	SthC	n&v	SthC	n&v
FAC	1Q	FAC	2Q	FAC	P	FAC	2Qr	FAC	2Q	FAC	3Q	FAC	P	FAC	P	FAC	P	FAC	1Q
FAT	1Q	FAT	1Q	FAT	P	FAT	P	FAT	1Q	FAT	1Q	FAT	1Q	FAT	1Q	FAT	1Q	FAT	2Q

HONOURS / RECORDS
FA Comps: None
League: Birmingham Combination 1948-49, 49-50.

County FA: Birmingham Senior Cup 1978-79, 80-81, 81-82.

Goalscorer: Peter Spacey - 1949-69
Appearances: Peter Spacey - 1949-69
Additional: Paid £1,750 to Hinckley Town for Colin Taylor 1991-92
Received £30,000 from Plymouth Argyle for Richard Landon

GROUND: The Oval, Coventry Road, Bedworth CV12 8NN
Ground Capacity: 2,900 **Seats:** 300 **Covered:** 300 **Clubhouse:** Yes **Shop:** Yes
Previous Grounds: British Queen Ground 1911-39
Record Attendance: 5,172 v Nuneaton Borough - Southern League Midland Division 23/02/1982

Nearest Railway Station Bedworth - 0.5km
Bus Route Bus stops at the Leisure Centre

BELPER TOWN

NPL Midlands

Founde 1883 **Nickname:** The Nailers **Club Colours:** Yellow & black

Club Contact Details
01773 825 549

Previous Names: None
Previous Leagues: Derbyshire Senior (Founder members) 1890-1911. Notts & Derbyshire (FM) 1911-12. Central Alliance 1957-61, Midland Counties 1961-82, Northern Counties East 1982-97

11-12		12-13		13-14		14-15		15-16		16-17		17-18		18-19		19-20		20-21	
NP1S	6	NP1S	3	NP1S	4	NP P	24	NP1S	13	NP1S	10	NP1S	16	NP1E	9	NPSE	n&v	NPSE	n&v
FAC	P	FAC	2Qr	FAC	2Q	FAC	1Qr	FAC	1Q	FAC	2Q	FAC	Pr	FAC	1Q	FAC	4Q	FAC	1Q
FAT	2Q	FAT	2Q	FAT	1Q	FAT	1Q	FAT	1Qr	FAT	P	FAT	P	FAT	Pr	FAT	P	FAT	2Q

HONOURS / RECORDS
FA Comps: None
League: Central Alliance 1958-59. Midland Counties 1979-80. Northern Counties East 1984-85.

County FA: Derbyshire Senior Cup 1958-59, 61-62, 63-64, 79-80, 2007-08.

Victory: 15-2 v Nottingham Forest 'A' - 1956
Defeat: 0-12 v Goole Town - 1965
Goalscorer: Mick Lakin - 231
Appearances: Craig Smithurst - 678
Additional: Paid £2,000 to Ilkeston Town for Jamie Eaton 2001. Received £2,000 from Hinckley United for Craig Smith.

GROUND: Christchurch Meadow, Bridge Street, Belper DE56 1BA
Ground Capacity: 2,650 **Seats:** 500 **Covered:** 850 **Clubhouse:** Yes **Shop:** Yes
Previous Grounds: Acorn Ground > 1951
Record Attendance: 3,200 v Ilkeston Town - 1955

Nearest Railway Station Belper - 0.4km
Bus Route The Lion Hotel - stop 200m away

CAMBRIDGE CITY

NPL Midlands

Founde 1908 **Nickname:** Lilywhites **Club Colours:** Black and white

Club Contact Details
07720 678 585 info@cambridge-city-fc.com

Previous Names: Cambridge Town 1908-51

Previous Leagues: Bury & District 1908-13, 19-20, Anglian 1908-10, Southern Olympian 1911-14. Southern Amateur 1913-35. Spartan 1935-50. Athenian 1950-58. Southern 1958-2004, 08-19. Conference 2004-08. Isthmian 2019-21.

11-12	12-13	13-14	14-15	15-16	16-17	17-18	18-19	19-20	20-21
SthP 5	SthP 8	SthP 3	SthP 13	SthP 18	SthP 21	Sth1E 6	SthC 12	IsthN n&v	IsthN n&v
FAC 1Qr	FAC 1Pr	FAC 2Q	FAC 1Q	FAC 1Q	FAC 2Q	FAC 2Qr	FAC 1Q	FAC P	FAC 4Q
FAT 2Q	FAT 1Q	FAT 2Qr	FAT 1Q	FAT 1Q	FAT 1Q	FAT 1Q	FAT 1Q	FAT 1Q	FAT 1Q

HONOURS / RECORDS

FA Comps: None

League: Southern 1962-63, Southern Division 1985-86.

County FA: Suffolk Senior Cup 1909-10. East Anglian x9. Cambridgeshire Professional Cup 2012-13, 14-15, Invitational Cup 2014-15.

Goalscorer: Gary Grogan

Appearances: Mal Keenan

Additional: Paid £8,000 to Rushden & Diamonds for Paul Coe
Received £100,000 from Millwall for Neil Harris 1998

GROUND: Histon FC, Bridge Road, Impington, Cambridge CB24 9PH

Ground Capacity: 3,250 **Seats:** 450 **Covered:** Yes **Clubhouse:** Yes **Shop:** Yes

Previous Grounds: City Ground.

Record Attendance: 12,058 v Leytonstone - FA Amateur Cup 1st Round 1949-50

Nearest Railway Station Cambridge - the following buses run every 20 minutes,

Bus Route Citi 8 and Guided Busway routes A, B and C

CARLTON TOWN

NPL Midlands

Founde 1904 **Nickname:** The Millers **Club Colours:** Yellow & blue

Club Contact Details
01159 403 192

Previous Names: Sneinton FC

Previous Leagues: Notts Alliance, Central Midlands, Northern Counties East

11-12	12-13	13-14	14-15	15-16	16-17	17-18	18-19	19-20	20-21
NP1S 2	NP1S 12	NP1S 10	NP1S 18	NP1S 18	NP1S 19	NP1S 19	NP1E 19	NPSE n&v	NPSE n&v
FAC 2Q	FAC 3Q	FAC 3Q	FAC 1Q	FAC P	FAC P	FAC P	FAC P	FAC EP	FAC 1Q
FAT P	FAT P	FAT Pr	FAT 1Qr	FAT 2Q	FAT 1Q	FAT 1Q	FAT 2Q	FAT 1Q	FAT 2Q

HONOURS / RECORDS

FA Comps: None

League: Notts Alliance 1905-06, 07-08, 08-09, 09-10, Division Two 1984-85, Division One 1992-93.
Central Midlands Supreme Division 2002-03. Northern Counties East Division One 2005-06.

County FA: Notts Senior Cup 2012-13, 16-17.

Best FA Cup Third Qualifying Round 2012-13, 13-14

Amateur Cup Third Round Proper 1910-11, 19-20, 30-31

FA Trophy Second Qualifying Round 2009-10, 15-16, 20-21

FA Vase Third Round Proper 2005-06

GROUND: Bill Stokeld Stadium, Stoke Lane, Gedling NG4 2QS

Ground Capacity: 1,500 **Seats:** 164 **Covered:** Yes **Clubhouse:** Yes **Shop:** No

Previous Grounds: Club played at several grounds before moving to Stoke Lane (Bill Stokeld Stadium) in the 1990s.

Record Attendance: 1,000 - Radio Trent Charity Match

Nearest Railway Station Carlton - 1.1km. Netherfield - 1.5km

Bus Route Stoke Lane - stop 50m away

CHASETOWN

NPL Midlands

Founde 1954 **Nickname:** The Scholars **Club Colours:** Royal blue & white

Club Contact Details
01543 682 222

Previous Names: Chase Terrace Old Scholars 1954-72
Previous Leagues: Cannock Youth 1954-58, Lichfield & District 1958-61, Staffordshire County 1961-72, West Midlands 1972-94, Midland Alliance 1994-2006, Southern 2006-09

11-12		12-13		13-14		14-15		15-16		16-17		17-18		18-19		19-20		20-21	
NP P	20	NP1S	5	NP1S	12	NP1S	13	NP1S	7	NP1S	17	NP1S	5	NP1W	13	NPSE	n&v	NPSE	n&v
FAC	2Q	FAC	2Q	FAC	1Qr	FAC	1Qr	FAC	3Qr	FAC	2Q	FAC	2Q	FAC	1Qr	FAC	2Q	FAC	2Q
FAT	2Q	FAT	2Q	FAT	1Q	FAT	3Q	FAT	Pr	FAT	P	FAT	2Q	FAT	1Q	FAT	1Q	FAT	2Q

HONOURS / RECORDS
FA Comps: None
League: West Midlands 1978. Midland Alliance 2004-05.

County FA: Walsall Senior Cup 1990-91, 92-93, 2004-05.

Victory: 14-1 v Hanford - Walsall Senior Cup 1991-92
Defeat: 1-8 v Telford United Reserves - West Midlands League
Goalscorer: Tony Dixon - 197. Mick Ward scored 39 goals during the 1987-88 season, whilst a player by the name of Keith Birch scored 11 in a 21-1 win over Lichfield Laundry.
Misc: Became the first club from the eighth tier of English football to reach the FA Cup Third Round Proper during the 2007-08 season.

GROUND: The Scholars, Church Street, Chasetown, Walsall WS7 3QL
Ground Capacity: 2,000 **Seats:** 151 **Covered:** 220 **Clubhouse:** Yes **Shop:** Yes
Previous Grounds: Burntwood Recreation
Record Attendance: 2,420 v Cardiff City - FA Cup Third Round Proper January 2008

Nearest Railway Station Hednesford - 6.4km
Bus Route Queen Street - stop 160m away

COLESHILL TOWN

NPL Midlands

Founde 1894 **Nickname:** The Coleman **Club Colours:** White & blue

Club Contact Details
01675 464 905

Previous Names: Coleshill & District. Coleshill FC. Coleshill United 1919.
Previous Leagues: Birmingham Youth & Old Boys 1906-07, 56-67. Sutton & Erdington 1907-08. Trent Valley 1912. Sutton & District 1919-56. Worcestershire Combination/Midland Combination 1967-2008. Midland Alliance 2008-2014. Southern 2014-21.

11-12		12-13		13-14		14-15		15-16		16-17		17-18		18-19		19-20		20-21	
MidAl	16	MidAl	15	MidAl	4	MFLP	2	MFLP	5	MFLP	2	MFLP	2	SthC	9	SthC	n&v	SthC	n&v
FAC	Pr	FAC	EPr	FAC	EP	FAC	1Q	FAC	3Q	FAC	1Q	FAC	1Q	FAC	EP	FAC	P	FAC	P
FAV	1Q	FAV	1Q	FAV	4P	FAV	2P	FAV	4P	FAV	SF	FAV	5P	FAT	EP	FAT	P	FAT	2P

HONOURS / RECORDS
FA Comps: None
League: Sutton & District Division One 1952-53, 54-5. Birmingham Youth & Old Boys Suburban Division 1958-59. Midland Combination Division Two 1969-70, Premier 07-08.
County FA: Walsall Senior Cup 1982-83

Best FA Cup Third Qualifying Round 2015-16
FA Vase Semi Finals 2016-17
FA Trophy Second Round Proper 2020-21

GROUND: Pack Meadow, Packington Lane, Coleshill B46 3JJ
Ground Capacity: 2,000 **Seats:** 570 **Covered:** **Clubhouse:** Yes **Shop:**
Previous Grounds: Memorial Ground >1974
Record Attendance: Not known

Nearest Railway Station Coleshill Parkway - 3.6km
Bus Route St Edmunds Primary School - 258m away

CORBY TOWN

NPL Midlands

Founde 1948 **Nickname:** The Steelmen **Club Colours:** Black and white

Club Contact Details

01536 406 640 media@corbytownfc.co.uk

Previous Names: Stewart & Lloyds (Corby) > 1947

Previous Leagues: United Counties 1935-52. Midland 1952-58. Southern 1958-2009, 13-15, 18-21. Football Conference 2009-13, 15-16. Northern Premier 2016-18.

11-12		12-13		13-14		14-15		15-16		16-17		17-18		18-19		19-20		20-21	
Conf N	17	Conf N	20	SthP	11	SthP	1	Nat N	22	NP P	21	NP1S	9	SthC	3	SthC	n&v	SthC	n&v
FAC	1P	FAC	4Q	FAC	1P	FAC	1Qr	FAC	2Qr	FAC	1Q	FAC	P	FAC	3Q	FAC	2Q	FAC	P
FAT	3Qr	FAT	2Pr	FAT	1Q	FAT	1Q	FAT	3Q	FAT	1Q	FAT	1Q	FAT	P	FAT	1Q	FAT	3Q

HONOURS / RECORDS

FA Comps: None

League: United Counties League 1950-51, 51-52. Southern League Premier Division 2008-09, 2014-15.

County FA: Northants Senior Cup 1950-51, 62-63, 75-76, 82-83, 2009-10, 12-13.

Goalscorer: David Holbauer - 159 (1984-95)

Appearances: Derek Walker - 601

Additional: Paid £2,700 to Barnet for Elwun Edwards 1981
Received £20,000 from Oxford United for Matt Murphy 1993

GROUND: Steel Park, Jimmy Kane Way, Rockingham Road, Corby NN17 2FB

Ground Capacity: 3,893 **Seats:** 577 **Covered:** 1,575 **Clubhouse:** Yes **Shop:** Yes

Previous Grounds: Occupation Road 1948-85.

Record Attendance: 2,240 v Watford - Friendly 1986-87

Nearest Railway Station Corby - 2.2km

Bus Route Dalton Road - stop 500m away

DAVENTRY TOWN

NPL Midlands

Founde 1886 **Nickname:** Purple Army **Club Colours:** Purple

Club Contact Details

01327 311 239 club.secretary@dtfc.co.uk

Previous Names: None

Previous Leagues: Northampton Town (pre-1987), Northants Comb 1987-89, United Counties 1989-2010, 16-19. Southern 2010-15, 19-21. Northern Premier 2015-16.

11-12		12-13		13-14		14-15		15-16		16-17		17-18		18-19		19-20		20-21	
SthC	16	SthC	8	SthC	4	SthC	19	NP1S	21	UCL 1	1	UCL P	10	UCL P	1	SthC	n&v	SthC	n&v
FAC	3Q	FAC	2Q	FAC	1P	FAC	1Q	FAC	P	FAC	EP	FAC	EP	FAC	1Q	FAC	EP	FAC	1Q
FAT	2Q	FAT	P	FAT	1P	FAT	P	FAT	P	FAV	1P	FAV	2Q	FAT	P	FAT	EP	FAT	2Q

HONOURS / RECORDS

FA Comps: None

League: Northants Combination Division One 1987-88, Premier 88-89.
United Counties Division One 1989-90, 90-91, 2000-01, 2007-08, 16-17, Premier Division 2009-10, 18-19.

County FA: Northants Junior Cup 1930-31, 60-61.

FA Cup First Round Proper 2013-14

FA Trophy First Round Proper 2013-14

FA Vase Fifth Round 2009-10

GROUND: Browns Road, Daventry, Northants NN11 4NS

Ground Capacity: 3,000 **Seats:** 250 **Covered:** 250 **Clubhouse:** Yes **Shop:**

Previous Grounds: Hollow Ground.

Record Attendance: 850 v Utrecht (Holland) - 1989

Nearest Railway Station Northampton

Bus Route D3 towards Daventry from Rail Station approach road - alight at Cherwell, 7min walk from there.

HALESOWEN TOWN

NPL Midlands

Founde 1873 **Nickname:** Yeltz **Club Colours:** All blue

Club Contact Details
0121 629 0727 secretary@halesowentown.com

Previous Names: None
Previous Leagues: Birmingham & District/West Midlands 1892-1905, 06-11, 46-86, Birmingham Combination 1911-39. Southern 1986-12, 18-21. Northern Premier 2012-18.

11-12		12-13		13-14		14-15		15-16		16-17		17-18		18-19		19-20		20-21	
Sthsw	12	NP1S	7	NP1S	1	NP P	11	NP P	13	NP P	19	NP P	23	SthPC	21	SthC	n&v	SthC	n&v
FAC	P	FAC	P	FAC	3Q	FAC	3Q	FAC	2Q	FAC	3Qr	FAC	2Q	FAC	2Q	FAC	3Q	FAC	3Q
FAT	P	FAT	2Q	FAT	1Q	FAT	1P	FAT	1Q	FAT	2Q	FAT	1Q	FAT	3Q	FAT		FAT	2Q

HONOURS / RECORDS
FA Comps: FA Vase 1984-85, 85-86
League: West Midlands (Reg) 1946-47, 82-83, 83-84, 84-85, 85-86. Southern League Midland Division 1989-90, Western Division 2001-02. Northern Premier Division One South 2013-14.
County FA: Worcestershire Senior Cup 1951-52, 61-62, 2002-03, 04-05. Birmingham Senior Cup 1983-84, 97-98. Staffordshire Senior Cup 1988-89.
Victory: 13-1 v Coventry Amateurs - Birmingham Senior cup 1956
Defeat: 0-8 v Bilston - West Midlands League 07/04/1962
Goalscorer: Paul Joinson - 369
Appearances: Paul Joinson - 608
Additional: Paid £7,250 to Gresley Rovers for Stuart Evans. Received £40,000 from Rushden & Diamonds for Jim Rodwell.

GROUND: The Grove, Old Hawne Lane, Halesowen B63 3TB
Ground Capacity: 3,150 **Seats:** 525 **Covered:** 930 **Clubhouse:** Yes **Shop:** Yes
Previous Grounds: None
Record Attendance: 5,000 v Hendon - FA Cup 1st Round Proper 1954

Nearest Railway Station Old Hill - 1.8km
Bus Route Cranmoor Crescent - stop 50m away

HISTON

NPL Midlands

Founde 1904 **Nickname:** The Stutes **Club Colours:** Red and black

Club Contact Details
01223 237 373 (Ground) enquiries@histonfc.co.uk

Previous Names: Histon Institute 1904-51.
Previous Leagues: Cambridgeshire 1904-48. Spartan 1948-60. Delphian 1960-63. Athenian 1963-65. Eastern Counties 1965-2000, 17-19. Southern 2000-05, 14-17. Conference 2005-14. Isthmian 2017-21.

11-12		12-13		13-14		14-15		15-16		16-17		17-18		18-19		19-20		20-21	
Conf N	16	Conf N	19	Conf N	21	SthP	18	SthP	22	SthC	21	ECP	6	ECP	1	IsthN	n&v	IsthN	n&v
FAC	2Qr	FAC	3Qr	FAC	3Q	FAC	2Qr	FAC	1Q	FAC	2Q	FAC	EP	FAC	1Qr	FAC	1Q	FAC	P
FAT	3Q	FAT	3Q	FAT	3Q	FAT	2Q	FAT	1Qr	FAT	Pr	FAV	2Q	FAV	2P	FAT	Pr	FAT	2Q

HONOURS / RECORDS
FA Comps: None
League: Spartan Division One Eastern 1950-51. Eastern Counties 1999-2000, 18-19. Southern League Premier 2004-05. Conference South 2006-07.
County FA: Cambridgeshire Professional Cup 2012-13, 15-16.

Victory: 11-0 v March Town - Cambridgeshire Invitation Cup 15/02/01
Defeat: 1-8 v Ely City - Eastern Counties Division One 1994
Goalscorer: Neil Kennedy - 292
Appearances: Neil Andrews and Neil Kennedy
Additional: Paid £6,000 to Chelmsford City for Ian Cambridge 2000. Received £30,000 from Man Utd for Guiliano Maiorana.

GROUND: Bridge Road, Impington, Cambridge CB24 9PH
Ground Capacity: 3,250 **Seats:** 450 **Covered:** 1,800 **Clubhouse:** Yes **Shop:** Yes
Previous Grounds: None
Record Attendance: 6,400 v King's Lynn - FA Cup 1956

Nearest Railway Station Cambridge - the following buses run every 20 minutes,
Bus Route Citi 8 and Guided Busway routes A, B and C

ILKESTON TOWN

NPL Midlands

Founde 2017 **Nickname:** The Robjns **Club Colours:** Red & white

Club Contact Details
01159 300 386

Previous Names: None
Previous Leagues: Midland 2017-19.

11-12	12-13	13-14	14-15	15-16	16-17	17-18	18-19	19-20	20-21
						MFL1 2	MFLP 1	NPSE n&v	NPSE n&v
								FAC EP	FAC 4Q
							FAV 2P	FAT P	FAT 3Q

HONOURS / RECORDS
FA Comps: None
League: Midland Premier 2018-19.

County FA: None

Victory: 8-1 v Loughborough University, Midland Premier, 27/04/2019
Defeat: 0-4 v Coventry Sphinx, Midland Premier, 15/12/2018
Best FA Cup Fourth Qualifying Round 2020-21
FA Vase Second Round Proper 2018-19
FA Trophy Third Qualifying Round 2020-21

GROUND: New Manor Ground, Awsworth Road, Ilkeston, Derbyshire DE7 8JF
Ground Capacity: 3,029 **Seats:** 550 **Covered:** 2,000 **Clubhouse:** Yes **Shop:** Yes
Previous Grounds: None.
Record Attendance: Not known

Nearest Railway Station Ilkeston
Bus Route 21, 27 & The Two

LOUGHBOROUGH DYNAMO

NPL Midlands

Founde 1955 **Nickname:** The Moes **Club Colours:** Gold & black

Club Contact Details
01509 215 972

Previous Names: None
Previous Leagues: Loughborough Alliance 1957-66, Leicestershire & District 1966-71, East Midlands 1971-72, Central Alliance 1972-89, Leicestershire Senior 1989-2004, Midland Alliance 2004-08

11-12	12-13	13-14	14-15	15-16	16-17	17-18	18-19	19-20	20-21
NP1S 8	NP1S 16	NP1S 14	NP1S 14	NP1S 20	NP1S 20	NP1S 14	NP1E 8	NPSE n&v	NPSE n&v
FAC 2Q	FAC 1Qr	FAC P	FAC P	FAC P	FAC P	FAC 1Q	FAC P	FAC 2Q	FAC 1Q
FAT P	FAT P	FAT P	FAT 2Q	FAT P	FAT P	FAT P	FAT Pr	FAT EP	FAT 3Q

HONOURS / RECORDS
FA Comps: None
League: Loughborough Alliance Division Three 1959-60, Division One 64-65. Leicester & District Division One 1969-70. Leicestershire Senior Division One 2001-02, Premier Division 2003-04.
County FA: Leicestershire Charity Cup 1987-88, 2003-04, 11-12, Senior Cup 2002-03, 03-04.

Best FA Cup Second Qualifying Round 2010-11, 11-12, 19-20
FA Trophy Second Qualifying Round 2014-15
FA Vase Second Round Proper 2004-05

GROUND: Watermead Lane, Loughborough LE11 3TN
Ground Capacity: 1,500 **Seats:** 75 **Covered:** Yes **Clubhouse:** Yes **Shop:** No
Previous Grounds: None
Record Attendance: Not known

Nearest Railway Station Loughborough - 4.6km
Bus Route Nursery School - stop 500m away

SHEPSHED DYNAMO

NPL Midlands

Founde 1994 **Nickname:** Dynamo **Club Colours:** Black & white

Club Contact Details

01509 650 992 dannypole@aol.com

Previous Names: Shepshed Albion/Charterhouse > 1994

Previous Leagues: Leics Sen 1907-16,19-27, 46-50, 51-81, Mid Co 81-82,N.C.E. 82-83, Sth 83-88, 96-04, N.P.L.88-93, 04-12, Mid Com 93-94, Mid All 94-95,13-14. UCL 12-13. Midland 2014-19. United Counties 2019-21.

11-12		12-13		13-14		14-15		15-16		16-17		17-18		18-19		19-20		20-21	
NP1S	22	UCL P	9	MidAl	16	MFLP	16	MFLP	4	MFLP	15	MFLP	7	MFLP	7	UCL P	n&v	UCL P	n&v
FAC	Pr	FAC	EP	FAC	P	FAC	1Q	FAC	1Qr	FAC	EP	FAC	2Q	FAC	EPr	FAC	EP	FAC	P
FAT	P	FAV	2P	FAV	2Q	FAV	2P	FAV	1Q	FAV	4P	FAV	3P	FAV	4P	FAV	3P	FAV	3P

HONOURS / RECORDS

FA Comps: None

League: Midland Counties 1981-82. Northern Counties East 1982-83.
Midland Alliance 1995-96.

County FA: Leicestershire Senior Cup x7

Goalscorer: Lee McGlinchey - 107

Appearances: Lee McGlinchey - 255

GROUND: The Dovecote, Butt Hole Lane, Shepshed, Leicestershire LE12 9BN

Ground Capacity: 2,050 **Seats:** 570 **Covered:** 400 **Clubhouse:** Yes **Shop:** Yes

Previous Grounds: Not known

Record Attendance: 2,500 v Leicester City - Friendly 1996-97

Bus Route Market Place stop - 229m away

SOHAM TOWN RANGERS

NPL Midlands

Founde 1947 **Nickname:** Greens, Town or Rangers **Club Colours:** Green & white

Club Contact Details

01353 720 732

Previous Names: Soham Town and Soham Rangers merged in 1947

Previous Leagues: Peterborough & District, Eastern Counties 1963-2008, Southern 2008-11. Isthmian 2011-21.

11-12		12-13		13-14		14-15		15-16		16-17		17-18		18-19		19-20		20-21	
Isth1N	19	Isth1N	7	Isth1N	8	Isth1N	11	Isth1N	17	Isth1N	19	Isth1N	13	IsthN	16	IsthN	n&v	IsthN	n&v
FAC	P	FAC	1Q	FAC	P	FAC	P	FAC	P	FAC	1Qr	FAC	1Qr	FAC	1Q	FAC	2Q	FAC	1Q
FAT	P	FAT	2Q	FAT	2Q	FAT	P	FAT	P	FAT	1Q	FAT	P	FAT	Pr	FAT	2Q	FAT	1Q

HONOURS / RECORDS

FA Comps: None

League: Peterborough & District 1959-60, 61-62. Eastern Counties Premier Division 2007-08.

County FA: Cambridgeshire Challenge Cup 1957-58. Cambridgeshire Invitation Cup 1990-91, 97-98, 98-99, 2005-06.

Best FA Cup Third Qualifying Round 1970-71

FA Trophy Second Qualifying Round 2012-13, 13-14

FA Vase Fifth Round 2004-05

GROUND: Julius Martin Lane, Soham, Ely, Cambridgeshire CB7 5EQ

Ground Capacity: 2,000 **Seats:** 250 **Covered:** 1,000 **Clubhouse:** Yes **Shop:** Yes

Previous Grounds: None

Record Attendance: 3,000 v Pegasus - FA Amateur Cup 1963

Nearest Railway Station Cambridge - catch Citi 1 towards Arbury alight at Jesus College, catch No.12 from Fair Street towards Ely.

Bus Route 12 - Julius Martin Lane - stop 200m away

SPALDING UNITED

NPL Midlands

Founde 1921 **Nickname:** Tulips **Club Colours:** Blue & yellow

Club Contact Details
01778 713 328

Previous Names: None

Previous Leagues: Peterborough, United Counties 1931-55,68-78,86-88,91-99,03-04, 11-14 Eastern Counties 1955-60, Central Alliance 1960-61, Midland Co. 1961-68, Northern Counties East 1982-86, Southern 1988-91, 99-03. NPL 2003-11.

11-12	12-13	13-14	14-15	15-16	16-17	17-18	18-19	19-20	20-21
UCL P 13	UCL P 3	UCL P 1	NP1S 7	NP1S 12	NP1S 3	NP1S 13	NP1E 18	NPSE n&v	NPSE n&v
FAC EP	FAC EP	FAC 2Q	FAC 2Q	FAC 3Qr	FAC 1Q	FAC Pr	FAC 1Q	FAC P	FAC EP
FAV 2P	FAV 5P	FAV 3P	FAT 1Qr	FAT P	FAT P	FAT 1Q	FAT P	FAT EP	FAT 2Q

HONOURS / RECORDS

FA Comps: None

League: Peterborough & District 1930-31. United Counties 1954-55, 75-75, 87-88, 98-99, 2003-04, 13-14.
Northern Counties East 1983-84.

County FA: Lincolnshire Senior Cup 1952-53.

Best FA Cup First Round Proper 1957-58, 64-65

FA Trophy Third Round Proper 1999-2000

FA Vase Quarter Finals 1989-90, 96-97

GROUND: Sir Halley Stewart Playing Fields, Winfrey Avenue, Spalding PE11 1DA

Ground Capacity: 3,500 **Seats:** 1,000 **Covered:** 1,000 **Clubhouse:** Yes **Shop:** Yes

Previous Grounds: Stadium known as the Black Swan Ground before being renamed after Halley Stewart MP in 1954.

Record Attendance: 6,972 v Peterborough - FA Cup 1982

Nearest Railway Station Spalding - 0.2km

Bus Route Broad Street - stop 100m away

SPORTING KHALSA

NPL Midlands

Founde 1991 **Nickname:** Sporting **Club Colours:** Yellow & blue

Club Contact Details
07976 220 444 manjit.gill@globeproperty.co.uk

Previous Names: None

Previous Leagues: Walsall & District Sunday 1991-96. West Midlands (Regional) 1996-97, 2005-15. Midland 2015-21.

11-12	12-13	13-14	14-15	15-16	16-17	17-18	18-19	19-20	20-21
WMP 14	WMP 11	WMP 6	WMP 1	MFLP 3	MFLP 3	MFLP 5	MFLP 3	MFLP n&v	MFLP n&v
	FAC Pr		FAC P	FAC 4Q	FAC P	FAC Pr	FAC P	FAC P	FAC EP
FAV 1Q	FAV 1Q	FAV 2Q	FAV 2Qr	FAV 1P	FAV QF	FAV 2P	FAV 5P	FAV 5P	FAV 3P

HONOURS / RECORDS

FA Comps: None

League: West Midlands (Regional) Premier Division 2014-15 (Won the title 27pts ahead of second place, finishing on a record 117pts).

County FA: None

Best FA Cup Fourth Qualifying Round 2015-16.

FA Vase Quarter finals 2016-17.

GROUND: Aspray Arena, Noose Lane, Willenhall WV13 3BB

Ground Capacity: 5,000 **Seats:** Yes **Covered:** Yes **Clubhouse:** Yes **Shop:** Yes

Previous Grounds: AFC Wulfrunians 2017-18 (for 6 months whilst Aspray Arena was redeveloped).

Record Attendance: 2,252 v FC United of Manchester, FAC 4Q, 24/10/15.

Nearest Railway Station Wolverhampton - 3.9km (Bus Station is adjacent to railway)

Bus Route 529 service stopping at the bottom of Noose Lane a 5-10 min walk from the ground.

STAMFORD

NPL Midlands

Founde 1896 **Nickname:** The Daniels **Club Colours:** Red with white trim

Club Contact Details
01780 751 471

Previous Names: Stamford Town and Rutland Ironworks amalgamated in 1894 to form Rutland Ironworks > 1896
Previous Leagues: Peterborough, Northants (UCL) 1908-55, Central Alliance 1955-61, Midland counties 1961-72, United Counties 1972-98, Southern 1998-2007

11-12		12-13		13-14		14-15		15-16		16-17		17-18		18-19		19-20		20-21	
NP1S	7	NP1S	4	NP P	18	NP P	20	NP P	21	NP1S	16	NP1S	6	NP1E	11	NPSE	n&v	NPSE	n&v
FAC	P	FAC	2Q	FAC	4Q	FAC	2Q	FAC	2Q	FAC	1P	FAC	P	FAC	Pr	FAC	2Q	FAC	2Q
FAT	1Q	FAT	3Q	FAT	1Q	FAT	1Q	FAT	1Q	FAT	1Q	FAT	2Q	FAT	3Qr	FAT	1Q	FAT	4P

HONOURS / RECORDS
FA Comps: FA Vase 1979-80.

League: United Counties 1911-12, 75-76, 77-78, 79-80, 80-81, 81-82, 96-97, 97-98.

County FA: Lincolnshire Senior Cup 2000-01, Senior Shield 2006-07, 08-09, 10-11, 13-14, 14-15.

Victory: 13-0 v Peterborough Reserves - Northants League 1929-30
Defeat: 0-17 v Rothwell - FA Cup 1927-28
Goalscorer: Bert Knighton - 248
Appearances: Dick Kwiatkowski - 462

GROUND: Borderville Sports Centre, Ryhall Road, Stamford PE9 1US
Ground Capacity: 2,000 **Seats:** 300 **Covered:** 1,250 **Clubhouse:** Yes **Shop:** Yes
Previous Grounds: Hanson's Field 1894-2014.
Record Attendance: 1,573 v Peterborough United, pre-season friendly, 10/07/2019.

Nearest Railway Station Stamford - 2.1km
Bus Route Gush Way - stop 300m away

SUTTON COLDFIELD TOWN

NPL Midlands

Founde 1879 **Nickname:** Royals **Club Colours:** All blue

Club Contact Details
0121 354 2997

Previous Names: Sutton Coldfield F.C. 1879-1921
Previous Leagues: Central Birmingham, Walsall Senior, Staffordshire County, Birmingham Combination 1950-54, West Midlands (Regional) 1954-65, 79-82, Midlands Combination 1965-79. Northern Premier 2010-18. Southern 2018-19.

11-12		12-13		13-14		14-15		15-16		16-17		17-18		18-19		19-20		20-21	
NP1S	12	NP1S	6	NP1S	6	NP1S	4	NP P	12	NP P	20	NP P	24	SthC	5	NPSE	n&v	NPSE	n&v
FAC	P	FAC	1Q	FAC	2Q	FAC	1Q	FAC	1Q	FAC	2Q	FAC	1Q	FAC	2Qr	FAC	3Q	FAC	P
FAT	1Q	FAT	P	FAT	P	FAT	P	FAT	1P	FAT	1Q	FAT	1Q	FAT	EP	FAT	2Q	FAT	2Q

HONOURS / RECORDS
FA Comps: None
League: West Midlands League 1979-80. Midland Combination x2.
NPL Division One South Play-off 2014-15.
County FA: Birmingham Senior Cup 2010-11.

Goalscorer: Eddie Hewitt - 288
Appearances: Andy Ling - 550
Additional: Paid £1,500 to Gloucester for Lance Morrison, to Burton Albion for Micky Clarke and to Atherstone United for Steve Farmer 1991. Received £25,000 from West Bromwich Albion for Barry Cowdrill 1979

GROUND: Central Ground, Coles Lane, Sutton Coldfield B72 1NL
Ground Capacity: 4,500 **Seats:** 200 **Covered:** 500 **Clubhouse:** Yes **Shop:** Yes
Previous Grounds: Meadow Plat 1879-89, Coles Lane 1890-1919
Record Attendance: 2,029 v Doncaster Rovers - FA Cup 1980-81

Nearest Railway Station Sutton Coldfield - 1.1km
Bus Route Douglas Road - stop 100m away

WISBECH TOWN

NPL Midlands

Founde 1920 **Nickname:** Fenmen **Club Colours:** All red

Club Contact Details
01945 581 511

Previous Names: None

Previous Leagues: Peterborough 1920-35. United Counties 1935-50, 2013-18. EC 1950-52, 70-97, 2003-13. Midland 1952-58. Southern 1958-70, 97-2002.

11-12		12-13		13-14		14-15		15-16		16-17		17-18		18-19		19-20		20-21	
ECP	4	ECP	2	UCL P	7	UCL P	3	UCL P	8	UCL P	6	UCL P	2	NP1E	17	NPSE	n&v	NPSE	n&v
FAC	1Q	FAC	1Qr	FAC	EP	FAC	1Q	FAC	P	FAC	P	FAC	1Q	FAC	1Q	FAC	1Q	FAC	P
FAV	4Pr	FAV	4P	FAV	QF	FAV	3P	FAV	1P	FAV	1Qr	FAV	4P	FAT	1Qr	FAT	P	FAT	2Q

HONOURS / RECORDS

FA Comps: None

League: United Counties 1946-47, 47-48. Southern Division one 1961-62.
Eastern Counties 1971-72, 76-77, 90-91.

County FA: None

Goalscorer: Bert Titmarsh - 246 (1931-37)
Appearances: Jamie Brighty - 731
Best FA Cup Second Round Proper 1957-58, 97-98
FA Trophy Second Round Proper 1999-2000
FA Vase Semi Finals 1984-85, 85-86

GROUND: Fenland Stadium, Lynn Road, Wisbech PE14 7AL

Ground Capacity: **Seats:** 118 **Covered:** Yes **Clubhouse:** Yes **Shop:**

Previous Grounds: Played on several grounds before moving to Fenland Park in 1947, then moving to their new stadium in 2008.

Record Attendance: 8,044 v Peterborough United, Midland League 25/08/1957

Nearest Railway Station Watlington
Bus Route Pumping Station - stop 370m away

YAXLEY

NPL Midlands

Founde 1962 **Nickname:** The Cuckoos **Club Colours:** Navy and orange

Club Contact Details
01733 244 928 info@yaxleyfc.com

Previous Names: Yaxley British Legion 1963-86. Coalite Yaxley 1986-90. Clarksteel Yaxley 1990.

Previous Leagues: Peterborough & District 1962-88. Eastern Counties (Founder Member) 1988-92. Huntingdonshire 1992-94. West Anglia 1994-95. United Counties 1995-2018. Southern 2018-21.

11-12		12-13		13-14		14-15		15-16		16-17		17-18		18-19		19-20		20-21	
UCL P	18	UCL P	12	UCL P	6	UCL P	4	UCL P	12	UCL P	3	UCL P	1	SthC	11	SthC	n&v	SthC	n&v
FAC	EP	FAC	P	FAC	EP	FAC	EP	FAC	1Q	FAC	Pr	FAC	1Q	FAC	P	FAC	P	FAC	P
FAV	1P	FAV	1P	FAV	1Q	FAV	4P	FAV	3P	FAV	1P	FAV	3P	FAT	2Qr	FAT	P	FAT	3Q

HONOURS / RECORDS

FA Comps: None

League: Peterborough & District Division Three South 1968-69, Division Two 70-71, Premier 76-77, 83-84.
West Anglia 1994-95. United Counties Division One 1996-97, Premier 2017-18.

County FA: Hunts Senior Cup 1974-75, 75-76, 82-83, 83-84, 98-99, 2003-04, 04-05, 07-08. Hunts Premier Cup 2004-05

Best FA Cup Second Qualifying Round 2002-03, 06-07
FA Vase Fourth Round Proper 2014-15
FA Trophy Second Qualifying Round 2018-19(r)

GROUND: In2itive Park, Holme Road, Yaxley, Peterborough PE7 3NA

Ground Capacity: 1,500 **Seats:** 150 **Covered:** yes **Clubhouse:** Yes **Shop:** Yes

Previous Grounds: Middleton Road 1962-94

Record Attendance: 300v Wisbech Town, FA Vase Preliminary Round 1982-83

Nearest Railway Station Peterborough - 8 miles
Bus Route Churhc Street stop 300m away

1874 NORTHWICH

NPL West

Founde 2012 **Nickname:** The 74 or The Greens **Club Colours:** Green and black

Club Contact Details
07975 679 624

Previous Names: None
Previous Leagues: North West Counties 2013-21.

11-12	12-13	13-14	14-15	15-16	16-17	17-18	18-19	19-20	20-21
		NWC1 3	NWCP 3	NWCP 4	NWCP 5	NWCP 7	NWCP 10	NWCP n&v	NWCP n&v
			FAC Pr	FAC P	FAC Pr	FAC 3Qr	FAC EPr	FAC 2Q	FAC EP
		FAV 1Q	FAV 3P	FAV 2P	FAV 2P	FAV SF	FAV 2P	FAV 1Q	FAV 2P

HONOURS / RECORDS
FA Comps: None
League: None

County FA: Mid-Cheshire Senior Cup 2015-16, 16-17

Best FA Cup Third Qualifying Round 2017-18(r)
FA Vase Semi-final 2017-18
Victory: 9-0 v Wigan Robin Park (H), FAV 2Q, 05/10/14 and v Litherland REMYCA, NWCP, 02/11/2019
Defeat: 0-4 v Ashton Athletic, NWCP, 06/10/2015

GROUND: Townfield, Townfield Lane, Barnton Northwich, Cheshire CW8 4LH
Ground Capacity: 6,000 **Seats:** Yes **Covered:** Yes **Clubhouse:** Yes **Shop:**
Previous Grounds: Winsford United FC >2019
Record Attendance: 1,693 v Thatcham Town, FA Vase Semi-final, 24/03/2018

Nearest Railway Station Greenbank
Bus Route No.4 from Northwich interchange. Embark at Beech Road which is a short walk from the ground.

BOOTLE

NPL West

Founde 1953 **Nickname:** Bucks **Club Colours:** All blue

Club Contact Details
07928 994 441

Previous Names: Langton Dock 1953 - 1973.
Previous Leagues: Liverpool Shipping. Lancashire Combination 1974-78. Cheshire County 1978-82. Liverpool County Combination 1982-2006. North West Counties 2006-21.

11-12	12-13	13-14	14-15	15-16	16-17	17-18	18-19	19-20	20-21
NWCP 3	NWCP 3	NWCP 8	NWCP 7	NWCP 8	NWCP 2	NWCP 5	NWCP 2	NWCP n&v	NWCP n&v
FAC P	FAC 1Q	FAC 1Qr	FAC EP	FAC EP	FAC P	FAC EP	FAC EP	FAC EP	FAC 1Q
FAV 2Q	FAV 2P	FAV 1P	FAV 1P	FAV 2Q	FAV 3P	FAV 2P	FAV 2Q	FAV 1P	FAV 1P

HONOURS / RECORDS
FA Comps: None
League: Liverpool County Combination 1964-65, 65-66, 67-68, 68-69, 69-70, 70-71, 71-72, 72-73, 73-74.
Lancashire Comb. 1975-76, 76-77. Cheshire County Div.2 1978-79. North West Counties Div.1 2008-09.
County FA: Liverpool County Senior Cup 2012-13.

GROUND: Vestey Road, Off Bridle Road, Bootle L30 1NY
Ground Capacity: 1,750 **Seats:** Yes **Covered:** Yes **Clubhouse:** Yes **Shop:**
Previous Grounds: Bucks Park 1953-2002.
Record Attendance: 1,078 v Everton Reserves, Liverpool Senior Cup Feb 2010.

Nearest Railway Station Aintree - 0.5km
Bus Route Hereford Drive stop - 251m away

CITY OF LIVERPOOL

NPL West

Founde 2015 **Nickname:** The Purps **Club Colours:** All purple

Club Contact Details
07831 494 885 contact@colfc.co.uk

Previous Names: None
Previous Leagues: North West Counties 2016-19.

11-12	12-13	13-14	14-15	15-16	16-17	17-18	18-19	19-20	20-21
					NWC1 4	NWCP 4	NWCP 1	NPNW n&v	NPNW n&v
						FAC 1Q	FAC 2Q	FAC 1Qr	FAC 1Q
						FAV 3P	FAV 1P	FAT EPr	FAT 2P

HONOURS / RECORDS
FA Comps: None
League: North West Counties Premier 2018-19.

County FA: None

Victory: 10-0 v Stockport Town, North West Counties Division One, 31/12/2016
FA Cup Second Qualifying Round 2018-19
FA Vase Third Round Proper 2017-18
FA Trophy Second Round Proper 2020-21

GROUND: Rivacre Road, Ellesmere Port, South Wirrall CH66 1NJ
Ground Capacity: **Seats:** Yes **Covered:** Yes **Clubhouse:** Yes **Shop:**
Previous Grounds: Vesty Road (Bootle FC) 2015-21.
Record Attendance: 1,099 v Warrington Town, FA Cup First Qualifying Round, 01/09/2019

Nearest Railway Station Overpool (1.4 miles) or Hooton (1.7)
Bus Route Special shuttle bus service from the City Centre.

CLITHEROE

NPL West

Founde 1877 **Nickname:** The Blues **Club Colours:** All blue

Club Contact Details
01200 423 344 secretary@clitheroefc.co.uk

Previous Names: Clitheroe Central 1877-1903.
Previous Leagues: Blackburn & District, Lancashire Combination 1903-04, 05-10, 25-82, North West Counties 1982-85

11-12	12-13	13-14	14-15	15-16	16-17	17-18	18-19	19-20	20-21
NP1N 19	NP1N 8	NP1N 17	NP1N 13	NP1N 7	NP1N 7	NP1N 12	NP1W 18	NPNW n&v	NPNW n&v
FAC 2Q	FAC 1Q	FAC P	FAC 1Q	FAC 1Q	FAC P	FAC 1Q	FAC 1Q	FAC EP	FAC P
FAT Pr	FAT Pr	FAT Pr	FAT 1Q	FAT P	FAT P	FAT 1Q	FAT 1Q	FAT P	FAT 3Q

HONOURS / RECORDS
FA Comps: None
League: Lancashire Combination Division Two 1959-60, Division One 1979-80.
North West Counties Division Three 1983-84, Division Two 1984-85, Division One 1985-86, 2003-04.
County FA: Lancashire Challenge Trophy 1892-93, 1984-85.

Goalscorer: Don Francis
Appearances: Lindsey Wallace - 670
Additional: Received £45,000 from Crystal Palace for Carlo Nash.

GROUND: Shawbridge, off Pendle Road, Clitheroe, Lancashire BB7 1LZ
Ground Capacity: 2,000 **Seats:** 250 **Covered:** 1,400 **Clubhouse:** Yes **Shop:** No
Previous Grounds: None
Record Attendance: 2,050 v Mangotsfield - FA Vase Semi-final 1995-96

Nearest Railway Station Clitheroe - 0.6km
Bus Route Hayhurst Street - 50m away

COLNE

NPL West

Founde 1996 **Nickname:** The Reds **Club Colours:** Red & white

Club Contact Details

01282 862 545 secretary@colnefootballclub.com

Previous Names: None

Previous Leagues: North West Counties 1996-2016.

11-12	12-13	13-14	14-15	15-16	16-17	17-18	18-19	19-20	20-21
NWCP 8	NWCP 8	NWCP 9	NWCP 4	NWCP 1	NP1N 5	NP1N 8	NP1W 4	NPNW n&v	NPNW n&v
FAC EP	FAC EPr	FAC EPr	FAC EP	FAC 1Q	FAC 1Q	FAC 1Q	FAC 2Q	FAC 4Q	FAC P
FAV 1P	FAV 2Q	FAV 2Q	FAV 1P	FAV 2P	FAT P	FAT P	FAT EP	FAT 3Q	FAT 3Q

HONOURS / RECORDS

FA Comps: None

League: North West Counties League Division Two 2003-04, Premier Division 2015-16.

County FA: None

Goalscorer: Geoff Payton

Appearances: Richard Walton

Best FA Cup Fourth Qualifying Round 2019-20

FA Vase Semi Final 2003-04

FA Trophy Third Qualifyning Round 2019-20, 20-21

GROUND: Harrison Drive, Colne, Lancashire BB8 9SL

Ground Capacity: 1,800 **Seats:** 160 **Covered:** 1,000 **Clubhouse:** Yes **Shop:** Yes

Previous Grounds: None

Record Attendance: 1,742 v AFC Sudbury F.A. Vase SF 2004. 2,762 (at Accrington Stanley) v FC United, NWC Challenge Cup, 13/11/05.

Nearest Railway Station Colne - 0.6km

Bus Route Tennyson Road - stop 100m away

GLOSSOP NORTH END

NPL West

Founde 1886 **Nickname:** Peakites / The Hillmen **Club Colours:** All royal blue

Club Contact Details

07740 265 711

Previous Names: Glossop North End1886-1896 and Glossop FC 1898-1992. Reformed in 1992.

Previous Leagues: North Cheshire 1890-94. Combination 1894-96. Midland 1896-98. The Football League 1898-1918. Lancashire Comb. 1919-20, 57-66. Manchester 1920-57, 66-78. Cheshire County (Founder member) 1978-82. North West Counties (FM)1982-2015.

11-12	12-13	13-14	14-15	15-16	16-17	17-18	18-19	19-20	20-21
NWCP 6	NWCP 13	NWCP 3	NWCP 1	NP1N 4	NP1N 8	NP1N 11	NP1W 17	NPSE n&v	NPSE n&v
FAC EP	FAC P	FAC 1Q	FAC 2Q	FAC 1Qr	FAC Pr	FAC P	FAC Pr	FAC 1Q	FAC P
FAV 3P	FAV 2Qr	FAV 2P	FAV F	FAT Pr	FAT 1Q	FAT 3Qr	FAT EP	FAT P	FAT 3Q

HONOURS / RECORDS

FA Comps: None

League: Manchester 1927-28. North West Counties Premier Division 2014-15.

County FA: Manchester FA Premier Cup 1996-97, 97-98. Derbyshire Senior Cup 2000-01.

Best FA Cup First Round Proper 1896-97

FA Trophy Third Qualifying Round 2017-18, 20-21

FA Vase Runners up 2014-15

GROUND: Surrey Street, Glossop, Derbys SK13 7AJ

Ground Capacity: 2,374 **Seats:** 209 **Covered:** 509 **Clubhouse:** Yes **Shop:** Yes

Previous Grounds: Pyegrove. Silk Street. Water Lane. Cemetery Road. North Road 1890-1955.

Record Attendance: 10,736 v Preston North End F.A. Cup 1913-1914

Nearest Railway Station Glossop - 0.4km

Bus Route St Mary's Road - stop 300m away

KENDAL TOWN

NPL West

Founde 1919 **Nickname:** The Mintcakes / The Field **Club Colours:** Black and white stripes

Club Contact Details
01539 738 818

Previous Names: Netherfield AFC 1919-2000
Previous Leagues: Westmorland, North Lancashire Combination 1945-68, Northern Premier 1968-83, North West Counties 1983-87

11-12		12-13		13-14		14-15		15-16		16-17		17-18		18-19		19-20		20-21	
NP P	11	NP P	21	NP1N	10	NP1N	16	NP1N	15	NP1N	12	NP1N	18	NP1W	19	NPNW	n&v	NPNW	n&v
FAC	3Q	FAC	3Q	FAC	P	FAC	Pr	FAC	2Q	FAC	P	FAC	1Q	FAC	1Q	FAC	EP	FAC	P
FAT	2Qr	FAT	1Qr	FAT	1Qr	FAT	P	FAT	1Q	FAT	2Q	FAT	1Q	FAT	P	FAT	P	FAT	2Q

HONOURS / RECORDS
FA Comps: None
League: Lancashire Combination 1948-49, 64-65.

County FA: Westmorlands Senior Cup x12. Lancashire Senior Cup 2002-03.

Victory: 11-0 v Great Harwood - 22/03/1947
Defeat: 0-10 v Stalybridge Celtic - 01/09/1984
Goalscorer: Tom Brownlee
Additional: Received £10,250 from Manchester City for Andy Milner 1995

GROUND: Parkside Road, Kendal, Cumbria LA9 7BL
Ground Capacity: 2,490 **Seats:** 450 **Covered:** 1000 **Clubhouse:** Yes **Shop:** Yes
Previous Grounds: None
Record Attendance: 5,184 v Grimsby Town - FA Cup 1st Round 1955

Nearest Railway Station Kendal - 1.3km
Bus Route Castle Circle - stop 200m away

KIDSGROVE ATHLETIC

NPL West

Founde 1952 **Nickname:** The Grove **Club Colours:** Blue & white

Club Contact Details
01782 782 412

Previous Names: None
Previous Leagues: Buslem and Tunstall 1953-63, Staffordshire County 1963-66, Mid Cheshire 1966-90, North West Counties 1990-2002

11-12		12-13		13-14		14-15		15-16		16-17		17-18		18-19		19-20		20-21	
NP1S	13	NP1S	18	NP1S	21	NP1S	20	NP1S	15	NP1S	12	NP1S	18	NP1W	10	NPSE	n&v	NPSE	n&v
FAC	4Q	FAC	P	FAC	1Q	FAC	P	FAC	Pr	FAC	2Q	FAC	2Q	FAC	4Q	FAC	3Q	FAC	P
FAT	1Q	FAT	1Q	FAT	2Q	FAT	P	FAT	2Qr	FAT	2Q	FAT	2Q	FAT	P	FAT	1Q	FAT	1P

HONOURS / RECORDS
FA Comps: None
League: Staffordshire County Division Two 1963-64, Premier 65-66. Mid-Cheshire 1970-71, 77-78, 86-87, 87-88. North West Counties Premier Division 1997-98, 2001-02.
County FA: Staffordshire Senior Cup 2003-04, 06-07, 08-09, 10-11, 11-12.

Victory: 23-0 v Cross Heath W.M.C. - Staffordshire Cup 1965
Defeat: 0-15 v Stafford Rangers - Staffordshire Senior Cup 20/11/2001
Goalscorer: Scott Dundas - 53 (1997-98)
Additional: Paid £10,000 to Stevenage Borough for Steve Walters
Received £3,000 for Ryan Baker 2003-04

GROUND: Hollinwood Road, Kidsgrove, Staffs ST7 1DH
Ground Capacity: 2,000 **Seats:** 1,000 **Covered:** 800 **Clubhouse:** Yes **Shop:** Yes
Previous Grounds: Vickers and Goodwin 1953-60
Record Attendance: 1,903 v Tiverton Town - FA Vase Semi-final 1998

Nearest Railway Station Kidsgrove - 0.8km
Bus Route Grove Avenue - stop 200m away

LEEK TOWN

NPL West

Founde 1946 **Nickname:** The Blues **Club Colours:** All blue

Club Contact Details
01538 399 278

Previous Names: None

Previous Leagues: Staffordshire Co., Manchester 1951-54, 57-73, West Midlands (B'ham) 1954-56,Cheshire Co. 1973-82, North West Counties 1982-87, Northern Premier 1987-94, 95-97, Southern 1994-95, Conference 1997-99

11-12		12-13		13-14		14-15		15-16		16-17		17-18		18-19		19-20		20-21	
NP1S	5	NP1S	10	NP1S	3	NP1S	2	NP1S	8	NP1S	9	NP1S	7	NP1W	3	NPSE	n&v	NPSE	n&v
FAC	3Qr	FAC	3Q	FAC	Pr	FAC	4Q	FAC	1Qr	FAC	1Q	FAC	1Q	FAC	2Q	FAC	3Q	FAC	1Q
FAT	2Qr	FAT	2Qr	FAT	2P	FAT	2Qr	FAT	P	FAT	2Q	FAT	2Q	FAT	1Qr	FAT	2Q	FAT	3Q

HONOURS / RECORDS

FA Comps: None

League: Staffordshire County 1949-50, 50-51. Manchester 1951-52, 71-72, 72-73. Cheshire County 1974-75. Northern Premier Division One 1989-90, Premier Division 1996-97.

County FA: Staffordshire Senior Cup 1995-96.

Goalscorer: Dave Sutton - 144

Appearances: Gary Pearce - 447

Additional: Paid £2,000 to Sutton Town for Simon Snow
Received £30,000 from Barnsley for Tony Bullock

GROUND: Harrison Park, Macclesfield Road, Leek, Cheshire ST13 8LD

Ground Capacity: 3,600 **Seats:** 650 **Covered:** 3,000 **Clubhouse:** Yes **Shop:** Yes

Previous Grounds: None

Record Attendance: 3,512 v Macclesfield Town - FA Cup 1973-74

Nearest Railway Station Congleton - 8.4 miles

Bus Route 109 & 18

MARINE

NPL West

Founde 1894 **Nickname:** Mariners **Club Colours:** White & black

Club Contact Details
0151 924 1743

Previous Names: None

Previous Leagues: Liverpool Zingari, Liverpool County Combination, Lancashire Combination 1935-39, 46-69, Cheshire County 1969-79

11-12		12-13		13-14		14-15		15-16		16-17		17-18		18-19		19-20		20-21	
NP P	7	NP P	11	NP P	20	NP P	21	NP P	15	NP P	18	NP P	19	NP P	20	NPNW	n&v	NPNW	n&v
FAC	1Q	FAC	4Q	FAC	1Q	FAC	3Q	FAC	3Q	FAC	2Qr	FAC	2Q	FAC	4Q	FAC	2Q	FAC	3P
FAT	3Q	FAT	1Q	FAT	2Q	FAT	2Q	FAT	3Q	FAT	1P	FAT	2P	FAT	1Q	FAT	EP	FAT	2P

HONOURS / RECORDS

FA Comps: None

League: I Zingari Division Two 1901-02, Division One 02-03, 03-04, 09-10, 19-20, 20-21, 22-23. Liverpool Combination Division One 1927-28, 30-31, 33-34, 34-35, 43-44. Cheshire County 1973-74, 75-76, 76-77. Northern Premier Premier Division 1993-94, 84-95.

County FA: Lancashire Amateur Cup 1921-22, 25-26, 30-31, Junior Cup /Trophy 78-79, 87-88, 90-91, 99-00. Liverpool Challenge Cup 42-43, 44-45, 71-72, Non-League Cup 1968-69, 75-76, 76-77, Senior Cup 78-79, 84-85, 87-88, 89-90, 93-94, 99-00, 07-08.

Victory: 14-0 v Sandhurst - FA Cup 1st Qualifying Round 01/10/1938

Defeat: 2-11 v Shrewsbury Town - FA Cup 1st Round 1995

Goalscorer: Paul Meachin - 200

Appearances: Peter Smith 952

Additional: Paid £6,000 to Southport for Jon Penman October 1985. Received £20,000 from Crewe for Richard Norris 1996.

GROUND: College Road, Crosby, Liverpool L23 3AS

Ground Capacity: 3,185 **Seats:** 400 **Covered:** 1,400 **Clubhouse:** Yes **Shop:** Yes

Previous Grounds: Waterloo Park 1894-1903

Record Attendance: 4,000 v Nigeria - Friendly 1949
Sold 30,697 virtual tickets for their FA Cup Third Round tie against Spurs 10/01/2021

Nearest Railway Station Blundellsands & Crosby - 0.5km

Bus Route Brompton Avenue - stop 175m away

MARKET DRAYTON TOWN

NPL West

Founde 1969 **Nickname:** None **Club Colours:** All red

Club Contact Details
07453 960 650

Previous Names: Little Drayton Rangers > 2003
Previous Leagues: West Midlands (Regional) 1969-2006, Midland Alliance 2006-09

11-12		12-13		13-14		14-15		15-16		16-17		17-18		18-19		19-20		20-21	
NP1S	16	NP1S	15	NP1S	19	NP1S	19	NP1S	11	NP1S	14	NP1S	21	NP1W	16	NPSE	n&v	NPSE	n&v
FAC	P	FAC	1Qr	FAC	P	FAC	1Q	FAC	1Q	FAC	P	FAC	1Q	FAC	Pr	FAC	P	FAC	P
FAT	P	FAT	P	FAT	P	FAT	1Qr	FAT	P	FAT	1Q	FAT	P	FAT	EP	FAT	P	FAT	1Q

HONOURS / RECORDS
FA Comps: None
League: West Midlands (Regional) 2005-06. Midland Alliance 2008-09.

County FA: None

Victory: (League) 9-0 Home vs. Racing Club Warwick 10/03/09
Best FA Cup Second Qualifying Round 2007-08, 10-11
FA Trophy First Qualifying Round 2010-11, 14-15, 15-16, 20-21
FA Vase Fifth Round Proper 2008-09

GROUND: Greenfields Sports Ground, Greenfields Lane, Market Drayton TF9 3SL
Ground Capacity: 1,000 **Seats:** Yes **Covered:** Yes **Clubhouse:** Yes **Shop:** No
Previous Grounds: Not known
Record Attendance: 440 vs. AFC Telford, Friendly 11/07/09. 229 vs. Witton Albion, Unibond South 25/08/09

Nearest Railway Station Prees
Bus Route 164 - Cemetery Road Jct - stop 400m away

MOSSLEY

NPL West

Founde 1903 **Nickname:** Lilywhites **Club Colours:** White & black

Club Contact Details
01457 832 369

Previous Names: Park Villa 1903-04, Mossley Juniors
Previous Leagues: Ashton, South East Lancashire, Lancashire Combination 1918-19, Cheshire County 1919-72, Northern Premier 1972-95, North West Counties 1995-2004

11-12		12-13		13-14		14-15		15-16		16-17		17-18		18-19		19-20		20-21	
NP1N	14	NP1N	5	NP1N	15	NP1N	7	NP1N	13	NP1N	17	NP1N	19	NP1W	8	NPNW	n&v	NPNW	n&v
FAC	Pr	FAC	P	FAC	Pr	FAC	Pr	FAC	Pr	FAC	1Q	FAC	1Qr	FAC	2Q	FAC	Pr	FAC	2Q
FAT	P	FAT	1Qr	FAT	2Q	FAT	1Q	FAT	1Q	FAT	1Q	FAT	1Q	FAT	EP	FAT	P	FAT	2Q

HONOURS / RECORDS
FA Comps: None
League: Ashton & District 1911-12, 14-15. Northern Premier 1978-79, 79-80, Division One 2005-06.

County FA: Manchester Premier Cup 1937-38, 48-49, 60-61, 66-67, 67-68, 88-89, 90-91, 2011-12, 12-13, 14-15, 15-16. Manchester Challenge Trophy 2011-12.
Victory: 9-0 v Urmston, Manchester Shield, 1947
Defeat: 2-13 v Witton Albion, Cheshire League, 1926
Goalscorer: David Moore - 235 (1974-84). Jackie Roscoe scored 58 during the 1930-31 season.
Appearances: Jimmy O'Connor - 613 (1972-87)
Additional: Paid £2,300 to Altrincham for Phil Wilson. Received £25,000 from Everton for Eamonn O'Keefe.

GROUND: Seel Park, Market Street, Mossley, Lancashire OL5 0ES
Ground Capacity: 4,000 **Seats:** 220 **Covered:** 1,500 **Clubhouse:** Yes **Shop:** Yes
Previous Grounds: Moved to Seel Park in 1911.
Record Attendance: 7,000 v Stalybridge Celtic 1950

Nearest Railway Station Mossley - 0.3km
Bus Route Stamford Street - 200m away

NEWCASTLE TOWN

NPL West

Founde 1964 **Nickname:** The Castle **Club Colours:** Blue & white

Club Contact Details

01782 662 350 secretary@newcastletownfc.co.uk

Previous Names: Parkway Hanley, Clayton Park & Parkway Clayton. Merged as NTFC in 1986.

Previous Leagues: Newcatle & District, Staffs Co & Mid Cheshire, North West Counties

11-12		12-13		13-14		14-15		15-16		16-17		17-18		18-19		19-20		20-21	
NP1S	15	NP1S	17	NP1S	8	NP1S	3	NP1S	14	NP1S	7	NP1S	20	NP1W	15	NPSE	n&v	NPSE	n&v
FAC	1Qr	FAC	P	FAC	1Qr	FAC	Pr	FAC	1Qr	FAC	P	FAC	1Q	FAC	P	FAC	P	FAC	P
FAT	1Qr	FAT	1Q	FAT	P	FAT	1Q	FAT	1Qr	FAT	P	FAT	1Qr	FAT	2Qr	FAT	P	FAT	3Q

HONOURS / RECORDS

FA Comps: None

League: Mid Cheshire Division Two 1982-83, 90-91, Division One 85-86. North West Counties Premier Division 2009-10.

County FA: Walsall Senior Cup 1993-94, 94-95. Staffordshire Senior Cup 2009-10.

Goalscorer: Andy Bott - 149

Appearances: Dean Gillick - 632

GROUND: Buckmaster Avenue, Newcastle-under-Lyme, Stoke-on-Trent ST5 3BX

Ground Capacity: 4,000 **Seats:** 300 **Covered:** 1,000 **Clubhouse:** Yes **Shop:** Yes

Previous Grounds: None

Record Attendance: 3,948 v Notts County - FA Cup 1996

Nearest Railway Station Stafford - take the 101 towards Hanley and alight at The Orange Tree - ground 14min walk

Bus Route 101, 11H, 25 & 9

PRESCOT CABLES

NPL West

Founde 1884 **Nickname:** Tigers **Club Colours:** Amber & black

Club Contact Details

0151 430 0507

Previous Names: Prescot > 1995

Previous Leagues: Liverpool County Combination, Lancashire Combination 1897-98, 1918-20, 27-33, 36-76, Mid Cheshire 1976-78, Cheshire County 1978-82, North West Counties 1982-2003

11-12		12-13		13-14		14-15		15-16		16-17		17-18		18-19		19-20		20-21	
NP1N	16	NP1N	17	NP1N	20	NP1N	20	NP1N	16	NP1N	16	NP1N	5	NP1W	7	NPNW	n&v	NPNW	n&v
FAC	P	FAC	1Q	FAC	1Q	FAC	1Q	FAC	P	FAC	P	FAC	Pr	FAC	P	FAC	P	FAC	2Q
FAT	P	FAT	1Q	FAT	P	FAT	1Q	FAT	P	FAT	1Q	FAT	1Qr	FAT	2Q	FAT	2Qr	FAT	2Q

HONOURS / RECORDS

FA Comps: None

League: Lancashire Combination Division Two 1951-52, Premier 1956-57. Mid-Cheshire 1976-77. Cheshire County Division Two 1979-80. North West Counties 2002-03.

County FA: Liverpool Challenge Cup 1927-28, 28-29, 29-30, 48-49, 61-62, 77-78. Liverpool Non-League Cup 1952-53, 58-59, 60-61. Liverpool Senior Cup 2016-17, 17-18.

Victory: 18-3 v Great Harwood - 1954-55

Defeat: 1-12 v Morecambe - 1936-37

Goalscorer: Freddie Crampton

Appearances: Harry Grisedale

GROUND: Volair Park, Eaton Street, Prescot L34 6HD

Ground Capacity: 3,200 **Seats:** 500 **Covered:** 600 **Clubhouse:** Yes **Shop:** Yes

Previous Grounds: None

Record Attendance: 8,122 v Ashton National - 1932

Nearest Railway Station Eccleston Park - 26min walk

Bus Route 10, 10A & 89

RAMSBOTTOM UNITED

NPL West

Founde 1966 **Nickname:** The Rams **Club Colours:** Blue & white

Club Contact Details
01706 822 799 secretary@rammyunited.co.uk

Previous Names: None
Previous Leagues: Bury Amateur 1966-69. Bolton Combination 1969-89. Manchester 1989-95. North West Counties 1995-2012.

11-12		12-13		13-14		14-15		15-16		16-17		17-18		18-19		19-20		20-21	
NWCP	1	NP1N	6	NP1N	5	NP P	17	NP P	24	NP1N	14	NP1N	14	NP1W	5	NPNW	n&v	NPNW	n&v
FAC	1Q	FAC	1Q	FAC	2Q	FAC	1Q	FAC	1Q	FAC	P	FAC	P	FAC	Pr	FAC	2Q	FAC	1Q
FAV	2P	FAT	2Q	FAT	3Q	FAT	1P	FAT	1Qr	FAT	3Q	FAT	2Q	FAT	3Pr	FAT	P	FAT	2Q

HONOURS / RECORDS
FA Comps: None
League: Bolton Combination Division One 1972-73, Premier Division 76-77. Manchester Division One 1990-91.
North West Counties Division Two 1996-97, Premier Division 2011-12.
County FA: None

Victory: 9-0 v Stantondale (H), NWCFL Division Two, 9th November 1996.
Defeat: 0-7 v Salford City (A), NWCFL Division One, 16th November 2002.
Goalscorer: Russell Brierley - 176 (1996-2003). Russell Brierley scored 38 during the 1999-2000 season.

GROUND: The Harry Williams Stadium, Acrebottom (off Bridge Street) BL0 0BS.
Ground Capacity: 2,000 **Seats:** Yes **Covered:** Yes **Clubhouse:** Yes **Shop:** No
Previous Grounds: None
Record Attendance: 2,104 v FC United of Manchester, Northern Premier League Premier Division, 04/04/15.

Bus Route 472 & 474

RUNCORN LINNETS

NPL West

Founde 2006 **Nickname:** Linnets **Club Colours:** Yellow & green

Club Contact Details
08454 860 705 secretary@runcornlinnetsfc.co.uk

Previous Names: None
Previous Leagues: North West Counties 2006-18.

11-12		12-13		13-14		14-15		15-16		16-17		17-18		18-19		19-20		20-21	
NWCP	5	NWCP	6	NWCP	2	NWCP	2	NWCP	2	NWCP	4	NWCP	1	NP1W	6	NPNW	n&v	NPNW	n&v
FAC	2Q	FAC	EPr	FAC	3Q	FAC	P	FAC	1Q	FAC	EP	FAC	P	FAC	P	FAC	P	FAC	2Q
FAV	1P	FAV	1P	FAV	1P	FAV	1P	FAV	2P	FAV	1P	FAV	3P	FAT	EP	FAT	3Q	FAT	1P

HONOURS / RECORDS
FA Comps: None
League: North West Counties Premier 2017-18.

County FA: None

Best FA Cup Third Qualifying Round 2013-14
FA Vase Third Round Proper 2008-09, 17-18
FA Trophy First Round Proper 2020-21

GROUND: Millbank Linnets Stadium, Stockham Lane, Murdishaw, Runcorn, Cheshire WA7 6GJ
Ground Capacity: 1,600 **Seats:** Yes **Covered:** Yes **Clubhouse:** Yes **Shop:**
Previous Grounds: Not known
Record Attendance: 1,037 v Witton Albion, pre season friendly July 2010

Nearest Railway Station Runcorn East - 1.2km
Bus Route Halton Arms stop - 62m away

TRAFFORD

NPL West

Founde 1990 **Nickname:** The North **Club Colours:** All white

Club Contact Details
0161 747 1727

Previous Names: North Trafford 1990-94
Previous Leagues: Mid Cheshire 1990-92, North West Counties 1992-97, 2003-08, Northern Premier 1997-2003

11-12		12-13		13-14		14-15		15-16		16-17		17-18		18-19		19-20		20-21	
NP1N	12	NP1N	4	NP P	10	NP P	23	NP1N	8	NP1N	6	NP1N	6	NP1W	9	NPNW	n&v	NPNW	n&v
FAC	1Q	FAC	3Q	FAC	3Q	FAC	1Q	FAC	P	FAC	2Q	FAC	Pr	FAC	2Q	FAC	2Q	FAC	1Q
FAT	P	FAT	2Q	FAT	2Q	FAT	2Q	FAT	P	FAT	2Q	FAT	P	FAT	P	FAT	P	FAT	2Q

HONOURS / RECORDS
FA Comps: None

League: North West Counties Division One 1996-97, 2007-08.

County FA: Manchester Challenge Trophy 2004-05.

Victory: 10-0 v Haslingden St.Mary's (Lancs Amt Shield 1991)
Goalscorer: Scott Barlow - 100
Appearances: Lee Southwood - 311
Additional: NWC League Record: 18 consecutive league wins in 2007-08
Most Points In One Season: 95 points from 38 games 2007-08

GROUND: Shawe View, Pennybridge Lane, Flixton Urmston M41 5DL
Ground Capacity: 2,500 **Seats:** 292 **Covered:** 740 **Clubhouse:** Yes **Shop:** Yes
Previous Grounds: None
Record Attendance: 803 v Flixton - Northern Premier League Division 1 1997-98.
2,238 (at Altrincham FC) FAC P v FC United 02/09/07.
Nearest Railway Station Urmston - 0.3km
Bus Route 245 & 255

WARRINGTON RYLANDS

NPL West

Founde 1906 **Nickname:** **Club Colours:** All blue

Club Contact Details
01925 635 880

Previous Names: Warrington Rylands merged with Crosfields and became Crosfields/Rylands between 2008-10. Rylands 2010-20.
Previous Leagues: Liverpool County Combination. Warrington & District. Mid-Cheshire 1968-2007. Cheshire 2008-18. North West Counties 2018-21.

11-12		12-13		13-14		14-15		15-16		16-17		17-18		18-19		19-20		20-21	
Ches1	12	Ches1	6	Ches1	8	ChesP	9	ChesP	14	ChesP	10	ChesP	11	NWC1S	1	NWCP	n&v	NWCP	n&v
																FAC	EP	FAC	2Q
														FAV	2Q	FAV	2P	FAV	F

HONOURS / RECORDS
FA Comps: FA Vase 2020-21.

League: Warrington & District Premier Division 1953-54, 54-55, 55-56, 56-57, 57-58, 58-59. Mid-Cheshire 1980-81, 83-84.
North West Counties Division One South 2018-19.
County FA: Liverpool Challenge Cup 1957-58

Best FA Cup Second Qualifying Round 2020-21
FA Vase Winners 2020-21

GROUND: Rylands Recreation Club, Gorsey Lane, Warrington WA2 7RZ
Ground Capacity: 1345 **Seats:** Yes **Covered:** Yes **Clubhouse:** Yes **Shop:**
Previous Grounds: None
Record Attendance: Not known

Nearest Railway Station Warrington Central (1.4 miles)
Bus Route No.3 from Warrington to Beresford Street

WIDNES

NPL West

Founde 2003 **Nickname:** Vikings **Club Colours:** White & black

Club Contact Details
07917 428 609

Previous Names: Formed as Dragons AFC in 2003. Widnes Dragons > 2012. Widnes Vikings 2012-14.
Previous Leagues: Junior Leagues 2003-12. West Cheshire 2012-13. North West Counties 2013-18.

11-12	12-13	13-14	14-15	15-16	16-17	17-18	18-19	19-20	20-21
	WCh3 4	NWC1 14	NWC1 16	NWC1 13	NWC1 1	NWCP 2	NP1W 12	NPNW n&v	NPNW n&v
						FAC EP	FAC EPr	FAC 1Q	FAC P
			FAV 2Q		FAV 2Q	FAV 1Q	FAT EP	FAT EP	FAT 2Q

HONOURS / RECORDS
FA Comps: None
League: North West Counties Division One 2016-17.

County FA: None

Victory: (League) 8-0 v St Helens Town, 08/04/2017
Defeat: (League) 1-10 v Northwich Manchester Villa, 13/12/2014

GROUND: Lowerhouse Lane, Widnes, Cheshire WA8 7DZ
Ground Capacity: 13,350 **Seats:** Yes **Covered:** Yes **Clubhouse:** Yes **Shop:**
Previous Grounds: The club moved to Halton Stadium in 2012.
Record Attendance: 462 v Charnock Richard, North West Counties Division One, 22/04/2017

Nearest Railway Station Widnes - 1.5km
Bus Route Cricketers Arms stop - 121m away

WORKINGTON

NPL West

Founde 1921 **Nickname:** Reds **Club Colours:** Red and white

Club Contact Details
01900 602 871

Previous Names: Workington AFC 1921-
Previous Leagues: North Eastern 1921-51, Football League 1951-77, Northern Premier 1977-2005. Conference 2005-14.

11-12	12-13	13-14	14-15	15-16	16-17	17-18	18-19	19-20	20-21
Conf N 13	Conf N 14	Conf N 22	NP P 2	NP P 5	NP P 4	NP P 11	NP P 21	NPNW n&v	NPNW n&v
FAC 2Q	FAC 4Q	FAC 4Q	FAC 2Q	FAC 2Q	FAC 3Qr	FAC 2Q	FAC 3Qr	FAC P	FAC 1Q
FAT 3Q	FAT 3Q	FAT 3Q	FAT 3Q	FAT 1Q	FAT 1Q	FAT 3Pr	FAT 1P	FAT 3Q	FAT 1P

HONOURS / RECORDS
FA Comps: None
League: North West Counties 1998-99

County FA: Cumberland County Cup x25 (Most recently 2016-17).

Victory: 17-1 v Cockermouth Crusaders - Cumberland Senior League 19/01/1901
Defeat: 0-9 v Chorley (A) - Northern Premier League 10/11/1987
Goalscorer: Billy Charlton - 193
Appearances: Bobby Brown - 469
Additional: Paid £6,000 to Sunderland for Ken Chisolm 1956. Received £33,000 from Liverpool for Ian McDonald 1974.

GROUND: Borough Park, Workington, Cumbria CA14 2DT
Ground Capacity: 3,101 **Seats:** 500 **Covered:** 1,000 **Clubhouse:** Yes **Shop:** Yes
Previous Grounds: Lonsdale Park 1921-37.
Record Attendance: 21,000 v Manchester United - FA Cup 3rd round 04/01/1958

Nearest Railway Station Workington - 0.6km
Bus Route Tesco - stop 100m away

Pre-season action - Photos Keith Clayton.

Richards (Crewe) Heath (Nantwich).jpg

Terry (Nantwich) saves from Murphy (Crewe).

Moody (Bottesford) breaks through the Gainsborough defence.

Spencer (Bottesford) goes close against Gainsborough.

AFC RUSHDEN & DIAMONDS

Southern League Central

Founde 2011 **Nickname:** The Diamonds **Club Colours:** White & blue

Club Contact Details
01933 359 206 secretary@afcdiamonds.com

Previous Names: None
Previous Leagues: United Counties 2012-15. Southern 2015-16. Northern Premier 2016-17.

11-12	12-13		13-14		14-15		15-16		16-17		17-18		18-19		19-20		20-21	
	UCL 1	2	UCL P	3	UCL P	1	SthC	5	NP1S	5	Sth1E	2	SthPC	9	SthPC	n&v	SthPC	n&v
			FAC	3Q	FAC	1Q	FAC	4Qr	FAC	3Q	FAC	2Qr	FAC	1Q	FAC	1Q	FAC	1Q
	FAV	3P	FAV	4P	FAV	2P	FAT	P	FAT	2Q	FAT	P	FAT	1Q	FAT	2Q	FAT	1P

HONOURS / RECORDS
FA Comps: None

League: United Counties Premier Division 2014-15.

County FA: Northamptonshire Senior Cup 2015-16.

Victory: 9-0 v Buckingham Town (A) 15/12/12 and v Desborough Town (A) 21/02/15
Goalscorer: Tom Lorraine - 54 in 150 appearances, 2014- present.
Appearances: Brad Harris - 213, 2013 - present
Additional: 28 matches unbeaten, 13/01/2015 - 31/10/2015.

GROUND: Rushden & Higham United FC, Hayden Road, Rushden NN10 0HX
Ground Capacity: 2,956 **Seats:** 100 **Covered:** 250 **Clubhouse:** Yes **Shop:** Yes
Previous Grounds: The Dog & Duck Wellingborough Town FC 2011-17.
Record Attendance: 1,162 v Barwell, 27/10/2015.

Nearest Railway Station Wellingborough and Bedford
Bus Route X46/X47, 49, 50, 26 to Rushden town centre a 10 min walk from the ground

ALVECHURCH

Southern League Central

Founde 1929 **Nickname:** The Church **Club Colours:** Amber & black.

Club Contact Details
0121 445 2929 info@alvechurchfc.club

Previous Names: Alvechurch FC >1993. Re-formed in 1994 as Alvechurch Villa > 1996.
Previous Leagues: Worcestershire Combination/Midland Combination 1961-73, 94-2003. West Midlands (Reg) 1973-78. Southern 1978-93. Midland Alliance 2003-14. Midland Football League 2014-17. Northern Premier 2017-18.

11-12		12-13		13-14		14-15		15-16		16-17		17-18		18-19		19-20		20-21	
MidAl	13	MidAl	11	MidAl	13	MFLP	15	MFLP	2	MFLP	1	NP1S	2	SthPC	4	SthPC	n&v	SthPC	n&v
FAC	1Q	FAC	EPr	FAC	EP	FAC	EP	FAC	P	FAC	P	FAC	3Q	FAC	2Q	FAC	1Q	FAC	3Q
FAV	2Q	FAV	2Q	FAV	3P	FAV	1Q	FAV	4P	FAV	2P	FAT	2Q	FAT	1Qr	FAT	1Q	FAT	3Q

HONOURS / RECORDS
FA Comps: None
League: Worcestershire Combination Division 1962-63, 64-65, 66-67. Midland Combination Division One 1971-72, Premier 2002-03. West Midlands (Reg) Premier 1973-74, 74-75, 75-76, 76-77. Southern Midland Division 1980-81. Midland Football Premier 2016-17.
County FA: Worcestershire Senior Cup 1972-73, 73-74, 76-77, Senior Urn 2003-04, 04-05, 07-08, 12-13.

Victory: 13-0 v (A) Alcester Town.
Defeat: 0-9 v (H) Coalville Town.
Goalscorer: Graham Allner. Keith Rostill scored 53 goals during the 2002-03 season.
Appearances: Kevin Palmer.
Additional: In 1971, the club played out the longest FA Cup tie in history when it took six games to beat Oxford City in the 4Q Round.

GROUND: Lye Meadow, Redditch Road, Alvechurch B48 7RS
Ground Capacity: 3,000 **Seats:** 100 **Covered:** 300 **Clubhouse:** Yes **Shop:**
Previous Grounds: Played in the local park until moving to Lye Meadow.
Record Attendance: 13,500 v Enfield, FA Amateur Cup Quarter-final, 1964-65.

Nearest Railway Station Alvechurch - 0.7km
Bus Route Bus stops at the ground.

BANBURY UNITED

Southern League Central

Founde 1931 **Nickname:** Puritans **Club Colours:** Red

Club Contact Details

01295 263 354 bworsley@btinternet.com

Previous Names: Spencer Villa 1931-34. Banbury Spencer. Club reformed in 1965 as Banbury United

Previous Leagues: Banbury Junior 1933-34, Oxon Senior 1934-35, Birmingham Combination 1935-54, West Midlands 1954-66, Southern 1966-90, Hellenic 1991-2000

11-12		12-13		13-14		14-15		15-16		16-17		17-18		18-19		19-20		20-21	
SthP	16	SthP	16	SthP	19	SthP	21	Sthsw	2	SthP	6	SthP	9	SthPC	17	SthPC	n&v	SthPC	n&v
FAC	1Q	FAC	1Qr	FAC	1Q	FAC	2Q	FAC	P	FAC	3Q	FAC	3Q	FAC	2Q	FAC	1Qr	FAC	1P
FAT	3Qr	FAT	1Qr	FAT	1Q	FAT	3Q	FAT	1Qr	FAT	1Q	FAT	2Qr	FAT	2Q	FAT	1Qr	FAT	3Q

HONOURS / RECORDS

FA Comps: None

League: Oxfordshire Junior Banbury Division 1933-34. Oxfordshire Senior 1934-35. Hellenic Premier 1999-2000.

County FA: Oxford Senior Cup 1978-79, 87-88, 2003-04, 05-06, 06-07, 14-15.

Victory: 12-0 v RNAS Culham - Oxon Senior Cup 1945-46

Defeat: 2-11 v West Bromwich Albion 'A' - Birmingham Combination 1938-39

Goalscorer: Dick Pike and Tony Jacques - 222 (1935-48 and 1965-76 respectively). Jacues also scored 62 in a single season, 1967-68.

Appearances: Jody McKay - 576

Additional: Paid £2,000 to Oxford United for Phil Emsden. Received £20,000 from Derby County for Kevin Wilson 1979.

GROUND: Station Approach, Banbury OX16 5AB

Ground Capacity: 4,000 **Seats:** 250 **Covered:** 250 **Clubhouse:** Yes **Shop:** Yes

Previous Grounds: Middleton Road 1931-34.

Record Attendance: 7,160 v Oxford City - FA Cup 3rd Qualifying Round 30/10/1948

Nearest Railway Station Banbury - 0.2km

Bus Route 500 & S4

BARWELL

Southern League Central

Founde 1992 **Nickname:** Canaries **Club Colours:** Green & yellow

Club Contact Details

07961 905 141 shirley.brown16@sky.com

Previous Names: Barwell Athletic FC and Hinckley FC amalgamated in 1992.

Previous Leagues: Midland Alliance 1992-2010, Northern Premier League 2010-11, 13-18. Southern 2011-13.

11-12		12-13		13-14		14-15		15-16		16-17		17-18		18-19		19-20		20-21	
SthP	9	SthP	7	NP P	14	NP P	8	NP P	9	NP P	14	NP P	10	SthPC	16	SthPC	n&v	SthPC	n&v
FAC	2Q	FAC	3Qr	FAC	1Q	FAC	4Q	FAC	1P	FAC	2Q	FAC	3Q	FAC	1Q	FAC	2Q	FAC	2Q
FAT	2Q	FAT	1Q	FAT	1Q	FAT	3Qr	FAT	1Q	FAT	2Q	FAT	2Q	FAT	1P	FAT	2Qr	FAT	3Q

HONOURS / RECORDS

FA Comps: None

League: Midland Alliance 2009-10.
Northern Premier Division One South 2010-11.

County FA: Leicestershire Challenge Cup 2014-15, 16-17.

Goalscorer: Andy Lucas

Appearances: Adrian Baker

Best FA Cup First Round Proper 2015-16

FA Trophy First Round Proper 2018-19

FA Vase Semi Finals 2009-10

GROUND: Kirkby Road Sports Ground, Kirkby Road, Barwell LE9 8FQ

Ground Capacity: 2,462 **Seats:** 256 **Covered:** 750 **Clubhouse:** Yes **Shop:** Yes

Previous Grounds: None

Record Attendance: 1,279 v Whitley Bay, FA Vase Semi-Final 2009-10.

Nearest Railway Station Hinckley - 7 miles away

Bus Route 158, 159 & 2

BIGGLESWADE TOWN

Southern League Central

Founde 1874 **Nickname:** The Waders **Club Colours:** Green & white

Club Contact Details

01767 318 802 (Matchdays) michaeldraxler@hotmail.com

Previous Names: Biggleswade FC. Biggleswade & District.

Previous Leagues: Biggleswade & District 1902-20. Bedford & District. Northamptsonshire/United Counties 1920-39 / 1951-55, 1963-80. Spartan 1945-51. Eastern Counties 1955-63. South Midlands/SSM 1980-2009.

11-12		12-13		13-14		14-15		15-16		16-17		17-18		18-19		19-20		20-21	
SthC	8	SthC	4	SthP	9	SthP	19	SthP	14	SthP	7	SthP	16	SthPC	7	SthPC	n&v	SthPC	n&v
FAC	2Qr	FAC	1Q	FAC	1P	FAC	3Q	FAC	2Q	FAC	2Q	FAC	3Q	FAC	1Q	FAC	2Q	FAC	2Q
FAT	1Q	FAT	P	FAT	1Q	FAT	2Q	FAT	1Q	FAT	2Qr	FAT	1Q	FAT	2P	FAT	3Q	FAT	1P

HONOURS / RECORDS

FA Comps: None

League: Biggleswade & District 1902-03. Spartan South Midlands Premier Division 2008-09.

County FA: Bedfordshire Senior Cup 1902-03, 07-08, 46-47, 50-51, 61-62, 62-63, 66-67, 73-74.
Bedfordshire Premier Cup 2009. Bedfordshire Senior Challenge Cup 2012-13.

Victory: 12-0 v Newmarket Town (A), Eastern Counties.

Best FA Cup First Round Proper 2013-14

FA Trophy Second Round Proper 2018-19

FA Vase Quarter Finals 2008-09

GROUND: The Langford Road Stadium, Langford Road, Biggleswade SG18 9JT

Ground Capacity: 3,500 **Seats:** 300 **Covered:** 400 **Clubhouse:** Yes **Shop:**

Previous Grounds: Fairfield

Record Attendance: 2,000

Nearest Railway Station Biggleswade - 1km

Bus Route 188, 190, 200 & 74

BROMSGROVE SPORTING

Southern League Central

Founde 2009 **Nickname:** The Rouslers **Club Colours:** Red & white

Club Contact Details

01527 876 949 info@bromsgrovesporting.co.uk

Previous Names: None

Previous Leagues: Midland Combination 2010-14.

11-12		12-13		13-14		14-15		15-16		16-17		17-18		18-19		19-20		20-21	
MCm1	3	MCmP	6	MCmP	2	MFL1	2	MFL1	2	MFL1	1	MFLP	1	SthC	2	SthPC	n&v	SthPC	n&v
						FAC	Pr	FAC	P	FAC	P	FAC	P	FAC	P	FAC	1Q	FAC	1Q
				FAV	1P	FAV	3P	FAV	1P	FAV	SF	FAV	5P	FAT	EP	FAT	1Q	FAT	3Q

HONOURS / RECORDS

FA Comps: None

League: Midland Football League Division One 2016-17, Premier 2017-18.

County FA: Worcestershire Senior Urn 2017-18

Best FA Cup Preliminary Round 2014-15(r), 15-16, 16-17, 17-18, 18-19

FA Vase Semi Final 2016-17

FA Trophy Third Qualifying Round 2020-21

GROUND: The Victoria Ground, Birmingham Road, Bromsgrove, Worcs, B61 0DR

Ground Capacity: 5,008 **Seats:** Yes **Covered:** Yes **Clubhouse:** Yes **Shop:** Yes

Previous Grounds: None

Record Attendance: 3,349 v Cleethorpes Town, FA Vase Semi Final First Leg, 11/03/2017

Nearest Railway Station Bromsgrove - 2km

Bus Route All Saints Road stop - 214m away

COALVILLE TOWN

Southern League Central

Founde 1926 **Nickname:** The Ravens **Club Colours:** Black & white

Club Contact Details
07496 792 650 coalvilletownfc@gmail.com

Previous Names: Ravenstoke Miners Ath. 1926-58. Ravenstoke FC 1958-95. Coalville 1995-98.
Previous Leagues: Coalville & Dist. Amateur. North Leicester. Leicestershire Senior. Midland Alliance > 2011. Northern Premier 2011-18.

11-12		12-13		13-14		14-15		15-16		16-17		17-18		18-19		19-20		20-21	
NP1S	14	NP1S	2	NP1S	2	NP1S	10	NP1S	3	NP P	17	NP P	20	SthPC	6	SthPC	n&v	SthPC	n&v
FAC	P	FAC	1Q	FAC	2Q	FAC	2Qr	FAC	2Q	FAC	2Q	FAC	2Q	FAC	3Qr	FAC	2Q	FAC	2Q
FAT	P	FAT	2Q	FAT	1Pr	FAT	P	FAT	1Q	FAT	1Q	FAT	3Q	FAT	1Qr	FAT	3Q	FAT	3Q

HONOURS / RECORDS
FA Comps: None
League: Coalville & District Amateur 1952-53. North Leicestershire 1988-89, 89-90. Leicestershire Senior 2001-02, 02-03. Midland Football Alliance 2010-11.
County FA: Leicestershire Senior Cup 1999-00. Leicestershire Challenge Cup 2012-13, 17-18.

Appearances: Nigel Simms.
Additional: 153 goals scored during 2010-11 season.

GROUND: Owen Street Sports Ground, Owen St, Coalville LE67 3DA
Ground Capacity: 2,500 **Seats:** 240 **Covered:** 240 **Clubhouse:** Yes **Shop:** Yes
Previous Grounds: None
Record Attendance: 1,500.

Nearest Railway Station Loughborough and Leicester
Bus Route Arriva No.137 can be taken to Coalville from both Loughborough and Leicester.

HEDNESFORD TOWN

Southern League Central

Founde 1880 **Nickname:** The Pitmen **Club Colours:** White and black

Club Contact Details
01543 422 870 office@hednesfordtownfc.com

Previous Names: Hednesford 1938-74
Previous Leagues: Walsall & District, Birmingham Comb. 1906-15, 45-53, West Mids 1919-39, 53-72, 74-84, Midland Counties 1972-74, Southern 1984-95, 2001-2005, 2009-11, Conference 1995-2001, 05-06, 13-16. Northern Premier 2006-09, 11-13, 16-19.

11-12		12-13		13-14		14-15		15-16		16-17		17-18		18-19		19-20		20-21	
NP P	5	NP P	2	Conf N	4	Conf N	8	Nat N	21	NP P	15	NP P	16	NP P	13	SthPC	n&v	SthPC	n&v
FAC	3Q	FAC	3Qr	FAC	1P	FAC	2Q	FAC	3Q	FAC	1Q	FAC	2Q	FAC	3Q	FAC	4Q	FAC	2Q
FAT	2Qr	FAT	1P	FAT	1P	FAT	3Q	FAT	3Q	FAT	2Qr	FAT	2Qr	FAT	1Qr	FAT	1Pr	FAT	1P

HONOURS / RECORDS
FA Comps: FA Trophy 2003-04.
League: Birmingham Combination 1909-10, 50-51. West Midlands (Reg) 1940-41, 77-78. Southern League Premier Division 1994-95.
County FA: Staffordshire Senior Cup 1897-98, 1969-70, 73-74, 2012-13. Birmingham Senior Cup 1935-36, 2008-09, 12-13.
Victory: 12-1 v Redditch United - Birmingham Combination 1952-53
Defeat: 0-15 v Burton - Birmingham Combination 1952-53
Goalscorer: Joe O'Connor - 220 in 430 games
Appearances: Kevin Foster - 470
Additional: Paid £12,000 to Macclesfield Town for Steve Burr. Received £40,000 from Blackpool for Kevin Russell.

GROUND: Keys Park, Park Road, Hednesford, Cannock WS12 2DZ
Ground Capacity: 6,039 **Seats:** 1,011 **Covered:** 5,335 **Clubhouse:** Yes **Shop:** Yes
Previous Grounds: The Tins 1880-1903. The Cross Keys 1903-95.
Record Attendance: 4,412 v FC United of Manchester, Northern Premier League Premier Division play-off final, 11/05/13.

Nearest Railway Station Hednesford - 1.6km
Bus Route Brickworks Road - stop 200m away

HITCHIN TOWN

Southern League Central

Founde 1865 **Nickname:** Canaries **Club Colours:** Yellow & green

Club Contact Details

01462 459 028 (match days only) roy.izzard@outlook.com

Previous Names: Hitchin FC 1865-1911. Re-formed in 1928

Previous Leagues: Spartan 1928-39, Herts & Middlesex 1939-45, Athenian 1945-63, Isthmian 1964-2004

11-12		12-13		13-14		14-15		15-16		16-17		17-18		18-19		19-20		20-21	
SthP	14	SthP	13	SthP	13	SthP	9	SthP	3	SthP	4	SthP	11	SthPC	18	SthPC	n&v	SthPC	n&v
FAC	1Q	FAC	3Qr	FAC	1Qr	FAC	2Q	FAC	3Qr	FAC	2Qr	FAC	1Qr	FAC	1P	FAC	3Q	FAC	2Q
FAT	2Q	FAT	3Q	FAT	1Qr	FAT	1Qr	FAT	3Q	FAT	1P	FAT	1Q	FAT	1Q	FAT	1Qr	FAT	2P

HONOURS / RECORDS

FA Comps: None

League: Spartan 1934-35. Isthmian League Division One 1992-93.

County FA: AFA Senior Cup 1931-32. London Senior Cup 1969-70. East Anglian Cup 1972-73.
Herts Senior Cup x14 Most recently 2016-17.

Victory: 13-0 v Cowley and v RAF Uxbridge - both Spartan League 1929-30

Defeat: 0-10 v Kingstonian (A) and v Slough Town (A) - 1965-66 and 1979-80 respectively

Goalscorer: Paul Giggle - 214 (1968-86)

Appearances: Paul Giggle - 769 (1968-86)

Additional: Paid £2,000 to Potton United for Ray Seeking. Received £30,000 from Cambridge United for Zema Abbey, Jan 2000

GROUND: Top Field, Fishponds Road, Hitchin SG5 1NU

Ground Capacity: 4,554 **Seats:** 500 **Covered:** 1,250 **Clubhouse:** Yes **Shop:** Yes

Previous Grounds: None

Record Attendance: 7,878 v Wycombe Wanderers - FA Amateur Cup 3rd Round 08/02/1956

Nearest Railway Station Hitchin - 1.3km

Bus Route Buss stops outside the ground

LEISTON

Southern League Central

Founde 1880 **Nickname:** The Blues **Club Colours:** Blue & red

Club Contact Details

01728 830 308 info@leistonfc.co.uk

Previous Names: Leiston Works Athletic 1919-35.

Previous Leagues: North Suffolk. Suffolk & Ipswich. South East Anglian/East Anglian. Essex & Suffolk Border. Norfolk & Suffolk.
Ipswich & District 1953-2001. Eastern Counties 2001-2011. Isthmian 2011-18.

11-12		12-13		13-14		14-15		15-16		16-17		17-18		18-19		19-20		20-21	
Isth1N	1	Isth P	12	Isth P	9	Isth P	9	Isth P	8	Isth P	7	Isth P	5	SthPC	19	SthPC	n&v	SthPC	n&v
FAC	1Q	FAC	2Q	FAC	1Q	FAC	2Q	FAC	3Q	FAC	4Q	FAC	3Q	FAC	2Q	FAC	1Q	FAC	4Q
FAT	P	FAT	3Qr	FAT	1Q	FAT	1P	FAT	2Q	FAT	1Pr	FAT	2Q	FAT	3Q	FAT	1Q	FAT	1P

HONOURS / RECORDS

FA Comps: None

League: Suffolk & Ipswich/Ipswich & District 1900-01, 01-02, 02-03, Division 2B 1937-38 / Division One 83-84.
Eastern Counties Premier Division 2010-11. Isthmian Division One North 2011-12.

County FA: Suffolk Junior Cup 1894-95, 82-83, 83-84, Premier Cup 2017-18.
East Anglian Cup 2007-08.

Goalscorer: Lee McGlone - 60 (League).

Appearances: Gareth Heath - 201 (League).

GROUND: The LTAA, Victory Road, Leiston IP16 4DQ

Ground Capacity: 2,350 **Seats:** 250 **Covered:** 500 **Clubhouse:** Yes **Shop:**

Previous Grounds: Leiston Recreation Ground 1880-1921.

Record Attendance: 1,250 v Fleetwood Town, FA Cup First round Proper, 2008-09.

Nearest Railway Station Saxmundham - 6 miles

Bus Route Alde Valley Sixth Form - stop 300m away

LOWESTOFT TOWN

Southern League Central

Founde 1880 **Nickname:** The Trawler Boys or Blues **Club Colours:** Blue & white

Club Contact Details

07719 031 2215 admin@lowestofttownfc.co.uk

Previous Names: Original club merged with Kirkley in 1887 to form Lowestoft and became Lowestoft Town in 1890

Previous Leagues: North Suffolk 1897-35, Eastern Counties 1935-2009. Isthmian 2009-2014, 16-18. Conference 2014-16.

11-12		12-13		13-14		14-15		15-16		16-17		17-18		18-19		19-20		20-21	
Isth P	3	Isth P	2	Isth P	4	Conf N	16	Nat N	20	Isth P	11	Isth P	22	SthPC	14	SthPC	n&v	SthPC	n&v
FAC	3Q	FAC	4Q	FAC	1Q	FAC	3Q	FAC	2Q	FAC	1Q	FAC	2Q	FAC	2Q	FAC	3Q	FAC	1Q
FAT	1P	FAT	1Q	FAT	1Q	FAT	1P	FAT	1P	FAT	1Q	FAT	1Q	FAT	1Q	FAT	1Q	FAT	1P

HONOURS / RECORDS

FA Comps: None

League: Eastern Counties League 1935-36 (shared), 37-38, 62-63, 64-65, 65-66, 66-67, 67-68, 69-70, 70-71, 77-78, 2005-06, 08-09. Isthmian League Division One North 2009-10.

County FA: Suffolk Senior Cup 1902-03, 22-23, 25-26, 31-32, 35-36, 46-47, 47-48, 48-49, 55-56, Premier Cup 1966-67, 71-72, 74-75, 78-79, 79-80, 99-00, 00-01, 04-05, 05-06, 08-09, 11-12, 14-15, 15-16. East Anglian Cup 1929-30, 70-71, 77-78.

Best FA Cup First Round Proper 1926-27, 38-39, 66-67, 67-68, 77-78, 2009-10

FA Trophy Second Round Proper 1971-72

FA Vase Runners-up 2007-08

GROUND: Crown Meadow, Love Road, Lowestoft NR32 2PA

Ground Capacity: 3,250 **Seats:** 466 **Covered:** 500 **Clubhouse:** Yes **Shop:** Yes

Previous Grounds: Crown Meadow Athletic Ground 1880-1889. North Denes 1889-94.

Record Attendance: 5,000 v Watford - FA Cup 1st Round 1967

Nearest Railway Station Lowestoft - 0.7km

Bus Route 99 & X1

NEEDHAM MARKET

Southern League Central

Founde 1919 **Nickname:** The Marketmen **Club Colours:** Red & black

Club Contact Details

01449 721 000 m.easlea@sky.com

Previous Names: None

Previous Leagues: Suffolk & Ipswich Senior, Eastern Counties. Isthmian 2010-2018.

11-12		12-13		13-14		14-15		15-16		16-17		17-18		18-19		19-20		20-21	
Isth1N	4	Isth1N	16	Isth1N	5	Isth1N	1	Isth P	20	Isth P	9	Isth P	19	SthPC	11	SthPC	n&v	SthPC	n&v
FAC	2Q	FAC	1Q	FAC	4Q	FAC	3Q	FAC	1Qr	FAC	1Q	FAC	3Q	FAC	2Qr	FAC	2Q	FAC	1Q
FAT	1Q	FAT	P	FAT	P	FAT	P	FAT	1Q	FAT	2Q	FAT	2Q	FAT	1P	FAT	2Q	FAT	2P

HONOURS / RECORDS

FA Comps: None

League: Eastern Counties Premier Division 2009-10. Isthmian Division One North 2014-15.

County FA: Suffolk Senior Cup 1989-90, 2004-05. Suffolk & Ipswich Senior League 1995-96. East Anglian Cup 2006-07. Suffolk Premier Cup 2016-17.

Victory: 10-1 v I[swich Wanderers (A) , FA Cup Preliminary Round, 01/09/2007

Defeat: 2-6 v Lowestoft Town (A), FA Trophy First round Qualifier, 19/10/2010

Goalscorer: Craig Parker - 111 (2007-2011) Most goals in a season - Craig Parker 40 (2011-11).

Appearances: Rhys Barber - 334 (2006-2012)

Additional: Most goals scored in a season - 196 in 70 games (2007-08)

GROUND: Bloomfields, Quinton Road, Needham Market IP6 8DA

Ground Capacity: 2,250 **Seats:** 250 **Covered:** 250 **Clubhouse:** Yes **Shop:** Yes

Previous Grounds: Young's Meadow 1919. Crowley Park >1996.

Record Attendance: 1,784 v Cambridge United, FAC Fourth Qualifying Round, 26/10/2013.

Nearest Railway Station Needham Market - 0.6km

Bus Route Quinton Road stop - 38m away

NUNEATON BOROUGH

Southern League Central

Founde 1889 **Nickname:** The Boro / The Town **Club Colours:** Blue and white

Club Contact Details

0247 518 6661 info@nuneatonboroughfc.com

Previous Names: Nuneaton St. Nicholas 1889-1894. Nuneaton Town 1894-37. Nuneaton Borough 1937-2008.

Previous Leagues: Local 1894-1906. Birmingham Jr/Comb 06-15, 26-33, 38-52. Birmingham 19-24, 33-37. Central Am. 37-38. Birmingham 52-58. Southern 24-25, 58-79 81-82, 87-99, 2003-04, 08-10. Conference/National 79-81, 82-87, 99-03, 04-08, 10-19.

11-12	12-13	13-14	14-15	15-16	16-17	17-18	18-19	19-20	20-21
Conf N 5	Conf 15	Conf 13	Conf 24	Nat N 6	Nat N 12	Nat N 13	Nat N 22	SthPC n&v	SthPC n&v
FAC 4Q	FAC 1Pr	FAC 4Q	FAC 4Qr	FAC 3Q	FAC 2Q	FAC 3Q	FAC 2Qr	FAC 1Q	FAC 3Q
FAT 1P	FAT 1P	FAT 2Pr	FAT 1P	FAT 1P	FAT 3P	FAT 1P	FAT 3Q	FAT 1Q	FAT 2P

HONOURS / RECORDS

FA Comps: None

League: Coventry & Dist. 1902-03. Coventry & North Warwicks' 1904-05. Birmingham Junior 1906-07, Combination 1914-15, 28-29, 30-31. Birmingham League North 1954-55, Div.One 55-56. Southern League Midland Div. 1981-82, 92-93, 95-96, Premier Division 1988-99.

County FA: Birmingham Senior Cup 1930-31, 48-49, 54-55, 59-60, 77-78, 79-80, 92-93, 2001-02, 09-10.

Victory: 11-1 - 1945-46 and 1955-56

Defeat: 1-8 - 1955-56 and 1968-69

Goalscorer: Paul Culpin - 201 (55 during season 1992-93)

Appearances: Alan Jones - 545 (1962-74)

Misc: Paid £35,000 to Forest green Rovers for Marc McGregor 2000

GROUND: Liberty Way, Nuneaton CV11 6RR

Ground Capacity: 4,500 **Seats:** 514 **Covered:** Yes **Clubhouse:** Yes **Shop:** Yes

Previous Grounds: Higham Lane/Rose Inn/Arbury Rd/Edward St. 1889-1903. Queens Rd 03-08. Newdegate Arms 08-15. Manor Pk 19-07.

Record Attendance: 22,114 v Rotherham Utd, FAC 3P 28/01/1967 (Manor Park). 3,480 v Luton Town, Conf. Prem., 22/02/14 (Liberty Way).

Nearest Railway Station Nuneaton - approx. 35min walk from the ground.

Bus Route 2 & 4

PETERBOROUGH SPORTS

Southern League Central

Founde 1919 **Nickname:** The Turbines **Club Colours:** Blue & yellow

Club Contact Details

01733 567 835 pslfc1908@outlook.com

Previous Names: Brotherhoods Engineering Works 1919-99. Bearings Direct during 1999-2001.

Previous Leagues: Northants League (former UCL) 1919-23. Peterborough & District 1923-2013. United Counties 2013-17. Northern Premier 2017-18.

11-12	12-13	13-14	14-15	15-16	16-17	17-18	18-19	19-20	20-21
P&D P 3	P&D P 3	UCL 1 16	UCL 1 5	UCL 1 1	UCL P 1	NP1S 12	SthC 1	SthPC n&v	SthPC n&v
				FAC 1Qr	FAC 1Q	FAC 1Q	FAC 3Q	FAC 4Q	FAC 3Q
			FAV 2P	FAV 1Q	FAV 4P	FAT P	FAT P	FAT 3Q	FAT 5P

HONOURS / RECORDS

FA Comps: None

League: Northants 1919-20, United Counties 1919-20, Division One 2015-16, Premier 2016-17. Peterborough & Dist Division Three 1925-26, Division Three South 1980-81, Premier 2006-07. Southern Div1 Central 18-19.

County FA: Northants Junior Cup 2006-07, 15-16,

Best FA Cup Fourth Qualifying Round 2019-20

FA Trophy Fifth Round Proper 2020-21

FA Vase Fourth Round Proper 2016-17

GROUND: Bea Arena, Lincoln Road, Peterborough PE1 3HA

Ground Capacity: 1,500 **Seats:** 350 **Covered:** Yes **Clubhouse:** Yes **Shop:** No

Previous Grounds: None

Record Attendance: Not known

Nearest Railway Station Peterborough - 3 miles

Bus Route 101 towards Bourne - alight at Boulevard Retail Park, 6min walk from there.

REDDITCH UNITED

Southern League Central

Founde 1891 **Nickname:** The Reds **Club Colours:** Red

Club Contact Details
01527 67450 info@redditchutdfc.co.uk

Previous Names: Redditch Town
Previous Leagues: Birmingham Combination 1905-21, 29-39, 46-53, West Midlands 1921-29, 53-72, Southern 1972-79, 81-2004, Alliance 1979-80. Conference 2004-11.

11-12		12-13		13-14		14-15		15-16		16-17		17-18		18-19		19-20		20-21	
SthP	15	SthP	19	SthP	10	SthP	6	SthP	2	SthP	17	SthP	14	SthPC	15	SthPC	n&v	SthPC	n&v
FAC	1Q	FAC	1Q	FAC	1Qr	FAC	1Qr	FAC	1Q	FAC	1Q	FAC	2Q	FAC	1Q	FAC	1Qr	FAC	1Q
FAT	1Q	FAT	1Q	FAT	3Q	FAT	3Q	FAT	1Q	FAV	2Q	FAT	1Q	FAT	1Q	FAT	3Q	FAT	3Q

HONOURS / RECORDS
FA Comps: None
League: Birmingham Combination 1913-14, 32-33, 52-53. Birmingham & District Southern Division 1954-55. Southern Division One North 1975-76, Western Division 2003-04.
County FA: Worcestershire Senior Cup 1893-94, 29-30, 74-75, 76-76, 2007-08, 13-14. Birmingham Senior Cup 1924-25, 31-32, 38-39, 76-77, 2004-05. Staffordshire Senior Cup 1990-91.
Misc: Paid £3,000 to Halesowen Town for Paul Joinson. Received £40,000 from Aston Villa for David Farrell. Played nine games in nine days at the end of the 1997-98 season.
Victory: 7-1 v Farnborough (H), Southern Premier, 06/01/2018

GROUND: Bromsgrove Road, Redditch B97 4RN
Ground Capacity: 4,000 **Seats:** 400 **Covered:** 2,000 **Clubhouse:** Yes **Shop:** Yes
Previous Grounds: HDA Sports Ground, Millsborough Road
Record Attendance: 5,500 v Bromsgrove Rovers - Wets Midlands League 1954-55

Nearest Railway Station Redditch - 0.4km
Bus Route Bus stops outside the ground

ROYSTON TOWN

Southern League Central

Founde 1875 **Nickname:** The Crows **Club Colours:** White & black

Club Contact Details
01763 241 204 secretary@roystontownfc.co.uk

Previous Names: None
Previous Leagues: Buntingford & District 1919-29. Cambridgeshire 1929-48. Herts County 1948-60, 63-77. South Midlands 1960-63, 77-84. Isthmian 1984-94. Spartan South Midlands 1994-2012.

11-12		12-13		13-14		14-15		15-16		16-17		17-18		18-19		19-20		20-21	
SSM P	1	SthC	7	SthC	7	SthC	2	SthC	2	SthC	1	SthP	7	SthPC	10	SthPC	n&v	SthPC	n&v
FAC	P	FAC	1Qr	FAC	2Q	FAC	P	FAC	Pr	FAC	P	FAC	2Qr	FAC	1Q	FAC	4Q	FAC	3Q
FAV	4P	FAT	1Qr	FAT	P	FAT	1Q	FAT	2Q	FAT	1Pr	FAT	3P	FAT	3Qr	FAT	4P	FAT	2P

HONOURS / RECORDS
FA Comps: None
League: Cambridgeshire Division Two 1929-30. Herts County Division One 1969-70, 72-73, Premier 1976-77. South Midlands Division One 1977-78, 2008-09, Premier Division 2011-12. Southern Division One Central 2016-17.
County FA: Herts Charity Shield 1981-82, 96-97. Herts Intermediate Cup 1988-89.

Best FA Cup Fourth Qualifying Round 2019-20
FA Trophy Fourth Round Proper 2019-20
FA Vase Fifth Round Proper 2009-10

GROUND: Garden Walk, Royston, Herts SG8 7HP
Ground Capacity: 1,980 **Seats:** 300 **Covered:** Yes **Clubhouse:** Yes **Shop:** No
Previous Grounds: Newmarket Road, Baldock Road and Mackerell Hall before acquiring Garden Walk in 1932.
Record Attendance: 876 v Aldershot Town, 1993-94.

Nearest Railway Station Royston - 0.7km
Bus Route St Mary's School - stop 150m away

RUSHALL OLYMPIC

Southern League Central

Founde 1951 **Nickname:** The Pics **Club Colours:** Amber and black

Club Contact Details
01922 641 021 secretary@rushallolympic.co.uk

Previous Names: None
Previous Leagues: Walsall Amateur 1952-55, Staffordshire County (South) 1956-78, West Midlands 1978-94, Midland Alliance 1994-2005, Southern 2005-08. Northern Premier 2008-18.

11-12		12-13		13-14		14-15		15-16		16-17		17-18		18-19		19-20		20-21	
NP P	8	NP P	6	NP P	7	NP P	9	NP P	10	NP P	12	NP P	8	SthPC	8	SthPC	n&v	SthPC	n&v
FAC	4Q	FAC	1Q	FAC	4Q	FAC	2Q	FAC	3Q	FAC	2Q	FAC	3Qr	FAC	1Qr	FAC	3Q	FAC	1Q
FAT	1Q	FAT	1P	FAT	2Q	FAT	3Qr	FAT	2Qr	FAT	1Q	FAT	2Q	FAT	1Q	FAT	1Q	FAT	1P

HONOURS / RECORDS
FA Comps: None
League: West Midlands (Reg) Division One 1979-80. Midland Alliance 2004-05.

County FA: Staffordshire Senior Cup 2015-16. Walsall Senior Cup 2015-16, 17-18.

Goalscorer: Graham Wiggin
Appearances: Alan Dawson - 400+

GROUND: Dales Lane off Daw End Lane, Rushall, Nr Walsall WS4 1LJ
Ground Capacity: 1,990 **Seats:** 200 **Covered:** 200 **Clubhouse:** Yes **Shop:** Yes
Previous Grounds: Rowley Place 1951-75, Aston University 1976-79
Record Attendance: 2,000 v Leeds United Ex players

Nearest Railway Station Walsall - 3km.
Bus Route Royal Oak - stop 50m away

ST. IVES TOWN

Southern League Central

Founde 1887 **Nickname:** The Ives **Club Colours:** Black & white

Club Contact Details
sitfcsecretary@aol.com

Previous Names: None
Previous Leagues: Cambridgeshire, Central Amateur, Hunts, Peterborough & District. United Counties > 2013.

11-12		12-13		13-14		14-15		15-16		16-17		17-18		18-19		19-20		20-21	
UCL P	3	UCL P	2	SthC	13	SthC	9	SthC	4	SthP	15	SthP	22	SthPC	13	SthPC	n&v	SthPC	n&v
FAC	Pr	FAC	P	FAC	2Q	FAC	Pr	FAC	2Q	FAC	1Q	FAC	2Q	FAC	3Q	FAC	2Qr	FAC	1Q
FAV	QF	FAV	2Pr	FAT	2Q	FAT	P	FAT	1Q	FAV	3Q	FAT	1Q	FAT	1Q	FAT	1Qr	FAT	2P

HONOURS / RECORDS
FA Comps: None
League: Southern Division One Central Play-offs 2015-16.

County FA: Hunts Senior Cup 1900/01, 11-12, 22-23, 25-26, 29-30, 81-82, 86-87, 87-88, 2006-07, 08-09, 11-12, 15-16. Hunts Premier Cup 2006-07, 08-09.
Victory: 0-6 v Stafford Rangers (A), FAT 1Q, 28/10/2017 & v Dorchester Town (A), Southern Premier, 16/12/2017
Best FA Cup Third Qualifying Round 2018-19
FA Vase Quarter Finals 2011-12
FA Trophy Second Round Proper 2020-21

GROUND: Westwood Road, St. Ives PE27 6DT
Ground Capacity: 2,000 **Seats:** Yes **Covered:** Yes **Clubhouse:** Yes **Shop:** No
Previous Grounds: Meadow Lane.
Record Attendance: 1,523 v AFC Rushden & Diamonds, Southern Division One Central Play-off Final, 02/05/2016.

Nearest Railway Station Huntingdon - 6.2 miles
Bus Route B the busway - alight at Langley Close. 7min walk from there.

STOURBRIDGE

Southern League Central

Founde 1876 **Nickname:** The Glassboys **Club Colours:** Red and white

Club Contact Details

01384 394 040 clive1974eades@gmail.com

Previous Names: Stourbridge Standard 1876-87

Previous Leagues: West Midlands (Birmingham League) 1892-1939, 54-71, Birmingham Combination 1945-53, Southern 1971-2000. Midland Alliance 2000-06. Southern 2006-14. Northern Premier 2014-18.

11-12		12-13		13-14		14-15		15-16		16-17		17-18		18-19		19-20		20-21	
SthP	6	SthP	2	SthP	5	NP P	16	NP P	6	NP P	3	NP P	11	SthPC	3	SthPC	n&v	SthPC	n&v
FAC	2P	FAC	1Qr	FAC	2P	FAC	3Qr	FAC	2P	FAC	3P	FAC	4Q	FAC	4Q	FAC	1Pr	FAC	1Q
FAT	3Q	FAT	1Q	FAT	3Qr	FAT	2Q	FAT	3P	FAT	1Q	FAT	2P	FAT	1Q	FAT	3Qr	FAT	3Q

HONOURS / RECORDS

FA Comps: None

League: Birmingham 1923-24. Birmingham Combination 1951-52. Southern Division One North 1973-74, Midland Division 1990-91. Midland Alliance 2001-02, 02-03.

County FA: Worcestershire Junior Cup 1927-28. Hereford Senior Cup 1954-55. Birmingham Senior Cup 1949-50, 58-59, 67-68, 2017-18. Worcestershire Senior Cup x11 - Firstly in 1904-05 and most recently in 2012-13.

Goalscorer: Ron Page - 269

Appearances: Ron Page - 427

Additional: Received £20,000 from Lincoln City for Tony Cunningham 1979

GROUND: War Memorial Athletic Ground, High Street, Amblecote DY8 4HN

Ground Capacity: 2,716 **Seats:** 250 **Covered:** 750 **Clubhouse:** Yes **Shop:** Yes

Previous Grounds: None

Record Attendance: 5,726 v Cardiff City - Welsh Cup Final 1st Leg 1974

Nearest Railway Station Stourbridge - 1km

Bus Route Bus 246 from Dudley, 256 from Wolverhampton and 257 all pass the War Memorial Athletic Ground.

STRATFORD TOWN

Southern League Central

Founde 1941 **Nickname:** The Bards **Club Colours:** Orange & navy

Club Contact Details

01789 269 336 info@stratfordtownfc.co.uk

Previous Names: Straford Rangers 1941-49. Stratford Town Amateurs 1964-70.

Previous Leagues: Local leagues > 1954. Worcestershire/Midland Combination 1954-57, 70-75, 77-94. Birmingham & District/West Midlands (Reg) 1957-70. Hellenic 1975-77. Midland Alliance (Founder Members) 1994-2013.

11-12		12-13		13-14		14-15		15-16		16-17		17-18		18-19		19-20		20-21	
MidAl	8	MidAl	1	Sthsw	10	Sthsw	3	SthP	19	SthP	14	SthP	15	SthPC	5	SthPC	n&v	SthPC	n&v
FAC	3Q	FAC	EP	FAC	P	FAC	P	FAC	1Q	FAC	1Q	FAC	3Qr	FAC	1Q	FAC	2Q	FAC	2Q
FAV	1P	FAV	2Q	FAT	Pr	FAT	2Q	FAT	2Q	FAT	1Qr	FAT	2Q	FAT	1P	FAT	1Q	FAT	3Q

HONOURS / RECORDS

FA Comps: None

League: Worcestershire/Midland Combination 1956-57, 86-87. Midland Alliance 2012-13.

County FA: Birmingham Senior Cup 1962-63.

Best FA Cup Third Qualifying Round 2004-05, 06-07, 11-12, 17-18(r)

Amateur Cup Third Round 1962-63

FA Trophy First Round Proper 2018-19

FA Vase Fifth Round Proper 2008-09

GROUND: The DCS Stadium, Knights Lane, Tiddington, Stratford Upon Avon CV37 7BZ

Ground Capacity: 3,000 **Seats:** Yes **Covered:** Yes **Clubhouse:** Yes **Shop:** Yes

Previous Grounds: A number of pitches before Alcester Road by the late 1940s where they stayed until 2007.

Record Attendance: 1,078 v Aston Villa, Birmingham Senior Cup, Oct. 1996.

Nearest Railway Station Stratford-upon-Avon - 2.8km

Bus Route Alveston Primary School - stop 50m away

TAMWORTH

Southern League Central

Founde 1933 **Nickname:** The Lambs **Club Colours:** Red & black

Club Contact Details

01827 657 98 clubsec@thelambs.co.uk

Previous Names: None

Previous Leagues: Birmingham Combination 1933-54. West Midlands (originally Birmingham & District League) 1954-72, 84-88. Southern 1972-79, 83-84, 89-2003. Northern Premier 1979-83. Conference/National 2003-18.

11-12		12-13		13-14		14-15		15-16		16-17		17-18		18-19		19-20		20-21	
Conf	18	Conf	19	Conf	23	Conf N	7	Nat N	7	Nat N	9	Nat N	21	SthPC	12	SthPC	n&v	SthPC	n&v
FAC	3P	FAC	4Q	FAC	2P	FAC	4Qr	FAC	2Q	FAC	2Q	FAC	2Q	FAC	1Q	FAC	4Q	FAC	3Q
FAT	1P	FAT	3P	FAT	QF	FAT	3Q	FAT	1P	FAT	3Qr	FAT	3Pr	FAT	2Q	FAT	2Q	FAT	1P

HONOURS / RECORDS

FA Comps: FA Vase 1988-89.

League: West Midlands League 1963-64, 65-66, 71-72, 87-88.
Southern League Divison One Midland 1996-97, Premier Division 2002-03. Conference North 2008-09.

County FA: Staffordshire Senior Cup 1958-59, 63-64, 65-66, 2001-02.
Birmingham Senior Cup 1960-61, 65-66, 68-69.

Victory: 14-4 v Holbrook Institue (H) - Bass Vase 1934

Defeat: 0-11 v Solihull (A) - Birmingham Combination 1940

Goalscorer: Graham Jessop - 195

Appearances: Dave Seedhouse - 869

Additional: Paid £7,500 to Ilkeston Town for David Hemmings, Dec 2000. Received £12,000 from Kidderminster H for Scott Rickards, 2003

GROUND: The Lamb Ground, Kettlebrook, Tamworth, Staffordshire B77 1AA

Ground Capacity: 4,565 **Seats:** 518 **Covered:** 1,191 **Clubhouse:** Yes **Shop:** Yes

Previous Grounds: Jolly Sailor Ground 1933-34

Record Attendance: 5,500 v Torquay United - FA Cup 1st Round 15/11/69

Nearest Railway Station Tamworth - within walking distance of the ground.

Bus Route 110 & 765

BEACONSFIELD TOWN

Southern League South

Founde 1994 **Nickname:** The Rams **Club Colours:** Red

Club Contact Details
01494 676 868 info@beaconsfieldtownfc.co.uk

Previous Names: Slough YCOB and Beaconsfield United merged in 1994. Beaconsfield SYCOB 1994-2017.
Previous Leagues: Spartan South Midlands 1004-2004, 07-08, Southern 2004-07.

11-12		12-13		13-14		14-15		15-16		16-17		17-18		18-19		19-20		20-21	
SthC	5	SthC	5	SthC	8	SthC	20	SthC	9	SthC	16	Sth1E	1	SthPS	12	SthPS	n&v	SthPS	n&v
FAC	2Qr	FAC	P	FAC	1Q	FAC	2Q	FAC	1Q	FAC	4Q	FAC	1Q	FAC	3Q	FAC	3Q	FAC	1Q
FAT	P	FAT	Pr	FAT	P	FAT	P	FAT	P	FAT	1Q	FAT	2Qr	FAT	1P	FAT	1Q	FAT	3Q

HONOURS / RECORDS
FA Comps: None
League: Spartan South Midlands 2000-01, 03-04, 07-08. Southern Division One East 2017-18.

County FA: Berks and Bucks Senior Trophy 2003-04, Senior Cup 2012-13.

Goalscorer: Allan Arthur
Appearances: Allan Arthur
Best FA Cup Fourth Qualifying Round 2016-17
FA Trophy First Round Proper 2018-19
FA Vase Second Round Proper 2003-04

GROUND: Holloways Park, Windsor Road, Beaconsfield, Bucks HP9 2SE
Ground Capacity: 2,900 **Seats:** Yes **Covered:** Yes **Clubhouse:** Yes **Shop:** No
Previous Grounds: None
Record Attendance: Not known

Nearest Railway Station Beaconsfield - 2.8km
Bus Route 101, 104 & X74

CHESHAM UNITED

Southern League South

Founde 1917 **Nickname:** The Generals **Club Colours:** White & Claret

Club Contact Details
01494 783 964 secretary@cheshamunited.co.uk

Previous Names: Chesham Town and Chesham Generals merged in 1917 to form Chesham United.
Previous Leagues: Spartan 1917-47, Corinthian 1947-63, Athenian 1963-73, Isthmian 1973-2004

11-12		12-13		13-14		14-15		15-16		16-17		17-18		18-19		19-20		20-21	
SthP	4	SthP	3	SthP	2	SthP	12	SthP	13	SthP	11	SthP	8	SthPS	10	SthPS	n&v	SthPS	n&v
FAC	2Q	FAC	1Q	FAC	1Q	FAC	1Qr	FAC	2P	FAC	1P	FAC	2Q	FAC	2Q	FAC	2Q	FAC	1Q
FAT	2Qr	FAT	2P	FAT	1P	FAT	1Q	FAT	1Pr	FAT	2Q	FAT	1P	FAT	2Q	FAT	1Q	FAT	3P

HONOURS / RECORDS
FA Comps: None
League: Spartan 1921-22, 22-23, 24-25, 32-33. Isthmian Division Two North 1986-87, Division One 1986-87, 97-97, Premier Division 1992-93.
County FA: Berks & Bucks Senior Cup x13. Most recently 2017-18

Goalscorer: John Willis
Appearances: Martin Baguley - 600+
Additional: Received £22,000 from Oldham Athletic for Fitz Hall
Victory: 13-1 v Merthyr Town (H), Southern Premier, 18/11/2017

GROUND: The Meadow, Amy Lane, Amersham Road, Chesham HP5 1NE
Ground Capacity: 3,000 **Seats:** 284 **Covered:** 2,500 **Clubhouse:** Yes **Shop:** Yes
Previous Grounds: None
Record Attendance: 5,000 v Cambridge United - FA Cup 3rd Round 1979

Nearest Railway Station Chesham underground - 0.7km
Bus Route The Wild Rover Pub - stop 250m away

DORCHESTER TOWN

Southern League South

Founde 1880 **Nickname:** The Magpies **Club Colours:** Black & white

Club Contact Details
01305 267 623 office@dorchestertownfc.co.uk

Previous Names: None
Previous Leagues: Dorset, Western 1947-72

11-12		12-13		13-14		14-15		15-16		16-17		17-18		18-19		19-20		20-21	
Conf S	11	Conf S	8	Conf S	22	SthP	17	SthP	12	SthP	18	SthP	19	SthPS	15	SthPS	n&v	SthPS	n&v
FAC	2Q	FAC	2P	FAC	2Q	FAC	4Q	FAC	1Qr	FAC	1Q	FAC	2Q	FAC	2Q	FAC	2Q	FAC	1Q
FAT	3Q	FAT	1Pr	FAT	3Q	FAT	1Q	FAT	2Qr	FAT	2Q	FAT	2Q	FAT	2P	FAT	1Qr	FAT	1P

HONOURS / RECORDS
FA Comps: None

League: Western Division One 1954-55. Southern Southern Division 1979-80, 86-87, Division One East 2002-03.

County FA: Dorset Senior Cup x12 - Firstly in 1950-51 and most recently in 2011-12.

Victory: 7-0 v Canterbury (A) - Southern League Southern Division 1986-87
Defeat: 0-13 v Welton Rovers (A) - Western League 1966
Appearances: Mark Jermyn - 600+ over 14 seasons
Additional: Denis Cheney scored 61 goals in one season. Paid £12,000 to Gloucester City for Chris Townsend 1990. Received £35,000 from Portsmouth for Trevor Sinclair.

GROUND: The Avenue Stadium, Weymouth Avenue, Dorchester DT1 2RY
Ground Capacity: 4,939 **Seats:** 710 **Covered:** 2,846 **Clubhouse:** Yes **Shop:** Yes
Previous Grounds: Council Recreation Ground, Weymouth Avenue 1908-1929, 1929-90, The Avenue Ground 1929
Record Attendance: 4,159 v Weymouth - Southern Premier 1999

Nearest Railway Station Dorchester South & West - 0.9km
Bus Route 10 & X12

FARNBOROUGH

Southern League South

Founde 1967 **Nickname:** Boro **Club Colours:** Yellow and blue

Club Contact Details
07950 394 150 info@farnboroughfc.co.uk

Previous Names: Farnborough Town 1967-2007
Previous Leagues: Surrey Senior 1968-72, Spartan 1972-76, Athenian 1976-77, Isthmian 1977-89, 99-2001, 15-16. Alliance/Conference 1989-90, 91-93, 94-99, 2010-15. Southern 1990-91, 93-94, 2007-10.

11-12		12-13		13-14		14-15		15-16		16-17		17-18		18-19		19-20		20-21	
Conf S	16	Conf S	13	Conf S	16	Conf S	20	Isth P	18	SthC	2	SthP	20	SthPS	9	SthPS	n&v	SthPS	n&v
FAC	2Qr	FAC	2Q	FAC	2Qr	FAC	2Qr	FAC	2Qr	FAC	2Q	FAC	1Q	FAC	1Qr	FAC	2Q	FAC	2Q
FAT	1Pr	FAT	1P	FAT	3Qr	FAT	3P	FAT	1Qr	FAT	P	FAT	3Q	FAT	1Q	FAT	1Q	FAT	3Q

HONOURS / RECORDS
FA Comps: None
League: Spartan 1972-73, 73-74, 74-75. London Spartan 1975-76. Athenian Division Two 1976-77. Isthmian Division Two 1978-79, Division One 84-85, Premier 2000-01. Southern Premier 1990-91, 93-94, 2009-10, Division One South & West 2007-08.
County FA: Hampshire Senior Cup 1974-75, 81-82, 83-84, 85-86, 90-91, 2003-04, 05-06.

Victory: 7-0 v Newport (I.O.W.) (A) - Southern League Division 1 South & West 01/12/2007
Defeat: 0-4 v Hednesford Town (A) - Southern League Premier Division 04/03/2010
Goalscorer: Dean McDonald - 35 (in 53+3 Appearances 2009-10)
Appearances: Nic Ciardini - 147 (2007-10)

GROUND: The Rushmoor Stadium, Cherrywood Road, Farnborough, Hants GU14 8DU
Ground Capacity: 6,500 **Seats:** 627 **Covered:** 1,350 **Clubhouse:** Yes **Shop:** Yes
Previous Grounds: Queens Road Recreation ground.
Record Attendance: 2,230 v Corby Town - Southern Premier 21/03/2009

Nearest Railway Station Frimley - 0.7km
Bus Route 194

GOSPORT BOROUGH

Southern League South

Founde 1944 **Nickname:** The 'Boro' **Club Colours:** Yellow & blue

Club Contact Details
023 9250 1042 enquiries@gosportboroughfc.co.uk

Previous Names: Gosport Borough Athletic
Previous Leagues: Portsmouth & District 1944-45, Hampshire 1945-78. Southern 1978-92, 2007-13. Wessex 1992-2007. Conference 2013-17.

11-12		12-13		13-14		14-15		15-16		16-17		17-18		18-19		19-20		20-21	
Sthsw	3	SthP	5	Conf S	12	Conf S	6	Nat S	9	Nat S	20	SthP	23	SthPS	19	SthPS	n&v	SthPS	n&v
FAC	P	FAC	4Qr	FAC	2Q	FAC	1P	FAC	3Qr	FAC	2Q	FAC	2Q	FAC	2Q	FAC	1Q	FAC	2Q
FAT	1P	FAT	2Q	FAT	F	FAT	2P	FAT	3Q	FAT	1P	FAT	2Q	FAT	1Q	FAT	3Qr	FAT	3Q

HONOURS / RECORDS
FA Comps: None
League: Portsmouth & District 1944-45. Hampshire 1945-46, 76-77, 77-78.
Wessex 2006-07.
County FA: Hampshire Senior Cup 1987-88, 2014-15.

Victory: 19-1 v Widbrook United, Portsmouth Senior Cup, 2016-17.
Defeat: 0-9 v Gloucester City - Southern Premier Division 1989-90 and v Lymington & N.M. - Wessex Lge 99-2000
Goalscorer: Justin Bennett- 257
Appearances: Tony Mahoney - 765

GROUND: Privett Park, Privett Road, Gosport, Hampshire PO12 3SX
Ground Capacity: 3,200 **Seats:** 1,000 **Covered:** Yes **Clubhouse:** Yes **Shop:** Yes
Previous Grounds: None
Record Attendance: 4,770 v Pegasus - FA Amateur Cup 1953

Nearest Railway Station Portsmouth Harbour
Bus Route X5 (to Southampton) & 9/9A (to Fareham)

HARROW BOROUGH

Southern League South

Founde 1933 **Nickname:** Boro or The reds **Club Colours:** All red

Club Contact Details
0208 422 5221 peter@harrowboro.co.uk

Previous Names: Roxonian 1933-38, Harrow Town 1938-66
Previous Leagues: Harrow & District 1933-34, Spartan 1934-40, 45-58, West Middlesex Combination 1940-41, Middlesex Senior 1941-45, Delphian 1956-63, Athenian 1963-75. Isthmian 1975-2018.

11-12		12-13		13-14		14-15		15-16		16-17		17-18		18-19		19-20		20-21	
Isth P	17	Isth P	15	Isth P	18	Isth P	16	Isth P	17	Isth P	21	Isth P	12	SthPS	7	SthPS	n&v	SthPS	n&v
FAC	2Q	FAC	1Q	FAC	1Qr	FAC	4Qr	FAC	1Qr	FAC	1P	FAC	1Q	FAC	1Q	FAC	2Q	FAC	2Q
FAT	2Qr	FAT	1Q	FAT	1Q	FAT	1Q	FAT	1Q	FAV	3Q	FAT	1Qr	FAT	1Q	FAT	1Q	FAT	3Q

HONOURS / RECORDS
FA Comps: None
League: Isthmian League 1983-84.

County FA: Middlesex Senior Cup 1982-83, 92-93, 2014-15. Middlesex Premier Cup 1981-82.
Middlesex Senior Charity Cup 1979-80, 92-93, 2005-06, 06-07, 14-15.
Victory: 13-0 v Handley Page (A) - 18/10/1941
Defeat: 0-8 on five occasions
Goalscorer: Dave Pearce - 153
Appearances: Les Currell - 582, Colin Payne - 557, Steve Emmanuel - 522

GROUND: Teh Rogers Family Stadium, Carlyon Avenue, South Harrow HA2 8SS
Ground Capacity: 3,068 **Seats:** 350 **Covered:** 1,000 **Clubhouse:** Yes **Shop:** Yes
Previous Grounds: Northcult Road 1933-34.
Record Attendance: 3,000 v Wealdstone - FA Cup 1st Qualifying Road 1946

Nearest Railway Station Northolt Underground - 1.1km
Bus Route 114, 282, 487, H10, H9 & X140

HARTLEY WINTNEY

Southern League South

Founde 1897 **Nickname:** The Row **Club Colours:** All orange

Club Contact Details
01252 843 586 (Clubhouse)

Previous Names: None
Previous Leagues: Basingstoke & District. Aldershot & District >1978. Founder members of the Home Counties League (renamed Combined Counties League) 1978- 2017.

11-12		12-13		13-14		14-15		15-16		16-17		17-18		18-19		19-20		20-21	
CC1	3	CCP	19	CCP	7	CCP	9	CCP	1	CCP	1	Sth1E	4	SthPS	8	SthPS	n&v	SthPS	n&v
FAC	3Q	FAC	P	FAC	4Q	FAC	Pr	FAC	3Q	FAC	EP	FAC	2Q	FAC	1Q	FAC	2Qr	FAC	4Q
FAV	1P	FAV	1Q	FAV	2P	FAV	2Q	FAV	5P	FAV	2P	FAT	1P	FAT	1Qr	FAT	3Q	FAT	3Q

HONOURS / RECORDS
FA Comps: None
League: Combined Counties League 1982-83, 2015-16, 16-17.

County FA: None

Best FA Cup Fourth Qualifying Round 2013-14, 20-21
FA Vase Fifth Round 2015-16
FA Trophy Third Qualifying Round 2020-21

GROUND: Memorial Playing Fields, Green Lane, Hartley Wintney RG27 8DL
Ground Capacity: 1,980 **Seats:** 113 **Covered:** Yes **Clubhouse:** Yes **Shop:** Yes
Previous Grounds: Causeway Farm 1897-1953.
Record Attendance: 1,392 v AFC Wimbledon , Combined Counties League Premier, 25/01/03.

Nearest Railway Station Winchfield - 1.9km
Bus Route Green Lane - stop 100m away

HAYES & YEADING UNITED

Southern League South

Founde 2007 **Nickname:** United **Club Colours:** Red

Club Contact Details
0208 573 2075 info@hyufc.com

Previous Names: Hayes - Botwell Mission 1909-29. Hayes and Yeading merged to form today's club in 2007
Previous Leagues: Isthmian. Conference 2007-16. Southern 2016-18.

11-12		12-13		13-14		14-15		15-16		16-17		17-18		18-19		19-20		20-21	
Conf	21	Conf S	17	Conf S	20	Conf S	19	Nat S	21	SthP	23	Sth1E	3	IsthSC	1	SthPS	n&v	SthPS	n&v
FAC	4Q	FAC	4Q	FAC	2Qr	FAC	2Q	FAC	2Q	FAC	2Q	FAC	3Q	FAC	2Q	FAC	4Qr	FAC	1P
FAT	1P	FAT	1P	FAT	1P	FAT	1P	FAT	3Qr	FAT	1Q	FAT	1Q	FAT	1P	FAT	3Q	FAT	3Q

HONOURS / RECORDS
FA Comps: None
League: Isthmian South Central 2018-19.

County FA: None

Victory: 8-2 v Hillingdon Borough (A) - Middlesex Senior Cup 11/11/08
Defeat: 0-8 v Luton Town (A) - Conference Premier 27/03/10
Goalscorer: Josh Scott - 40 (2007-09)
Appearances: James Mulley - 137 (2007-10)

GROUND: SKYex Community Stadium, Beaconsfield Road, Hayes UB4 0SL
Ground Capacity: 1.950 **Seats:** Yes **Covered:** Yes **Clubhouse:** Yes **Shop:** Yes
Previous Grounds: Kingfield Stadium (Woking FC) 2012-13.
Record Attendance: 1,881 v Luton Town - Conference Premier 06/03/2010

Nearest Railway Station Hayes & Harlington - 5-10min taxi ride from ground
Bus Route From Uxbridge Underground take bus towards Shep Bush, alight at Springfield Rd

HENDON

Southern League South

Founde 1908 **Nickname:** Dons or Greens **Club Colours:** Green, black and white

Club Contact Details
07773 312 110 Secretaryhendonfc@gmail.com

Previous Names: Christ Church Hampstead > 1908, Hampstead Town > 1933, Golders Green > 1946
Previous Leagues: Finchley & District 1908-11, Middlesex 1910-11, London 1911-14, Athenian 1914-63. Isthmian 1963-2018.

11-12		12-13		13-14		14-15		15-16		16-17		17-18		18-19		19-20		20-21	
Isth P	7	Isth P	10	Isth P	8	Isth P	2	Isth P	19	Isth P	19	Isth P	3	SthPS	16	SthPS	n&v	SthPS	n&v
FAC	4Q	FAC	1P	FAC	2P	FAC	3Q	FAC	1Q	FAC	4Q	FAC	1Qr	FAC	3Q	FAC	3Q	FAC	2Q
FAT	1Q	FAT	1Q	FAT	1P	FAT	3Q	FAT	1Q	FAT	1Q	FAT	2P	FAT	2Q	FAT	1Q	FAT	3Q

HONOURS / RECORDS
FA Comps: FA Amateur Cup 1959-60, 64-65, 71-72. European Amateur Champions 1972-73.
League: Finchley & District Division Three 1908-09, DivisioN Two 09-10, Division One 10-11. Middlesex 1912-13, 13-14. Athenian 1952-53, 55-56, 60-61. Isthmian 1964-65, 72-73.
County FA: London Senior Cup 1963-64, 68-69, 2008-09, 11-12 14-15. Middlesex Senior Cup x16 - Firstly in 1933-34 / Most recently 2017-18. Middlesex Intermediate Cup 1964-65, 66-67, 72-73. London Intermediate Cup 1962-63, 64-65, 72-73, 75-76, 79-80.
Victory: 13-1 v Wingate - Middlesex County Cup 02/02/1957
Defeat: 2-11 v Walthamstowe Avenue, Athenian League 09/11/1935
Goalscorer: Freddie Evans - 176 (1929-35)
Appearances: Bill Fisher - 787 - (1940-64)
Additional: Received £30,000 from Luton Town for Iain Dowie

GROUND: Silver Jubilee Park, Townsend Lane, Kingsbury, London NW9 7NE
Ground Capacity: 1,990 **Seats:** 350 **Covered:** 1,000 **Clubhouse:** Yes **Shop:**
Previous Grounds: Claremont Road. Vale Farm (Wembley FC). Earlsmead (Harrow Borough FC).
Record Attendance: 9,000 v Northampton Town - FA Cup 1st Round 1952

Nearest Railway Station Hendon - 1.1km
Bus Route Queensbury Road - 700m away

KING'S LANGLEY

Southern League South

Founde 1886 **Nickname:** Kings **Club Colours:** White & black

Club Contact Details
07730 410 330

Previous Names: None
Previous Leagues: West Herts (Founder Member) 1891-1920, 22-34. Southern Olympian 1934-39. Hertfordshire County 1920-22, 46-52, 55-2001. Parthenon 1952-55. Spartan South Midlands 2001-2015.

11-12		12-13		13-14		14-15		15-16		16-17		17-18		18-19		19-20		20-21	
SSM1	4	SSM1	6	SSM1	2	SSM P	1	SthC	1	SthP	20	SthP	21	SthPS	6	SthPC	n&v	SthPC	n&v
FAC	EP	FAC	EPr	FAC	1Q	FAC	Pr	FAC	P	FAC	2Q	FAC	2Q	FAC	2Qr	FAC	4Q	FAC	2Q
FAV	2Q	FAV	1Q	FAV	1Q	FAV	2P	FAT	1Q	FAT	3Q	FAT	1Q	FAT	1Q	FAT	2Q	FAT	1P

HONOURS / RECORDS
FA Comps: None
League: West Herts Div.3 1911-12, Div.2 1919-20, 30-31, 34-35. Southern Olympian Div.1 1936-37. Herts County 1949-50, 51-52, 65-66, 66-67, Div.1 1975-76. Spartan South Midlands Div.2 2007-08, Premier 2014-15. Southern Div.1 Central 2015-16.
County FA: Herts Charity Shield 1966-67. Herts Intermediate Cup 2006-07, 07-08. Herts Senior Centenary Trophy 2011-12.

Misc: 47 consecutive matches unbeaten in all competitions between 15-09-07 and 15-10-08.

GROUND: The Orbital Fasteners Stadium, Hempstead Road, Kings Langley Herts WD4 8BS
Ground Capacity: 1,900 **Seats:** Yes **Covered:** Yes **Clubhouse:** Yes **Shop:**
Previous Grounds: Groomes Meadow. Blackwell Meadow. Kings Langley Common. Home Park 1913-80. Oxhey, Rolls Royce & Buncefield Lane and Leavesden Hospital Ground between 1980-97.
Record Attendance: Not known

Nearest Railway Station Kings Langley - 1.6km
Bus Route 500

MERTHYR TOWN

Southern League South

Founde 2010 **Nickname:** Martyrs **Club Colours:** White & black

Club Contact Details
01685 359 074 merthyrsec@gmail.com

Previous Names: None
Previous Leagues: Western League 2010-12.

11-12		12-13		13-14		14-15		15-16		16-17		17-18		18-19		19-20		20-21	
WestP	1	Sthsw	3	Sthsw	2	Sthsw	1	SthP	10	SthP	3	SthP	17	SthPS	13	SthPS	n&v	SthPS	n&v
FAC	1Qr	FAC	3Q	FAC	1Q	FAC	P	FAC	2Q	FAC	3Q	FAC	2Q	FAC	2Q	FAC	2Q		
FAV	2Q	FAT	1P	FAT	3Q	FAT	3Qr	FAT	3Qr	FAT	2Qr	FAT	1Q	FAT	2Q	FAT	1Qr		

HONOURS / RECORDS
FA Comps: None
League: Western League Division One 2010-11, Premier Division 2011-12.
Southern Division One South & West 2014-15.
County FA: None

Victory: 9-0 v Bishops Cleeve, Southern Division One South & West, 06/04/2015.
Defeat: 1-13 v Chesham United (A), Southern Premier, 18/11/2017

GROUND: Penydarren Park, Park Terrance CF47 8RF
Ground Capacity: 4,000 **Seats:** Yes **Covered:** Yes **Clubhouse:** Yes **Shop:**
Previous Grounds: Rhiw Dda'r (Taff's Well AFC) 2010-11.
Record Attendance: Not known

Nearest Railway Station Merthyr Tydfil - 0.6km
Bus Route St Mary's Church - stop 100m away

METROPOLITAN POLICE

Southern League South

Founde 1919 **Nickname:** The Blues **Club Colours:** All blue

Club Contact Details
020 8398 7358

Previous Names: None
Previous Leagues: Spartan 1928-60, Metropolitan 1960-71, Southern 1971-78. Isthmian 1978-2018.

11-12		12-13		13-14		14-15		15-16		16-17		17-18		18-19		19-20		20-21	
Isth P	12	Isth P	6	Isth P	17	Isth P	5	Isth P	12	Isth P	18	Isth P		SthPS	3	SthPS	n&v	SthPS	n&v
FAC	1Q	FAC	1P	FAC	1Qr	FAC	2Q	FAC	1Qr	FAC	2Q	FAC	2Q	FAC	1P	FAC	1Qr	FAC	2Q
FAT	1Q	FAT	2Qr	FAT	2Q	FAT	3Q	FAT	3Q	FAV	1Q	FAT	3Q	FAT	1Qr	FAT	2Qr	FAT	3Q

HONOURS / RECORDS
FA Comps: None
League: Spartan League Eastern Division and overall 1928-29, 29-30, 36-37, 38-39, 46-47, 53-54, 54-55, Central Division 45-46.
Isthmian League Division One South 2010-11.
County FA: Middlesex Senior Cup 1927-28, Surrey Senior Cup 1932-33, 2014-15. London Senior Cup 2009-10.

Victory: 10-1 v Tilbury - 1995
Defeat: 1-11 v Wimbledon - 1956
Goalscorer: Mario Russo
Appearances: Pat Robert

GROUND: Imber Court, Ember Lane, East Molesey, Surrey KT8 0BT
Ground Capacity: 3,100 **Seats:** 297 **Covered:** 1,800 **Clubhouse:** Yes **Shop:** No
Previous Grounds: None
Record Attendance: 4,500 v Kingstonian - FA Cup 1934

Nearest Railway Station Thames Ditton - 0.8km
Bus Route 411

POOLE TOWN

Southern League South

Founde 1890 **Nickname:** The Dolphins **Club Colours:** Black & gold

Club Contact Details
07771 604 289 secretary@pooletownfc.co.uk

Previous Names: Poole Rovers and Poole Hornets merged in 1890 to form Poole FC > 1934 (Known as Poole & St. Mary's 1919-20).
Previous Leagues: Dorset 1896-1903, 04-05, 10-11. Hampshire 1903-04, 05-10, 11-23, 34-35, 96-2004. Western 1923-26, 30-34, 35-57. Southern 1926-30, 57-96, 2011-16. Wessex 2004-11. National 2016-18.

11-12		12-13		13-14		14-15		15-16		16-17		17-18		18-19		19-20		20-21	
Sthsw	2	Sthsw	1	SthP	7	SthP	2	SthP	1	Nat S	5	Nat S	20	SthPS	5	SthPS	n&v	SthPS	n&v
FAC	3Q	FAC	P	FAC	4Qr	FAC	2Qr	FAC	4Q	FAC	2Q	FAC	3Q	FAC	4Q	FAC	4Qr	FAC	2Q
FAT	1Qr	FAT	2Qr	FAT	2Q	FAT	1P	FAT	1Q	FAT	3Qr	FAT	3Q	FAT	3Q	FAT	1Q	FAT	2P

HONOURS / RECORDS
FA Comps: None
League: Western 1956-57. Hampshire Division One 1999-00. Wessex Premier Division 2008-09, 09-10, 10-11. Southern Division One South & West 2012-13, Premier 2015-16.
County FA: Dorset Senior Cup 1894-95, 96-97, 98-99, 1901-02, 03-04, 06-07, 25-26, 26-27, 37-38, 46-47, 74-75, 88-89, 97-98, 2008-09, 12-13, 13-14.
Victory: 12-0 v Welton Rovers (H) Western League 26/04/1939.
Defeat: 1-12 v Boscombe (A) Hampshire League (West) 20/12/1913.
Additional: Transfer fee paid £5,000 for Nicky Dent 1990.
Transfer fee received reported as £180,000 for Charlie Austin from Swindon Town 2009.

GROUND: Black Gold Stadium, Oakdale School, School Lane, Poole BH15 3JR
Ground Capacity: 3,100 **Seats:** 268 **Covered:** Yes **Clubhouse:** Yes **Shop:** Yes
Previous Grounds: Ye Old Farm Ground. Wimborne Road Rec > 1933. Poole Stadium 1933-94. Hamworthy Utd 1994-96. Holt Utd 1996.
Record Attendance: 6,575 v Watford, FAC 1Pr, 1962-63 (at Poole Stadium). 2,203 v Corby, Southern Prem, 2014-15 (at Tatnam).

Nearest Railway Station Poole - 3/4 mile from the ground.
Bus Route 10, 6, M1, M2, X6 & X8

SALISBURY

Southern League South

Founde 2015 **Nickname:** The Whites **Club Colours:** White and black

Club Contact Details
01722 776 655 jimayres@salisburyfc.co.uk

Previous Names: None
Previous Leagues: Wessex 2015-16.

11-12		12-13		13-14		14-15		15-16		16-17		17-18		18-19		19-20		20-21	
								WexP	1	Sthsw	2	Sth1W	2	SthPS	4	SthPS	n&v	SthPS	n&v
										FAC	2Q	FAC	2Q	FAC	2Qr	FAC	3Q	FAC	1Q
								FAV	SF	FAT	1Q	FAT	P	FAT	2P	FAT	2P	FAT	1P

HONOURS / RECORDS
FA Comps: None
League: Wessex Premier Division 2015-16.

County FA: None

Victory: 9-1 v Bournemouth - Wessex Premier 25/08/15.
Defeat: 4-1 v AFC Porchester - Wessex Premier 30/04/16.
Goalscorer: Sam Wilson - 40 - 2015-16.
Appearances: Thomas Whelan - 54 - 2015-16.

GROUND: Raymond McEnhill Stadium, Partridge Way, Old Sarum SP4 6PU
Ground Capacity: 4,000 **Seats:** 500 **Covered:** 2,247 **Clubhouse:** Yes **Shop:**
Previous Grounds: None
Record Attendance: 3,450 v Hereford FC, FA Vase Semi-final 2nd leg, 2015-16.

Nearest Railway Station Salisbury - 4km
Bus Route Bus stops outside the ground

SWINDON SUPERMARINE

Southern League South

Founde 1992 **Nickname:** The Marine or Spitfires **Club Colours:** All blue

Club Contact Details
01793 828 778 supermarinefc@aol.com

Previous Names: Club formed after the amalgamation of Swindon Athletic and Supermarine
Previous Leagues: Wiltshire, Hellenic1992-2001.

11-12		12-13		13-14		14-15		15-16		16-17		17-18		18-19		19-20		20-21	
SthP	21	Sthsw	4	Sthsw	5	Sthsw	14	Sthsw	4	Sthsw	7	Sth1W	5	SthPS	11	SthPS	n&v	SthPS	n&v
FAC	2Q	FAC	1Q	FAC	P	FAC	2Q	FAC	1Q	FAC	3Q	FAC	3Q	FAC	2Qr	FAC	2Q	FAC	2Q
FAT	1P	FAT	1Q	FAT	1Q	FAT	P	FAT	2Q	FAT	1Q	FAT	1Q	FAT	1Qr	FAT	1Q	FAT	3P

HONOURS / RECORDS
FA Comps: None
League: Hellenic League Premier Division 1997-98, 2000-01.

County FA: Wiltshire Premier Shield 1996-97, 2006-07. Senior Cup 2016-17.

Goalscorer: Damon York - 136 (1990-98)
Appearances: Damon York - 314 (1990-98)
Additional: Paid £1,000 to Hungerford Town for Lee Hartson

GROUND: The Webbswood Stadium, South Marston, Swindon SN3 4BZ
Ground Capacity: 2,000 **Seats:** 325 **Covered:** Yes **Clubhouse:** Yes **Shop:** Yes
Previous Grounds: Supermarine: Vickers Airfield > Mid 1960s
Record Attendance: 1,550 v Aston Villa

Nearest Railway Station Swindon - 5.8km
Bus Route Stanton Fitzwarren Turn - stop 300m away

TAUNTON TOWN

Southern League South

Founde 1947 **Nickname:** The Peacocks **Club Colours:** Claret and sky blue

Club Contact Details
01823 254 909 admin@tauntontown.com

Previous Names: Taunton > 1968
Previous Leagues: Western 1954-77, 83-2002, Southern 1977-83

11-12		12-13		13-14		14-15		15-16		16-17		17-18		18-19		19-20		20-21	
Sthsw	17	Sthsw	18	Sthsw	8	Sthsw	4	Sthsw	3	Sthsw	4	Sth1W	1	SthP	2	SthPS	n&v	SthPS	n&v
FAC	1Qr	FAC	1Qr	FAC	Pr	FAC	1Q	FAC	2Qr	FAC	1Pr	FAC	1Qr	FAC	4Qr	FAC	2Q	FAC	4Q
FAT	1Q	FAT	2Q	FAT	P	FAT	Pr	FAT	2Q	FAT	3Q	FAT	1P	FAT	1Q	FAT	2Qr	FAT	3Q

HONOURS / RECORDS
FA Comps: FA Vase 2000-01.
League: Western League 1968-69, 89-90, 95-96, 98-99, 99-2000, 2000-01.
Southern Division One 2017-18.
County FA: Somerset Senior Cup 1969-70, Premier Cup 2002-03, 05-06, 13-14, 14-15, 16-17.

Victory: 12-0 v Dawlish Town (A) - FA Cup Preliminary Round 28/08/1993
Defeat: 0-8 v Cheltenham Town (A) - FA Cup 2nd Qualifying Round 28/09/1991
Goalscorer: Tony Payne. Reg Oram scored 67 in one season
Appearances: Tony Payne

GROUND: Wordsworth Drive, Taunton, Somerset TA1 2HG
Ground Capacity: 3,000 **Seats:** 300 **Covered:** 1,000 **Clubhouse:** Yes **Shop:** Yes
Previous Grounds: Mountfields. French Weir. Victoria Park. Huish Old Boys. Denman's Park > 1953.
Record Attendance: 3,284 v Tiverton Town - FA Vase Semi-final 1999

Nearest Railway Station Taunton - 1.4km
Bus Route Milford Road - stop 20m away

TIVERTON TOWN

Southern League South

Founde 1913 **Nickname:** Tivvy **Club Colours:** All yellow

Club Contact Details
01884 252 397 johnandtraceyfournier@btinternet.com

Previous Names: Tiverton Athletic.
Previous Leagues: East Devon 1913-28. North Devon 1928-32. Exeter & District 1932-73. Western 1973-99.

11-12		12-13		13-14		14-15		15-16		16-17		17-18		18-19		19-20		20-21	
Sthsw	9	Sthsw	16	Sthsw	3	Sthsw	16	Sthsw	8	Sthsw	3	SthP	6	SthPS	18	SthPS	n&v	SthPS	n&v
FAC	P	FAC	P	FAC	P	FAC	1Qr	FAC	P	FAC	Pr	FAC	1Q	FAC	3Qr	FAC	2Q	FAC	2Q
FAT	3Q	FAT	1Q	FAT	3Qr	FAT	1Q	FAT	2Q	FAT	1Q	FAT	2Qr	FAT	2Q	FAT	1Qr	FAT	3Q

HONOURS / RECORDS
FA Comps: FA Vase 1997-98, 98-99.
League: East Devon Senior Division 1924-25, 25-26, 26-27, 27-28. North Devon 1931-32.
Exeter & District 1933-34, 64-65, 65-66. Western 1993-94, 94-95, 96-97, 97-98.
County FA: Devon Senior Cup 1955-56, 65-66.
Devon St Luke's Cup 1990-91, 91-92, 92-93, 93-94, 94-95, 96-97, 1999-2000, 02-03, 05-06, 16-17.
Victory: 14-1 v University College SW, 11/02/1933.
Defeat: 0-10 v Dawlish Town, 27/12/1969.
Goalscorer: Phil Everett - 378.
Appearances: Tom Gardner - 510.

GROUND: Ladysmead, Bolham Road, Tiverton, Devon EX16 6SG
Ground Capacity: 2,983 **Seats:** 520 **Covered:** 2,300 **Clubhouse:** Yes **Shop:** Yes
Previous Grounds: Athletic Ground (Amory Park) 1913-21. Elm Field (The Elms) 1921-46.
Record Attendance: 3,000 v Leyton Orient - FA Cup 1st Round Proper 12/11/1994.

Nearest Railway Station Tiverton Parkway - 2km
Bus Route Park Road - stop 300m away

TRURO CITY

Southern League South

Founde 1889 **Nickname:** City, White Tigers, The Tinmen **Club Colours:** All white

Club Contact Details
01872 225 400 info@trurocityfc.net

Previous Names: None
Previous Leagues: Cornwall County. Plymouth & District >1951. South Western (FM) 1951-2006. Western 2006-08. Southern 2008-11, 13-15. Conference 2011-13.

11-12		12-13		13-14		14-15		15-16		16-17		17-18		18-19		19-20		20-21	
Conf S	14	Conf S	22	SthP	17	SthP	3	Nat S	4	Nat S	19	Nat S	7	Nat S	20	SthPS	n&v	SthPS	n&v
FAC	3Q	FAC	2Q	FAC	2Q	FAC	1Q	FAC	3Q	FAC	2Q	FAC	1P	FAC	2Qr	FAC	2Q	FAC	3Q
FAT	1P	FAT	3Q	FAT	1Q	FAT	3Q	FAT	2Pr	FAT	1Pr	FAT	3Q	FAT	2P	FAT	1Qr	FAT	3P

HONOURS / RECORDS
FA Comps: FA Vase 2006-07.
League: Plymouth & District 1936-37. South Western League 1960-61, 69-70, 92-93, 95-96, 97-98. Western Div. One 2006-07,
Premier Division 07-08. Southern Division One South & West 2008-09, Premier Division 2010-11.
County FA: Cornwall Senior Cup 1894-95, 1901-02, 02-03, 10-11, 23-24, 26-27, 27-28, 37-38, 58-59, 66-67, 69-70, 94-95, 97-98, 2005-06, 06-07, 07-08.
Misc: 115 points & 185 goals, Western League Division One (42 games) 2006-07.
Became first British club to achieve five promotions in six seasons.

GROUND: Plymouth Parkway FC, Bolitho Park, St Peters Road, Plymouth PL5 3JH
Ground Capacity: 3,200 **Seats:** Yes **Covered:** Yes **Clubhouse:** Yes **Shop:** Yes
Previous Grounds: Truro School. Tolgarrick > mid-1900s Treyew Road Mid 1900s-2018, 19-21. Plainmoor (Torquay Utd FC) 18-19.
Record Attendance: Not known

Nearest Railway Station Plymouth

WALTON CASUALS

Southern League South

Founde 1948 **Nickname:** The Stags **Club Colours:** Orange and black

Club Contact Details
01932 260 300 info@waltoncasuals.com

Previous Names: None
Previous Leagues: Surrey Intermediate 1948-69. Surrey Senior 1969-71. Suburban 1971-92. Surrey County 1992-95. Combined Counties 1995-2005.

11-12		12-13		13-14		14-15		15-16		16-17		17-18		18-19		19-20		20-21	
Isth1S	15	Isth1S	22	Isth1S	9	Isth1S	18	Isth1S	16	Isth1S	13	Isth1S	6	SthPS	17	SthPS	n&v	SthPS	n&v
FAC	P	FAC	P	FAC	P	FAC	Pr	FAC	P	FAC	3Q	FAC	1Q	FAC	2Q	FAC	1Q	FAC	3Q
FAT	Pr	FAT	P	FAT	Pr	FAT	1Q	FAT	1Qr	FAT	1P	FAT	1Q	FAT	3Q	FAT	1Q	FAT	1P

HONOURS / RECORDS
FA Comps: None
League: Surban Southern Section 1982-83, Premier B 2012-13. Combined Counties Premier Division 2004-05.

County FA: None

Goalscorer: Paul Mills - 111 in 123 appearances (1993-99).
Appearances: Lawrence Ennis - 288
Victory: 10-0 v Chessington United, Combined Counties Premier, 28/12/2004.
Defeat: 0-7 v Redhill, Surrey Senior Cup 1st Rnd, 08/12/98. v Chipstead, Combined Counties Premier, 09/11/2002. v Faversham Town, Isthmian Division One, 08/12/2012. v Faversham Town, Isthmian Division One, 09/04/2016.

GROUND: Elmbridge Sports Hub, Waterside Drive, Walton-on-Thames, Surrey KT12 2JP
Ground Capacity: 2,217 **Seats:** 153 **Covered:** 403 **Clubhouse:** Yes **Shop:** Yes
Previous Grounds: Elm Grove Rec. 1948-69. Franklyn Road 69-71. Stompond Lane 71-72. Liberty Lane 72-80. Waterside Stadium 80-2015. Moatside 2015-16. Church Road 2016-17.
Record Attendance: 1,748 v AFC Wimbledon - Combined Counties League 12/04/2004

Nearest Railway Station Both Walton and Hersham stations about 43min walk.
Bus Route Nos. 461 & 459 stop nearest the hub.

WESTON-SUPER-MARE

Southern League South

Founde 1887 **Nickname:** Seagulls **Club Colours:** White

Club Contact Details
01934 621 618 enquiries@wsmafc.co.uk

Previous Names: Borough or Weston-super-Mare
Previous Leagues: Western League 1900-02, 10-18, 48-92. Bristol & District and Somerset County 1921-45. Southern 1992-04.

11-12		12-13		13-14		14-15		15-16		16-17		17-18		18-19		19-20		20-21	
Conf S	13	Conf S	7	Conf S	11	Conf S	17	Nat S	16	Nat S	15	Nat S	12	Nat S	22	SthPS	n&v	SthPS	n&v
FAC	4Q	FAC	3Qr	FAC	3Q	FAC	1P	FAC	4Q	FAC	2Q	FAC	2Q	FAC	1P	FAC	3Qr	FAC	4Q
FAT	3Q	FAT	3Q	FAT	1Pr	FAT	1P	FAT	2P	FAT	3Q	FAT	2Pr	FAT	1P	FAT	1Q	FAT	1P

HONOURS / RECORDS
FA Comps: None
League: Western League 1991-92.

County FA: Somerset Senior Cup 1926-67.
Somerset Premier Cup 2010-11, 11-12, 17-18.
Victory: 11-0 v Paulton Rovers
Defeat: 1-12 v Yeovil Town Reserves
Goalscorer: Matt Lazenby - 180
Appearances: Harry Thomas - 740
Additional: Received £20,000 from Sheffield Wednesday for Stuart Jones

GROUND: Winterstoke Road, Weston-super-Mare BS24 9AA
Ground Capacity: 3,500 **Seats:** 350 **Covered:** 2,000 **Clubhouse:** Yes **Shop:** Yes
Previous Grounds: 'Great Ground' Locking Road >1955. Langford Road 1955-83. Woodspring Park 1983-2004.
Record Attendance: 2,949 v Doncaster Rovers, FA Cup First Round Proper, 18th November 2014.

Nearest Railway Station Weston-Super-Mare - 25-30 minute walk away.
Bus Route 3

WIMBORNE TOWN

Southern League South

Founde 1878 **Nickname:** Magpies **Club Colours:** Black and white

Club Contact Details
01202 884 821 info@wimbornetownfc.co.uk

Previous Names: None
Previous Leagues: Dorset, Dorset Combination, Western 1981-86, Wessex 1986-2010

11-12		12-13		13-14		14-15		15-16		16-17		17-18		18-19		19-20		20-21	
Sthsw	19	Sthsw	12	Sthsw	13	Sthsw	13	Sthsw	17	Sthsw	11	Sth1W	3	SthPS	14	SthPS	n&v	SthPS	n&v
FAC	P	FAC	P	FAC	P	FAC	1Q	FAC	2Q	FAC	Pr	FAC	Pr	FAC	1Qr	FAC	1Q	FAC	4Q
FAT	P	FAT	2Q	FAT	P	FAT	1P	FAT	P	FAT	2Q	FAT	1Q	FAT	1Q	FAT	1Qr	FAT	3Q

HONOURS / RECORDS
FA Comps: FA Vase 1991-92.
League: Dorset Division One 1980-81. Wessex 1991-92, 93-94, 99-2000.

County FA: Dorset Minor Cup 1912-13, Senior Amateur Cup 1936-37, 63-64, Senior Cup 91-92, 96-97.

Goalscorer: Jason Lovell
Appearances: James Sturgess

GROUND: The New Cuthbury, 16 Ainsley Road, Wimborne, Dorset BH21 2FU
Ground Capacity: 2,500 **Seats:** Yes **Covered:** Yes **Clubhouse:** Yes **Shop:** Yes
Previous Grounds: Cuthbury, Cowgrave Road >2021.
Record Attendance: 3,250 v Bamber Bridge

Nearest Railway Station Poole - 8 miles
Bus Route First School - stop 400m away

YATE TOWN

Southern League South

Founde 1906 **Nickname:** The Bluebells **Club Colours:** White & navy blue

Club Contact Details
01454 228 103 yatetownfootballclub@outlook.com

Previous Names: Yate Rovers 1906-1930s. Yate YMCA 1933-58.
Previous Leagues: Bristol Premier Combination > 1968, Gloucestershire County 1968-83, Hellenic 1983-89, 2000-03, Southern 1989-2000

11-12		12-13		13-14		14-15		15-16		16-17		17-18		18-19		19-20		20-21	
Sthsw	13	Sthsw	6	Sthsw	9	Sthsw	6	Sthsw	16	Sthsw	18	Sth1W	14	SthS	3	SthPS	n&v	SthPS	n&v
FAC	2Qr	FAC	1P	FAC	3Qr	FAC	1Q	FAC	P	FAC	P	FAC	P	FAC	1Qr	FAC	Pr	FAC	1Q
FAT	2Q	FAT	Pr	FAT	Pr	FAT	P	FAT	P	FAT	1Q	FAT	1Q	FAT	1Qr	FAT	1P	FAT	3Q

HONOURS / RECORDS
FA Comps: None
League: Hellenic 1987-88, 88-89.

County FA: Gloucestershire Senior Cup 2004-05, 05-06.

Victory: 13-3 v Clevedon - Bristol Premier Combination 1967-68
Goalscorer: Kevin Thaws
Appearances: Gary Hewlett
Additional: Paid £2,000 to Chippenham Town for Matt Rawlings 2003
Received £15,000 from Bristol Rovers for Mike Davis

GROUND: Lodge Road, Yate, Bristol BS37 7LE
Ground Capacity: 2,300 **Seats:** 236 **Covered:** 400 **Clubhouse:** Yes **Shop:** Yes
Previous Grounds: Yate Aerodrome 1954-60. Sunnyside Lane 1960-84.
Record Attendance: 2,000 v Bristol Rovers v Bristol Rovers Past XI - Vaughan Jones testimonial 1990

Nearest Railway Station Yate - 1km
Bus Route North Road - stop 100m away

AFC DUNSTABLE

Southern League D1 Central

Founde 1981 **Nickname:** Od's **Club Colours:** All blue

Club Contact Details
01582 891 433 aireydavid@hotmail.com

Previous Names: Old Dunstablians 1981- 2004.
Previous Leagues: Dunstable Alliance 1981-83. Luton District & South Bedfordshire 1983-95. South Midlands/Spartan South Midlands 1995-2016.

11-12		12-13		13-14		14-15		15-16		16-17		17-18		18-19		19-20		20-21	
SSM P	3	SSM P	8	SSM P	9	SSM P	3	SSM P	1	SthC	7	Sth1E	5	SthC	10	SthC	n&v	SthC	n&v
FAC	P	FAC	2Qr	FAC	EP	FAC	P	FAC	1Q	FAC	2Q	FAC	P	FAC	Pr	FAC	Pr	FAC	2Q
FAV	2Q	FAV	1P	FAV	1Qr	FAV	3P	FAV	4P	FAT	P	FAT	P	FAT	P	FAT	1Q	FAT	1Q

HONOURS / RECORDS
FA Comps: None

League: Spartan South Midlands Division Two 2003-04, 06-07, Premier Division 2015-16.

County FA: Bedfordshire Junior Cup 1989-90. Bedfordshire Senior Trophy 2006-07, 07-08. Bedfordshire Senior Cup 2016-17.

Best FA Cup Second Qualifying Round 2012-13(r), 16-17
FA Trophy Preliminary Round 2016-17, 17-18, 18-19
FA Vase Fourth Round Proper 2015-16

GROUND: Creasey Park, Creasey Park Drive, Brewers Hill Road LU6 1BB
Ground Capacity: 3,065 **Seats:** 350 **Covered:** 1,000 **Clubhouse:** Yes **Shop:** Yes
Previous Grounds: Manshead School 1981-94. Dunstable Cricket Club (Totternhoe) 1994-2009.
Record Attendance: Not known.

Nearest Railway Station Luton Leagrave - 4 miles
Bus Route 34, C & F77

AYLESBURY UNITED

Southern League D1 Central

Founde 1897 **Nickname:** The Ducks **Club Colours:** Green

Club Contact Details
01296 487 367 (Office) info@aylesburyunitedfc.co.uk

Previous Names: None
Previous Leagues: Post War: Spartan1908-51, Delphian 51-63, Athenian 63-76, Southern 76-88, 2004-10, Conf. 88-89, Isthmian 89-2004. Spartan South Midlands 2010-13.

11-12		12-13		13-14		14-15		15-16		16-17		17-18		18-19		19-20		20-21	
SSM P	4	SSM P	2	SthC	12	SthC	13	SthC	19	SthC	13	Sth1E	13	SthC	15	SthC	n&v	SthC	n&v
FAC	Pr	FAC	P	FAC	2Q	FAC	P	FAC	P	FAC	P	FAC	3Q	FAC	1Qr	FAC	1Q	FAC	1Q
FAV	2Q	FAV	1P	FAT	1Q	FAV	P	FAT	P	FAT	1Q	FAT	Pr	FAT	P	FAT	1Q	FAT	3Q

HONOURS / RECORDS
FA Comps: None
League: Spartan 1908-09, Western Division 28-29. Delphian 1953-54. Southern 1987-88.

County FA: Berks & Bucks Senior Cup 1913-14, 85-86, 96-97, 99-00. Berks & Bucks Senior Shield 2012-13.

Victory: 10-0 v Hornchurch & Upminster (H), Delphain League 17/04/1954
Defeat: 0-9 v Bishop's Stortford (A), Delphain League 08/10/1955
Goalscorer: Cliff Hercules - 301 (1984-2002)
Appearances: Cliff Hercules - 651+18 (1984-2002)

GROUND: Chesham United FC, The Meadow, Amy Lane, Chesham HP5 1NE
Ground Capacity: 5,000 **Seats:** 284 **Covered:** Yes **Clubhouse:** Yes **Shop:** No
Previous Grounds: Turnfurlong Lane. Buckingham Road >2006. Meadow View Park (Thame Utd) 2006-17.
Record Attendance: Turnfurlong Lane - 7,440 v Watford FAC 1st Rnd 1951-52. Buckingham Road - 6,031 v England 04/06/1988.

Nearest Railway Station Chesham underground - 0.7km
Bus Route The Wild Rover Pub - stop 250m away

BARTON ROVERS

Southern League D1 Central

Founde 1898 **Nickname:** Rovers **Club Colours:** All royal blue

Club Contact Details
01582 707 772 bartonrovers@talktalk.net

Previous Names: None
Previous Leagues: Local village football leagues >1939. Luton & District 1947-54, South Midlands 1954-79, Isthmian 1979-2004

11-12		12-13		13-14		14-15		15-16		16-17		17-18		18-19		19-20		20-21	
SthC	11	SthC	14	SthC	6	SthC	5	SthC	18	SthC	3	Sth1E	20	SthC	16	SthC	n&v	SthC	n&v
FAC	1Qr	FAC	1Q	FAC	2Qr	FAC	3Q	FAC	1Q	FAC	2Q	FAC	P	FAC	1Q	FAC	2Q	FAC	P
FAT	1Q	FAT	1Q	FAT	P	FAT	P	FAT	Pr	FAT	P	FAT	P	FAT	EP	FAT	2Q	FAT	2Q

HONOURS / RECORDS
FA Comps: None
League: South Midlands Division Two 1954-55, Division One 64-65, Premier 70-71, 71-72, 72-73, 74-75, 75-76, 76-77, 77-78, 78-79.

County FA: Bedfordshire Senior Cup 1971-72, 72-73, 80-81, 81-82, 89-90, 97-98, 98-99, 2014-15, Premier Cup 1995-96, Senior Challenge Cup 2015-16.
Goalscorer: Richard Camp - 152 (1989-98)
Appearances: Tony McNally - 598 (1988-2005)
Additional: Paid £1,000 to Hitchin Town for Bill Baldry 1980
Received £2,000 from AFC Wimbledon for Paul Barnes

GROUND: Sharpenhoe Road, Luton Road, Barton-le-Clay, Bedford MK45 4LQ
Ground Capacity: 2,000 **Seats:** 160 **Covered:** 1,120 **Clubhouse:** Yes **Shop:** Yes
Previous Grounds: None
Record Attendance: 1,900 v Nuneaton Borough - FA Cup 4th Qualifying Round 1976

Nearest Railway Station Harlington - 4.6km
Bus Route The Memorial - stop 200m away

BEDFORD TOWN

Southern League D1 Central

Founde 1989 **Nickname:** The Eagles **Club Colours:** All blue

Club Contact Details
01234 831 558 james.smiles@bedfordeagles.net

Previous Names: Original Bedford Town founded in 1908 folded in 1982
Previous Leagues: South Midlands 1989-94, Isthmian 1994-2004, Southern 2004-06, Conference 2006-07

11-12		12-13		13-14		14-15		15-16		16-17		17-18		18-19		19-20		20-21	
SthP	10	SthP	10	SthP	22	SthC	17	SthC	14	SthC	8	Sth1E	8	SthC	4	SthC	n&v	SthC	n&v
FAC	1Q	FAC	1Q	FAC	2Q	FAC	Pr	FAC	1Q	FAC	P	FAC	1Q	FAC	2Q	FAC	P	FAC	P
FAT	1Q	FAT	2Q	FAT	1Qr	FAT	3Qr	FAT	2Q	FAT	P	FAT	1Qr	FAT	2P	FAT	P	FAT	2P

HONOURS / RECORDS
FA Comps: None
League: South Midlands Division One 1992-93, Premier Division 93-94. Isthmian Division Two 1998-99.

County FA: Bedfordshire Senior Cup 1994-95.

Defeat: 0-10 v Merthyr Tydfil, 1950-51, v Yeovil Town 1960-61
Goalscorer: Jason Reed. Joe Chamberlain scored 9 v Rushden Fosse, December 1911
Appearances: David Skinn
Victory: 9-0 v Weymouth, Southern League, 1954-55, v Poole 1958-59, v Ickleford, v Cardington

GROUND: The Eyrie, Meadow Lane, Cardington, Bedford MK44 3LW
Ground Capacity: 3,000 **Seats:** 300 **Covered:** 1,000 **Clubhouse:** Yes **Shop:** Yes
Previous Grounds: Allen Park, Queens Park, Bedford Park Pitch 1991-93
Record Attendance: 3,000 v Peterborough United - Ground opening 06/08/1993. At Queens Park - 18,407 v Everton, FAC, 1965-66

Nearest Railway Station Bedford St Johns - 3.8km
Bus Route Meadow Lane - stop 150m away

BERKHAMSTED

Southern League D1 Central

Founde 2009 **Nickname:** Comrades or Berko **Club Colours:** Yellow and blue

Club Contact Details
07525 872 914

Previous Names: None
Previous Leagues: Spartan South Midlands 2009-18.

11-12		12-13		13-14		14-15		15-16		16-17		17-18		18-19		19-20		20-21	
SSM P	7	SSM P	11	SSM P	5	SSM P	6	SSM P	5	SSM P	8	SSM P	2	SthC	6	SthC	n&v	SthC	n&v
FAC	1Qr	FAC	2Q	FAC	1Q	FAC	EP	FAC	P	FAC	EP	FAC	1Q	FAC	1Qr	FAC	1Q	FAC	P
FAV	2Q	FAV	2P	FAV	2P	FAV	1P	FAV	5P	FAV	4P	FAV	3P	FAT	1Q	FAT	1Q	FAT	3Q

HONOURS / RECORDS
FA Comps: None

League: Spartan South Midlands Division Two 2009-10, Division One 10-11.

County FA: Hertfordshire Charity Shield 2016-17

Victory: 12-1 v Stotfold, FA Cup Extra Preliminary Round, 05/08/2017
Defeat: 1-7 v Hanwell Town, Spartan South Midlands Premier Division, 2011-12

GROUND: Broadwater, Lower Kings Road, Berkhamsted HP4 2AL
Ground Capacity: 1,500 **Seats:** 170 **Covered:** 350 **Clubhouse:** Yes **Shop:** Yes
Previous Grounds: None
Record Attendance: 366 v Slough Town, FA Cup First Qualifying Round, 02/09/2017

Nearest Railway Station Berkhamsted - 0.3km
Bus Route Castel Hill Avenue - stop 190m away

BIGGLESWADE FC

Southern League D1 Central

Founde 2016 **Nickname:** FC **Club Colours:** Green & white

Club Contact Details
01234 831 558 biggleswadefc@outlook.com

Previous Names: Based on Biggleswade Town's U18 side.
Previous Leagues: Spartan South Midlands 2016-19.

11-12	12-13	13-14	14-15	15-16	16-17		17-18		18-19		19-20		20-21	
					SSM1	1	SSM P	5	SSM P	1	SthC	n&v	SthC	n&v
							FAC	EP	FAC	P	FAC	2Q	FAC	2Q
					FAV	2P	FAV	4P	FAV	2P	FAT	EPr	FAT	1Q

HONOURS / RECORDS
FA Comps: None

League: Spartan South Midlands Division One 2016-17, Premier Division 2018-19.

County FA: None

FA Cup Second Qualifying Round 2019-20, 20-21
FA Vase Fourth Round Proper 2017-18
FA Tropjhy First Qualifying Round 2020-21

GROUND: Bedford Town FC, The Eyrie, Meadow Lane, Cardington, Bedford MK44 3LW
Ground Capacity: 3,000 **Seats:** 300 **Covered:** 1,000 **Clubhouse:** Yes **Shop:**
Previous Grounds: Langford Road.
Record Attendance: Not known

Nearest Railway Station Bedford St Johns - 3.8km
Bus Route Meadow Lane - stop 150m away

COLNEY HEATH

Southern League D1 Central

Founde 1907 **Nickname:** Magpies **Club Colours:** Black & white stripes

Club Contact Details
01727 824 325

Previous Names: None
Previous Leagues: Herts Senior County League 1953-2000. Spartan South Midlands >2021.

11-12	12-13	13-14	14-15	15-16	16-17	17-18	18-19	19-20	20-21
SSM P 8	SSM P 13	SSM P 3	SSM P 14	SSM P 20	SSM P 18	SSM P 11	SSM P 6	SSM P n&v	SSM P n&v
FAC P	FAC 1Q	FAC EP	FAC P			FAC 2Qr	FAC P	FAC 1Q	FAC EP
FAV 1Q	FAV 2P	FAV 3Pr	FAV 1P		FAV 1P	FAV 1P	FAV 1Pr	FAV 2P	FAV 3P

HONOURS / RECORDS
FA Comps: None

League: Herts County Division Two 1953-54 Division One A 55-56, Prem 58-99, 99-00, Division One 88-89,
Spartan South Midlands Division One 2005-06.

County FA: Hertfordshire Intermediate Cup 1959-60, Senior Centenary Trophy 1995-96, 96-97, Charity Shield 2013-14, 17-18, 18-19.

Best FA Cup Second Qualifying Round 2017-18
FA Vase Third Round Proper 2013-14(r), 20-21

GROUND: The Recreation Ground, High St, Colney Heath, St Albans AL4 0NP
Ground Capacity: 2,000 **Seats:** Yes **Covered:** Yes **Clubhouse:** Yes **Shop:**
Previous Grounds: The Meadow and The Warren on Coursers Road. Fuzzen Field until 1952.
Record Attendance: Not known

Nearest Railway Station Welham Green - 3.6km
Bus Route Crooked Billet Ph - stop 50m away

DIDCOT TOWN

Southern League D1 Central

Founde 1907 **Nickname:** Railwaymen **Club Colours:** Red & white

Club Contact Details
01235 813 138
info@didcottownfc.co.uk

Previous Names: Didcot Village and Northbourne Wanderers amalgamated to form Didcot Town in 1907.
Previous Leagues: Metropolitan 1957-63, Hellenic 1963-2006

11-12	12-13	13-14	14-15	15-16	16-17	17-18	18-19	19-20	20-21
Sthsw 16	Sthsw 17	Sthsw 12	Sthsw 7	Sthsw 10	Sthsw 12	Sth1W 6	SthC 7	SthC n&v	SthC n&v
FAC 1Qr	FAC 4Q	FAC 3Q	FAC P	FAC 1P	FAC P	FAC 1Q	FAC 2Qr	FAC 1Q	FAC P
FAT 1P	FAT 3Q	FAT Pr	FAT 1Pr	FAT 1Q	FAT P	FAT P	FAT 2Q	FAT P	FAT 2Q

HONOURS / RECORDS
FA Comps: FA Vase 2004-05.
League: Hellenic Premier Division 1953-54, 2005-06, Division One 1976-77, 87-88.

County FA: Berks & Bucks Senior Trophy 2001-02, 02-03, 05-06.

Goalscorer: Ian Concanon
Best FA Cup First Round Proper 2015-16
FA Trophy First Round Proper 2011-12, 14-15(r)

GROUND: Loop Meadow Stadium, Bowmont Water, Didcot OX11 7GA
Ground Capacity: 3,000 **Seats:** 350 **Covered:** 200 **Clubhouse:** Yes **Shop:** Yes
Previous Grounds: Fleet Meadow. Edmonds Park. Cow Lane. Haydon Road. Station Road 1923-99.
Record Attendance: 2,707 - v Exeter City, FA Cup 1st Round, 08/11/2015

Nearest Railway Station Didcot Parkway - 0.4km
Bus Route X2 & X32

FC ROMANIA

Southern League D1 Central

Founde 2006 **Nickname:** The Wolves **Club Colours:** Red

Club Contact Details

01992 625 793 ionutvintilafcr@gmail.com

Previous Names: None

Previous Leagues: Sunday London Weekend 2006-07. Essex Business Houses 2007-10. Middlesex County 2010-13. Essex Senior 2013-18. Isthmian 2018-21.

11-12		12-13		13-14		14-15		15-16		16-17		17-18		18-19		19-20		20-21	
MidxP	2	MidxP	2	ESen	5	ESen	6	ESen	3	ESen	3	ESen	3	IsthSC	16	IsthSC	n&v	IsthSC	n&v
						FAC	2Q	FAC	EP	FAC	EP	FAC	2Qr	FAC	2Q	FAC	Pr	FAC	P
		FAV	2Q	FAV	1Q	FAV	2Q	FAV	4P	FAV	3Pr	FAV	2Pr	FAT	P	FAT	P	FAT	2Q

HONOURS / RECORDS

FA Comps: None

League: None

County FA: None

Best FA Cup Second Qualifying Round 2014-15, 17-18(r), 18-19

FA Vase Fourth Round Proper 2015-16

FA Trophy Second Qualifying Round 2020-21

GROUND: Cheshunt FC, Theobalds Lane, Cheshunt, Herts EN8 8RU

Ground Capacity: 3,500 **Seats:** 424 **Covered:** 600 **Clubhouse:** Yes **Shop:**

Previous Grounds: Hackey Marshes 2006-07. Low Hall Rec Walthamstow 2007-10. Leyton Sport Centre 2010-12.

Record Attendance: Not known

Nearest Railway Station Theobalds Grove – 5 mins walk

Bus Route N279

HARLOW TOWN

Southern League D1 Central

Founde 1879 **Nickname:** Hawks **Club Colours:** Red & white

Club Contact Details

01279 443 196

Previous Names: Harlow & Burnt Mill 1898-1902.

Previous Leagues: East Hertfordshire > 1932, Spartan 1932-39, 46-54, London 1954-61, Delphian 1961-63, Athenian 1963-73, Isthmian 1973-92, 93-2004, 06-21. Inactive 1992-93, Southern 2004-06.

11-12		12-13		13-14		14-15		15-16		16-17		17-18		18-19		19-20		20-21	
Isth1N	7	Isth1N	21	Isth1N	4	Isth1N	2	Isth1N	3	Isth P	10	Isth P	21	Isth P	22	IsthSC	n&v	IsthSC	n&v
FAC	P	FAC	P	FAC	2Q	FAC	1Qr	FAC	4Q	FAC	2Q	FAC	3Qr	FAC	1Qr	FAC	Pr	FAC	1Q
FAT	3Q	FAT	Pr	FAT	P	FAT	1Q	FAT	2Q	FAT	2P	FAT	3Q	FAT	2Q	FAT	EPr	FAT	2Q

HONOURS / RECORDS

FA Comps: None

League: East Herts Division One 1911-12, 22-23, 28-29, 29-30. Athenian Division One 1971-72. Isthmian Division One 1978-79, Division Two North 1988-89.

County FA: Essex Senior cup 1978-79

Victory: 14-0 v Bishop's Stortford - 11/04/1925

Defeat: 0-11 v Ware (A) - Spartan Division 1 East 06/03/1948

Goalscorer: Dick Marshall scored 64 during 1928-29, Alex Read scored 52 during 2013-14.

Appearances: Norman Gladwin - 639 (1951-70)

GROUND: The Harlow Arena, off Elizabeth Way, The Pinnacles, Harlow CM19 5BE

Ground Capacity: 3,500 **Seats:** 500 **Covered:** 500 **Clubhouse:** Yes **Shop:** Yes

Previous Grounds: Green Man Field 1879-60. Harlow Sportcentre 1960-2006.

Record Attendance: 9,723 v Leicester City - FA Cup 3rd Round replay 08/01/1980

Nearest Railway Station Canons Gate - 12min walk

Bus Route 381 & 6

HERTFORD TOWN

Southern League D1 Central

Founde 1901 **Nickname:** The Blues **Club Colours:** Blue & white

Club Contact Details
01992 583 716

Previous Names: Port Vale Rovers 1901.

Previous Leagues: Herts Senior County 1908-20. Middlsex 1920-21. Spartan 1921-59. Delphian 1959-63. Athenian 1963-72. Eastern Counties 1972-73. Spartan South Midlands 1973-2017. Isthmian 2017-21.

11-12		12-13		13-14		14-15		15-16		16-17		17-18		18-19		19-20		20-21	
SSM P	16	SSM P	17	SSM P	16	SSM P	11	SSM P	8	SSM P	2	Isth1N	15	IsthSC	18	IsthSC	n&v	IsthSC	n&v
FAC	1Q	FAC	EP	FAC	1Q	FAC	1Q	FAC	EPr	FAC	P	FAC	2Q	FAC	1Q	FAC	P	FAC	P
FAV	1Q	FAV	3P	FAV	1Q	FAV	1P	FAV	3P	FAV	1P	FAT	1Q	FAT	P	FAT	EP	FAT	2Q

HONOURS / RECORDS

FA Comps: None

League: Spartan Division One Eastern Section 1949-50. Delphian 1960-61, 61-62.

County FA: Herts Senior Cup 1966-67. East Anglian Cup 1962-63, 69-70.

Appearances: Robbie Burns
Best FA Cup Fourth Qualifying Round 1973-74
FA Trophy Second Round Proper 1979-80
FA Vase Third Round Proper 1986-87, 2003-04, 12-13, 15-16

GROUND: Hertingfordbury Park, West Street, Hertford SG13 8EZ
Ground Capacity: 6,500 **Seats:** 200 **Covered:** 1,500 **Clubhouse:** Yes **Shop:** Yes
Previous Grounds: Hartham Park 1901-08.
Record Attendance: 5,000 v Kingstonian FA Am Cup 2nd Round 1955-56.

Nearest Railway Station Hertford North - 0.8km
Bus Route 310, 341, 351, 641 & H4

KEMPSTON ROVERS

Southern League D1 Central

Founde 1884 **Nickname:** Walnut Boys **Club Colours:** Red, white & black

Club Contact Details
01234 852 346 administrator@kempston-rovers.co.uk

Previous Names: Kempston Rovers 1884-2004. AFC Kempston Rovers 2004-16.

Previous Leagues: Bedford & District. Biggleswade & District. Bedfordshire & District County/South Midlands 1927-53. United Counties 1957-2016.

11-12		12-13		13-14		14-15		15-16		16-17		17-18		18-19		19-20		20-21	
UCL P	10	UCL P	17	UCL P	12	UCL P	8	UCL P	1	SthC	6	Sth1E	7	SthC	13	SthC	n&v	SthC	n&v
FAC	EP	FAC	1Q	FAC	EP	FAC	P	FAC	P	FAC	2Qr	FAC	2Q	FAC	3Q	FAC	1Q	FAC	P
FAV	2Q	FAV	2Q	FAV	1Q	FAV	2P	FAV	2P	FAT	1Q	FAT	P	FAT	1Qr	FAT	EP	FAT	2Q

HONOURS / RECORDS

FA Comps: None

League: Bedford & District Division One 1907-08, 08-09, Division Two South 22-23, 33-34. Biggleswade & District 1910-11. United Counties Premier Division 1957-58, 73-74, 2015-16, Division One 85-86, 2010-11, Division Two 1955-56,

County FA: Bedfordshire Senior Cup 1908-09, 37-38, 76-77, 91-92. Huntingdonshire Premier Cup 1999-2000, 00-01.

Best FA Cup Fourth Qualifying Round 1978-79
FA Trophy Second Qualifying Round 2020-21
FA Vase Fifth Round Proper 1974-75, 80-81

GROUND: Hillgrounds Leisure, Hillgrounds Road, Kempston, Bedford MK42 8SZ
Ground Capacity: 2,000 **Seats:** 100 **Covered:** 250 **Clubhouse:** Yes **Shop:** Yes
Previous Grounds: None
Record Attendance: Not known

Nearest Railway Station Bedford - 1.3km
Bus Route Prentice Gardens - stop 100m away

KIDLINGTON

Southern League D1 Central

Founde 1909 **Nickname:** Greens **Club Colours:** Green

Club Contact Details
01865 849 777

Previous Names: None.
Previous Leagues: Villages Leagues > 1945. Oxford City Junior 1945-51. Oxfordshire Senior 1951-54. Hellenic 1954-2016.

11-12		12-13		13-14		14-15		15-16		16-17		17-18		18-19		19-20		20-21	
Hel P	18	Hel P	13	Hel P	6	Hel P	4	Hel P	1	SthC	12	Sth1W	12	SthC	18	SthC	n&v	SthC	n&v
FAC	P	FAC	EPr	FAC	EPr	FAC	P	FAC	2Q	FAC	P	FAC	2Q	FAC	P	FAC	2Q	FAC	2Q
FAV	2Q	FAV	3P	FAV	3P	FAV	1Q	FAV	QFr	FAT	P	FAT	1Q	FAT	P	FAT	EP	FAT	3Q

HONOURS / RECORDS
FA Comps: None
League: Oxfordshire Senior 1952-53. Hellenic Premier Division 2015-16.

County FA: Oxfordshire Intermediate Cup 1952-53, 69-70, 84-85.

Best FA Cup Second Qualifying Round 2015-16, 17-18, 19-20, 20-21
FA Trophy Third Qualifying Round 2020-21
FA Vase Fifth Round 1976-77

GROUND: Yarnton Road, Kidlington, Oxford OX5 1AT
Ground Capacity: 2,086 **Seats:** Yes **Covered:** Yes **Clubhouse:** Yes **Shop:** No
Previous Grounds: None
Record Attendance: 2,000 v Showbiz XI, 1973.

Nearest Railway Station Oxford Parkway - 1.9km
Bus Route Treeground Place - stop 100m away

NORTH LEIGH

Southern League D1 Central

Founde 1908 **Nickname:** The Millers **Club Colours:** Yellow and black

Club Contact Details
01993 880 157
commercial@northleighfc.co.uk

Previous Names: None
Previous Leagues: Witney & District, Hellenic 1990-2008

11-12		12-13		13-14		14-15		15-16		16-17		17-18		18-19		19-20		20-21	
Sthsw	6	Sthsw	9	Sthsw	7	Sthsw	8	Sthsw	9	Sthsw	6	Sth1W	18	SthC	17	SthC	n&v	SthC	n&v
FAC	1Q	FAC	3Q	FAC	1Q	FAC	P	FAC	3Q	FAC	4Q	FAC	1Qr	FAC	P	FAC	2Q	FAC	P
FAT	P	FAT	1Qr	FAT	1Q	FAT	1Q	FAT	1Q	FAT	1Pr	FAT	P	FAT	Pr	FAT	EP	FAT	1P

HONOURS / RECORDS
FA Comps: None
League: Witney & District Premier 1985-86, 86-87, 87-88, 88-89, 89-90. Hellenic Premier Division 2002-03, 07-08.

County FA: Oxfordshire Senior Cup 2011-12, 16-17.

Goalscorer: P Coles
Appearances: P King
Best FA Cup Fourth Qualifying Round 2016-17
FA Trophy First Round Proper 2016-17, 20-21
FA Vase Fourth Round Proper 2003-04

GROUND: Eynsham Hall Park, North Leigh, Witney, Oxon OX29 6SL
Ground Capacity: 1,500 **Seats:** 175 **Covered:** 200 **Clubhouse:** Yes **Shop:** No
Previous Grounds: None
Record Attendance: 426 v Newport County - FA Cup 3rd Qualifying Round 16/10/2004

Nearest Railway Station Combe - 3.3km
Bus Route 233

ST. NEOTS TOWN

Southern League D1 Central

Founde 1879 **Nickname:** Saints **Club Colours:** Dark blue & light blue

Club Contact Details

01480 470 012 enquiries@stneotstownfc.co.uk

Previous Names: St Neots 1879-1924. St. Neots & District 1924-1957.

Previous Leagues: Biggleswade & Dist. Bedfordshire & Dist/South Midlands 1927-36, 46-49. United Co. 1936-39, 51-56, 66-69, 73-88, 94-2011. Metropolitan (Founder Members) 1949-51, 60-66. Central Alliance 1956-60. Eastern Co. 1969-73. Hunts Junior 1990-94.

11-12		12-13		13-14		14-15		15-16		16-17		17-18		18-19		19-20		20-21	
SthC	1	SthP	12	SthP	16	SthP	5	SthP	20	SthP	19	SthP	12	SthPC	20	SthC	n&v	SthC	n&v
FAC	P	FAC	2Q	FAC	2Qr	FAC	1Qr	FAC	2Qr	FAC	1Qr	FAC	1Q	FAC	4Q	FAC	1Qr	FAC	P
FAT	2Q	FAT	1Q	FAT	2Q	FAT	3Qr	FAT	2Q	FAT	2Qr	FAT	2Q	FAT	2Q	FAT	EP	FAT	2P

HONOURS / RECORDS

FA Comps: None

League: South Midlands 1932-33. Metropolitan 1949-50. United Counties 1967-68, 2010-11, Division One 1994-95. Huntingdonshire 1990-91, 91-92, 92-93, 93-94. Southern Division One Central 2011-12.

County FA: Huntingdonshire Senior Cup x38 - Firstly in 1888-89 and most recently in 2017-18. Huntingdonshire Premier Cup 2001-02.

Misc: 105 points obtained in the 2010-11 season - a United Counties record.

In 1968-69 the club won the Huntingdonshire Senior Cup for the 12th consecutive time - an English record for Senior cups.

GROUND: Rowley Park, Kester Way, Cambridge Road, St Neots, PE19 6SN

Ground Capacity: 3,500 **Seats:** 250 **Covered:** 850 **Clubhouse:** Yes **Shop:** No

Previous Grounds: Town Common 1879-1899. Shortsands 1899-1988. Priory Park 1990-93. Old Rowley Park 1993-2008.

Record Attendance: 2,000 v Wisbech 1966

Nearest Railway Station St Neots - 06.km

Bus Route 150 & 66

THAME UNITED

Southern League D1 Central

Founde 1883 **Nickname:** Red Kites **Club Colours:** Red & black

Club Contact Details

01844 214 401 jake@jcpc.org.uk

Previous Names: Thame F.C.

Previous Leagues: Oxon Senior. Hellenic 1959-88, 2006-17. South Midlands 1988-91. Isthmian 1991-2004. Southern 2004-06.

11-12		12-13		13-14		14-15		15-16		16-17		17-18		18-19		19-20		20-21	
Hel P	9	Hel P	9	Hel P	10	Hel P	5	Hel P	6	Hel P	1	Sth1E	11	SthC	8	SthC	n&v	SthC	n&v
FAC	2Q	FAC	P	FAC	EP	FAC	1Q	FAC	EPr	FAC	P	FAC	1Q	FAC	P	FAC	Pr	FAC	P
FAV	2Q	FAV	2P	FAV	2Q	FAV	2P	FAV	3P	FAV	1P	FAT	3Q	FAT	2Q	FAT	1Q	FAT	1P

HONOURS / RECORDS

FA Comps: None

League: Hellenic 1961-62, 69-70, 2016-17, Division One East 2009-10. South Midlands League 1990-91. Isthmian Division Two 1994-95.

County FA: None

Appearances: Steve Mayhew

Best FA Cup Fourth Qualifying Round 2003-04, 04-05

FA Trophy Third Round Proper 2002-03

FA Vase Semi Finals 1998-99

GROUND: Meadow View Park, Tythrop Way, Thame, Oxon OX9 3RN

Ground Capacity: 3,000 **Seats:** Yes **Covered:** Yes **Clubhouse:** Yes **Shop:**

Previous Grounds: Windmill Road 1883-2005. Aylesbury United FC 2005-06. AFC Wallingford 2006-11.

Record Attendance: 1,382 v Oxford United Jan 2011.

Nearest Railway Station Haddenham & Thame Parkway - 2.9km

Bus Route Queens Close - stop 350m away

WALTHAM ABBEY

Southern League D1 Central

Founde 1944 **Nickname:** Abbotts **Club Colours:** Green and white hoops

Club Contact Details

01992 711 287

Previous Names: Abbey Sports amalgamated with Beechfield Sports in 1974 to form Beechfields. Club then renamed to Waltham Abbey in 1976

Previous Leagues: London Spartan/Spartan. Essex & Herts Border. Essex Senior. Isthmian >2021.

11-12		12-13		13-14		14-15		15-16		16-17		17-18		18-19		19-20		20-21	
Isth1N	14	Isth1N	12	Isth1N	18	Isth1N	10	Isth1N	21	Isth1N	20	Isth1N	18	IsthSC	9	IsthSC	n&v	IsthSC	n&v
FAC	1Q	FAC	2Q	FAC	1Q	FAC	3Q	FAC	P	FAC	1Q	FAC	P	FAC	P	FAC	1Qr	FAC	2Q
FAT	Pr	FAT	1Q	FAT	1Q	FAT	P	FAT	2Q	FAT	1Q	FAT	1Q	FAT	EP	FAT	P	FAT	2Q

HONOURS / RECORDS

FA Comps: None

League: London Spartan Division One 1977-78, Senior Division 1978-79.

County FA: London Senior Cup 1998-99. Essex Senior Cup 2004-05.

Best FA Cup Third Qualifying Round 2014-15

FA Trophy Second Qualifying Round 2020-21

FA Vase Second Round Proper 1997-98

GROUND: Capershotts, Sewardstone Road, Waltham Abbey, Essex EN9 1NX

Ground Capacity: 3,500 **Seats:** 200 **Covered:** 500 **Clubhouse:** Yes **Shop:** No

Previous Grounds: None

Record Attendance:

Nearest Railway Station Waltham Cross - 2km

Bus Route Catersfield - stop 100m away

WANTAGE TOWN

Southern League D1 Central

Founde 1892 **Nickname:** Alfredians or The Freds **Club Colours:** Green & white

Club Contact Details

01235 764 781 (Ground) wantagetownfc-secretary@outlook.com

Previous Names: None.

Previous Leagues: Swindon & District. North Berkshire. Reading & District. Hellenic > 2014, 17-19. Southern 2014-17.

11-12		12-13		13-14		14-15		15-16		16-17		17-18		18-19		19-20		20-21	
Hel P	12	Hel P	2	Hel P	1	Sthsw	20	Sthsw	20	Sthsw	21	Hel P	4	Hel P	1	SthC	n&v	SthC	n&v
FAC	P	FAC	1Q	FAC	P	FAC	1Qr	FAC	P	FAC	1Qr	FAC	P	FAC	2Qr	FAC	1Q	FAC	1Q
FAV	3P	FAV	2P	FAV	2P	FAT	P	FAT	P	FAT	1Qr	FAV	2P	FAT	1Q	FAT	P	FAT	3Q

HONOURS / RECORDS

FA Comps: None

League: Swindon & District 1907-08, 33-34, 52-53, 55-56. North Berks Division One 1919-20, 21-22. Hellenic Division 1 East 1980-81, 03-04, Premier Division 2010-11, 13-14, 18-19.

County FA: Berks & Bucks Intermediate Cup 1954-55. Reading Senior Cup 1982-83.

FA Cup Second Qualifying Round 2018-19

FA Trophy Third Qualifying Round 2020-21

FA Vase Third Round Proper 1974-75, 83-84, 86-87, 2010-11, 11-12

GROUND: Alfredian Park, Manor Road, Wantage OX12 8DW

Ground Capacity: 1,500 **Seats:** 50 **Covered:** 300 **Clubhouse:** Yes **Shop:**

Previous Grounds: Not known

Record Attendance: 550 v Oxford United, July 2003.

Nearest Railway Station Didcot Parkway

Bus Route From Parkway Station take the X32 Connector towards Wantage - alight at Market Place, 11min walk from there.

WARE

Southern League D1 Central

Founde 1892 **Nickname:** Blues **Club Colours:** Blue & white

Club Contact Details
01920 462 064

Previous Names: Ware Town.

Previous Leagues: East Herts, North Middlesex 1907-08, Herts County 1908-25, Spartan 1925-55, Delphian 1955-63, Athenian 1963-75, Isthmian 1975-2015, 16-21. Southern 2015-16.

11-12		12-13		13-14		14-15		15-16		16-17		17-18		18-19		19-20		20-21	
Isth1N	21	Isth1N	19	Isth1N	21	Isth1N	10	SthC	11	Isth1N	22	Isth1N	20	IsthSC	7	IsthSC	n&v	IsthSC	n&v
FAC	P	FAC	1Q	FAC	P	FAC	P	FAC	P	FAC	P	FAC	2Q	FAC	1Q	FAC	3Q	FAC	P
FAT	P	FAT	P	FAT	Pr	FAT	1Q	FAT	P	FAT	2Q	FAT	1Q	FAT	P	FAT	1Q	FAT	2Q

HONOURS / RECORDS

FA Comps: None

League: East Herts 1897-88, 98-99, 99-1900, 02-03, 03-04, 05-06 (shared), 06-07. Herts County 1908-09, 21-22. Spartan Division Two B 1926-27, Division One 51-52, Premier 52-53. Isthmian Division Two 2005-06.

County FA: Herts Senior Cup 1898-99, 1903-04, 06-07, 21-22, 53-54. Herts Charity Shield 1926-27, 52-53, 56-57, 58-59, 62-63, 85-86. East Anglian Cup 1973-74.

Victory: 10-1 v Wood Green Town

Defeat: 0-11 v Barnet

Goalscorer: George Dearman scored 98 goals during 1926-27

Appearances: Gary Riddle - 654

GROUND: Wodson Park, Wadesmill Road, Ware, Herts SG12 0UQ

Ground Capacity: 3,300 **Seats:** 500 **Covered:** 312 **Clubhouse:** Yes **Shop:** Yes

Previous Grounds: Highfields, Canons Park, London Road, Presdales Lower Park 1921-26

Record Attendance: 3,800 v Hendon - FA Amateur Cup, January 1957.

Nearest Railway Station Ware - 1.9km

Bus Route Wodson Park - stop 100m away

WELWYN GARDEN CITY

Southern League D1 Central

Founde 1921 **Nickname:** Citizens **Club Colours:** Red & white

Club Contact Details
01707 329 358 welwyngardencityfc@gmail.com

Previous Names: Original club folded in 1935 and was reformed in 1937.

Previous Leagues: Mid-Herts 1922-26, 44-45. Beds & Dist 26-27. Spartan 27-35, 37-39, 45-51, 55-59. East, North & Mid-Herts Comb. 1939. Beds & Herts Comb 1940. London 51-55. Herts Senior Co 59-70. Greater London 70-71. Met London (FM) 71-73.

11-12		12-13		13-14		14-15		15-16		16-17		17-18		18-19		19-20		20-21	
SSM1	17	SSM1	13	SSM1	4	SSM1	1	SSM P	4	SSM P	6	SSM P	1	SthC	14	SthC	n&v	SthC	n&v
						FAC	1Q	FAC	1Q	FAC	P	FAC	EP	FAC	P	FAC	P	FAC	1Q
FAV	1Q	FAV	1Q	FAV	3P	FAV	1P	FAV	1P	FAV	3P	FAV	3P	FAT	P	FAT	EP	FAT	3P

HONOURS / RECORDS

FA Comps: None

League: South Midlands 1973-74, Division One 1981-82. Spartan South Midlands Division One 2014-15, Premier 17-18.

County FA: Hertfordshire FA Charity Shield 1927-28, 86-87, 87-88. Herts FA Senior Centenary Trophy 1984-85.

Best FA Cup Third Qualifying Round 1998-99(r), 2005-06

FA Vase Fourth Round Proper Replay 2005-06

FA Trophy Third Round Proper 2020-21

Goalscorer: Jason Caswell scored 51 goals during the 2014-15 season

GROUND: Herns Lane, Welwyn Garden City, Herts AL7 1TA

Ground Capacity: 2,500 **Seats:** Yes **Covered:** Yes **Clubhouse:** Yes **Shop:**

Previous Grounds: Several before moving to Herns Lane in 1968

Record Attendance: Unknown

Nearest Railway Station Welwyn Garden City - 1.9km

Bus Route Hernes Way - stop 160m away

AFC TOTTON

Southern League D1 South

Founde 1886 **Nickname:** Stags **Club Colours:** Blue and white

Club Contact Details
02380 868 981 secretary.afctotton@gmail.com

Previous Names: Totton FC until merger with Totton Athletic in 1975
Previous Leagues: New Forest (Founder Members) 1904. Southampton Senior. Hampshire 1920-86, Wessex 1986-2008.

11-12		12-13		13-14		14-15		15-16		16-17		17-18		18-19		19-20		20-21	
SthP	3	SthP	14	SthP	21	Sthsw	15	Sthsw	15	Sthsw	19	Sth1W	10	SthS	10	SthS	n&v	SthS	n&v
FAC	2P	FAC	4Q	FAC	1Q	FAC	1Q	FAC	P	FAC	P	FAC	1Q	FAC	P	FAC	P	FAC	P
FAT	1Q	FAT	1P	FAT	1Q	FAT	1Q	FAT	P	FAT	Pr	FAT	Pr	FAT	2Q	FAT	2Q	FAT	2Q

HONOURS / RECORDS
FA Comps: None

League: New Forest 1905-06, 10-11, 13-14, 19-20, 25-26, 26-27, 47-48, 60-61, 61-62. Hampshire West 1924-25. Hampshire Division Two 1930-31, 66-67, Division One 81-82, 84-85. Wessex Premier Division 2007-08. Southern Division South & West 2010-11.
County FA: Hampshire Junior Cup 1913-14, Intermediate Cup 1946-47, 66-67, 81-82, 82-83, Senior Cup 2009-10, 10-11.

Appearances: Michael Gosney - 427
Best FA Cup Second Round Proper 2011-12
FA Trophy Third Qualifying Round 2006-07, 08-09(r)
FA Vase Runners-up 2008-09

GROUND: The Snows Stadium, Salisbury Road, Calmore, Totton SO40 2RW
Ground Capacity: 2,375 **Seats:** 500 **Covered:** 500 **Clubhouse:** Yes **Shop:** Yes
Previous Grounds: South Testwood Park 1886-1933.
Record Attendance: 2,315 v Bradford Park Avenue, 12/11/2011.

Nearest Railway Station Totton - 2.9km
Bus Route Cooks Lane - stop 300m away

BARNSTAPLE TOWN

Southern League D1 South

Founde 1904 **Nickname:** Barum **Club Colours:** Red & black

Club Contact Details
01271 343 469

Previous Names: Pilton Yeo Vale
Previous Leagues: North Devon, Devon & Exeter, South Western. Western >2016.

11-12		12-13		13-14		14-15		15-16		16-17		17-18		18-19		19-20		20-21	
WestP	15	WestP	20	West1	3	West1	1	WestP	2	Sthsw	17	Sth1W	21	SthS	19	SthS	n&v	SthS	n&v
FAC	P	FAC	EP	FAC	EP	FAC	EP	FAC	1Q	FAC	1Q	FAC	1Q	FAC	P	FAC	EP	FAC	1Q
FAV	3P	FAV	1P	FAV	2P	FAV	2Q	FAV	2P	FAT	1Q	FAT	P	FAT	P	FAT	P	FAT	2Q

HONOURS / RECORDS
FA Comps: None
League: North Devon 1904-05, 08-09. Exeter & District 1946-47. Western 1952-53, 79-80, Division One 1993-94, 2014-15.

County FA: Devon Pro Cup 1952-53, 62-63, 64-65, 67-68, 69-70, 71-72, 72-73, 74-75, 76-77, 77-78, 78-79, 79-80. 80-81. Devon St Lukes Cup 1987-88. Devon Senior Cup 1992-93.
Victory: 12-1 v Tavistock, F.A. Cup 3rd Qualifying Round 1954.
Defeat: 0-11 v Odd Down, Western, 25/04/2013.
Appearances: Ian Pope
Additional: Paid £4,000 to Hungerford Town for Joe Scott.
Received £6,000 from Bristol City for Ian Doyle.

GROUND: Mill Road, Barnstaple, North Devon EX31 1JQ
Ground Capacity: 2,000 **Seats:** 250 **Covered:** 1,000 **Clubhouse:** Yes **Shop:** Yes
Previous Grounds: None
Record Attendance: 6,200 v Bournemouth & Boscombe Athletic, FA Cup 1st Round, 1951-52.

Nearest Railway Station Barnstaple - 1km
Bus Route 21, 21A & 5B

BIDEFORD

Southern League D1 South

Founde 1947 **Nickname:** The Robins **Club Colours:** All red

Club Contact Details
01237 474 974 enquiries@bidefordafc.com

Previous Names: Bideford Town
Previous Leagues: Devon & Exeter 1947-49, Western 1949-72, 75-2010, Southern 1972-75

11-12		12-13		13-14		14-15		15-16		16-17		17-18		18-19		19-20		20-21	
Sthsw	1	SthP	20	SthP	8	SthP	15	SthP	23	Sthsw	10	Sth1W	8	SthS	9	SthS	n&v	SthS	n&v
FAC	2Q	FAC	2Q	FAC	2Q	FAC	2Q	FAC	2Q	FAC	1Q	FAC	3Q	FAC	Pr	FAC	1Q	FAC	1Q
FAT	1Q	FAT	1Q	FAT	2Q	FAT	1Qr	FAT	3Q	FAT	P	FAT	P	FAT	P	FAT	P	FAT	1P

HONOURS / RECORDS
FA Comps: None

League: Western 1963-64, 70-71, 71-72, 81-82, 82-83, 2001-02, 03-04, 04-05, 05-06, 09-10, Division Two 1951-52, Division Three 1949-50. Southern Division One South & West 2011-12.

County FA: Devon Pro Cup 1960-61, 61-62, 63-64, 65-66, 66-67, 68-69, 70-71. Devon Senior Cup 1979-80. Devon St Lukes Bowl 1981-82, 83-84, 85-86, 95-96, 2009-10.

Victory: 16-1 v Soundwell, 1950-51
Defeat: 1-10 v Taunton Town, 1998-99
Goalscorer: Tommy Robinson - 259
Appearances: Derek May - 647

GROUND: The Sports Ground, Kingsley Road, Bideford EX39 2NG
Ground Capacity: 4,000 **Seats:** 375 **Covered:** 1,000 **Clubhouse:** Yes **Shop:**
Previous Grounds: None
Record Attendance: 5,975 v Gloucester City - FA Cup 4th Qualifying Round 1949

Nearest Railway Station Barnstaple - 9 miles
Bus Route The Dairy - stop 100m away

BRISTOL MANOR FARM

Southern League D1 South

Founde 1960 **Nickname:** The Portwaymen **Club Colours:** Red, white & black

Club Contact Details
0117 968 3571

Previous Names: None
Previous Leagues: Bristol Suburban 1964-69. Somerset Senior 1969-77. Western 1977-2017.

11-12		12-13		13-14		14-15		15-16		16-17		17-18		18-19		19-20		20-21	
WestP	8	WestP	18	WestP	2	WestP	4	WestP	3	WestP	1	Sth1W	9	SthS	15	SthS	n&v	SthS	n&v
FAC	EPr	FAC	EP	FAC	2Qr	FAC	P	FAC	1Q	FAC	EPr	FAC	P	FAC	3Qr	FAC	3Qr	FAC	3Q
FAV	2Q	FAV	2Q	FAV	1P	FAV	2P	FAV	QF	FAV	5P	FAT	1Q	FAT	1Q	FAT	P	FAT	2Q

HONOURS / RECORDS
FA Comps: None
League: Western Division One 1982-83, Premier 2016-17.

County FA: Gloucestershire Challenge Trophy 1987-88, 2015-16. Gloucestershire Amateur Cup 1989-90.

Appearances: M. Baird
Victory: 10-0 v Devizes Town, Les Phillips Cup, 19/11/2016.
Defeat: 0-11 v Bristol City, Community Match, 09/07/2017

GROUND: The Creek, Portway, Sea Mills, Bristol BS9 2HS
Ground Capacity: 1,700 **Seats:** 200 **Covered:** 350 **Clubhouse:** Yes **Shop:** No
Previous Grounds: None
Record Attendance: 1,417 v Bristol City, pre-season friendly, 09/07/2017.

Nearest Railway Station Sea Mills - 0.3km
Bus Route Riverleaze - stop 50m away

CINDERFORD TOWN

Southern League D1 South

Founde 1922 **Nickname:** The Foresters **Club Colours:** White and black

Club Contact Details
01594 824 080

Previous Names: None

Previous Leagues: Gloucestershire Northern Senior 1922-39, 60-62, Western 1946-59, Warwickshire Combination 1963-64, West Midlands 1965-69, Gloucestershire Co. 1970-73, 85-89, Midland Comb. 1974-84, Hellenic 1990-95

11-12		12-13		13-14		14-15		15-16		16-17		17-18		18-19		19-20		20-21	
Sthsw	10	Sthsw	10	Sthsw	15	Sthsw	9	Sthsw	1	SthP	24	Sth1W	13	SthS	5	SthS	n&v	SthS	n&v
FAC	2Q	FAC	1Qr	FAC	P	FAC	P	FAC	1Q	FAC	1Q	FAC	3Q	FAC	2Q	FAC	2Q	FAC	1Q
FAT	P	FAT	1Q	FAT	P	FAT	Pr	FAT	P	FAT	1Q	FAT	P	FAT	1Qr	FAT	3Q	FAT	3Q

HONOURS / RECORDS

FA Comps: None

League: Western Division Two 1956-57. Warwickshire Combination Western Division 1964-65. Hellenic Premier Division 1994-95. Southern Division One South & West 2015-16.

County FA: Gloucestershire Senior Amateur Cup North x6. Gloucestershire Junior Cup North 1980-81. Gloucestershire Senior Cup 2000-01.

Victory: 13-0 v Cam Mills - 1938-39

Defeat: 0-10 v Sutton Coldfield - 1978-79

Appearances: Russel Bowles - 528

GROUND: The Causeway, Edgehills Road, Cinderford, Gloucestershire GL14 2QH

Ground Capacity: 2,200 **Seats:** 250 **Covered:** 1,000 **Clubhouse:** Yes **Shop:** Yes

Previous Grounds: Mousel Lane, Royal Oak

Record Attendance: 4,850 v Minehead - Western League 1955-56

Nearest Railway Station Gloucester - 15 miles

Bus Route Forest High School - stop 200m away

CIRENCESTER TOWN

Southern League D1 South

Founde 1889 **Nickname:** Centurions **Club Colours:** Red & black

Club Contact Details
01285 654 543 enquiries@cirentownfc.com

Previous Names: None

Previous Leagues: Cheltenham 1889-1935. Gloucestershire Northern Senior 1935-68. Gloucestershire County (Founder Members) 1968-69. Hellenic 1969-96.

11-12		12-13		13-14		14-15		15-16		16-17		17-18		18-19		19-20		20-21	
SthP	22	Sthsw	11	Sthsw	1	SthP	8	SthP	15	SthP	22	Sth1W	7	SthS	2	SthS	n&v	SthS	n&v
FAC	1Q	FAC	P	FAC	3Q	FAC	1Qr	FAC	2Q	FAC	2Q	FAC	P	FAC	3Q	FAC	2Q	FAC	1Q
FAT	2Q	FAT	P	FAT	1Q	FAT	1Q	FAT	1Pr	FAT	1Q	FAT	1Qr	FAT	P	FAT	P	FAT	2Q

HONOURS / RECORDS

FA Comps: None

League: Cheltenham Division One 1927-28, 29-30, 48-49, 54-55, 55-56. Gloucestershire Northern Senior 1966-67, 67-68. Hellenic Division One 1973-74, Premier Division 95-96. Southern Division One South & West 2013-14.

County FA: Gloucestershire Senior Amateur Cup 1989-90. Gloucestershire Senior Challenge Cup 1995-96, 2015-16.

Misc: Paid £4,000 to Gloucester City for Lee Smith

Best FA Cup Fourth Qualifying Round 2001-02, 03-04

FA Trophy Third Round Proper 2002-03

FA Vase Third Round Proper 1975-76, 76-77

GROUND: The Corinium Stadium, Kingshill Lane, Cirencester GL7 1HS

Ground Capacity: 2,564 **Seats:** 550 **Covered:** 1,250 **Clubhouse:** Yes **Shop:** Yes

Previous Grounds: Smithfield Stadium >2002.

Record Attendance: 2,600 v Fareham Town - 1969

Nearest Railway Station Kemble - 6 miles

Bus Route Kingshill School - stop 150m away

EVESHAM UNITED

Southern League D1 South

Founde 1945 **Nickname:** The Robins **Club Colours:** Red and white

Club Contact Details
01386 442 303 eveshamunitedsecretary@hotmail.com

Previous Names: None
Previous Leagues: Worcester, Birmingham Combination, Midland Combination 1951-55, 65-92, West Midlands (Regional) 1955-62

11-12		12-13		13-14		14-15		15-16		16-17		17-18		18-19		19-20		20-21	
SthP	20	Sthsw	14	Sthsw	16	Sthsw	2	Sthsw	6	Sthsw	5	Sth1W	4	SthS	7	SthS	n&v	SthS	n&v
FAC	3Q	FAC	P	FAC	1Q	FAC	4Q	FAC	P	FAC	1Qr	FAC	Pr	FAC	P	FAC	1Q	FAC	2Q
FAT	1Qr	FAT	P	FAT	1Q	FAT	1Qr	FAT	2Q	FAT	1Qr	FAT	P	FAT	EP	FAT	P	FAT	2P

HONOURS / RECORDS
FA Comps: None
League: Midland Combination Premier Division 1991-92, Division One 1965-66, 67-68, 68-69. Southern Division One Midlands 2007-08.
County FA: Worcestershire Senior Urn 1976-77, 77-78, Senior Cup 2008-09, 17-18.

Victory: 11-3 v West Heath United
Defeat: 1-8 v Ilkeston Town
Goalscorer: Sid Brain
Appearances: Rob Candy
Additional: Paid £1,500 to Hayes for Colin Day 1992. Received £5,000 from Cheltenham Town for Simon Brain.

GROUND: Jubilee Stadium, Cheltenham Road, Evesham WR11 2LZ
Ground Capacity: 3,000 **Seats:** Yes **Covered:** Yes **Clubhouse:** Yes **Shop:** Yes
Previous Grounds: The Crown Meadow > 1968, Common Reed 1968-2006. Ground shared with Worcester City 2006-12.
Record Attendance: 2,338 v West Bromwich Albion - Friendly 18/07/1992

Nearest Railway Station Evesham - 2.9km
Bus Route Lavender Walk - stop 400m away

FROME TOWN

Southern League D1 South

Founde 1904 **Nickname:** The Robins **Club Colours:** Red

Club Contact Details
07305 244 643 secretary@frometownfc.co.uk

Previous Names: None
Previous Leagues: Wiltshire Premier 1904, Somerset Senior 1906-19, Western 1919, 63-2009

11-12		12-13		13-14		14-15		15-16		16-17		17-18		18-19		19-20		20-21	
SthP	12	SthP	18	SthP	14	SthP	20	SthP	16	SthP	8	SthP	13	SthPS	21	SthS	n&v	SthS	n&v
FAC	2Qr	FAC	2Q	FAC	1Qr	FAC	3Qr	FAC	1Qr	FAC	1Q	FAC	2Q	FAC	1Qr	FAC	P	FAC	2Q
FAT	1Q	FAT	1Q	FAT	1Qr	FAT	1Q	FAT	3Qr	FAT	3Q	FAT	1Q	FAT	1Q	FAT	2Q	FAT	3P

HONOURS / RECORDS
FA Comps: None
League: Somerset County 1906-07, 08-09, 10-11. Western Division Two 1919-20, Division One 2001-02, Premier Division 1978-79.
County FA: Somerset Senior Cup 1932-33, 33-34, 50-51 Somerset Premier Cup 1966-67, 68-69 (shared), 82-83, 2008-09.

Victory: 7-2 v kings Langley (A), Southern Premier, 09/12/2017
Defeat: 0-7 v Gosport Borough (A), Southern Premier, 21/04/2018

GROUND: Badgers Hill, Berkley Road, Frome BA11 2EH
Ground Capacity: 2,331 **Seats:** 250 **Covered:** Yes **Clubhouse:** Yes **Shop:** Yes
Previous Grounds: None
Record Attendance: 8,000 v Leyton Orient - FA Cup 1st Round 1958

Nearest Railway Station Frome - 0.9km
Bus Route Bus stops outside the ground

HIGHWORTH TOWN

Southern League D1 South

Founde 1893 **Nickname:** Worthians **Club Colours:** Red

Club Contact Details
01793 766 263

Previous Names: None.
Previous Leagues: Cirencester & District. Swindon & District. Wiltshire Combination. Hellenic >2018.

11-12		12-13		13-14		14-15		15-16		16-17		17-18		18-19		19-20		20-21	
Hel P	6	Hel P	16	Hel P	11	Hel P	7	Hel P	7	Hel P	6	Hel P	3	SthS	14	SthS	n&v	SthS	n&v
FAC	EP	FAC	1Q	FAC	EP	FAC	P	FAC	P	FAC	2Q	FAC	P	FAC	EPr	FAC	2Q	FAC	1Q
FAV	2Pr	FAV	1Qr	FAV	1Q	FAV	SF	FAV	3P	FAV	2P	FAV	1P	FAT	EP	FAT	Pr	FAT	3Q

HONOURS / RECORDS
FA Comps: None
League: Cirencester & District Division Two 1931-32. Swindon & District Division Three 1933-34, 54-55, Two 1955-56, One 1956-57, Premier 57-58, 58-59, 60-61, 61-62, 62-63, 63-64, 65-66, 66-67, 67-68. Hellenic Premier 2004-05.
County FA: Wiltshire Senior Cup 1963-64, 72-73, 95-96, 97-98.

Goalscorer: Kevin Higgs
Appearances: Rod Haines

GROUND: Elms Recreation Ground, Highworth SN6 7DD
Ground Capacity: 1,365 **Seats:** 150 **Covered:** 250 **Clubhouse:** Yes **Shop:** No
Previous Grounds: Unknown
Record Attendance: 2,000 v QPR, opening of floodlights.

Nearest Railway Station Swindon - 7 miles
Bus Route Swindon Street stop - 90m away

LARKHALL ATHLETIC

Southern League D1 South

Founde 1914 **Nickname:** Larks **Club Colours:** All royal blue

Club Contact Details
01225 334 952

Previous Names: None
Previous Leagues: Somerset Senior. Western 1976-2014.

11-12		12-13		13-14		14-15		15-16		16-17		17-18		18-19		19-20		20-21	
WestP	3	WestP	5	WestP	1	Sthsw	5	Sthsw	11	Sthsw	13	Sth1W	15	SthS	13	SthS	n&v	SthS	n&v
FAC	1Q	FAC	1Qr	FAC	1Q	FAC	2Qr	FAC	2Qr	FAC	P	FAC	P	FAC	P	FAC	P	FAC	3Q
FAV	5P	FAV	5P	FAV	5P	FAT	P	FAT	1Q	FAT	P	FAT	1Q	FAT	Pr	FAT	1Qr	FAT	3Q

HONOURS / RECORDS
FA Comps: None
League: Western Division One 1988-89, 08-09, Premier Division 2010-11, 13-14.

County FA: Somerset Junior Cup 1962-63, Senior Cup 1975-76, 2003-04.

Victory: 8-0 v Oldland Abbotonians, 2007
Defeat: 1-6 v Exmouth Town, 2001
Goalscorer: Ben Highmore scored 52 goals during the 2008-09 season.
Appearances: Luke Scott - 600+ (as at July 2014)

GROUND: Plain Ham, Charlcombe Lane, Larkhall, Bath BA1 8DJ
Ground Capacity: 1,429 **Seats:** Yes **Covered:** 50 **Clubhouse:** Yes **Shop:** No
Previous Grounds: None
Record Attendance: 280 v Tunbridge Wells, FA Vase, Feb 2013

Nearest Railway Station Bath Spa - 2.8km
Bus Route Charlcombe Lane - stop 200m away

LYMINGTON TOWN

Southern League D1 South

Founde 1998 **Nickname:** Town **Club Colours:** Red and white

Club Contact Details

01590 671 305 secretary.lymingtontownfc@yahoo.com

Previous Names: None

Previous Leagues: Hampshire 1998-2004. Wessex 2004-21.

11-12		12-13		13-14		14-15		15-16		16-17		17-18		18-19		19-20		20-21	
WexP	14	WexP	19	WexP	14	WexP	9	WexP	13	WexP	9	WexP	8	WexP	10	WexP	n&v	WexP	n&v
FAC	Pr	FAC	EP	FAC	P	FAC	EP	FAC	EP	FAC	EPr	FAC	EP	FAC	2Q	FAC	P	FAC	P
FAV	1Q	FAV	2Q	FAV	1P	FAV	2Qr	FAV	2P	FAV	1Q	FAV	1P	FAV	2Q	FAV	1P	FAV	1P

HONOURS / RECORDS

FA Comps: None

League: Hampshire East Section 1922-23, West Section 26-27, Division Three 67-68. Wessex Division Two 2004-05.

County FA: None

Best FA Cup Second Qualifying Round 2018-19

FA Vase Fourth Round Proper 2007-08

GROUND: The Sports Ground, Southampton Road, Lymington SO41 9ZG

Ground Capacity: 2,200 **Seats:** 200 **Covered:** 300 **Clubhouse:** Yes **Shop:**

Previous Grounds: None

Record Attendance: Not known

Nearest Railway Station Lymington Town - 0.6km

Bus Route Town Hall - Stop 110m away

MANGOTSFIELD UNITED

Southern League D1 South

Founde 1950 **Nickname:** The Field **Club Colours:** Maroon and sky blue

Club Contact Details

0117 956 0119 davidj693@hotmail.co.uk

Previous Names: None

Previous Leagues: Bristol & District 1950-67. Avon Premier Combination 1967-72. Western 1972-2000.

11-12		12-13		13-14		14-15		15-16		16-17		17-18		18-19		19-20		20-21	
Sthsw	14	Sthsw	13	Sthsw	11	Sthsw	10	Sthsw	14	Sthsw	8	Sth1W	16	SthS	16	SthS	n&v	SthS	n&v
FAC	P	FAC	1Q	FAC	2Q	FAC	1Q	FAC	1Q	FAC	P	FAC	P	FAC	P	FAC	1Q	FAC	P
FAT	2Qr	FAT	Pr	FAT	2Q	FAT	2Q	FAT	2Q	FAT	P	FAT	P	FAT	1Qr	FAT	EP	FAT	2Q

HONOURS / RECORDS

FA Comps: None

League: Bristol & District Div.7 1951-52, Div.6 52-53, Div.4 53-54, Div.3 54-55, Div.2 55-56, Premier Comb Div.1 68-69. Somerset Senior Div.3 74-75, Div.2 75-76, 97-98, Prem 2004-05. Western 1990-91. Southern Division One West 2004-05.

County FA: Gloucestershire Senior Cup 1968-69, 75-76, 2002-03, 12-13. Gloucestershire F.A. Trophy x6. Somerset Premier Cup 1987-88.

Victory: 17-0 v Hanham Sports (H) - 1953 Bristol & District League

Defeat: 3-13 v Bristol City United - Bristol & District League Division One

Goalscorer: John Hill. **Appearances:** John Hill - 600+

Misc: In the last 10 matches of the 2003/04 season, the club went 738 minutes (just over 8 games) without scoring and then finished the campaign with 13 goals in the last two, which included a 9-0 away win.

GROUND: Cossham Street, Mangotsfield, Bristol BS16 9EN

Ground Capacity: 3,038 **Seats:** 300 **Covered:** 800 **Clubhouse:** Yes **Shop:** Yes

Previous Grounds: None

Record Attendance: 1,253 v Bath City - F.A. Cup 1974

Nearest Railway Station Bristol Parkway - 5 miles. Temple Meads - 7 miles.

Bus Route Cossham Street - stop 50m away

MELKSHAM TOWN

Southern League D1 South

Founde 1876 **Nickname:** Town **Club Colours:** Yellow and black

Club Contact Details
01225 302 977

Previous Names: Melksham FC 1876-1951.
Previous Leagues: Wiltshire (Founder Members) 1894-1974. Western 1974-2018.

11-12		12-13		13-14		14-15		15-16		16-17		17-18		18-19		19-20		20-21	
West1	2	WestP	13	WestP	7	WestP	1	WestP	5	WestP	3	WestP	2	SthS	12	SthS	n&v	SthS	n&v
FAC	P	FAC	1Q	FAC	EPr	FAC	EPr	FAC	EPr	FAC	EP	FAC	EP	FAC	1Q	FAC	Pr	FAC	2Q
FAV	2P	FAV	2Q	FAV	2Q	FAV	4P	FAV	2P	FAV	4Pr	FAV	QF	FAT	2Q	FAT	2Q	FAT	1Q

HONOURS / RECORDS
FA Comps: None

League: Wiltshire 1903-04, Premier 1993-94.
Western Division One 1979-80, 96-97, Premier Division 2014-15.
County FA: Wiltshire Senior Cup 1904-05, 69-70, 77-78, 2002-03, 07-08, 12-13, 13-14, 15-16.

Best FA Cup Third Qualifying Round 1954-55, 57-58
FA Trophy Second Qualifying Round 1982-83, 84085, 85-86, 87-87, 87-88, 2018-19
FA Vase Quarter Finals 2017-18
Goalscorer: Gareth Lewis scored 72 goals during the 1968-69 season

GROUND: Oakfield Stadium, Eastern Way, Melksham SN12 7GU
Ground Capacity: 3,000 **Seats:** Yes **Covered:** Yes **Clubhouse:** Yes **Shop:**
Previous Grounds: Challymead Common 1876-83. Old Bear Field 1883-1920. Conigre 1920-2017.
Record Attendance: 2,821 v Trowbridge Town, FA Cup 1957-58.

Nearest Railway Station Melksham - 2.7km
Bus Route New Road - stop 300m away

PAULTON ROVERS

Southern League D1 South

Founde 1881 **Nickname:** The Robins or Rovers **Club Colours:** Claret and white

Club Contact Details
01761 412 907

Previous Names: None
Previous Leagues: Wiltshire Premier, Somserset Senior, Western

11-12		12-13		13-14		14-15		15-16		16-17		17-18		18-19		19-20		20-21	
Sthsw	7	Sthsw	5	Sthsw	4	SthP	10	SthP	24	Sthsw	15	Sth1W	19	SthS	17	SthS	n&v	SthS	n&v
FAC	P	FAC	Pr	FAC	P	FAC	2Qr	FAC	2Q	FAC	1Q	FAC	4Q	FAC	1Qr	FAC	P	FAC	P
FAT	2Q	FAT	Pr	FAT	1Q	FAT	2Q	FAT	1Q	FAT	P	FAT	2Q	FAT	P	FAT	3Qr	FAT	1Q

HONOURS / RECORDS
FA Comps: None
League: None

County FA: Somerset Junior Cup 1898-99, Senior Cup x12 - Firstly in 1900-01 and most recently in 1974-75, Premier Cup 2012-13.

Goalscorer: Graham Colbourne
Appearances: Steve Tovey
Best FA Cup First Round Proper 2009-10
FA Trophy First Round Proper 2004-05
FA Vase Fifth Round Proper 1989-90

GROUND: Athletic Ground, Winterfield Road, Paulton, Bristol BS39 7RF
Ground Capacity: 2,500 **Seats:** 253 **Covered:** 2,500 **Clubhouse:** Yes **Shop:** Yes
Previous Grounds: Chapel Field, Cricket Ground, Recreation Ground
Record Attendance: 2,000 v Crewe Alexandra - FA Cup 1906-07

Nearest Railway Station Bath Spa - 13 miles
Bus Route Alexandra Park - stop 150m away

PLYMOUTH PARKWAY AFC

Southern League D1 South

Founde 1988 **Nickname:** The Parkway **Club Colours:** Yellow & blue

Club Contact Details

07786 571 308 gennyt@sky.com

Previous Names: None

Previous Leagues: Plymouth & District. South West Peninsula 2007-18. Western 2018-21.

11-12	12-13	13-14	14-15	15-16	16-17	17-18	18-19	19-20	20-21
SWPP 6	SWPP 2	SWPP 1	SWPP 5	SWPP 4	SWPP 7	SWPP 1	WestP 2	WestP n&v	WestP n&v
	FAC 1Qr	FAC 1Q	FAC P	FAC 1Q	FAC 1Q	FAC EP	FAC 2Q	FAC 1Q	FAC EP
FAV 1P	FAV 1Q	FAV 3P	FAV 2P	FAV 2P	FAV 1Pr	FAV 3P	FAV 1P	FAV QF	FAV 5P

HONOURS / RECORDS

FA Comps: None

League: Plymouth & District Division Two 1990-91.
South West Peninsula Premier Division 2013-14, 17-18.

County FA: None

Best FA Cup Second Qualifying Round 2018-19

FA Vase Quarter final 2019-20

GROUND: Bolitho Park, St Peters Road, Manadon, Plymouth PL5 3JG

Ground Capacity: 3,500 **Seats:** 250 **Covered:** Yes **Clubhouse:** Yes **Shop:**

Previous Grounds: Not known

Record Attendance: Not known

Nearest Railway Station St Budeaux Road - 2.8km

Bus Route St Peters Road - stop 10m away

SHOLING

Southern League D1 South

Founde 1884 **Nickname:** The Boatmen **Club Colours:** Red & white stripes

Club Contact Details

07496 804 555 secretary@sholingfc.com

Previous Names: Woolston Works, Thornycrofts (Woolston) 1918-52, Vospers 1960-2003, Vosper Thorneycroft FC/VTFC 2003-10

Previous Leagues: Hampshire 1991-2004, Wessex 2004-09, 2013-14, 15-19. Southern 2009-13, 2014-15.

11-12	12-13	13-14	14-15	15-16	16-17	17-18	18-19	19-20	20-21
Sthsw 4	Sthsw 7	WexP 1	Sthsw 17	WexP 2	WexP 3	WexP 3	WexP 1	SthS n&v	SthS n&v
FAC 2Q	FAC 3Q	FAC 2Q	FAC 1Q	FAC P	FAC 1Q	FAC EP	FAC 2Qr	FAC 2Q	FAC 4Q
FAT 1Q	FAT 3Q	FAV F	FAT 3Q	FAV 2P	FAV 1P	FAV 3P	FAT 3Q	FAT 1P	FAT 2Q

HONOURS / RECORDS

FA Comps: FA Vase 2013-14.

League: Hampshire Premier Division 2000-01, 03-04.
Wessex Premier 2013-14, 18-19.

County FA: Southampton Senior Cup 2001-02, 03-04, 05-06, 06-07, 07-08, 09-10, 13-14, 16-17

Goalscorer: George Diaper - 100+

FA Cup Third Qualifying Round 2012-13

FA Trophy First Round Proper 2019-20

GROUND: Portsmouth Road, Sholing, SO19 9PW

Ground Capacity: 2,000 **Seats:** 150 **Covered:** 250 **Clubhouse:** Yes **Shop:**

Previous Grounds: Not known

Record Attendance: 150

Nearest Railway Station Netley - 1.9km

Bus Route Bus stop outside the ground.

SLIMBRIDGE

Southern League D1 South

Founde 1899 **Nickname:** The Swans **Club Colours:** All blue

Club Contact Details

01453 899 982 info@slimbridgeafc.co.uk

Previous Names: None

Previous Leagues: Stroud & District. Gloucester Northern. Gloucestershire County >2009. Hellenic 2009-2013. Western 2013-15.

11-12		12-13		13-14		14-15		15-16		16-17		17-18		18-19		19-20		20-21	
Hel P	5	Hel P	6	WestP	16	WestP	3	Sthsw	18	Sthsw	20	Sth1W	20	SthS	18	SthS	n&v	SthS	n&v
FAC	P	FAC	EP	FAC	EPr	FAC	P	FAC	2Q	FAC	2Q	FAC	P	FAC	Pr	FAC	Pr	FAC	P
FAV	1P	FAV	1Q	FAV	2Q	FAV	2Pr	FAT	P	FAT	P	FAT	P	FAT	P	FAT	P	FAT	2Q

HONOURS / RECORDS

FA Comps: None

League: Stroud & District Division Three 1951-52, Division Two 1952-53, Division one 1953-54, 98-99, Division Four 1989-90. Hellenic Division 1 West 2003-04, 09-10, Premier 06-07. Gloucester Northern 2007-08. Gloucestershire County 2008-09.

County FA: Gloucester Challenge Trophy 2003-04, 05-06, 06-07. Gloucester Northern Senior Cup 2000-01.

Victory: 12-1 v Cheltenham Civil Service, Reg Davis Cup, 18/08/2007

Defeat: 0-9 v Cinderford Town (A), 19/04/2018 and v Taunton Town (A), 24/04/2018

Goalscorer: Marvyn Roberts - 104 (in 221 appearances)

Appearances: Fred Ward - 505

GROUND: Thornhill Park, Wisloe Road, Cambridge, Glos GL2 7AF

Ground Capacity: 1,500 **Seats:** Yes **Covered:** Yes **Clubhouse:** Yes **Shop:** Yes

Previous Grounds: Various venues around Slimbridge before moving to Wisloe Road (now Thornhill Park) in 1951.

Record Attendance: 525 v Shortwood United, Hellenic Premier, 24/08/2003.

Nearest Railway Station Cam & Dursley - 1 mile

Bus Route Wisloe Road - stop 300m away

WILLAND ROVERS

Southern League D1 South

Founde 1946 **Nickname:** Rovers **Club Colours:** White and blue

Club Contact Details

01884 33885

Previous Names: None.

Previous Leagues: Devon & Exeter >1992. Devon County (Founder Members) 1992-2001. Western 2001-19.

11-12		12-13		13-14		14-15		15-16		16-17		17-18		18-19		19-20		20-21	
WestP	5	WestP	11	WestP	8	WestP	6	WestP	6	WestP	6	WestP	3	WestP	1	SthS	n&v	SthS	n&v
FAC	EP	FAC	EP	FAC	EP	FAC	4Q	FAC	EP	FAC	EPr	FAC	1Q	FAC	P	FAC	1Q	FAC	P
FAV	4P	FAV	2P	FAV	1P	FAV	1Q	FAV	2Q	FAV	1P	FAV	2P	FAV	QF	FAT	P	FAT	1P

HONOURS / RECORDS

FA Comps: None

League: Devon County 1998-99, 2000-01, Western Division One 2004-05, Premier 18-19.

County FA: None

Goalscorer: Paul Foreman

FA Cup Fourth Qualifying Round 2014-15

FA Vase Quarter final 2018-19

FA Trophy First Round Proper 2020-21

GROUND: Silver Street, Willand, Collumpton, Devon EX15 2RG

Ground Capacity: 1,663 **Seats:** 75 **Covered:** 150 **Clubhouse:** Yes **Shop:**

Previous Grounds: Not known

Record Attendance: 650 v Newton Abbot 1992-3

Nearest Railway Station Tiverton Parkway - 3.2km

Bus Route Garage (Silver St) - stop 50m away

WINCHESTER CITY

Southern League D1 South

Founde 1884 **Nickname:** The Capitals **Club Colours:** Red & black

Club Contact Details

07495 735 609 secretary.wcfc@outlook.com

Previous Names: None

Previous Leagues: Hampshire 1898-71, 73-03. Southern 1971-73, 2006-09, 2012-13. Wessex 2003-06. 2009-12, 13-15.

11-12		12-13		13-14		14-15		15-16		16-17		17-18		18-19		19-20		20-21	
WexP	1	SthC	22	WexP	5	WexP	2	Sthsw	5	Sthsw	14	Sth1W	11	SthS	6	SthS	n&v	SthS	n&v
FAC	P	FAC	1Q	FAC	1Q	FAC	3Q	FAC	2Qr	FAC	3Q	FAC	1Q	FAC	4Q	FAC	1Q	FAC	2Q
FAV	2P	FAT	P	FAV	1P	FAV	1P	FAT	1Q	FAT	3Q	FAT	P	FAT	EPr	FAT	Pr	FAT	2Q

HONOURS / RECORDS

FA Comps: FA Vase 2004.

League: Hampshire Division Two 1973-74, 91-92, Division One 2000-01, Premier Division 2002-03.
Wessex Division One 2003-04, 05-06, Premier Division 2011-12.

County FA: Hants Senior Cup 1930-31, 2004-05.

Goalscorer: Andy Forbes.

Appearances: Ian Mancey.

GROUND: Hillier Way, Winchester SO23 7SR

Ground Capacity: 3,000 **Seats:** 180 **Covered:** 275 **Clubhouse:** Yes **Shop:** Yes

Previous Grounds: None

Record Attendance: 1,818 v Bideford, FA Vase Semi-final.

Nearest Railway Station Winchester - 0.9km

Bus Route Simonds Court - stop 250m away

ABBEY RANGERS

Combined Counties Premier North

Founded 1976 Nickname: **Club Colours:** Black & white

Club Contact Details 01932 422 962 graham.keable@ntlworld.com

Previous Names: None
Previous Leagues: Surrey Elite 2011-2015

HONOURS
FA Comps: None
League: Surrey & Hants Border League 2004-05.
Surrey Intermediate League (Western) Division One 2008-09.

11-12	12-13	13-14	14-15	15-16	16-17	17-18	18-19	19-20	20-21
SuEl 10	SuEl 7	SuEl 3	SuEl 4	CC1 3	CCP 10	CCP 17	CCP 3	CCP n&v	CCP n&v
					FAC EP	FAC EP	FAC EP	FAC 3Q	FAC P
				FAV 2P	FAV 3P	FAV 2Q	FAV 2P	FAV 2P	FAV 2Q

GROUND: Addlestone Moor, Addlestone, KT15 2QH
Nearest Railway Station Addlestone
Bus Route No.461

CLUB MOVEMENTS

PREMIER NORTH - IN: Burnham, Reading City, Virginia Water & Windsor (LM - HLP). Edgware Town, North Greenford United and Wembley (LM - SSMP). Holyport and Wokingham & Emmbrook (P - HL1E). St Panteleimon (P - SSM1). Tadley Calleva (LM - WXP).
OUT: Sutton Common Rovers (P - Isth SC).

ASCOT UNITED

Combined Counties Premier North

Founded 1965 Nickname: Yellaman **Club Colours:** Yellow and blue

Club Contact Details 01344 291 107 (Ground)

Previous Names: None.
Previous Leagues: Reading Senior. Hellenic >2019.

HONOURS
FA Comps: None
League: Reading Senior Division 2006-07.

11-12	12-13	13-14	14-15	15-16	16-17	17-18	18-19	19-20	20-21
Hel P 14	Hel P 7	Hel P 3	Hel P 3	Hel P 4	Hel P 15	Hel P 14	Hel P 7	CCP n&v	CCP n&v
FAC EP	FAC P	FAC EP	FAC P	FAC EP	FAC 1Qr	FAC P	FAC P	FAC EPr	FAC EP
FAV 2Q	FAV QFr	FAV 2P	FAV QF	FAV 3Pr	FAV 2P	FAV 1Q	FAV 1Q	FAV 3P	FAV 1P

GROUND: Ascot Racecourse, Car Park 7&8, Winkfield Road, Ascot SL5 7LJ **Capacity:** 1,150
Nearest Railway Station Ascot - 1.3km
Bus Route Hilltop Close (Cheapside Rd) stop - 934m

BURNHAM

Combined Counties Premier North

Founded 1878 Nickname: The Blues **Club Colours:** Blue & white

Club Contact Details 01628 668 654 (Ground) burnhamfcsec@aol.com

Previous Names: Burnham & Hillingdon 1985-87
Previous Leagues: Hellenic 1971-77, 95-99, 2016-21. Athenian 1977-84. London Spartan 1984-85. Southern 1985-95, 99-16.

HONOURS
FA Comps: None
League: Hellenic 1975-76, 98-99, Division One East 2018-19. London Spartan 1984-85.
Southern Division One Central 2012-13.

11-12	12-13	13-14	14-15	15-16	16-17	17-18	18-19	19-20	20-21
SthC 15	SthC 1	SthP 20	SthP 23	Sthsw 21	Hel P 17	Hel P 20	Hel1E 1	Hel P n&v	Hel P n&v
FAC 3Q	FAC P	FAC 2Q	FAC 2Q	FAC Pr	FAC EP	FAC EP	FAC 2Q	FAC 1Q	FAC 2Q
FAT Pr	FAT 2Q	FAT 2Q	FAT 2Qr	FAT P	FAV 2Q	FAV 2Q	FAV 2Q	FAV 1Q	FAV 1Q

GROUND: The Gore, Wymers Wood Road, Burnham, Slough SL1 8JG **Capacity:** 2,500
Nearest Railway Station Taplow - 1.9km
Bus Route Pink Lane stop - 239m away

CB HOUNSLOW UNITED

Combined Counties Premier North

Founded 1989 Nickname: The Dragons **Club Colours:** Green and black

Club Contact Details 07958 718 930 cbhounslowunitedfc.com

Previous Names: CB United 1989-94. (Named after Cater Bank, a company owned by the father of the club chairman.)
Previous Leagues: Hounslow & District 1989-94. Middlesex County 1994-2006.
HONOURS
FA Comps: None
League: Combined Counties League Division One 2015-16.

11-12	12-13	13-14	14-15	15-16	16-17	17-18	18-19	19-20	20-21
CC1 15	CC1 8	CC1 14	CC1 7	CC1 1	CCP 20	CCP 9	CCP 17	CCP n&v	CCP n&v
					FAC 1Q	FAC P	FAC P	FAC P	FAC P
			FAV 1Q	FAV 2Q	FAV 2Q	FAV 2Q	FAV 1P	FAV 1Q	FAV 1P

GROUND: The Lair, Hounslow Sports Club, Green Lane, Hounslow TW4 6DH **Capacity:** 1200
Nearest Railway Station Hatton Cross (Underground) Piccadilly Line **Seats:** 100
Bus Route London Transport 423 stops almost opposite the ground, 482 & 203 stop on Gt South West Rd close to Green Lane **Covered:** Yes

EDGWARE TOWN

Combined Counties Premier North

Founded 1939 Nickname: The Wares **Club Colours:** Green and white

Club Contact Details 0208 205 1645

Previous Names: Edgware 1972-87. Original Edgware Town folded in 2008 and re-formed in 2014.
Previous Leagues: Corinthian 1946-63. Athenian 1963-84. Spartan 1984-90, 2006-07, 14-21. Isthmian 1990-2006, 2007-08.
HONOURS
FA Comps: None
League: Middlesex Senior 1939-40, 43-44, 44-45 (shared). London Western Section 1945-46. London Spartan Premier 1987-88, 89-90. Isthmian Division Three 1991-92. Spartan South Midlands Premier 2006-07, Division One 2015-16.

11-12	12-13	13-14	14-15	15-16	16-17	17-18	18-19	19-20	20-21
			SSM1 9	SSM1 1	SSM P 17	SSM P 10	SSM P 13	SSM P n&v	SSM P n&v
					FAC P	FAC EPr	FAC EP	FAC EP	FAC P
				FAV 3P	FAV 2Q	FAV 1P	FAV 2Q	FAV 2Q	FAV 1P

GROUND: Silver Jubilee Park, Townsend Lane, London NW9 7NE **Capacity:** 1,990
Nearest Railway Station Hendon - 1.1km **Seats:** 298
Bus Route Queensbury Road - stop 660m away

EGHAM TOWN

Combined Counties Premier North

Founded 1877 Nickname: Sarnies **Club Colours:** Red & white

Club Contact Details 01784 437 055

Previous Names: Runnymead Rovers 1877-1905. Egham F.C. 05-63.
Previous Leagues: West Surrey. Surrey Senior 1922-28, 33-39, 65-67. Spartan 1928-33, 67-74. Athenian 1964-77. Isthmian 1977-2004, 05-06, 18-19. Southern 2004-05, 13-18. Combined Counties 2006-13.
HONOURS
FA Comps: None
League: West Surrey 1921-22. Surrey Senior 1922-23. Spartan 1971-72. Athenian Division Two 1974-75. Combined Counties 2012-13.

11-12	12-13	13-14	14-15	15-16	16-17	17-18	18-19	19-20	20-21
CCP 4	CCP 1	SthC 11	SthC 15	SthC 3	SthC 5	Sth1E 16	IsthSC 20	CCP n&v	CCP n&v
FAC Pr	FAC P	FAC P	FAC P	FAC Pr	FAC 4Q	FAC 1Qr	FAC 2Qr	FAC P	FAC P
FAV 2P	FAV 1P	FAT 2Q	FAT 1Q	FAT 1Q	FAT P	FAT 2Q	FAT P	FAV 1P	FAV 1Q

GROUND: Runnymead Stadium, Tempest Road, Egham TW20 8XD **Capacity:** 5500
Nearest Railway Station Egham - 1km **Seats:** 262
Bus Route Charta Road - stop 200m away **Covered:** 3300

HANWORTH VILLA

Combined Counties Premier North

Founded 1976 Nickname: The Vilans **Club Colours:** Red & white

Club Contact Details 0208 831 9391 db1959@btinternet.com

Previous Names: None
Previous Leagues: Hounslow & District Lge. West Middlesex Lge. Middlesex County League.
HONOURS
FA Comps: None
League: Hounslow & District Div.1 & Prem. West Middlesex Division One & Division Two.
Middlesex County 2002-03, 04-05.

11-12		12-13		13-14		14-15		15-16		16-17		17-18		18-19		19-20		20-21	
CCP	3	CCP	9	CCP	8	CCP	19	CCP	7	CCP	3	CCP	11	CCP	15	CCP	n&v	CCP	n&v
FAC	4Q	FAC	P	FAC	P	FAC	Pr	FAC	EP	FAC	P	FAC	P	FAC	Pr	FAC	P	FAC	P
FAV	3Pr	FAV	4P	FAV	4P	FAV	3P	FAV	1P	FAV	1Q	FAV	2P	FAV	1P	FAV	2Q	FAV	5P

GROUND: Rectory Meadows, Park Road, Hanworth TW13 6PN **Capacity:** 600
Nearest Railway Station Feltham or Hampton **Seats:** 100
Bus Route London United 111 or H25 **Covered:** Yes

HOLYPORT

Combined Counties Premier North

Founded 1934 Nickname: The Villagers **Club Colours:** Claret & green

Club Contact Details 07515 789 415 richardtyrell@googlemail.com

Previous Names: None
Previous Leagues: Hellenic 1934-2021.
HONOURS
FA Comps: None
League: Hayes & Giles Premier Division 1998-99, 99-2000, 01-02.
Hellenic Division One East 2010-11.

11-12		12-13		13-14		14-15		15-16		16-17		17-18		18-19		19-20		20-21	
Hel P	13	Hel P	14	Hel P	18	Hel P	16	Hel1E	7	Hel1E	13	Hel1E	5	Hel1E	4	Hel1E	n&v	Hel1E	n&v
FAC	EP	FAC	EP	FAC	EP	FAC	EPr	FAC	EP					FAC	EP				
FAV	1Q	FAV	1P	FAV	2Q	FAV	1Q	FAV	1Qr	FAV	1Q	FAV	2Q	FAV	1Pr	FAV	2Q	FAV	1Q

GROUND: Summerleaze Park, 35 North Town Moor, Maidenhead SL6 7JR
Nearest Railway Station Furze Platt - 1km
Bus Route Veterinary Hospital stop - 133m away

NORTH GREENFORD UNITED

Combined Counties Premier North

Founded 1944 Nickname: Blues **Club Colours:** Royal blue & white

Club Contact Details 0208 422 8923

Previous Names: None
Previous Leagues: London Spartan, Combined Counties 2002-10, 16-18. Southern 2010-16. Spartan SM 2018-21.
HONOURS
FA Comps: None
League: Combined Counties League Premier Division 2009-10

11-12		12-13		13-14		14-15		15-16		16-17		17-18		18-19		19-20		20-21	
SthC	18	SthC	19	SthC	20	SthC	21	SthC	22	CCP	13	CCP	13	SSM P	16	SSM P	n&v	SSM P	n&v
FAC	3Qr	FAC	P	FAC	3Q	FAC	2Q	FAC	1Qr	FAC	1Q	FAC	P	FAC	P	FAC	P	FAC	EP
FAT	P	FAT	P	FAT	2Q	FAT	P	FAT	P	FAV	2Q	FAV	1Q	FAV	1P	FAV	2Q	FAV	2P

GROUND: Berkeley Fields, Berkley Avenue, Greenford UB6 0NX **Capacity:** 2,000
Nearest Railway Station Greenford or Sudbury Hill (Piccadilly Line). **Seats:** 150
Bus Route No.92 **Covered:** 100

READING CITY

Combined Counties Premier North

Founded 2001 Nickname: Mighty Moor **Club Colours:** Blue

Club Contact Details 07918 880 777 media@readingcity.co.uk

Previous Names: Highmoor and Ibis merged to form today's club in 2001. Highmoor Ibis 2001-18.

Previous Leagues: Reading 2001-2011. Hellenic 2011-21.

HONOURS

FA Comps: None

League: Reading Senior Division 2003-04, 10-11.

11-12		12-13		13-14		14-15		15-16		16-17		17-18		18-19		19-20		20-21	
Hel1E	2	Hel P	12	Hel P	4	Hel P	2	Hel P	11	Hel P	14	Hel P	17	Hel P	18	Hel P	n&v	Hel P	n&v
				FAC	1Q	FAC	P	FAC	EP	FAC	P	FAC	P	FAC	EPr	FAC	P	FAC	EP
		FAV	2Q	FAV	1P	FAV	1P	FAV	1P	FAV	1P	FAV	1Q	FAV	1Q	FAV	2Q	FAV	1P

GROUND: The Rivermoor, Scours Lane, Tilehurst, Reading RG30 6AY

Nearest Railway Station Tilehurst - 1.2km

Bus Route Cold Store stop - 277m away

SOUTHALL

Combined Counties Premier North

Founded 1871 Nickname: None **Club Colours:** Red and white

Club Contact Details enquiries@southallfc.com

Previous Names: Southall 1871-1975. Southall & Ealing Borough 1975-80.

Previous Leagues: West London (FM) 1892-93. Southern 1896-1905. Great Western Suburban 1907-14. Athenian 1919-73. Isthmian 1973-75, 80--2000. Combined Counties 2000-06. Middlesex County 2006-12. Spartan South Midlands 2012-18.

HONOURS

FA Comps: None

League: Great Western Suburban 1912-13. Athenian 1926-27.
Spartan South Midlands Division One 2017-18.

11-12		12-13		13-14		14-15		15-16		16-17		17-18		18-19		19-20		20-21	
MidxP	3	SSM1	9	SSM1	11	SSM1	12	SSM1	12	SSM1	5	SSM1	1	CCP	4	CCP	n&v	CCP	n&v
												FAC	P	FAC	EP	FAC	P	FAC	1Q
				FAV	1Q	FAV	2Q	FAV	1P	FAV	QF	FAV	2P	FAV	2P	FAV	3P	FAV	2P

GROUND: Ashford Town (Mddx) FC, Robert Parker Stadium, Short Lane, Stanwell TW19 7BH **Capacity:** 2,550

Nearest Railway Station Heathrow Terminal 4 Underground - 1.5km **Seats:** 250

Bus Route Genesis Close - stop 400m away **Covered:** 250

SPELTHORNE SPORTS

Combined Counties Premier North

Founded 1922 Nickname: Spelly **Club Colours:** Navy & sky blue

Club Contact Details 01932 961 055

Previous Names: None

Previous Leagues: Surrey Intermediate (West) > 2009. Surrey Elite Intermediate 2009-11.

HONOURS

FA Comps: None

League: Surrey Elite Intermediate League 2010-11. Combined Counties Division One 2013-14.

11-12		12-13		13-14		14-15		15-16		16-17		17-18		18-19		19-20		20-21	
CC1	7	CC1	6	CCP	1	CCP	6	CCP	11	CCP	9	CCP	10	CCP	6	CCP	n&v	CCP	n&v
								FAC	P	FAC	P	FAC	EP	FAC	1Q	FAC	1Q	FAC	P
						FAV	1P	FAV	1Q	FAV	1Qr	FAV	1P	FAV	2P	FAV	1Q	FAV	1Q

GROUND: Spelthorne Sports Club, 296 Staines Rd West, Ashford Common, TW15 1RY **Capacity:** 1,500

Nearest Railway Station Sunbury **Seats:** 50

Bus Route 290 to outside the club. **Covered:** Yes

ST PANTELEIMON

Combined Counties Premier North

Founded 2015 Nickname: The Saints **Club Colours:** Yellow & blue

Club Contact Details

Previous Names: None

Previous Leagues: KOPA. Middlesex County 2018-19. Spartan SM 2019-21.

HONOURS

FA Comps: None

League: Middlesex County Division One (Central & East) 2018-19.

11-12	12-13	13-14	14-15	15-16	16-17	17-18	18-19	19-20	20-21
				KOPA	KOPA	KOPA	Midx1SE 1	SSM1 n&v	SSM1 n&v
							FAV 1P	FAV 1Q	FAV 2Q

GROUND: Queen Elizabeth Stadium, Donkey Lane, Enfield EN1 3PL **Capacity:** 2,500

Nearest Railway Station Southbury - 1.2km **Seats:** Yes

Bus Route 191 towards Brimsdown from Enfield stops outside the ground. **Covered:** Yes

TADLEY CALLEVA

Combined Counties Premier North

Founded 1989 Nickname: The Tadders **Club Colours:** All yellow

Club Contact Details 07926 830 806 secretarytcfc@gmail.com

Previous Names: Tadley FC 1989-99. Tadley Town 1999-2004.

Previous Leagues: Hampshire 1994-2004. Wessex 2004-21.

HONOURS

FA Comps: None

League: Wessex Division One 2007-08.

11-12	12-13	13-14	14-15	15-16	16-17	17-18	18-19	19-20	20-21
Wex1 17	Wex1 7	Wex1 5	Wex1 3	Wex1 3	Wex1 7	Wex1 3	WexP 8	WexP n&v	WexP n&v
		FAC P	FAC EPr	FAC EP	FAC EP		FAC EP	FAC EP	FAC 1Q
	FAV 1Q	FAV 2Q	FAV 2Q	FAV 3Pr	FAV 1Q	FAV 2Q	FAV 2Q	FAV 1P	FAV 2Q

GROUND: Barlows Park Silchester Road Tadley Hampshire RG26 3PX **Capacity:** 1,000

Nearest Railway Station Midgham - 5.1km

Bus Route Tadley Common Road - stop 60m away

VIRGINIA WATER

Combined Counties Premier North

Founded 1920 Nickname: The Waters **Club Colours:** Maroon

Club Contact Details 01753 860 656 (Ground) gp738@hotmail.com

Previous Names:

Previous Leagues: Surrey Senior 1968-75. London Spartan 1975-79. Combined Co 1979-87, 93-94. Surrey Co Premier 1992-93, 94-2002. Surrey Intermediate (West) 2002-10. Surrey Elite Intermediate 2010-17. Hellenic 2017-21.

HONOURS

FA Comps: None

League: Surrey County Premier Division 1992-93, 96-97. Surrey Elite Intermediate 2016-17.
Hellenic Division One East 2017-18.

11-12	12-13	13-14	14-15	15-16	16-17	17-18	18-19	19-20	20-21
SuEl 14	SuEl 11	SuEl 8	SuEl 7	SuEl 5	SuEl 1	Hel1E 1	Hel P 14	Hel P n&v	Hel P n&v
								FAC EP	FAC EP
							FAV 2Q	FAV 1Q	FAV 1Q

GROUND: Windsor FC, Stag Meadow, St Leonards Road Windsor SL4 3DR **Capacity:** 4,500

Nearest Railway Station Windsor & Eton Central - 1.5km **Seats:** 450

Bus Route Stag Meadow stop - 131m away **Covered:** 650

WEMBLEY

Combined Counties Premier North

Founded 1946 Nickname: The Lions **Club Colours:** Red

Club Contact Details 0208 904 8169

Previous Names: None

Previous Leagues: Middlesex Senior. Spartan 1949-51. Delphian 1951-56. Corinthian 1956-63. Athenian 1963-75. Isthmian 1975-2006. Combined Counties 2006-14. Spartan SM 2014-21.

HONOURS

FA Comps: None

League: Middlesex Senior 1947-48. Spartan Division One Western 1950-51.

11-12		12-13		13-14		14-15		15-16		16-17		17-18		18-19		19-20		20-21	
CCP	10	CCP	15	CCP	9	SSM P	7	SSM P	11	SSM P	4	SSM P	9	SSM P	12	SSM P	n&v	SSM P	n&v
FAC	1Q	FAC	Pr	FAC	1Q	FAC	EPr	FAC	Pr	FAC	Pr	FAC	P	FAC	EP	FAC	P	FAC	EP
FAV	2Qr	FAV	1P	FAV	1P	FAV	2P	FAV	1Q	FAV	3P	FAV	2P	FAV	2Q	FAV	2Q	FAV	1Q

GROUND: Vale Farm, Watford Road, Sudbury, Wembley HA0 3HG.
Nearest Railway Station Sudbury Town Underground - 1km Sudbury & Harrow Road
Bus Route Butlers Green - stop 150m away

Capacity: 2450
Seats: 350
Covered: 950

WINDSOR

Combined Counties Premier North

Founded 1892 Nickname: The Royals **Club Colours:** Red, white & green

Club Contact Details 01753 860 656 (Ground) secretary@windsorfc.net

Previous Names: Formed when Windsor Phoenix and Windsor St. Albans merged in 1892. Windsor & Eton 1892-2011.

Previous Leagues: W.Berks, Gt Western, Suburban, Athenian 22-29,63-81, Spartan 29-39, Gt W.Comb. Corinthian 45-50, Met 50-60, Delphian 60-63, Isthmian 1963-2006, Southern 2006-11. Combined Counties 2011-17. Hellenic 2017-21.

HONOURS

FA Comps: None

League: Athenian League 1979-80, 80-81. Isthmian League Division 1 1983-84.
Southern League Division 1 South & West 2009-10.

11-12		12-13		13-14		14-15		15-16		16-17		17-18		18-19		19-20		20-21	
CCP	2	CCP	6	CCP	6	CCP	5	CCP	12	CCP	11	Hel P	8	Hel P	6	Hel P	n&v	Hel P	n&v
		FAC	1Q	FAC	P	FAC	P	FAC	EP	FAC	EP	FAC	EP	FAC	P	FAC	EP	FAC	P
FAV	2Q	FAV	1P	FAV	1P	FAV	1P	FAV	1P	FAV	1Q	FAV	QF	FAV	5P	FAV	2P	FAV	1Q

GROUND: Stag Meadow, St Leonards Road, Windsor, Berks SL4 3DR
Nearest Railway Station Windsor & Eton - 1.5km
Bus Route Stag Meadow stop - 131m away

Capacity: 4,500
Seats: 450
Covered: 650

WOKINGHAM & EMMBROOK

Combined Counties Premier North

Founded 2004 Nickname: Satsumas (Sumas) **Club Colours:** Orange and black

Club Contact Details 07525 736 797 senior@wefc.club

Previous Names: Club formed when Wokingham Town and Emmbrook Sports merged.

Previous Leagues: Isthmian (Wokingham). Reading (Emmbrook Sports). Hellenic 2004-21.

HONOURS

FA Comps: None

League: Hellenic Division One East 2014-15.

11-12		12-13		13-14		14-15		15-16		16-17		17-18		18-19		19-20		20-21	
Hel P	10	Hel P	8	Hel1E	2	Hel1E	1	Hel P	20	Hel1E	12	Hel1E	6	Hel1E	6	Hel1E	n&v	Hel1E	n&v
FAC	1Q	FAC	EP																
FAV	2Q	FAV	1P					FAV	1P							FAV	2Q	FAV	2Q

GROUND: Emmbrook Sports & Social Club, Lowther Road, Wokingham RG41 1JB
Nearest Railway Station Winnersh - 1.6km
Bus Route Toutley Close stop - 154m away

AFC CROYDON ATHLETIC

Combined Counties Premier South

Founded 2012 Nickname: The Rams **Club Colours:** All maroon

Club Contact Details 020 8689 5322 secretary@afccroydonathletic.co.uk

Previous Names: None
Previous Leagues: Combined Counties 2012-15. Southern Counties East 2015-21.
HONOURS
FA Comps: None
League: None

11-12	12-13	13-14	14-15	15-16	16-17	17-18	18-19	19-20	20-21
	CC1 8	CC1 7	CC1 2	SCE 11	SCEP 7	SCEP 13	SCEP 15	SCEP n&v	SCEP n&v
		FAC EP	FAC EP	FAC EP	FAC EP	FAC P	FAC 1Q	FAC Pr	FAC EP
	FAV 1P	FAV 1P	FAV 2Q	FAV 1Pr	FAV 2Q	FAV 2Q	FAV 2P	FAV 1Q	FAV 1Q

GROUND: Mayfield Stadium, off Mayfield Road, Thornton Heath CR7 6DN
Nearest Railway Station Croydon
Capacity: 3,000 **Seats:** 301 **Covered:** 660

CLUB MOVEMENTS

PREMIER SOUTH - IN: AFC Croydon Athletic, Balham & Beckenham Town (LM - SCEP). Farnham Town, Jersey Bulls and Walton & Hersham (P - CC1). Fleet Town (LM - WXP). Horley Town (LM - SCP).

BADSHOT LEA

Combined Counties Premier South

Founded 1907 Nickname: Baggies **Club Colours:** Claret & sky blue

Club Contact Details badshotleafootballclub.co.uk

Previous Names: None
Previous Leagues: Surrey Intermediate. Hellenic > 2008.
HONOURS
FA Comps: None
League: Surrey Intermediate Division One 1936-37, 37-38, 85-86, Division Two 92-93

11-12	12-13	13-14	14-15	15-16	16-17	17-18	18-19	19-20	20-21
CCP 17	CCP 7	CCP 15	CCP 8	CCP 17	CCP 21	CC1 3	CCP 9	CCP n&v	CCP n&v
FAC P	FAC 3Q	FAC P	FAC P	FAC P	FAC P	FAC P	FAC EP	FAC 2Q	FAC P
FAV 2Q	FAV 1Q	FAV 1Q	FAV 1Q	FAV 2Q	FAV 2Q	FAV 2Q	FAV 2P	FAV 2P	FAV 2Q

GROUND: Westfield Lane, Wrecclesham, Farnham, Surrey GU10 4QP
Nearest Railway Station Aldershot
Bus Route Stagecoach 18 from Aldershot bus station - about 28min journey via 31 stops to Westfield Lane.
Capacity: 1,200 **Seats:** Yes **Covered:** Yes

BALHAM

Combined Counties Premier South

Founded 2011 Nickname: **Club Colours:** Red and white

Club Contact Details 020 8942 8062

Previous Names: None
Previous Leagues: Surrey South Eastern Combination 2011-15. Surrey Elite Intermediate 2015-2016. Combined Counties 2016-20. Southern Counties East 2020-21.
HONOURS
FA Comps: None
League: Surrey South Eastern Combination Intermediate Division One 2013-14.

11-12	12-13	13-14	14-15	15-16	16-17	17-18	18-19	19-20	20-21
SSECJ1 4	SSECI2 3	SSECI1 1	SuEI 3	SuEI 2	CC1 3	CCP 5	CCP 18	CCP n&v	SCEP n&v
							FAC P	FAC 2Q	FAC EP
						FAV 1P	FAV 1Q	FAV 1Q	FAV 2Q

GROUND: Wibbandune Sports Ground, Lincoln Green, Wimbledon SW20 0AA
Nearest Railway Station Raynes Park
Bus Route London Transport 265
Capacity: 2,000 **Seats:** 102 **Covered:** 100

BANSTEAD ATHLETIC

Combined Counties Premier South

Founded 1944 Nickname: The A's **Club Colours:** Amber & black

Club Contact Details 01737 350 982 terrymolloy@leyfield.eclipse.co.uk

Previous Names: Banstead Juniors 1944-46.

Previous Leagues: Surrey Senior 1949-65. Spartan 1965-75. London Spartan 1975-79. Athenian 1979-85. Isthmian 1985-2006.

HONOURS

FA Comps: None

League: Surrey Senior League 1950-51, 51-52, 52-53, 53-54, 56-57, 64-65.
Combined Counties League Division One 2016-17.

11-12	12-13	13-14	14-15	15-16	16-17	17-18	18-19	19-20	20-21
CCP 22	CC1 17	CC1 12	CC1 6	CC1 6	CC1 1	CCP 19	CCP 8	CCP n&v	CCP n&v
FAC 1Q	FAC EP			FAC EPr	FAC Pr	FAC 1Q	FAC EP	FAC EP	FAC EP
FAV 2Q	FAV 2Q	FAV 2Q	FAV 1P	FAV 2Q	FAV 1P	FAV 1Q	FAV 2P	FAV 1Qr	FAV 1Q

GROUND: Merland Rise, Tadworth, Surrey KT20 5JG
Nearest Railway Station Tattenham Corner
Bus Route Metro 420 & 460
Capacity: 4000
Seats: 250
Covered: 800

BECKENHAM TOWN

Combined Counties Premier South

Founded 1887 Nickname: Reds **Club Colours:** All red

Club Contact Details 07774 728 758 peterpalmer3@sky.com

Previous Names: Original club folded in 1969 and reformed based on the Stanhope Rovers Junior team in 1971.

Previous Leagues: London 1923-35, 51-61. Kent County Amateur 1935-51. Aetolian 1961-64. Greater London 1964-69. South East London Amateur 1971-75. London Spartan 1975-82. Kent/Southern Counties East 1982-2021.

HONOURS

FA Comps: None

League: London Division One 1927-28.

11-12	12-13	13-14	14-15	15-16	16-17	17-18	18-19	19-20	20-21
Kent P 6	Kent P 11	SCE 8	SCE 9	SCE 12	SCEP 18	SCEP 4	SCEP 5	SCEP n&v	SCEP n&v
FAC 2Qr	FAC 1Q	FAC EP	FAC EP	FAC P	FAC P	FAC EP	FAC 1Qr	FAC P	FAC P
FAV 1P	FAV 1P	FAV 3P	FAV 2Q	FAV 2P	FAV 1P	FAV 3P	FAV 1P	FAV 1Pr	FAV 1Q

GROUND: Eden Park Avenue, Beckenham Kent BR3 3JL
Nearest Railway Station Eden Park - 0.3km
Capacity: 4,000
Seats: 120
Covered: 120

CAMBERLEY TOWN

Combined Counties Premier South

Founded 1895 Nickname: The Krooners **Club Colours:** Red and white stripes

Club Contact Details 01276 65 392

Previous Names: St Michael's FC (St Michael's Camberley) 1895-1901. Camberley & Yorktown 1901-46. Camberley 1946-67.

Previous Leagues: East & West Surrey (West Surrey) 1898-99, 1910-22. Aldershot Comb 1902-03. Ascot & Dist 1903-10. Surrey Senior 1922-73. Spartan 1973-75. Athenian 1975-77, 82-84. Isthmian 1977-82, 84-2006.

HONOURS

FA Comps: None

League: Ascot & Dist. 1904-05, 07-08, 08-09, 09-10. Aldershot Sen. Civilian 1912-13. West Surrey 1913-14. Surrey Senior 1930-31, 31-32, 32-33.

11-12	12-13	13-14	14-15	15-16	16-17	17-18	18-19	19-20	20-21
CCP 6	CCP 16	CCP 2	CCP 2	CCP 3	CCP 6	CCP 7	CCP 16	CCP n&v	CCP n&v
FAC P	FAC P	FAC 1Qr	FAC EP	FAC EP	FAC 1Q	FAC P	FAC EP	FAC EP	FAC P
FAV 1P	FAV 2Q	FAV 2Q	FAV 1P	FAT QF	FAV 2P	FAV 1P	FAV 2Q	FAV 2Q	FAV 1Q

GROUND: Krooner Park, Wilton Road, Camberley, Surrey GU15 2QW
Nearest Railway Station Camberley
Bus Route Stagecoach 1
Capacity: 1,976
Seats: 196
Covered: 300

COBHAM

Combined Counties Premier South

Founded 1892 Nickname: Hammers **Club Colours:** Red & black

Club Contact Details 07813 643 336

Previous Names: None

Previous Leagues: Kingston & District. Surrey Senior 1937-78.

HONOURS

FA Comps: None

League: Kingston & District Division One 1928-29, 29-30.

11-12		12-13		13-14		14-15		15-16		16-17		17-18		18-19		19-20		20-21	
CC1	11	CC1	11	CC1	16	CC1	11	CC1	7	CC1	11	CC1	2	CCP	14	CCP	n&v	CCP	n&v
FAC	EPr	FAC	EPr											FAC	P	FAC	EPr	FAC	1Q
FAV	1Q	FAV	2Q	FAV	2Q	FAV	2Q	FAV	2Q	FAV	2Q	FAV	1P	FAV	1P	FAV	2Q	FAV	5P

GROUND: Leg O'Mutton Field, Downside Bridge Road, Cobham KT11 1AA **Capacity:** 2000

Nearest Railway Station Cobham **Seats:** 112

Bus Route Green Line 715 **Covered:** 200

COLLIERS WOOD UNITED

Combined Counties Premier South

Founded 1874 Nickname: The Wood **Club Colours:** Royal blue & black

Club Contact Details 0208 942 8062 collierswoodunited@yahoo.co.uk

Previous Names: Vandyke 1874-1997. Vandyke Colliers United 1997-99.

Previous Leagues: Wimbledon & Sutton. Surrey Intermediate. Surrey County Senior

HONOURS

FA Comps: None

League: Surrey County Premier League 1997-98.

11-12		12-13		13-14		14-15		15-16		16-17		17-18		18-19		19-20		20-21	
CCP	19	CCP	18	CCP	16	CCP	11	CCP	8	CCP	15	CCP	16	CCP	13	CCP	n&v	CCP	n&v
FAC	EPr	FAC	P	FAC	P	FAC	EP	FAC	EP	FAC	2Qr	FAC	Pr	FAC	EPr	FAC	EP	FAC	EP
FAV	1P	FAV	3P	FAV	1Q	FAV	4P	FAV	3P	FAV	1Q	FAV	1Q	FAV	2Q	FAV	1P	FAV	2Q

GROUND: Wibbandune Sports Ground, Lincoln Green, Wimbledon SW20 0AA **Capacity:** 2000

Nearest Railway Station Raynes Park **Seats:** 102

Bus Route London Transport 265 **Covered:** 100

FARNHAM TOWN

Combined Counties Premier South

Founded 1906 Nickname: The Town **Club Colours:** Claret & sky blue

Club Contact Details 01252 715 305

Previous Names: Formed after the merger of Farnham Bungs and Farnham Star.

Previous Leagues: Surrey Intermediate. Surrey Senior 1947-71. Spartan 1971-75, London Spartan 1975-80, Combined Co. 1980-92, 93-2006, Isthmian 1992-93 (resigned pre-season).

HONOURS

FA Comps: None

League: Surrey Intermediate 1929-30, 30-31. Surrey Senior 1965-66, 66-67, 67-68.
Combined Counties 1990-91, 91-92, Division One 2006-07.

11-12		12-13		13-14		14-15		15-16		16-17		17-18		18-19		19-20		20-21	
CCP	12	CCP	8	CCP	15	CCP	10	CCP	10	CCP	18	CCP	22	CC1	4	CC1	n&v	CC1	n&v
FAC	P	FAC	EP	FAC	P	FAC	EP	FAC	1Q	FAC	P	FAC	P	FAC	EP	FAC	EPr	FAC	EP
FAV	1P	FAV	2Q	FAV	1P	FAV	1Pr	FAV	1P	FAV	1Q	FAV	2P	FAV	2Q	FAV	2Q	FAV	2Q

GROUND: The Club House, Mead Lane, Farnham GU9 7DY **Capacity:** 1,500

Nearest Railway Station Farnham **Seats:** 50

Bus Route Stagecoach 5, 14, 18, 19, 46, 64, 71, 536

FLEET TOWN

Combined Counties Premier South

Founded 1890 Nickname: The Blues **Club Colours:** Blue & white

Club Contact Details 01252 623 804 Match day only secretary@fleettownfc.co.uk

Previous Names: Fleet FC 1890-1963

Previous Leagues: Hampshire 1961-77, Athenian, Combined Counties, Chiltonian, Wessex 1989-95, 2000-02, 19-21. Southern 1995-2000, 02-04, 07-08, 11-19. Isthmian 2004-07, 2008-11.

HONOURS

FA Comps: None

League: Wessex 1994-95.

11-12		12-13		13-14		14-15		15-16		16-17		17-18		18-19		19-20		20-21	
SthC	21	SthC	18	Sthsw	21	Sthsw	19	SthC	17	SthC	14	Sth1E	19	SthS	20	WexP	n&v	WexP	n&v
FAC	1Q	FAC	P	FAC	P	FAC	2Q	FAC	1Qr	FAC	1Qr	FAC	Pr	FAC	1Q	FAC	1Q	FAC	EP
FAT	1Q	FAT	Pr	FAT	P	FAT	1Q	FAT	P	FAT	1Q	FAT	Pr	FAT	1Q	FAV	1Qr	FAV	1P

GROUND: Calthorpe Park, Crookham Road, Fleet, Hants GU51 5FA **Capacity:** 2,000

Nearest Railway Station Fleet - 2.1km **Seats:** 250

Bus Route Leawood Road - stop 150m away **Covered:** 250

FRIMLEY GREEN

Combined Counties Premier South

Founded 1919 Nickname: The Green **Club Colours:** All blue

Club Contact Details 01252 835 089

Previous Names: None

Previous Leagues: Surrey Senior 1960-74. London Spartan 1974-75. London Spartan 1975-81. Combined Counties 1981-94. Surrey County Premier 1999-2002.

HONOURS

FA Comps: None

League: Combined Counties Division One 2012-13.

11-12		12-13		13-14		14-15		15-16		16-17		17-18		18-19		19-20		20-21	
CC1	10	CC1	1	CCP	12	CCP	21	CC1	12	CC1	13	CC1	7	CC1	2	CCP	n&v	CCP	n&v
				FAC	P	FAC	EP	FAC	EP					FAC	P	FAC	EP	FAC	1Q
FAV	1Q	FAV	2P	FAV	1Q	FAV	2Q	FAV	2Q	FAV	2Q	FAV	1P	FAV	1Q	FAV	2Q	FAV	1P

GROUND: Frimley Green Rec. Ground, Frimley Green, Camberley GU16 6SY **Capacity:** 2000

Nearest Railway Station Frimley **Seats:** No

Bus Route Stagecoach 3, Arriva 49 **Covered:** Yes

GUILDFORD CITY

Combined Counties Premier South

Founded 1996 Nickname: The Sweeney **Club Colours:** Red & white stripes

Club Contact Details 01483 443 322

Previous Names: AFC Guildford 1996-2005. Guildford United 2005-06.

Previous Leagues: Surrey Senior. Combined Counties > 2012. Southern 2012-14.

HONOURS

FA Comps: None

League: Southern League 1937-38, 55-56, League cup 1962-63, 66-67.
Combined Counties Division One 2003-04, Premier Division 2010-11, 11-12

11-12		12-13		13-14		14-15		15-16		16-17		17-18		18-19		19-20		20-21	
CCP	1	SthC	9	Sthsw	22	CCP	17	CCP	14	CCP	16	CCP	12	CCP	7	CCP	n&v	CCP	n&v
FAC	EP	FAC	1Q	FAC	P	FAC	EP	FAC	P	FAC	1Q	FAC	1Q	FAC	EP	FAC	P	FAC	P
FAV	2P	FAT	1Q	FAT	P	FAV	1P	FAV	1Q	FAV	1Q	FAV	1Q	FAV	2Q	FAV	1Q	FAV	3P

GROUND: Spectrum Leisure Centre, Parkway, Guildford GU1 1UP **Capacity:** 1,320

Nearest Railway Station Guildford Main Line (2 miles) & Guildford (London Rd) (1 mile) **Seats:** 255

Bus Route Arriva 100 **Covered:** Yes

HORLEY TOWN

Combined Counties Premier South

Founded 1896 Nickname: The Clarets **Club Colours:** Claret & blue

Club Contact Details 01293 822 000 mark@avocettm.co.uk

Previous Names: Horley >1975

Previous Leagues: Surrey Intermediate 1925-51, 55- Surrey Senior 1951-55, 71-78, London Spartan 1978-81, Athenian 1981-84, Combined Counties 1984-96, 03-19. Surrey County Senior 2002-03. Southern Combination 2019-21.

HONOURS

FA Comps: None

League: Surrey Intermediate 1926-27, Eastern Section 1950-51. Surrey Senior 1976-77.

11-12		12-13		13-14		14-15		15-16		16-17		17-18		18-19		19-20		20-21	
CCP	7	CCP	12	CCP	19	CCP	12	CCP	6	CCP	7	CCP	14	CCP	10	SCP	n&v	SCP	n&v
FAC	1Q	FAC	Pr	FAC	1Q	FAC	EP	FAC	Pr	FAC	EP	FAC	P	FAC	P	FAC	1Q	FAC	P
FAV	2Q	FAV	1P	FAV	1Q	FAV	3P	FAV	1Q	FAV	1P	FAV	4P	FAV	2P	FAV	1P	FAV	2P

GROUND: The New Defence, Anderson Way, Horley RH6 8SP

Nearest Railway Station Horley

Bus Route Metrobus 100, 526

Capacity: 1800
Seats: 150
Covered: 100

JERSEY BULLS

Combined Counties Premier South

Founded 2018 Nickname: Bulls **Club Colours:** Red & white

Club Contact Details info@bulls.je 01534 449615 (Stadium)

Previous Names: None

Previous Leagues: None

HONOURS

FA Comps: None

League: None

11-12		12-13		13-14		14-15		15-16		16-17		17-18		18-19		19-20		20-21	
																CC1	n&v	CC1	n&v

GROUND: Springfield Stadium, Janvrin Road, Saint Helier, Jersey JE2 4LF

Bus Route No.15 from Jersey Airport.

Capacity: 7,000
Seats: 992

KNAPHILL

Combined Counties Premier South

Founded 1924 Nickname: The Knappers **Club Colours:** Red and black

Club Contact Details 01483 475 150

Previous Names: None

Previous Leagues: Woking & District. Surrey Intermediate (Western) > 2007

HONOURS

FA Comps: None

League: Woking & District League 1978-79.
Surrey Intermediate League Division Three 1980-81, Division One 2005-06, Premier 06-07.

11-12		12-13		13-14		14-15		15-16		16-17		17-18		18-19		19-20		20-21	
CC1	12	CC1	12	CC1	3	CCP	13	CCP	5	CCP	14	CCP	8	CCP	11	CCP	n&v	CCP	n&v
						FAC	1Q	FAC	EP	FAC	EPr	FAC	2Q	FAC	EP	FAC	P	FAC	EP
FAV	1Q	FAV	1Q	FAV	2P	FAV	2P	FAV	4P	FAV	3P	FAV	2Q	FAV	1Q	FAV	2Q	FAV	1Q

GROUND: Brookwood Country Park, Redding Way, Knaphill GU21 2AY

Nearest Railway Station Brookwood or Woking

Bus Route Arriva 34, 35

Capacity: 1,000
Seats: 100

MOLESEY

Combined Counties Premier South

Founded 1946 Nickname: The Moles **Club Colours:** White & black

Club Contact Details 020 8979 4823

Previous Names: None.

Previous Leagues: Surrey Intermediate 1946-53. Surrey Senior 1953-59. Spartan 1959-73. Athenian 1973-77. Isthmian 1977-2008, 15-19. Combined Counties 2008-15.

HONOURS

FA Comps: None

League: Surrey Intermediate 1946-47. Surrey Senior 1957-58. Combined Counties Premier Division 2014-15.

11-12		12-13		13-14		14-15		15-16		16-17		17-18		18-19		19-20		20-21	
CCP	5	CCP	10	CCP	11	CCP	1	Isth1S	9	Isth1S	19	Isth1S	23	IsthSC	19	CCP	n&v	CCP	n&v
FAC	EP	FAC	EP	FAC	Pr	FAC	P	FAC	1Q	FAC	P	FAC	P	FAC	Pr	FAC	EPr	FAC	EP
FAV	1P	FAV	1Q	FAV	1Q	FAV	2Q	FAT	3Q	FAT	P	FAT	P	FAT	1Q	FAV	2Q	FAV	2Q

GROUND: 412 Walton Road, West Molesey KT8 2JG
Nearest Railway Station Hampton - 1.5km
Bus Route Grange Road - stop 150m away

Capacity: 4,000
Seats: 160
Covered: Yes

RAYNES PARK VALE

Combined Counties Premier South

Founded 1995 Nickname: The Vale **Club Colours:** Blue and yellow

Club Contact Details 0208 540 8843

Previous Names: Malden Vale and Raynes Park merged in 1995

Previous Leagues: None

HONOURS

FA Comps: None

League: Combined Counties Division One 2002-03.

11-12		12-13		13-14		14-15		15-16		16-17		17-18		18-19		19-20		20-21	
CCP	9	CCP	11	CCP	10	CCP	15	CCP	15	CCP	23	CC1	5	CCP	5	CCP	n&v	CCP	n&v
FAC	P	FAC	Pr	FAC	Pr	FAC	Pr	FAC	EP	FAC	EP	FAC	EP	FAC	Pr	FAC	EP	FAC	EP
FAV	1P	FAV	2Q	FAV	1Q	FAV	1P	FAV	1Q	FAV	1Q	FAV	1Q	FAV	1Q	FAV	2P	FAV	2P

GROUND: Grand Drive, Raynes Park SW20 9DZ
Nearest Railway Station Raynes Park (9 mins away). **Underground:** Morden (take 163 bus for 10 mins, walk from Blenheim Road)
Bus Route London Buses 152 & 163

Capacity: 1500
Seats: 120
Covered: 100

REDHILL

Combined Counties Premier South

Founded 1894 Nickname: Reds/Lobsters **Club Colours:** Red & white

Club Contact Details 01737 762 129

Previous Names: None

Previous Leagues: E & W Surrey. Spartan 1909-10. Southern Sub. London 1921-23. Athenian 1923-84. Sussex County 1984-2013. Isthmian 2013-15.

HONOURS

FA Comps: None

League: London League 1922-23. Athenian League 1924-25, 83-84.

11-12		12-13		13-14		14-15		15-16		16-17		17-18		18-19		19-20		20-21	
SxC1	10	SxC1	2	Isth1S	22	Isth1S	23	CCP	20	CC1	2	CCP	6	CCP	12	CCP	n&v	CCP	n&v
FAC	1Q	FAC	1Q	FAC	1Q	FAC	3Q	FAC	EP	FAC	P	FAC	P	FAC	EP	FAC	P	FAC	EP
FAV	2Q	FAV	1Q	FAT	P	FAT	Pr	FAV	2Q	FAV	1Q	FAV	1Q	FAV	1P	FAV	2P	FAV	2Q

GROUND: Kiln Brow, Three Arch Road, Redhill, Surrey RH1 5AE
Nearest Railway Station Redhill (mainline) Earlswood
Bus Route 100, 400, 420, 430, 435, 460

Capacity: 2,000
Seats: 150
Covered: 150

SHEERWATER

Combined Counties Premier South

Founded 1958 Nickname: Sheers **Club Colours:** All royal blue

Club Contact Details 07791 612 008

Previous Names: None

Previous Leagues: Woking & District 1958-67. Surrey County Intermediate 1967-78. Surrey Senior 1972-78. Combined Counties 1978-82. Surrey Premier (FM) 1982-93, 94-2000. Surrey County Senior 2000-03.

HONOURS

FA Comps: None

League: Combined Counties Division One 2018-19

11-12		12-13		13-14		14-15		15-16		16-17		17-18		18-19		19-20		20-21	
CC1	18	CC1	15	CC1	11	CC1	14	CC1	13	CC1	9	CC1	4	CC1	1	CCP	n&v	CCP	n&v
																FAC	EP	FAC	EP
														FAV	1P	FAV	1Q	FAV	1P

GROUND: Woking FC, The Laithwaite Community Stadium, Kingfield Rd, Woking, Surrey GU22 9AA **Capacity:** 6,200

Nearest Railway Station Woking - about 15 mins from the ground. **Seats:** 2,500

Bus Route 34 & 462 **Covered:** 3,900

WALTON & HERSHAM

Combined Counties Premier South

Founded 1945 Nickname: Swans **Club Colours:** Red and white

Club Contact Details waltonhersham2019@gmail.com

Previous Names: Walton FC (Founded in 1895) amalgamated with Hersham FC in 1945.

Previous Leagues: Corinthian 1945-50, Athenian 1950-71. Isthmian 1971-2016.

HONOURS

FA Comps: Amateur Cup 1972-73

League: Corinthian 1946-47, 47-48, 48-49. Athenian League 1968-69.

11-12		12-13		13-14		14-15		15-16		16-17		17-18		18-19		19-20		20-21	
Isth1S	11	Isth1S	18	Isth1S	21	Isth1S	17	Isth1S	22	CCP	5	CCP	4	CCP	20	CC1	n&v	CC1	n&v
FAC	1Q	FAC	1Qr	FAC	P	FAC	P	FAC	P	FAC	Pr	FAC	Pr	FAC	EP	FAC	EP		
FAT	P	FAT	1Q	FAT	P	FAT	1Q	FAT	P	FAV	2P	FAV	3P	FAV	1P	FAV	2Q	FAV	4P

GROUND: Waterside Drive, Walton-on-Thames, Surrey KT12 2JP **Capacity:** 5,000

Nearest Railway Station Walton-on-Thames less a mile from the ground. **Seats:** 400

Covered: 2,500

CLUB MOVEMENTS

DIVISION ONE - IN: AFC Aldermaston, Chalvey Sports, Langley & Woodley Utd (LM - HL1E). Berks County (P - TVL). Enfield Borough, Hillingdon Borough, London Lions & Rayners Lane (LM - SSM1). Hilltop and London Samurai (P - MCL).

OUT: Ash United and Fleet Spurs (LM - WX1). Chessington & Hook, Tooting Bec and Westside (LM - SCE1). Dorking Wanderers Res, Epsom & Ewell and Godalming (LM - SC1). Farnham Town, Jersey Bulls and Walton & Hersham (P - CCPS).

AFC ALDERMASTON

Combined Counties Division One

Founded 1952 Nickname: The Atomics **Club Colours:** Red & black

Club Contact Details secretary@afcaldermaston.co.uk

HONOURS FA Comps: None

League: None

11-12	12-13	13-14	14-15	15-16	16-17	17-18	18-19	19-20	20-21
HantP 9	HantP 8	HantP 10	ReadP 5	ReadP 7	Hel1E 7	Hel1E 11	Hel1E 3	Hel1E n&v	Hel1E n&v
						FAV 1Q		FAV 2Q	

GROUND: Thatcham Town FC, Waterside Park, Crookham Hill, Thatcham RG19 4PA

Nearest Railway Station Thatcham - 1.6km.

Bus Route Vincent Road stop - 287m away.

AFC HAYES

Combined Counties Division One

Founded 1976 Nickname: The Brooks **Club Colours:** Blue and white stripes

Club Contact Details 020 8845 0110

HONOURS FA Comps: None

League: Spartan South Midlands Premier South 1997-98.

11-12	12-13	13-14	14-15	15-16	16-17	17-18	18-19	19-20	20-21
SthC 10	SthC 15	SthC 18	SthC 22	CCP 16	CCP 17	CCP 18	CCP 19	CC1 n&v	CC1 n&v
FAC 1Q	FAC P	FAC P	FAC 1Q	FAC Pr	FAC P	FAC EP	FAC EP	FAC EPr	
FAT 1Q	FAT P	FAT 1Q	FAT Pr	FAV 2Q	FAV 1Q	FAV 2Q	FAV 1Q	FAV 1P	

GROUND: Farm Park, Kingshill Avenue, Hayes UB4 8DD

Nearest Railway Station Northholt or Haye & Harlington

Bus Route No.90

BAGSHOT

Combined Counties Division One

Founded 1906 Nickname: **Club Colours:** Yellow & blue

Club Contact Details 07971 147 315

HONOURS FA Comps: None

League: Aldershot & District Division Two 2005-06, Division One 2008-09,
Senior Division 2011-12, 12-13, 13-14, 15-16.

11-12	12-13	13-14	14-15	15-16	16-17	17-18	18-19	19-20	20-21
A&DS 1	A&DS 1	A&DS 1	A&DS 1	A&DS 1	CC1 8	CC1 19	CC1 13	CC1 n&v	CC1 n&v
						FAV 1Q	FAV 1Q	FAV 2Q	FAV 1Q

GROUND: Badshot Lea FC, Westfield Lane, Wrecclesham, Farnham GU10 4QP

Nearest Railway Station Aldershot

Bus Route Stagecoach 18 from Aldershot Bus Station - about 28 min journey via 31 stops to Westfield Lane.

BEDFONT & FELTHAM

Combined Counties Division One

Founded 2012 Nickname: The Yellows **Club Colours:** Yellow & blue

Club Contact Details 020 8890 7264

HONOURS FA Comps: None

League: None

11-12	12-13	13-14	14-15	15-16	16-17	17-18	18-19	19-20	20-21
	CC1 13	CC1 5	CC1 5	CC1 2	CCP 22	CC1 17	CC1 5	CC1 n&v	CC1 n&v
			FAC 1Q	FAC 1Q	FAC EP	FAC EP	FAC EP		
	FAV 2Q	FAV 1P	FAV 1Q	FAV 1Q	FAV 2Q	FAV 1Q	FAV 1P	FAV 2P	FAV 1Q

GROUND: The Orchard, Hatton Road, Bedfont TW14 9QT

Nearest Railway Station Hatton Cross (Piccadilly Line)

Bus Route London Transport 203, H25, H26

BERKS COUNTY

Combined Counties Division One

Founded 2009 Nickname: Club Colours: Maroon & light blue

Club Contact Details 07810 853 986

HONOURS FA Comps: None

League: None

11-12	12-13	13-14	14-15	15-16	16-17	17-18	18-19	19-20	20-21
			THVaP 9	THVaP 13	THVaP 11	THVaP 10	THVaP 5	THVaP n&v	THVaP 2

GROUND: Binfield FC, Hill Farm Lane, Bracknell, Bracknell Forest RG42 5NR

Nearest Railway Station Bracknell - 3.9km

Bus Route Church Lane North - 628m

BRITISH AIRWAYS

Combined Counties Division One

Founded 1947 Nickname: Club Colours: Blue and white

Club Contact Details britishairwaysfc.co.uk

HONOURS FA Comps: None

League: Middlesex County Premier Division 2012-13, 17-18.

11-12	12-13	13-14	14-15	15-16	16-17	17-18	18-19	19-20	20-21
LonCom 1	MidxP 1	MidxP 7	MidxP 11	MidxP 6	MidxP 2	MidxP 1	CC1 10	CC1 n&v	CC1 n&v
							FAV 1Q	FAV 1Q	FAV 1Q

GROUND: Bedfont & Feltham FC, The Orchard, Hatton Road, Bedfont TW14 9QT

Nearest Railway Station Hatton Cross (Piccadilly Line)

Bus Route London Transport 203, H25, H26

CHALVEY SPORTS

Combined Counties Division One

Founded 1885 Nickname: The Stab-monks Club Colours: Blue & black

Club Contact Details 07525 441 926

HONOURS FA Comps: None

League: Great Western Combination 1954-55. East Berkshire Division One 1992-93, Premier 96-97.
Hellenic Division Two East 2016-17, 17-18.

11-12	12-13	13-14	14-15	15-16	16-17	17-18	18-19	19-20	20-21
EBkP 8	EBkP 7	EBkP 2	EBkP 2	EBkP 2	Hel2E 1	Hel2E 1	Hel1E 8	Hel1E n&v	Hel1E n&v
								FAV 1Q	FAV 1Q

GROUND: Arbour Park, Stoke Road, Slough SL2 5AY

Nearest Railway Station Slough

Bus Route First Group 1, 13, 12, 14, 353.

COVE

Combined Counties Division One

Founded 1897 Nickname: None Club Colours: Yellow and black

Club Contact Details 01252 543 615

HONOURS FA Comps: None

League: Combined Counties League 2000-01.

11-12	12-13	13-14	14-15	15-16	16-17	17-18	18-19	19-20	20-21
CCP 11	CCP 3	CCP 5	CCP 4	CCP 22	CC1 17	CC1 18	CC1 18	CC1 n&v	CC1 n&v
FAC EP	FAC P	FAC 1Q	FAC EP	FAC P	FAC EP				
FAV 2Q	FAV 2Q	FAV 2P	FAV 1Q	FAV 1P	FAV 1Q	FAV 1Q	FAV 1Q	FAV 1Q	FAV 1Q

GROUND: Oak Farm Fields, 7 Squirrels Lane, Farnborough GU14 8PB

Nearest Railway Station Farnborough Main - 16min walk from there.

Bus Route No. 1 to Farnborough Rail station (17 min walk to ground), No. 10 to Beta Road (6 min walk)

ENFIELD BOROUGH

Combined Counties Division One

Founded 2016 Nickname: Panthers **Club Colours:** Red & black

Club Contact Details 07493 377 484

HONOURS FA Comps: None

League: None

11-12	12-13	13-14	14-15	15-16	16-17	17-18	18-19	19-20	20-21
					SSM2 3	SSM1 10	SSM1 9	SSM1 n&v	SSM1 n&v
						FAV 2P	FAV 1P	FAV 2Q	FAV 2Q

GROUND: Wingate & Finchley FC, Maurice Rebak Stadium, Summers Lane, N12 0PD

Nearest Railway Station New Southgate - 2.3km

Bus Route 134, 263 & 382

EVERSLEY & CALIFORNIA

Combined Counties Division One

Founded 1910 Nickname: The Boars **Club Colours:** Yellow and blue

Club Contact Details eversleyandcalifornia.co.uk

HONOURS FA Comps: None

League: Surrey Elite Intermediate 2008-09.

11-12	12-13	13-14	14-15	15-16	16-17	17-18	18-19	19-20	20-21
CC1 5	CC1 4	CC1 2	CC1 9	CC1 5	CC1 6	CC1 9	CC1 16	CC1 n&v	CC1 n&v
						FAC EP			
			FAV 2Q		FAV 2Q	FAV 1Q	FAV 1P	FAV 1Q	FAV 1Q

GROUND: ESA Sports Complex, Halls Way, off Fox Lane, Eversley RG27 0NS

Nearest Railway Station Sandhurst (Great Western)

Bus Route Nos 14 & 7

FC DEPORTIVO GALICIA

Combined Counties Division One

Founded 1968 Nickname: Depor **Club Colours:** Blue and white

Club Contact Details fcdeportivogalicia.com

HONOURS FA Comps: None

League: Middlesex County Premier Division 2016-17.

11-12	12-13	13-14	14-15	15-16	16-17	17-18	18-19	19-20	20-21
MidxP 12	MidxP 13	MidxP 6	MidxP 12	MidxP 13	MidxP 1	CC1 12	CC1 14	CC1 n&v	CC1 n&v
					FAV 1Q	FAV 2Q	FAV 1P	FAV 2Q	FAV 2Q

GROUND: Hatten Road, Feltham, Middlesex TW14 9JR

Nearest Railway Station Hatton Cross or Feltham BR

Bus Route London Transport 203, H25, H26

HILLINGDON BOROUGH

Combined Counties Division One

Founded 1990 Nickname: The Hillmen, Boro **Club Colours:** White & royal blue

Club Contact Details 01895 639 544 accounts@middlesexstadium.com

HONOURS FA Comps: None

League: None

11-12	12-13	13-14	14-15	15-16	16-17	17-18	18-19	19-20	20-21
SSM P 10	SSM P 19	SSM P 11	SSM P 22	SSM1 16	SSM1 9	SSM1 16	SSM1 16	SSM1 n&v	SSM1 n&v
FAC EP	FAC EP	FAC P	FAC EP	FAC EPr					
FAV 1P	FAV 2Q	FAV 1P	FAV 2Q	FAV 1Q	FAV 2Q	FAV 2Q		FAV 2Q	

GROUND: Middlesex Stadium, Breakspear Rd, Ruislip HA4 7SB

Nearest Railway Station Willow Lawn - 737m

Bus Route Howletts Lane - stop 98m away

HILLTOP

Combined Counties Division One

Founded 2005 | Nickname: | **Club Colours:** White and Blue

Club Contact Details

HONOURS FA Comps: None

League: Middlesex County Division Two 2017-18, Division One West 2018-19.

11-12	12-13	13-14	14-15	15-16	16-17	17-18	18-19	19-20	20-21
			Midx2 7	Midx2 9	MidxCom 2	Midx2 1	Midx1W 1	MidxP n&v	MidxP n&v

GROUND: Hillingdon Borough FC, Middlesex Stadium, Breakspear Road, Ruislip HA4 7SB

Nearest Railway Station Willow Lawn - 737m

Bus Route Howletts Lane - stop 98m away

KENSINGTON & EALING BOROUGH

Combined Counties Division One

Founded 2012 | Nickname: | **Club Colours:** Green and white

Club Contact Details

HONOURS FA Comps: None

League: None

11-12	12-13	13-14	14-15	15-16	16-17	17-18	18-19	19-20	20-21
		Midx2 3	Midx1SE 6	SSM2 5	SSM1 12	CC1 15	CC1 15	CC1 n&v	CC1 n&v
						FAV 1P	FAV 2P	FAV 1Q	

GROUND: Middlesex FA, Rectory Park, Ruislip Road, Northolt UB5 5FA

Nearest Railway Station Greenford (Great Western & Central Line), South Greenford (Great Western).

Bus Route 297, E10, E2, E7 & E9 stop within walking distance.

LANGLEY

Combined Counties Division One

Founded | Nickname: The Villagers | **Club Colours:** Red and white

Club Contact Details 07935 046 504 langleyfc2016@gmail.com

HONOURS FA Comps: None

League: East Berkshire Division One 2013-14, Premier Division 2016-17.

11-12	12-13	13-14	14-15	15-16	16-17	17-18	18-19	19-20	20-21
		EBk1 1	EBkP 5	EBkP 4	EBkP 1	EBkP 2	Hel2E 2	Hel1E n&v	Hel1E n&v
								FAV 1Q	

GROUND: Slough Town FC, Arbour Park, Stoke Road, Slough SL2 5AY

Nearest Railway Station Slough

Bus Route First Group 1, 13, 12, 14, 353.

LONDON LIONS

Combined Counties Division One

Founded 1995 | Nickname: Lions | **Club Colours:** All blue

Club Contact Details 0208 441 6051

HONOURS FA Comps: None

League: Hertfordshire Senior County Division One 1999-2000, Premier 09-10, 16-17. Spartan South Midlands Division One 2012-13.

11-12	12-13	13-14	14-15	15-16	16-17	17-18	18-19	19-20	20-21
SSM1 7	SSM1 1	SSM P 22	SSM1 17	HertP 5	HertP 1	SSM1 6	SSM1 6	SSM1 n&v	SSM1 n&v
	FAC 1Q	FAC EPr					FAC P		FAC EP
FAV 1Q	FAV 2P	FAV 2Q			FAV 1Q	FAV 2P	FAV 2Q	FAV 1Q	FAV 2Q

GROUND: Maccabi London Sports Ground, Rowley Lane, Barnet EN5 3HW

Nearest Railway Station Elstree & Borehamwood - 2.4km

Bus Route Buses stop on Rowley Lane

LONDON SAMURAI ROVERS

Combined Counties Division One

Founded 2017 Nickname: **Club Colours:** Red & black

Club Contact Details

HONOURS FA Comps: None

League: None

11-12	12-13	13-14	14-15	15-16	16-17	17-18	18-19	19-20	20-21
						Midx1SE 10	Midx1SE 4	MidxP n&v	MidxP n&v

GROUND: CB Hounslow Sports Club, Green Lane, Hounslow TW4 6DH
Nearest Railway Station Hatton Cross (underground) Piccadilly Line.
Bus Route London Transport 423 stops almost opposite the ground, 482 & 203 stop on Great South West Rd close to Green Lane.

RAYNERS LANE

Combined Counties Division One

Founded 1933 Nickname: The Lane **Club Colours:** Yellow and green

Club Contact Details 0208 868 8724

HONOURS FA Comps: None

League: Hellenic Division One 1982-83, Division One East 2012-13.

11-12	12-13	13-14	14-15	15-16	16-17	17-18	18-19	19-20	20-21
Hel1E 3	Hel1E 1	Hel1E 9	Hel1E 7	Hel1E 5	Hel1E 11	SSM1 13	SSM1 12	SSM1 n&v	SSM1 n&v
				FAV 2Q	FAV 2Q	FAV 2Q	FAV 1P	FAV 1Q	FAV 1Q

GROUND: Tithe Farm Social Club, Rayners Lane, South Harrow HA2 0XH
Nearest Railway Station Rayners Lane underground - 680m
Bus Route Clitheroe Avenue - stop 64m away

SANDHURST TOWN

Combined Counties Division One

Founded 1910 Nickname: Fizzers **Club Colours:** Red and black

Club Contact Details info@sandhursttownfc.org

HONOURS FA Comps: None

League: Reading & Disttrict Division One 1932-33, Premier 33-34.
Aldershot & District Division One 1980-81.

11-12	12-13	13-14	14-15	15-16	16-17	17-18	18-19	19-20	20-21
CCP 15	CCP 21	CC1 13	CC1 16	CC1 11	Hel1E 8	Hel1E 4	CC1 6	CC1 n&v	CC1 n&v
FAC EP	FAC EP	FAC EPr					FAC EPr		FAC EP
FAV 1Q	FAV 1P	FAV 1Q			FAV 1Q	FAV 1P	FAV 1Q	FAV 1Q	FAV 1P

GROUND: Bracknell Town FC, Larges Lane, Bracknell RG12 9AN (Until refurb complete at Bottom Meadow)
Nearest Railway Station Bracknell - 0.5km from the ground.
Bus Route Bracknell bus station 0.5km from the ground.

WALLINGFORD TOWN

Combined Counties Division One

Founded 1995 Nickname: Wally **Club Colours:** Red & white

Club Contact Details 01491 835 044

HONOURS FA Comps: None

League: None

11-12	12-13	13-14	14-15	15-16	16-17	17-18	18-19	19-20	20-21
NBk 1 11	NBk 1 9	NBk 1 9	NBk 1 4	NBk 1 6	NBk 1 3	Hel1E 7	Hel1E 7	Hel1E n&v	Hel1E n&v
FAV 1Q						FAV 2Q	FAV 1Q		FAV 1Q

GROUND: Wallingford Sports Park, Hithercroft Road, Wallingford OX10 9RB
Nearest Railway Station Wallingford - 366m
Bus Route Moses Winter Way stop - 58m away

WOODLEY UNITED

Combined Counties Division One

Founded 1904 Nickname: Woods or United **Club Colours:** Sky blue

Club Contact Details 0118 9453 555 info@woodleyunitedfc.co.uk

HONOURS FA Comps: None

League: Wargrave & District 1909-10, 26-27. Reading & District Division Three 28-29, Division One 32-33, Division Two 50-51, Premier 57-58, 58-59, 85-86. Reading Division Four Kennet 91-92, Division Three Kennet 92-93, Senior Division 2008-09.

11-12	12-13	13-14	14-15	15-16	16-17	17-18	18-19	19-20	20-21
Hel1E 5	Hel1E 3	Hel1E 14	Hel1E 8	Hel1E 13	Hel1E 2	Hel P 19	Hel1E 11	Hel1E n&v	Hel1E n&v
						FAC EP	FAC EP		
			FAV 2Q	FAV 1Q	FAV 1Q	FAV 1Q	FAV 1Q	FAV 1Q	FAV 2Q

GROUND: Reading City FC, Scours Lane, Tilehurst, Reading, Berkshire, RG30 6AY

Nearest Railway Station Tilehurst - 1.2km

Bus Route Cold Store stop - 277m away

BRANTHAM ATHLETIC

Eastern Counties Premier

Founded 1887 Nickname: The Imps **Club Colours:** All blue

Club Contact Details 01206 392 506 (ground) secretary@branthamathletic.com

Previous Names: Brantham & Stutton United 1996-98.
Previous Leagues: Eastern Counties. Suffolk & Ipswich.

HONOURS

FA Comps: None
League: Essex & Suffolk Border 1972-73, 73-74, 75-76, 76-77. Suffolk & Ipswich Senior League 2007-08.

11-12		12-13		13-14		14-15		15-16		16-17		17-18		18-19		19-20		20-21	
ECP	3	ECP	4	ECP	11	ECP	8	ECP	11	ECP	8	ECP	5	ECP	8	ECP	n&v	ECP	n&v
FAC	P	FAC	P	FAC	1Q	FAC	EPr	FAC	1Q	FAC	EP	FAC	P	FAC	2Q	FAC	EP	FAC	2Q
FAV	1P	FAV	5P	FAV	4P	FAV	3P	FAV	1P	FAV	2Q	FAV	1Q	FAV	2Q	FAV	1P	FAV	1Q

GROUND: Brantham Leisure Centre, New Village, Brantham CO11 1RZ **Capacity:** 1,200
Nearest Railway Station Manningtree - 1.5km **Seats:** 200
Bus Route Temple Pattle (Brooklands Close) - 120m **Covered:** 200

CLUB MOVEMENTS

PREMIER DIVISION - IN: Fakenham Town, Lakenheath, March Town United and Mulbarton Wanderers (P - EC1N).

OUT: FC Clacton and Stanway Rovers (LM - ES). Stowmarket Town (P - IsthN).

ELY CITY

Eastern Counties Premier

Founded 1885 Nickname: Robins **Club Colours:** Red

Club Contact Details 01353 662 035 (ground) derek.oakey11@gmail.com

Previous Names: None.
Previous Leagues: Cambridgeshire 1901-02, 03-51. Peterborough & District 1951-58. Central Alliance 1958-60.

HONOURS

FA Comps: None
League: Peterborough & District 1955-56.
Eastern Counties Division One 1996-97.

11-12		12-13		13-14		14-15		15-16		16-17		17-18		18-19		19-20		20-21	
ECP	2	ECP	11	ECP	17	ECP	20	EC1	2	ECP	13	ECP	14	ECP	18	ECP	n&v	ECP	n&v
FAC	1Qr	FAC	Pr	FAC	EP	FAC	EP	FAC	EPr	FAC	EP	FAC	EP	FAC	EP	FAC	Pr	FAC	1Q
FAV	1Q	FAV	4P	FAV	2Pr	FAV	1Q	FAV	2Q	FAV	5P	FAV	2P	FAV	2Q	FAV	1Q	FAV	1Q

GROUND: The Ellgia Stadium, Downham Road, Ely CB6 2SH **Capacity:** 1,500
Nearest Railway Station Ely - 2.5km **Seats:** 200
Bus Route 12, 125, 39 & 9 **Covered:** 350

FAKENHAM TOWN

Eastern Counties Premier

Founded 1884 Nickname: Ghosts **Club Colours:** Amber & black

Club Contact Details 01328 851 735 (ground)

Previous Names: None
Previous Leagues: Norwich & District. Norfolk & Suffolk/Anglian Combination 1935-88.

HONOURS

FA Comps: None
League: Anglian Combination Division One 1971-72.

11-12		12-13		13-14		14-15		15-16		16-17		17-18		18-19		19-20		20-21	
EC1	11	EC1	5	EC1	2	ECP	13	ECP	17	ECP	15	ECP	22	EC1N	6	EC1N	n&v	EC1N	n&v
		FAC	EP	FAC	EP	FAC	EPr	FAC	P	FAC	EP	FAC	EP	FAC	EP	FAC	EP		
FAV	1Q	FAV	2Q	FAV	2Q	FAV	2P	FAV	2Q	FAV	2Q	FAV	1Q	FAV	1Q	FAV	1Q	FAV	4P

GROUND: Clipbush Park, Clipbush Lane, Fakenham, Norfolk NR21 8SW

Bus Route Sanders Coaches No.9

GORLESTON

Eastern Counties Premier

Founded 1887 Nickname: The Greens **Club Colours:** Green

Club Contact Details 01493 602 802 (Ground) colin-bray@sky.com

Previous Names: None

Previous Leagues: Aldred/Yamouth & District 1900-08. Norfolk & Suffolk/Anglian Combination 1908-35, 60-69. Eastern Counties 1935-60.

HONOURS

FA Comps: None

League: Yamouth & District 1905-06, 07-08. Norfolk & Suffolk/Anglian Comb. 1920-21, 25-26, 29-30, 31-32, 32-33, 33-34, 34-35, 68-69. Eastern Counties 1952-53, 72-73, 79-80, 80-81, Division One 1995-96, 2010-11.

11-12		12-13		13-14		14-15		15-16		16-17		17-18		18-19		19-20		20-21	
ECP	12	ECP	3	ECP	4	ECP	12	ECP	16	ECP	4	ECP	7	ECP	15	ECP	n&v	ECP	n&v
FAC	1Q	FAC	P	FAC	1Q	FAC	EP	FAC	EP	FAC	EP	FAC	1Q	FAC	EP	FAC	P	FAC	P
FAV	2Q	FAV	1P	FAV	1P	FAV	1P	FAV	2P	FAV	4P	FAV	3P	FAV	2Q	FAV	1Q	FAV	3P

GROUND: Emerald Park, Woodfarm Lane, Gorleston, Norfolk NR31 9AQ

Nearest Railway Station Great Yarmouth

Bus Route 580, 881 & X1

HADLEIGH UNITED

Eastern Counties Premier

Founded 1892 Nickname: Brettsiders **Club Colours:** Navy blue

Club Contact Details 01473 822 165 (Ground) waffhenderson@aol.com

Previous Names: None

Previous Leagues: Ipswich & District/Suffolk & Ipswich 1929-91.

HONOURS

FA Comps: None

League: Suffolk & Ipswich 1953-54, 56-57, 73-74, 76-77, 78-79, Division Two 1958-59. Eastern Counties 1993-94, 2013-14.

11-12		12-13		13-14		14-15		15-16		16-17		17-18		18-19		19-20		20-21	
ECP	11	ECP	8	ECP	1	ECP	7	ECP	7	ECP	18	ECP	21	ECP	16	ECP	n&v	ECP	n&v
FAC	P	FAC	1Q	FAC	P	FAC	1Q	FAC	EP	FAC	EP	FAC	P	FAC	P	FAC	EP	FAC	EP
FAV	1Q	FAV	QF	FAV	5P	FAV	2P	FAV	2Q	FAV	2Q	FAV	2Q	FAV	2Q	FAV	1P	FAV	1Q

GROUND: The Millfield, Tinkers Lane, Duke St, Hadleigh IP7 5NF

Nearest Railway Station Manningtree

Bus Route 91

Capacity: 3,000
Seats: 250
Covered: 500

HAVERHILL ROVERS

Eastern Counties Premier

Founded 1886 Nickname: Rovers **Club Colours:** Red

Club Contact Details 01440 702 137 (ground) barbarajoneshrfc@outlook.com

Previous Names: None.

Previous Leagues: East Anglian. Essex & Suffolk Border.

HONOURS

FA Comps: None

League: Essex & Suffolk Border 1947-48, 62-63, 63-64. Eastern Counties 1978-79.

11-12		12-13		13-14		14-15		15-16		16-17		17-18		18-19		19-20		20-21	
ECP	14	ECP	10	ECP	7	ECP	17	ECP	12	ECP	16	ECP	19	ECP	12	ECP	n&v	ECP	n&v
FAC	1Q	FAC	P	FAC	P	FAC	EPr	FAC	EP	FAC	EP	FAC	Pr	FAC	2Q	FAC	EP	FAC	1Q
FAV	1P	FAV	1P	FAV	1Q	FAV	2Q	FAV	1Q	FAV	2Q	FAV	1Q	FAV	2Q	FAV	2Q	FAV	1P

GROUND: The New Croft, Chalkstone Way, Haverhill, Suffolk CB9 0BW

Nearest Railway Station Cambridge - take 13 Gold towards Haverhill - alight at Chalkstone Way Underpass, 1min walk from there.

Bus Route 13, 13A, 15 & 18

Capacity: 3,000
Seats: 200
Covered: 200

KIRKLEY & PAKEFIELD

Eastern Counties Premier

Founded 1886 Nickname: The Royals **Club Colours:** Royal blue

Club Contact Details 01502 513 549 (ground) secretarykpfc@outlook.com

Previous Names: Kirkley. Kirkley & Waveney 1929-33. Merged with Pakefield in 2007.

Previous Leagues: North Suffolk. Norfolk & Suffolk. Anglian Combination.

HONOURS

FA Comps: None

League: North Suffolk 1894-95, 96-97, 1901-02, 05-06, 07-08, 08-09.
Anglian Combination Premier Division 2001-02, 02-03.

11-12		12-13		13-14		14-15		15-16		16-17		17-18		18-19		19-20		20-21	
ECP	13	ECP	12	ECP	12	ECP	4	ECP	5	ECP	11	ECP	10	ECP	5	ECP	n&v	ECP	n&v
FAC	EP	FAC	P	FAC	P	FAC	P	FAC	2Q	FAC	P	FAC	EP	FAC	EPr	FAC	EPr	FAC	EP
FAV	1Q	FAV	1Q	FAV	2Q	FAV	2P	FAV	2P	FAV	1Q	FAV	2Q	FAV	2P	FAV	4P	FAV	2P

GROUND: The Bungalow, Walmer Road, Lowestoft NR33 7LE
Capacity: 2,000
Nearest Railway Station Oulton Broad South - 1.8km
Seats: 150
Bus Route 146 & 99
Covered: 150

LAKENHEATH

Eastern Counties Premier

Founded Nickname: **Club Colours:** Green & white

Club Contact Details lakenheathfc.secretary@gmail.com

Previous Names: None

Previous Leagues: Ouse Valley 1908. Essex & Suffolk Border. Norfolk & Suffolk >1964. Anglian Combination. Cambridgeshire County >2018.

HONOURS

FA Comps: None

League: Cambridgeshire County Senior Division A 2007-08, Premier 10-11.

11-12		12-13		13-14		14-15		15-16		16-17		17-18		18-19		19-20		20-21	
CamP	2	CamP	9	CamP	5	CamP	2	CamP	6	CamP	3	CamP	8	EC1N	5	EC1N	n&v	EC1N	n&v
																FAV	1Q	FAV	2Q

GROUND: The Nest, Wings Road, Lakenheath IP27 9HW
Nearest Railway Station Lakenheath 4.5km walk
Bus Route 201 from Mildenhall, 200 from Thetford

LONG MELFORD

Eastern Counties Premier

Founded 1868 Nickname: The Villagers **Club Colours:** Black & white

Club Contact Details 01787 312 187 (Ground) richardjpowell@outlook.com

Previous Names: N/A

Previous Leagues: Essex & Suffolk Border > 2003

HONOURS

FA Comps: None

League: Essex & Suffolk Border Champions x5.
Eastern Counties Division One 2014-15.

11-12		12-13		13-14		14-15		15-16		16-17		17-18		18-19		19-20		20-21	
EC1	9	EC1	13	EC1	11	EC1	1	ECP	9	ECP	17	ECP	16	ECP	17	ECP	n&v	ECP	n&v
FAC	P	FAC	EP					FAC	P	FAC	P	FAC	P	FAC	1Qr	FAC	P	FAC	1Q
FAV	1Q	FAV	1P	FAV	2Q	FAV	2Q	FAV	2Q	FAV	2Q	FAV	1Q	FAV	1Q	FAV	2Q	FAV	1Q

GROUND: Stoneylands Stadium, New Road, Long Melford, Suffolk CO10 9JY
Nearest Railway Station Sudbury - 4.6km
Bus Route 236

MARCH TOWN UNITED

Eastern Counties Premier

Foundec 1885 Nickname: Hares **Club Colours:** Amber & black

Club Contact Details 01354 653 073 (ground) chris@gbshealthandsafety.co.uk

Previous Names: March Town > 1950

Previous Leagues: United Counties 1948-54.

HONOURS

FA Comps: None

League: United Counties Division One 1953-54. Eastern Counties 1987-88.

11-12	12-13	13-14	14-15	15-16	16-17	17-18	18-19	19-20	20-21
EC1 4	EC1 14	EC1 19	EC1 8	EC1 11	EC1 16	EC1 17	EC1N 4	EC1N n&v	EC1N n&v
FAC Pr	FAC EP							FAC 1Q	
FAV 1Q	FAV 1Q	FAV 2Q			FAV 2Q	FAV 1Q	FAV 2Q	FAV 1P	FAV 2Q

GROUND: GER Sports Ground, Robin Goodfellows Lane, March, Cambs PE15 8HS

Nearest Railway Station March - 0.7km

Bus Route Darthill Road stop - 290m away

MILDENHALL TOWN

Eastern Counties Premier

Foundec 1898 Nickname: The Hall **Club Colours:** Amber & black

Club Contact Details 01638 713 449 (ground) mtfc@safepac.co.uk

Previous Names: None

Previous Leagues: Bury & District. Cambridgeshire. Cambridgeshire Premier. Eastern Counties > 2017. Isthmian 2017-19.

HONOURS

FA Comps: None

League: Eastern Counties Premier Division 2016-17.

11-12	12-13	13-14	14-15	15-16	16-17	17-18	18-19	19-20	20-21
ECP 7	ECP 7	ECP 10	ECP 10	ECP 6	ECP 1	Isth1N 22	IsthN 20	ECP n&v	ECP n&v
FAC EP	FAC EP	FAC 1Qr	FAC 1Q	FAC 2Q	FAC EP	FAC 1Qr	FAC P	FAC EP	FAC 1Q
FAV 2Q	FAV 1Q	FAT 1Pr	FAT 2Q	FAT 2P	FAT 2Q	FAT 3Q	FAT 1Q	FAV 2P	FAV 2P

GROUND: Recreation Way, Mildenhall, Suffolk IP28 7HG

Nearest Railway Station Kennett

Bus Route 727

Capacity: 2,000
Seats: 100
Covered: 200

MULBARTON WANDERERS

Eastern Counties Premier

Foundec 2002 Nickname: Wanderers **Club Colours:** Blue & black

Club Contact Details 07545 470 130 j.nurse21@btinternet.com

Previous Names: None

Previous Leagues: Central & South Norfolk 2002-09. Anglian Combination 2009-18.

HONOURS

FA Comps: None

League: Anglian Combination Division Five 2010-11, Division Four 11-12, Division One 14-15.

11-12	12-13	13-14	14-15	15-16	16-17	17-18	18-19	19-20	20-21
AnC4 1	AnC3 2	AnC3 2	AnC1 1	AnCP 8	AnCP 3	AnCP 2	EC1N 3	EC1N n&v	EC1N n&v
								FAC EPr	
							FAV 2Q	FAV 2Q	FAV 4P

GROUND: Mulberry Park, Mulbarton Common, Norfolk NR14 8AE

Nearest Railway Station Norwich (6.5 miles away)

Bus Route Regular services from Norwich City centre to the village of Mulbarton.

NEWMARKET TOWN

Eastern Counties Premier

Founded 1877 Nickname: The Jockeys **Club Colours:** Yellow & royal blue

Club Contact Details 01638 663 637 (ground) newmarket.secretary@gmail.com

Previous Names: None

Previous Leagues: Cambridgeshire Senior. Bury & District. Suffolk & Ipswich >1937. Eastern Counties 1937-52. Peterborough & District 1952-59.

HONOURS

FA Comps: None

League: Cambridgeshire Senior 1919-20. Bury & District 1926-27. Suffolk & Ipswich 1931-32, 32-33, 33-34. Peterborough & District 1957-58. Eastern Counties Division One 2008-09.

11-12	12-13	13-14	14-15	15-16	16-17	17-18	18-19	19-20	20-21
ECP 20	EC1 2	ECP 9	ECP 6	ECP 13	ECP 3	ECP 9	ECP 10	ECP n&v	ECP n&v
FAC EP	FAC EP	FAC Pr	FAC 1Q	FAC P	FAC EP	FAC P	FAC 1Q	FAC EPr	FAC P
FAV 2Q	FAV 2Q	FAV 2P	FAV 2Q	FAV 1P	FAV 2Q	FAV 1P	FAV 1P	FAV 2Qr	FAV 1Q

GROUND: The Tristel Stadium, Cricket Field Road, Off Cheveley Rd, Newmarket CB8 8BT

Nearest Railway Station Newmarket - 0.4km

Bus Route 11, 12,16, 18, 903 & 904

Capacity: 2,750 **Seats:** 144 **Covered:** 250

NORWICH UNITED

Eastern Counties Premier

Founded 1903 Nickname: Planters **Club Colours:** Yellow & blue

Club Contact Details 01603 716 963 (ground) norwich.utd.fc@gmail.com

Previous Names: Poringland & District > 1987

Previous Leagues: Norwich & District. Anglian Combination. Eastern Counties >2016. Isthmian 2016-18.

HONOURS

FA Comps: None

League: Anglian Combination Premier Division 1988-99.
Eastern Counties Division One 1990-91, 01-02, Premier Division 2014-15, 15-16.

11-12	12-13	13-14	14-15	15-16	16-17	17-18	18-19	19-20	20-21
ECP 9	ECP 13	ECP 6	ECP 1	ECP 1	Isth1N 9	Isth1N 24	ECP 11	ECP n&v	ECP n&v
FAC EP	FAC 1Q	FAC EP	FAC 2Qr	FAC Pr	FAC P	FAC P	FAC EP	FAC EP	FAC EP
FAV 2Q	FAV 2Q	FAV 4P	FAV 5P	FAV 2P	FAT P	FAT P	FAV 1Q	FAV 2P	FAV 3P

GROUND: Plantation Park, Blofield, Norwich NR13 4PL

Nearest Railway Station Brundall - 2.1km

Bus Route Surgery (Plantation Rd) stop - 48m away.

Capacity: 3,000 **Seats:** 100 **Covered:** 1,000

SWAFFHAM TOWN

Eastern Counties Premier

Founded 1892 Nickname: Pedlars **Club Colours:** Black & white

Club Contact Details 01760 722 700 (ground) rayewart@aol.com

Previous Names: None

Previous Leagues: Anglian Combination

HONOURS

FA Comps: None

League: Anglian Combination Division Two 1973-74.
Eastern Counties Division One 2000-01, Division One North 18-19.

11-12	12-13	13-14	14-15	15-16	16-17	17-18	18-19	19-20	20-21
EC1 13	EC1 9	EC1 7	EC1 2	ECP 18	ECP 21	EC1 4	EC1N 1	ECP n&v	ECP n&v
		FAC P	FAC EP	FAC EP	FAC EP	FAC P	FAC EP	FAC EP	FAC EP
FAV 1Q	FAV 1P	FAV 1Pr	FAV 1Q	FAV 1P	FAV 1P	FAV 2Q	FAV 3Pr	FAV 1Q	FAV 2Q

GROUND: The Pavillion, Shoemakers Lane, Swaffham, Norfolk PE37 7NS

Nearest Railway Station Peterborough - take A excel towards Norwich City Centre - alight at the Kings Arms, 10min walk from there.

Bus Route 6 & 61

THETFORD TOWN

Eastern Counties Premier

Founded 1883 Nickname: Brecklanders **Club Colours:** Claret

Club Contact Details 01842 766 120 (Ground) becsraynor@hotmail.com

Previous Names: None

Previous Leagues: Norwich & District. Norfolk & Suffolk. Founder member of Eastern Counties League

HONOURS

FA Comps: None

League: Norfolk & Suffolk League 1954-55.

11-12		12-13		13-14		14-15		15-16		16-17		17-18		18-19		19-20		20-21	
EC1	2	ECP	19	ECP	16	ECP	14	ECP	19	ECP	7	ECP	12	ECP	14	ECP	n&v	ECP	n&v
FAC	EP	FAC	EP	FAC	P	FAC	P	FAC	P	FAC	EP	FAC	EP	FAC	P	FAC	EP	FAC	P
FAV	2P	FAV	2Q	FAV	1P	FAV	2Q	FAV	1Q	FAV	2P	FAV	2P	FAV	2P	FAV	2Q	FAV	2Q

GROUND: Recreation Ground, Mundford Road, Thetford, Norfolk IP24 1NB

Nearest Railway Station Thetford - 0.5km

Bus Route 201, 84 & 86

WALSHAM LE WILLOWS

Eastern Counties Premier

Founded 1888 Nickname: The Willows **Club Colours:** Red & yellow

Club Contact Details 01359 259 298 (Ground) gordonaross2@gmail.com

Previous Names: None

Previous Leagues: St Edmundsbury/Bury & District 1907-89. Suffolk & Ipswich 1989-2004.

HONOURS

FA Comps: None

League: Suffolk & Ipswich Senior Division 2001-02, 02-03. Eastern Counties Division One 2006-07.

11-12		12-13		13-14		14-15		15-16		16-17		17-18		18-19		19-20		20-21	
ECP	17	ECP	6	ECP	8	ECP	15	ECP	14	ECP	14	ECP	17	ECP	9	ECP	n&v	ECP	n&v
FAC	Pr	FAC	EP	FAC	EP	FAC	EPr	FAC	EP	FAC	EPr	FAC	EPr	FAC	EP	FAC	EP	FAC	EP
FAV	1P	FAV	1Pr	FAV	2P	FAV	2Q	FAV	2Q	FAV	1P	FAV	2Q	FAV	2Q	FAV	2Q	FAV	2P

GROUND: Walsham-le-Willows Sports Club, Sumner Road, Walsham-le-Willows IP31 3AH

Seats: 100

Bus Route 338 **Covered:** 100

WHITTON UNITED

Eastern Counties Premier

Founded 1926 Nickname: The Boyos **Club Colours:** Green and white

Club Contact Details 07487 738 583 secretary@whittonunited.co.uk

Previous Names: None

Previous Leagues: Ipswich & District >68. Essex & Border. Ipswich District/Suffolk & Ipswich >1995.

HONOURS

FA Comps: None

League: Suffolk & Ipswich Senior 1946-47, 47-48, 65-66, 67-68, 92-93, 94-95.
Eastern Counties Division One 2013-14.

11-12		12-13		13-14		14-15		15-16		16-17		17-18		18-19		19-20		20-21	
EC1	3	EC1	7	EC1	1	ECP	11	ECP	20	EC1	11	EC1	3	ECP	13	ECP	n&v	ECP	n&v
FAC	EP	FAC	P	FAC	Pr	FAC	P	FAC	P	FAC	EPr			FAC	P	FAC	1Q	FAC	P
FAV	2P	FAV	1P	FAV	2Q	FAV	1P	FAV	1P	FAV	1Q	FAV	1P	FAV	2Q	FAV	1P	FAV	2Q

GROUND: King George V Playing Fields, Old Norwich Road, Ipswich IP1 6LE

Nearest Railway Station Westerfield - 2.9km

Bus Route Maypole (Old Norwich Rd) - 52m away

WOODBRIDGE TOWN

Eastern Counties Premier

Founded 1885 Nickname: The Woodpeckers **Club Colours:** Black & white

Club Contact Details 01394 385 308 (ground) marywtfc@gmail.com

Previous Names: None.

Previous Leagues: Ipswich & District. Suffolk & Ipswich.

HONOURS

FA Comps: None

League: Ipswich & District/Suffolk & Ipswich Senior 1912-13, 88-89, Division One 1986-87, 70-71.
Eastern Counties Division One 2017-18.

11-12		12-13		13-14		14-15		15-16		16-17		17-18		18-19		19-20		20-21	
ECP	6	ECP	15	ECP	20	EC1	17	EC1	9	EC1	4	EC1	1	ECP	2	ECP	n&v	ECP	n&v
FAC	EPr	FAC	EP	FAC	EP	FAC	EP					FAC	EP	FAC	1Q	FAC	P	FAC	EP
FAV	1Pr	FAV	2Q	FAV	2Q	FAV	1P	FAV	2Q	FAV	2Q	FAV	2Q	FAV	2P	FAV	4P	FAV	2P

GROUND: Notcutts Park, Fynn Road, Woodbridge IP12 4LS

Nearest Railway Station Woodbridge - 1.7km

Bus Route Ashton House (California) - 201m away

Capacity: 3,000
Seats: 50
Covered: 200

WROXHAM

Eastern Counties Premier

Founded 1892 Nickname: Yachtsmen **Club Colours:** Royal blue & white

Club Contact Details 01603 783 936 (ground) greenc@btinternet.com

Previous Names: None

Previous Leagues: East Norfolk. Norwich City. East Anglian. Norwich & Dist. Anglian Comb.

HONOURS

FA Comps: None

League: Anglian County League 1981-82, 82-83, 83-84, 84-85, 86-87.
Eastern Counties Division One 1988-89, Prem 91-92, 92-93, 93-94, 96-97, 97-98, 98-99, 2006-07, 11-12.

11-12		12-13		13-14		14-15		15-16		16-17		17-18		18-19		19-20		20-21	
ECP	1	Isth1N	14	Isth1N	22	Isth1N	8	Isth1N	22	Isth1N	23	ECP	13	ECP	7	ECP	n&v	ECP	n&v
FAC	3Q	FAC	1Q	FAC	1Q	FAC	2Q	FAC	1Q	FAC	P	FAC	EP	FAC	EPr	FAC	P	FAC	1Q
FAV	1P	FAT	1Qr	FAT	1Q	FAT	P	FAT	P	FAT	1Q	FAV	2Q	FAV	1P	FAV	QF	FAV	2P

GROUND: Trafford Park, Skinners Lane, Wroxham NR12 8SJ

Nearest Railway Station Hoveton & Wroxham - 1.6km

Bus Route 722, 724 and 717.

Capacity: 2,500
Seats: 50
Covered: 250

CLUB MOVEMENTS

DIVISION ONE NORTH - IN: FC Parson Drove and Peterborough North End Sports (P - PD).
Harlestone Town and UEA (P - AC). Huntingdon Town and Whittlesey Athletic (LM - UC1).
OUT: AFC Sudbury Reserves, Conard United, Haverhill Borough, Ipswich Wanderers and Park View (LM - ECD1S).
Fakenham Town, Lakenheath, March Town United and Mulbarton Wanderers (P - ECP).
Kings Lynn Town Reserves withdrew.

DIVISION ONE SOUTH - IN: AFC Sudbury Reserves, Conard United, Haverhill Borough, Ipswich Wanderers and Park View (LM - ECD1N). Buckhurst Hill (P - EO).
OUT: AFC Sudbury Reserves, Conard United, Haverill Borough and Park View (LM - ECD1S).
Athletic Newham, Little Oakley and White Ensign (P - ESP).
Fakenham Town, Lakenheath, March Town United and Mulbarton Wanderers (P - ECP).

DEBENHAM LC

Eastern Counties Division One North

Founded 1991 Nickname: The Hornets **Club Colours:** Yellow & black

Club Contact Details 01728 861 101 (ground)

HONOURS FA Comps: None

League: Suffolk & Ipswich Division Seven 1991-92, Four 96-97, Three 99-2000, One 03-04.

11-12	12-13	13-14	14-15	15-16	16-17	17-18	18-19	19-20	20-21
EC1 7	EC1 15	EC1 12	EC1 7	EC1 13	EC1 12	EC1 7	EC1N 11	EC1N n&v	EC1N n&v
FAC EP	FAC EP			FAC EP					
FAV 2Q	FAV 1Qr	FAV 1P	FAV 2Q	FAV 2Q	FAV 1Q	FAV 1Pr	FAV 1Pr	FAV 2Q	FAV 2Q

GROUND: Debenham Leisure Centre, Gracechurch Street, Debenham IP14 6BL

DISS TOWN

Eastern Counties Division One North

Founded 1888 Nickname: Tangerines **Club Colours:** Tangerine & navy

Club Contact Details 01379 651 223 (ground) pamdisstownfc@gmail.com

HONOURS FA Comps: FA Vase 1993-94.

League: Anglian Combination Division One 1967-68, 73-74, Premier 76-77, 78-79.
Eastern Counties Division One 1991-92.

11-12	12-13	13-14	14-15	15-16	16-17	17-18	18-19	19-20	20-21
ECP 16	ECP 17	ECP 18	ECP 19	EC1 7	EC1 6	EC1 12	EC1N 15	EC1N n&v	EC1N n&v
FAC EP	FAC EP	FAC EP	FAC EP	FAC EP		FAC EP			FAC P
FAV 3P	FAV 2P	FAV 1P	FAV 1Q	FAV 1P	FAV 2Q	FAV 2Q	FAV 1Q	FAV 1Q	FAV 1Q

GROUND: Brewers Green Lane, Diss, Norfolk IP22 4QP

Nearest Railway Station Diss - 0.5 miles

DOWNHAM TOWN

Eastern Counties Division One North

Founded 1881 Nickname: Town **Club Colours:** Red

Club Contact Details george.dickson@me.com

HONOURS FA Comps: None

League: Peterborough & District 1962-63, 73-74, 78-79, 86-87, 87-88.

11-12	12-13	13-14	14-15	15-16	16-17	17-18	18-19	19-20	20-21
EC1 14	EC1 16	EC1 17	EC1 9	EC1 16	EC1 14	EC1 9	EC1N 8	EC1N n&v	EC1N n&v
FAV 2Q	FAV 2Q	FAV 1Q		FAV 2Q	FAV 2Q	FAV 1Q	FAV 1Q	FAV 1Q	FAV 2Q

GROUND: Memorial Field, Lynn Road, Downham Market PE38 9AU

Nearest Railway Station Downham Market - 1.25 miles

FC PARSON DROVE

Eastern Counties Division One North

Founded 1921 Nickname: Drove **Club Colours:** Red & black

Club Contact Details

HONOURS FA Comps: None

League: Peterborough & District Division Two 2017-18, Division One 2018-19.

11-12	12-13	13-14	14-15	15-16	16-17	17-18	18-19	19-20	20-21
						P&D 2 1	P&D 1 1	P&D P n&v	P&D P n&v

GROUND: Main Road, Parson Drove, Wisbech PE13 4LA

Nearest Railway Station March

Bus Route No.56 from March Railway Station to Wisbech, then No. 46 to Parson Drove.

FRAMLINGHAM TOWN

Eastern Counties Division One North

Founded 1887 Nickname: The Castlemen **Club Colours:** Green & white

Club Contact Details fionawhatling@tiscali.co.uk

HONOURS FA Comps: None

League: Suffolk & Ipswich Division Two 1980-81, Senior Division 91-92.

11-12	12-13	13-14	14-15	15-16	16-17	17-18	18-19	19-20	20-21
S&I S 16	S&I 1 10	S&I 1 5	S&I 1 2	S&I S 5	EC1 7	EC1 2	ECP 20	EC1N n&v	EC1N n&v
						FAC P	FAC EPr	FAC P	FAC EP
FAV 2Q					FAV 1Q	FAV 2P	FAV 2Qr	FAV 1Q	FAV 1Q

GROUND: Framingham Sports Club, Badingham Road, Framlingham IP13 9HS

Nearest Railway Station Wickham

Bus Route Katch from Wickham Railway Station.

GREAT YARMOUTH TOWN

Eastern Counties Division One North

Founded 1897 Nickname: The Bloaters **Club Colours:** Yellow & black

Club Contact Details gytfcsecretary@gmail.com

HONOURS FA Comps: None

League: Norfolk & Suffolk 1913-14, 26-27, 27-28. Eastern Counties 1968-69, Division One 2009-10.

11-12	12-13	13-14	14-15	15-16	16-17	17-18	18-19	19-20	20-21
ECP 21	EC1 10	EC1 8	EC1 4	EC1 3	ECP 5	ECP 15	ECP 19	EC1N n&v	EC1N n&v
FAC EP	FAC P	FAC EP	FAC P	FAC EP	FAC EP	FAC 1Q	FAC EP	FAC P	
FAV 2Q	FAV 2Q	FAV 2P	FAV 3P	FAV 1P	FAV 1P	FAV 2Q	FAV 2P	FAV 2Q	FAV 2Q

GROUND: The Wellesley, Sandown Road, Great Yarmouth NR30 1EY

Nearest Railway Station Great Yarmouth - 1/2 mile away.

HARLESTON TOWN

Eastern Counties Division One North

Founded 1885 Nickname: **Club Colours:** Black & white

Club Contact Details ajm@cornerstonelimited.co.uk

HONOURS FA Comps: None

League: Anglian Combination Division Three 1980-81, 2010-11,
Division Two 1981-82, 2011-12, Premier 2017-18

11-12	12-13	13-14	14-15	15-16	16-17	17-18	18-19	19-20	20-21
AnC2 1	AnC1	AnC1 2	AnCP 3	AnCP 3	AnCP 2	AnCP 1	EC1N 2	AnCP n&v	AnCP n&v

GROUND: Harleston Recreation Ground, Wilderness Lane, Harleston IP20 9DD

Nearest Railway Station Diss

Bus Route 38A network Norwich - High School bus stop.

HUNTINGDON TOWN

Eastern Counties Division One North

Founded 1995 Nickname: The Hunters **Club Colours:** Red & black

Club Contact Details 07974 664 818

HONOURS FA Comps: None

League: Cambridgeshire Division 1B 1999-2000.
United Counties Division One 2011-12.

11-12	12-13	13-14	14-15	15-16	16-17	17-18	18-19	19-20	20-21
UCL 1 1	UCL P 4	UCL P 2	UCL P 16	UCL P 22	UCL P 22	UCL 1 12	UCL 1 18	UCL 1 n&v	UCL 1 n&v
FAC 1Q	FAC 1Q	FAC 1Q	FAC EP	FAC EPr	FAC EP	FAC EP			
FAV 2Q	FAV 1Q	FAV 3P	FAV 2P	FAV 1Q	FAV 2Q	FAV 2Q	FAV 1Q	FAV 1P	FAV 1Q

GROUND: Jubilee Park, Kings Ripton Road,, Huntingdon, Cambridgeshire PE28 2NR

Nearest Railway Station Huntingdon - 3.4km

Bus Route Newnham Close - stop 1km away

LEISTON RESERVES

Eastern Counties Division One North

Foundec 1880 Nickname: Blues **Club Colours:** All blue

Club Contact Details 01728 830 308 (ground)

HONOURS FA Comps: None

League: None

11-12	12-13	13-14	14-15	15-16	16-17	17-18	18-19	19-20	20-21
			EC1 19	EC1 6	EC1 21	EC1 13	EC1N 9	EC1N n&v	EC1N n&v

GROUND: The LTAA, Victory Road, Leiston, Suffolk IP16 4DQ

Nearest Railway Station Saxmundham - 6 miles

Bus Route Alde Valley Sixth Form - stop 300m away

NEEDHAM MARKET RESERVES

Eastern Counties Division One North

Foundec 1919 Nickname: The Marketmen **Club Colours:** Red

Club Contact Details 01449 721 000 (ground) m.easlea@sky.com

HONOURS FA Comps: None

League: None

11-12	12-13	13-14	14-15	15-16	16-17	17-18	18-19	19-20	20-21
		EC1 15	EC1 16	EC1 19	EC1 19	EC1 20	EC1N 17	EC1N n&v	EC1N

GROUND: Bloomfields, Quinton Road, Needham Market IP6 8DA.

Nearest Railway Station Needham Market - 0.6km

Bus Route Quinton Road stop - 38m away

NORWICH CBS

Eastern Counties Division One North

Foundec 1888 Nickname: **Club Colours:** Blue

Club Contact Details 01603 748 944 (ground) norwichcbsfc@outlook.com

HONOURS FA Comps: None

League: Anglian Combination Premier Division 2016-17.

11-12	12-13	13-14	14-15	15-16	16-17	17-18	18-19	19-20	20-21
AnCP 4	AnCP 2	AnCP 2	AnCP 5	AnCP 2	AnCP 1	EC1 8	EC1N 7	EC1N n&v	EC1N n&v
								FAC EP	
						FAV 4P	FAV 2P	FAV 1Q	FAV 3P

GROUND: The FDC, Bowthorpe Park, Clover Hill Road, Norwich NR5 9ED

Bus Route Breckland Road stop - 176m away

PETERBOROUGH NORTH END SPORTS

Eastern Counties Division One North

Foundec 2019 Nickname: Ghosts **Club Colours:** Blue & yellow

Club Contact Details seamusmorgan16@gmail.com

HONOURS FA Comps: None

League:

11-12	12-13	13-14	14-15	15-16	16-17	17-18	18-19	19-20	20-21
								P&D P n&v	P&D P n&v

GROUND: Bee Arena, Lincoln Road, Peterborough PE1 3HA

Nearest Railway Station Peterborough - 3 miles

Bus Route 101 towards Bourne - alight at Boulevard Retail Park, 6min walk from there.

SHERINGHAM

Eastern Counties Division One North

Founded 1897 Nickname: The Shannocks **Club Colours:** Red

Club Contact Details 07961 435261 (Secretary) suze0509@hotmail.com

HONOURS FA Comps: None

League: Norfolk & Suffolk 1957-58. Anglian Combination Premier 1969-70, 2008-09, 18-19, Division Three 02-03, Division Two 03-04, Division One 04-05.

11-12	12-13	13-14	14-15	15-16	16-17	17-18	18-19	19-20	20-21
AnCP 11	AnCP 14	AnCP 13	AnCP 16	AnC1 6	AnC1 11	AnC1 2	AnCP 1	EC1N n&v	EC1N n&v

GROUND: Sheringham Recreation, Weybourne Road, Sheringham NR26 8WD

Nearest Railway Station Abellio Greater Anglia line.

Bus Route 5, Coasthopper & X44

UEA

Eastern Counties Division One North

Founded 1960 Nickname: **Club Colours:** Navy blue

Club Contact Details 01362 690 460 p.neary@uea.ac.uk

HONOURS FA Comps: None

League: Anglian Combination Division Three 2012-13, Division Two 16-17, Division One 18-19.

11-12	12-13	13-14	14-15	15-16	16-17	17-18	18-19	19-20	20-21
AnC3 3	AnC3 1	AnC2 6	AnC2 9	AnC2 5	AnC2 1	AnC1 5	AnC1 1	AnCP n&v	AnCP n&v

GROUND: Dereham Town FC, Aldiss Park, Norwich Road, Dereham, Norfolk NR20 3PX

Nearest Railway Station Peterborough - take B excel bus towards Norwich City Centre, alight at Hornbeam Drive

Bus Route 8 & X1

WHITTLESEY ATHLETIC

Eastern Counties Division One North

Founded 2014 Nickname: **Club Colours:** Royal blue & black

Club Contact Details wafcfootballsec@mail.com

HONOURS FA Comps: None

League: None

11-12	12-13	13-14	14-15	15-16	16-17	17-18	18-19	19-20	20-21
				P&D P 2	UCL 1 Exp	P&D P 3	P&D P 5	UCL 1 n&v	UCL 1 n&v

GROUND: Feldale Field, Drybread Road, Whittlesey, PE7 1YP

WISBECH ST MARY

Eastern Counties Division One North

Founded 1993 Nickname: The Saints **Club Colours:** Purple

Club Contact Details 01945 410 243 (ground) martin@jsholmes.com

HONOURS FA Comps: None

League: Cambridgeshire County Division 1B 2008-09, Senior B 10-11,

11-12	12-13	13-14	14-15	15-16	16-17	17-18	18-19	19-20	20-21
CamSA 3	CamP 7	CamP 8	CamP 15	CamP 5	EC1 13	EC1 18	EC1N 18	EC1N n&v	EC1N n&v
				FAV 2Q	FAV 1Q	FAV 2P	FAV 1Q	FAV 1Q	

GROUND: ABC Meats Stadium, Beechings Close, Wisbech St Mary PE13 4SS

Bus Route St Mary's Close (High Rd) stop - 362m away

AFC SUDBURY RESERVES

Eastern Counties Division One South

Founded 1999 Nickname: AFC **Club Colours:** Yellow & blue

Club Contact Details 01787 376 213 secretary@afcsudbury.co.uk

HONOURS FA Comps: None

League: None

11-12	12-13	13-14	14-15	15-16	16-17	17-18	18-19	19-20	20-21
		EC1 16	EC1 14	EC1 10	EC1 18	EC1 11	EC1N 13	EC1N n&v	EC1N n&v

GROUND: Kings Marsh Stadium, Brundon Lane, Sudbury CO10 7HN

Nearest Railway Station Sudbury - 1.5km

Bus Route Bulmer Road - stop 100m away

BARKINGSIDE

Eastern Counties Division One South

Founded 1898 Nickname: The Side / Sky Blues **Club Colours:** Sky blue & navy

Club Contact Details 020 8552 3995 confclothing@aol.com

HONOURS FA Comps: None

League: Spartan Premier Division 1996-97. Spartan South Midlands 1998-99.

11-12	12-13	13-14	14-15	15-16	16-17	17-18	18-19	19-20	20-21
ESen 8	ESen 2	Isth1N 20	Isth1N 22	Isth1N 23	ESen 10	ESen 16	ESen 19	EC1S n&v	EC1S n&v
FAC EP	FAC EPr	FAC P	FAC 1Q	FAC P	FAC P	FAC EP	FAC EPr	FAC P	
FAV 2Qr	FAV 1Q	FAT P	FAT 2Q	FAT P	FAV 2Q	FAV 2Q	FAV 2Q	FAV 1Q	FAV 1Q

GROUND: Cricketfield Stadium, 3 Cricklefield Place, Ilford IG1 1FY

Nearest Railway Station Ilford (underground) / Seven Kings (BR) ½ mile

Bus Route 86 outside ground

BENFLEET

Eastern Counties Division One South

Founded 1922 Nickname: **Club Colours:** Sky and navy blue

Club Contact Details 01268 682 991 (Canvey Island FC) michael.dixon@benfleetfc.com

HONOURS FA Comps: None

League: Essex Olympian Division One 1988-89, Division Two 2006-07, Division Three 15-16.

11-12	12-13	13-14	14-15	15-16	16-17	17-18	18-19	19-20	20-21
EsxO1 11	EsxO1 9	EsxO1 11	EsxO2 Exp	EsxO3 1	EsxO2 3	EsxO2 4	EC1S 12	EC1S n&v	EC1S n&v
									FAC EP
								FAV 1Q	FAV 2Q

GROUND: Canvey Island FC, Frost Financial Stadium, 1 Park Lane SS8 7PX

Nearest Railway Station Leigh-on-Sea - 3.2km

Bus Route Transport Museum - stop 100m away

BRIMSDOWN

Eastern Counties Division One South

Founded 2013 Nickname: The Limers **Club Colours:** White & green

Club Contact Details 01375 843 093 (ground) s.alptekin@hotmail.co.uk

HONOURS FA Comps: None

League: None

11-12	12-13	13-14	14-15	15-16	16-17	17-18	18-19	19-20	20-21
		SSM2 13	SSM2 4	SSM1 15	SSM1 17	SSM1 11	SSM1 18	SSM1 n&v	EC1S n&v
				FAV 2Q		FAV 1Q	FAV 1P	FAV 1Q	FAV 1Q

GROUND: Tilbury FC, Chadfields, St Chads Road, Tilbury, Essex RM18 8NL

Nearest Railway Station Tilbury Town - 1.1km

Bus Route Raphael Avenue - stop 75m away

BUCKHURST HILL

Eastern Counties Division One South

Founded 1985 Nickname: **Club Colours:** Blue & black

Club Contact Details katie.edmans@bhfc.co.uk

HONOURS FA Comps: None

League: Essex Olympian Division One 2017-18, Premier 18-19, 20-21 (Ranked on PPG).

11-12	12-13	13-14	14-15	15-16	16-17	17-18	18-19	19-20	20-21
EsxOP 4	EsxOP 9	EsxOP 5	EsxOP 12	EsxOP 10	EsxOP 14	EsxO1 1	EsxOP 1	EsxOP n&v	EsxOP 1

GROUND: Roding Lane, Buckhurst Hill IG9 6BJ

BURNHAM RAMBLERS

Eastern Counties Division One South

Founded 1900 Nickname: Ramblers **Club Colours:** Blue & black

Club Contact Details 01621 784 383 (Ground) martin.leno@btopenworld.com

HONOURS FA Comps: None

League: Mid-Essex 1927-28, 54-55, 62-63. Essex Olympian 1966-67. Essex Senior League 2012-13.

11-12	12-13	13-14	14-15	15-16	16-17	17-18	18-19	19-20	20-21
ESen 4	ESen 1	Isth1N 17	Isth1N 24	ESen 14	ESen 21	ESen 20	EC1S 13	EC1S n&v	EC1S n&v
FAC Pr	FAC P	FAC 1Q	FAC P	FAC EP	FAC EP	FAC EP	FAC EP		
FAV 1P	FAV 2P	FAT 1Q	FAT P	FAV 1Qr	FAV 2Q	FAV 1P	FAV 1Q	FAV 1Q	FAV 2Q

GROUND: Leslie Fields Stadium, Springfield Road CM0 8TE

Nearest Railway Station Burnham on Crouch (Greater Anglia).

Bus Route 31X (Eastern National)

COGGESHALL UNITED

Eastern Counties Division One South

Founded 2017 Nickname: Weavers **Club Colours:** Blue

Club Contact Details 01376 562 843 (Ground) briansawyer@hotmail.co.uk

HONOURS FA Comps: None

League: None

11-12	12-13	13-14	14-15	15-16	16-17	17-18	18-19	19-20	20-21
						EsSuP 2	EC1S 2	EC1S n&v	EC1S n&v
								FAC EP	
							FAV 2Q	FAV 2P	FAV 1P

GROUND: West Street, Coggeshall, Essex CO6 1NT

CORNARD UNITED

Eastern Counties Division One South

Founded 1964 Nickname: Ards **Club Colours:** All blue

Club Contact Details 07834 773 416 paulw_66@outlook.com

HONOURS FA Comps: None

League: Colchester & East Essex Div.6 1971-72, Div.5 72-73, Div.4 73-74, Div.3 74-75
Essex & Suffolk Border 1988-89. Eastern Counties Division One 1989-90.

11-12	12-13	13-14	14-15	15-16	16-17	17-18	18-19	19-20	20-21
EC1 16	EC1 18	EC1 18	EC1 18	EC1 15	EC1 15	EC1 15	EC1N 12	EC1N n&v	EC1N n&v
FAV 2Q	FAV 1Q	FAV 2Q	FAV 1Q	FAV 1Q	FAV 1Q	FAV 1Q	FAV 1Q	FAV 1Q	FAV 2Q

GROUND: Backhouse Lane, Great Cornard, Sudbury, Suffolk CO10 0NL

Nearest Railway Station Sudbury - 2.2km

FRENFORD

Eastern Counties Division One South

Founded 1945 Nickname: Club Colours: Red & white

Club Contact Details 020 8518 0992 (ground)

HONOURS FA Comps: None

League: Ilford & District Premier 1975-76. Essex Olympian Division Two 1995-96, Premier 2011-12, 12-13.

11-12		12-13		13-14		14-15		15-16		16-17		17-18		18-19		19-20		20-21	
EsxOP	1	EsxOP	1	EsxOP	3	EsxOP	7	EsxOP	7	EsxOP	5	EsxOP	2	EC1S	9	EC1S	n&v	EC1S	n&v
																FAV	2P	FAV	1Q

GROUND: Jack Carter Centre, The Drive, Ilford, Essex, IG1 3PS

HACKNEY WICK

Eastern Counties Division One South

Founded 1995 Nickname: The Wickers Club Colours: Yellow & black

Club Contact Details 01376 511 198 (Ground)

HONOURS FA Comps: None

League: Essex Sunday Corinthian 2011-12.

11-12		12-13		13-14		14-15		15-16		16-17		17-18		18-19		19-20		20-21	
EsxSC	1	ESen	10	ESen	20	ESen	15	ESen	8	ESen	17	ESen	21	EC1S	6	EC1S	n&v	EC1S	n&v
								FAC	EP	FAC	EP	FAC	EP	FAC	P	FAC	EP		
						FAV	2Q	FAV	1Q	FAV	1P	FAV	1Q	FAV	2Q	FAV	1P	FAV	1Q

GROUND: Witham Town FC, Spa Road, Witham CM8 1UN

Nearest Railway Station Witham - 1.1km

Bus Route Cuppers Close - stop 200m away

HALSTEAD TOWN

Eastern Counties Division One South

Founded 1879 Nickname: Humbugs Club Colours: Black & white

Club Contact Details 01787 472 082 (ground) halsteadtownfc@aol.com

HONOURS FA Comps: None

League: Essex & Suffolk Border Premier Division 1957-58, 68-69, 77-78.
Eastern Counties 1994-95, 95-96, Division One 2002-03.

11-12		12-13		13-14		14-15		15-16		16-17		17-18		18-19		19-20		20-21	
EC1	6	EC1	11	EC1	6	EC1	10	EC1	4	EC1	9	EC1	10	EC1S	3	EC1S	n&v	EC1S	n&v
FAC	EP	FAC	P	FAC	EP	FAC	EPr			FAC	1Q					FAC	P	FAC	P
FAV	1P	FAV	2Q	FAV	2Q	FAV	1Q	FAV	2Q	FAV	2Q	FAV	2Q	FAV	1Q	FAV	1Q	FAV	2Q

GROUND: Rosemary Lane, Broton Industrial Estate, Halstead, Essex CO9 1HR

HARWICH & PARKESTON

Eastern Counties Division One South

Founded 1875 Nickname: Shrimpers Club Colours: Black & white stripes

Club Contact Details 01255 503 643

HONOURS FA Comps: None

League: Essex & Suffolk Border Senior Division 1908-09, 13-14, 20-21, 21-22, 22-23, 28-29, 31-32, 32-33, 33-34. Eastern Counties 1935-36 (joint). Essex County 1937-38. Athenian Division Two 1964-65

11-12		12-13		13-14		14-15		15-16		16-17		17-18		18-19		19-20		20-21	
EsSuP	2	EsSuP	5	EsSuP	3	EsSu1	5	EsSuP	9	EsSuP	6	EsSuP	10	EC1S	5	EC1S	n&v	EC1S	n&v
																FAC	P		
																FAV	1Q	FAV	1Q

GROUND: Royal Oak, Main Road, Dovercourt, Harwich CO12 4AA

HAVERHILL BOROUGH

Eastern Counties Division One South

Founded 2011 Nickname: Borough **Club Colours:** Blue

Club Contact Details 01440 702 137 (Ground)

HONOURS FA Comps: None

League: Essex & Suffolk Border Division One 2011-12.

11-12	12-13	13-14	14-15	15-16	16-17	17-18	18-19	19-20	20-21
EsSu1 1	EsSuP 2	EC1 4	EC1 6	EC1 8	EC1 3	ECP 20	EC1N 16	EC1N n&v	EC1N n&v
			FAC 1Q	FAC EP		FAC 1Q	FAC EP		
		FAV 1Q	FAV 1P	FAV 1Q	FAV 1P	FAV 1Q	FAV 1P	FAV 2Q	FAV 1Q

GROUND: The New Croft, Chalkestone Way, Haverhill, Suffolk CB9 0BW

HOLLAND

Eastern Counties Division One South

Founded 2006 Nickname: **Club Colours:** Orange

Club Contact Details 07778 142 118 (ground) mark.sorrell@btinternet.com

HONOURS FA Comps: None

League: Essex & Suffolk Border Division One 2008-09.

11-12	12-13	13-14	14-15	15-16	16-17	17-18	18-19	19-20	20-21
EsSuP 12	EsSuP 4	EsSuP 10	EsSuP 4	EsSuP 4	EC1 5	EC1 16	EC1S 11	EC1S n&v	EC1S n&v
						FAV 1P	FAV 2Q	FAV 1Q	FAV 2Q

GROUND: Eastcliff Sports Ground, Dulwich Road, Holland-on-Sea CO15 5HP

Nearest Railway Station Clacton-on-Sea - 1.7km

IPSWICH WANDERERS

Eastern Counties Division One South

Founded 1980 Nickname: Wanderers **Club Colours:** All blue

Club Contact Details 01473 720 691 (Ground) ipswichwanderers@mail.com

HONOURS FA Comps: None

League: Eastern Counties Division One 1997-98, 04-05.

11-12	12-13	13-14	14-15	15-16	16-17	17-18	18-19	19-20	20-21
EC1 12	EC1 4	EC1 3	ECP 9	ECP 15	ECP 10	ECP 23	EC1N 10	EC1N n&v	EC1N n&v
FAC Pr	FAC EP	FAC P	FAC 1Qr	FAC 2Q	FAC EPr	FAC EP	FAC EP		FAC EP
FAV 2Q	FAV 1P	FAV 1P	FAV 2P	FAV 5Pr	FAV 2P	FAV 1Q	FAV 1Q	FAV 1Q	FAV 1P

GROUND: SEH Sports Centre, Humber Doucy Lane, Ipswich IP4 3NR

Nearest Railway Station Derby Road (Ipswich) 2.1km.

MAY & BAKER E.C.

Eastern Counties Division One South

Founded Nickname: Bakers **Club Colours:** Red & black

Club Contact Details 0208 919 2156 / 3156 mwright@cvc.com

HONOURS FA Comps: None

League: Essex Olympian Division One 2009/10.

11-12	12-13	13-14	14-15	15-16	16-17	17-18	18-19	19-20	20-21
EsxOP 11	EsxOP 8	EsxOP 10	EsxOP 9	EsxOP 11	EsxOP 3	EsxOP 7	EC1S 8	EC1S n&v	EC1S n&v
							FAV 2P	FAV 1Q	FAV 2P

GROUND: Parkside, Park Lane, Aveley RM15 4PX

Nearest Railway Station Purfleet

NEWBURY FOREST

Eastern Counties Division One South

Founded 2003 Nickname: **Club Colours:** Navy blue

Club Contact Details 0208 550 3611 secretary@newburyforestfc.co.uk

HONOURS FA Comps: None

League: Romford & District Senior 2009-10.

11-12	12-13	13-14	14-15	15-16	16-17	17-18	18-19	19-20	20-21
	EsxO1 3	EsxOP 7	EsxOP 10	EsxOP 14	EsxO1 6	EsxO1 8	EC1S 17	EC1S n&v	EC1S n&v
				FAV 2Q	FAV 1Q		FAV 1P	FAV 2Q	FAV 1P

GROUND: Redbridge FC, Oakside Stadium, Station Road, Barkingside, IG6 1NB

Nearest Railway Station Barkingside Underground - 186m

Bus Route Barkingside - 395m away

PARK VIEW

Eastern Counties Division One South

Founded 1991 Nickname: **Club Colours:** Navy & royal blue

Club Contact Details awuku1@yahoo.com

HONOURS FA Comps: None

League: Middlesex County Division One C&E 2007-08. London Commercial Division One 12-13. Amateur Combination Intermediate Division One North 2014-15, Senior Division Two North 15-15, Senior Division One 16-17. Spartan SM Divison Two 17-18.

11-12	12-13	13-14	14-15	15-16	16-17	17-18	18-19	19-20	20-21
	LonCom 1	LonCom 2	AMCI1N 1	AmC2N 1	AmC1 1	SSM2 1	SSM1 13	SSM1 n&v	SSM1 n&v
									FAC EP
								FAV 1Q	FAV 2Q

GROUND: New River Stadium, White Hart Lane, Wood Green N22 5QW

WIVENHOE TOWN

Eastern Counties Division One South

Founded 1925 Nickname: The Dragons **Club Colours:** Blue & white

Club Contact Details lorraineosman1969@yahoo.com

HONOURS FA Comps: None

League: Brightlingsea & Dist 1932-33, 36-37, 47-48. Colchester & East Essex Prem 1952-53, 55-56, D1 59-60, 69-70. Essex & Suffolk D2 1971-72, D1 72-73, Prem 78-79. Isth D2N 1987-88, D1 1989-90. Eastern C. D1 2015-16.

11-12	12-13	13-14	14-15	15-16	16-17	17-18	18-19	19-20	20-21
ECP 19	ECP 18	ECP 19	ECP 18	EC1 1	ECP 19	ECP 24	EC1S 14	EC1S n&v	EC1S n&v
	FAC EPr	FAC EPr	FAC P	FAC EP	FAC EP	FAC EP	FAC EP		
FAV 1Q	FAV 2Qr	FAV 1Q	FAV 1P	FAV 2Q	FAV 1Q	FAV 1Q	FAV 1Q	FAV 2Q	FAV 1Q

GROUND: Broad Lane Ground, Elmstead Road, Wivenhoe CO7 7HA

Nearest Railway Station Wivenhoe - 2.4km.

Bus Route No.62.

WORMLEY ROVERS

Eastern Counties Division One South

Founded 1921 Nickname: **Club Colours:** Red & black

Club Contact Details 01992 460 650 (ground)

HONOURS FA Comps: None

League: Herts Senior County Division Three 1976-77, Division One 86-87.

11-12	12-13	13-14	14-15	15-16	16-17	17-18	18-19	19-20	20-21
HertP 8	HertP 7	HertP 8	HertP 5	HertP 15	HertP 8	HertP 5	EC1S 10	EC1S n&v	EC1S n&v
							FAV 1Q	FAV 2Q	FAV 2Q

GROUND: Wormley Sports Club, Church Lane, Wormley EN10 6LB

ATHLETIC NEWHAM

Essex Senior

Founded 2015 Nickname: The Kings **Club Colours:** Red & white

Club Contact Details 0300 124 0123 secretary.anfc@gmail.com

Previous Names: Lopes Tavares London (Youth) 2015-16. Lopes Tavares 2016-20.
Previous Leagues: Essex Alliance 2016-18. Eastern Counties 2018-21.
HONOURS
FA Comps: None
League: None

11-12	12-13	13-14	14-15	15-16	16-17	17-18	18-19	19-20	20-21
					EsxAlP 8	EsxAlP 5	EC1S 16	EC1S n&v	EC1S n&v
								FAV 1P	FAV 1Q

GROUND: Clapton FC, Terence MacMillan Stadium, Plaistow E13 8SD **Seats:** 192
Nearest Railway Station Plaistow, Prince Regent and Canning Town. **Underground:** District and Jubilee & DLR
Bus Route 115, 147, 262, 276, 300 and 473

CLUB MOVEMENTS

IN: Athletic Newham, Little Oakley and White Ensign (P - ECD1S). FC CLacton and Stanway Rovers (LM - ECP).
OUT: Hashtag United (P- IsthN). Hadley (LM - SSMP).

CLAPTON

Essex Senior

Founded 1878 Nickname: Tons **Club Colours:** Red & white

Club Contact Details 0203 652 2951 (ground) secretary@claptonfc.com

Previous Names: None
Previous Leagues: Southern (FM). London. Isthmian (FM) 1905-2006.
HONOURS
FA Comps: FA Amateur Cup 1906-07, 08-09, 14-15, 23-24, 24-25.
League: Isthmian 1910-11, 22-23, Division Two 1982-83.

11-12	12-13	13-14	14-15	15-16	16-17	17-18	18-19	19-20	20-21
ESen 17	ESen 18	ESen 10	ESen 8	ESen 7	ESen 2	ESen 6	ESen 11	ESen n&v	ESen n&v
FAC EP	FAC EP	FAC P	FAC EPr	FAC EP	FAC P	FAC 1Q	FAC EPr	FAC EP	FAC EP
FAV 2Q	FAV 1P	FAV 1P	FAV 2Q	FAV 2Q	FAV 1Q	FAV 1P	FAV 2Q	FAV 1Q	FAV 1P

GROUND: Terence MacMillan Stadium, Plaistow E13 8SD **Seats:** 192
Nearest Railway Station Plaistow, Prince Regent and Canning Town. **Underground:** District and Jubilee & DLR
Bus Route 115, 147, 262, 276, 300 and 473

COCKFOSTERS

Essex Senior

Founded 1921 Nickname: Fosters **Club Colours:** All red

Club Contact Details arynhold@googlemail.com

Previous Names: Cockfosters Athletic 1921-68.
Previous Leagues: Barnet 1921-30s. Wood Green 1930s-46. Northern Suburban Int. 1946-66. Hertfordshire County 1966-1991. Spartan 1991-97. Spartan South Midlands 1997-2019.
HONOURS
FA Comps: None
League: Wood green Division Two 1931-32, Division One 33-34, Premier 38-39. Northern Suburban Inter. Division One 1949-50, 60-61, Premier 61-62. Hertfordshire Senior County Division One 1966-67, Premier 78-79, 80-81, 83-84

11-12	12-13	13-14	14-15	15-16	16-17	17-18	18-19	19-20	20-21
SSM1 9	SSM1 2	SSM P 8	SSM P 18	SSM P 9	SSM P 3	SSM P 20	SSM P 18	ESen n&v	ESen n&v
FAC P	FAC P	FAC 1Qr	FAC P	FAC 1Q	FAC EP	FAC 1Q	FAC EP	FAC P	FAC P
FAV 1Q	FAV 2P	FAV 2P	FAV 1P	FAV 1Qr	FAV 2P	FAV 1P	FAV 1Q	FAV 1Q	FAV 1P

GROUND: Cockfosters Sports Ground, Chalk Lane, Cockfosters, Herts EN4 9JG
Nearest Railway Station New Barnet - 1.5km
Bus Route 299, 298 & 384

ENFIELD 1893 FC

Essex Senior

Founded 1893 Nickname: The E's **Club Colours:** White & royal blue

Club Contact Details enfieldfc@sky.com

Previous Names: Enfield Spartans > 1900. Enfield > 2007.

Previous Leagues: Tottenham & District. North Middlesex. London 1903-12, 20-21. Athenian 1912-14, 21-63. Isthmian 1963-81, 90-2005, 06-07. Conference 1981-90. Southern 2005-06.

HONOURS

FA Comps: FA Amateur Cup 1966-67, 69-70. FA Trophy 1981-82, 87-88.

League: Alliance 1982-83, 85-86. Essex Senior 2010-11.

11-12		12-13		13-14		14-15		15-16		16-17		17-18		18-19		19-20		20-21	
ESen	7	ESen	9	ESen	3	ESen	16	ESen	20	ESen	18	ESen	9	ESen	14	ESen	n&v	ESen	n&v
FAC	Pr	FAC	EP	FAC	EPr	FAC	EP	FAC	EP	FAC	EP	FAC	EP	FAC	EP	FAC	EP	FAC	EP
FAV	4P	FAV	4P	FAV	4P	FAV	1P	FAV	1Q	FAV	2Q	FAV	3P	FAV	2P	FAV	1P	FAV	1Q

GROUND: Bishop's Stortford FC, Dunmow Road, Bishop's Stortford CM23 5RG
Nearest Railway Station Bishop's Stortford - less than a mile away.
Bus Route 508, 7 & 7A

Capacity: 4,000
Seats: 525
Covered: 700

FC CLACTON

Essex Senior

Founded 1892 Nickname: The Seasiders **Club Colours:** White & royal blue

Club Contact Details dannycoyle007@gmail.com

Previous Names: Clacton Town > 2007

Previous Leagues: Eastern Counties 1935-37, 38-58, 64-2021. Essex County 1937-38. Southern League 1958-64.

HONOURS

FA Comps: None

League: North Essex D2 1898-99, 99-1900. Clacton & District 1905-06. South East Anglian D2 1907-08. Colchester & District D2 1909-10. East Anglian 1910-11. Southern D1 1959-60. Eastern Counties D1 1994-95, 98-99.

11-12		12-13		13-14		14-15		15-16		16-17		17-18		18-19		19-20		20-21	
ECP	15	ECP	20	ECP	15	ECP	16	ECP	10	ECP	20	ECP	18	ECP	6	ECP	n&v	ECP	n&v
FAC	P	FAC	EP	FAC	2Qr	FAC	P	FAC	P	FAC	EP	FAC	EP	FAC	P	FAC	Pr	FAC	1Q
FAV	1P	FAV	2Q	FAV	1Q	FAV	2Q	FAV	1P	FAV	1Q	FAV	1Q	FAV	3P	FAV	3P	FAV	1P

GROUND: Rush Green Bowl, Rush Green Rd, Clacton-on-Sea CO16 7BQ
Nearest Railway Station Clacton-on-Sea - 1.8km
Bus Route 5 or 6 to Coopers Lane - left at the end of Coopers Lane, ground 5 min walk from there.

Capacity: 3,000
Seats: 200
Covered: Yes

HODDESDON TOWN

Essex Senior

Founded 1879 Nickname: Lilywhites **Club Colours:** White & black

Club Contact Details jdsinden1@gmail.com

Previous Names: None

Previous Leagues: Hertfordshire County 1920-25. Spartan 1925-75. London Spartan 1975-77. Athenian 1977-84. Spartan SM 1984-2018.

HONOURS

FA Comps: FA Vase 1974-75 (1st Winners).

League: Spartan 1970-71, Division One 1935-36, Division Two 'B' 1927-28.

11-12		12-13		13-14		14-15		15-16		16-17		17-18		18-19		19-20		20-21	
SSM1	3	SSM1	3	SSM P	6	SSM P	19	SSM P	3	SSM P	7	SSM P	12	ESen	9	ESen	n&v	ESen	n&v
FAC	EP	FAC	EPr	FAC	EPr	FAC	P	FAC	3Qr	FAC	P	FAC	EP	FAC	P	FAC	P	FAC	EP
FAV	1P	FAV	1P	FAV	2Q	FAV	2Q	FAV	1P	FAV	3P	FAV	1Q	FAV	2Q	FAV	1Q	FAV	1P

GROUND: The Stewart Edwards Stadium, Lowfield, Park View, Hoddesdon, Herts. EN11 8PX
Nearest Railway Station Broxbourne
Bus Route 310 - Hoddesdon High Street

Capacity: 3,000
Seats: 150
Covered: Yes

ILFORD

Essex Senior

Founded 1987 Nickname: The Foxes **Club Colours:** Blue and white hoops

Club Contact Details joe.kuzsel@gmail.com

Previous Names: Reformed as Ilford in 1987 after the original club merged with Leytonstone in 1980.

Previous Leagues: Spartan 1987-94, Essex Senior 1996-2004, Isthmian 2004-05, 2006-13, Southern 2005-06.

HONOURS

FA Comps: FA Amateur Cup 1928-29, 29-30.

League: Isthmian 1906-07, 20-21, 21-22, Division Two 2004-05.

11-12		12-13		13-14		14-15		15-16		16-17		17-18		18-19		19-20		20-21	
Isth1N	20	Isth1N	22	ESen	16	ESen	10	ESen	5	ESen	6	ESen	13	ESen	10	ESen	n&v	ESen	n&v
FAC	Pr	FAC	P	FAC	EP	FAC	EP	FAC	P	FAC	P	FAC	P	FAC	EP	FAC	EP	FAC	EP
FAT	P	FAT	1Q	FAV	1P	FAV	2Q	FAV	1P	FAV	1P	FAV	2Q	FAV	1Q	FAV	1Q	FAV	2P

GROUND: Cricklefield Stadium, 486 High Road, Ilford, Essex IG1 1FY **Capacity:** 3,500

Nearest Railway Station Seven Kings (BR), approx. ½ mile. **Underground:** Newbury Park. **Seats:** 216

Bus Route 86, outside ground

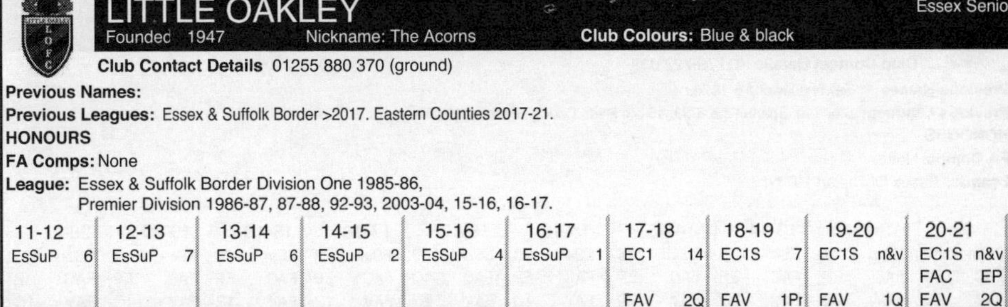

LITTLE OAKLEY

Essex Senior

Founded 1947 Nickname: The Acorns **Club Colours:** Blue & black

Club Contact Details 01255 880 370 (ground)

Previous Names:

Previous Leagues: Essex & Suffolk Border >2017. Eastern Counties 2017-21.

HONOURS

FA Comps: None

League: Essex & Suffolk Border Division One 1985-86,
Premier Division 1986-87, 87-88, 92-93, 2003-04, 15-16, 16-17.

11-12		12-13		13-14		14-15		15-16		16-17		17-18		18-19		19-20		20-21	
EsSuP	6	EsSuP	7	EsSuP	6	EsSuP	2	EsSuP	4	EsSuP	1	EC1	14	EC1S	7	EC1S	n&v	EC1S	n&v
																		FAC	EP
												FAV	2Q	FAV	1Pr	FAV	1Q	FAV	2Q

GROUND: Memorial Ground, Harwich Road, Little Oakley, Harwich CO12 5ED

Nearest Railway Station Harwich International - 3.3km

Bus Route Mayes Lane stop - 173m away

REDBRIDGE

Essex Senior

Founded 1958 Nickname: Motormen **Club Colours:** Royal blue

Club Contact Details r.holloway338@btinternet.com r.holloway338@btinternet.com

Previous Names: Ford United 1958-2004

Previous Leagues: Aetolian 1959-64, Greater London 1964-71, Metropolitan London 1971-74, Essex Senior 1974-97, Isthmian 1997-2004, 05-16. Conference 2004-05.

HONOURS

FA Comps: None

League: Aetolian 1959-60, 61-62. Greater London 1970-71. Essex Senior 1991-92, 96-97.
Isthmian Division Three 1998-99, Division One 2001-02.

11-12		12-13		13-14		14-15		15-16		16-17		17-18		18-19		19-20		20-21	
Isth1N	6	Isth1N	20	Isth1N	14	Isth1N	23	Isth1N	24	ESen	14	ESen	4	ESen	12	ESen	n&v	ESen	n&v
FAC	2P	FAC	P	FAC	P	FAC	Pr	FAC	P	FAC	EP	FAC	P	FAC	EP	FAC	EP	FAC	EP
FAT	3Q	FAT	1Q	FAT	P	FAT	P	FAT	1Q	FAV	2Q	FAV	2Qr	FAV	3P	FAV	2Q	FAV	1Q

GROUND: Oakside Stadium, Station Road, Barkingside, Essex IG6 1NB **Capacity:** 3,000

Nearest Railway Station Barkingside Underground - 186m

Bus Route Barkingside - 395m away

SAFFRON WALDEN TOWN

Essex Senior

Founded 1872 Nickname: The Bloods **Club Colours:** Red & black

Club Contact Details 07711 225 680

Previous Names: Saffron Walden > 1967. Resigned from ECo in August 2011 rejoining for 2012-13 season.

Previous Leagues: Herts County 1955-71. Essex Senior 1971-74, 96-2003. Eastern Counties 1974-84 2004-11, 12-18. Isthmian 1984-96.

HONOURS

FA Comps: None

League: Essex Senior 1973-74, 99-00. Eastern Counties 1982-83.

11-12		12-13		13-14		14-15		15-16		16-17		17-18		18-19		19-20		20-21	
		EC1	6	ECP	5	EC1	3	ECP	8	ECP	9	ECP	11	ESen	4	ESen	n&v	ESen	n&v
				FAC	EP	FAC	Pr	FAC	1Q	FAC	1Q	FAC	Pr	FAC	1Qr	FAC	P	FAC	P
		FAV	2Q	FAV	2Q	FAT	4P	FAV	3P	FAV	1P	FAV	1Q	FAV	2Q	FAV	2P	FAV	1Q

GROUND: Catons Lane Stadium, Saffron Walden, Essex CB10 2DU

Nearest Railway Station Audley End - 3.5km

Bus Route Saffron Walden High Street

SAWBRIDGEWORTH TOWN

Essex Senior

Founded 1897 Nickname: Robins **Club Colours:** Red & black

Club Contact Details 01279 722 039 rich.hogg@virgin.net

Previous Names: Sawbridgeworth > 1976.

Previous Leagues: Stortford. Spartan 1936-39, 46-53. Herts County. Essex Olympian.

HONOURS

FA Comps: None

League: Essex Olympian 1971-72.

11-12		12-13		13-14		14-15		15-16		16-17		17-18		18-19		19-20		20-21	
ESen	6	ESen	14	ESen	6	ESen	5	ESen	10	ESen	5	ESen	8	ESen	18	ESen	n&v	ESen	n&v
FAC	EP	FAC	EP	FAC	EP	FAC	EP	FAC	EP	FAC	1Q	FAC	EP	FAC	EP	FAC	EP	FAC	P
FAV	2Q	FAV	2Q	FAV	2Q	FAV	1Q	FAV	1Q	FAV	2Q	FAV	1P	FAV	1P	FAV	1Q	FAV	1Q

GROUND: Crofters End, West Road, Sawbridgeworth CM21 0DE

Nearest Railway Station Sawbridgeworth, approx. ½ mile

Bus Route 510 & 511, approx. ½ mile

Capacity: 2,500
Seats: 175
Covered: 300

SOUTHEND MANOR

Essex Senior

Founded 1955 Nickname: The Manor **Club Colours:** Yellow & black

Club Contact Details southendmanorfc1955@outlook.com

Previous Names: None

Previous Leagues: Southend Borough Combination. Southend & District Alliance.

HONOURS

FA Comps: None

League: Southend Borough Combination 1971-72, 73-74, 78-79, 79-80, 80-81, 81-82.
Southend & District Alliance 1983-84, 84-85. Essex Senior 1990-91.

11-12		12-13		13-14		14-15		15-16		16-17		17-18		18-19		19-20		20-21	
ESen	2	ESen	7	ESen	19	ESen	18	ESen	16	ESen	7	ESen	14	ESen	17	ESen	n&v	ESen	n&v
FAC	4Q	FAC	1Q	FAC	EPr	FAC	EP	FAC	P	FAC	EPr	FAC	P	FAC	EP	FAC	EPr	FAC	EP
FAV	3Pr	FAV	3P	FAV	2Q	FAV	2Q	FAV	2Qr	FAV	2Q	FAV	1Q	FAV	1P	FAV	1Q	FAV	1Q

GROUND: The Arena, Southchurch Park, Northumberland Crescent, Southend SS1 2XB

Nearest Railway Station Southend East (C2C), ½ mile to ground

Bus Route Southend Sea Front and Marlborough Road - 5 min walk away

Capacity: 2,000
Seats: 500
Covered: 700

SPORTING BENGAL UNITED

Essex Senior

Founded 1996 Nickname: Bengal Tigers **Club Colours:** Green & red

Club Contact Details shakil@sportingfoundation.com

Previous Names: None.

Previous Leagues: Asian League. London Intermediate, Kent 2003-11.

HONOURS

FA Comps: None

League: None

11-12	12-13	13-14	14-15	15-16	16-17	17-18	18-19	19-20	20-21
ESen 10	ESen 11	ESen 13	ESen 20	ESen 12	ESen 19	ESen 10	ESen 8	ESen n&v	ESen n&v
	FAC EPr	FAC EPr	FAC EP	FAC EP	FAC 1Q	FAC EP	FAC Pr	FAC EP	FAC P
FAV 3P	FAV 1P	FAV 1P	FAV 1Q	FAV 2P	FAV 1P	FAV 1Q	FAV 2Q	FAV 1Q	FAV 2Q

GROUND: Mile End Stadium, Rhodeswell Rd, Off Burdett Rd E14 7TW **Capacity:** 2,000

Nearest Railway Station Mile End – approx. 5 mins walk

Bus Route 277, 309, D6, D7 – outside ground

ST MARGARETSBURY

Essex Senior

Founded 1894 Nickname: The Bury **Club Colours:** Red & black

Club Contact Details sbarksy@gmail.com

Previous Names: Stanstead Abbots > 1962

Previous Leagues: East Herts, Hertford & District, Waltham & District 1947-48, Herts Senior County 1948-92. Spartan SM 1992-2018.

HONOURS

FA Comps: None

League: Spartan 1995-96.

11-12	12-13	13-14	14-15	15-16	16-17	17-18	18-19	19-20	20-21
SSM P 12	SSM P 4	SSM P 4	SSM P 8	SSM P 19	SSM P 20	SSM P 16	ESen 7	ESen n&v	ESen n&v
FAC EP	FAC 1Q	FAC 1Q	FAC P	FAC P	FAC EP	FAC 1Q	FAC P	FAC EP	
FAV 2Q	FAV 2Q	FAV 1P	FAV 3P	FAV 1Q	FAV 3P	FAV 1Qr	FAV 1Q	FAV 2Q	

GROUND: Recreation Ground, Station Road, St Margarets SG12 8EH **Capacity:** 1,000

Nearest Railway Station St Margarets - 5mins from the ground **Seats:** 60

Covered: 60

STANSTED

Essex Senior

Founded 1892 Nickname: Blues **Club Colours:** Royal blue

Club Contact Details 07921 403 842 stanstedfc@btinternet.com

Previous Names: None.

Previous Leagues: Spartan 1946-53. London 1953-56. Herts Premier 1956-71.

HONOURS

FA Comps: FA Vase 1983-84.

League: East Herts 1934-35. Essex Senior 2009-10.

11-12	12-13	13-14	14-15	15-16	16-17	17-18	18-19	19-20	20-21
ESen 16	ESen 17	ESen 17	ESen 7	ESen 9	ESen 8	ESen 18	ESen 2	ESen n&v	ESen n&v
FAC 1Q	FAC EP	FAC EPr	FAC EP	FAC Pr	FAC EP	FAC EP	FAC P	FAC EP	FAC 2Q
FAV 2P	FAV 2Q	FAV 2Q	FAV 2Q	FAV 1Q	FAV 1Q	FAV 1Q	FAV 1Q	FAV 3P	FAV 1P

GROUND: Hargrave Park, Cambridge Road, Stansted CM24 8BX **Capacity:** 2,000

Nearest Railway Station Stansted Mountfitchet - ¼ mile **Seats:** 200

Bus Route 301 100 yards from ground **Covered:** 400

STANWAY ROVERS

Essex Senior

Founded 1956 Nickname: Rovers **Club Colours:** Yellow & black

Club Contact Details 01206 578 187 (ground) ivan_senter@tiscali.co.uk

Previous Names: None.

Previous Leagues: Colchester & East Essex. Essex & Suffolk Border. Eastern Counties >2018. Essex Senior 2018-19. Eastern Counties 2019-21.

HONOURS

FA Comps: None

League: Colchester & East Essex Premier Division 1973-74. Essex & Suffolk Border Division Two 1981-82, 85-86. Eastern Counties Division One 2005-06.

11-12		12-13		13-14		14-15		15-16		16-17		17-18		18-19		19-20		20-21	
ECP	5	ECP	9	ECP	13	ECP	3	ECP	3	ECP	6	ECP	8	ESen	15	ECP	n&v	ECP	n&v
FAC	EP	FAC	EP	FAC	EPr	FAC	EP	FAC	2Q	FAC	1Q	FAC	EP	FAC	P	FAC	P	FAC	EP
FAV	2Q	FAV	2Q	FAV	2Q	FAV	5P	FAV	3P	FAV	2P	FAV	2Q	FAV	2Q	FAV	3Pr	FAV	2P

GROUND: Hawthorns, New Farm Road, Stanway, Colchester CO3 0PG **Capacity:** 1,500

Nearest Railway Station Colchester - 3.7km **Seats:** 100

Bus Route 65, 70 & 71 to Lucy Lane **Covered:** 250

TAKELEY

Essex Senior

Founded 1903 Nickname: **Club Colours:** Royal blue

Club Contact Details 07831 845 466 Takeleyfc@mail.com

Previous Names: None.

Previous Leagues: Essex Intermediate/Olympian.

HONOURS

FA Comps: None

League: Essex Olympian/Intermediate 1987-88, 2001-02, Division Two 1993-94.

11-12		12-13		13-14		14-15		15-16		16-17		17-18		18-19		19-20		20-21	
ESen	3	ESen	3	ESen	7	ESen	11	ESen	18	ESen	4	ESen	5	ESen	5	ESen	n&v	ESen	n&v
FAC	EPr	FAC	P	FAC	EP	FAC	EPr	FAC	EP	FAC	EP	FAC	1Q	FAC	1Q	FAC	1Q	FAC	EP
FAV	2Q	FAV	2P	FAV	2P	FAV	1Q	FAV	2Qr	FAV	2Q	FAV	1P	FAV	1P	FAV	1P	FAV	1Q

GROUND: Station Road, Takeley, Bishop's Stortford CM22 6QA **Capacity:** 2,000

Nearest Railway Station Stansted Airport (overground) Epping (underground)

Bus Route from Stansted Airport to Four Ashes Pub.

WALTHAMSTOW

Essex Senior

Founded 1964 Nickname: The Stags **Club Colours:** Royal blue

Club Contact Details 07748 983 792 andrewpeter perkins@hotmail.com

Previous Names: Pennant 1964-88. Walthamstow Pennant 88-95. Merged with Leyton to form Leyton Pennant 95-2003. Waltham Forest 03-18.

Previous Leagues: Isthmian 2003-04, 06-14. Southern 2004-06.

HONOURS

FA Comps: None

League: None

11-12		12-13		13-14		14-15		15-16		16-17		17-18		18-19		19-20		20-21	
Isth1N	17	Isth1N	18	Isth1N	23	ESen	9	ESen	19	ESen	12	ESen	17	ESen	3	ESen	n&v	ESen	n&v
FAC	2Q	FAC	2Q	FAC	P	FAC	EP	FAC	EP	FAC	2Q	FAC	EPr	FAC	1Q	FAC	2Qr	FAC	2Q
FAT	1Q	FAT	1Q	FAT	P	FAV	1P	FAV	2Q	FAV	1P	FAV	1Q	FAV	1Q	FAV	2P	FAV	1P

GROUND: Wadham Lodge, Kitchener Road, Walthamstow E17 4JP **Capacity:** 3,500

Nearest Railway Station Walthamstow Central - Victoria Line/London Overground. **Seats:** 216

Bus Route 158

WEST ESSEX

Essex Senior

Founded 1989 Nickname: Club Colours: Red & black

Club Contact Details 07956 557 438

Previous Names: None

Previous Leagues: Ilford & District 1989-94. Essex Business Houses 1994-2010. Middlesex County 2010-2016.

HONOURS

FA Comps: None

League: Essex Business Houses Division One 2008-09.
Middlesex County Division One (Central & East) 2010-11, Premier Division 2015-16.

11-12	12-13	13-14	14-15	15-16	16-17	17-18	18-19	19-20	20-21
MidxP 11	MidxP 10	MidxP 9	MidxP 7	MidxP 1	ESen 13	ESen 7	ESen 13	ESen n&v	ESen n&v
						FAC P	FAC P	FAC EP	FAC P
					FAV 1Q	FAV 2Q	FAV 1P	FAV 2Q	FAV 2Q

GROUND: Barking FC, Mayesbrook Park, Lodge Avenue, Dagenham RM8 2JR **Capacity:** 2,500
Nearest Railway Station Barking. Upney (District Line) 2 miles **Seats:** 200
Bus Route 5, 62, 145, 364, 368 **Covered:** 600

WHITE ENSIGN

Essex Senior

Founded 1951 Nickname: Club Colours: Red & navy

Club Contact Details 01702 217 812 (ground)

Previous Names: None

Previous Leagues: Southend Borough Combination 1951-2002. Eastern Counties 2002-21.

HONOURS

FA Comps: None

League: Essex Intermediate/Olympian Division Two 2002-03, Division One 03-04, 04-05, 06-07, 07-08.

11-12	12-13	13-14	14-15	15-16	16-17	17-18	18-19	19-20	20-21
EsxOP 8	EsxOP 7	EsxOP 13	EsxO1 2	EsxOP 5	EsxOP 12	EsxOP 4	EC1S 4	EC1S n&v	EC1S n&v
								FAC Pr	
							FAV 1Q	FAV 2P	FAV 1P

GROUND: Burroughs Park, Little Wakering Hall Lane, Great Wakering SS3 0HH **Capacity:** 3,000
Nearest Railway Station Rochord **Seats:** 250
Bus Route Barrow Hall Road (Little Wakering Road) - 631m **Covered:** Yes

WOODFORD TOWN

Essex Senior

Founded 1937 Nickname: The Woods Club Colours: Blue

Club Contact Details info@woodfordtownfc.com

Previous Names: Changed the name of reformed Bush Hill Rangers to Woodford Town in 2017.

Previous Leagues: Delphian (FM) 1937-61. Metropolitan 1961-67, 70-71. Greater London 1967-69. Southern 1971-72, 82-87. Essex Senior 1976-79, 87-93, 99-2003. Athenian 1979-82. Spartan SM 1993-98. London Intermediate 1998-99, 2001-03.

HONOURS

FA Comps: None

League: None

11-12	12-13	13-14	14-15	15-16	16-17	17-18	18-19	19-20	20-21
						ESen 12	ESen 6	ESen n&v	ESen n&v
								FAC EPr	FAC P
							FAV 1Qr	FAV 1Q	FAV 2Q

GROUND: Ashton Playing Fields, 598 Chigwell Road, Woodford Green IG8 8AA

BISHOP'S CLEEVE

Hellenic Premier

Founded 1905 Nickname: The Mitres **Club Colours:** Green & white

Club Contact Details 01242 676 166 (Ground) themitres@outlook.com

Previous Names: None

Previous Leagues: Cheltenham. North Gloucestershire. Hellenic 1983-2006. Southern 2006-18.

HONOURS

FA Comps: None

League: Cheltenham Division Two 1924-25, 30-31, 58-59, Division One 31-32, 34-35, 61-62, 63-64, 65-66, 66-67. Gloucestershire Northern Senior Division Two 1967-68, Division One 68-69, 69-70, 72-73. Hellenic Division One 1986-87.

11-12		12-13		13-14		14-15		15-16		16-17		17-18		18-19		19-20		20-21	
Sthsw	11	Sthsw	21	Sthsw	20	Sthsw	21	Sthsw	12	Sthsw	16	Sth1W	22	Hel P	4	Hel P	n&v	Hel P	n&v
FAC	P	FAC	2Q	FAC	Pr	FAC	1Q	FAC	P	FAC	Pr	FAC	1Q	FAC	1Q	FAC	P	FAC	EP
FAT	P	FAT	1Q	FAT	P	FAT	1Q	FAT	P	FAT	2Q	FAT	P	FAV	2Q	FAV	1P	FAV	2P

GROUND: Kayte Lane, Bishop's Cleeve, Cheltenham GL52 3PD **Capacity:** 1,500

Nearest Railway Station Cheltenham Spa - 4.9km **Seats:** 50

Bus Route Bus stops outside the ground **Covered:** 50

CLUB MOVEMENTS

PREMIER DIVISION - IN: Bradford Town, Chipping Sodbury Town, Cribbs, Hallen, Roman Glass St George and Westbury United (LM - WLP). Calne Town and Corsham Town (P - WL1). Hereford Lads Club, Malvern Town and Thornbury Town (P - HL1W). **OUT:** Ardley United, Flackwell Heath and Holmer Green (LM - SSSP). Binfield (P - IsthSC). Easington Sports (LM - UCPS).

BRADFORD TOWN

Hellenic Premier

Founded 1992 Nickname: Bobcats **Club Colours:** All royal blue

Club Contact Details 07912 184 104 secretary@bradfordtownfc.com

Previous Names: None

Previous Leagues: Wiltshire County 1992-2005. Western 2005-21.

HONOURS

FA Comps: None

League: Western Division One 2013-14.

11-12		12-13		13-14		14-15		15-16		16-17		17-18		18-19		19-20		20-21	
West1	5	West1	3	West1	1	WestP	8	WestP	8	WestP	5	WestP	4	WestP	7	WestP	n&v	WestP	n&v
FAC	EP	FAC	EP	FAC	EP	FAC	1Q	FAC	2Q	FAC	EP	FAC	EP	FAC	P	FAC	1Q	FAC	EP
FAV	1P	FAV	2Q	FAV	1P	FAV	5P	FAV	4P	FAV	4P	FAV	5P	FAV	3P	FAV	5P	FAV	2P

GROUND: Bradford Sports & Social Club, Trowbridge Road, Bradford on Avon BA15 1EX

Nearest Railway Station Bradford-upon-Avon - 0.3km

Bus Route Junction Road _ stop 30m away

BRIMSCOMBE & THRUPP

Hellenic Premier

Founded 1886 Nickname: Lilywhites **Club Colours:** White and blue

Club Contact Details 07889 675 503 scottybolts1995@hotmail.com

Previous Names: Brimscombe AFC 1886- late 1970s. Brimscombe and Thrupp merged.

Previous Leagues: Stroud & District. Gloucestershire Northern Senior. Gloucestershire County

HONOURS

FA Comps: None

League: Stroud & Dist. 1902-03, 06-07, 07-08, 12-13. Gloucestershire Northern Senior 1922-23, 30-31, 47-48, Division Two 2004 -05. Gloucestershire County 2010-11. Hellenic Division One West 2012-13.

11-12		12-13		13-14		14-15		15-16		16-17		17-18		18-19		19-20		20-21	
Hel1W	4	Hel1W	1	Hel P	12	Hel P	10	Hel P	5	Hel P	7	Hel P	6	Hel P	2	Hel P	n&v	Hel P	n&v
					N/A	FAC	EP	FAC	Pr	FAC	3Q	FAC	P	FAC	P	FAC	P	FAC	P
				FAV	2P	FAV	1P	FAV	3Pr	FAV	2Pr	FAV	1Q	FAV	1P	FAV	1P	FAV	3P

GROUND: 'The Meadow', London Road, Brimscombe Stroud, Gloucestershire GL5 2SH **Capacity:** 1,500

Nearest Railway Station Stroud - 2.9km

Bus Route Brewery Lane stop - 261m away

CALNE TOWN

Hellenic Premier

Founded 1886 Nickname: Lilywhites **Club Colours:** White and black

The Lilywhites **Club Contact Details** 07795 833 702 wmm498@msn.com

Previous Names: None
Previous Leagues: Western >2021.
HONOURS
FA Comps: None
League: None

11-12	12-13	13-14	14-15	15-16	16-17	17-18	18-19	19-20	20-21
West1 4	West1 9	West1 13	West1 15	West1 15	West1 21	West1 17	West1 8	West1 n&v	West1 n&v
FAC EP	FAC EP	FAC EP							FAC EP
FAV 2Q	FAV 1P	FAV 1Q	FAV 2Q	FAV 1P	FAV 1P	FAV 2Q	FAV 1Q	FAV 1Q	FAV 1Q

GROUND: Bremhill View, Calne, Wiltshire SN11 9RY **Capacity:** 2,500
Seats: 150
Bus Route Northend - stop 80m away

CHIPPING SODBURY TOWN

Hellenic Premier

Founded 1885 Nickname: The Sods **Club Colours:** Black & white

Club Contact Details 07745 299 351 leslietheobald@btinternet.com

Previous Names: None
Previous Leagues: Gloucester County 2008-2015. Western 2015-21.
HONOURS
FA Comps: None
League: Western Division One 2015-16.

11-12	12-13	13-14	14-15	15-16	16-17	17-18	18-19	19-20	20-21
GlCo 18	GlCo 15	GlCo 11	GlCo 3	West1 1	WestP 13	WestP 13	WestP 10	WestP n&v	WestP n&v
						FAC P	FAC 1Q	FAC EP	FAC EP
					FAV 1Q	FAV 1Q	FAV 2Q	FAV 1Q	FAV 1Q

GROUND: The Ridings, Wickwar Road, Chipping Sodbury, Bristol BS37 6GA
Nearest Railway Station Yate - 2.7km
Bus Route Wickwar Road - stop 50m away

CORSHAM TOWN

Hellenic Premier

Founded 1883 Nickname: The Peacocks **Club Colours:** Red & white

Club Contact Details 07712 342 251 ctfccorshamsecretary@gmail.com

Previous Names: None.
Previous Leagues: Wiltshire County. Western >2021.
HONOURS
FA Comps: None
League: Wiltshire Division Two 1960-61, Division One 97-98.
Western Premier Division 2006-07.

11-12	12-13	13-14	14-15	15-16	16-17	17-18	18-19	19-20	20-21
WestP 18	West1 4	West1 7	West1 9	West1 10	West1 19	West1 20	West1 3	West1 n&v	West1 n&v
FAC EP	FAC EP	FAC 1Qr	FAC EP						FAC P
FAV 1Qr	FAV 1Q	FAV 2Q	FAV 2Q	FAV 1P	FAV 2Q	FAV 1Q	FAV 2Q	FAV 2Q	FAV 1Q

GROUND: Southbank Ground, Lacock Road, Corsham SN13 9HS **Capacity:** 1,200
Nearest Railway Station Chippenham - 5.8km **Seats:** 112
Bus Route St Patrick's School - stop 50m away

CRIBBS

Hellenic Premier

Founded 1976 Nickname: Cribbs **Club Colours:** Blue

Club Contact Details 0117 950 2303 welshwizard1973@aol.com

Previous Names: Sun Life Assurance 1976. AXA>2011. Cribbs Friends Life 2011-13

Previous Leagues: Bristol & Avon. Avon Premier Combination. Gloucestershire County > 2012. Western 2012-21.

HONOURS

FA Comps: None

League: Gloucester County 2011-12.

11-12	12-13	13-14	14-15	15-16	16-17	17-18	18-19	19-20	20-21
GlCo 1	West1 8	West1 5	West1 3	WestP 5	WestP 8	WestP 11	WestP 8	WestP n&v	WestP n&v
			FAC P	FAC EP	FAC EPr	FAC EP	FAC EP	FAC P	FAC 1Q
		FAV 2Q	FAV 1Q	FAV 1Q	FAV 1Q	FAV 2Q	FAV 4P	FAV 3P	FAV 2P

GROUND: The Lawns, Station Road, Henbury, Bristol BS10 7TB **Capacity:** 1,000

Nearest Railway Station Pilning - 4.3km. Sea Mills - 4.5km. Patchway - 4.5km **Seats:** 100

Bus Route Rugby Club - stop 400m away

FAIRFORD TOWN

Hellenic Premier

Founded 1891 Nickname: The Reds **Club Colours:** Red & maroon

Club Contact Details 01285 712 071 (Ground) andyfiddler1706@gmail.com

Previous Names: None.

Previous Leagues: Cirencester & District. Swindon & District.

HONOURS

FA Comps: None

League: Swindon & District Prmeier Division 1964-65, 68-69.
Hellenic Division One A 1971-72, Division One West 2016-17.

11-12	12-13	13-14	14-15	15-16	16-17	17-18	18-19	19-20	20-21
Hel P 20	Hel1W 4	Hel1W 4	Hel1W 14	Hel1W 4	Hel1W 1	Hel P 18	Hel P 13	Hel P n&v	Hel P n&v
FAC P	FAC EP	FAC EP	FAC EP		FAC EP	FAC EPr	FAC EP	FAC P	FAC 1Q
FAV 1P	FAV 1P	FAV 2Q	FAV 1Q	FAV 1P	FAV 1P	FAV 1Q	FAV 1Q	FAV 2P	FAV 1Q

GROUND: Cinder Lane, London Road, Fairford GL7 4AX **Capacity:** 2,000

Nearest Railway Station Swindon or Kemble **Seats:** 100

Bus Route Hatherop Lane stop - 124m **Covered:** 250

HALLEN

Hellenic Premier

Founded 1949 Nickname: The Armadillos **Club Colours:** Blue & black

Club Contact Details 01179 505 559 sinbad88@hotmail.co.uk

Previous Names: Lawrence Weston Athletic, Lawrence Weston Hallen

Previous Leagues: Bristol & District. Bristol Premier. Gloucestershire County 1987-92. Hellenic 1992-2000. Western 2000-21.

HONOURS

FA Comps: None

League: Gloucestershire County 1988-89, 92-93. Hellenic Division One 1996-97. Western Division One 2003-04.

11-12	12-13	13-14	14-15	15-16	16-17	17-18	18-19	19-20	20-21
WestP 4	WestP 9	WestP 15	WestP 17	WestP 17	WestP 18	WestP 17	WestP 12	WestP n&v	WestP n&v
FAC 1Qr	FAC P	FAC 1Q	FAC P	FAC EPr	FAC EP	FAC EPr	FAC P	FAC EP	FAC EP
FAV 2Q	FAV 1P	FAV 5P	FAV 2P	FAV 2P	FAV 2Q	FAV 1Q	FAV 1Q	FAV 1Q	FAV 2Q

GROUND: Hallen Centre, Moorhouse Lane, Hallen Bristol BS10 7RU **Capacity:** 2,000

Nearest Railway Station St Andrews Road - 2.7km **Seats:** 200

Bus Route Moorhouse Park - stop 250m away **Covered:** 200

HEREFORD LADS CLUB

Hellenic Premier

Founded 1925 Nickname: Lads Club **Club Colours:** Blue

Club Contact Details 07557 128 790 dmoon1982@hotmail.co.uk

Previous Names: None
Previous Leagues: Herefordshire. West Midlands (Regional) 2011-19. Hellenic 2019-21.
HONOURS
FA Comps: None
League: Herefordshire Division One 2002-03.
West Midlands Division One 2016-17.

11-12	12-13	13-14	14-15	15-16	16-17	17-18	18-19	19-20	20-21
WM2 2	WM2 3	WM1 10	WM1 5	WM1 2	WM1 1	WMP 12	WMP 7	Hel1W n&v	Hel1W n&v
						FAV 1Q	FAV 2P		

GROUND: Widemarsh Common, Hereford HR4 9NA
Nearest Railway Station Hereford - 1km
Bus Route Priory Place - stop 150m away

LONGLEVENS AFC

Hellenic Premier

Founded 1954 Nickname: Levens **Club Colours:** Red & black

Club Contact Details 07526 958 972 bill1853@outlook.com

Previous Names: None
Previous Leagues: Gloucestershire Northern Senior > 2011. Gloucestershire County 2011-14.
HONOURS
FA Comps: None
League: Gloucestershire Northern Division One 2008-09. Gloucestershire County 2012-13, 13-14.
Hellenic Division One West 2014-15.

11-12	12-13	13-14	14-15	15-16	16-17	17-18	18-19	19-20	20-21
GlCo 9	GlCo 1	GlCo 1	Hel1W 1	Hel P 10	Hel P 12	Hel P 9	Hel P 16	Hel P n&v	Hel P n&v
					FAC P	FAC P	FAC P	FAC 1Q	FAC EP
				FAV 1Q	FAV 2Q	FAV 1P	FAV 1P	FAV 2P	FAV 2P

GROUND: Saw Mills End, Corinium Avenue, Gloucester GL4 3DG **Capacity:** 500
Nearest Railway Station Gloucester - 1.9km
Bus Route Budgen's Garage stop - 146m away

LYDNEY TOWN

Hellenic Premier

Founded 1911 Nickname: The Town **Club Colours:** Black & white

Club Contact Details 01594 844 523 (Ground) rogersansom@outlook.com

Previous Names: None
Previous Leagues: Local leagues 1911-52. Gloucestershire Northern Senior 1952-80, 84-. Hellenic 1980-84. Gloucestershire County 2005-06.
HONOURS
FA Comps: None
League: Gloucesteeshire Northern Senior 1979-80. Gloucestershire County 2005-06. Hellenic League Division One West 2006-07.

11-12	12-13	13-14	14-15	15-16	16-17	17-18	18-19	19-20	20-21
Hel1W 13	Hel1W 10	Hel1W 2	Hel1W 3	Hel P 12	Hel P 9	Hel P 16	Hel P 11	Hel P n&v	Hel P n&v
FAC EP					FAC EP	FAC EP	FAC 1Qr	FAC EP	FAC EP
FAV 1P	FAV 2Q	FAV 2Q		FAV 2Q	FAV 1P	FAV 2Q	FAV 1Q	FAV 1Q	FAV 2Q

GROUND: Lydney Recreation Ground, Swan Road, Lydney GL15 5RU **Capacity:** 1,000
Nearest Railway Station Lydney Town - 144m
Bus Route Forest Parade - 156m away

MALVERN TOWN

Hellenic Premier

Founded 1947 Nickname: The Hillsiders **Club Colours:** Sky blue and claret

Club Contact Details 01684 564 746 marg@malverntown.co.uk

Previous Names: None

Previous Leagues: Midland Alliance >2011. West Midlands (Regional) 2011-19.

HONOURS

FA Comps: None

League: Midland Combination Division One 1955-56.

11-12		12-13		13-14		14-15		15-16		16-17		17-18		18-19		19-20		20-21	
WMP	13	WMP	13	WMP	14	WMP	5	WMP	3	WMP	4	WMP	3	WMP	4	Hel1W	n&v	Hel1W	n&v
FAC	EPr							FAC	EP	FAC	EP	FAC	P	FAC	P	FAC	EP		
FAV	1Q	FAV	1Q	FAV	1Q	FAV	1Q	FAV	2Q	FAV	1P	FAV	1Q	FAV	1Q	FAV	3P	FAV	4P

GROUND: Langland Avenue, Malvern WR14 2EQ — **Capacity:** 2,500

Nearest Railway Station Great Malvern - 1.2km. Malvern Link - 1.5km — **Seats:** 150

Bus Route Bus stops outside the ground — **Covered:** 310

ROMAN GLASS ST GEORGE

Hellenic Premier

Founded 1872 Nickname: The Glass **Club Colours:** White and black

Club Contact Details 07770 331 491 adamwolves2@hotmail.com

Previous Names: St George. Bristol St George. Merged with Roman Glass in 1995 to form today's club.

Previous Leagues: Bristol & District/Western (Founder Members) 1892-1903, 1928-35, 2007-21. Bristol & District 1935-57. Bristol Premier Combination (FM) 1957-68. Gloucestershire County (FM) 1968-87, 99-2007. County of Avon Premier Comb 1987-95.

HONOURS

FA Comps: None

League: Bristol & District Div.1 1949-50. Bristol Premier Com. Div.1 1963-64, 64-65, 65-66, 66-67, 67-68, 88-89, Prem 92-93. .Gloucestershire County 1969-70, 2001-02, 06-07.

11-12		12-13		13-14		14-15		15-16		16-17		17-18		18-19		19-20		20-21	
West1	8	West1	17	West1	12	West1	20	West1	18	West1	15	West1	2	WestP	17	WestP	n&v	WestP	n&v
														FAC	EP	FAC	P	FAC	EP
		FAV	2Q	FAV	2Q	FAV	2Q	FAV	1Qr	FAV	2Q	FAV	2Q	FAV	1P	FAV	3P	FAV	1P

GROUND: Oaklands Park, Gloucester Road, Almondsbury BS32 4AG — **Capacity:** 2,000

Nearest Railway Station Patchway - 2.6km

Bus Route Alondsbury Depot - stop 100m away

ROYAL WOOTTON BASSETT

Hellenic Premier

Founded 1882 Nickname: Bassett **Club Colours:** All blue

Club Contact Details 01793 853 880 (Ground) ian.thomas@wbtfc.co.uk

Previous Names: Wootton Bassett Town > 2015.

Previous Leagues: Vale of White 1898-99. Swindon & District 1899-1903. Wiltshire County 1903-08, 35-69, 76-88. Calne & District 1930. Wiltshire Combination 1969-76.

HONOURS

FA Comps: None

League: Calne & District 1931-32, 34-35, 35-36.
Wiltshire Division One 1958-59, Division Two 1984-85, Division One 1987-88.

11-12		12-13		13-14		14-15		15-16		16-17		17-18		18-19		19-20		20-21	
Hel1W	5	Hel1W	2	Hel P	14	Hel P	11	Hel P	15	Hel P	11	Hel P	15	Hel P	10	Hel P	n&v	Hel P	n&v
FAC	EP	FAC	2Q	FAC	EP	FAC	P	FAC	EP	FAC	EP	FAC	EP	FAC	Pr	FAC	EPr	FAC	2Q
FAV	1Q	FAV	1Q	FAV	2Q	FAV	2Q	FAV	2Q	FAV	2Q	FAV	2P	FAV	2Q	FAV	2Q	FAV	2P

GROUND: Gerrard Buxton Sports Ground, Malmesbury Road, Royal Wootton Bassett SN4 8DS — **Capacity:** 4,500

Seats: 550

Bus Route The Farm stop - 69m — **Covered:** 1,250

SHRIVENHAM

Hellenic Premier

Founded 1900 Nickname: Shrivvy **Club Colours:** Blue & white

Club Contact Details 07711 263 113 m.hirst@shrivenhamfc.co.uk

Previous Names: None.
Previous Leagues: North Berkshire.
HONOURS
FA Comps: None
League: North Berks Division Two 1994-95, Division One 1997-98, 2000-01.
Hellenic Division One West 2004-05.

11-12		12-13		13-14		14-15		15-16		16-17		17-18		18-19		19-20		20-21	
Hel P	16	Hel P	19	Hel P	15	Hel P	19	Hel1W	8	Hel1W	7	Hel1W	2	Hel P	5	Hel P	n&v	Hel P	n&v
FAC	EP	FAC	P	FAC	EP	FAC	P	FAC	EP							FAC	P	FAC	EP
FAV	2Q	FAV	2Q	FAV	2Q	FAV	1Q	FAV	2Q	FAV	1Q			FAV	2Q	FAV	1P	FAV	2Q

GROUND: The Recreation Ground, Barrington Park, Shrivenham SN6 8BJ **Capacity:** 1,500

Bus Route Green (Townsend Rd) stop - 268m away

THORNBURY TOWN

Hellenic Premier

Founded 1898 Nickname: Thorns **Club Colours:** Red & black

Club Contact Details 07970 009 132 pengelly.mike@gmail.com

Previous Names: Thornbury Sports 1933. Thornbury >1974
Previous Leagues: Dursley Wotton. Bristol & Suburban. Bristol Premier Comb. 1946-68, 77-2001. Gloucestershire County (FM) 1968-77, 2001-18
HONOURS
FA Comps: None
League: Bristol Premier Combination x2. Gloucestershire County 2009-10, 17-18.

11-12		12-13		13-14		14-15		15-16		16-17		17-18		18-19		19-20		20-21	
GlCo	16	GlCo	14	GlCo	6	GlCo	4	GlCo	4	GlCo	4	GlCo	1	Hel1W	3	Hel1W	n&v	Hel1W	n&v
																FAC	EP		
																FAV	2P	FAV	2Q

GROUND: Mundy Playing Fields, Kington Lane, Thornbury BS35 1NA
Nearest Railway Station Bristol Parkway - 40min bus journey from the ground.
Bus Route No.77 (Thornbury) to Rock Street - 14min walk to ground from there.

TUFFLEY ROVERS

Hellenic Premier

Founded 1929 Nickname: Rovers **Club Colours:** Claret & blue

Club Contact Details 07545 492 261 admin@tuffleyroversfc.co.uk

Previous Names: None
Previous Leagues: Gloucestershire County 1988-91, 2007-13. Hellenic 1991-06. Gloucestershire Northern 2006-07.
HONOURS
FA Comps: None
League: Gloucester County 1990-91. Gloucestershire Northern Division One 2006-07.

11-12		12-13		13-14		14-15		15-16		16-17		17-18		18-19		19-20		20-21	
GlCo	3	GlCo	2	Hel1W	6	Hel1W	2	Hel P	17	Hel P	10	Hel P	10	Hel P	15	Hel P	n&v	Hel P	n&v
								FAC	1Q	FAC	EP	FAC	1Q	FAC	EP	FAC	EPr	FAC	EP
						FAV	1P	FAV	1Q	FAV	2P	FAV	1Q	FAV	2Qr	FAV	1Q	FAV	1Q

GROUND: Glevum Park, Lower Tuffley Lane, Tuffley, Gloucester GL2 5DT **Capacity:** 1,000
Nearest Railway Station Gloucester - 3.5km **Seats:** 100
Bus Route Pearce Way stop - 197m away

WESTBURY UNITED

Hellenic Premier

Founded 1920 Nickname: White Horse Men **Club Colours:** Green and black

Club Contact Details 01373 764 197 vikkiburbidge@gmail.com

Previous Names: Formed after the merger of Westbury Old Comrades FC and Westbury Great Western Railway XI

Previous Leagues: Wiltshire County 1920-1984. Western 1984-21.

HONOURS

FA Comps: None

League: Wiltshire 1934-35, 37-38, 38-39, 49-50, 50-51, 55-56.
Western Division One 1991-92, 2017-18.

11-12	12-13	13-14	14-15	15-16	16-17	17-18	18-19	19-20	20-21
West1 17	West1 19	West1 20	West1 22	West1 22	West1 12	West1 1	WestP 5	WestP n&v	WestP n&v
							FAC 1Q	FAC EP	FAC EP
FAV 1Q	FAV 1P	FAV 1Q	FAV 1Q	FAV 1Q	FAV 2Q	FAV 2Q	FAV 1P	FAV 1P	FAV 1P

GROUND: Meadow Lane, Westbury, Wiltshire BA13 3AF

Nearest Railway Station Westbury - 1.1km

Bus Route Springfield Road - stop 200m away

WESTFIELDS

Hellenic Premier

Founded 1966 Nickname: The Fields **Club Colours:** All Maroon & sky blue

Club Contact Details 07860 410 548 andrewmorris@westfieldsfc.com

Previous Names: None.

Previous Leagues: Herefordshire Sunday 1966-73. Worcester & Dist. 1973-78. West Midlands (Regional) 1978-04. Midland Alliance 2004-14. Midland 2014-19.

HONOURS

FA Comps: None

League: West Midlands (Regional) Division One 1986-87, Premier 2002-03.

11-12	12-13	13-14	14-15	15-16	16-17	17-18	18-19	19-20	20-21
MidAl 2	MidAl 2	MidAl 12	WMP 8	MFLP 16	MFLP 5	MFLP 12	MFLP 4	Hel P n&v	Hel P n&v
FAC EP	FAC 2Qr	FAC EP	FAC P	FAC 1Q	FAC 1P	FAC 2Q	FAC EP	FAC P	FAC 1Q
FAV 1P	FAV 1P	FAV 4P	FAV 3P	FAV 1P	FAV 3P	FAV 4P	FAV 3P	FAV 3P	FAV 4P

GROUND: Allpay Park, Widemarsh Common, Hereford HR4 9NA **Capacity:** 2,250

Nearest Railway Station Hereford - 1km **Seats:** 220

Bus Route Priory Place stop - 165m away **Covered:** 400

CLUB MOVEMENTS

DIVISION ONE - IN: FC Stratford (P - ML2). Littleton, Pershore Town and Worcester Raiders (LM - WMRL). Studley (LM - ML1).

OUT: Abingdon Town (W - pre 2021-22 after failing to reach an agreement with Culham Road's new owners.)
Hereford Lads Club, Malvern Town and Thornbury Town (P - HLP).
Tytherington Rocks (LM - WL1).

ABINGDON UNITED

Hellenic Division One

Founded 1946 Nickname: The Yellows **Club Colours:** Yellow and blue

Club Contact Details 01235 203 203 secretaryaufc@virginmedia.com

HONOURS FA Comps: None

League: North Berks 1952-53.

11-12	12-13	13-14	14-15	15-16	16-17	17-18	18-19	19-20	20-21
Sthsw 18	Sthsw 20	Hel P 17	Hel P 15	Hel P 19	Hel1W 2	Hel P 13	Hel P 19	Hel1E n&v	Hel1E n&v
FAC 1Q	FAC P	FAC EPr	FAC 2Q	FAC EP	FAC EPr		FAC EPr	FAC EP	FAC EP
FAT P	FAT P	FAV 1P	FAV 2Pr	FAV 1Q	FAV 1P	FAV 2Q	FAV 1P	FAV 1P	FAV 1P

GROUND: The Northcourt, Northcourt Road, Abingdon OX14 1PL

Nearest Railway Station Radley - 2.5km

Bus Route Boundary House (Oxford Road) stop - 215m

BOURTON ROVERS

Hellenic Division One

Founded 1894 Nickname: Rovers **Club Colours:** All blue

Club Contact Details 01451 821 977

HONOURS FA Comps: None

League: Hellenic Division Two West 2016-17

11-12	12-13	13-14	14-15	15-16	16-17	17-18	18-19	19-20	20-21
					Hel2W 1	Hel2W 2	Hel2W 5	Hel1W n&v	Hel1W n&v

GROUND: Rissington Road, Bourton-on-the-Water, Cheltenham GL54 2EB

Nearest Railway Station Cirencester

Bus Route 801 - alight at Edinburgh Wool Shop, 11min walk from there.

CHELTENHAM SARACENS

Hellenic Division One

Founded 1964 Nickname: The Sarries **Club Colours:** All blue

Club Contact Details 07468 515 471 saracenschairman@outlook.com

HONOURS FA Comps: None

League: Hellenic Division One 1999-2000.

11-12	12-13	13-14	14-15	15-16	16-17	17-18	18-19	19-20	20-21
Hel P 15	Hel P 11	Hel P 16	Hel P 20	Hel1W 2	Hel1W 14	Hel1W 10	Hel1W 2	Hel1W n&v	Hel1W n&v
		FAC Pr	FAC P	FAC 1Q				FAC EP	FAC EP
FAV 1Q	FAV 1P	FAV 1Q	FAV 1Q	FAV 1Q			FAV 2Q	FAV 1Q	FAV 1Q

GROUND: Petersfield Park, Tewkesbury Road GL51 9DY

Nearest Railway Station Cheltenham Spa - 1.4km

Bus Route Moors Avenue stop - 171m away

CIRENCESTER TOWN DEV.

Hellenic Division One

Founded 2011 Nickname: Centurions **Club Colours:** Red & black

Club Contact Details 01285 654 543 scott.griffin@cirentownfc.com

HONOURS FA Comps: None

League: None

11-12	12-13	13-14	14-15	15-16	16-17	17-18	18-19	19-20	20-21
	Hel2W 3	Hel2W 3	Hel1W 4	Hel1W 11	Hel1W 5	Hel1W 5	Hel1W 8	Hel1W n&v	Hel1W n&v

GROUND: Corinium Stadium, Kingshill Lane, Cirencester Glos GL7 1HS

Nearest Railway Station Cirencester

Bus Route Kingshill School Grounds stop - 55m away

CLANFIELD 85

Hellenic Division One

Founded 1890 Nickname: Robins **Club Colours:** All red

Club Contact Details 01367 810 770 peter.osborne1@virgin.net

HONOURS FA Comps: None

League: North Berks Division Two 1924-25.
Hellenic Division One 1969-70.

11-12	12-13	13-14	14-15	15-16	16-17	17-18	18-19	19-20	20-21
Hel1W 8	Hel1W 11	Hel1W 5	Hel1W 9	Hel1W 12	Hel1W 10	Hel1W 8	Hel1W 5	Hel1W n&v	Hel1W n&v
FAC EP								FAC EP	FAC EP
FAT 1P	FAV 1Q					FAV 2Q	FAV 2Q	FAV 2Q	FAV 1P

GROUND: Radcot Road, Clanfield OX18 2ST

Bus Route Carter Institute stop - 399m away

FC STRATFORD

Hellenic Division One

Founded 2009 Nickname: **Club Colours:** Blue

Club Contact Details 07957 694 472 (Sec)

HONOURS FA Comps:

League:

11-12	12-13	13-14	14-15	15-16	16-17	17-18	18-19	19-20	20-21
MCm2 7	MCm2 10	MCm2 14	MFL3 12	MFL3 4	MFL3 6	MFL3 3	MFL2 14	MFL2 n&v	MFL2 n&v
							FAV 1Q	FAV 2Q	

GROUND: Home Guard Club, Main Road, Tiddington CV37 7AY

Nearest Railway Station Strtaford-upon-Avon - just under 3 miles away.

Bus Route No.15 from Alcester Road outside train station stops almost outside the club on Tiddington Road.

HEREFORD PEGASUS

Hellenic Division One

Founded 1955 Nickname: The Redmen or Peggy **Club Colours:** Red and white

Club Contact Details 07931 971 765 nikmarsh1982@gmail.com

HONOURS FA Comps: None

League: Hellenic Division One 1984-85, 98-99.

11-12	12-13	13-14	14-15	15-16	16-17	17-18	18-19	19-20	20-21
WMP 17	WMP 7	WMP 2	WMP 9	WMP 9	WMP 9	WMP 19	WMP 20	Hel1W n&v	Hel1W n&v
FAC EPr	FAC P	FAC EP	FAC EPr	FAC EP					
FAV 1Q	FAV 1P	FAV 1Q	FAV 2P	FAV 1Q	FAV 2Q	FAV 1Q	FAV 1Q	FAV 1Q	FAV 1Q

GROUND: Old School Lane, Hereford HR1 1EX

Nearest Railway Station Hereford - 1.3km

Bus Route Bus stops outside the ground

LITTLETON

Hellenic Division One

Founded 1890 Nickname: The Ton **Club Colours:** Red/red/white

Club Contact Details 01905 909 125

HONOURS FA Comps: None

League: Midland Combination Division Three 2001-02.

11-12	12-13	13-14	14-15	15-16	16-17	17-18	18-19	19-20	20-21
MCm1 2	MCmP 2	MCmP 11	MFL1 9	MFL1 9	MFL1 9	MFL1 8	MFL1 17	WMP n&v	WMP n&v
				FAV 2Q	FAV 2Q	FAV 2Q	FAV 2Q	FAV 1Q	FAV 2Q

GROUND: 5 Acres, Pebworth Road, North Littleton, Evesham, Worcs, WR11 8QL

Nearest Railway Station Honeybourne - 3.1km

Bus Route The Ivy Inn stop - 1.2km away

MALMESBURY VICTORIA

Hellenic Division One

Foundec 1896 Nickname: The Vics **Club Colours:** Black & white

Club Contact Details 01666 822 141 brendon@innov.co.uk

HONOURS FA Comps: None

League: Wiltshire Premier 1999-00, 2014-15.

11-12	12-13	13-14	14-15	15-16	16-17	17-18	18-19	19-20	20-21
Hel1W 16	Hel1W 15	Hel1W 12	Wilt 1	Wilt 3	West1 9	West1 15	Hel1W 4	Hel1W n&v	Hel1W n&v
								FAC EP	
		FAV 1Q	FAV 1P	FAV 2Q	FAV 1Q	FAV 2Q	FAV 2P	FAV 1P	FAV 2Q

GROUND: Flying Monk Ground, Gloucester Road, SN16 9JS

Bus Route Bus stops outside the Supermarket

MILTON UNITED

Hellenic Division One

Foundec 1909 Nickname: Miltonians **Club Colours:** Claret & sky blue

Club Contact Details 01235 832 999 milton.united.fc@hotmail.co.uk

HONOURS FA Comps: None

League: Hellenic 1990-91, Division One East 2013-14.

11-12	12-13	13-14	14-15	15-16	16-17	17-18	18-19	19-20	20-21
Hel1E 14	Hel1E 14	Hel1E 1	Hel P 14	Hel P 18	Hel1W 12	Hel1E 13	Hel1E 10	Hel1E n&v	Hel1E n&v
FAC EP			FAC 1Q	FAC P	FAC EP				
FAV 2Q	FAV 2Q	FAV 1P	FAV 2Q	FAV 2Q	FAV 2Q	FAV 1Q	FAV 1Q	FAV 1Q	FAV 1P

GROUND: The Heights, Potash Lane, Milton Heights, OX13 6AG

Nearest Railway Station Didcot Parkway - 4.7km. Appleford - 5.9km

Bus Route The Pack Horse stop - 69m away

MORETON RANGERS

Hellenic Division One

Foundec 1997 Nickname: The Townsmen **Club Colours:** Claret and blue

Club Contact Details 07568 469 120

HONOURS FA Comps: None

League: Cheltenham Division One 2009-10. Hellenic Division Two West 2018-19

11-12	12-13	13-14	14-15	15-16	16-17	17-18	18-19	19-20	20-21
				Hel2W 3	Hel2W 5	Hel2W 3	Hel2W 1	Hel1W n&v	Hel1W n&v

GROUND: London Road, Moreton-in-Marsh, Glos GL56 0HN

Nearest Railway Station Moreton-in-Marsh - 1min walk away

NEWENT TOWN AFC

Hellenic Division One

Foundec Nickname: The Daff's **Club Colours:** Yellow & blue

Club Contact Details 01531 821 509 (Ground) phil@calendarlady.co.uk

HONOURS FA Comps: None

League: North Gloucestershire Premier 2012-13. Hellenic Division Two West 2017-18

11-12	12-13	13-14	14-15	15-16	16-17	17-18	18-19	19-20	20-21
NGIP 3	NGIP 1	GIN2 3	GIN1 14	GIN1 3	GIN1 7	Hel2W 1	Hel1W 9	Hel1W n&v	Hel1W n&v
									FAC EP
								FAV 2Q	FAV 1Q

GROUND: Wildsmith Meadow, Malswick, Newent GL18 1HE

Nearest Railway Station Gloucester

Bus Route 32

PERSHORE TOWN

Hellenic Division One

Founded 1988 | Nickname: Town | **Club Colours:** Blue & white

Club Contact Details

HONOURS FA Comps: None

League: Midland Combination Division Two 1989-90, Premier 1993-94.

11-12	12-13	13-14	14-15	15-16	16-17	17-18	18-19	19-20	20-21
MCmP 16	MCmP 13	MCmP 15	MFL1 11	MFL1 14	MFL1 18	MFL1 18	WMP 14	WMP n&v	WMP n&v
FAV 2Q	FAV 2Q	FAV 2Q	FAV 2Q	FAV 1Q	FAV 1Q	FAV 2Q	FAV 1Q	FAV 1Qr	FAV 2Q

GROUND: King George V Playing Field, King George's Way, Pershore WR10 1QU

Nearest Railway Station Pershore - 2.1km

Bus Route Abbey Tea Rooms stop - 167m away

SHORTWOOD UNITED

Hellenic Division One

Founded 1900 | Nickname: The Wood | **Club Colours:** Red and white

Club Contact Details 07931 971 765 jimcunneen1951@gmail.com

HONOURS FA Comps: None

League: Gloucestershire 1981-82. Hellenic 1984-85, 91-92.

11-12	12-13	13-14	14-15	15-16	16-17	17-18	18-19	19-20	20-21
Hel P 2	Sthsw 8	Sthsw 6	Sthsw 11	Sthsw 7	Sthsw 9	Sthsw 17	WestP 20	Hel1W n&v	Hel1W n&v
FAC Pr	FAC P	FAC 1P	FAC 3Qr	FAC 2Q	FAC P	FAC P	FAC EP	FAC P	
FAV QF	FAT 3Qr	FAT 1Q	FAT 1Q	FAT P	FAT P	FAT 3Q	FAV 2Q	FAV 2Q	FAV 1Q

GROUND: Meadowbank, Shortwood, Nailsworth GL6 0SJ

Bus Route Homefield Turn - stop 250m away

STONEHOUSE TOWN

Hellenic Division One

Founded 1898 | Nickname: The Magpies | **Club Colours:** Black and white

Club Contact Details 07849 551 656

HONOURS FA Comps: None

League: Dursley & Dist 1900-01. Stroud & Dist 1908-09, 20-12, 27-28. North Glos 1919-20. Glos Nth Senior 1934-35, 35-36, 36-37, Div.2 2008-09, Wiltshire 1967-68. Glos Co 1968-69. Western Div.2 1950-51.

11-12	12-13	13-14	14-15	15-16	16-17	17-18	18-19	19-20	20-21
					GlCo 3	GlCo 4	GlCo 3	Hel1W n&v	Hel1W n&v
									FAV 2Q

GROUND: Oldends Lane, Stonehouse, Glos GL10 2DG

Nearest Railway Station Stonehouse - 3min walk to Wycliffe College bus stop.

Bus Route No.61 (Woodmancote) from Wycliffe College 5min journey to Oldends Lane.

STUDLEY

Hellenic Division One

Founded 1971 | Nickname: Bees | **Club Colours:** Sky blue and navy

Club Contact Details 07745 310 077 bobtheat@hotmail.co.uk

HONOURS FA Comps: None

League: Midland Combination Division One 1991-92.

11-12	12-13	13-14	14-15	15-16	16-17	17-18	18-19	19-20	20-21
MidAl 17	MidAl 21	MCmP 6	MFL1 10	MFLP 12	MFLP 15	MFL1 9	MFL1 9	MFL1 n&v	MFL1 n&v
FAC P	FAC P	FAC P	FAC EP						
FAV 2Q	FAV 1Q	FAV 2Q	FAV 1P	FAV 2Q	FAV 1Q	FAV 2Q	FAV 2Q	FAV 2Q	FAV 1P

GROUND: The Beehive, Abbeyfields Drive, Studley B80 7BF

Nearest Railway Station Redditch - 4.6km

Bus Route Red Hill Close stop - 49m away

WELLINGTON

Hellenic Division One

Founded 1968 Nickname: The Wellies **Club Colours:** Orange

Club Contact Details 07842 186 643 (MD) wellingtonherefordfc@gmail.com

HONOURS FA Comps: None

League: West Midlands (Reg) Division One South 1998-99.

11-12		12-13		13-14		14-15		15-16		16-17		17-18		18-19		19-20		20-21	
WMP	11	WMP	15	WMP	8	WMP	11	WMP	11	WMP	5	WMP	10	WMP	9	Hel1W	n&v	Hel1W	n&v
FAC	EP	FAC	P			FAC	P					FAC	EP					FAC	EP
FAV	2Q	FAV	1Q	FAV	1Q	FAV	1P	FAV	2Q	FAV	2Q	FAV	1P	FAV	1Pr	FAV	1Q	FAV	1Q

GROUND: Wellington Playing Field, Wellington, Hereford HR4 8AZ

Nearest Railway Station Hereford

Bus Route Wellington Village - stop 270m away

WORCESTER RAIDERS

Hellenic Division One

Founded 2001 Nickname: Raiders **Club Colours:** Red and black

Club Contact Details 07532 266 897

HONOURS FA Comps: None

League: West Mildlands (Regional) Division One 2018-19.

11-12		12-13		13-14		14-15		15-16		16-17		17-18		18-19		19-20		20-21	
				WM2	3	WM1	14	WM1	12	WM1	3	WM1	7	WM1	1	WMP	n&v	WMP	n&v
																		FAV	1Q

GROUND: Claines Lane, Worcester, Worcestershire WR3 7SS

Nearest Railway Station Worcester Foregate Street

Bus Route 303 from Foregate Street Station to Bevere Lane (10min journey), ground 14min walk from there.

Wardle (Witton Albion) Clare (Macclesfield) - pre-season. Photo Keith Clayton.

AFC WULFRUNIANS

Midland Football League Premier

Founded 2005 | Nickname: The Wulfs | **Club Colours:** Red and black

Club Contact Details 07870 164 631 simoncater@hotmail.com

Previous Names: None
Previous Leagues: West Midlands (Regional). Midland Alliance 2013-14.
HONOURS
FA Comps: None
League: West Midlands (Regional) League Division Two 2005-06, Premier Division 2008-09, 12-13.

11-12	12-13	13-14	14-15	15-16	16-17	17-18	18-19	19-20	20-21
WMP 5	WMP 1	MidAl 8	MFLP 7	MFLP 13	MFLP 17	MFLP 17	MFLP 12	MFLP n&v	MFLP n&v
FAC 1Q	FAC 1Q	FAC 2Q	FAC P	FAC 1Q	FAC EP	FAC Pr	FAC EP	FAC P	FAC EP
FAV 2Q	FAV 3P	FAV 2P	FAV 1Pr	FAV 4P	FAV 2P	FAV 1Pr	FAV 2Q	FAV 1Q	FAV 1Q

GROUND: CKW Stadium, Castlecroft Road, Wolverhampton WV3 8NA **Capacity:** 2,000
Nearest Railway Station Wolverhampton - 5km
Bus Route Castlecroft Hotel stop - 218m away

CLUB MOVEMENTS

PREMIER DIVISION - IN: Bewdley Town, Shifnal Town and Wolverhampton Casuals (P - WMRL). Hanley Town and Whitchurch Alport (LM - NWCP). Lichfield City and Uttoxeter Town (P - ML1). Stone Old Alleynians (P - NWCS). **OUT:** Sporting Khalsa (P - NPLM). Gresley, Heather St Johns, Long Eaton United, Newark, and Selston (LM - UCPN). Coventry Sphinx and Coventry United (LM - UCPS).

BEWDLEY TOWN

Midland Football League Premier

Founded 1978 | Nickname: None | **Club Colours:** Royal blue & yellow

Club Contact Details 07739 626 169 stevegodfrey09@gmail.com

Previous Names: Formed by the merger of Bewdley Old Boys and Woodcolliers.
Previous Leagues: Kidderminster & District 1978-99. West Midlands (Reg) 1999-2021.
HONOURS
FA Comps: None
League: West Midlands (Reg) Division One South 2002-03, Division One 2004-05.

11-12	12-13	13-14	14-15	15-16	16-17	17-18	18-19	19-20	20-21
WMP 4	WMP 8	WMP 7	WMP 17	WMP 16	WMP 6	WMP 7	WMP 6	WMP n&v	WMP n&v
FAC 1Q	FAC 1Q	FAC EP	FAC EP			FAC EP			FAC EP
FAV 1Q	FAV 1P	FAV 1Q	FAV 1Q	FAV 1Q	FAV 2Q	FAV 1Q	FAV 1P	FAV 1Q	FAV 2P

GROUND: Ribbesford Meadows, Ribbesford, Bewdley, Worcs DY12 2TJ
Bus Route Burlish Farm - stop 1km away

BOLDMERE ST. MICHAELS

Midland Football League Premier

Founded 1883 | Nickname: The Mikes | **Club Colours:** White & black

Club Contact Details 07866 122 254 clivefaulkner457@gmail.com

Previous Names: None.
Previous Leagues: West Midlands (Regional) 1949-63. Midland Combination. Midland Alliance > 2014.
HONOURS
FA Comps: None
League: Midland Combination Premier 1985-86, 88-89, 89-90.

11-12	12-13	13-14	14-15	15-16	16-17	17-18	18-19	19-20	20-21
MidAl 12	MidAl 9	MidAl 2	MFLP 9	MFLP 11	MFLP 12	MFLP 14	MFLP 5	MFLP n&v	MFLP n&v
FAC 1Q	FAC EP	FAC EP	FAC 1Q	FAC EPr	FAC P	FAC 1Q	FAC EPr	FAC 1Q	FAC EP
FAV 2P	FAV 2Q	FAV 2Q	FAV 1P	FAV 1P	FAV 2Q	FAV 2Q	FAV 2P	FAV 1P	FAV 2P

GROUND: Trevor Brown Memorial Ground, Church Road, Boldmere B73 5RY **Capacity:** 2,500
Nearest Railway Station Chester Road - 0.9km **Seats:** 230
Bus Route Church Road stop - 106m away **Covered:** 400

HANLEY TOWN

Midland Football League Premier

Founded 1966 Nickname: **Club Colours:** All royal blue

Club Contact Details 07306 109 634 secretary@hanley-townfc.co.uk

Previous Names: None

Previous Leagues: London 1966-67. Staffordshire County Senior 1967-76. Mid-Cheshire 1976-88, 96-98. Midland/Staffordshire County 1998-2013. North West Counties 2013-21.

HONOURS

FA Comps: None

League: London 1966-67. Staffordshire County Div.2 67-68, Div.1 68-69, Premier 72-73, 75-76. Mid-Cheshire Div.1 81-82. Midland/Staffordshire County Senior 2004-05, 2006-07, 11-12, 12-13. North West Counties Div.1 2015-16.

11-12	12-13	13-14	14-15	15-16	16-17	17-18	18-19	19-20	20-21
StfSP 1	StfSP 1	NWC1 4	NWC1 4	NWC1 1	NWCP 10	NWCP 8	NWCP 17	NWCP n&v	NWCP n&v
				FAC P	FAC EPr	FAC P	FAC EPr	FAC EP	FAC 2Q
			FAV 1P	FAV 1Q	FAV 1P	FAV 1P	FAV 1P	FAV 1P	FAV 3P

GROUND: Payaro Stadium, Abbey Lane, Bucknall, Stoke-on-Trent, Staffordshire ST2 8AJ

Nearest Railway Station Stoke-on-Trent - 3.2km

Bus Route Abbey Lane stop - 229m away

HAUGHMOND

Midland Football League Premier

Founded 1980 Nickname: Academicals **Club Colours:** White and black

Club Contact Details 07785 531 754 stuartlwilliams@btinternet.com

Previous Names: None

Previous Leagues: West Midlands >2017. Midland Football 2017-18. West Midlands 2018-19.

HONOURS

FA Comps: None

League: Shropshire County Premier Division 2010-11. West Midlands Division Two 2011-12, Premier Division 2016-17.

11-12	12-13	13-14	14-15	15-16	16-17	17-18	18-19	19-20	20-21
WM2 1	WM1 4	WM1 2	WMP 8	WMP 5	WMP 1	MFLP 20	WMP 2	MFLP n&v	MFLP n&v
					FAC EP	FAC 2Qr	FAC 1Q	FAC P	FAC EP
				FAV 2P	FAV 1P	FAV 1P	FAV 1Q	FAV 1P	FAV 1Q

GROUND: Sundorne Sports Village, Sundorne Road, Shrewsbury. SY1 4RQ

Nearest Railway Station Shrewsbury - 2.6km

Bus Route Ta Centre stop - 109m away

HIGHGATE UNITED

Midland Football League Premier

Founded 1948 Nickname: Red or Gate **Club Colours:** All red

Club Contact Details 07591 172 318 jimmymerry777@gmail.com

Previous Names: None.

Previous Leagues: Worcestershire/Midland Combination. Midland Alliance 2008-14.

HONOURS

FA Comps: None

League: Midland Combination Premier 1972-73, 73-74, 74-75.

11-12	12-13	13-14	14-15	15-16	16-17	17-18	18-19	19-20	20-21
MidAl 20	MidAl 19	MidAl 3	MFL1 1	MFLP 9	MFLP 7	MFLP 3	MFLP 14	MFLP n&v	MFLP n&v
FAC P	FAC EPr				FAC 2Q	FAC EPr	FAC 1Q	FAC EP	FAC EP
FAV 1P	FAV 2Q			FAV 2P	FAV 2Q	FAV 3P	FAV 1P	FAV 2Q	FAV 2Q

GROUND: The Coppice, Tythe Barn Lane, Shirley Solihull B90 1PH **Capacity:** 2,000

Nearest Railway Station Whitlocks End - 0.4km

Bus Route Whitlocks End stop - 302m away

LICHFIELD CITY

Midland Football League Premier

Founded 1970 Nickname: **Club Colours:** All royal blue

Club Contact Details 07779 295 033 darrenleaver@outlook.com

Previous Names: Lichfield FC 1970-94

Previous Leagues: West Midlands (Regional) 1970-96. Sunday League 1996-2008. Midland Combination 2008-14.

HONOURS

FA Comps: None

League: None

11-12		12-13		13-14		14-15		15-16		16-17		17-18		18-19		19-20		20-21	
MCm1	4	MCmP	10	MCmP	7	MFL1	12	MFL1	7	MFL1	7	MFL1	10	MFL1	4	MFL1	n&v	MFL1	n&v
						FAC	P			FAC	P					FAC	1Q	FAC	EP
				FAV	1Q	FAV	2Q	FAV	1Q	FAV	2P	FAV	1Q	FAV	1Q	FAV	1P	FAV	2Q

GROUND: Brownsfield Road, Lichfield, Staffs, WS13 6AY **Capacity:** 1,500

Nearest Railway Station Lichfield Trent Valley High Level/Lichfield Trent Valley - 1.4km

Bus Route Netherstowe Lane stop - 78m away

LYE TOWN

Midland Football League Premier

Founded 1930 Nickname: The Flyers **Club Colours:** All blue

Club Contact Details 07429 887 570 dprobbo@gmail.com

Previous Names: Lye & Wollescote 1930-31.

Previous Leagues: Worcestershire Combination 1931-39. Birmingham & Dist/West Midlands (Regional) 1947-62/1962-2014.

HONOURS

FA Comps: None

League: West Midlands (Regional) 2013-14.

11-12		12-13		13-14		14-15		15-16		16-17		17-18		18-19		19-20		20-21	
WMP	15	WMP	2	WMP	1	MFLP	6	MFLP	8	MFLP	4	MFLP	16	MFLP	10	MFLP	n&v	MFLP	n&v
FAC	EP	FAC	P	FAC	P	FAC	EP	FAC	EPr	FAC	P					FAC	EP	FAC	EP
FAV	1Q	FAV	1P	FAV	1Q	FAV	2Q	FAV	2Q	FAV	1Q			FAV	4P	FAV	3P	FAV	1P

GROUND: Sports Ground, Stourbridge Road, Lye, Stourbridge, West Mids DY9 7DH **Capacity:** 1,000

Nearest Railway Station Lye - 0.5km

Bus Route Cemetery Road stop - 93m away

RACING CLUB WARWICK

Midland Football League Premier

Founded 1919 Nickname: Racers **Club Colours:** Gold and black

Club Contact Details 07926 188 553 pja.murphy@hotmail.co.uk

Previous Names: Warwick Saltisford Rovers > 1970.

Previous Leagues: Warwick. Leamington & District. West Midlands (regional) 1967-72. Midland Combination 1972-89, 2009-14. Southern 1989-2003. Midland Alliance 2003-09.

HONOURS

FA Comps: None

League: Warwick 1933-34, 34-35, 35-36. Leamington & District 37-38, 45-46, 46-47, 47-48. Midland Combination Premier Division 1987-88.

11-12		12-13		13-14		14-15		15-16		16-17		17-18		18-19		19-20		20-21	
MCmP	13	MCmP	17	MCmP	12	MFL1	18	MFL1	10	MFL1	6	MFL1	5	MFL1	2	MFLP	n&v	MFLP	n&v
														FAC	1Q	FAC	EP	FAC	EP
FAV	2P	FAV	2Q	FAV	1P	FAV	1Q	FAV	2P	FAV	1Q	FAV	3P	FAV	2Q	FAV	1P	FAV	1P

GROUND: Townsend Meadow, Hampton Road, Warwick, Warwickshire CV34 6JP **Capacity:** 1,300

Nearest Railway Station Warwick Parkway - 1.4km

Bus Route Shakespeare Avenue stop - 131m away

ROMULUS

Midland Football League Premier

Founded 1979 Nickname: The Roms **Club Colours:** Red and white stripes/red/red

Club Contact Details 07528 177 046 paterson_r3@sky.com

Previous Names: None

Previous Leagues: Midland Combination 1999-2004, Midland Alliance 2004-07, Southern 2007-2010. Northern Premier 2010-18.

HONOURS

FA Comps: None

League: Midland Combination Division One 1999-00, Premier Division 2003-04.

11-12	12-13	13-14	14-15	15-16	16-17	17-18	18-19	19-20	20-21
NP1S 20	NP1S 19	NP1S 11	NP1S 12	NP1S 10	NP1S 13	NP1S 22	MFLP 17	MFLP n&v	MFLP n&v
FAC 1Q	FAC P	FAC P	FAC 1Q	FAC P	FAC 1Qr	FAC 1Q	FAC 2Q	FAC 1Q	FAC EP
FAT 2Q	FAT 3Q	FAT Pr	FAT 1Q	FAT Pr	FAT Pr	FAT P	FAV 2P	FAV 1Q	FAV 1P

GROUND: Vale Stadium, Farnborough Road, Castle Vale, Birmingham B35 7LQ

SHIFNAL TOWN

Midland Football League Premier

Founded 1964 Nickname: The Town or Reds **Club Colours:** Navy blue & yellow

Club Contact Details 07432 573 763 victoriatranter@hotmail.co.uk

Previous Names: St Andrews Youth Club 1964. Shifnal Juniors >1972.

Previous Leagues: Wellington & District 1964-69. Shropshire County 1969-76, 85-93. West Midlands (Regional) 1976-85, 06-21. Midland Combination 1993-94, 2003-06. Midland Alliance (FM) 1994-2003.

HONOURS

FA Comps: None

League: Wellington & District Division Two 1968-69. Shropshire County 1975-76. West Midlands (Regional) Division One 1978-79, 2015-16, Premier Division 1980-81, 81-82, 2006-07.

11-12	12-13	13-14	14-15	15-16	16-17	17-18	18-19	19-20	20-21
WMP 16	WMP 19	WMP 19	WMP 21	WM1 1	WMP 11	WMP 15	WMP 19	WMP n&v	WMP n&v
FAC EPr	FAC EP								FAC EP
FAV 1Q	FAV 1P	FAV 1Q	FAV 2Q	FAV 1Q	FAV 1P	FAV 1P	FAV 1Q	FAV 2Q	FAV 2Q

GROUND: Coppice Green Lane, Shifnal, Shrops TF11 8PD

Nearest Railway Station Shifnal - 0.8km

Bus Route Green (Barn Rd) - stop 100m away

STONE OLD ALLEYNIANS

Midland Football League Premier

Founded 1962 Nickname: **Club Colours:** White & black

Club Contact Details 07585 328 049 secretarysoafc@hotmail.com

Previous Names: None

Previous Leagues: Stafford Amateur 1962-80. North Staffs Alliance 1980-92. Staffordshire County 1992-2007. West Midlands (Reg) 2007-18. North West Counties 2018-21.

HONOURS

FA Comps: None

League: Stafford Amateur Division Two, Division One 1970-71 + x3 more. Mid Staffordshire Division Two 1965-66, 80-81, Division One 71-72, 74-75, 78-79.

11-12	12-13	13-14	14-15	15-16	16-17	17-18	18-19	19-20	20-21
WM1 5	WM1 10	WM1 8	WM1 2	WMP 14	WMP 12	WMP 13	NWC1S 3	NWC1S n&v	NWC1S n&v
								FAC EP	FAC EP
			FAV 2Q	FAV 2Q	FAV 2Qr	FAV 2Q	FAV 2Q	FAV 1Q	FAV 2P

GROUND: Kings Park, Hilderstone Road, Meir Heath, Stoke On Trent, ST3 7NT

Nearest Railway Station Blythe Bridge (East Midlands Railway).

Bus Route 6A & 455

STOURPORT SWIFTS

Midland Football League Premier

Founded 1882 Nickname: Swifts **Club Colours:** Gold & black

Club Contact Details 07780 997 758 ghaighway@hotmail.co.uk

Previous Names: None

Previous Leagues: Kidderminster/Worcestershire/West Midlands (Regional) > 1998, Midland Alliance 1998-2001, 12-14, Southern 2001-12.

HONOURS

FA Comps: None

League: Midland Alliance 2000-01.

11-12	12-13	13-14	14-15	15-16	16-17	17-18	18-19	19-20	20-21
Sthsw 21	MidAl 5	MidAl 10	MFLP 10	MFLP 10	MFLP 13	MFLP 15	MFLP 13	MFLP n&v	MFLP n&v
						FAC EPr	FAC 1Q	FAC Pr	FAC EP
						FAV 5P	FAV 2P	FAV 1Q	FAV 4P

GROUND: Walshes Meadow, Harold Davis Drive, Stourport on Severn DY13 0AA

Nearest Railway Station Hartlebury - 4.2km

Bus Route Swimming Pool stop - 104m away

Capacity: 2,000 **Seats:** 250 **Covered:** 150

TIVIDALE

Midland Football League Premier

Founded 1953 Nickname: The Dale **Club Colours:** Yellow

Club Contact Details 07939 234 813 leontividale@hotmail.com

Previous Names: Tividale Hall Youth Club 1953-56

Previous Leagues: Warwickshire & West Midlands Alliance 1956-66. West Midlands (Regional) 1966- 2011. Midland Alliance 2011-14.

HONOURS

FA Comps: None

League: Warwickshire & West Midlands Alliance Premier 1964-65. West Midlands (Reg) Division One 1972-73, Premier Division 2010-11, 18-19. Midland Alliance 2013-14.

11-12	12-13	13-14	14-15	15-16	16-17	17-18	18-19	19-20	20-21
MidAl 4	MidAl 8	MidAl 1	NP1S 8	NP1S 22	MFLP 22	WMP 2	WMP 1	MFLP n&v	MFLP n&v
FAC EP	FAC 2Q	FAC 1Q	FAC 2Qr	FAC 1Q	FAC P	FAC 1Q	FAC EP	FAC P	FAC EP
FAV 5P	FAV 2Q	FAV 2Q	FAT P	FAT P	FAV 1Q	FAV 1Q	FAV 2Q	FAV 2Q	FAV 2Q

GROUND: The Beeches, Packwood Road, Tividale, West Mids B69 1UL

Nearest Railway Station Dudley Port - 1.6km

Bus Route Regent Road - stop 100m away

Capacity: 3,000 **Seats:** 200

UTTOXETER TOWN

Midland Football League Premier

Founded 1972 Nickname: Town **Club Colours:** All Yellow

Club Contact Details 07816 068 454 uttoxetertfc@gmail.com

Previous Names: None

Previous Leagues: Staffordshire County 1972-late 70s. Sunday League late 70s- early 2000s. Staffordshire County Senior >2014, 15-16. Midland (FM) 2014-15.

HONOURS

FA Comps: None

League: Staffordshire County Senior Division One 2012-13.

11-12	12-13	13-14	14-15	15-16	16-17	17-18	18-19	19-20	20-21
	StfS1 1	StfSP 2	MFL1 5	StfSP 6	MFL1 11	MFL1 11	MFL1 7	MFL1 n&v	MFL1 n&v
				FAV 3P	FAV 2P	FAV 2Q	FAV 2Qr	FAV 2P	FAV 2Q

GROUND: Oldfields Sports Ground, Springfield Road, Uttoxeter, ST14 7JX

Nearest Railway Station Uttoxeter - 1.1km

Bus Route Smithfield Road stop - 178m away

Capacity: 1,000

WALSALL WOOD

Midland Football League Premier

Founded 1915 Nickname: Wood or Prims **Club Colours:** All Red

Club Contact Details 07565 358 902 trace.hunt@hotmail.co.uk

Previous Names: Walsall Borough (formed when Walsall Wood & Walsall Sportsco merged) 1982-96.

Previous Leagues: Midland Combinataion 1986-92, 2006-13. Staffordshire Senior 1992-93. West Midlands 1993-2006. Mid Alliance 2013-14.

HONOURS

FA Comps: None

League: Worcestershire/Midland Combination 1951-52, 2012-13. Midland Football Division One 2017-18.

11-12	12-13	13-14	14-15	15-16	16-17	17-18	18-19	19-20	20-21
MidCo 14	MidCo 1	MidAl 6	WMP 4	MFLP 7	MFLP 20	MFL1 1	MFLP 2	MFLP n&v	MFLP n&v
FAC EP		FAC 1Qr	FAC P	FAC EPr	FAC EP	FAC P	FAC 1Q	FAC EP	FAC P
FAV 2Q	FAV QFr	FAV 2P	FAV 4Pr	FAV 3P	FAV 1P	FAV 3P	FAV 3P	FAV 4P	FAV SF

GROUND: BBG Stadium, Lichfield Road, Walsall Wood, Walsall WS9 9NP **Capacity:** 1,000

Nearest Railway Station Walsall (West Midlands Railway).

Bus Route 10 & X35 from Walsall - Oak Park.

WHITCHURCH ALPORT

Midland Football League Premier

Founded 1946 Nickname: **Club Colours:** Red and white

Club Contact Details 07758 160 059 wandrewhough@gmail.com

Previous Names: None

Previous Leagues: Cheshire >2011. Mercian Regional League >2015. North West Counties 2015-21.

HONOURS

FA Comps: WFA Am Cup 1973-74

League: Shrewsbury & District 1947-48. Mid Cheshire 1969-70.

11-12	12-13	13-14	14-15	15-16	16-17	17-18	18-19	19-20	20-21
Ches2 7	MerRP 11	MerRP 5	MerRP 4	NWC1 18	NWC1 5	NWC1 4	NWCP 14	NWCP n&v	NWCP n&v
						FAC EP	FAC P	FAC 1Q	FAC P
					FAV 1Q	FAV 1Q	FAV 2Q	FAV 1P	FAV 1Q

GROUND: Yockings Park, Black Park Road, Whitchurch SY13 1PG

Nearest Railway Station Whitchurch - 0.4km

Bus Route Railway Station stop - 501m away

WOLVERHAMPTON CASUALS

Midland Football League Premier

Founded 1899 Nickname: The Cassies **Club Colours:** Green

Club Contact Details 07738 820320 tudor.p@outlook.com

Previous Names: None

Previous Leagues: West Midlands (Regional) 1982-2021.

HONOURS

FA Comps: None

League: West Midlands (Reg) Division One 1994-95.

11-12	12-13	13-14	14-15	15-16	16-17	17-18	18-19	19-20	20-21
WMP 3	WMP 3	WMP 3	WMP 6	WMP 7	WMP 2	WMP 9	WMP 3	WMP n&v	WMP n&v
FAC EP	FAC 1Qr	FAC P	FAC EP	FAC EP	FAC EPr	FAC P		FAC EPr	
FAV 1Q	FAV 1Q	FAV 2Q	FAV 1Q	FAV 2Q	FAV 2P	FAV 1Q	FAV 2Q	FAV 2Q	FAV 1Q

GROUND: Brinsford Stadium, Brinsford Lane, Wolverhampton WV10 7PR **Seats:** 150

Nearest Railway Station Billbrook - 4.8km

Bus Route Old Heath House - stop 350m away

WORCESTER CITY

Midland Football League Premier

Founded 1902 Nickname: City **Club Colours:** Blue & white

Club Contact Details 07811 076 933 kevinpreece1987@gmail.com

Previous Names: Formed when Berwick Rangers and Worcester Rovers amalgamated

Previous Leagues: Birmingham & District 1902-38. Southern 1938-79, 85-2004. Alliance 1979-85. Conference 2004-17.

HONOURS

FA Comps: None

League: Birmingham League 1913-14, 24-25, 28-29, 29-30.
Southern League Division One North 1967-68, 76-77, Premier 1978-79.

11-12		12-13		13-14		14-15		15-16		16-17		17-18		18-19		19-20		20-21	
Conf N	7	Conf N	15	Conf N	15	Conf N	9	Nat N	17	Nat N	20	MFLP	4	MFLP	11	MFLP	n&v	MFLP	n&v
FAC	2Q	FAC	4Q	FAC	4Qr	FAC	2Pr	FAC	1P	FAC	3Q	FAC	Pr	FAC	EPr	FAC	P	FAC	1Q
FAT	3Q	FAT	3Q	FAT	2P	FAT	1P	FAT	1Pr	FAT	1P	FAV	2P	FAV	2P	FAV	5Pr	FAV	2P

GROUND: County Sports Ground, Claines Lane, Worcester, WR3 7SS

Nearest Railway Station Worcester Shrub Hill (GWR & West Midlands).

Bus Route 355 - Creswell Close 15 min walk away.

CLUB MOVEMENTS

DIVISION ONE - IN: AFC Bridgnorth, Bilston Town Community, Black Country Rangers, Cradley Town, Darlaston Town, Dudley Sports, Dudley Town, Shawbury United, Wednesfield, and Wolverhampton Sporting Community (LM - WMRL).

OUT: Brocton, Rocester and Stafford Town (LM - NWC1S).
Cadbury Athletic (W - ML2). GNP Sports (W).
Hinckley and Kirby Muxloe (LM - UC1). Leicester Road (P - UCPS).
Lichfield City and Uttoxeter Town (P - MLP).

Moody (Bottesford) breaks through the Gainsborough defence during this pre-season friendly. Photo Keith Clayton.

AFC BRIDGNORTH

Midland Football League Division One

Founded 2013 Nickname: Meadow Men **Club Colours:** Royal blue

Club Contact Details 07748 302650 steve_groome2003@yahoo.co.uk

HONOURS FA Comps: None

League: West Midlands (Reg) Division One 2013-14.

11-12	12-13	13-14	14-15	15-16	16-17	17-18	18-19	19-20	20-21
		WM1 1	WMP 2	WMP 2	WMP 8	WMP 18	WMP 12	WMP n&v	WMP n&v
				FAC P	FAC EP				FAC P
			FAV 1P	FAV 2P	FAV 1Q	FAV 1Q	FAV 1Q	FAV 1Q	FAV 2P

GROUND: Crown Meadow, Innage Lane, Bridgnorth WV16 4HS

Bus Route Bus stops outside the ground.

ASHBY IVANHOE

Midland Football League Division One

Founded 1948 Nickname: The Knights **Club Colours:** Royal blue

Club Contact Details 07854 194099 stuart.mann@hotmail.co.uk

HONOURS FA Comps: None

League: North Leicestershire 1994-95, 96-97, 98-99, 2002-03.
Leicestershire Senior Premier Division 2010-11.

11-12	12-13	13-14	14-15	15-16	16-17	17-18	18-19	19-20	20-21
LeicSP 8	LeicSP 4	LeicSP 3	EMC 6	EMC 3	EMC 10	EMC 17	EMC 14	MFL1 n&v	MFL1 n&v
					FAC 1Q				
FAV 2Q				FAV 1Q	FAV 1P	FAV 2Q	FAV 2Q	FAV 2Q	FAV 2Q

GROUND: NFU Sports Ground, Lower Packington Road, Ashby de la Zouch LE65 1TS

ATHERSTONE TOWN

Midland Football League Division One

Founded 2004 Nickname: The Adders **Club Colours:** Red & white

Club Contact Details 07889 737493 maria@atcfc.co.uk

HONOURS FA Comps: None

League: Midland Combination Division 1 2004-05, Premier Division 2005-06. Midland Alliance 2007-08.

11-12	12-13	13-14	14-15	15-16	16-17	17-18	18-19	19-20	20-21
MidAl 21	MCmP 9	MCmP 9	MFL1 13	MFL1 13	MFL1 4	MFL1 3	MFL1 3	MFL1 n&v	MFL1 n&v
FAC P	FAC EP	FAC 3Q	FAC EPr			FAC EP	FAC 2Q	FAC EP	FAC EP
FAV 1P	FAV 1Q	FAV 1P	FAV 2Q	FAV 1Q	FAV 2Q	FAV 1P	FAV 2Q	FAV QF	FAV 2P

GROUND: Sheepy Road, Atherstone, Warwickshire CV9 3AD

Nearest Railway Station Atherstone - 0.6km

Bus Route Lister Road stop - 118m away

BILSTON TOWN COMMUNITY

Midland Football League Division One

Founded 1894 Nickname: The Steelmen **Club Colours:** Orange & black

Club Contact Details 07751 168 986 hales_05@hotmail.co.uk

HONOURS FA Comps: None

League: Walsall & District 1895-96, 1900-01, 01-02, 32-33, 35-36, 47-48. Birmingham & District/West Mids (Reg) Division One 1956-57, Premier 60-61, 72-73.

11-12	12-13	13-14	14-15	15-16	16-17	17-18	18-19	19-20	20-21
WM1 9	WM1 2	WMP 16	WMP 13	WMP 20	WMP 15	WMP 11	WMP 13	WMP n&v	WMP n&v
	FAV 1P	FAV 2Q	FAV 1Q	FAV 2Q	FAV 2Q	FAV 2Q		FAV 1Q	FAV 1Q

GROUND: Queen Street Stadium, Queen Street, Bilston WV14 7EX

Nearest Railway Station Bilston Central - 550m

Bus Route Bus stops outside the ground

CHELMSLEY TOWN

Midland Football League Division One

Founded 1927 Nickname: Club Colours: Sky blue, white & black

Club Contact Details 07837 509 752 louisehelenhughes@gmail.com

HONOURS FA Comps: None

League: Midland Combination Division One 1987-88.

11-12	12-13	13-14	14-15	15-16	16-17	17-18	18-19	19-20	20-21
MCm2 3	MCm1 13	MCm1 6	MCm2 6	MCm2 2	MCm1 17	MFL1 16	MFL1 12	MFL1 n&v	MFL1 n&v
									FAC EP
						FAV 2Q	FAV 1P	FAV 1Q	FAV 2Q

GROUND: Coleshill FC, Pack Meadow, Packington Lane, Coleshill, B46 3JJ

Nearest Railway Station Coleshill Parkway - 3.6km

Bus Route St Edwards Primary School stop - 258m away

COVENTRY COPSEWOOD

Midland Football League Division One

Founded 1923 Nickname: The G's Club Colours: All blue

Club Contact Details 07884 585 440 davide.wilson@hotmail.co.uk

HONOURS FA Comps: None

League: Midland Combination Division One 1996-97.

11-12	12-13	13-14	14-15	15-16	16-17	17-18	18-19	19-20	20-21
MCmP 3	MCmP 12	MCmP 16	MFL1 8	MFL1 11	MFL1 12	MFL1 13	MFL1 15	MFL1 n&v	MFL1 n&v
FAV 1P	FAV 1Q	FAV 1Q	FAV 1Q	FAV 1Q	FAV 1P	FAV 2Q	FAV 2Q	FAV 2Q	FAV 1Q

GROUND: Copsewood Sports & Social Club, Allard Way, Coventry CV3 1JP

CRADLEY TOWN

Midland Football League Division One

Founded 1948 Nickname: The Lukes or Hammers Club Colours: Red and black

Club Contact Details 07708 659636 d.attwood@sky.com

HONOURS FA Comps: None

League: West Midlands (Reg) Division One 1990-91.

11-12	12-13	13-14	14-15	15-16	16-17	17-18	18-19	19-20	20-21
WMP 8	WMP 9	WMP 10	WMP 15	WMP 8	WMP 10	WMP 8	WMP 11	WMP n&v	WMP n&v
FAC EPr	FAC Pr	FAC EP			FAC EPr				
FAV 1Q	FAV 2Q	FAV 1P	FAV 2Q	FAV 1P	FAV 1Q	FAV 2Q	FAV 2Q	FAV 1Q	FAV 1Q

GROUND: The Beeches, Beeches View Avenue, Cradley, Halesowen B63 2HB

Nearest Railway Station Cradley Heath - 2km

Bus Route Hedgefield Grove - stop 200m away

DARLASTON TOWN (1874)

Midland Football League Division One

Founded 1874 Nickname: Club Colours: Blue and white

Club Contact Details 07956 679056 s.cox@darlastontown1874fc.com

HONOURS FA Comps: None

League: West Midlands (Regional) Division One 2006-07.

11-12	12-13	13-14	14-15	15-16	16-17	17-18	18-19	19-20	20-21
WMP 22	WMP 21		WM2 3	WM1 5	WM1 7	WM1 6	WM1 2	WMP n&v	WMP n&v

GROUND: Bentley Leisure Pavilion, Bentley Road North, Bentley WS2 0EA

DUDLEY SPORTS

Midland Football League Division One

Founded 1925 Nickname: The Piemen **Club Colours:** Green & white

Club Contact Details 07305 005989 kath-john.lewis@blueyonder.co.uk

HONOURS FA Comps: None

League: None

11-12	12-13	13-14	14-15	15-16	16-17	17-18	18-19	19-20	20-21
WMP 12	WMP 17	WMP 17	WMP 12	WMP 6	WMP 17	WMP 16	WMP 15	WMP n&v	WMP n&v
	FAC EPr				FAC P				
FAV 2Q	FAV 1Q	FAV 2Q	FAV 1Q	FAV 2Q	FAV 2Q	FAV 2Q	FAV 2Q	FAV 1Q	FAV 2P

GROUND: Hillcrest Avenue, Brierley Hill, West Mids DY5 3QH

Nearest Railway Station Lye - 2.1km Stourbridge - 2.5km Cradley Heath - 2.8km

Bus Route Lancaster Road - stop 60m away

DUDLEY TOWN

Midland Football League Division One

Founded 1888 Nickname: The Duds or Robins **Club Colours:** Red, white & black

Club Contact Details 07986 549675 davef.dtfc@blueyonder.co.uk

HONOURS FA Comps: None

League: Birmingham Combination 1933-34. Southern Midland Division 1984-85.

11-12	12-13	13-14	14-15	15-16	16-17	17-18	18-19	19-20	20-21
WMP 7	WMP 6	WMP 9	WMP 14	WMP 13	WMP 18	WMP 17	WMP 10	WMP n&v	WMP n&v
	FAC 1Q	FAC EPr	FAC P						
FAV 2Q	FAV 1Q	FAV 2P	FAV 2Q	FAV 1Q	FAV 1Q	FAV 2Q	FAV 2Q	FAV 2P	FAV 2Q

GROUND: Sporting Khalsa FC, Noose Lane, Willenhall WV13 3BB

Nearest Railway Station Wolverhampton - 3.9km

Bus Route Fibbersley Bridge stop - 125m away

HEATH HAYES

Midland Football League Division One

Founded 1965 Nickname: The Hayes **Club Colours:** Blue

Club Contact Details 07974 851 604 tony.hhfc@gmail.com

HONOURS FA Comps: None

League: Staffordshire County Division One 1977-78. West Midlands (Regional) Division One North 1998-99. Midland Combination Premier Division 2009-10.

11-12	12-13	13-14	14-15	15-16	16-17	17-18	18-19	19-20	20-21
MidAl 14	MidAl 18	MidAl 8	MFLP 22	MFL1 8	MFL1 14	MFL1 14	MFL1 18	MFL1 n&v	MFL1 n&v
FAC EP	FAC P	FAC EP	FAC EP	FAC EP	FAC EP				
FAV 1P	FAV 1Q	FAV 1Q	FAV 1Q	FAV 1Q	FAV 1Q	FAV 2Q	FAV 2Q	FAV 1Q	FAV 1Q

GROUND: Coppice Colliery Grd, Newlands Lane, Heath Hayes, Cannock, WS12 3HH

Nearest Railway Station Cannock - 2.7km

Bus Route Five Ways Inn stop - 253m away

KHALSA FOOTBALL FEDERATION

Midland Football League Division One

Founded 1987 Nickname: **Club Colours:** Navy blue & yellow

Club Contact Details 07974 429171 gurdawar.dhaliwal@gmail.com

HONOURS FA Comps: None

League: None

11-12	12-13	13-14	14-15	15-16	16-17	17-18	18-19	19-20	20-21

GROUND: Tividale FC, The Beeches, Packwood Road, Tividale, B69 1UL

Nearest Railway Station Dudley Port - 1.6km

Bus Route Regent Road - stop 100m away

NUNEATON GRIFF

Midland Football League Division One

Founded 1972 Nickname: The Heartlanders **Club Colours:** Blue & white

Club Contact Details 07944 457 250 nuneatongriff@sky.com

HONOURS FA Comps: None

League: Coventry Alliance Premier 1996-97, 97-98.
Midland Combination Premier Division 1999-2000, 00-01.

11-12	12-13	13-14	14-15	15-16	16-17	17-18	18-19	19-20	20-21
MCmP 11	MCmP 4	MCmP 3	MFL1 17	MFL1 3	MFL1 10	MFL1 19	MFL1 19	MFL1 n&v	MFL1 n&v
FAC EP	FAC 2Q	FAC EP	FAC EP		FAC EPr				
FAV 1Q	FAV 2Q	FAV 2Q	FAV 1P	FAV 5P	FAV 3P	FAV 1Q	FAV 2Q	FAV 2Q	FAV 1Q

GROUND: The Pingles Stadium, Avenue Road, Nuneaton, Warwickshire CV11 4LX

OJM BLACK COUNTRY RANGERS

Midland Football League Division One

Founded 1996 Nickname: **Club Colours:** Red

Club Contact Details 07455 203920 chrisbuttswork@gmail.com

HONOURS FA Comps: None

League: West Midlands (Reg) Division Two 2009-10, Division One 10-11.

11-12	12-13	13-14	14-15	15-16	16-17	17-18	18-19	19-20	20-21
WMP 2	WMP 5	WMP 5	WMP 10	WMP 15	WMP 13	WMP 4	WMP 8	WMP n&v	WMP n&v
		FAC P	FAC EP						
	FAV 2P	FAV 1Q	FAV 1Q	FAV 1Pr	FAV 2Q		FAV 1P	FAV 2Q	FAV 2Q

GROUND: The Sports Ground, Stourbridge Road, Lye, DY9 7DH

PAGET RANGERS

Midland Football League Division One

Founded 2011 Nickname: Bears or The Wee Gers **Club Colours:** Yellow and black

Club Contact Details 07581 794238 michelleparker66@outlook.com

HONOURS FA Comps: None

League: None

11-12	12-13	13-14	14-15	15-16	16-17	17-18	18-19	19-20	20-21
		MCm2 3	MFL2 11	MFL2 4	MFL2 2	MFL1 12	MFL1 10	MFL1 n&v	MFL1 n&v
				FAV 1Q	FAV 2P	FAV 2Q	FAV 1P	FAV 2Q	FAV 1P

GROUND: Central Ground, Coles Lane, Sutton Coldfield, B72 1NL

SHAWBURY UNITED

Midland Football League Division One

Founded 1992 Nickname: **Club Colours:** Black & white

Club Contact Details 07739 915 089 daibando161274@aol.com

HONOURS FA Comps: None

League: West Midlands (Regional) Premier Division 2015-16.

11-12	12-13	13-14	14-15	15-16	16-17	17-18	18-19	19-20	20-21
WMP 10	WMP 4	WMP 4	WMP 7	WMP 1	MFLP 19	MFLP 21	WMP 6	WMP n&v	WMP n&v
					FAC EPr	FAC EP	FAC EP		
FAV 2Q	FAV 2P	FAV 1P	FAV 2Q	FAV 1Q	FAV 1P	FAV 1Q	FAV 1Q	FAV 1Pr	FAV 1Q

GROUND: Ludlow FC, Bromfield Road, Ludlow SY8 2BN

STAPENHILL

Midland Football League Division One

Founded 1947 Nickname: The Swans Club Colours: All red

Club Contact Details 07411 832 333 stapenhillsecretary@yahoo.com

HONOURS FA Comps: None

League: Leicestershire Senior 1958-59, 59-60, 86-87, 88-89, 2006-07.

11-12		12-13		13-14		14-15		15-16		16-17		17-18		18-19		19-20		20-21	
LeicSP	5	LeicS1	5	EMC	2	EMC	15	EMC	12	EMC	11	EMC	13	MFL1	13	MFL1	n&v	MFL1	n&v
						FAC	EPr												
		FAV	1Q	FAV	1Q	FAV	1Q	FAV	1Q	FAV	2Q	FAV	1Q	FAV	1Q	FAV	1Q	FAV	1P

GROUND: Edge Hill, Maple Grove, Stapenhill DE15 9NN.

Nearest Railway Station Burton-on-Trent - 3km

WEDNESFIELD

Midland Football League Division One

Founded 1961 Nickname: The Cottagers Club Colours: Red & white

Club Contact Details 07964 941637 hydkvn@yahoo.co.uk

HONOURS FA Comps: None

League: West Midlands Division One A 1976-77, Division One 77-78, Premier 95-96, 96-97.

11-12		12-13		13-14		14-15		15-16		16-17		17-18		18-19		19-20		20-21	
WMP	6	WMP	18	WMP	15	WMP	22	WM1	4	WM1	2	WMP	5	WMP	5	WMP	n&v	WMP	n&v
														FAC	Pr	FAC	EP		
		FAV	1Q	FAV	1Q	FAV	1Q	FAV	1Q	FAV	1Q	FAV	1P	FAV	1P	FAV	1Q	FAT	1Q

GROUND: Cottage Ground, Amos Lane, Wednesfield WV11 1ND

Nearest Railway Station Wolverhampton - 3km

Bus Route Cottages Homes - stop 20m away

WOLVERHAMPTON SPORTING COMM'

Midland Football League Division One

Founded 2001 Nickname: Wolves Sporting Club Colours: Orange & black

Club Contact Details 07553 371070 wolvessporting@yahoo.co.uk

HONOURS FA Comps: None

League: West Midlands (Reg) Division Two 2006-07, Premier 2017-18.

11-12		12-13		13-14		14-15		15-16		16-17		17-18		18-19		19-20		20-21	
WMP	19	WMP	10	WMP	18	WMP	16	WMP	4	WMP	3	WMP	1	MFLP	20	WMP	n&v	WMP	n&v
										FAC	EP	FAC	EP	FAC	EP	FAC	EP		
FAV	2Q	FAV	2Q	FAV	1Q	FAV	1Q	FAV	1Q	FAV	1P	FAV	5P	FAV	2P	FAV	2Q	FAV	1Q

GROUND: Pride Park, Hazel Lane, Great Wyrley, Staffs WS6 6AA

Nearest Railway Station Ladywood - 1km

Bus Route Hazel Lane - stop 270m away

AFC LIVERPOOL

North West Counties Premier

Founded 2008 | Nickname: Little Reds | **Club Colours:** All red

Club Contact Details 0151 924 1743 or 0151 286 9101

Previous Names: None
Previous Leagues: None
HONOURS
FA Comps: None
League: None

11-12		12-13		13-14		14-15		15-16		16-17		17-18		18-19		19-20		20-21	
NWCP	19	NWCP	11	NWCP	7	NWCP	9	NWCP	17	NWCP	12	NWCP	20	NWC1N	3	NWC1N	n&v	NWC1N	n&v
FAC	EPr	FAC	P	FAC	P	FAC	EP	FAC	1Q	FAC	EPr	FAC	EP	FAC	EPr	FAC	EP		
FAV	2Qr	FAV	1P	FAV	1Q	FAV	2Q	FAV	1Q	FAV	1P	FAV	2Q	FAV	1Q	FAV	1Q	FAV	1P

GROUND: Marine FC, College Road, Crosby, Liverpool L23 3AS
Nearest Railway Station Blundellsands & Crosby - 0.5km
Bus Route Brompton Avenue stop - 175m away

Capacity: 3,185
Seats: 400
Covered: 1,400

CLUB MOVEMENTS

PREMIER DIVISION - IN: AFC Liverpool, Lower Breck, and Prestwich Heys (P - NWC1N).
Vauxhall Motors and Wythenshawe Town (P - NWC1S). Macclesfield FC (N).
OUT: 1874 Northwich, Bootle and Warrington Rylands (P - NPLW)

ASHTON ATHLETIC

North West Counties Premier

Founded 1968 | Nickname: Yellows | **Club Colours:** Yellow and blue

Club Contact Details 01942 716 360

Previous Names: None.
Previous Leagues: Lancashire Combination 1978-82. Manchester Amateur League
HONOURS
FA Comps: None
League: None

11-12		12-13		13-14		14-15		15-16		16-17		17-18		18-19		19-20		20-21	
NWCP	14	NWCP	20	NWCP	6	NWCP	5	NWCP	7	NWCP	9	NWCP	12	NWCP	5	NWCP	n&v	NWCP	n&v
FAC	Pr	FAC	Pr	FAC	P	FAC	EP	FAC	EPr	FAC	2Q	FAC	3Q	FAC	2Q	FAC	EP	FAC	EP
FAV	2Q	FAV	1Q	FAV	2Q	FAV	2Q	FAV	1Qr	FAV	2Q	FAV	3P	FAV	1Q	FAV	1P	FAV	2Q

GROUND: Brocstedes Park, Downall Green, Ashton in Makerfield WN4 0NR
Nearest Railway Station Bryn - 1.6km.
Bus Route 156/157 St Helens/Bryn route

Capacity: 600
Seats: 100
Seats: 300

AVRO

North West Counties Premier

Founded 1936 | Nickname: | **Club Colours:** Blue, black and white

Club Contact Details 07920 779 382

Previous Names:
Previous Leagues: Manchester.
HONOURS
FA Comps: None
League: Manchester Division One 1988-89, 2003-04, Premier 09-10, 10-11, 17-18.

11-12		12-13		13-14		14-15		15-16		16-17		17-18		18-19		19-20		20-21	
MancP	6	MancP	5	MancP	9	MancP	3	MancP	9	MancP	11	MancP	1	NWC1N	2	NWCP	n&v	NWCP	n&v
																FAC	EP	FAC	EP
														FAV	3P	FAV	1Q	FAV	2Q

GROUND: Vestacare Stadium, White Bank Road, Oldham OL8 3JH
Nearest Railway Station Manchester Victoria or Moston (mainline). Hollinwood (metrolink) 20 mins walk or 180 bus.
Bus Route No.180 from Oldham Street (Manchester City centre) to Hollins Road/Oak Road, then 5 mins down Oak Road to ground.

BARNOLDSWICK TOWN

North West Counties Premier

Founded 1972 Nickname: Town or Barlick **Club Colours:** All blue

Club Contact Details 07958 169 095

Previous Names: Today's club formed after the merger of Barnoldswick United and Barnoldswick Park Rovers in 2003

Previous Leagues: Craven, East Lancashire, West Lancashire.

HONOURS

FA Comps: None

League: West Lancashire Division One 1998-99.

11-12	12-13	13-14	14-15	15-16	16-17	17-18	18-19	19-20	20-21
NWCP 4	NWCP 9	NWCP 16	NWCP 19	NWCP 9	NWCP 11	NWCP 9	NWCP 11	NWCP n&v	NWCP n&v
FAC EP	FAC EP	FAC EPr	FAC EP	FAC EP	FAC EPr	FAC 1Q	FAC P	FAC EP	FAC P
FAV 2P	FAV 3P	FAV 2Q	FAV 2Q	FAV 2Q	FAV 1P	FAV 1Q	FAV 2Q	FAV 2P	FAV 1Q

GROUND: Silentnight Stadium, West Close Road, Barnoldswick, Colne, BB18 5LJ

Nearest Railway Station Colne or Skipton

Bus Route Greenberfield Road stop - 97m away

BURSCOUGH

North West Counties Premier

Founded 1946 Nickname: Linnets **Club Colours:** Green & black

Club Contact Details 01704 896 776

Previous Names: None

Previous Leagues: Liverpool County Combination 1946-53, Lancashire Combination 1953-70, Cheshire County 1970-82, North West Counties 1982-98, Northern Premier League 1998-2007, 09-17, Conference 2007-09.

HONOURS

FA Comps: FA Trophy 2002-03.

League: Lancashire Combination Division Two 1953-54. North West Counties Division One 1982-83. Northern Premier Premier Division 2006-07.

11-12	12-13	13-14	14-15	15-16	16-17	17-18	18-19	19-20	20-21
NP P 22	NP1N 11	NP1N 14	NP1N 15	NP1N 5	NP1N 22	NWCP 18	NWCP 12	NWCP n&v	NWCP n&v
FAC 1Qr	FAC 1Q	FAC 2Q	FAC 1Q	FAC 3Q	FAC 2Q	FAC Pr	FAC 1Q	FAC P	FAC EP
FAT 1Q	FAT 2Q	FAT 1Qr	FAT P	FAT 1Pr	FAT P	FAV 1P	FAV 2Q	FAV 1Qr	FAV 1Q

GROUND: The Community Ground, Booby Langton Way, Burscough L40 0SD

Nearest Railway Station Burscough Bridge - 0.2km

Bus Route 2A

CHARNOCK RICHARD

North West Counties Premier

Founded 1955 Nickname: **Club Colours:** Green

Club Contact Details 01257 792 558

Previous Names: None

Previous Leagues: Chorley Alliance (Sunday). Preston & District. West Lancashire >2016

HONOURS

FA Comps: None

League: Chorley Alliance 1947-48, 56-57. Preston & District 1960-61, 66-67, 67-68, 68-69, 89-90. West Lancashire Division One 1997-98, Premier 2002-03, 08-09, 11-12, 12-13, 13-14, 14-15.

11-12	12-13	13-14	14-15	15-16	16-17	17-18	18-19	19-20	20-21
WLaP 1	WLaP 1	WLaP 1	WLaP 1	WLaP 2	NWC1 2	NWCP 6	NWCP 6	NWCP n&v	NWCP n&v
						FAC EP	FAC Pr	FAC 1Q	FAC 1Q
					FAV 2P	FAV 1P	FAV 1P	FAV 1P	FAV 2P

GROUND: Mossie Park, Charter Lane, Charnock Richard, Chorley PR7 5LZ

Nearest Railway Station Euxton Balshaw Lane - 3km

Bus Route Leeson Avenue stop - 299m away

CONGLETON TOWN

North West Counties Premier

Founded 1901 Nickname: Bears **Club Colours:** Amber & black

Club Contact Details 01260 274 460

Previous Names: Congleton Hornets

Previous Leagues: Crewe & District 1901-05. North Staffs 1905-20. Cheshire County 1920-39, 46-65, 78-82. Manchester 1965-68. Mid Cheshire 1968-78. NW Co (FM) 1982-87, 2001-21. NPL 1987-2001.

HONOURS

FA Comps: None

League: Crewe & District 1901-02, 02-03, 03-04. North Staffs & District 1919-20. Macclesfield & District 1939-40. Mid Cheshire 1973-74, 75-76, 77-78. Cheshire County D2 1981-82.

11-12	12-13	13-14	14-15	15-16	16-17	17-18	18-19	19-20	20-21
NWCP 11	NWCP 7	NWCP 10	NWCP 8	NWCP 6	NWCP 16	NWCP 15	NWCP 3	NWCP n&v	NWCP n&v
FAC P	FAC P	FAC Pr	FAC Pr	FAC 2Q	FAC P	FAC P	FAC 1Q	FAC EPr	FAC P
FAV 1Q	FAV 1P	FAV 4P	FAV 2P	FAV 1P	FAV 1P	FAV 2Qr	FAV 1Q	FAV 3Pr	FAV 5P

GROUND: Ivy Gardens, Booth Street, Crescent Road, Congleton, Cheshire CW12 4GA **Capacity:** 1,450
Nearest Railway Station Congleton - 1.9km **Seats:** 250
Bus Route Booth Street stop - 75m away **Covered:** 1,200

IRLAM

North West Counties Premier

Founded 1935 Nickname: Mitchells/Shack **Club Colours:** All blue

Club Contact Details 07969 946 277

Previous Names: Mitchell Shackleton.

Previous Leagues: Manchester Amateur. Manchester.

HONOURS

FA Comps: None

League: Manchester Amateur Division Three 1973-74, Division Two 74-75. Manchester Premier Division 2002-03.

11-12	12-13	13-14	14-15	15-16	16-17	17-18	18-19	19-20	20-21
NWC1 10	NWC1 14	NWC1 10	NWC1 14	NWC1 2	NWCP 8	NWCP 13	NWCP 13	NWCP n&v	NWCP n&v
FAC EP	FAC P				FAC EP	FAC EP	FAC 2Q	FAC 2Q	FAC P
FAV 1Q	FAV 1Q	FAV 1Q	FAV 1Q	FAV 1Qr	FAV 1P	FAV 1P	FAV 5P	FAV 2P	FAV 1P

GROUND: Silver Street, Irlam, Manchester M44 6JJ
Nearest Railway Station Flixton - 2.3km **Seats:** 150
Bus Route Nos 67 and 100. Silver Street stop - 23m away

LITHERLAND REMYCA

North West Counties Premier

Founded 1959 Nickname: The REMY **Club Colours:** Red and black

Club Contact Details 0151 288 6288

Previous Names: St Thomas. Bootle Church Lads Brigade. REMYCA United 1968-2013.

Previous Leagues: Liverpool County >2015.

HONOURS

FA Comps: None

League: Zingari Premier Division 1987-88, 93-94, 94-95, 95-96, Division Two 2005-06. Liverpool County Division Two 2006-07.

11-12	12-13	13-14	14-15	15-16	16-17	17-18	18-19	19-20	20-21
LivCP 15	LivCP 9	LivCP 5	NWC1 9	NWC1 9	NWC1 3	NWC1 2	NWCP 15	NWCP n&v	NWCP n&v
						FAC P	FAC EP	FAC P	FAC 1Q
				FAV 1Q	FAV 1P	FAV 1P	FAV 1P	FAV 1Q	FAV 1Q

GROUND: Litherland Sports Park, Boundary Road, Litherland, Liverpool L21 7LA
Nearest Railway Station Seaforth & Litherland - 20min walk away. **Seats:** 100
Bus Route 56 from Sir Thomas Street in Liverpool City Centre to Dunnings Bridge Road, Bootle Golf Course.

LONGRIDGE TOWN

North West Counties Premier

Founded 1996 Nickname: **Club Colours:** All red

Club Contact Details 07966 632 082

Previous Names:

Previous Leagues: Preston & District 1996-2009.

HONOURS

FA Comps: None

League: Preston & District Division Three 2003-04. West Lancashire Division One 2011-12, Premier 16-17.
North West Counties Division One North 2018-19.

11-12	12-13	13-14	14-15	15-16	16-17	17-18	18-19	19-20	20-21
WLa1 1	WLaP 3	WLaP 12	WLaP 6	WLaP 4	WLaP 1	WLaP 3	NWC1N 1	NWCP n&v	NWCP n&v
								FAC Pr	FAC 3Q
							FAV 1Q	FAV 5P	FAV 3P

GROUND: The Mike Riding Ground, Inglewhite Road, Longridge, Preston PR3 2NA
Nearest Railway Station Preston (7.7 miles)
Bus Route No.1 bus Preston to Berry Lane Longridge

LOWER BRECK

North West Counties Premier

Founded 2010 Nickname: **Club Colours:** Red

Club Contact Details 0151 263 6186

Previous Names: The Famous Grapes 2010-13.

Previous Leagues: I Zingari Combination 2010-13. Liverpool County 2013-18.

HONOURS

FA Comps: None

League: Liverpool County Division Two 2012-13, Premier 17-18.

11-12	12-13	13-14	14-15	15-16	16-17	17-18	18-19	19-20	20-21
	LivC2 1	LivC1 4	LivCP 11	LivCP 3	LivCP 2	LivCP 1	NWC1N 4	NWC1N n&v	NWC1Nn&v
								FAC EP	
							FAV 1P	FAV 3P	FAV 2P

GROUND: Anfield Sports & Community Centre, Lower Breck Rd, Liverpool L6 0AG
Nearest Railway Station Liverpool Lime Street
Bus Route Arriva Bus 68 stops at the ground

MACCLESFIELD FC

North West Counties Premier

Founded 1874 Nickname: The Silkmen **Club Colours:** Blue & white

Club Contact Details 01625 426 708

Previous Names: Macclesfield Football & Athletic Club, Hallifield FC, Macclesfield FC, Macclesfield Town 1946-2020.

Previous Leagues: Manchester. Cheshire County 1946-68. Northern Premier 1968-87. Conference 1987-97, 2012-18.
Football League 1997-2012, 18-20. Folded summer 2020.

HONOURS

FA Comps: FA Trophy 1969-70, 95-96.

League: Manchester 1908-09, 10-11. Cheshire County 1931-32, 32-33, 53-54, 60-61, 63-64, 67-68.
Northern Premier League 1968-69, 69-70, 86-87. Conference 1994-95, 96-97. National 2017-18.

11-12	12-13	13-14	14-15	15-16	16-17	17-18	18-19	19-20	20-21
FL 2 24	Conf 11	Conf 15	Conf 6	Nat 10	Nat 9	Nat 1	FL 2 22	FL 2 23	
FAC 3Pr	FAC 4P	FAC 3Pr	FAC 4Qr	FAC 1P	FAC 2Pr	FAC 1P	FAC 1P	FAC 1P	
FLC 2P	FAT 1P	FAT 1P	FAT 1P	FAT 3Pr	FAT F	FAT 1P	FLC 3P	FLC 2P	

GROUND: Moss Rose Ground, London Road, Macclesfield SK11 7SP 6,335
Nearest Railway Station Macclesfield - roughly 20min walk away. 2,599
Bus Route Nos. 9 & 14 from the bus station. Yes

NORTHWICH VICTORIA

North West Counties Premier

Founded 1874 Nickname: Vics, Greens or Trickies **Club Colours:** Green and white

Club Contact Details 01606 43008

Previous Names: None

Previous Leagues: The Combination 1890-92, 1894-98, Football League 1892-94, Cheshire 1898-1900, Manchester 1900-12 Lancashire 1912-19, Cheshire County 1919-68, Northern Premier 1968-79, Conference 1979-2010

HONOURS

FA Comps: FA Trophy 1983-84.

League: Manchester 1902-03. Cheshire County 1956-57. Conference North 2005-06.

11-12	12-13	13-14	14-15	15-16	16-17	17-18	18-19	19-20	20-21
NP P 2	NP1S 8	NP1N 9	NP1N 4	NP1N 3	NP1S 22	NWCP 16	NWCP 4	NWCP n&v	NWCP n&v
FAC 2Q	FAC Pr	FAC 1Q	FAC 1Qr	FAC 2P	FAC P	FAC EPr	FAC P	FAC 1Qr	FAC P
FAT 3P	FAT 1Q	FAT 1Pr	FAT 1Qr	FAT 1Q	FAT Pr	FAV 1Q	FAV SF	FAV 2Pr	FAV 2Q

GROUND: Wincham Park, Chapel Street, Northwich CW9 6DA

Nearest Railway Station Northwich (1.3 miles)

PADIHAM

North West Counties Premier

Founded 1878 Nickname: Caldersiders **Club Colours:** All blue.

Club Contact Details 01282 773 742

Previous Names: None

Previous Leagues: Lancashire Combination 1894-98, 1900-06, 10-16, 49-68, 77-82. East Lancs Am. North East Lancs. West Lancs. North West Counties > 2013. NPL 2013-15.

HONOURS

FA Comps: None

League: West Lancashire Division Two 1971-72, 76-77, Division One 1999-00.
North West Counties 2012-13.

11-12	12-13	13-14	14-15	15-16	16-17	17-18	18-19	19-20	20-21
NWCP 15	NWCP 1	NP1N 19	NP1N 22	NWCP 11	NWCP 7	NWCP 17	NWCP 18	NWCP n&v	NWCP n&v
FAC EP	FAC P	FAC 1Q	FAC P	FAC 1Q	FAC P	FAC EP	FAC EP	FAC Pr	FAC EP
FAV 2P	FAV 1Q	FAT P	FAT 1Q	FAV 1Q	FAV 2P	FAV 1Q	FAV 2Qr	FAV 1P	FAV 1P

GROUND: Arbories Memorial Sports Ground, Well Street, Padiham BB12 8LE

Capacity: 1,688

Seats: 159

Nearest Railway Station Hapton - 2.2km

Bus Route Memorial Park stop - 110m away

PRESTWICH HEYS

North West Counties Premier

Founded 1938 Nickname: The Heys **Club Colours:** Red and white

Club Contact Details 0161 7773 8888 (MD)

Previous Names:

Previous Leagues: Manchester >2016

HONOURS

FA Comps: None

League: Lancashire Combination 1970-71. Manchester Division One 1996-97, Premier Division 2004-05, 04-05, 05-06, 06-07, 15-16.

11-12	12-13	13-14	14-15	15-16	16-17	17-18	18-19	19-20	20-21
MancP 13	MancP 8	MancP 4	MancP 6	MancP 1	NWC1 8	NWC1 3	NWC1N 5	NWC1N n&v	NWC1N n&v
							FAC P		
						FAV 1Q	FAV 2Pr	FAV 2Q	FAV 1Q

GROUND: Adie Moran Park, Sandgate Road, Whitefield M45 6WG

Nearest Railway Station Besses o'th' Barn metrolink - 0.7 miles.

Bus Route 135 from Manchester to Bury - alight at Besses o' th' Barn.

RUNCORN TOWN

North West Counties Premier

Founded 1967 Nickname: Town **Club Colours:** Sky and navy blue

Club Contact Details 07808 737 773

Previous Names: Mond Rangers 1967-2005 (Amalgamated with ICI Weston 1974-75).

Previous Leagues: Runcorn Sunday 1967-73, Warrington & District 1973-84, West Cheshire 1984-10.

HONOURS

FA Comps: None

League: West Cheshire League Division Two 2006-07.

11-12		12-13		13-14		14-15		15-16		16-17		17-18		18-19		19-20		20-21	
NWCP	2	NWCP	4	NWCP	5	NWCP	13	NWCP	13	NWCP	3	NWCP	3	NWCP	7	NWCP	n&v	NWCP	n&v
FAC	1Q	FAC	1Q	FAC	P	FAC	3Q	FAC	P	FAC	EP	FAC	P	FAC	1Q	FAC	2Q	FAC	1Q
FAV	4Pr	FAV	5P	FAV	2P	FAV	2P	FAV	3Pr	FAV	1P	FAV	1P	FAV	3P	FAV	2Q	FAV	1P

GROUND: Sandy Lane, Weston Point, Runcorn WA7 4ET **Capacity:** 1,530

Nearest Railway Station Runcorn - 1.6km

Bus Route 3c or 3A from Runcorn bus station or railway station.

SKELMERSDALE UNITED

North West Counties Premier

Founded 1882 Nickname: Skem / Blueboys **Club Colours:** All blue

Club Contact Details pitchero.com/clubs/skelmersdaleunited

Previous Names: Skelmsdale Young Rovers. Skelmersdale Wesleyans.

Previous Leagues: Liverpool County Combination, Lancashire Combination 1891-93, 1903-07, 21-24, 55-56, 76-78, Cheshire County 1968-71, 78-82, Northern Premier 1971-76, 06-19. North West Counties 1983-2006.

HONOURS

FA Comps: FA Amateur Cup 1970-71. Barassi Anglo-Italian Cup 1970-71.

League: Northern Premier Division One North 2013-14.

11-12		12-13		13-14		14-15		15-16		16-17		17-18		18-19		19-20		20-21	
NP1N	7	NP1N	1	NP P	6	NP P	7	NP P	16	NP P	24	NP1N	21	NP1W	20	NWCP	n&v	NWCP	n&v
FAC	P	FAC	2Q	FAC	2Q	FAC	2Q	FAC	2Q	FAC	1Qr	FAC	1Q	FAC	P	FAC	P	FAC	1P
FAT	P	FAT	3P	FAT	1Q	FAT	1Q	FAT	1Pr	FAT	1Q	FAT	P	FAT	P	FAV	2Q	FAV	1Q

GROUND: JMO Sports Park, Livepool Road, Skelmersdale WN8 8BX

Nearest Railway Station Rainford - 3.6 miles

Bus Route 310, 375 & 385

SQUIRES GATE

North West Counties Premier

Founded 1948 Nickname: Gate **Club Colours:** All blue.

Club Contact Details 01253 348 512

Previous Names: Squires Gate British Legion FC >1953.

Previous Leagues: Blackpool & District Amateur 1958-61. West Lancashire 1961-91.

HONOURS

FA Comps: None

League: Blackpool & District Amateur League Division One 1955-56, 56-57.
West Lancashire League Division Two 1980-81.

11-12		12-13		13-14		14-15		15-16		16-17		17-18		18-19		19-20		20-21	
NWCP	16	NWCP	21	NWCP	19	NWCP	6	NWCP	19	NWCP	19	NWCP	11	NWCP	8	NWCP	n&v	NWCP	n&v
FAC	1Qr	FAC	EP	FAC	EP	FAC	1Qr	FAC	EPr	FAC	1Q	FAC	EP	FAC	1Q	FAC	EP	FAC	P
FAV	3P	FAV	2Q	FAV	2Q	FAV	1Q	FAV	2Q	FAV	1Q	FAV	1Q	FAV	2P	FAV	2Q	FAV	1Q

GROUND: Brian Addison Stadium, School Road, Marton, Blackpool, Lancs FY4 5DS **Capacity:** 1,000

Nearest Railway Station Blackpool South **Seats:** 100

Bus Route No.14 from Blackpool Town Centre stops outside the Shovels Pub - 5 min walk away.

VAUXHALL MOTORS

North West Counties Premier

Founded 1963 Nickname: The Motormen **Club Colours:** White and navy

Club Contact Details 0151 327 2294

Previous Names: Vauxhall Motors 1963-87, Vauxhall GM 1995-99

Previous Leagues: Ellesmere Port, Wirral Combination, West Cheshire 1966-87, 92-95, 2014-18, North West Co. 1987-92, 95-2000, Northern Premier 2000-04. Conference 2004-14.

HONOURS

FA Comps: None

League: North West Counties Division Two 1988-89, 95-96, Division One 99-2000.

11-12	12-13	13-14	14-15	15-16	16-17	17-18	18-19	19-20	20-21
Conf N 18	Conf N 12	Conf N 18	WCh1 4	WCh1 4	WCh1 8	WCh1 2	NWC1S 2	NWC1S n&v	NWC1S n&v
FAC 2Qr	FAC 2Q	FAC 4Q						FAC EP	
FAT 1Pr	FAT 3Q	FAT 3Q	FAV 1Q	FAV 2Q	FAV 2Q	FAV 1Q	FAV 2P	FAV 4P	FAV 3P

GROUND: Rivacre Road, Ellesmere Port, South Wirrall CH66 1NJ

Nearest Railway Station Overpool (1.4 miles) or Hooton (1.7)

Bus Route None near the ground

Capacity: 3,500
Seats: 266
Covered: 1,000

WINSFORD UNITED

North West Counties Premier

Founded 1883 Nickname: Blues **Club Colours:** Navy blue and white

Club Contact Details 01606 558 447

Previous Names: Over Wanderers 1883-1887

Previous Leagues: The Combination 1902-04. Cheshire County 1919-40, 47-82. Northern Premier League 1987-2001.

HONOURS

FA Comps: None

League: Cheshire County 1920-21, 76-77.
North West Counties League Division Two 2006-07.

11-12	12-13	13-14	14-15	15-16	16-17	17-18	18-19	19-20	20-21
NWCP 7	NWCP 5	NWCP 14	NWCP 12	NWCP 14	NWCP 13	NWCP 14	NWCP 16	NWCP n&v	NWCP n&v
FAC EPr	FAC P	FAC P	FAC EP	FAC EPr	FAC 1Qr	FAC EP	FAC EP	FAC Pr	FAC EP
FAV 2P	FAV 3P	FAV 2Pr	FAV 1P	FAV 1P	FAV 1Q	FAV 2Q	FAV 1P	FAV 1Q	FAV 2Q

GROUND: The Barton Stadium, Kingsway, Winsford, Cheshire CW7 3AE

Nearest Railway Station Winsford - 1.2km.

Bus Route Several buses stop near the ground - ask for Wharton Road or Station Road.

Capacity: 3,000
Seats: 200
Covered: 5,000

WYTHENSHAWE TOWN

North West Counties Premier

Founded 1946 Nickname: **Club Colours:** Royal Blue

Club Contact Details

Previous Names: North Withington AFC

Previous Leagues: South Manchester & Wythenshawe 1946-58. Lancashire & Cheshire Am. 1958-72. Manchester 1972-2014. Cheshire 2014-18.

HONOURS

FA Comps: None

League: Sth Manc & Wythen Div.2 1949-50. Lancs & Ches Div.C 1958-59, Div.3 59-60, Div.2 64-65, Div.1 66-67, 68-69, 69-70, 70-71. Manc Div.2 73-74, Div.1 2011-12. Cheshire Div.2 2014-15, Div.1 15-16.

11-12	12-13	13-14	14-15	15-16	16-17	17-18	18-19	19-20	20-21
Manc1 1	MancP 10	MancP 15	Ches2 1	Ches1 1	ChesP 7	ChesP 8	NWC1S 5	NWC1S n&v	NWC1S n&v
							FAV 1Q	FAV 3Pr	FAV 1P

GROUND: Ericstan Park, Timpson Road, Wythenshawe M23 9LL

Nearest Railway Station Baguley tram stop is only a 5-10 minute walk from Ericstan Park.

Bus Route 11 / 11a / 109 - Altrincham Road stop is the nearest to the ground, 3-5 min walk away.

AFC BLACKPOOL

North West Counties Division 1N

Founded 1947 Nickname: Mechanics **Club Colours:** Tangerine

Club Contact Details 01253 761 721

HONOURS FA Comps: None

League: West Lancashire League 1960-61, 61-62.
North West Counties League Division Three 1985/86, Division One 2010-11.

11-12		12-13		13-14		14-15		15-16		16-17		17-18		18-19		19-20		20-21	
NWCP	9	NWCP	10	NWCP	13	NWCP	18	NWCP	22	NWC1	19	NWC1	7	NWC1N	13	NWC1N	n&v	NWC1N	n&v
FAC	Pr	FAC	EP	FAC	EP	FAC	EP	FAC	1Q	FAC	EP								
FAV	1Q	FAV	2Q	FAV	1P	FAV	1Q	FAV	1Q	FAV	2Q	FAV	1Q	FAV	2Q	FAV	2Q	FAV	1P

GROUND: Jepson Way, Common Edge Road, Blackpool FY4 5DY

Nearest Railway Station Squires Gate - 2.2km

Bus Route No.17 from Blackpool Town Centre.

AFC DARWEN

North West Counties Division 1N

Founded 2009 Nickname: Salmoners **Club Colours:** All red

Club Contact Details 07778 191 788

HONOURS FA Comps: None

League: None

11-12		12-13		13-14		14-15		15-16		16-17		17-18		18-19		19-20		20-21	
NWC1	13	NWC1	5	NWC1	9	NWC1	3	NWCP	18	NWCP	18	NWCP	23	NWC1N	10	NWC1N	n&v	NWC1N	n&v
								FAC	EP	FAC	EPr	FAC	EP	FAC	P			FAC	EP
FAV	1P			FAV	2Q	FAV	2P	FAV	2Q	FAV	1Q	FAV	1P	FAV	2Q	FAV	1Q	FAV	2Q

GROUND: WEC Group Anchor Ground, Anchor Road, Darwen, Lancs BB3 0BB

Nearest Railway Station Darwen - 1.7km

Bus Route Anchor stop on the Blackburn to Bolton route.

ASHTON TOWN

North West Counties Division 1N

Founded 1953 Nickname: The Town **Club Colours:** All red

Club Contact Details 01942 724 448

HONOURS FA Comps: None

League: St Helens Combination Division Two 1957-58.
Warrington & District League Division One 1959-60, 60-61, 62-63, 63-64, 64-65, 69-70.

11-12		12-13		13-14		14-15		15-16		16-17		17-18		18-19		19-20		20-21	
NWC1	18	NWC1	6	NWC1	12	NWC1	17	NWC1	11	NWC1	22	ChesP	6	NWC1N	9	NWC1N	n&v	NWC1N	n&v
				FAC	EP														
FAV	1Q	FAV	2Q	FAV	1Q	FAV	1P	FAV	2Q	FAV	1P	FAV	1Q	FAV	2Q	FAV	1Q	FAV	1Q

GROUND: Edge Green Street, Ashton-in-Makerfield, Wigan, WN4 8SL

Nearest Railway Station Bryn

Bus Route 600 or 601

ATHERTON LABURNUM ROVERS

North West Counties Division 1N

Founded 1956 Nickname: The Panthers **Club Colours:** Yellow and royal blue

Club Contact Details 01942 878 715

HONOURS FA Comps: None

League: Bolton Combination Division Two A 1965-66.
North West Counties 1992-93, 93-94.

11-12		12-13		13-14		14-15		15-16		16-17		17-18		18-19		19-20		20-21	
NWCP	22	NWC1	13	NWC1	3	NWC1	12	NWC1	17	NWC1	20	NWC1	18	NWC1N	20	NWC1N	n&v	NWC1N	n&v
FAC	P	FAC	P																
FAV	1P	FAV	1Q	FAV	1P			FAV	2Q	FAV	1P	FAV	1Q	FAV	2Q	FAV	1Q		

GROUND: Crilly Park, Spa Road, Atherton, Manchester M46 9XG

Nearest Railway Station Atherton - 0.3km

Bus Route 582 - alight at Atherton train station.

BACUP BOROUGH

North West Counties Division 1N

Founded 1875 Nickname: The Boro **Club Colours:** White and black

Club Contact Details 01706 878 655

HONOURS FA Comps: None

League: Lancashire Combination 1946-47.
North West Counties Division Two 2002-03

11-12	12-13	13-14	14-15	15-16	16-17	17-18	18-19	19-20	20-21
NWCP 17	NWCP 17	NWCP 21	NWCP 21	NWC1 5	NWC1 18	NWC1 17	NWC1N 8	NWC1N n&v	NWC1N n&v
FAC EP	FAC P			FAC EP	FAC EP				
FAV 2P	FAV 1Qr			FAV 2Q	FAV 2Q	FAV 2Q	FAV 2Q	FAV 1Q	FAV 1P

GROUND: Brian Boys Stadium, Cowtoot Lane, Blackthorn, Bacup OL13 8EE

Nearest Railway Station Rochdale, Todmorden & Burnley

Bus Route Thorn Cp School stop - 119m away

BURY AFC

North West Counties Division 1N

Founded 2019 Nickname: The Shakers **Club Colours:** White & blue

Club Contact Details 07754 125 768

HONOURS FA Comps: None

League: None

11-12	12-13	13-14	14-15	15-16	16-17	17-18	18-19	19-20	20-21
									NWC1N n&v
									FAV 1Q

GROUND: Radcliffe FC, Stainton Park, Pilkington Road, Radcliffe M26 3PE

Nearest Railway Station Radcliffe Tram (from Manchester) - 20 min walk away.

Bus Route No.98 from Manchester to Radcliffe.

CAMPION

North West Counties Division 1N

Founded 1963 Nickname: **Club Colours:** Red & black

Club Contact Details 01274 491 919

HONOURS FA Comps: None

League: West Riding Amateur Division Two 1989-90, Division One 92-93.

11-12	12-13	13-14	14-15	15-16	16-17	17-18	18-19	19-20	20-21
WRCP 9	WRCP 12	WRCP 3	WRCP 3	WRCP 3	NCE1 8	NCE1 9	NCE1 2	NCE1 n&v	NCE1 n&v
								FAC EP	FAC EP
						FAV 1Q	FAV 1Q	FAV 1Q	FAV 2Q

GROUND: Scotchman Road, Bradford BD9 5AT.

Nearest Railway Station Frizinghall - 1.9km

Bus Route 620/621 from Bradford Interchange - alight at Westfield Road stop.

CHADDERTON

North West Counties Division 1N

Founded 1946 Nickname: Chaddy **Club Colours:** All red

Club Contact Details 07506 104 005 (MD)

HONOURS FA Comps: None

League: Manchester Amateur League 1955-56, Division One 1962-63.
Manchester League Division Two 1964-65, Division One 1966-67.

11-12	12-13	13-14	14-15	15-16	16-17	17-18	18-19	19-20	20-21
NWC1 6	NWC1 12	NWC1 13	NWC1 6	NWC1 14	NWC1 9	NWC1 16	NWC1N 16	NWC1N n&v	NWC1N n&v
FAC EP	FAC P			FAC EP					
FAV 2Q	FAV 2Q	FAV 1P	FAV 4P	FAV 2P	FAV 1P	FAV 2Q	FAV 1Q	FAV 1P	FAV 1P

GROUND: Andrew Street, Chadderton, Oldham, Greater Manchester OL9 0JT

Nearest Railway Station Werneth

Bus Route 59 from Middleton or Oldham and 181 from Macnhester Piccadilly - alight at Chadderton Arcade (2 min walk to ground).

CLEATOR MOOR CELTIC

North West Counties Division 1N

Founded 1909 Nickname: **Club Colours:** Green and white

Club Contact Details 07368 135 835

HONOURS FA Comps: None

League: None

11-12	12-13	13-14	14-15	15-16	16-17	17-18	18-19	19-20	20-21
Wear 7	Wear 4	Wear 4	Wear 3	Wear 4	Wear 3	Wear 2	NWC1N 11	NWC1N n&v	NWC1Nn&v
FAV 1Q								FAV 2Q	FAV 1Q

GROUND: McGrath Park, Birks Road, Cleator Moor, Cumbria CA25 5HP

Nearest Railway Station Whitehaven

Bus Route Buses run on a regular basis from Whitehaven to Cleator Moor.

DAISY HILL

North West Counties Division 1N

Founded 1894 Nickname: The Daisies **Club Colours:** All royal blue and white

Club Contact Details 01942 818 544

HONOURS FA Comps: None

League: Wigan & District 1896-97.
Bolton Combination Premier Division 1962-63, 72-73, 75-76, 77-78.

11-12	12-13	13-14	14-15	15-16	16-17	17-18	18-19	19-20	20-21
NWC1 12	NWC1 16	NWC1 18	NWC1 8	NWC1 12	NWC1 16	NWC1 21	NWC1N 19	NWC1N n&v	NWC1Nn&v
	FAC EP								FAC EP
FAV 1Q	FAV 2Q	FAV 1Q	FAV 1P	FAV 2P	FAV 2Q	FAV 1Q	FAV 2Q	FAV 1Q	FAV 1Q

GROUND: New Sirs, St James Street, Westhoughton, Bolton BL5 2EB

Nearest Railway Station Daisy Hill - 0.7km

Bus Route Nos 516 or 517 Horwich - Leigh. No 540 Bolton - Wigan.

GARSTANG

North West Counties Division 1N

Founded 1895 Nickname: **Club Colours:** Red and black

Club Contact Details 07967 337 411

HONOURS FA Comps: None

League: West Lancashire Premier 2007-08, 17-18.

11-12	12-13	13-14	14-15	15-16	16-17	17-18	18-19	19-20	20-21
WLaP 16	WLa1 2	WLaP 10	WLaP 5	WLaP 9	WLaP 4	WLaP 1	NWC1N 7	NWC1N n&v	NWC1Nn&v
							FAV 2P	FAV 1Q	FAV 1Q

GROUND: The Riverside, Lancaster Road, Garstang PR3 1EB

Nearest Railway Station Lancaster (12 miles) or Preston (14.5)

Bus Route From Preston (40/41), Lancaster/ (40/41/42) and Blackpool (42) - stop High Street.

GOLCAR UNITED

North West Counties Division 1N

Founded 1904 Nickname: **Club Colours:** Green and black

Club Contact Details 07825 744 829

HONOURS FA Comps: None

League: West Riding County Amateur Premier Division 2004-05, 17-18, 18-19

11-12	12-13	13-14	14-15	15-16	16-17	17-18	18-19	19-20	20-21
WRCP 7	WRCP 6	WRCP 6	WRCP 2	WRCP 7	WRCP 5	WRCP 1	WRCP 1	NWC1N n&v	NWC1Nn&v
									FAV 1Q

GROUND: Longfield Avenue, Golcar, Huddersfield HD7 4AZ

Nearest Railway Station Huddersfield - 2.9 miles or Slaithwaite - 3.7 miles.

Bus Route 301/302 Golcar Circular.

HOLKER OLD BOYS

North West Counties Division 1N

Founded 1936 Nickname: Cobs **Club Colours:** Green and white

Club Contact Details 01229 828 176

HONOURS FA Comps: None

League: West Lancashire 1986-87.

11-12	12-13	13-14	14-15	15-16	16-17	17-18	18-19	19-20	20-21
NWC1 9	NWC1 7	NWC1 6	NWC1 5	NWC1 8	NWC1 17	NWC1 9	NWC1N 18	NWC1N n&v	NWC1N n&v
FAC P	FAC 1Q		FAC EPr	FAC P					
FAV 2Q	FAV 1Q	FAV 1P	FAV 1P	FAV 2Q	FAV 1P	FAV 1Q	FAV 1Q	FAV 1Q	FAV 2P

GROUND: Rakesmoor, Rakesmoor Lane, Hawcoat, Barrow-in-Furness LA14 4QB

Nearest Railway Station Barrow-in-Furness - 2.6km

Bus Route No.1 from Barrow-in-Furness Town Centre to the Hospital.

ILKLEY TOWN

North West Counties Division 1N

Founded 1995 Nickname: **Club Colours:** Navy Blue

Club Contact Details football@ilkleytownafc.co.uk

HONOURS FA Comps: None

League: Harrogate Senior Premier 2002-03.

11-12	12-13	13-14	14-15	15-16	16-17	17-18	18-19	19-20	20-21
WYk1 7	WYk1	WYk1 3	WYk1 6	WYk1 4	WYkP 12	WYkP 5	WYkP 4	WYkP n&v	WYkP n&v

GROUND: Ben Rhydding Sports Club, Leeds Road, ILKLEY LS29 8AW

Nearest Railway Station Ben Rhydding - 7 min walk away.

Bus Route From Leeds take the X84 to Ilkley.

NELSON

North West Counties Division 1N

Founded 1881 Nickname: Admirals **Club Colours:** All blue

Club Contact Details 01772 794 103

HONOURS FA Comps: None

League: Lancashire 1895-96. Lancashire Combination 1949-50, 51-52. Football League Division Three North 1922-23. North West Counties Division One 2013-14.

11-12	12-13	13-14	14-15	15-16	16-17	17-18	18-19	19-20	20-21
NWC1 15	NWC1 10	NWC1 1	NWCP 11	NWCP 16	NWCP 21	NWC1 22	NWC1N 14	NWC1N n&v	NWC1N n&v
			FAC EP	FAC EP	FAC P	FAC EP			
	FAV 2Q	FAV 1P	FAV 2Qr	FAV 2Q	FAV 1Q	FAV 2Q	FAV 1P	FAV 1Q	FAV 2Q

GROUND: Little Wembley, Lomeshaye Way, Nelson, Lancs BB9 7BN.

Nearest Railway Station Nelson - 1km

Bus Route No.8 - stops outside of the ground.

PILKINGTON

North West Counties Division 1N

Founded 1938 Nickname: **Club Colours:** White & green

Club Contact Details

HONOURS FA Comps: None

League: Cheshire Premier Division 2018-19.

11-12	12-13	13-14	14-15	15-16	16-17	17-18	18-19	19-20	20-21
ChesP 9	ChesP 13	ChesP 15	ChesP 16	Ches1 6	Ches1 3	Ches1 2	ChesP 1	NWC1N n&v	NWC1N n&v
								FAV 2Q	FAV 1Q

GROUND: Ruskin Drive, Dentons Green, St Helens WA10 6RP

Nearest Railway Station St Helens Central

Bus Route The 37, 38 and 38A go past the end of Ruskin Drive.

SOUTH LIVERPOOL

North West Counties Division 1N

Founded 1935 Nickname: The South **Club Colours:** White, black & red

Club Contact Details south.liverpoolfc@btinternet.com

HONOURS FA Comps: Welsh FA Cup 1938-39.

League: Lancashire Combination 1937, 38, 39, 66, D2 1913. West Cheshire D1 2014-15, 15-16, 17-18, 20-21, D2 12-13, D3, 11-12.

11-12	12-13	13-14	14-15	15-16	16-17	17-18	18-19	19-20	20-21
WCh3 1	WCh2 1	WCh1 4	WCh1 1	WCh1 1	WCh1 3	WCh1 1	WCh1 5	WCh1 n&v	WCh1 1

GROUND: Jericho Lane Sports Hub, Otterspool Drive, Liverpool L17 5AL

Nearest Railway Station Aigburth or St Michaels on Liverpool Central to Hunts Cross Line - 20 min walk.

Bus Route 500 direct from City Centre and Liverpool Airport.

ST HELENS TOWN

North West Counties Division 1N

Founded 1946 Nickname: Town or Saints **Club Colours:** All blue

Club Contact Details

HONOURS FA Comps: FA Vase 1986-87.

League: Lancashire Combination Division Two 1950-51, Premier 1971-72 .

11-12	12-13	13-14	14-15	15-16	16-17	17-18	18-19	19-20	20-21
NWCP 21	NWCP 19	NWCP 17	NWCP 20	NWC1 7	NWC1 13	NWC1 20	NWC1N 17	NWC1N n&v	NWC1N n&v
FAC EP	FAC EP	FAC EPr	FAC EP	FAC EP					FAC P
FAV 2Q	FAV 1P	FAV 1Q	FAV 3P	FAV 2Q	FAV 1Q	FAV 1Q	FAV 1Q	FAV 1Q	FAV 1Q

GROUND: Ruskin Drive, Dentons Green, St Helens WA10 6RP

Nearest Railway Station St Helens Central - 1.9km

Bus Route 37, 38 and 38A Ruskin Drive stop - 153m away

STEETON

North West Counties Division 1N

Founded 1905 Nickname: **Club Colours:** All green

Club Contact Details

HONOURS FA Comps: None

League: Keighley & District 1937-38, 38-39, 54-55. Craven & District 1959-60.
West Riding County Amateur Division Two 1988-89, 2000-01, Division One 2009-10.

11-12	12-13	13-14	14-15	15-16	16-17	17-18	18-19	19-20	20-21
WRCP 6	WRCP 2	WRCP 5	WRCP 7	WRCP 10	WRCP 3	WRCP 3	NWC1N 15	NWC1N n&v	NWC1N n&v
							FAV 1P	FAV 2Q	FAV 1Q

GROUND: Marley Stadium, Aireworth Road, Keighley BD21 4DB

Nearest Railway Station Keighly (BR)

ABBEY HEY

North West Counties Division 1S

Founded 1902 Nickname: Red Rebels **Club Colours:** Red, white and black

Club Contact Details 0161 231 7147

HONOURS FA Comps: None

League: Manchester Amateur League 1964-65. South East Lancashire 1966-67, 68-69.
Manchester League Division One 1970-71, Premier 1981-82, 88-89, 88-89, 91-92, 93-94, 94-95.

11-12	12-13	13-14	14-15	15-16	16-17	17-18	18-19	19-20	20-21
NWC1 3	NWC1 2	NWCP 20	NWCP 14	NWCP 10	NWCP 14	NWCP 19	NWCP 20	NWC1S n&v	NWC1S n&v
	FAC 2Q	FAC EP	FAC EP	FAC 2Q	FAC EP	FAC 1Qr	FAC EP	FAC EP	
FAV 2Q	FAV 1Q	FAV 1Q	FAV 2Q	FAV 1P	FAV 2Q	FAV 1Q	FAV 1Q	FAV 1P	FAT 2P

GROUND: The Abbey Stadium, Goredale Avenue, Gorton, Manchester M18 7HD

Nearest Railway Station Ryder Brow - 0.5km

Bus Route 201, 203, 205, and 7 - Ryder Brow Road stop - 124m away

ABBEY HULTON UNITED

North West Counties Division 1S

Founded 1947 Nickname: **Club Colours:** Orange and black

Club Contact Details 01782 570 302

HONOURS FA Comps: None

League: Staffordshire County Senior Premier Division 2016-17.

11-12	12-13	13-14	14-15	15-16	16-17	17-18	18-19	19-20	20-21
StfSP 5	StfSP 4	StfSP 7	StfSP 3	StfSP 8	StfSP 1	NWC1 13	NWC1S 8	NWC1S n&v	NWC1S n&v
							FAV 1Q	FAV 2Qr	FAV 2P

GROUND: Birches Head Road, Abbey Hulton, Stoke-on-Trent ST2 8DD

Nearest Railway Station Stoke-on-Trent - 4.2km

Bus Route No.5 from Haley Bus Station to Abbey Hulton - alight at Birches Head Road stop.

ALSAGER TOWN

North West Counties Division 1S

Founded 1968 Nickname: The Bullets **Club Colours:** White & black

Club Contact Details 07888 750 532

HONOURS FA Comps: None

League: None

11-12	12-13	13-14	14-15	15-16	16-17	17-18	18-19	19-20	20-21
NWCP 13	NWCP 15	NWCP 18	NWCP 17	NWCP 20	NWC1 7	NWC1 8	NWC1S 17	NWC1S n&v	NWC1S n&v
FAC EP	FAC EP	FAC EP	FAC EP	FAC 1Q	FAC P	FAC EP			
FAV 1Q	FAV 2Q	FAV 2Q	FAV 1Q	FAV 3P	FAV 2Q	FAV 2P	FAV 1Q	FAV 1P	FAV 1Q

GROUND: Woodpark Stadium, Woodland Court, Alsager ST7 2DP

Nearest Railway Station Alsager - 0.9km

Bus Route No.3 from Hanley and Crewe, No.78 from Sandbach - nearest bus stop 900m away.

BARNTON

North West Counties Division 1S

Founded 1946 Nickname: Villagers **Club Colours:** Black and white

Club Contact Details 07484 793 822

HONOURS FA Comps: None

League: Mid-Cheshire/Cheshire 1979-80, 82-83, 88-89, 96-97, 97-98, 98-99, 99-2000, 2000-01, 01-02, 02-03, 04-05, Division Two 2012-13.

11-12	12-13	13-14	14-15	15-16	16-17	17-18	18-19	19-20	20-21
Ches2 13	Ches2 1	Ches1 5	NWC1 7	NWC1 3	NWCP 17	NWCP 22	NWC1S 12	NWC1S n&v	NWC1S n&v
					FAC EP	FAC EP	FAC EP		
				FAV 2Q	FAV 2Q	FAV 2Q	FAV 2Q		FAV 2P

GROUND: Townfield, Townfield Lane, Barnton, Cheshire CW8 4LH

Nearest Railway Station Greenbank - 2.6km

Bus Route No.4 from Northwich Interchange - alight at Beech Road.

BROCTON

North West Counties Division 1S

Founded 1937 Nickname: The Badgers **Club Colours:** Green and white

Club Contact Details 07791 841 774 terryhomer@yahoo.co.uk

HONOURS FA Comps: None

League: Midland Combination Premier 2013-14.

11-12	12-13	13-14	14-15	15-16	16-17	17-18	18-19	19-20	20-21
MCmP 6	MCmP 5	MCmP 1	MFLP 13	MFLP 15	MFLP 21	MFL1 17	MFL1 11	MFL1 n&v	MFL1 n&v
FAC EP	FAC EPr	FAC 1Q	FAC Pr	FAC EP	FAC P	FAC 1Q			FAC EP
FAV 3Pr	FAV 1Q	FAV 4P	FAV 4P	FAV 3P	FAV 2Q	FAV 2P	FAV 2P	FAV 1Q	FAV 1Q

GROUND: Silkmore Lane Sports Grd, Silkmore Lane, Stafford, Staffordshire ST17 4JH

Nearest Railway Station Stafford - 2km

Bus Route Silkmore Crescent stop - 30m away

CAMMELL LAIRD 1907

North West Counties Division 1S

Founded 1907 Nickname: Lairds **Club Colours:** All royal blue

Club Contact Details 0151 645 3121

HONOURS FA Comps: None

League: West Cheshire x19 (Firstly in 1954-55 and most recently 2000-01).
North West Counties Division Two 2004-05, Division One 2005-06.

11-12	12-13	13-14	14-15	15-16	16-17	17-18	18-19	19-20	20-21
NP1N 22	NP1N 2	NP1N 11	NWC1 2	NWCP 15	NWCP 22	NWC1 6	NWC1S 15	NWC1S n&v	NWC1S n&v
FAC 1Q	FAC 1Q	FAC 2Q	FAC EP			FAC P			FAC EP
FAT P	FAT 3Q	FAT 1Q	FAV 1Q			FAV 1Q	FAV 1P	FAV 1Q	FAV 2Q

GROUND: Kirklands, St Peter's Road, Rock Ferry, Birkenhead CH42 1PY

Nearest Railway Station Rock Ferry - 0.7km

Bus Route No.1 Stagecoach, Liverpool-Chester alight at Rock Ferry Bus Depot and 41/42 to Mill Park from Birkenhead.

CHEADLE HEATH NOMADS

North West Counties Division 1S

Founded 2004 Nickname: Nomads **Club Colours:** Maroon and blue

Club Contact Details

HONOURS FA Comps: None

League: Cheshire Premier 2014-15.

11-12	12-13	13-14	14-15	15-16	16-17	17-18	18-19	19-20	20-21
Ches1 6	Ches1 12	Ches1 10	ChesP 1	ChesP 2	ChesP 5	ChesP 4	NWC1S 9	NWC1S n&v	NWC1S n&v
								FAV 2Q	FAV 1Q

GROUND: The Heath, Norbreck Avenue, Cheadle, Stockport SK8 2ET

Nearest Railway Station Stockport

Bus Route 11, 11a and 309

CHEADLE TOWN

North West Counties Division 1S

Founded 1961 Nickname: **Club Colours:** Red and white

Club Contact Details 0161 428 2510

HONOURS FA Comps: None

League: Manchester Division One 1979-80.

11-12	12-13	13-14	14-15	15-16	16-17	17-18	18-19	19-20	20-21
NWC1 8	NWC1 7	NWC1 11	NWC1 10	NWC1 6	NWC1 12	NWC1 12	NWC1S 16	NWC1S n&v	NWC1S n&v
FAC P	FAC EPr	FAC EP			FAC 1Q				
FAV 1P	FAV 1P	FAV 2P	FAV 1Q	FAV 2Q	FAV 1Q	FAV 1Q	FAV 2Qr	FAV 1P	FAV 1P

GROUND: Park Road Stadium, Cheadle, Cheshire SK8 2AN

Nearest Railway Station Gatley - 1.8km

Bus Route Stockport Road stop - 161m away

ECCLESHALL

North West Counties Division 1S

Founded 1971 Nickname: The Eagles **Club Colours:** All blue

Club Contact Details 01785 851 351 (MD)

HONOURS FA Comps: None

League: Staffordshire County Premier 1982-83. Staffordshire Senior 1989-90.
Midland 2001-02, 02-03.

11-12	12-13	13-14	14-15	15-16	16-17	17-18	18-19	19-20	20-21
NWC1 7	NWC1 15	NWC1 17	NWC1 15	NWC1 16	NWC1 21	NWC1 15	NWC1S 13	NWC1S n&v	NWC1S n&v
FAC Pr	FAC EP								
FAV 1Q	FAV 1P	FAV 2Q	FAV 1P	FAV 2Q	FAV 1Q	FAV 1Q	FAV 1Q	FAV 1Q	FAV 2Q

GROUND: Pershall Park, Chester Road, Eccleshall ST21 6NE

Nearest Railway Station Stafford - 8.5 miles

Bus Route D&G Bus No.14 - Stafford (Chell Road) to Eccleshall (Castle Street).

ELLESMERE RANGERS

North West Counties Division 1S

Founded 1969 Nickname: The Rangers **Club Colours:** Sky blue & navy blue

Club Contact Details 07947 864 357 john.edge2@homecall.co.uk

HONOURS FA Comps: None

League: West Midlands (Reg) Division One 2005-06, Premier 2009-10.

11-12	12-13	13-14	14-15	15-16	16-17	17-18	18-19	19-20	20-21
MidAl 15	MidAl 22	WMP 11	WMP 4	WMP 10	WMP 7	WMP 6	NWC1S 19	NWC1S n&v	NWC1S n&v
FAC EP	FAC EP	FAC P	FAC EP	FAC EP			FAC EP		
FAV 2P	FAV 1Qr	FAV 2Q	FAV EP	FAV 1P	FAV 1Q	FAV 1Q	FAV 1Q	FAV 1Q	FAV 2Q

GROUND: Beech Grove, Ellesmere, Shropshire SY12 0BZ

Nearest Railway Station Gobowen (7 miles)

Bus Route Shrewsbury - Ellesmere No. 501 or Gobowen to Ellesmere No. 53.

FC ISLE OF MAN

North West Counties Division 1S

Founded 2019 Nickname: **Club Colours:** Red & black

Club Contact Details 07624 490 460 info@fcisleofman.im

HONOURS FA Comps: None

League: None

11-12	12-13	13-14	14-15	15-16	16-17	17-18	18-19	19-20	20-21

GROUND: The Bowl, Pulrose Road, Douglas, Isle of Man IM2 1AD

Bus Route Island served by Bus Vannin and can be caught from the ferry port. From IoM Airport take Nr 1 bus to Power Station.

MAINE ROAD

North West Counties Division 1S

Founded 1955 Nickname: Blues **Club Colours:** All sky blue.

Club Contact Details 0161 861 0344

HONOURS FA Comps: None

League: Manchester Amateur Sunday 1971-72. Manchester Premier 1982-83, 83-84, 84-85, 85-86.
North West Counties Division Two 1989-90.

11-12	12-13	13-14	14-15	15-16	16-17	17-18	18-19	19-20	20-21
NWCP 18	NWCP 2	NWCP 4	NWCP 15	NWCP 12	NWCP 15	NWCP 21	NWC1S 14	NWC1S n&v	NWC1S n&v
FAC 1Q	FAC 1Q	FAC EP	FAC EP	FAC P	FAC 1Q	FAC Pr	FAC EP		FAC EP
FAV 2Q	FAV 1P	FAV 2P	FAV 1P	FAV 2Q	FAV 1Q	FAV 1Q	FAV 2Q	FAV 2P	FAV 2Q

GROUND: Brantingham Road, Chorlton-cum-Hardy M21 0TT

Nearest Railway Station Chorlton (Manc. Metrolink) - 768m

Bus Route Nos 85 & 168 from Manchester City Centre - stops at Wilbraham Road.

NEW MILLS

North West Counties Division 1S

Founded pre1890 Nickname: The Millers **Club Colours:** Amber & black

Club Contact Details 01663 747 435

HONOURS FA Comps: None

League: Manchester Premier Division 1924, 26, 56, 63, 65, 66, 67, 68, 70, 71.
North West Counties Division Two 2007-08, Premier Division 2010-11.

11-12	12-13	13-14	14-15	15-16	16-17	17-18	18-19	19-20	20-21
NP1S 9	NP1N 3	NP1N 16	NP1N 21	NP1N 22	NWCP 20	NWC1 14	NWC1S 18	NWC1S n&v	NWC1S n&v
FAC 1Q	FAC 2Q	FAC 1Qr	FAC P	FAC P	FAC EP	FAC EP			
FAT P	FAT 3Q	FAT P	FAT 2Q	FAT P	FAV 2Q	FAV 1Q	FAV 1Q	FAV 1Q	FAV 2P

GROUND: Church Lane, New Mills SK22 4NP

Nearest Railway Station New Mills Central - 0.7km

Bus Route No.358 from Stockport.

ROCESTER

North West Counties Division 1S

Founded 1876 Nickname: Romans **Club Colours:** Amber & black

Club Contact Details 01889 591 301

HONOURS FA Comps: None

League: Staffordshire Senior 1985-86, 86-87. West Mids (Regional) Division One 1987-88.
Midland Alliance 1998-99, 2003-04.

11-12		12-13		13-14		14-15		15-16		16-17		17-18		18-19		19-20		20-21	
MidAl	6	MidAl	13	MidAl	20	MFLP	12	MFLP	12	MFLP	16	MFLP	22	MFL1	14	MFL1	n&v	MFL1	n&v
FAC	1Q	FAC	P	FAC	EPr	FAC	EPr	FAC	Pr	FAC	P	FAC	EPr	FAC	EP				
FAV	1Q	FAV	4P	FAV	2P	FAV	1P	FAV	1P	FAV	2P	FAV	2Q	FAV	1Q	FAV	1P	FAV	2Q

GROUND: Hillsfield, Mill Street, Rocester, Uttoxeter ST14 5JX

Bus Route Ashbourne Road Garage stop - 152m away

SANDBACH UNITED

North West Counties Division 1S

Founded 2004 Nickname: **Club Colours:** Blue and white

Club Contact Details 07974 710 924

HONOURS FA Comps: None

League: None

11-12		12-13		13-14		14-15		15-16		16-17		17-18		18-19		19-20		20-21	
Ches2	5	Ches2	6	Ches2	2	ChesP	11	ChesP	4	NWC1	6	NWC1	5	NWC1S	7	NWC1S	n&v	NWC1S	n&v
														FAC	EP				
												FAV	2Q	FAV	1P	FAV	1P	FAV	1Q

GROUND: Hind Heath Road, Sandbach CW11 3LZ

Nearest Railway Station Sandbach - 1.4km

Bus Route Salt Line Way stop - 260m away

ST MARTINS

North West Counties Division 1S

Founded 1897 Nickname: Saints **Club Colours:** Yellow and black

Club Contact Details 01691 684 840

HONOURS FA Comps: None

League: Oswestry & District 1919-20, 52-53, 54-55. West Shropshire Alliance Division Three 1973-74, Premier 89-90, 2000-01.
Shropshire County Division One 1997-98, 2007-08, Premier 2009-10.

11-12		12-13		13-14		14-15		15-16		16-17		17-18		18-19		19-20		20-21	
WM2	5	WM1	16	WM1	14	WM1	3	WM1	6	WM1	8	WM1	4	NWC1S	11	NWC1S	n&v	NWC1S	n&v
												FAV	1Q	FAV	1Q	FAV	1Q	FAV	1Q

GROUND: The Venue, Burma Road, Parkhall, Oswestry, Shrops. SY11 4AS

Nearest Railway Station Gobowen - 1.9 miles

Bus Route No.53, Oswestry/Gobowen/Ellesmere, bus stop is 500 yards from the ground.

STAFFORD TOWN

North West Counties Division 1S

Founded 1976 Nickname: Reds or Town **Club Colours:** All red

Club Contact Details 01785 213 396 staffordtown@hotmail.co.uk

HONOURS FA Comps: None

League: Midland Combination Division Two 1978-79.
West Midlands (Regional) Division One 1993-94, Premier 1999-2000.

11-12		12-13		13-14		14-15		15-16		16-17		17-18		18-19		19-20		20-21	
WMP	18	MCmP	11	MCmP	8	MFL1	14	MFL1	18	MFL1	16	MFL1	20	StfSP	5	MFL1	n&v	MFL1	n&v
				FAC	EP	FAC	P												
FAV	2P	FAV	2Q	FAV	2Q	FAV	1Q	FAV	2Q	FAV	1Q	FAV	1P	FAV	1Q	FAV	1Q	FAV	1Q

GROUND: Evans Park, Riverway, Stafford ST16 3TL

Nearest Railway Station Stafford - 1.1km

Bus Route Hatherton Street stop - 99m away

STOCKPORT TOWN

North West Counties Division 1S

Founded 2014 Nickname: The Lions **Club Colours:** Red & black

Club Contact Details 0161 494 3140

HONOURS FA Comps: None

League: None

11-12	12-13	13-14	14-15	15-16	16-17	17-18	18-19	19-20	20-21
				NWC1 4	NWC1 10	NWC1 10	NWC1S 10	NWC1S n&v	NWC1S n&v
					FAV 1P	FAV 2Q	FAV 2Q	FAV 2Q	FAV 2Q

GROUND: Lambeth Grove, Woodley, Stockport SK6 1QX

Nearest Railway Station Woodley - 0.7km. Bredbury - 0.8km

Bus Route No 330 from Stockport to Ashton.

WEST DIDSBURY & CHORLTON

North West Counties Division 1S

Founded 1908 Nickname: West **Club Colours:** White and black

Club Contact Details

HONOURS FA Comps: None

League: Lancashire & Cheshire Amateur Division Two 1987-88, Division One 88-89
Manchester League Division One 2010-11.

11-12	12-13	13-14	14-15	15-16	16-17	17-18	18-19	19-20	20-21
MancP 7	NCE1 3	NWCP 12	NWCP 16	NWCP 5	NWCP 6	NWCP 10	NWCP 19	NWC1S n&v	NWC1S n&v
		FAC Pr	FAC P	FAC EP	FAC P	FAC Pr	FAC EP	FAC Pr	
FAV 2Q	FAV 1Q	FAV 1P	FAV 1P	FAV 1P	FAV 2Q	FAV 1P	FAV 1Q	FAV 1P	FAV 2Q

GROUND: End of Brookburn Road, Chorlton, Manchester M21 8FE

Nearest Railway Station Chorlton Metrolink - 0.9 miles

Bus Route No.86 - Manchester Piccadilly Gardens to Barlow Moor road Bus Station.

WYTHENSHAWE AMATEURS

North West Counties Division 1S

Founded 1946 Nickname: The Ammies **Club Colours:** Blue & white

Club Contact Details 0161 428 0517

HONOURS FA Comps: None

League: Lancashire & Cheshire Division Two 1954-55, Division One 56-57, Premier 61-62.
Manchester Division One 1972-73, Premier 89-90, 92-93, 2002-03.

11-12	12-13	13-14	14-15	15-16	16-17	17-18	18-19	19-20	20-21
MancP 9	MancP 13	MancP 8	MancP 7	MancP 10	MancP 2	MancP 2	NWC1S 4	NWC1S n&v	NWC1S n&v
									FAC P
								FAV 2Q	FAV 2Q

GROUND: Hollyhedge Park, Altrincham Road, Wythenshawe M22 4US

Nearest Railway Station Benchill Metrolink

Bus Route 102, 103 to Altrincham Road from Mancheter City Centre

CLUB MOVEMENTS

DIVISION ONE NORTH - IN: Campion (LM - NCE1). Ilkley Town (P - WYL). South Liverpool (P - WCL).
OUT: AFC Liverpool, Lower Breck, and Prestwich Heys (P - NWCP). Isle of Man (LM - NWC1S). Shelley (W).

DIVISION ONE SOUTH - IN: Brocton, Rocester and Stafford Town (LM - ML1). Isle of Man (LM - NWC1N). Wem Town (LM - WMRL).
OUT: Vauxhall Motors and Wythenshawe Town (P - NWCP). Wem Town (W - ahead of the new season).

AFC MANSFIELD

Northern Counties East Premier

Founded 2012 Nickname: The Bulls **Club Colours:** All red

Club Contact Details 01623 238 500 (MD)

Previous Names: None
Previous Leagues: Central Midlands North 2012-14. Northern Counties East 2014-18. Northern Premier 2018-19 (demoted due to ground grading).
HONOURS
FA Comps: None
League: Central Midlands North 2013-14.

11-12	12-13	13-14	14-15	15-16	16-17	17-18	18-19	19-20	20-21
	CMN 2	CMN 1	NCE1 7	NCE1 2	NCEP 7	NCEP 3	NP1E 15	NCEP n&v	NCEP n&v
				FAC EP	FAC 3Q	FAC 3Q	FAC 2Q	FAC 1Q	FAC 2Q
		FAV 2Pr	FAV 5P	FAV 2Pr	FAV 4P	FAV 2P	FAT 2Qr	FAV 3P	FAV 1P

GROUND: Forest Town Stadium, Clipstone Road West, Forest Town, Mansfield NG19 0EE
Nearest Railway Station Mansfield - 2.7km
Bus Route Stagecoach East Midlands Nos 14, 15 & 16 from Mansfield.

CLUB MOVEMENTS

PREMIER DIVISION - IN: Emley AFC and Winterton Rangers (P - NCE1). Sherwood Collery (P - EMCP).
OUT: Bridlington Town, Liversedge and Yorkshire Amateur (P - NPLE).

ALBION SPORTS

Northern Counties East Premier

Founded 1974 Nickname: Lions **Club Colours:** Yellow and royal blue

Club Contact Details 0113 255 7292 contact@albionsports.co.uk

Previous Names: None
Previous Leagues: Bradford Amateur Sunday 1974-2007. West Riding County Amateur 2007-11.
HONOURS
FA Comps: None
League: Bradford Amateur Sunday Premier Division 1995-96, 99-2000, 00-01, 02-03, 04-05, 05-06. Northern Counties East Division One 2012-13.

11-12	12-13	13-14	14-15	15-16	16-17	17-18	18-19	19-20	20-21
NCE1 4	NCE1 1	NCEP 6	NCEP 10	NCEP 11	NCEP 8	NCEP 14	NCEP 16	NCEP n&v	NCEP n&v
		FAC 1Q	FAC P	FAC EPr	FAC EPr	FAC 2Q	FAC Pr	FAC EP	FAC P
	FAV 2Q	FAV 2Q	FAV 2Q	FAV 1Q	FAV 1Q	FAV 1Q	FAV 2Q	FAV 2Q	FAV 1Q

GROUND: The Citadel Stadium, Newlands, Farsley, Leeds, LS28 5BE. **Capacity:** 3,500
Nearest Railway Station New Pudsey - 1km **Seats:** 1,750
Bus Route Town St Slaters Rd - stop 340m away **Covered:** 1,750

ATHERSLEY RECREATION

Northern Counties East Premier

Founded 1979 Nickname: Penguins **Club Colours:** Black and white

Club Contact Details 07910 121 070 petegoodlad@yahoo.co.uk

Previous Names: Athersley North Juniors 1979-86.
Previous Leagues: Barnsley Junior. Barnsley Association. Sheffield & Hallamshire County Senior 1997-2012.
HONOURS
FA Comps: None
League: Barnsley Junior 1986-87. Barnsley Association 91-92, 92-93, 94-95, 95-96, 96-97. Sheffield & Hallamshire County Senior Division Two 1997-98, Premier Division 1999-2000, 03-04, 04-05, 06-07, 08-09, 11-12

11-12	12-13	13-14	14-15	15-16	16-17	17-18	18-19	19-20	20-21
SHSP 1	NCE1 2	NCEP 10	NCEP 13	NCEP 18	NCEP 10	NCEP 17	NCEP 17	NCEP n&v	NCEP n&v
			FAC P	FAC EP	FAC EP	FAC EP	FAC EP	FAC EP	FAC EP
		FAV 2P	FAV 2Q	FAV 1P	FAV 1Q	FAV 1Q	FAV 1Q	FAV 1Q	FAV 1Q

GROUND: Sheerien Park, Ollerton Road, Athersley North, Barnsley, S71 3DP **Capacity:** 2,000
Nearest Railway Station Barnsley - 3.4km **Seats:** 150
Bus Route No.11 - Trowell Way - stop 80m away **Covered:** 420

BARTON TOWN

Northern Counties East Premier

Founded 1995 Nickname: Swans **Club Colours:** Sky blue & navy blue

Club Contact Details 01652 636 964 bartontown@gmail.com

Previous Names: Barton Town Old Boys >2017.

Previous Leagues: Lincolnshire 1995-2000, Humber (Founder member) 2000-01, Central Midlands 2001-07.

HONOURS

FA Comps: None

League: Lincolnshire 1996-97. Central Midlands Supreme Division 2005-06.

11-12	12-13	13-14	14-15	15-16	16-17	17-18	18-19	19-20	20-21
NCEP 11	NCEP 8	NCEP 3	NCEP 5	NCEP 10	NCEP 20	NCEP 12	NCEP 11	NCEP n&v	NCEP n&v
FAC Pr	FAC P	FAC P	FAC P	FAC P	FAC EP	FAC EP	FAC EPr	FAC P	FAC P
FAV 2P	FAV 1Q	FAV 2Q	FAV 2P	FAV 1Q	FAV 1Q	FAV 2Q	FAV 2P	FAV 2Q	FAV 1Q

GROUND: The Easy Buy Stadium, off Falkland Way, Barton upon Humber DN18 5RL

Nearest Railway Station Barton-on-Humber - 0.5km

Bus Route Butts Road - stop 133m away

Capacity: 3,000
Seats: 240
Covered: 540

BOTTESFORD TOWN

Northern Counties East Premier

Founded 1974 Nickname: The Poachers **Club Colours:** Blue & yellow

Club Contact Details 01724 871 883 andrew.susworth@googlemail.com

Previous Names: None

Previous Leagues: Lincolnshire 1974-2000. Central Midlands 2000-07.

HONOURS

FA Comps: None

League: Lincolnshire 1989-90, 90-91, 91-92. Central Midlands Supreme Division 2006-07.

11-12	12-13	13-14	14-15	15-16	16-17	17-18	18-19	19-20	20-21
NCE1 16	NCE1 15	NCE1 3	NCE1 8	NCE1 3	NCEP 12	NCEP 8	NCEP 12	NCEP n&v	NCEP n&v
			FAC EP	FAC P	FAC P	FAC 1Q	FAC 1Q	FAC EP	FAC P
FAV 2Q	FAV 2P	FAV 1Q	FAV 1Pr	FAV 2Q	FAV 3P	FAV 2Q	FAV 1Pr	FAV 2P	FAV 1Q

GROUND: Birch Park, Ontario Road, Bottesford, Scunthorpe DN17 2TQ

Nearest Railway Station Scunthorpe - 3.6km

Bus Route Maple Leaf - stop 149m away

Capacity: 1,000
Seats: 90
Covered: 300

ECCLESHILL UNITED

Northern Counties East Premier

Founded 1948 Nickname: The Eagles **Club Colours:** Blue & white

Club Contact Details 01274 615 739

Previous Names: -

Previous Leagues: Bradford Amateur. West Riding County Amateur >1985

HONOURS

FA Comps: None

League: West Riding County Amateur 1976-77.
Northern Counties East Division One 1996-97.

11-12	12-13	13-14	14-15	15-16	16-17	17-18	18-19	19-20	20-21
NCE1 6	NCE1 14	NCE1 4	NCE1 13	NCE1 13	NCE1 9	NCE1 4	NCEP 10	NCEP n&v	NCEP n&v
FAC 1Q	FAC 1Q		FAC EP				FAC EP	FAC Pr	FAC EP
FAV 2P	FAV 1Q	FAV 1P	FAV 1Q	FAV EP	FAV 1Q	FAV 1Q	FAV 1Q	FAV 1Q	FAV 1Q

GROUND: Kingsway, Wrose, Bradford BD2 1PN

Nearest Railway Station Frizinghall - 1.7km

Bus Route Kingsway Plumpton Drive - stop 97m away

Capacity: 2,225
Seats: 225
Covered: 415

EMLEY AFC

Northern Counties East Premier

Founded 2005 Nickname: Pewits **Club Colours:** Claret and sky blue

Club Contact Details 01924 849 392

Previous Names:
Previous Leagues: West Yorkshire 2005-06. Northern Counties East 2006-19. North West Counties 2019-20.
HONOURS
FA Comps: None
League: None

11-12		12-13		13-14		14-15		15-16		16-17		17-18		18-19		19-20		20-21	
NCE1	10	NCE1	7	NCE1	8	NCE1	5	NCE1	4	NCE1	3	NCE1	12	NCE1	12	NWC1N	n&v	NCE1	n&v
FAC	EP	FAC	EP	FAC	P	FAC	P	FAC	P	FAC	P	FAC	EP						
FAV	1P	FAV	4P	FAV	1P	FAV	1P	FAV	2Q	FAV	2P	FAV	1P	FAV	1Q	FAV	2Q	FAV	1Q

GROUND: The Welfare Ground, Off Upper Lane, Emley, nr Huddersfield HD8 9RE. **Capacity:** 2,000
Nearest Railway Station Denby Dale - 5km **Seats:** 330
Bus Route No. 232 - Upper Lane Church Street - stop 61m away **Covered:** 1,000

GARFORTH TOWN

Northern Counties East Premier

Founded 1964 Nickname: The Miners **Club Colours:** Blue

Club Contact Details 0113 287 7567 secretary@garforthtown.net

Previous Names: Garforth Miners 1964-85
Previous Leagues: Leeds Sunday Comb. 1972-76, West Yorkshire 1976-78, Yorkshire 1978-82, NCE 1982-2007. Northern Premier 2007-13.
HONOURS
FA Comps: None
League: Northern Counties East Division 1 1997-98

11-12		12-13		13-14		14-15		15-16		16-17		17-18		18-19		19-20		20-21	
NP1N	5	NP1N	22	NCEP	14	NCEP	14	NCEP	16	NCEP	15	NCEP	13	NCEP	14	NCEP	n&v	NCEP	n&v
FAC	1Q	FAC	1Q	FAC	EP	FAC	P	FAC	EP	FAC	EP	FAC	EP	FAC	1Q	FAC	P	FAC	EP
FAT	1Q	FAT	P	FAV	1P	FAV	2Q	FAV	2P	FAV	1Q	FAV	1P	FAV	1P	FAV	2Q	FAV	2Q

GROUND: Bannister Prentice Stadium, Cedar Ridge, Garforth, Leeds LS25 2PF **Capacity:** 3,000
Nearest Railway Station East Garforth - 1km. Garforth - 1.2km. **Seats:** 278
Bus Route Aberford Road - stop 128m away **Covered:** 200

GOOLE AFC

Northern Counties East Premier

Founded 1997 Nickname: The Vikings **Club Colours:** Red

Club Contact Details 01405 762 794 (Match days) jumbosmith96@icloud.com

Previous Names: Replacement for Goole Town which folded at the end of the 1995-96 season.
Previous Leagues: Central Midlands 1997-98. Northern Counties East 2000-04. Northern Premier 2004-18.
HONOURS
FA Comps: None
League: Central Midlands 1997-98.
Northern Counties East Division One 1999-2000, Premier Division 2003-04.

11-12		12-13		13-14		14-15		15-16		16-17		17-18		18-19		19-20		20-21	
NP1S	10	NP1N	21	NP1S	13	NP1S	16	NP1S	19	NP1N	21	NP1N	22	NCEP	18	NCEP	n&v	NCEP	n&v
FAC	Pr	FAC	P	FAC	P	FAC	Pr	FAC	1Qr	FAC	P	FAC	P	FAC	EP	FAC	Pr	FAC	EP
FAT	1Q	FAT	Pr	FAT	P	FAT	2Q	FAT	1Q	FAT	1Qr	FAT	P	FAV	1Q	FAV	1Q	FAV	2Q

GROUND: Victoria Pleasure Gardens, Marcus Road, Goole DN14 6SL **Capacity:** 3,000
Nearest Railway Station Goole - 0.5km **Seats:** 300
Bus Route Goole Newport Street - stop 200m away **Covered:** 800

GRIMSBY BOROUGH

Northern Counties East Premier

Founded 2003 Nickname: The Wilderness Boys **Club Colours:** All red

Club Contact Details 07496 113 736 nigelfanthorpe@hotmail.co.uk

Previous Names: None
Previous Leagues: Lincolnshire 2003-04. Central Midlands 2004-08.
HONOURS
FA Comps: None
League: None

11-12	12-13	13-14	14-15	15-16	16-17	17-18	18-19	19-20	20-21
NCE1 18	NCE1 17	NCE1 16	NCE1 22	NCE1 19	NCE1 4	NCE1 3	NCE1 1	NCEP n&v	NCEP n&v
FAC EP						FAC 1Q	FAC 1Q	FAC EP	FAC EP
FAV 2Q	FAV 1Q	FAV 2Q	FAV 1Q		FAV 2Q	FAV 1Q	FAV 1Q	FAV 3P	FAV 2P

GROUND: The Bradley Football Development Centre, Bradley Road, Grimsby, DN37 0AG
Nearest Railway Station Grimsby Town - 3km
Bus Route Crowland Avenue - stop 463m away

Capacity: 1,000
Seats: 180
Covered: 200

HANDSWORTH

Northern Counties East Premier

Founded 1986 Nickname: Ambers **Club Colours:** Amber & black

Club Contact Details 07930 443 453 johnbrunsmeer@hotmail.co.uk

Previous Names: Parramore Sports > 2010. Sheffield Parramore 2010-2011. Worksop Parramore 2011-14. Handsworth Parramore 2014-19.
Previous Leagues: Sheffield & Hallam County Senior 1986-2008. Central Midlands 2008-11
HONOURS
FA Comps: None
League: Central Midland Supreme Division 2010-11.

11-12	12-13	13-14	14-15	15-16	16-17	17-18	18-19	19-20	20-21
NCE1 3	NCEP 7	NCEP 4	NCEP 7	NCEP 2	NCEP 4	NCEP 4	NCEP 8	NCEP n&v	NCEP n&v
			FAC P	FAC P	FAC 3Q	FAC 2Qr	FAC P	FAC P	FAC EP
			FAV 1P	FAV 3P	FAV 1P	FAV 1P	FAV 1P	FAV 2Q	FAV 1Q

GROUND: Handsworth Junior Sporting Club, Olivers Mount, Sheffield S9 4PA
Nearest Railway Station Darnell - 1mile away

HEMSWORTH MINERS WELFARE

Northern Counties East Premier

Founded 1981 Nickname: Wells **Club Colours:** Royal blue

Club Contact Details 01977 614 997

Previous Names: None
Previous Leagues: Doncaster Senior. West Riding County Amateur 1995-2008.
HONOURS
FA Comps: None
League: West Riding County Amateur Division One 1996-97.
Northern Counties East Division One 2015-16.

11-12	12-13	13-14	14-15	15-16	16-17	17-18	18-19	19-20	20-21
NCE1 8	NCE1 13	NCE1 17	NCE1 3	NCE1 1	NCEP 9	NCEP 6	NCEP 4	NCEP n&v	NCEP n&v
FAC EP	FAC P			FAC EP	FAC P	FAC EP	FAC EPr	FAC P	FAC EP
FAV 2Q	FAV 1Q	FAV 2Q	FAV 2Q	FAV 2P	FAV 2P	FAV 2Q	FAV 2P	FAV 1P	FAV 1P

GROUND: Prince Drive, Fitzwilliam, Pontefract WF9 5FD
Nearest Railway Station Fitzwilliam - 0.4km
Bus Route Wakefield Road - stop 22m away

Capacity: 2,000
Seats: 100
Covered: 100

KNARESBOROUGH TOWN

Northern Counties East Premier

Founded 1902 Nickname: The Boro **Club Colours:** Red and black

Club Contact Details 01423 868 042 knaresboroughtownafc@gmail.com

Previous Names: None

Previous Leagues: York 1902-09, 11-31, 32-38, 51-56. Northern 1909-11. West Yorkshire 1956-61, 69-2012. Harrogate & District 1961-69.

HONOURS

FA Comps: None

League: York 1902-03, 03-04, 04-05, 08-09, 24-25, 25-26, 28-29, 33-34, 34-35, Div.2 51-52, Div.1 52-53. Harrogate & District 64-65, 65-66, 66-67. West Yorkshire Prem 2008-09. Northern Counties East Division One 2017-18.

11-12	12-13	13-14	14-15	15-16	16-17	17-18	18-19	19-20	20-21
WYkP 3	NCE1 8	NCE1 6	NCE1 12	NCE1 8	NCE1 7	NCE1 1	NCEP 9	NCEP n&v	NCEP n&v
			FAC P				FAC 2Q	FAC EP	FAC P
		FAV 2Q	FAV 1Q	FAV 1Q	FAV 1Q	FAV 2P	FAV 1Q	FAV 1P	FAV 1Q

GROUND: Manse Lane, Knaresborough, HG5 8LF
Nearest Railway Station Knaresborough - 1.5km
Bus Route Aspin Park School - stop 168 away

Capacity: 1,000
Seats: 73
Covered: 173

MALTBY MAIN

Northern Counties East Premier

Founded 1916 Nickname: Miners **Club Colours:** Red and black

Club Contact Details 07795 693 683 john_mills_@hotmail.co.uk

Previous Names: Maltby Miners Welfare 1970-96

Previous Leagues: Sheffield Association 1919-29, 39-41, 45-49, 65-70, 72-73. Rotherham Minor 1929-36. Sheffield Amateur 1936-39. Rotherham Association 1942-45, 55-58. Yorkshire League 1949-55, 73-82. Doncaster & District 1958-65.

HONOURS

FA Comps: None

League: Sheffield Association 1925-26, 26-27.

11-12	12-13	13-14	14-15	15-16	16-17	17-18	18-19	19-20	20-21
NCEP 18	NCEP 14	NCEP 15	NCEP 19	NCEP 7	NCEP 14	NCEP 5	NCEP 6	NCEP n&v	NCEP n&v
FAC EP	FAC 1Q	FAC EP	FAC P	FAC 1Q	FAC EP	FAC EP	FAC 1Q	FAC 1Q	FAC P
FAV 1Q	FAV 2Q	FAV 1Q	FAV 2Qr	FAV 2P	FAV 1Q	FAV 2Q	FAV 2Q	FAV 1Q	FAV 2P

GROUND: Muglet Lane, Maltby, Rotherham S66 7JQ
Nearest Railway Station Rotherham Central - 8 miles
Bus Route Duke Avenue - stop 78m away

Capacity: 2,000
Seats: 150
Covered: 300

PENISTONE CHURCH

Northern Counties East Premier

Founded 1906 Nickname: None **Club Colours:** Black & white

Club Contact Details 01226 370 095 penistonechurchfc@gmail.com

Previous Names: Formed after the merger of Penistone Choirboys and Penistone Juniors.

Previous Leagues: Sheffield Junior 1906-07. Sheffield Amateur 1907-48. Hatchard League/Sheffield Association 1948-83. Sheffield & Hallamshire County Senior (Founder Members) 1983-14.

HONOURS

FA Comps: None

League: Sheffield & Hallamshire County Senior Division One 1993-94, 2000-01.

11-12	12-13	13-14	14-15	15-16	16-17	17-18	18-19	19-20	20-21
Sh&HP 4	Sh&HP 3	Sh&HP 4	NCE1 9	NCE1 5	NCE1 6	NCEP 7	NCEP 2	NCEP n&v	NCEP n&v
				FAC EP	FAC EP	FAC 2Q	FAC P	FAC EPr	FAC EP
		FAV 1Q	FAV 1Q	FAV 2Q	FAV 1P	FAV 1Q	FAV 1Q	FAV 1P	FAV 2P

GROUND: Church View Road, Penistone, Sheffield S36 6AT
Nearest Railway Station Penistone - 0.2km
Bus Route Church View Road - stop 149m away

Capacity: 1,000
Seats: 100
Covered: 150

SHERWOOD COLLIERY

Northern Counties East Premier

Founded 2008 Nickname: The Wood **Club Colours:** Black and blue

Club Contact Details 01623 631 747 kirkland9294@gmail.com

Previous Names: None
Previous Leagues: Central Midlands 2012-18. East Midlands 2018-21.
HONOURS
FA Comps: None
League: None

11-12	12-13	13-14	14-15	15-16	16-17	17-18	18-19	19-20	20-21
	CMN 15	CMN 11	CMN 17	CMN 5	CMN 3	CMN 2	EMC 3	EMC n&v	EMC n&v
								FAC Pr	FAC EP
					FAV 2P	FAV 2Q	FAV 2Q	FAV 2P	FAV 2Q

GROUND: Debdale Lane, Mansfield Woodhouse, Mansfield NG19 7NS
Nearest Railway Station Mansfield Woodhouse - 6min walk from the ground.
Bus Route 1, 12B, 23 & 53

SILSDEN

Northern Counties East Premier

Founded 1904 Nickname: The Cobbydalers **Club Colours:** Red and black

Club Contact Details 01535 958 850 john.silsdenfc@hotmail.co.uk

Previous Names: Reformed in 1980.
Previous Leagues: Craven & District. West Riding County Amateur. North West Counties >2019.
HONOURS
FA Comps: None
League: Craven Premier Division 1998-99. West Riding County Am. Division Two 99-2000, Division One 2000-01, Premier Division 2002-03. North West Counties Division One 2017-18.

11-12	12-13	13-14	14-15	15-16	16-17	17-18	18-19	19-20	20-21
NWCP 12	NWCP 18	NWCP 15	NWCP 10	NWCP 21	NWC1 11	NWC1 1	NWCP 9	NCEP n&v	NCEP n&v
FAC Pr	FAC EP	FAC EP	FAC EP	FAC P	FAC EPr		FAC EP	FAC EPr	FAC P
FAV 1Q		FAV 2Q	FAV 1P	FAV 1P	FAV 2Q	FAV 2Q	FAV 3P	FAV 1Q	FAV 2Q

GROUND: Keighley Road, Keighley Road, Silsden BD20 0EH
Nearest Railway Station Steeton & Silsden - 1.1km
Bus Route Keighley Road stop - 55m away

STAVELEY MINERS WELFARE

Northern Counties East Premier

Founded 1989 Nickname: The Trojans **Club Colours:** Blue & white

Club Contact Details 01246 471 441 staveleyed@hotmail.co.uk

Previous Names: None
Previous Leagues: Chesterfield & District Amateur 1989-91. Sheffield & Hallamshire County Senior 1991-93.
HONOURS
FA Comps: None
League: Sheffield & Hallamshire County Senior Division Three 1991-92, Division Two 1992-93.
Northern Counties East Division One 2010-11.

11-12	12-13	13-14	14-15	15-16	16-17	17-18	18-19	19-20	20-21
NCEP 5	NCEP 13	NCEP 17	NCEP 9	NCEP 8	NCEP 6	NCEP 16	NCEP 7	NCEP n&v	NCEP n&v
FAC 2Q	FAC Pr	FAC P	FAC 1Q	FAC EP	FAC EP	FAC P	FAC 2Q	FAC 1Q	FAC EP
FAV SF	FAV 2P	FAV 3P	FAV 1Q	FAV 1Q	FAV 3P	FAV 1P	FAV 1Pr	FAV 1Q	FAV 1Q

GROUND: Inkersall Road, Staveley, Chesterfield, S43 3JL
Nearest Railway Station Chesterfield - 5,4km
Bus Route Market Street - stop 156m away

Capacity: 5,000
Seats: 220
Covered: 400

THACKLEY

Northern Counties East Premier

Founded 1930 Nickname: Dennyboys **Club Colours:** Red and white

Club Contact Details 01274 615 571 mick.lodge@btinternet.com

Previous Names: Thackley Wesleyians 1930-39

Previous Leagues: Bradford Amateur, West Riding County Amateur, West Yorkshire, Yorkshire 1967-82

HONOURS

FA Comps: None

League: West Riding County Amateur x5. West Yorkshire 1965-66, 66-67. Yorkshire Division Two 1973-74.

11-12		12-13		13-14		14-15		15-16		16-17		17-18		18-19		19-20		20-21	
NCEP	10	NCEP	10	NCEP	13	NCEP	12	NCEP	12	NCEP	5	NCEP	15	NCEP	15	NCEP	n&v	NCEP	n&v
FAC	P	FAC	EP	FAC	EP	FAC	EP	FAC	1Qr	FAC	EP	FAC	EP	FAC	EP	FAC	EP	FAC	EP
FAV	1P	FAV	3P	FAV	3P	FAV	1Q	FAV	1Qr	FAV	1Q	FAV	2Q	FAV	2P	FAV	2Q	FAV	2Q

GROUND: Dennyfield, Ainsbury Avenue, Thackley, Bradford BD10 0TL **Capacity:** 3000
Nearest Railway Station Baildon - 1.4km **Seats:** 300
Bus Route Thackley Road - stop 200m away **Covered:** 600

WINTERTON RANGERS

Northern Counties East Premier

Founded 1930 Nickname: Rangers **Club Colours:** All blue

Club Contact Details 01724 732 628 wintertonrangers2018@mail.com

Previous Names:

Previous Leagues: Scunthorpe & District. 1945-65. Lincolnshire 1965-70. Yorkshire 1970-82.

HONOURS

FA Comps: None

League: Yprkshire Division One 1971-72, 76-77, 78-79.
Northern Counties East Division Two 1989-90, Premier 2007-08.

11-12		12-13		13-14		14-15		15-16		16-17		17-18		18-19		19-20		20-21	
NCEP	6	NCEP	19	NCEP	22	NCE1	18	NCE1	8	NCE1	12	NCE1	10	NCE1	4	NCE1	n&v	NCE1	n&v
FAC	EP	FAC	EP	FAC	EP	FAC	P									FAC	P		
FAV	2Q	FAV	2Q	FAV	2Q	FAV	1P	FAV	1Q	FAV	1Q	FAV	1Q	FAV	3P	FAV	1P	FAV	2Q

GROUND: West Street, Winterton, Scunthorpe DN15 9QF. **Capacity:** 3,000
Nearest Railway Station Scunthorpe - 6¼ miles **Seats:** 245
Bus Route Post Office - stop 150m away **Covered:** 200

CLUB MOVEMENTS

DIVISION ONE - IN: Clipstone, Ollerton, Rainworth MW, Shirebrook Town and Teversal (LM - EMCP).
OUT: Emley AFC and Winterton Rangers (P - NCEP). Skegness Town (P - UCPN).

ARMTHORPE WELFARE

Northern Counties East Division One

Founded 1926 Nickname: Wellie Club Colours: All blue

Club Contact Details armthorpe.welfare@hotmail.co.uk

HONOURS FA Comps: None

League: Doncaster & District Senior 1952-53, 53-54, 54-55, 56-57, 57-58, 60-61, 61-62, 64-65, 82-83, Div.3 77-78, Div.2 78-79, Div.1 81-82. NCE Div.1 Central 1984-85.

11-12		12-13		13-14		14-15		15-16		16-17		17-18		18-19		19-20		20-21	
NCEP	13	NCEP	20	NCEP	18	NCEP	17	NCEP	19	NCEP	21	NCE1	16	NCE1	17	NCE1	n&v	NCE1	n&v
FAC	1Qr	FAC	EP	FAC	EP	FAC	P	FAC	2Q	FAC	EP	FAC	EPr						
FAV	3P	FAV	2P	FAV	2P	FAV	2Q	FAV	1P	FAV	1Q	FAV	2Q	FAV	1Q	FAV	1Q	FAV	1Q

GROUND: Welfare Ground, Church Street, Armthorpe, Doncaster DN3 3AG

Nearest Railway Station Kirk Sandall - 3.4km

Bus Route Beech Road - stop 13m away

BRIGG TOWN

Northern Counties East Division One

Founded 1864 Nickname: Zebras Club Colours: Black and white

Club Contact Details 01652 794 275 gavinduncanbriggtownfc@gmail.com

HONOURS FA Comps: FAV 1995-96, 2002-03

League: Midland Counties 1977-78. Northern Counties East Premier 2000-01. Lincolnshire League x8,

11-12		12-13		13-14		14-15		15-16		16-17		17-18		18-19		19-20		20-21	
NP1S	17	NP1S	13	NP1S	18	NP1S	22	NCEP	21	NCE1	14	NCE1	21	Lincs	2	NCE1	n&v	NCE1	n&v
FAC	P	FAC	P	FAC	1Qr	FAC	P	FAC	EP	FAC	1Q								
FAT	1Q	FAT	P	FAT	2Q	FAT	Pr	FAV	1Q	FAV	1Q					FAV	2Q	FAV	1Q

GROUND: The Hawthorns, Hawthorn Avenue, Brigg DN20 8PG

Nearest Railway Station Brigg - 0.9km

Bus Route Vale of Ancholme School - stop 189m away

CLIPSTONE

Northern Counties East Division One

Founded 1928 Nickname: The Cobras Club Colours: Black & white

Club Contact Details enquiries@clipstonefc.co.uk

HONOURS FA Comps: None

League: Central Midlands 1993-94, 96-97. Northern Counties East Division One 2014-15.

11-12		12-13		13-14		14-15		15-16		16-17		17-18		18-19		19-20		20-21	
CMN	4	NCE1	11	NCE1	7	NCE1	1	NCEP	13	NCEP	16	NCEP	22	EMC	18	EMC	n&v	EMC	n&v
						FAC	1Q	FAC	1Q	FAC	EP	FAC	P	FAC	P				
				FAV	2Q	FAV	2Q	FAV	1P	FAV	2Q	FAV	1P	FAV	1Q	FAV	1Q	FAV	1Q

GROUND: The Lido Ground, Clipstone Road East, Clipstone Village NG21 9AB

Nearest Railway Station Mansfield Woodhouse - 4.9km

Bus Route Station Road - stop 27m away

DRONFIELD TOWN

Northern Counties East Division One

Founded 1998 Nickname: None Club Colours: Red & black

Club Contact Details secretary@dronfieldtownfc.com

HONOURS FA Comps: None

League: Hope Valley B Div 2001-02, A Div 2002-03, Prem 2003-04. Midland Regional Alliance Division One 2005-06, Premier 2007-08. Central Midlands North 2012-13.

11-12		12-13		13-14		14-15		15-16		16-17		17-18		18-19		19-20		20-21	
CMN	3	CMN	1	NCE1	14	NCE1	19	NCE1	15	NCE1	19	NCE1	14	NCE1	6	NCE1	n&v	NCE1	n&v
						FAV	1P	FAV	1P	FAV	1Q	FAV	1P	FAV	2P	FAV	2Q	FAV	2Q

GROUND: Stonelow Playing Fields, Stonelow Road, Dronfield, S18 2EU

Nearest Railway Station Dronfield - 0.9km

Bus Route Oakhill Road Bottom - stop 270m away

FC HUMBER UNITED

Northern Counties East Division One

Founded   Nickname: Carnegie, EYC   **Club Colours:** Navy blue

Club Contact Details 01757 241 368   info@fchumberunited.co.uk

HONOURS FA Comps: None

League: East Riding County Division One 2009-10, Premier Division 2013-14.
Humber Premier Division One 2014-15

11-12	12-13	13-14	14-15	15-16	16-17	17-18	18-19	19-20	20-21
ERCP 5	ERCP 4	ERCP 1	Humb1 1	HumbP 14	HumbP 5	NCE1 18	NCE1 13	NCE1 n&v	NCE1 n&v
								FAV 2Q	

GROUND: Richard Street, Selby YO8 4BN
Nearest Railway Station Selby 3/4 mile away.

GLASSHOUGHTON WELFARE

Northern Counties East Division One

Founded 1964   Nickname: Welfare or Blues   **Club Colours:** Royal blue & white

Club Contact Details 01977 511 234   frankmaclachlan499@gmail.com

HONOURS FA Comps: None

League: None

11-12	12-13	13-14	14-15	15-16	16-17	17-18	18-19	19-20	20-21
NCE1 2	NCEP 16	NCEP 16	NCEP 21	NCE1 16	NCE1 11	NCE1 6	NCE1 11	NCE1 n&v	NCE1 n&v
FAC Pr	FAC EP	FAC EP	FAC EP	FAC EPr			FAC EP		FAC EP
FAV 2P	FAV 2Q	FAV 2Q	FAV 1Q	FAV 1Q	FAV 2Qr	FAV 2Q	FAV 1P	FAV 1P	FAV 2Q

GROUND: Glasshoughton Centre, Leeds Road, Glasshoughton, Castleford WF10 4PF
Nearest Railway Station Glasshoughton - 0.8km
Bus Route Leeds Road Carr Lane - stop 83m away

HALL ROAD RANGERS

Northern Counties East Division One

Founded 1959   Nickname: Rangers   **Club Colours:** Blue & white

Club Contact Details hallroadrangers@live.co.uk

HONOURS FA Comps: None

League: Yorkshire Division Three 1972-73, 79-80. Northern Counties East Division One 2016-17.

11-12	12-13	13-14	14-15	15-16	16-17	17-18	18-19	19-20	20-21
NCEP 16	NCEP 22	NCE1 11	NCE1 17	NCE1 17	NCE1 1	NCEP 19	NCEP 20	NCE1 n&v	NCE1 n&v
FAC Pr	FAC EP	FAC EP				FAC EP		FAC EP	FAC EP
FAV 2Q	FAV 1P	FAV 1Q	FAV 2Q	FAV 2Q	FAV 2P	FAV 2P		FAV 2Q	FAV 1Q

GROUND: Hawroth Park, Dawson Drive, Hull HU6 7DY
Nearest Railway Station Cottingham - 3.5km
Bus Route Larard Avenue - stop 158m away

HALLAM

Northern Counties East Division One

Founded 1860   Nickname: Countrymen   **Club Colours:** Blue and white

Club Contact Details 0114 230 9484   enquiry@hallamfc.co.uk

HONOURS FA Comps: None

League: Hatchard 1902-03, 48-49. Sheffield Amateur 1922-23, 26-27.
Sheffield Association 1949-50. Yorkshire Division Two 1960-61.

11-12	12-13	13-14	14-15	15-16	16-17	17-18	18-19	19-20	20-21
NCE1 14	NCE1 12	NCE1 20	NCE1 14	NCE1 6	NCE1 5	NCE1 8	NCE1 3	NCE1 n&v	NCE1 n&v
FAC EP	FAC EP				FAC EP	FAC P	FAC EP	FAC EP	FAC EP
FAV 1Q	FAV 1Q	FAV 1Q	FAV 2Q	FAV 2P	FAV 2P	FAV 2Q	FAV 2P	FAV 1Q	FAV 2P

GROUND: Sandygate Road, Crosspool, Sheffield S10 5SE
Nearest Railway Station Sheffield - 4.5km
Bus Route Ringstead Crescent - stop 19m away

HARROGATE RAILWAY ATHLETIC

Northern Counties East Division One

Founded 1935 Nickname: The Rail **Club Colours:** Red and green

Club Contact Details 01423 883 104 shep@therailfc.com

HONOURS FA Comps: None

League: West Yorkshire 1953-54.
Northern Counties East Division Two North 1983-84, Division one 1989-99.

11-12	12-13	13-14	14-15	15-16	16-17	17-18	18-19	19-20	20-21
NP1N 21	NP1N 18	NP1N 13	NP1N 8	NP1N 21	NCEP 19	NCEP 20	NCEP 19	NCE1 n&v	NCE1 n&v
FAC 1Q	FAC Pr	FAC Pr	FAC 2Q	FAC Pr	FAC 1Q	FAC Pr	FAC EP	FAC EP	
FAT 1Q	FAT 1Q	FAT P	FAT P	FAT P	FAV 2Q	FAV 1P	FAV 1Q	FAV 1Q	FAV 1P

GROUND: Station View, Starbeck, Harrogate, North Yorkshire HG2 7JA

Nearest Railway Station Starbeck - 0.1km

Bus Route Henry Peacock - stop 134m away

NORTH FERRIBY

Northern Counties East Division One

Founded 2019 Nickname: The Villagers **Club Colours:** Green and white

Club Contact Details 01482 634 601 info@northferriby.co.uk

HONOURS FA Comps: None

League: None

11-12	12-13	13-14	14-15	15-16	16-17	17-18	18-19	19-20	20-21
								NCE1 n&v	NCE1 n&v
									FAV 4P

GROUND: The Dransfield Stadium, Grange Lane, Church Road, North Ferriby HU14 3AB

Nearest Railway Station Ferriby - 5 min walk from the ground.

NOSTELL MINERS WELFARE

Northern Counties East Division One

Founded 1928 Nickname: The Welfare **Club Colours:** Yellow and black

Club Contact Details 01924 866 010 nostwellmwfc@hotmail.com

HONOURS FA Comps: None

League: West Yorkshire Premier Division 2004-05

11-12	12-13	13-14	14-15	15-16	16-17	17-18	18-19	19-20	20-21
NCEP 17	NCEP 18	NCEP 21	NCEP 15	NCEP 22	NCE1 22	NCE1 17	NCE1 5	NCE1 n&v	NCE1 n&v
FAC EP	FAC EP	FAC EP	FAC EP	FAC EPr	FAC EPr			FAC EPr	
FAV 2Qr	FAV 1P	FAV 1Q	FAV 2Q	FAV 1Q	FAV 2Q	FAV 2Q	FAV 1Q	FAV 1P	FAV 2Q

GROUND: The Welfare Ground, Crofton Co. Centre, Middle Lane, New Crofton WF4 1LB

Nearest Railway Station Streethouse - 2.9km

Bus Route The Slipper Pub - stop 372m away

OLLERTON TOWN

Northern Counties East Division One

Founded 1988 Nickname: The Town **Club Colours:** Red and black

Club Contact Details 07504 416 879 craigemb99@gmail.com

HONOURS FA Comps: None

League: Notts Alliance Division Two 1992-93, Division One 95-96.
Central Midlands Premier Division 2007-08.

11-12	12-13	13-14	14-15	15-16	16-17	17-18	18-19	19-20	20-21
CMN 7	CMN 6	CMN 8	CMN 10	CMN 2	NCE1 17	NCE1 15	NCE1 16	NCE1 n&v	EMC n&v
FAV 2Q	FAV 1Q	FAV 2Q		FAV 1Q	FAV 1Q	FAV 2Q	FAV 2Q	FAV 1Q	FAV 2Q

GROUND: The Lane, Walesby Lane, New Ollerton, Newark NG22 9UT

Nearest Railway Station Worksop

Bus Route Rosewood Centre - stop 214m away

PARKGATE

Northern Counties East Division One

Founded 1969 Nickname: The Steelmen **Club Colours:** Red & black

Club Contact Details 01709 826 600 brucebickerdike@hotmail.co.uk

HONOURS FA Comps: None

League: Northern Counties East Division One 2006-07.

11-12	12-13	13-14	14-15	15-16	16-17	17-18	18-19	19-20	20-21
NCEP 7	NCEP 9	NCEP 19	NCEP 16	NCEP 17	NCEP 17	NCEP 21	NCE1 8	NCE1 n&v	NCE1 n&v
FAC 1Q	FAC EP	FAC EP	FAC EP	FAC EP	FAC P	FAC P	FAC 1Qr		
FAV 3P	FAV 3P	FAV 2P	FAV 1Q	FAV 1Q	FAV 1Q	FAV 2Q	FAV 2Q	FAV 1Q	FAV 2Q

GROUND: Roundwood Sports Complex, Green Lane, Rawmarsh S62 6LA

Nearest Railway Station Swinton - 3.4km

Bus Route Roundwood Grove - stop 57m away

RAINWORTH MINERS WELFARE

Northern Counties East Division One

Founded 1922 Nickname: The Wrens **Club Colours:** White & navy blue

Club Contact Details 01623 792 495 leslie.lee7@ntlworld.com

HONOURS FA Comps: None

League: Notts Alliance 1971-72, 77-78, 78-79, 79-80, 80-81, 81-82, 82-83, 90-91, 95-96, 96-97.

11-12	12-13	13-14	14-15	15-16	16-17	17-18	18-19	19-20	20-21
NP1S 19	NP1N 14	NP1S 15	NP1S 21	NCEP 9	NCEP 18	NCEP 10	EMC 17	EMC n&v	EMC n&v
FAC P	FAC 1Qr	FAC Pr	FAC P	FAC EPr	FAC EP	FAC EP	FAC P		
FAT P	FAT 1Q	FAT P	FAT Pr	FAV 1Q	FAV 1Q	FAV 1Q	FAV 1Q	FAV 2Q	FAV 2P

GROUND: Welfare Ground, Kirklington Road, Rainworth, Mansfield NG21 0JY

Nearest Railway Station Mansfield - 4¼ miles

Bus Route Garden Avenue - stop 24m away

RETFORD

Northern Counties East Division One

Founded 2015 Nickname: The Choughs **Club Colours:** All blue

Club Contact Details 07766 700 536 kevswarfc@gmail.com

HONOURS FA Comps: None

League: Central Midlands North Division 2018-19

11-12	12-13	13-14	14-15	15-16	16-17	17-18	18-19	19-20	20-21
				CMN 7	CMN 6	CMN 5	CMN 1	NCE1 n&v	NCE1 n&v
					FAV 2Q			FAV 1Q	FAV 1Q

GROUND: Babworth Road, Retford DN22 6NJ

Nearest Railway Station Retford - 0.8 miles from the ground.

ROSSINGTON MAIN

Northern Counties East Division One

Founded 1919 Nickname: The Colliery **Club Colours:** All blue

Club Contact Details 01302 864 870 (MD) g-parsons2@sky.com

HONOURS FA Comps: None

League: Doncaster & District Senior 1944-45.
Central Midlands Premier Division 1984-85.

11-12	12-13	13-14	14-15	15-16	16-17	17-18	18-19	19-20	20-21
NCE1 7	NCE1 18	NCE1 13	NCE1 15	NCE1 20	NCE1 15	NCE1 13	NCE1 14	NCE1 n&v	NCE1 n&v
FAC EPr	FAC EP								
FAV 2Q	FAV 1Q	FAV 2Q	FAV 2Q	FAV 2Q	FAV 2Q	FAV 1P	FAV 2Q	FAV 2Q	FAV 1Q

GROUND: Welfare Ground, Oxford Street, Rossington, Doncaster DN11 0TE

Nearest Railway Station Doncaster - 6.4km

Bus Route Grantham Street - stop 149m away

SELBY TOWN

Northern Counties East Division One

Founded 1919 Nickname: The Robins **Club Colours:** All red

Club Contact Details 01757 241 368 toonarkley@yahoo.co.uk

HONOURS FA Comps: None

League: Yorkshire 1932-33, 34-35, 35-36, 52-53, 53-54.
Northern Counties East Division One 1995-96.

11-12	12-13	13-14	14-15	15-16	16-17	17-18	18-19	19-20	20-21
NCEP 20	NCE1 16	NCE1 12	NCE1 11	NCE1 10	NCE1 10	NCE1 7	NCE1 9	NCE1 n&v	NCE1 n&v
FAC EP	FAC EP						FAC Pr		
FAV 1P	FAV 2Q	FAV 1Q	FAV 1P	FAV 1P	FAV 1Q	FAV 1Q	FAV 1Q	FAV 2P	FAV 2Q

GROUND: Richard Street, Scott Road, Selby YO8 4BN
Nearest Railway Station Selby - 0.8km
Bus Route Leisure Centre - stop 73m away

SHIREBROOK TOWN

Northern Counties East Division One

Founded 1985 Nickname: None **Club Colours:** Red and black

Club Contact Details 01623 742 535 aimeeradford@yahoo.co.uk

HONOURS FA Comps: None

League: Central Midlands League Supreme Division 2000-01, 01-02.
Northern Counties East Division One 2003-04.

11-12	12-13	13-14	14-15	15-16	16-17	17-18	18-19	19-20	20-21
NCE1 13	NCE1 6	NCE1 5	NCE1 4	NCE1 7	NCE1 18	NCE1 5	NCE1 18	EMC n&v	EMC n&v
FAC Pr	FAC EP	FAC Pr	FAC EPr	FAC EP	FAC EPr		FAC EP		
FAV 2Q	FAV 2Pr	FAV 2Q	FAV 1Q	FAV 2P	FAV 2Q	FAV 1P	FAV 2Q	FAV 2Q	FAV 1P

GROUND: Langwith Road, Shirebrook, Mansfield, NG20 8TF
Nearest Railway Station Shirebrook - 0.2km
Bus Route Langwith Road End - stop 36m away

SWALLOWNEST

Northern Counties East Division One

Founded 2006 Nickname: None **Club Colours:** All royal blue

Club Contact Details 0114 287 2510 kent97@btinternet.com

HONOURS FA Comps: None

League: South Yorkshire Amateur Premier Division 2007-08.
Sheffield & Hallamshire County Senior Div.2 2008-09, Prem 10-11, 16-17.

11-12	12-13	13-14	14-15	15-16	16-17	17-18	18-19	19-20	20-21
Sh&HP 3	Sh&HP 6	Sh&HP 5	Sh&HP 3	Sh&HP 7	Sh&HP 1	NCE1 11	NCE1 10	NCE1 n&v	NCE1 n&v
							FAV 1P	FAV 1Q	FAV 2Q

GROUND: Rotherham Road, Sheffield S26 4UR.
Nearest Railway Station Woodhouse - 2.2km
Bus Route Park Street - stop 61m away

TEVERSAL

Northern Counties East Division One

Founded 1918 Nickname: Tevie Boys **Club Colours:** Red and black

Club Contact Details 07711 358 060 enquiries@teversalfc.co.uk

HONOURS FA Comps: None

League: Central Midlands Division Two 1987-88.

11-12	12-13	13-14	14-15	15-16	16-17	17-18	18-19	19-20	20-21
NCE1 15	NCE1 10	NCE1 15	NCE1 20	NCE1 14	NCE1 16	EMC 3	EMC 15	EMC n&v	EMC n&v
	FAC EP	FAC EP					FAC EP		
FAV 2Q	FAV 2Q	FAV 2Q	FAV 1Q	FAV 2Q	FAV 1Q	FAV 2Q	FAV 2Q	FAV 1Q	FAV 1Q

GROUND: Teversal Grange Sports and Social Centre, Carnarvon Street, Teversal, NG17 3HJ
Nearest Railway Station Sutton Parkway - 4.5 miles
Bus Route Trent Barton No.241 from Mansfield bus station to Teversal (Carnarvon Street) - 1/4 mile to ground.

WORSBROUGH BRIDGE ATHLETIC

Northern Counties East Division One

Founded 1923 Nickname: The Briggers **Club Colours:** All red

Club Contact Details 01226 284 452 mrsmooth705@gmail.com

HONOURS FA Comps: None

League: Barnsley Division One 1952-53, 58-59, 59-60.
Sheffield Association Division One 1965-66, 69-70.

11-12	12-13	13-14	14-15	15-16	16-17	17-18	18-19	19-20	20-21
NCE1 11	NCE1 9	NCE1 10	NCE1 16	NCE1 21	NCE1 20	NCE1 19	NCE1 7	NCE1 n&v	NCE1 n&v
FAV 2Q	FAV 1Q	FAV 2Q	FAV 2Q	FAV 1Q		FAV 1Q	FAV 2Q	FAV 1Q	FAV 1Q

GROUND: Park Road, Worsbrough Bridge, Barnsley S70 5LJ

Nearest Railway Station Barnsley - 3.1km

Bus Route West Street - stop 29m away

Gainsborough trialist clears from Jones (Bottesford) during this pre-season friendly. Photo Keith Clayton.

Barlow (Winterton) picks his spot during pre-season. Photo Keith Clayton.

ASHINGTON

Northern League Division One

Founded 1883 Nickname: The Colliers **Club Colours:** White & black

Club Contact Details 01670 811 991

Previous Names: None

Previous Leagues: East Northumberland. Northern Alliance 1892-93, 1902-14, 69-70. North Eastern 1914-21, 29-58, 62-64. Football League 1921-29. Midland 1958-60. Northern Counties 1960-62. Wearside 1964-65. North Regional 1965-68. N.P.L. 1968-69.

HONOURS

FA Comps: None

League: East Northumberland 1897-98. Northern Alliance 1913-14.
Northern Division Two 2000-01, 03-04.

11-12		12-13		13-14		14-15		15-16		16-17		17-18		18-19		19-20		20-21	
NL 1	5	NL 1	7	NL 1	6	NL 1	13	NL 1	12	NL 1	16	NL 1	12	NL 1	16	NL 1	n&v	NL 1	n&v
FAC	4Q	FAC	1Q	FAC	P	FAC	1Qr	FAC	P	FAC	EP	FAC	P	FAC	EP	FAC	P	FAC	P
FAV	5P	FAV	4P	FAV	4P	FAV	2P	FAV	2P	FAV	2Q	FAV	1P	FAV	2P	FAV	1Q	FAV	1P

GROUND: Woodhorn Lane, Ashington NE63 9FW

Bus Route No.1 - alight at Wansbeck Hospital - 71m away

Capacity: 2,000
Seats: 400
Covered: 900

CLUB MOVEMENTS

DIVISION ONE - IN: Crook Town, Redcar Athletic and West Allotment Celtic (P - NL2).

OUT: Hebburn Town, Shildon and Stockton Town (P - NPLE).

BILLINGHAM TOWN

Northern League Division One

Founded 1967 Nickname: Billy Town **Club Colours:** All blue

Club Contact Details 01642 560 800

Previous Names: Billingham Social Club

Previous Leagues: Stockton & District 1968-74 Teesside 1974-82

HONOURS

FA Comps: None

League: Stockton & District Division Two 1968-69. Teesside 1978-79, 81-82.
Northern Division Two 2018-19.

11-12		12-13		13-14		14-15		15-16		16-17		17-18		18-19		19-20		20-21	
NL 1	17	NL 1	20	NL 1	23	NL 2	18	NL 2	11	NL 2	5	NL 2	9	NL 2	1	NL 1	n&v	NL 1	n&v
FAC	P	FAC	P	FAC	EP	FAC	EP					FAC	EP			FAC	P	FAC	P
FAV	2P	FAV	1Q	FAV	2Qr	FAV	2Q	FAV	1Q	FAV	4P	FAV	2P	FAV	1P	FAV	1P	FAV	1Q

GROUND: Bedford Terrace, Billingham, Cleveland TS23 4AE

Nearest Railway Station Billingham - 0.4km

Bus Route Warwick Crescent - stop 136m away

Capacity: 3,000
Seats: 176
Covered: 600

BISHOP AUCKLAND

Northern League Division One

Founded 1886 Nickname: Two Blues **Club Colours:** Light & dark blue

Club Contact Details 01388 604 605

Previous Names: Auckland Town 1889-1893

Previous Leagues: Northern Alliance 1890-91, Northern League 1893-1988, Northern Premier 1988-2006

HONOURS

FA Comps: FA Amateur Cup 1895-96, 1899-1900, 1913-14, 20-21, 21-22, 34-35, 38-39, 54-55, 55-56, 56-57.

League: Northern League 1898-99, 1900-01, 01-02, 08-09, 09-10, 11-12, 20-21, 30-31, 38-39, 46-47, 49-50, 50-51,
51-52, 53-54, 54-55, 55-56, 66-67, 84-85, 85-86.

11-12		12-13		13-14		14-15		15-16		16-17		17-18		18-19		19-20		20-21	
NL 1	8	NL 1	6	NL 1	8	NL 1	11	NL 1	8	NL 1	8	NL 1	19	NL 1	3	NL 1	n&v	NL 1	n&v
FAC	EP	FAC	2Q	FAC	1Qr	FAC	1Q	FAC	P	FAC	4Q	FAC	EPr	FAC	EP	FAC	EP	FAC	1Q
FAV	2Q	FAV	1P	FAV	2Q	FAV	2P	FAV	1P	FAV	2Q	FAV	2Q	FAV	1P	FAV	2P	FAV	1Q

GROUND: Heritage Park, Stadium Way, Bishop Auckland, Co. Durham DL14 9AE

Nearest Railway Station Bishop Auckland - 2.2km

Bus Route Bus stops right outside the ground.

Capacity: 2,004
Seats: 250
Covered: 722

CONSETT

Northern League Division One

Founded 1899 Nickname: Steelman **Club Colours:** All white

Club Contact Details 01207 588 886

Previous Names: Consett Celtic 1899-1922.

Previous Leagues: Northern Alliance 1919-26, 35-37, North Eastern 1926-35, 37-58, 62-64, Midland 1958-60, Northern Counties 1960-62, Wearside 1964-70.

HONOURS

FA Comps: None

League: North Eastern 1939-40, Division Two 26-27. Northern Counties 1961-62. Northern Division Two 1988-89, 05-06.

11-12		12-13		13-14		14-15		15-16		16-17		17-18		18-19		19-20		20-21	
NL 1	15	NL 1	9	NL 1	11	NL 1	9	NL 1	7	NL 1	7	NL 1	9	NL 1	4	NL 1	n&v	NL 1	n&v
FAC	EP	FAC	EPr	FAC	EP	FAC	1Q	FAC	2Q	FAC	2Qr	FAC	1Q	FAC	2Qr	FAC	EPr	FAC	2Q
FAV	3P	FAV	2P	FAV	2Q	FAV	4P	FAV	2P	FAV	2Q	FAV	2Q	FAV	2Q	FAV	F	FAV	3P

GROUND: Belle View Stadium, Deleves Lane, Consett DH8 7BF

Capacity: 2,950
Seats: 200
Covered: 200

Bus Route Mortons Garage - stop 174m away

CROOK TOWN

Northern League Division One

Founded 1889 Nickname: Black & Ambers **Club Colours:** Amber and black

Club Contact Details 01388 762 959

Previous Names: Crook C.W.

Previous Leagues: Durham Central 1941-45.

HONOURS

FA Comps: FA Am C 00-01,53-54, 58-59, 61-62, 63-64.

League: Northern 1914-15, 26-27, 52-53, 58-59, 62-63, Division Two 2012-13.

11-12		12-13		13-14		14-15		15-16		16-17		17-18		18-19		19-20		20-21	
NL 2	10	NL 2	1	NL 1	15	NL 1	22	NL 2	18	NL 2	17	NL 2	18	NL 2	9	NL 2	n&v	NL 2	n&v
FAC	EP	FAC	Pr	FAC	1Q	FAC	EP	FAC	EP									FAC	P
FAV	2P	FAV	1Q	FAV	2P	FAV	2Q	FAV	1Q	FAV	1Q	FAV	2Q	FAV	2Q	FAV	1P	FAV	2Q

GROUND: The Sir Tom Cowie Millfield, West Road, Crook, Co.Durham DL15 9PW

Capacity: 1,500

Bus Route Bus stops right outside the ground

GUISBOROUGH TOWN

Northern League Division One

Founded 1973 Nickname: Priorymen **Club Colours:** Red & white

Club Contact Details 01287 636 925

Previous Names: None

Previous Leagues: Middlesbrough & District 1973-77. Northern Alliance 1977-80. Midland 1980-82. Northern Counties East 1982-85.

HONOURS

FA Comps: None

League: Northern Alliance 1979-80.

11-12		12-13		13-14		14-15		15-16		16-17		17-18		18-19		19-20		20-21	
NL 1	16	NL 1	11	NL 1	4	NL 1	3	NL 1	3	NL 1	20	NL 1	15	NL 1	15	NL 1	n&v	NL 1	n&v
FAC	P	FAC	Pr	FAC	3Q	FAC	EPr	FAC	1Qr	FAC	P	FAC	P	FAC	1Q	FAC	P	FAC	P
FAV	1Pr	FAV	1P	FAV	1P	FAV	2P	FAV	2P	FAV	1P	FAV	1Q	FAV	1Pr	FAV	2P	FAV	2P

GROUND: King George V Ground, Howlbeck Road, Guisborough TS14 6LE

Bus Route Howlbeck Road - stop 49m away

NEWCASTLE BENFIELD

Northern League Division One

Founded 1988 Nickname: The Lions **Club Colours:** Blue & white

Club Contact Details 07525 275 641

Previous Names: Heaton Corner House. Newcastle Benfield Saints.

Previous Leagues: Northern Alliance 1988-2003

HONOURS

FA Comps: None

League: Northern Alliance Division Two 1989-90, Division One 1994-95, 2002-03.
Northern Division One 2008-09.

11-12		12-13		13-14		14-15		15-16		16-17		17-18		18-19		19-20		20-21	
NL 1	12	NL 1	21	NL 1	14	NL 1	10	NL 1	18	NL 1	10	NL 1	7	NL 1	10	NL 1	n&v	NL 1	n&v
FAC	1Q	FAC	EP	FAC	EP	FAC	2Q	FAC	P	FAC	1Q	FAC	3Q	FAC	1Qr	FAC	1Q	FAC	P
FAV	4P	FAV	2P	FAV	QF	FAV	3P	FAV	1P	FAV	2P	FAV	4P	FAV	4P	FAV	3P	FAV	1P

GROUND: Sam Smiths Park, Benfield Road, Walkergate NE6 4NU **Capacity:** 2,000
Nearest Railway Station Walkergate - 492m **Seats:** 150
Bus Route Benfield Comprehensive School - 96m away **Covered:** 250

NEWTON AYCLIFFE

Northern League Division One

Founded 1965 Nickname: Aycliffe **Club Colours:** Blue

Club Contact Details 01325 312 768

Previous Names: None

Previous Leagues: Wearside 1984-94, 2008-09. Darlington & District. Durham Alliance > 2008.

HONOURS

FA Comps: None

League: Darlington & District Division 'A' 2004-05. Durham Alliance 2007-08. Wearside 2008-09.
Northern Division Two 2010-11.

11-12		12-13		13-14		14-15		15-16		16-17		17-18		18-19		19-20		20-21	
NL 1	9	NL 1	17	NL 1	18	NL 1	18	NL 1	6	NL 1	9	NL 1	14	NL 1	12	NL 1	n&v	NL 1	n&v
FAC	EP	FAC	EPr	FAC	Pr	FAC	EP	FAC	2Qr	FAC	EPr	FAC	P	FAC	EPr	FAC	EP	FAC	EP
FAV	1Qr	FAV	1P	FAV	1Q	FAV	1Q	FAT	5P	FAV	3P	FAV	1Q	FAV	1Qr	FAV	2Q	FAV	1P

GROUND: Moore Lane Park, Moore Lane, Newton Aycliffe, Co. Durham DL5 5AG
Nearest Railway Station Newton Aycliffe - 2km
Bus Route Shafto Way - stop 271m away

NORTH SHIELDS

Northern League Division One

Founded 1896 Nickname: Robins **Club Colours:** All red

Club Contact Details 07929 336 645

Previous Names: North Shields Athletic 1896-15, Preston Colliery 1919-1928, North Shields FC 1928-92. North Shields Athletic 1995-99.

Previous Leagues: Northern Combination. Northern Alliance. North Eastern. Midland. Northern Counties/North Eastern 1960-64. Northern 1964-89. Northern Counties East 1989-92. Wearside 1992-2004.

HONOURS

FA Comps: FA Amateur Cup 1968-69. FA Vase 2014-15.

League: Northern Alliance 1906-07, 07-08. North Eastern Div.2 28-29, Div.1 49-50. Northern Counties 60-61.
Northern Div.1 68-69, Div.2 2013-14. Northern Counties East Prem 91-92. Wearside 98-99, 01-02, 03-04.

11-12		12-13		13-14		14-15		15-16		16-17		17-18		18-19		19-20		20-21	
NL 2	8	NL 2	8	NL 2	1	NL 1	4	NL 1	5	NL 1	3	NL 1	8	NL 1	9	NL 1	n&v	NL 1	n&v
FAC	EPr	FAC	EPr	FAC	EP	FAC	Pr	FAC	Pr	FAC	P	FAC	EPr	FAC	EP	FAC	EPr	FAC	EP
FAV	1Q	FAV	1Q	FAV	1Pr	FAV	F	FAV	4P	FAV	3P	FAV	3P	FAV	1Q	FAV	1Q	FAV	2P

GROUND: Daren Persson Staduim, West Percy Road, Chirton, North Shields NE29 6UA **Capacity:** 1,500
Nearest Railway Station Meadow Well - 392m
Bus Route Waterville Road - stop 29m away

NORTHALLERTON TOWN

Northern League Division One

Founded 1994 Nickname: Town **Club Colours:** Black & white

Club Contact Details 01609 778 337

Previous Names: Northallerton FC 1994.
Previous Leagues: Harrogate & District.

HONOURS
FA Comps: None
League: Northern Division Two 1996-97.

11-12	12-13	13-14	14-15	15-16	16-17	17-18	18-19	19-20	20-21
NL 2 9	NL 2 6	NL 2 7	NL 2 10	NL 2 8	NL 2 9	NL 2 4	NL 2 3	NL 1 n&v	NL 1 n&v
FAC P	FAC EP	FAC EP	FAC P		FAC P		FAC EP	FAC P	FAC EP
FAV 2Q	FAV 1Pr	FAV 1Q	FAV 1Q	FAV 1Q	FAV 2Q	FAV 2Q	FAV 2Q	FAV 2Q	FAV 2Q

GROUND: The Calvert Stadium, Ainderby Road, Northallerton DL7 8HJ
Nearest Railway Station Northallerton - 0.3km
Bus Route Chantry Road - stop 81m away

Seats: 200
Covered: 400

PENRITH

Northern League Division One

Founded 1894 Nickname: Blues **Club Colours:** Blue and white

Club Contact Details 01768 865 990 ianwhite77@hotmail.com

Previous Names: Penrith 1894-2007. Penrith Town 2007-08. Back to Penrith after a merger with Penrith United.
Previous Leagues: North Eastern. Northern 1947-82. North West Counties 1982-87, 90-97. Northern Premier League 1987-90.

HONOURS
FA Comps: None
League: Northern Division Two 2002-03, 07-08.

11-12	12-13	13-14	14-15	15-16	16-17	17-18	18-19	19-20	20-21
NL 1 19	NL 1 13	NL 1 13	NL 1 14	NL 1 14	NL 1 12	NL 1 17	NL 1 18	NL 1 n&v	NL 1 n&v
FAC 1Q	FAC EP	FAC 3Q	FAC EP	FAC EP	FAC Pr	FAC Pr	FAC EP	FAC EP	FAC P
FAV 2Q	FAV 1P	FAV 1P	FAV 1Q	FAV 1Q	FAV 3P	FAV 2Q	FAV 2Q	FAV 1Q	FAV 1P

GROUND: Atkinson Builders Stadium, Carleton, Frenchfield, Penrith CA11 8UU
Nearest Railway Station Penrith North Lakes - 2.3km
Bus Route Oak Road - stop 727m away

Capacity: 1,500
Seats: 200
Covered: 1,000

REDCAR ATHLETIC

Northern League Division One

Founded 1993 Nickname: **Club Colours:** Red and navy

Club Contact Details 07870 848 362

Previous Names: Teesside Athletic 1993-2010.
Previous Leagues: Teesside 1993-2005. Wearside 2005-18.

HONOURS
FA Comps: None
League: Wearside 2017-18.

11-12	12-13	13-14	14-15	15-16	16-17	17-18	18-19	19-20	20-21
Wear 2	Wear 5	Wear 3	Wear 4	Wear 2	Wear 2	Wear 1	NL 2 7	NL 2 n&v	NL 2 n&v
							FAV 2Q	FAV 1Q	FAV 1P

GROUND: Green Lane, Redcar TS10 3RW
Nearest Railway Station Redcar
Bus Route X3 & X4

SEAHAM RED STAR

Northern League Division One

Founded 1973 Nickname: The Star **Club Colours:** Red & white

Club Contact Details 07834 473 001

Previous Names: Seaham Colliery Welfare Red Star 1978-87.

Previous Leagues: Houghton & District 1973-74. Northern Alliance 1974-79. Wearside 1979-83.

HONOURS

FA Comps: None

League: Wearside 1981-82.
Northern League Division Two 2014-15.

11-12	12-13	13-14	14-15	15-16	16-17	17-18	18-19	19-20	20-21
NL 2 20	NL 2 10	NL 2 4	NL 2 1	NL 1 9	NL 1 14	NL 1 18	NL 1 14	NL 1 n&v	NL 1 n&v
		FAC EP	FAC P	FAC EPr	FAC EP	FAC EP	FAC P	FAC 1Q	FAC EP
FAV 1Q	FAV 1Q	FAV 1Q	FAV 3P	FAV 3P	FAV 1Q	FAV 2Q	FAV 1P	FAV 1P	FAV 3Pr

GROUND: Seaham Town Park, Stockton Road, Seaham, Co.Durham SR7 0HP **Capacity:** 500

Nearest Railway Station Seaham - 1.5km

Bus Route Mill Inn (Stockton Rd) - stop 201m away

SUNDERLAND R.C.A.

Northern League Division One

Founded 1961 Nickname: The CA **Club Colours:** Red & white

Club Contact Details 07802 523 533

Previous Names: Ryhope Youth Club 1961-71. Ryhope Community Association 1971-99. Kennek Ryhope CA 1999-2007.

Previous Leagues: Seham & District. Houghton & District. Northern Alliance 1978-82.

HONOURS

FA Comps: None

League: None

11-12	12-13	13-14	14-15	15-16	16-17	17-18	18-19	19-20	20-21
NL 1 4	NL 1 22	NL 1 19	NL 1 16	NL 1 13	NL 1 11	NL 1 4	NL 1 5	NL 1 n&v	NL 1 n&v
FAC P	FAC EPr	FAC EP	FAC EPr	FAC EPr	FAC EP	FAC 2Q	FAC Pr	FAC 1Qr	FAC 1Q
FAV 1P	FAV 2P	FAV 1P	FAV 2P	FAV 5P	FAV 5P	FAV 2Pr	FAV 4P	FAV 2P	FAV 2Q

GROUND: Meadow Park, Beachbrooke, Stockton Road, Ryhope, Sunderland SR2 0NZ **Capacity:** 1,500

Nearest Railway Station Seaham - 3.3km **Seats:** 150

Bus Route Ryhope Hospital - 94m away **Covered:** 200

SUNDERLAND RYHOPE C.W.

Northern League Division One

Founded 1892 Nickname: Colliery Welfare **Club Colours:** Red & white

Club Contact Details 07901 545 760

Previous Names: Vaux Ryhope 1988-92 (After merging with Sporting Club Vaux - previously South Hetton). Ryhope C.W. 1992-2015

Previous Leagues: Wearside >2012, 2013-14. Northern 2012-13.

HONOURS

FA Comps: None

League: Wearside 1927-28, 61-62, 62-63, 63-64, 65-66, 2010-11, 11-12.

11-12	12-13	13-14	14-15	15-16	16-17	17-18	18-19	19-20	20-21
Wear 1	NL 2 2	Wear 2	NL 2 6	NL 2 2	NL 1 17	NL 1 11	NL 1 11	NL 1 n&v	NL 1 n&v
				FAC EPr	FAC EPr	FAC EP	FAC EP	FAC EPr	FAC EP
			FAV 2P	FAV 1Q	FAV 2P	FAV 2P	FAV 2Q	FAV 2P	FAV 3P

GROUND: Ryhope Recreation Park, Ryhope Street, Ryhope, Sunderland SR2 0AB

Nearest Railway Station Sunderland - 3.8km

Bus Route Ryhope Street-post office - stop 79m away

THORNABY

Northern League Division One

Founded 1980 Nickname: The Blues **Club Colours:** All blue

Club Contact Details 07860 780 446

Previous Names: Stockton Cricket Club 1965-1980, Stockton 1980-99 and Thornaby-on-Tees 1999-2000

Previous Leagues: Wearside 1980-85.

HONOURS

FA Comps: None

League: Northern Division Two 1987-88, 91-92.

11-12	12-13	13-14	14-15	15-16	16-17	17-18	18-19	19-20	20-21
NL 2 19	NL 2 19	NL 2 14	NL 2 7	NL 2 7	NL 2 16	NL 2 6	NL 2 2	NL 1 n&v	NL 1 n&v
				FAC EP	FAC EP			FAC 1Qr	FAC P
FAV 1Q	FAV 1Q	FAV 1Q	FAV 1Q	FAV 1Q	FAV 1Q	FAV 2P	FAV 1Q	FAV 2P	FAV 2Q

GROUND: Teesdale Park, Acklam Road, Thornaby, Cleveland TS17 7JU

Nearest Railway Station Thornaby - 1.2km

Bus Route Millfield Close - stop 143m away

WEST ALLOTMENT CELTIC

Northern League Division One

Founded 1928 Nickname: Celtic **Club Colours:** Green & white

Club Contact Details 0191 2160308

Previous Names:

Previous Leagues: Tynemouth & District. Northern Amateur. Northern Alliance.

HONOURS

FA Comps: None

League: Northern Am. 1956-57, 57-58, 58-59, 59-60, 81-82, 82-83, Div 2: 38-39.
Northern All. 1986-87, 90-91, 91-92, 97-98, 98-99, 99-2000, 01-02, 03-04. Northern Div 2 2004-05

11-12	12-13	13-14	14-15	15-16	16-17	17-18	18-19	19-20	20-21
NL 2 7	NL 2 7	NL 2 2	NL 1 19	NL 1 19	NL 1 22	NL 2 15	NL 2 6	NL 2 n&v	NL 2 n&v
FAC EPr	FAC P	FAC EP	FAC 1Q	FAC EP	FAC EP	FAC EP			FAC 1Q
FAV 1Q	FAV 1Q	FAV 2Q	FAV 1P	FAV 2Q	FAV 1Q	FAV 1Q	FAV 2Q	FAV 1P	FAV 1Q

GROUND: East Palmersville Sports Pavilion, Palm Court, Palmersville, Newcastle upon Tyne NE12 9HW

Nearest Railway Station Manors - Newcastle upon Tyne NE1 2LA

Bus Route 53, 55, 653 and 654N stop outside the ground (Great Lime Road-Laurel Avenue).

WEST AUCKLAND TOWN

Northern League Division One

Founded 1893 Nickname: West **Club Colours:** Yellow and black

Club Contact Details 07812 361 388

Previous Names: West Auckland 1893-1914.

Previous Leagues: Wear Valley 1896-1900. South Durham Alliance 1900-05. Mid Durham 1905-08.

HONOURS

FA Comps: None

League: Northern 1959-60, 60-61, Division Two 1990-91.

11-12	12-13	13-14	14-15	15-16	16-17	17-18	18-19	19-20	20-21
NL 1 2	NL 1 4	NL 1 5	NL 1 5	NL 1 17	NL 1 18	NL 1 5	NL 1 8	NL 1 n&v	NL 1 n&v
FAC EPr	FAC 2Qr	FAC 3Qr	FAC Pr	FAC P	FAC P	FAC EP	FAC P	FAC EP	FAC 1Q
FAV F	FAV 2P	FAV F	FAV 2P	FAV 1P	FAV 2Q	FAV 4P	FAV QF	FAV 5P	FAV 5P

GROUND: Darlington Road, West Auckland, Co. Durham DL14 9AQ

Nearest Railway Station Bishop Auckland - 4.1km

Bus Route Oakley Grange Farm - stop 128m away

Capacity: 2,000
Seats: 250
Covered: 250

WHICKHAM

Northern League Division One

Founded 1944 Nickname: The Home Guard **Club Colours:** Black & white

Club Contact Details 0191 420 0186

Previous Names: Founded as Axwell Park Colliery Welfare.

Previous Leagues: Derwent Valley. Northern Combination. Wearside 1974-88.

HONOURS

FA Comps: FA Vase 1980-81.

League: Northern Combination 1969-70, 72-73, 73-74.
Wearside 1977-78, 87-88. Northern Division Two 1994-95.

11-12		12-13		13-14		14-15		15-16		16-17		17-18		18-19		19-20		20-21	
NL 2	15	NL 2	16	NL 2	8	NL 2	8	NL 2	12	NL 2	6	NL 2	3	NL 1	17	NL 1	n&v	NL 1	n&v
FAC	EP					FAC	P	FAC	EP					FAC	EP	FAC	P	FAC	EP
FAV	1Q			FAV	4P	FAV	2P	FAV	2Q	FAV	1Q	FAV	1P	FAV	1P	FAV	1Q	FAV	2Q

GROUND: Glebe Sports Club, Rose Street, Whickham NE16 4NA
Nearest Railway Station Metrocentre - 2.1km
Bus Route Whaggs Lane-south - stop 105m away

Capacity: 4,000
Seats: Yes
Covered: Yes

WHITLEY BAY

Northern League Division One

Founded 1897 Nickname: The Seahorses **Club Colours:** Blue & white

Club Contact Details 0191 291 3637

Previous Names: Whitley Bay Athletic 1950-58

Previous Leagues: Tyneside 1909-10, Northern Alliance 1950-55, North Eastern 1955-58, Northern 1958-88. Northern Premier League 1988-00.

HONOURS

FA Comps: FA Vase 2001-02, 08-09, 09-10, 10-11.

League: Northern Alliance 1952-53, 53-54. Northern 1964-65, 65-66, 06-07.
Northern Premier League Division One 1990-91.

11-12		12-13		13-14		14-15		15-16		16-17		17-18		18-19		19-20		20-21	
NL 1	6	NL 1	3	NL 1	10	NL 1	15	NL 1	16	NL 1	6	NL 1	16	NL 1	13	NL 1	n&v	NL 1	n&v
FAC	1Q	FAC	P	FAC	EP	FAC	EPr	FAC	3Q	FAC	EPr	FAC	1Q	FAC	2Q	FAC	EP	FAC	2Q
FAV	5P	FAV	4P	FAV	3P	FAV	3P	FAV	2P	FAV	2Q	FAV	3P	FAV	2Q	FAV	1Q	FAV	1Q

GROUND: Hillheads Park, Rink Way, Whitley Bay NE25 8HR
Nearest Railway Station Monkseaton - 768m
Bus Route Whitley Bay Ice Rink - stop 149m away

Capacity: 4,500
Seats: 450
Covered: 650

CLUB MOVEMENTS

DIVISION TWO - IN: Blyth Town and Redcar Town (P - NAL). Bordon CA and Horden CW (P - WL)

OUT: Crook Town, Redcar Athletic and West Allotment Celtic (P - NL1).

BEDLINGTON TERRIERS

Northern League Division Two

Founded 1949 Nickname: Terriers **Club Colours:** All red.

Club Contact Details 07777 651 332

HONOURS FA Comps: None

League: Northern Combination 1954-55. Northern Alliance 1966-67.
Northern DivisioN Two 1993-94, Division One 97-98, 98-99, 99-00, 2000-01, 01-02.

11-12		12-13		13-14		14-15		15-16		16-17		17-18		18-19		19-20		20-21	
NL 1	7	NL 1	15	NL 1	20	NL 1	17	NL 1	22	NL 2	12	NL 2	16	NL 2	14	NL 2	n&v	NL 2	n&v
FAC	2Q	FAC	1Q					FAC	EPr	FAC	EP								
FAV	2P	FAV	2P					FAV	2Q	FAV	1Q	FAV	2P	FAV	2P	FAV	1Q	FAV	1Q

GROUND: Doctor Pitt Welfare Park, Park Road, Bedlington NE22 5DP

Nearest Railway Station Cramlington - 5km

Bus Route Allgood Terrace - stop 216m away

BILLINGHAM SYNTHONIA

Northern League Division Two

Founded 1923 Nickname: Synners **Club Colours:** Green & white

Club Contact Details 01642 530 203

HONOURS FA Comps: None

League: Teeside 1936-37.
Northern 1956-57, 88-89, 89-90, 95-96. Division Two 86-87.

11-12		12-13		13-14		14-15		15-16		16-17		17-18		18-19		19-20		20-21	
NL 1	11	NL 1	12	NL 1	20	NL 1	20	NL 2	5	NL 2	3	NL 1	22	NL 2	10	NL 2	n&v	NL 2	n&v
FAC	P	FAC	EP	FAC	Pr	FAC	EP	FAC	EPr	FAC	1Qr	FAC	EP	FAC	EPr				
FAV	5Pr	FAV	3P	FAV	3P	FAV	1P	FAV	2Q	FAV	1P	FAV	2Qr	FAV	2Q	FAV	2Q	FAV	2Q

GROUND: Norton (Teesside) Sports Complex, Station Road, Norton TS20 1PE

Nearest Railway Station Billingham - 2.7km

Bus Route Jameson Road - stop 400m away

BIRTLEY TOWN

Northern League Division Two

Founded 1993 Nickname: The Hoops **Club Colours:** Green & white

Club Contact Details

HONOURS FA Comps: None

League: Wearside Division Two 1994-95, Division One 2002-03, 06-07.

11-12		12-13		13-14		14-15		15-16		16-17		17-18		18-19		19-20		20-21	
NL 2	6	NL 2	17	NL 2	13	NL 2	17	NL 2	21	NAl P	8	NAl P	2	NL 2	13	NL 2	n&v	NL 2	n&v
FAC	EP	FAC	P																
FAV	2Q	FAV	1Q	FAV	2Q	FAV	2Q	FAV	1Q	FAV	2Q			FAV	2Q	FAV	1Q	FAV	2Q

GROUND: Birtley Sports Complex, Durham Road, Birtley DH3 3TB

Nearest Railway Station Chester-Le-Street

Bus Route Numbers 21 & 81 stop near the ground

BLYTH TOWN

Northern League Division Two

Founded 1995 Nickname: The Braves **Club Colours:** White

Club Contact Details 07730 058 814

HONOURS FA Comps: None

League: Northern Alliance Division Two 2002-03, Premier Division 2013-14, 14-15, 15-16, Division One 2018-19.

11-12		12-13		13-14		14-15		15-16		16-17		17-18		18-19		19-20		20-21	
NAl P	11	NAl P	2	NAl P	1	NAl P	1	NAl P	1	NL 2	8	NAl 2	5	NAl 1	1	NAl P	n&v	NAl P	n&v
										FAV	1Q								

GROUND: South Newsham Pavillion, Blyth NE24 3PW

Nearest Railway Station Cramlington

BOLDON C.A.

Northern League Division Two

Founded 1892 Nickname: Club Colours: Black & white

Club Contact Details 07770 781 476

HONOURS FA Comps: None

League: Wearside 1974-75, 96-97.

11-12	12-13	13-14	14-15	15-16	16-17	17-18	18-19	19-20	20-21
Wear 9	Wear 16	Wear 19	Wear 14	Wear 11	Wear 5	Wear 5	Wear 11	Wear	Wear n&v

GROUND: Boldon Colliery Welfare, New Road, Boldon Colliery NE35 9DS

BRANDON UNITED

Northern League Division Two

Founded 1968 Nickname: United Club Colours: All red

Club Contact Details 07768 763 871

HONOURS FA Comps: None

League: Durham & District Sunday Div.2 1969-70, Div.1 73-74, 74-75, 75-76, 76-77.
Northern Alliance Div.2 77-78, 78-79. Northern 2002-03, Div.2 84-85, 99-2000.

11-12	12-13	13-14	14-15	15-16	16-17	17-18	18-19	19-20	20-21
NL 2 17	NL 2 18	NL 2 19	NL 2 22	NL 2 15	NL 2 14	NL 2 19	NL 2 19	NL 2 n&v	NL 2 n&v
FAV 2Q	FAV 1Q		FAV 1Q	FAV 1Q	FAV 1Q	FAV 1Q	FAV 1P	FAV 1Q	FAV 2Q

GROUND: Welfare Park, Rear Commercial Street, Brandon DH7 8PL

Nearest Railway Station Durham - 4.4km

Bus Route S Lukes Church - stop 52m away

CARLISLE CITY

Northern League Division Two

Founded 1975 Nickname: Sky Blues Club Colours: All sky blue

Club Contact Details 01228 523 777

HONOURS FA Comps: None

League: Northern Alliance Division One 1991-92.

11-12	12-13	13-14	14-15	15-16	16-17	17-18	18-19	19-20	20-21
NAI P 5	NAI P 3	NAI P 2	NAI P 2	NAI P 3	NWC1 14	NWC1 11	NWC1N 6	NL 2 n&v	NL 2 n&v
					FAV 1Q	FAV 2Q	FAV 2Q	FAV 1Q	FAV 1Q

GROUND: Gillford Park Stadium, Petteril Bank Road, Carlisle CA1 3AF

Nearest Railway Station Carlisle - 1.9km

Bus Route Ridgemount Road stop - 321m away

CHESTER-LE-STREET TOWN

Northern League Division Two

Founded 1972 Nickname: Cestrians Club Colours: Blue & white

Club Contact Details 0191 388 7283

HONOURS FA Comps: None

League: Washington 1975-76. Wearside 1980-81.
Northern Division Two 1983-84, 97-98.

11-12	12-13	13-14	14-15	15-16	16-17	17-18	18-19	19-20	20-21
NL 2 12	NL 2 13	NL 2 11	NL 2 13	NL 2 3	NL 1 21	NL 2 14	NL 2 5	NL 2 n&v	NL 2 n&v
FAC EPr	FAC EPr				FAC P	FAC EP			
FAV 1Q	FAV 2Q	FAV 1Q	FAV 2Q	FAV 1P	FAV 2P	FAV 1Q	FAV 1Q	FAV 1Q	FAV 1Q

GROUND: Chester Moor Park, Chester Moor, Chester-le-Street, Co.Durham DH2 3BX

Nearest Railway Station Chester-le-Street - 2.2km

Bus Route Inn (A167) - stop 69m away

DURHAM CITY

Northern League Division Two

Founded 1949 Nickname: City **Club Colours:** Black & red

Club Contact Details 01388 745 912

HONOURS FA Comps: None

League: Northern 1994-95, 2007-08, Division Two 98-99.
Northern Premier Division One North 2008-09.

11-12		12-13		13-14		14-15		15-16		16-17		17-18		18-19		19-20		20-21	
NP1N	9	NL 1	14	NL 1	9	NL 1	12	NL 1	20	NL 2	10	NL 2	11	NL 2	20	NL 2	n&v	NL 2	n&v
FAC	P	FAC	1Q	FAC	Pr	FAC	P	FAC	EP	FAC	EP							FAC	EP
FAT	2Qr	FAV	1P	FAV	2Q	FAV	2Q	FAV	1P	FAV	1Q	FAV	2Q	FAV	1Q	FAV	2Q	FAV	1Q

GROUND: Hall Lane, Willington, County Durham DL15 0QG

Nearest Railway Station Durham

Bus Route Mortons Garage - stop 174m away

EASINGTON COLLIERY

Northern League Division Two

Founded 1913 Nickname: The Colliery **Club Colours:** All green

Club Contact Details 07967 286 559

HONOURS FA Comps: None

League: Wearside 1929-30, 31-32, 32-33, 47-48, 48-49.

11-12		12-13		13-14		14-15		15-16		16-17		17-18		18-19		19-20		20-21	
NL 2	22	Wear	21	Wear	6	Wear	2	NL 2	6	NL 2	7	NL 2	10	NL 2	16	NL 2	n&v	NL 2	n&v
										FAC	EP								
FAV	2Q							FAV	2Q	FAV	1P	FAV	1Q			FAV	2Q	FAV	2Q

GROUND: Welfare Park, Memorial Avenue, Seaside Lane, Easington Colliery SR8 3PL

Bus Route Black Diamond - stop 43m away

ESH WINNING

Northern League Division Two

Founded 1885 Nickname: Stags **Club Colours:** Yellow and green

Club Contact Details 07432 648 072

HONOURS FA Comps: None

League: Northern 1912-13.
Durham & District Sunday 1978-79, 79-80, Division Two 72-73.

11-12		12-13		13-14		14-15		15-16		16-17		17-18		18-19		19-20		20-21	
NL 2	11	NL 2	20	NL 2	22	NL 2	20	NL 2	20	NL 2	21	NL 2	13	NL 2	17	NL 2	n&v	NL 2	n&v
FAC	EP	FAC	P																
FAV	2Q	FAV	2P	FAV	1Q	FAV	2Q	FAV	1Q	FAV	2Q	FAV	1Q	FAV	1Q	FAV	2Q	FAV	2Q

GROUND: West Terrace, Waterhouse, Durham DH7 9BQ

Bus Route Church (Russell St) - stop 158m away

HEATON STANNINGTON

Northern League Division Two

Founded 1910 Nickname: The Stan **Club Colours:** Black & white stripes

Club Contact Details 0191 281 9230

HONOURS FA Comps: None

League: Northern Amateur 1936-37, 85-86. Tyneside Amateur 1983-84.
Northern Alliance Premier Division 2011-12, 12-13.

11-12		12-13		13-14		14-15		15-16		16-17		17-18		18-19		19-20		20-21	
NAI P	1	NAI P	1	NL 2	5	NL 2	9	NL 2	9	NL 2	4	NL 2	5	NL 2	4	NL 2	n&v	NL 2	n&v
								FAC	P	FAC	EP	FAC	P	FAC	EPr			FAC	EP
						FAV	2Q	FAV	2Q	FAV	2Q	FAV	1Q	FAV	1Q	FAV	1Q	FAV	2Q

GROUND: Grounsell Park, Newton Road, Newcastle upon Tyne NE7 7HP

Nearest Railway Station Longbenton - 1.2km

Bus Route No.38 stops at the ground

HORDEN COMMUNITY WELFARE

Northern League Division Two

Founded 1908 Nickname: Marras **Club Colours:** Red & black

Club Contact Details 07725 997 106

HONOURS FA Comps: None.

League: North Eastern 1937-38, 63-64. Northern D2 2008-09.

11-12	12-13	13-14	14-15	15-16	16-17	17-18	18-19	19-20	20-21
NL 2 21	NL 2 22	Wear 11	Wear 6	Wear 6		DuAl 2	Wear 8	Wear n&v	Wear1 n&v
FAV 1Q	FAV 2Q								

GROUND: Horden Welfare Park, Eden Street, Horden SR8 4LX

JARROW

Northern League Division Two

Founded 1894 Nickname: **Club Colours:** Blue

Club Contact Details 0191 489 3743

HONOURS FA Comps: None

League: Northern Alliance 1898-99. Wearside 2016-17.

11-12	12-13	13-14	14-15	15-16	16-17	17-18	18-19	19-20	20-21
Wear 6	Wear 9	Wear 10	Wear 12	Wear 8	Wear 1	NL 2 12	NL 2 11	NL 2 n&v	NL 2 n&v
							FAV 1Q	FAV 1P	FAV 2P

GROUND: Perth Green Community Assoc., Inverness Road, Jarrow NE32 4AQ

Nearest Railway Station Brockley Whins - 530m

Bus Route Imverness Road-youth club - stop 75m away

NEWCASTLE UNIVERSITY

Northern League Division Two

Founded Nickname: **Club Colours:** Red

Club Contact Details 07971 852 468

HONOURS FA Comps: None

League: Northern Alliance Premier Division 2017-18.

11-12	12-13	13-14	14-15	15-16	16-17	17-18	18-19	19-20	20-21
NAl 1 8	NAl 1 13	NAl 1 7	NAl 1 8	NAl 1 2	NAl P 2	NAl P 1	NAl P 2	NL 2 n&v	NL 2 n&v
								FAV 1Q	FAV 1P

GROUND: Kimberley Park, Broomhouse Road NE42 5EH

Nearest Railway Station Newcastle

Bus Route No.686 stops 50 metres to the East on Broomhouse Road.

REDCAR TOWN

Northern League Division Two

Founded 2014 Nickname: **Club Colours:** Blue & white

Club Contact Details 01642 502 198

HONOURS FA Comps: None

League: Teesside Division Two 2014-15.

11-12	12-13	13-14	14-15	15-16	16-17	17-18	18-19	19-20	20-21
			Tee2 1	Tee1 10	Tee1 4	NRidP 3	NRidP 6	NRidP n&v	NRidP n&v

GROUND: The Vibrant Stadium, Mo Mowlam Memorial Park, Trunk Road, Redcar TS10 5BW

RYTON & CRAWCROOK ALBION

Northern League Division Two

Founded 1970 Nickname: The Albion **Club Colours:** Black & royal blue

Club Contact Details 0191 413 4448

HONOURS FA Comps: None

League: Northern Alliance Division One 1996-97.

11-12		12-13		13-14		14-15		15-16		16-17		17-18		18-19		19-20		20-21	
NL 2	18	NL 2	14	NL 2	21	NL 2	12	NL 2	16	NL 2	20	NL 2	17	NL 2	12	NL 2	n&v	NL 2	n&v
FAC	EP																		
FAV	2Q	FAV	2Q	FAV	2Q	FAV	1Qr	FAV	1Q	FAV	2Q	FAV	1Q	FAV	2Q	FAV	2Q	FAV	1Q

GROUND: Kingsley Park, Stannerford Road, Crawcrook NE40 3SN

Nearest Railway Station Wylam - 1.5km

Bus Route Stannerford Road - stop 121m away

SUNDERLAND WEST END

Northern League Division Two

Founded 2006 Nickname: **Club Colours:** Red & white

Club Contact Details 0800 0431 442

HONOURS FA Comps: None

League: None

11-12		12-13		13-14		14-15		15-16		16-17		17-18		18-19		19-20		20-21	
Wear	4	Wear	8	Wear	9	Wear	8	Wear	3	Wear	10	Wear	3	Wear	2	NL 2	n&v	NL 2	n&v
																FAV	2Q	FAV	1Q

GROUND: Ford Quarry Football Hub, Keelmans Lane, South Hylton, Sunderland SR4 0HB

TOW LAW TOWN

Northern League Division Two

Founded 1890 Nickname: Lawyers **Club Colours:** Black & white

Club Contact Details 01388 731 443

HONOURS FA Comps: None

League: Northern 1923-24, 24-25, 94-95.

11-12		12-13		13-14		14-15		15-16		16-17		17-18		18-19		19-20		20-21	
NL 1	21	NL 2	11	NL 2	10	NL 2	21	NL 2	14	NL 2	13	NL 2	8	NL 2	15	NL 2	n&v	NL 2	n&v
FAC	EP	FAC	EP	FAC	EP														
FAV	2Q	FAV	1Q	FAV	1Q	FAV	1Q	FAV	2Q	FAV	1Q	FAV	2P	FAV	2Q	FAV	1Q	FAV	1Q

GROUND: Ironworks Ground, Tow Law, Bishop Auckland DL13 4EQ

Nearest Railway Station Wolsingham - 4.8km

Bus Route Mart (Castle Bank) - stop 241m away

WASHINGTON

Northern League Division Two

Founded 1947 Nickname: Mechanics **Club Colours:** Navy & yellow

Club Contact Details 0800 0431442

HONOURS FA Comps: None

League: North Eastern Division Two 1927-28. Washington Amateur 1955-56, 56-57,57-58, 58-59, 59-60, 61-62,62-63.

11-12		12-13		13-14		14-15		15-16		16-17		17-18		18-19		19-20		20-21	
NL 2	14	NL 2	12	NL 2	9	NL 2	2	NL 1	10	NL 1	19	NL 1	21	NL 2	18	NL 2	n&v	NL 2	n&v
		FAC	EP			FAC	P	FAC	2Qr	FAC	1Q	FAC	EP	FAC	EP				
FAV	1Q	FAV	2Q	FAV	2Q	FAV	2Q	FAV	2Q	FAV	1Q	FAV	2Q	FAV	2Q	FAV	1Q	FAV	1Q

GROUND: Ford Quarry Football Hub, Keelmans Lane, South Hylton, Sunderland SR4 0HB

WILLINGTON

Northern League Division Two

Founded 1906 Nickname: The Blue & Whites **Club Colours:** Blue & white

Club Contact Details 01388 745 912

HONOURS FA Comps: FA Amateur Cup 1949-50.

League: Northern 1913-14, 25-26, 29-30.

11-12		12-13		13-14		14-15		15-16		16-17		17-18		18-19		19-20		20-21	
Wear	5	Wear	2	NL 2	15	NL 2	11	NL 2	19	NL 2	18	NL 2	7	NL 2	8	NL 2	n&v	NL 2	n&v
FAV	2Q	FAV	2Q	FAV	2Q	FAV	1Q	FAV	1Q	FAV	1Q	FAV	2Q	FAV	1Qr	FAV	1Q	FAV	1Q

GROUND: Hall Lane, Willington, Co. Durham DL15 0QG

Bus Route Police House - stop 129m away

Vasalo (Winterton NCEP) tackled by the Louth full back.

Anderson (Winterton) makes it 2-0 against Louth in this pre-season friendly. Photos Keith Clayton.

AXMINSTER TOWN

South West Peninsula Premier East

Founded 1903 Nickname: The Tigers **Club Colours:** Amber and black

Club Contact Details stuartandjulie.w@googlemail.com

HONOURS FA Comps: None

League: None

11-12	12-13	13-14	14-15	15-16	16-17	17-18	18-19	19-20	20-21
SW1E 16	SW1E 11	SW1E 12	SW1E 18	SW1E 8	SW1E 6	SW1E 10	SW1E 6	SWPE n&v	SWPE n&v
						FAV 1Q	FAV 2Q	FAV 2Q	FAV 2Q

GROUND: Tiger Way EX13 5HN
Nearest Railway Station Axminster
Bus Route 885 & 30

BOVEY TRACEY

South West Peninsula Premier East

Founded 1950 Nickname: Moorlanders **Club Colours:** Red

Club Contact Details rachel@defc.co.uk

HONOURS FA Comps: None

League: South Devon Premier 2007-08.

11-12	12-13	13-14	14-15	15-16	16-17	17-18	18-19	19-20	20-21
SWPP 16	SWPP 15	SWPP 15	SWPP 19	SW1E 16	SW1E 13	SW1E 3	SW1E 2	SWPE n&v	SWPE n&v
									FAC EP
								FAV 1P	FAV 2Q

GROUND: Mill Marsh Park, Ashburton Rd, Bovey TQ13 9FF - Temporarily at Coach Road (Devon FA) for 2021
Nearest Railway Station Newton Abbot
Bus Route 178 & 39

BRIXHAM AFC

South West Peninsula Premier East

Founded 2012 Nickname: The Fishermen **Club Colours:** All blue

Club Contact Details deanhops@talktalk.net

HONOURS FA Comps: None

League: None

11-12	12-13	13-14	14-15	15-16	16-17	17-18	18-19	19-20	20-21
	SDevP 4	SDevP 2	SW1E 9	SW1E 9	SW1E 5	SW1E 13	SW1E 3	SWPE n&v	SWPE n&v
									FAV 1Q

GROUND: Wall Park Road TQ5 9UE
Nearest Railway Station Paignton
Bus Route 92

CREDITON UNITED

South West Peninsula Premier East

Founded 1910 Nickname: The Kirton **Club Colours:** All blue

Club Contact Details 01363 774 671 maryavery210@btinternet.com

HONOURS FA Comps: None

League: None

11-12	12-13	13-14	14-15	15-16	16-17	17-18	18-19	19-20	20-21
SW1E 4	SW1E 16	SW1E 6	SW1E 11	SW1E 14	SW1E 8	SW1E 6	SW1E 10	SWPE n&v	SWPE n&v
FAV 2Q	FAV 1Q		FAV 1P	FAV 2Q	FAV 1Q	FAV 1P	FAV 1Q	FAV 1Q	FAV 2Q

GROUND: Lords Meadow, Commercial Road, Crediton EX17 1ER
Nearest Railway Station Crediton
Bus Route 5 & 5B

CULLOMPTON RANGERS

South West Peninsula Premier East

Founded 1945 Nickname: The Cully **Club Colours:** Red & black

Club Contact Details 01884 33090 alanslark1@gmail.com

HONOURS FA Comps: None

League: East Devon Senior Division One 1950-51, 78-79.
Devon & Exeter Premier Division 1961-62, 63-64.

11-12	12-13	13-14	14-15	15-16	16-17	17-18	18-19	19-20	20-21
SWPP 15	SWPP 17	SWPP 18	SWPP 12	SWPP 13	SWPP 9	SWPP 13	SWPP 8	SWPE n&v	SWPE n&v
FAV 2P	FAV 2Q	FAV 2Q	FAV 1Q	FAV 1Q	FAV 2Pr	FAV 2P	FAV 2Q	FAV 1P	FAV 1Q

GROUND: Speeds Meadow, Cullompton EX15 1DW

Nearest Railway Station Tiverton Parkway

Bus Route Falcon - alight at The Weary Traveller, 20min walk from there.

DARTMOUTH AFC

South West Peninsula Premier East

Founded 1999 Nickname: The Darts **Club Colours:** Red & white

Club Contact Details 01803 832 902 kathygreeno@hotmail.com

HONOURS FA Comps: None

League: Devon 2001-02, 02-03, 06-07. South Devon Division One 2013-14.

11-12	12-13	13-14	14-15	15-16	16-17	17-18	18-19	19-20	20-21
SWPP 14	SDev1 4	SDev1 1	SDevP 3	SDevP 2	SDevP 5	SDevP 6	SDevP 3	SWPE n&v	SWPE n&v

GROUND: Longcross, Dartmouth TQ5 9LW

Nearest Railway Station Totnes

Bus Route 3, 120

ELBURTON VILLA

South West Peninsula Premier East

Founded 1982 Nickname: The Villa **Club Colours:** Red & white stripes

Club Contact Details 01752 480 025 janinaaugustynowicz@elburtonvillafc.com

HONOURS FA Comps: None

League: Plymouth & District Division One 1990-91.

11-12	12-13	13-14	14-15	15-16	16-17	17-18	18-19	19-20	20-21
SWPP 11	SWPP 3	SWPP 12	SWPP 18	SWPP 20	SW1W 2	SW1W 3	SWPP 15	SWPE n&v	SWPE n&v
			FAV 1Q	FAV 1Q	FAV 1Q	FAV 1Q	FAV 1P	FAV 1Q	FAV 2Q

GROUND: Haye Road, Elburton, Plymouth PL9 8HS

Nearest Railway Station Plymouth

ELMORE

South West Peninsula Premier East

Founded 1947 Nickname: Eagles **Club Colours:** All green

Club Contact Details 01884 252 341 graham.wood@gw3consulting.co.uk

HONOURS FA Comps: None

League: Devon & Exeter Premier Division 2017-18.

11-12	12-13	13-14	14-15	15-16	16-17	17-18	18-19	19-20	20-21
West1 14	West1 12	SWPP 17	SWPP Exp	D&EP 5	D&EP 3	D&EP 1	SW1E 5	SWPE n&v	SWPE n&v
	FAC EP								
FAV 2Q	FAV 1Q	FAV 1Qr	FAV 1Q						

GROUND: Horsdon Park, Heathcoat Way, Tiverton, Devon EX16 6DB

Nearest Railway Station Tiverton Parkway

HOLSWORTHY AFC

South West Peninsula Premier East

Founded 1891 Nickname: The Magpies **Club Colours:** Black & white

Club Contact Details 01409 254 295 secretary@holsworthyafc.co.uk

HONOURS FA Comps: None

League: None

11-12	12-13	13-14	14-15	15-16	16-17	17-18	18-19	19-20	20-21
SW1W 15	SW1W 13	SW1W 15	SW1W 13	SW1W 11	SW1W 15	SW1W 11	SW1E 8	SWPE n&v	SWPE n&v

GROUND: Upcott Field, North Road, Holsworthy EX22 6HF

Bus Route 85

HONITON TOWN

South West Peninsula Premier East

Founded 1950 Nickname: The Hippos **Club Colours:** Red & black

Club Contact Details 01404 42379 alanmackay2009@hotmail.com

HONOURS FA Comps: None

League: Devon & Exeter Division One 2014-15, Premier Division 16-17.

11-12	12-13	13-14	14-15	15-16	16-17	17-18	18-19	19-20	20-21
D&E2 8	D&E2 5	D&E1 2	D&E1 1	D&EP 3	D&EP 1	SW1E 14	SW1E 14	SWPE n&v	SWPE n&v

GROUND: Moutbatten Park, Ottery Moor Lane, Honiton EX14 1AW

Nearest Railway Station Honiton

IVYBRIDGE TOWN

South West Peninsula Premier East

Founded 1925 Nickname: The Ivys **Club Colours:** Green & black

Club Contact Details 01752 896 686 secretary@ivybridgefc.com

HONOURS FA Comps: None

League: Devon County 2005-06.

11-12	12-13	13-14	14-15	15-16	16-17	17-18	18-19	19-20	20-21
SWPP 19	SWPP 13	SWPP 4	SWPP 4	SWPP 9	SWPP 17	SWPP 18	SWPP 12	SWPE n&v	SWPE n&v
				FAV 2Q	FAV 1Q	FAV 1P	FAV 2P	FAV 2Q	FAV 2Q

GROUND: Erme Valley, Ermington Road, Ivybridge PL21 9ES

Nearest Railway Station Ivybridge - 1.8km

Bus Route Community Centre - stop 251m away

NEWTON ABBOT SPURS

South West Peninsula Premier East

Founded 1938 Nickname: The Spurs **Club Colours:** Blue

Club Contact Details 01626 365 343 jake.elms.11@gmail.com

HONOURS FA Comps: None

League: None

11-12	12-13	13-14	14-15	15-16	16-17	17-18	18-19	19-20	20-21
SW1E 9	SW1E 4	SW1E 11	SW1E 17	SW1E 7	SW1E 4	SW1E 2	SW1E 12	SWPE n&v	SWPE n&v
									FAC P
							FAV 2Q	FAV 1P	FAV 2P

GROUND: Recreation Ground, Marsh Road, Newton Abbot TQ12 2AR

Nearest Railway Station Newton Abbot

OKEHAMPTON ARGYLE

South West Peninsula Premier East

Founded 1926 Nickname: The Okey **Club Colours:** Blue

Club Contact Details 01837 53997 chris.wills1985@outlook.com

HONOURS FA Comps: None

League: None

11-12	12-13	13-14	14-15	15-16	16-17	17-18	18-19	19-20	20-21
SW1E 8	SW1E 9	SW1E 14	SW1E 8	SW1E 18	D&EP 5			D&EP n&v	DevSWn&v

GROUND: Simmons Park, Mill Road, Okehampton EX20 1PR

OTTERY ST MARY

South West Peninsula Premier East

Founded 1911 Nickname: The Otters **Club Colours:** Blue

Club Contact Details csallen1969@gmail.com

HONOURS FA Comps: None

League: Devon & Exeter Senior 1953-54, 61-62, Premier 1973-74. Western Division One 1989-90.

11-12	12-13	13-14	14-15	15-16	16-17	17-18	18-19	19-20	20-21
SW1E 17	D&E3							DevSW n&v	DevSWn&v

GROUND: Washbrook Meadows, Butts Road, Ottery St Mary EX11 1EL

PLYMOUTH MAJON

South West Peninsula Premier East

Founded 2008 Nickname: The Johns **Club Colours:** Blue and black

Club Contact Details csmietanka@majon.ac.uk

HONOURS FA Comps: None

League: Plymouth & West Devon Premier Division 2015-16.

11-12	12-13	13-14	14-15	15-16	16-17	17-18	18-19	19-20	20-21
PWDevP 6	PWDevP 4	PWDevP 8	PWDevP	PWDevP 1	SW1W 10	SW1W 12	SW1W 9	SWPE n&v	SWPE n&v

GROUND: University of Mark & St Johns, Derriford Road PL6 8BH

Nearest Railway Station Plymouth

SIDMOUTH TOWN

South West Peninsula Premier East

Founded 1895 Nickname: The Vikings **Club Colours:** Green and black

Club Contact Details 01395 577 087 geoffwest45@aol.com

HONOURS FA Comps: None

League: Devon & Exeter Premier Division 2010-11

11-12	12-13	13-14	14-15	15-16	16-17	17-18	18-19	19-20	20-21
SW1E 14	SW1E 15	SW1E 13	SW1E 10	SW1E 12	SW1E 11	SW1E 11	SW1E 9	SWPE n&v	SWPE n&v
							FAV 1P	FAV 2Q	FAV 1Q

GROUND: Manstone Recreation Ground, Manstone Lane, Sidmouth EX10 9TF

Nearest Railway Station Sidmouth

STOKE GABRIEL & TORBAY POLICE

South West Peninsula Premier East

Founded 1905 Nickname: The Railwaymen **Club Colours:** Blue & red

Club Contact Details 01803 782 913 stokegabrielfc@gmail.com

HONOURS FA Comps: None

League: Devon County 1994-95, 96-97.
South West Peninsula Division One East 2013-14, 16-17, 18-19.

11-12	12-13	13-14	14-15	15-16	16-17	17-18	18-19	19-20	20-21
SW1E 2	SW1E 2	SW1E 1	SWPP 14	SWPP 19	SW1E 1	SWPP 12	SW1E 1	SWPE n&v	SWPE n&v

GROUND: G J Churchward Memorial TQ9 6RR

Nearest Railway Station Paignton - 4.3km

Bus Route Ramslade Touring Park - stop 344m away

TORPOINT ATHLETIC

South West Peninsula Premier East

Founded 1887 Nickname: The Point **Club Colours:** Gold

Club Contact Details 01752 812 889 robbietafc81@live.co.uk

HONOURS FA Comps: None

League: South Western 1964-65, 66-67.

11-12	12-13	13-14	14-15	15-16	16-17	17-18	18-19	19-20	20-21
SWPP 12	SWPP 14	SWPP 10	SWPP 13	SWPP 8	SWPP 12	SWPP 11	SWPP 7	SWPE n&v	SWPE n&v
FAC P	FAC EP		FAC EP						
FAV 2P		FAV 1Q	FAV 2Q	FAV 2P	FAV 3P	FAV 1Q	FAV 1P	FAV 1P	FAV 2Q

GROUND: The Mill, Mill Lane, Carbeile Road, Torpoint PL11 2RE

Nearest Railway Station Dockyard (plymouth) - 2.5km

Bus Route Carbeile Inn - stop 338m away

TORRIDGESIDE

South West Peninsula Premier East

Founded 1989 Nickname: T-Side **Club Colours:** Claret and blue

Club Contact Details andreasussex@btinternet.com

HONOURS FA Comps: None

League: North Devon Premier Division 2012-13.

11-12	12-13	13-14	14-15	15-16	16-17	17-18	18-19	19-20	20-21
NDevP 5	NDevP 1	NDevP 8	NDevP 3	NDevP 2	SW1E 7	SW1E 8	SW1E 4	SWPE n&v	SWPE n&v

GROUND: Donnacroft, Torrington EX38 7HT

TORRINGTON

South West Peninsula Premier East

Founded 1908 Nickname: The Super Greens **Club Colours:** All green

Club Contact Details cm@torringtonafc.co.uk

HONOURS FA Comps: None

League: Western Division One 2002-03. North Devon Senior Division 2008-09.

11-12	12-13	13-14	14-15	15-16	16-17	17-18	18-19	19-20	20-21
NDevP 15	NDevP 2	NDevP 3	NDevP 10	NDevP 4	NDevP 7	NDevP 7	NDevP 5	SWPE n&v	SWPE n&v
									FAC EP
									FAV 2Q

GROUND: Vicarage Field, Torrington EX38 7AJ

AFC ST. AUSTELL

South West Peninsula Premier West

Founded 1890 Nickname: The Lillywhites **Club Colours:** White and black

Club Contact Details secretaryafcstaustell@gmail.com

HONOURS FA Comps: None

League: South Western 1968-69. South West Peninsula Premier 2014-15.

11-12	12-13	13-14	14-15	15-16	16-17	17-18	18-19	19-20	20-21
SWPP 8	SWPP 4	SWPP 9	SWPP 1	SWPP 2	SWPP 4	SWPP 6	SWPP 5	SWPW n&v	SWPW n&v
		FAC EP	FAC P	FAC P	FAC EPr	FAC EPr		FAC EP	FAC EP
	FAV 2P	FAV 1Q	FAV SF	FAV 2P	FAV 2Q	FAV 2Q	FAV 4P	FAV 2P	FAV 1Q

GROUND: Poltair Park, Trevarthian Road, St Austell PL25 4LR

Nearest Railway Station St Austell - 0.3km

Bus Route Poltair Road - stop 33m away

BODMIN TOWN

South West Peninsula Premier West

Founded 1889 Nickname: Black & Ambers **Club Colours:** Yellow & black

Club Contact Details 01208 78165 nickgiles@live.co.uk

HONOURS FA Comps: None

League: Bodmin & District 1922-23, 26-27. South Western 1990-91, 93-94, 2005-06.
South West Peninsula Premier Division 2007-08, 08-09, 11-12, 12-13, 15-16.

11-12	12-13	13-14	14-15	15-16	16-17	17-18	18-19	19-20	20-21
SWPP 1	SWPP 1	SWPP 7	SWPP 2	SWPP 1	SWPP 3	SWPP 5	SWPP 9	SWPW n&v	SWPW n&v
FAC 3Qr	FAC 1Qr	FAC P	FAC 1Qr	FAC 2Q	FAC Pr	FAC 2Qr	FAC Pr		FAC P
FAV 2Pr	FAV 5P	FAV 4P	FAV 4P	FAV 4P	FAV 3P	FAV 2P	FAV 3P	FAV 2Q	FAV 1Q

GROUND: Priory Park, Bodmin, Cornwall PL31 2AE

Nearest Railway Station Bodmin General - 587m

CALLINGTON TOWN

South West Peninsula Premier West

Founded 1989 Nickname: The Pasty Men **Club Colours:** Red

Club Contact Details 01579 382 647

HONOURS FA Comps: None

League: East Cornwall Combination 1997-98, 98-99.
South West Peninsula Division One West 2013-14.

11-12	12-13	13-14	14-15	15-16	16-17	17-18	18-19	19-20	20-21
SW1W 6	SW1W 5	SW1W 1	SWPP 11	SWPP 16	SWPP 15	SWPP 19	SWPP 17	SWPW n&v	SWPW n&v
							FAV 1Q	FAV 1Q	FAV 1Q

GROUND: Ginsters Marshfield Parc PL17 7BT

Nearest Railway Station Gunnislake

CAMELFORD

South West Peninsula Premier West

Founded 1893 Nickname: Camels **Club Colours:** White & blue

Club Contact Details hilarykent35@gmail.com

HONOURS FA Comps: None

League: South West Peninsula Division One West 2010-11.

11-12	12-13	13-14	14-15	15-16	16-17	17-18	18-19	19-20	20-21
SWPP 9	SWPP 9	SWPP 14	SWPP 17	SWPP 15	SWPP 14	SWPP 10	SWPP 18	SWPW n&v	SWPW n&v
		FAV 2Q	FAV 1Qr	FAV 1P	FAV 1Q	FAV 2Q	FAV 2Qr	FAV 1P	FAV 1P

GROUND: Trefew Park, PL32 9TS

DOBWALLS

South West Peninsula Premier West

Founded 1922 Nickname: The Reds **Club Colours:** Red and black

Club Contact Details dodwallsfootball@gmail.com

HONOURS FA Comps: None

League: None

11-12	12-13	13-14	14-15	15-16	16-17	17-18	18-19	19-20	20-21
SW1W 10	SW1W 8	SW1W 8	SW1W 12	SW1W 15	SW1W 11	SW1W 14	SW1W 10	SWPW n&v	SWPW n&v

GROUND: Lantoom Park, Duloe Road, Dobwalls PL14 4FL

Nearest Railway Station Liskeard

FALMOUTH TOWN

South West Peninsula Premier West

Founded 1949 Nickname: The Ambers **Club Colours:** Amber & black

Club Contact Details 01326 375 156 richardpascoe25@btinternet.com

HONOURS FA Comps: None

League: South Western 1961-62, 65-66, 67-68, 70-71, 71-72, 72-73, 73-74, 85-86, 86-87, 88-89, 89-90, 91-92, 96-97, 99-2000. Western 74-75, 75-76, 76-77, 77-78. Cornwall Comb 83-84.

11-12	12-13	13-14	14-15	15-16	16-17	17-18	18-19	19-20	20-21
SWPP 3	SWPP 16	SWPP 16	SWPP 16	SWPP 11	SWPP 10	SWPP 3	SWPP 6	SWPW n&v	SWPW n&v
FAC EP									
FAV 3P			FAV 1P	FAV 1Q			FAV 2P	FAV 3P	FAV 3P

GROUND: Bickland Park, Bickland Water Road, Falmouth TR11 4PB

Nearest Railway Station Penmere - 1.3km

Bus Route Conway Road - stop 54m away

GODOLPHIN ATLANTIC (NEWQUAY)

South West Peninsula Premier West

Founded 1980 Nickname: G Army **Club Colours:** Sky blue & white

Club Contact Details godolphin.arms@btconnect.com

HONOURS FA Comps: None

League: South West Peninsula Division One West 2012-13.

11-12	12-13	13-14	14-15	15-16	16-17	17-18	18-19	19-20	20-21
SW1W 4	SW1W 1	SWPP 5	SWPP 7	SWPP 5	SWPP 13	SWPP 17	SWPP 14	SWPW n&v	SWPW n&v
						FAV 1Q	FAV 2Q	FAV 1Q	FAV 1Q

GROUND: Godolphin Way, Newquay TR7 3BU

Nearest Railway Station Newquay - 1.2km

Bus Route Brook House Inn - stop 136m away

LAUNCESTON

South West Peninsula Premier West

Founded 1891 Nickname: The Clarets **Club Colours:** All claret

Club Contact Details 01566 773 279 launcestonfc@aol.com

HONOURS FA Comps: None

League: South Western 1994-95.

11-12	12-13	13-14	14-15	15-16	16-17	17-18	18-19	19-20	20-21
SWPP 5	SWPP 5	SWPP 8	SWPP 10	SWPP 14	SWPP 11	SWPP 7	SWPP 16	SWPW n&v	SWPW n&v
							FAV 2Q	FAV 1Q	FAV 1Q

GROUND: Pennygillam Ind. Est., Launceston PL15 7ED

LISKEARD ATHLETIC

South West Peninsula Premier West

Founded 1946 Nickname: The Blues **Club Colours:** All blue

Club Contact Details 01579 342 665 liannewilliams08@btinternet.com

HONOURS FA Comps: None

League: South Western 1976-77, 78-79. Western Premier Division 1987-88.
South West Peninsula Division One West 2018-19.

11-12	12-13	13-14	14-15	15-16	16-17	17-18	18-19	19-20	20-21
SWPP 7	SWPP 18	SWPP 20	SW1W 6	SW1W 7	SW1W 8	SW1W 5	SW1W 1	SWPW n&v	SWPW n&v
FAV 1P					FAV 1Q		FAV 1Q	FAV 1Q	FAV 1Q

GROUND: Lux Park PL14 3HZ

Nearest Railway Station Liskeard

NEWQUAY

South West Peninsula Premier West

Founded 1890 Nickname: The Peppermints **Club Colours:** Red & white

Club Contact Details 01637 872 935 sbr.newquayafcsecretary@gmail.com

HONOURS FA Comps: None

League: South Western 1958-59, 59-60, 77-78, 79-80, 81-82, 83-84, 87-88.
South West Peninsula Division One West 2011-12.

11-12	12-13	13-14	14-15	15-16	16-17	17-18	18-19	19-20	20-21
SW1W 1	SWPP 12	SWPP 11	SWPP 15	SWPP 18	SWPP 19	SWPP 14	SWPP 13	SWPW n&v	SWPW n&v
		FAV EP	FAV 1P	FAV 2Q			FAV 1P	FAV 1Q	FAV 1Q

GROUND: Mount Wise TR7 2BU

Nearest Railway Station Newquay - 0.8km

Bus Route Windsor Court - stop 117m away

PENRYN ATHLETIC

South West Peninsula Premier West

Founded 1963 Nickname: The Borough **Club Colours:** Red & black

Club Contact Details thomasblewett193@gmail.com

HONOURS FA Comps: None

League: Cornwall Combination 1981-82, 82-83, 84-85, 86-87, 89-90, 92-93, 93-94, 95-96, 99-2000, 03-04.

11-12	12-13	13-14	14-15	15-16	16-17	17-18	18-19	19-20	20-21
SWPW 3	SWPW 7	SWPW 5	SWPW 3	SWPW 4	SWPW 5	CornC 9	CornC 2	St.PW n&v	St.PW n&v

GROUND: Kernick Road, Penryn TR10 9DG

PENZANCE

South West Peninsula Premier West

Founded 1888 Nickname: The Magpies **Club Colours:** White and black

Club Contact Details 01736 361 964 christopherfarley@sky.com

HONOURS FA Comps: None

League: South Western 1955-56, 56-57, 74-75. South West Peninsula League Division One West 2008-09.

11-12	12-13	13-14	14-15	15-16	16-17	17-18	18-19	19-20	20-21
SWPP 17	SWPP 19	SW1W 14	SW1W 14	SW1W 10	SW1W 17	SW1W 10	SW1W 12	SWPW n&v	SWPW n&v
FAV 2Q									

GROUND: Penlee Park, Alexandra Place, Penzance TR18 4NE

Nearest Railway Station Penzance

PORTHLEVEN

South West Peninsula Premier West

Founded 1898 Nickname: The Fisher Men **Club Colours:** Yellow and black

Club Contact Details 01326 569 655 vidaljames@me.com

HONOURS FA Comps: None

League: None

11-12	12-13	13-14	14-15	15-16	16-17	17-18	18-19	19-20	20-21
SW1W 12	SW1W 11	SW1W 11	SW1W 11	SW1W 16	SW1W 12	SW1W 6	SW1W 3	SWPW n&v	SWPW n&v
FAV 1Q	FAV 2Q		FAV 1Q	FAV 1Q			FAV 2Q	FAV 2Q	FAV 1Q

GROUND: Gala Parc, Mill Lane, Porthleven TR13 9LQ

ST. BLAZEY

South West Peninsula Premier West

Founded 1896 Nickname: The Green & Blacks **Club Colours:** Green & black

Club Contact Details 01725 814 110 stblazeyfootballsec@gmail.com

HONOURS FA Comps: None

League: South Western 1954-55, 57-58, 62-63, 63-64, 80-81, 82-83, 98-99, 2000-01, 01-02, 02-03, 03-04, 04-05, 06-07.

11-12	12-13	13-14	14-15	15-16	16-17	17-18	18-19	19-20	20-21
SWPP 18	SWPP 8	SWPP 13	SWPP 9	SWPP 17	SWPP 20	SW1W 7	SW1W 11	SWPW n&v	SWPW n&v
FAC P		FAC P							
FAV 2Q	FAV 3P	FAV 2Q	FAV 2P	FAV 2Q		FAV 1Q		FAV 2Q	FAV 1P

GROUND: Blaise Park, Station Road, St Blazey PL24 2ND

ST. DENNIS

South West Peninsula Premier West

Founded 1902 Nickname: The Saints **Club Colours:** Blue

Club Contact Details 01726 822 635 stdennisfootball@gmail.com

HONOURS FA Comps: None

League: Cornwall Combination 1975-76. East Cornwall Premier 1991-92, 99-00, 10-11, Division One 09-10.

11-12	12-13	13-14	14-15	15-16	16-17	17-18	18-19	19-20	20-21
SW1W 9	SW1W 6	SW1W 9	SW1W 4	SW1W 6	SW1W 7	SW1W 8	SW1W 5	SWPW n&v	SWPW n&v

GROUND: Boscawen Park, St Dennis PL26 8DW

STICKER

South West Peninsula Premier West

Founded 1911 Nickname: The Sticky **Club Colours:** Yellow and blue

Club Contact Details 01726 71003 chrisjohnosborne@aol.com

HONOURS FA Comps: None

League: South West Peninsula Division One West 2016-17.

11-12	12-13	13-14	14-15	15-16	16-17	17-18	18-19	19-20	20-21
ECP 2	SW1W 4	SW1W 4	SW1W 5	SW1W 3	SW1W 1	SWPP 15	SWPP 19	SWPW n&v	SWPW n&v

GROUND: Burngullow Park PL26 7EN

Nearest Railway Station St Austell - 4.4km

Bus Route Hewas Inn (Fore St) - stop 1.1km away

WADEBRIDGE TOWN

South West Peninsula Premier West

Founded 1894 Nickname: The Bridgers **Club Colours:** All red

Club Contact Details 01208 812 537 emmanuel.606@btinternet.com

HONOURS FA Comps: None

League: South West Peninsula League Division One West 2007-08.

11-12	12-13	13-14	14-15	15-16	16-17	17-18	18-19	19-20	20-21
SW1W 11	SW1W 3	SW1W 7	SW1W 10	SW1W 14	SW1W 14	SW1W 9	SW1W 4	SWPW n&v	SWPW n&v
FAV 2Q	FAV 1Q	FAV 2Q	FAV 2Q	FAV 2Q					FAV 2Q

GROUND: Bodieve Park, Bodieve Road, Wadebridge PL27 6EA

WENDRON UNITED

South West Peninsula Premier West

Founded 1986 Nickname: The Dron **Club Colours:** Claret and blue

Club Contact Details 01209 860 046 nick.scoley@btinternet.com

HONOURS FA Comps: None

League: None

11-12	12-13	13-14	14-15	15-16	16-17	17-18	18-19	19-20	20-21
CornC 11	CornC 12	CornC 2	CornC 2	SW1W 9	SW1W 13	SW1W 13	SW1W 6	SWPW n&v	SWPW n&v

GROUND: Underlane TR13 0EH

CLUB MOVEMENTS

PREMIER DIVISION EAST - IN: Okehampton Argyle and Ottery St Mary (P - DVL).
Stoke Gabriel & Torbay Police (Merger between Stoke Gabriel & Torbay Police (SDL).

OUT: Ilfracombe Town and Millbrook (P - WLP).

PREMIER DIVISION WEST - IN: Penryn Athletic (P - STP).

OUT: Helston Athletic, Mousehole and Saltash United (P - WLP).

AFC UCKFIELD TOWN

Southern Combination Premier

Founded 1988 Nickname: The Oakmen **Club Colours:** Red & black

Club Contact Details 01825 890 905 grahamsullivan27@gmail.com

Previous Names: Wealden 1988-2010. AFC Uckfield & Uckfield Town merged in 2014.

Previous Leagues: None

HONOURS

FA Comps: None

League: Sussex County Division Two 2010-11.

11-12	12-13	13-14	14-15	15-16	16-17	17-18	18-19	19-20	20-21
SxC1 8	SxC1 21	SxC1 10	SxC2 2	SCP 15	SCP 18	SCP 14	SCP 7	SCP n&v	SCP n&v
					FAC EP	FAC EPr	FAC 2Q	FAC Pr	FAC EP
				FAV 1Q	FAV 2Q	FAV 2Q	FAV 4P	FAV 3P	FAV 2P

GROUND: The Oaks, Old Eastbourne Road, Uckfield TN22 5QL

Nearest Railway Station Uckfield - 2.1km

CLUB MOVEMENTS

PREMIER DIVISION - IN: AFC Varndeanians, Bexhill United and Littlehampton Town (P - SC1).

OUT: Horley Town (LM - CCPS). Langney Wanderers (F). Lancing (P - IsthSE).

AFC VARNDEANIANS

Southern Combination Premier

Founded 1929 Nickname: **Club Colours:** Red & black

Club Contact Details stevematthews@utilitymatters.com

Previous Names: Secondary Old Boys Club renamed in 1929 to form Old Varndeanians - named as such until 2015.

Previous Leagues: Brighton, Hove & District 1929-56, 73-2003. Sussex County 1956-73. Mid Sussex 2003-15.

HONOURS

FA Comps: None

League: Sussex County Division Two 1959-60. Brighton, Hove & District Division One 1973-74, 99-2000, 00-01, 02-03. Mid Sussex Premier 2003-04, 06-07, 08-09. Southern Combination Division Two 2015-16.

11-12	12-13	13-14	14-15	15-16	16-17	17-18	18-19	19-20	20-21
MSuxP 5	MSuxP 7	MSuxP 2	MSuxP 7	SC2 1	SC1 18	SC1 14	SC1 3	SC1 n&v	SC1 n&v
								FAC 1Q	
							FAV 2Q	FAV 1Q	FAV 2Q

GROUND: Withdean Stadium, Tongdean Lane, Brighton BN1 5JD

Nearest Railway Station Preston Park - 0.9km

Bus Route Bottom of Valley Drive - stop 91m away

ALFOLD

Southern Combination Premier

Founded 1928 Nickname: Fold **Club Colours:** Maroon

Club Contact Details info@alfoldfc.com

Previous Names: Formed after the split of Loxwood and Alfold FC (Established 1920) in 1928.

Previous Leagues: Cranleigh & District. Horsham & District. West Sussex > 2016.

HONOURS

FA Comps: None

League: Horsham & District 1953-54. West Sussex Division Two North 1980-81, 93-94, Premier 2002-03. Southern Combination Division One 2018-19.

11-12	12-13	13-14	14-15	15-16	16-17	17-18	18-19	19-20	20-21
	WSux2 2	WSux1 9	WSux1 6	SC2 13	SC2 14	SC2 4	SC1 1	SCP n&v	SCP n&v
									FAC P
								FAV 1Q	FAV 2Q

GROUND: Recreation Ground, Dunsfold Road, Alfold, Surrey GU6 8JB

Seats: 50

Bus Route 42

BEXHILL UNITED

Southern Combination Premier

Founded 2002 Nickname: The Pirates **Club Colours:** White and black

Club Contact Details

Previous Names: Formed by merger of Bexhill Town (formerly Bexhill Town Athletic >1969) and Bexhill AAC in 2002
Previous Leagues: None
HONOURS
FA Comps: None
League: None

11-12	12-13	13-14	14-15	15-16	16-17	17-18	18-19	19-20	20-21
SxC2 7	SxC2 11	SxC2 8	SxC2 6	SC1 14	SC1 10	SC1 7	SC1 4	SC1 n&v	SC1 n&v
				FAC P				FAC EP	
			FAV 2Q	FAV 1Q	FAV 1Q	FAV 2Q	FAV 1Q	FAV 2Q	FAV 1Q

GROUND: The Polegrove, Brockley Road, Bexhill on Sea TN39 3EX
Nearest Railway Station Collington - 0.3km
Bus Route Polegrove - stop 91m away

BROADBRIDGE HEATH

Southern Combination Premier

Founded 1919 Nickname: The Bears **Club Colours:** All royal blue

Club Contact Details 01403 283 654

Previous Names: None
Previous Leagues: Horsham & District >1971. West Sussex 1971-79. Southern Counties Combination 1979-83.
HONOURS
FA Comps: None
League: West Sussex Division One 1975-76.

11-12	12-13	13-14	14-15	15-16	16-17	17-18	18-19	19-20	20-21
SxC2 5	SxC2 6	SxC2 2	SxC1 9	SCP 9	SCP 8	SCP 15	SCP 6	SCP n&v	SCP n&v
						FAC EP	FAC EP	FAC P	FAC P
			FAV 2Q	FAV 2Q	FAV 1Q	FAV 2P	FAV 2Q	FAV 1Q	FAV 1Q

GROUND: Countryside Stadium, Wickhurst Lane, Broadbridge Heath RH12 3YS
Nearest Railway Station Dorking - 93 towards Horsham, alight at Shelley Arms, 20min walk from there. **Seats:** 100
Bus Route 63, 68 & 93 **Covered:** 50

CRAWLEY DOWN GATWICK

Southern Combination Premier

Founded 1993 Nickname: The Anvils **Club Colours:** All Red

Club Contact Details 07973 620 759

Previous Names: Crawley Down United > 1993. Crawley Down Village > 1999. Crawley Down > 2012.
Previous Leagues: Mid Sussex, Sussex County > 2011. Isthmian 2011-14.
HONOURS
FA Comps: None
League: Mid-Sussex Premier Division 1994-95. Sussex County Division One 2010-11.

11-12	12-13	13-14	14-15	15-16	16-17	17-18	18-19	19-20	20-21
Isth1S 16	Isth1S 13	Isth1S 23	SxC1 19	SC1 2	SCP 11	SCP 12	SCP 9	SCP n&v	SCP n&v
FAC 1Q	FAC P	FAC P	FAC EPr	FAC EP	FAC P	FAC EP	FAC EP	FAC EP	FAC 1Q
FAT P	FAT 1Q	FAT 1Q	FAV 2P	FAV 1Q	FAV 1Q	FAV 2Q	FAV 1Q	FAV 2Q	FAV 2Q

GROUND: The Haven Centre, Hophurst Lane, Crawley Down RH10 4LJ **Capacity:** 1,000
Nearest Railway Station Three Bridges - 291 towards Tunbridge Wells, alight at the War Memorial, 4min walk from there.
Bus Route 291 **Covered:** 50

EAST PRESTON

Southern Combination Premier

Founded 1966 Nickname: EP **Club Colours:** Black and white

Club Contact Details 01903 776 026

Previous Names: None

Previous Leagues: Worthing & District 1966-68. West Sussex 1968-83.

HONOURS

FA Comps: None

League: West Sussex Premier Division 1977-78, 80-81, 81-82, 82-83.
Sussex County Division Three 1983-84, Division Two 1997-98, 2011-12, Division One 2013-14.

11-12	12-13	13-14	14-15	15-16	16-17	17-18	18-19	19-20	20-21
SxC2 1	SxC1 3	SxC1 1	SxC1 11	SCP 19	SC1 3	SCP 13	SCP 14	SCP n&v	SCP n&v
	FAC P	FAC 1Q	FAC 2Q	FAC EP	FAC 1Q	FAC P	FAC EP	FAC EP	FAC EP
FAV 1P	FAV 2Q	FAV 5P	FAV 2P	FAV 1Q	FAV 2Q	FAV 1Qr	FAV 1P	FAV 1Q	FAV 2Q

GROUND: Roundstone Recreation Ground, Lashmar Road, East Preston BN16 1ES

Nearest Railway Station Angmering - 0.8km

Bus Route Windlesham Gardens - stop 209m away

EASTBOURNE TOWN

Southern Combination Premier

Founded 1881 Nickname: Town **Club Colours:** Yellow and blue

Club Contact Details 01323 724 328 eastbournetownfc@live.co.uk

Previous Names: Devonshire Park 1881-89

Previous Leagues: Southern Amateur 1907-46, Corinthian 1960-63, Athenian 1963-76, Sussex County 1976-2007. Isthmian 2007-14.

HONOURS

FA Comps: None

League: Sussex County 1976-77, 2006-07.

11-12	12-13	13-14	14-15	15-16	16-17	17-18	18-19	19-20	20-21
Isth1S 14	Isth1S 11	Isth1S 24	SxC1 4	SCP 2	SCP 5	SCP 5	SCP 3	SCP n&v	SCP n&v
FAC P	FAC 2Q	FAC 2Q	FAC P	FAC 3Q	FAC 1Q	FAC 1Q	FAC EP	FAC P	FAC P
FAT 1Q	FAT 1Q	FAT 1Qr	FAV 1P	FAV 3P	FAV 4P	FAV 4P	FAV 3P	FAV 3P	FAV 1P

GROUND: The Saffrons, Compton Place Road, Eastbourne BN21 1EA

Capacity: 3,000

Nearest Railway Station Eastbourne - 0.4km

Seats: 200

Bus Route Saffrons Road Cricket Club - stop 100m away

EASTBOURNE UNITED ASSOCIATION

Southern Combination Premier

Founded 1894 Nickname: The U's **Club Colours:** Red and blue

Club Contact Details 01323 726 989 secretary@eastbourneunitedafc.com

Previous Names: 1st Sussex Royal Engineers. Eastbourne Old Comrades 1922. Eastbourne United (merged with Shinewater Assoc in 2000)

Previous Leagues: Sussex County 1921-28, 32-56. Spartan 1928-32. Metropolitan 1956-64. Athenian 1964-77.
Isthmian 1977-92.

HONOURS

FA Comps: None

League: Athenian Division Two 1966-67, Division One 68-69. Sussex County Division One 1954-55, 55-56, 2008-09,Division Two 2013-14.

11-12	12-13	13-14	14-15	15-16	16-17	17-18	18-19	19-20	20-21
SxC2 6	SxC2 4	SxC2 1	SxC1 12	SCP 10	SCP 7	SCP 16	SCP 18	SCP n&v	SCP n&v
		FAC 1Q	FAC P	FAC 1Q	FAC 1Q	FAC P	FAC EP	FAC EP	FAC EP
	FAV 1Q	FAV SF	FAV 2P	FAV 2Q	FAV 2P	FAV 1Q	FAV 1Q	FAV 1Q	FAV 1Q

GROUND: The Oval, Channel View Road, Eastbourne, BN22 7LN

Capacity: 3,000

Nearest Railway Station Eastbourne - 2km

Seats: 160

Bus Route Desmond Road - stop 240m away

Covered: 160

HASSOCKS

Southern Combination Premier

Founded 1902 Nickname: The Robins **Club Colours:** Red and black

Club Contact Details 01273 846 040

Previous Names: None
Previous Leagues: Mid Sussex, Brighton & Hove & District >1981.

HONOURS
FA Comps: None
League: Brighton, Hove & District Division Two 1965-66, Division One 71-72.
Sussex County Division Three 1991-92.

11-12		12-13		13-14		14-15		15-16		16-17		17-18		18-19		19-20		20-21	
SxC1	4	SxC1	7	SxC1	6	SxC1	15	SCP	13	SCP	13	SCP	18	SCP	12	SCP	n&v	SCP	n&v
FAC	EP	FAC	EP	FAC	1Q	FAC	EP					FAC	EP	FAC	EP	FAC	Pr	FAC	P
FAV	2Qr	FAV	1P	FAV	1P	FAV	2P			FAV	1Q	FAV	2Q	FAV	1Q	FAV	2Q	FAV	1Q

GROUND: The Beacon, Brighton Road, Hassocks BN6 9LU **Capacity:** 1,800
Nearest Railway Station Hassocks - 1.2km **Seats:** 270
Bus Route Friars Oak Cottages - stop 211m away **Covered:** 100

HORSHAM YMCA

Southern Combination Premier

Founded 1898 Nickname: YM's **Club Colours:** White and black

Club Contact Details 01403 283 818 ymcafootballclub@btconnect.com

Previous Names: None
Previous Leagues: Horsham & District, Brighton & Hove, Mid Sussex, Sussex County 1959-2006, 08-09. Isthmian 2006-08, 09-11.

HONOURS
FA Comps: None
League: Sussex County 2004-05, 05-06.

11-12		12-13		13-14		14-15		15-16		16-17		17-18		18-19		19-20		20-21	
SxC1	16	SxC1	10	SxC1	4	SxC1	5	SCP	7	SCP	10	SCP	4	SCP	2	SCP	n&v	SCP	n&v
FAC	EPr	FAC	EP	FAC	EP	FAC	Pr	FAC	2Qr	FAC	EP	FAC	EP	FAC	1Q	FAC	1Q	FAC	EP
FAV	1P	FAV	2P	FAV	1Q	FAV	2P	FAV	2Q	FAV	3P	FAV	1P	FAV	1P	FAV	1P	FAV	2Q

GROUND: Gorings Mead, Horsham, West Sussex RH13 5BP **Capacity:** 1,575
Nearest Railway Station Horsham - 0.9km **Seats:** 150
Bus Route Brighton Road - stop 205m away **Covered:** 200

LINGFIELD

Southern Combination Premier

Founded 1893 Nickname: The Lingers **Club Colours:** Red & Yellow

Club Contact Details 01342 834 269

Previous Names: None.
Previous Leagues: Redhill. Surrey Intermediate. Combined Counties. Mid Sussex. Sussex County > 2014. Southern Counties East 2014-15.

HONOURS
FA Comps: None
League: POST WAR: Edenbridge & Caterham 1952-53. Surrey Intermediate Prem B 76-77,
Prem A 77-78, 78-79. Mid Sussex Prem 92-93. Sussex County Division Three 97-98.

11-12		12-13		13-14		14-15		15-16		16-17		17-18		18-19		19-20		20-21	
SxC1	7	SxC1	6	SxC1	15	SCE	17	SC1	8	SC1	5	SC1	3	SCP	8	SCP	n&v	SCP	n&v
FAC	1Qr	FAC	1Q	FAC	EP	FAC	EP	FAC	EP			FAC	EP	FAC	EP	FAC	EP	FAC	EP
FAV	1Q	FAV	1P	FAV	1P	FAV	3P	FAV	2Q	FAV	1P	FAV	1Q	FAV	2Q	FAV	1Q	FAV	2Q

GROUND: Sports Pavillion, Godstone Road, Lingfield, Surrey RH7 6BT **Capacity:** 2,000
Nearest Railway Station Lingfield - 1.2km
Bus Route Godstone Road - stop 391m away

LITTLE COMMON

Southern Combination Premier

Founded 1966 Nickname: The Green Lane Boys **Club Colours:** Claret & blue

Club Contact Details 01424 845 861

Previous Names: Albion United 1966-86
Previous Leagues: East Sussex. Sussex County
HONOURS
FA Comps: None
League: East Sussex 1975-76, 76-77, 2004-05. Southern Combination Division One 2017-18.

11-12		12-13		13-14		14-15		15-16		16-17		17-18		18-19		19-20		20-21	
SxC2	16	SxC2	3	SxC2	4	SxC2	7	SC1	7	SC1	2	SC1	1	SCP	16	SCP	n&v	SCP	n&v
												FAC	EP	FAC	EPr	FAC	1Q	FAC	1Q
								FAV	1Q	FAV	2Q	FAV	1Q	FAV	2Q	FAV	1Q	FAV	1Q

GROUND: The Oval, Channel View Road, Eastbourne BN22 7LN **Capacity:** 3,000
Nearest Railway Station Eastbourne - 25min walk **Seats:** 160
Bus Route Desmond Road - stop 240m away **Covered:** 160

LITTLEHAMPTON TOWN

Southern Combination Premier

Founded 1896 Nickname: Marigolds **Club Colours:** Gold and black

Club Contact Details 01903 716 390

Previous Names: Littlehampton 1896-1938.
Previous Leagues: None
HONOURS
FA Comps: None
League: Sussex County Division Two 1996-97, 2003-04, 12-13, Division One 1990-91, 2014-15.

11-12		12-13		13-14		14-15		15-16		16-17		17-18		18-19		19-20		20-21	
SxC2	4	SxC2	1	SxC1	3	SxC1	1	SCP	11	SCP	16	SCP	20	SC1	6	SC1	n&v	SC1	n&v
FAC	EP	FAC	1Q	FAC	1Q	FAC	1Q	FAC	P	FAC	EP	FAC	1Qr	FAC	EPr				
FAV	2P	FAV	2Pr	FAV	2P	FAV	3Pr	FAV	1P	FAV	2Qr	FAV	1Q	FAV	2Q	FAV	1Q	FAV	3P

GROUND: St Flora Sportsfield, St Flora's Road, Littlehampton BN17 6BD **Capacity:** 4,000
Nearest Railway Station Littlehampton - 1km
Bus Route Parkside Avenue - stop 79m away

LOXWOOD

Southern Combination Premier

Founded 1920 Nickname: Magpies **Club Colours:** White and black

Club Contact Details 07791 766 857 secretary@loxwoodfc.co.uk

Previous Names: None
Previous Leagues: West Sussex 1995-2006.
HONOURS
FA Comps: None
League: West Sussex Division Two North 1998-99, 2001-02.
Sussex County Division Three 2007-08.

11-12		12-13		13-14		14-15		15-16		16-17		17-18		18-19		19-20		20-21	
SxC2	5	SxC2	9	SxC2	3	SxC1	6	SCP	8	SCP	6	SCP	11	SCP	17	SCP	n&v	SCP	n&v
								FAC	EP	FAC	P	FAC	P	FAC	Pr	FAC	EPr	FAC	EP
						FAV	2P	FAV	2P	FAV	1Q	FAV	1Q	FAV	1Q	FAV	2Q	FAV	1Q

GROUND: Loxwood Sports Ass., Plaistow Road, Loxwood RH14 0SX
Seats: 100
Bus Route Plaistow Road - stop 28m away

NEWHAVEN

Southern Combination Premier

Founded 1887 Nickname: The Dockers **Club Colours:** Red & yellow

Club Contact Details 01273 513 940 newhavenfootballclub@gmail.com

Previous Names: None

Previous Leagues: Brighton, Hove & District 1887-1920.

HONOURS

FA Comps: None

League: Sussex County Division One 1953-54, 73-74, Division Two 1971-72, 90-91, Division Three 2011-12.

11-12		12-13		13-14		14-15		15-16		16-17		17-18		18-19		19-20		20-21	
SxC3	1	SxC2	2	SxC1	13	SxC1	7	SCP	3	SCP	9	SCP	9	SCP	4	SCP	n&v	SCP	n&v
										FAC	EPr	FAC	Pr	FAC	P	FAC	P	FAC	P
FAV	2Q	FAV	1Q	FAV	1Pr	FAV	1Q	FAV	2P	FAV	3P	FAV	2Q	FAV	2P	FAV	3P	FAV	2P

GROUND: The Trafalgar Ground, Fort Road Newhaven East Sussex BN9 9DA

Nearest Railway Station Newhaven Harbour - 0.4km

Bus Route Court Farm Road - stop 20m away

PAGHAM

Southern Combination Premier

Founded 1903 Nickname: The Lions **Club Colours:** White and black

Club Contact Details 01243 266 112 paghamfootballclub@outlook.com

Previous Names: None

Previous Leagues: Bognor & Chichester 1903-50, West Sussex 50-69

HONOURS

FA Comps: None

League: West Sussex Division One South 1962-63, Prmeier 65-66, 68-69, 69-70.
Sussex County Division Two 1978-79, 86-87, 2006-07, Division One 80-81, 87-88, 88-89.

11-12		12-13		13-14		14-15		15-16		16-17		17-18		18-19		19-20		20-21	
SxC1	6	SxC1	5	SxC1	7	SxC1	3	SCP	6	SCP	4	SCP	3	SCP	11	SCP	n&v	SCP	n&v
FAC	EP	FAC	1Qr	FAC	EP	FAC	1Q	FAC	1Q	FAC	1Q	FAC	1Q	FAC	1Q	FAC	EPr	FAC	P
FAV	2P	FAV	1Pr	FAV	2Q	FAV	2P	FAV	2P	FAV	2Q	FAV	1P	FAV	3P	FAV	1Q	FAV	1P

GROUND: Nyetimber Lane, Pagham, West Sussex PO21 3JY **Capacity:** 1,500

Nearest Railway Station Bognor Regis - 4.3km **Seats:** 200

Bus Route The Bear Inn - stop 119m away **Seats:** 200

PEACEHAVEN & TELSCOMBE

Southern Combination Premier

Founded 1923 Nickname: The Tye **Club Colours:** Black and white

Club Contact Details 01273 582 471 peacehavenfc@hotmail.com

Previous Names: Formed when Peacehaven Rangers and Telscombe Tye merged.

Previous Leagues: Sussex County 1969-2013. Isthmian 2013-16.

HONOURS

FA Comps: None

League: Brighton, H&D Junior 1951-52, Intermediate 63-64, Senior 68-69. Sussex County Division One 1978-79, 81-82, 82-83, 91-92, 92-93, 94-95, 95-96, 2012-13, Division Three 2005-06, Division Two 2008-09. Isthmian Division One South 2013-14.

11-12		12-13		13-14		14-15		15-16		16-17		17-18		18-19		19-20		20-21	
SxC1	5	SxC1	1	Isth1S	1	Isth P	21	Isth1S	24	SCP	14	SCP	7	SCP	10	SCP	n&v	SCP	n&v
FAC	P	FAC	P	FAC	1Q	FAC	1Qr	FAC	P	FAC	1Q	FAC	EPr	FAC	EP	FAC	EPr	FAC	EP
FAV	3P	FAV	4P	FAT	1Q	FAT	3Q	FAT	1Q	FAV	2Q	FAV	1Q	FAV	2P	FAV	1P	FAV	1P

GROUND: The Sports Park, Piddinghoe Ave, Peacehaven, BN10 8RJ **Capacity:** 3,000

Nearest Railway Station Newhaven - 3.2km **Seats:** 350

Bus Route Slindon Avenue - stop 140m away

SALTDEAN UNITED

Southern Combination Premier

Founded 1966 Nickname: The Tigers **Club Colours:** Red & black

Club Contact Details 01273 309 898 secretary@saltdeanunitedfc.co.uk

Previous Names: None
Previous Leagues: None
HONOURS
FA Comps: None
League: Sussex County/Southern Combination Division Three 1988-89, Division Two 95-96 / Division One 2016-17.

11-12	12-13	13-14	14-15	15-16	16-17	17-18	18-19	19-20	20-21
SxC3 2	SxC2 18	SxC2 13	SxC2 13	SC1 17	SC1 1	SCP 8	SCP 5	SCP n&v	SCP n&v
						FAC EP	FAC Pr	FAC P	FAC EP
FAV 1Q	FAV 1Q	FAV 1Q	FAV 1Q		FAV 1Q	FAV 1P	FAV 1P	FAV 1Q	FAV 2P

GROUND: Hill Park, Coombe Vale Saltdean Brighton East Sussex BN2 8HJ
Nearest Railway Station Southease - 5km
Bus Route Saltdean Vale Shops - stop 175m away

STEYNING TOWN

Southern Combination Premier

Founded 1892 Nickname: The Barrowmen **Club Colours:** Red & white

Club Contact Details 01903 814 601 steyningtownfc@gmail.com

Previous Names: Steyning FC 1892-1979.
Previous Leagues: West Sussex (FM) 1896-1919. Brighton, Hove & District 1919-64. Sussex County 1964-86. Wessex (FM) 1986-88. Combined Counties 1988-93.
HONOURS
FA Comps: None
League: Brighton, H&D Division Two 1933-34, 38-39.
Sussex County Division Two 1977-78, Division One 1984-85, 85-86.

11-12	12-13	13-14	14-15	15-16	16-17	17-18	18-19	19-20	20-21
SxC2 13	SxC2 10	SxC2 11	SxC2 10	SC1 10	SC1 6	SC1 11	SC1 2	SCP n&v	SCP n&v
						FAC P		FAC P	FAC 1Q
FAV 1Q	FAV 1Q	FAV 1Q	FAV 2Q	FAV 2P	FAV 1Q	FAV 2Q	FAV 3P	FAV 1Qr	FAV 2P

GROUND: The Shooting Field, Steyning, West Sussex BN44 3RX
Bus Route Middle Mead - stop 52m away

CLUB MOVEMENTS

PREMIER DIVISION - IN: Dorking Wanderers Reserves, Epsom & Ewell and Godalming Town (LM - CC1). Forest Row (P - MSX). Montpelier Villa (SC2).

OUT: AFC Varndeanians, Bexhill United and Littlehampton Town (P - SCP).

ARUNDEL

Southern Combination Division One

Founded 1889 Nickname: Mulletts **Club Colours:** Red and white

Club Contact Details 01903 882 548 mullets@btinternet.com

HONOURS FA Comps: None

League: Sussex County Division One 1957-58, 58-59, 86-87.

11-12		12-13		13-14		14-15		15-16		16-17		17-18		18-19		19-20		20-21	
SxC1	17	SxC1	14	SxC1	12	SxC1	10	SCP	12	SCP	15	SCP	17	SCP	19	SC1	n&v	SC1	n&v
FAC	P	FAC	EP	FAC	EPr	FAC	EP	FAC	Pr	FAC	1Q	FAC	EP	FAC	P	FAC	1Qr		
FAV	2Q	FAV	2Q	FAV	2Q	FAV	1P	FAV	2Q	FAV	1Q	FAV	1Q	FAV	1Q	FAV	2Q	FAV	1Q

GROUND: Mill Road, Arundel, W. Sussex BN18 9PA

Nearest Railway Station Arundel - 1.6km

BILLINGSHURST

Southern Combination Division One

Founded 1891 Nickname: Hurst **Club Colours:** Red & black

Club Contact Details 01403 786 445 kevtilley@btinternet.com

HONOURS FA Comps: None

League: West Sussex Premier Division 2011-12.

11-12		12-13		13-14		14-15		15-16		16-17		17-18		18-19		19-20		20-21	
WSuxP	1	SxC3	4	SxC3	11	SxC3	6	SC2	5	SC1	15	SC1	16	SC1	12	SC1	n&v	SC1	n&v
																		FAC	EP
												FAV	2Q	FAV	1Q			FAV	2Q

GROUND: Jubilee Fields, Newbridge Road, Billingshurst, West Sussex RH14 9HZ

Nearest Railway Station Billinghurst - 1.7km

Bus Route Hole Farm - stop 126m away

DORKING WANDERERS RESERVES

Southern Combination Division One

Founded 1999 Nickname: Wanderers **Club Colours:** Red & white

Club Contact Details info@dorkingwanderers.com

HONOURS FA Comps: None

League: None

11-12		12-13		13-14		14-15		15-16		16-17		17-18		18-19		19-20		20-21	
								CC1	15					CC1	11	CC1	n&v	CC1	n&v

GROUND: Meadowbank Stadium, Mill Lane, Dorking RH4 1DX

Nearest Railway Station Dorking West and Dorking Deepdene

Bus Route 21 & 455

EPSOM & EWELL

Southern Combination Division One

Founded 1960 Nickname: E's or Salts **Club Colours:** Royal blue & white

Club Contact Details 01737 553 250

HONOURS FA Comps: None

League: Surrey Senior 1925-26, 26-27, 27-28, 74-75. London 1927-28. Isthmian Division Two 1977-78.

11-12		12-13		13-14		14-15		15-16		16-17		17-18		18-19		19-20		20-21	
CCP	14	CCP	5	CCP	3	CCP	7	CCP	4	CCP	4	CCP	21	CC1	8	CC1	n&v	CC1	n&v
FAC	P	FAC	1Q	FAC	EPr	FAC	Pr	FAC	EP	FAC	P	FAC	EP	FAC	Pr				
FAV	2Q	FAV	1Q	FAV	2Q	FAV	1P	FAV	1Q	FAV	2P	FAV	2P	FAV	1Q	FAV	1Q	FAV	1P

GROUND: Leatherhead FC, Fetcham Grove, Guildford Road, Leatherhead, Surrey KT22 9AS

Nearest Railway Station Leatherhead - half a mile away

Bus Route 21, 465 & 479

FOREST ROW

Southern Combination Division One

Founded 1892 Nickname: Frow **Club Colours:** Green

Club Contact Details

HONOURS FA Comps: None

League: Mid-Sussex Division Two 1951-52 (joint), 71-72, Division Four 59-60, 2000-01, Division Three 62-63, 71-72, Division One 75-76.

11-12	12-13	13-14	14-15	15-16	16-17	17-18	18-19	19-20	20-21
MSuxC 11	MSux1	MSux1	MSuxC 2	MSuxP 10	MSuxP 5	MSuxP 8	MSuxP 5	MSuxP n&v	MSuxP n&v

GROUND: Oakwood Park, Tinsley Lane, Crawley RH10 8AT

GODALMING TOWN

Southern Combination Division One

Founded 1950 Nickname: The G's **Club Colours:** Yellow & green

Club Contact Details 01483 417 520 godalmingtownfootballclub@gmail.com

HONOURS FA Comps: None

League: Combined Counties Premier Division 1983-84, 2005-06.

11-12	12-13	13-14	14-15	15-16	16-17	17-18	18-19	19-20	20-21
Isth1S 5	SthC 3	Sthsw 18	SthC 8	SthC 10	Isth1S 24	CCP 20	CC1 12	CC1 n&v	CC1 n&v
FAC 4Q	FAC 1Qr	FAC P	FAC 1Qr	FAC 1Q	FAC 1Q	FAC 1Q	FAC EP		
FAT 2Q	FAT P	FAT P	FAT P	FAT P	FAT P	FAV 2Q	FAV 1Q	FAV 2Q	FAV 1Q

GROUND: The Bill Kyte Stadium, Wey Court, Meadrow, Guildford, Surrey GU7 3JE

Nearest Railway Station Farncombe - 1/2 a mile from the ground.

HAILSHAM TOWN

Southern Combination Division One

Founded 1885 Nickname: The Stringers **Club Colours:** Yellow & green

Club Contact Details 01323 840 446 robvsquires@yahoo.co.uk

HONOURS FA Comps: None

League: Southern Counties Combination 1975-76.

11-12	12-13	13-14	14-15	15-16	16-17	17-18	18-19	19-20	20-21
SxC2 2	SxC1 12	SxC1 16	SxC1 17	SCP 18	SCP 20	SC1 8	SC1 8	SC1 n&v	SC1 n&v
FAC EP	FAC EP	FAC EP	FAC EP	FAC EP	FAC EP	FAC EP			
FAV 1Q	FAV 1Q	FAV 1Q	FAV 1P	FAV 2P	FAV 1Q	FAV 1Q	FAV 2Q	FAV 1Q	FAV 1Q

GROUND: The Beaconfield, Western Road, Hailsham BN27 3DN

Nearest Railway Station Polegate - 4.4km

Bus Route Bramble Drive - stop 190m away

MIDHURST & EASEBOURNE

Southern Combination Division One

Founded 1946 Nickname: The Stags **Club Colours:** All blue

Club Contact Details 07736 164 416 midhurstfc@gmail.com

HONOURS FA Comps: None

League: West Sussex 1955-56, 62-63, 64-65, Premier 67-68.
Sussex County Division Three 94-95, 2002-03.

11-12	12-13	13-14	14-15	15-16	16-17	17-18	18-19	19-20	20-21
SxC2 15	SxC2 8	SxC2 14	SxC2 8	SC1 15	SC1 9	SC1 13	SC1 16	SC1 n&v	SC1 n&v
						FAV 2Q	FAV 1Q	FAV 2Q	

GROUND: Rotherfield, Dodsley Lane, Easebourne, Midhurst GU29 9BE

Bus Route Dodsley Grove - Stop 125m away

MILE OAK

Southern Combination Division One

Founded 1960 Nickname: The Oak **Club Colours:** Tangerine and black

Club Contact Details 01273 423 854

HONOURS FA Comps: None

League: Brighton & Hove District Div.8 1960-61, Div.4 65-66, Div.2 72-73, Div.1 73-74, Prem 1980-81. Sussex County Division Two 94-95.

11-12	12-13	13-14	14-15	15-16	16-17	17-18	18-19	19-20	20-21
SxC2 10	SxC2 7	SxC2 7	SxC2 5	SC1 6	SC1 4	SC1 6	SC1 7	SC1 n&v	SC1 n&v
FAC EPr				FAC EP	FAC EP	FAC EP			FAC EP
FAV 2Q		FAV 1Qr	FAV 2Q	FAV 2Q	FAV 2Q	FAV 2Q	FAV 1Qr	FAV 1P	FAV 1Q

GROUND: Mile Oak Recreation Ground, Chalky Road, Portslade BN41 2WF

Nearest Railway Station Fishersgate - 2.1km

Bus Route New England Rise - stop 11m away

MONTPELIER VILLA

Southern Combination Division One

Founded 1991 Nickname: The Villa **Club Colours:** Blue & white

Club Contact Details 07988 692 283 montpeliervilla@gmail.com

HONOURS FA Comps: None

League: Brighton & District Division Six 1991-92, Division Four 93-94, Division Two 94-95, Division One 95-96, Premier Division 2009-10, 10-11.

11-12	12-13	13-14	14-15	15-16	16-17	17-18	18-19	19-20	20-21
	MSuxC 3	MSuxP 10	MSuxP 8	SC2 8	SC2 10	SC2 9	SC2 7	SC2 n&v	SC2 n&v

GROUND: Lancing FC, Culver Road BN15 9AX

Nearest Railway Station Lancing - 0.2km

Bus Route North Road Post Office - 123m away

OAKWOOD

Southern Combination Division One

Founded 1962 Nickname: The Oaks **Club Colours:** Red & black

Club Contact Details 01293 515 742 sarah.daly13@hotmail.co.uk

HONOURS FA Comps: None

League: Crawley Division One 1973-74. Sussex County Division Three 1984-85, Division Two 2005-06.

11-12	12-13	13-14	14-15	15-16	16-17	17-18	18-19	19-20	20-21
SxC2 18	SxC2 15	SxC2 12	SxC2 4	SC1 3	SC1 14	SC1 17	SC1 15	SC1 n&v	SC1 n&v
					FAC EP				FAC EP
FAV 1Q	FAV 1Q	FAV 1Q	FAV 1Q	FAV 2Q	FAV 2Q	FAV 1Q	FAV 1Q	FAV 2Q	FAV 1Q

GROUND: Tinsley Lane, Three Bridges, Crawley RH10 8AT

Nearest Railway Station Three Bridges - 1.3km

Bus Route Maxwell Way - Stop 98m away

ROFFEY

Southern Combination Division One

Founded 1901 Nickname: **Club Colours:** Blue and white

Club Contact Details roffeyfc@gmail.com

HONOURS FA Comps: None

League: Mid Sussex Division One 2009-10.

11-12	12-13	13-14	14-15	15-16	16-17	17-18	18-19	19-20	20-21
SxC3 16	SxC3 8	SxC3 3	SxC3 8	SC2 2	SC2 7	SC2 6	SC2 3	SC1 n&v	SC1 n&v

GROUND: Chennells, Bartholomew Way, Horsham RH12 5JL

SEAFORD TOWN

Southern Combination Division One

Founded 1888 Nickname: The Badgers **Club Colours:** All red

Club Contact Details 01323 890 211 secretary@seafordtownfc.com

HONOURS FA Comps: None

League: Lewes 1907-08.
Sussex County Division Three 1985-86, Division Two 1988-89, 2005-06.

11-12	12-13	13-14	14-15	15-16	16-17	17-18	18-19	19-20	20-21
SxC2 17	SxC2 12	SxC2 17	SxC2 15	SC1 16	SC1 13	SC1 12	SC1 11	SC1 n&v	SC1 n&v
FAV 1P	FAV 2Q	FAV 1Q	FAV 2Q	FAV 1Q	FAV 2Q	FAV 1Q	FAV 2Q	FAV 2P	FAV 1P

GROUND: The Crouch, Bramber Road, Seaford BN25 1AF

Nearest Railway Station Seaford - 0.6km

Bus Route Seaford Head Lower School - stop 168m away

SELSEY

Southern Combination Division One

Founded 1903 Nickname: Blues **Club Colours:** All blue

Club Contact Details 01243 603 420 selseyfootballclub@yahoo.com

HONOURS FA Comps: None

League: West Sussex Division One 1938-39, 54-55, 56-57, 57-58, 58-59, 60-61.
Sussex County Division Two 1963-64, 75-76.

11-12	12-13	13-14	14-15	15-16	16-17	17-18	18-19	19-20	20-21
SxC1 12	SxC1 18	SxC1 17	SxC1 20	SC1 13	SC1 7	SC1 9	SC1 5	SC1 n&v	SC1 n&v
FAC P	FAC EP	FAC EP	FAC EP	FAC EP				FAC EP	
FAV 1Q	FAV 1Q	FAV 1Q	FAV 1Q	FAV 2Q	FAV 2Q	FAV 2Q	FAV 2Q	FAV 1Q	FAV 1Q

GROUND: The Bunn Leisure Stadium, High Street, Selsey, Chichester, PO20 0QG

Bus Route Medical Centre - stop 92m away

SHOREHAM

Southern Combination Division One

Founded 1892 Nickname: Musselmen **Club Colours:** Blue & white

Club Contact Details 01273 454 261 shorehamfootballclub@gmail.com

HONOURS FA Comps: None

League: West Sussex Junior Division 1897-98, Senior Division 1902-03, 04-05, 05-06. Sussex County Division One 1951-52, 52-53, 77-78, Division Two 1961-62, 76-77, 84-85, 93-94. Southern Combination Premier Division 2016-17.

11-12	12-13	13-14	14-15	15-16	16-17	17-18	18-19	19-20	20-21
SxC1 18	SxC1 17	SxC1 14	SxC1 16	SCP 17	SCP 1	Isth1S 24	SCP 20	SC1 n&v	SC1 n&v
FAC 1Q	FAC EPr	FAC 1Q	FAC P	FAC 1Q	FAC P	FAC 1Q	FAC P	FAC P	FAC EP
FAV 2Q	FAV 1Q	FAV 2Q	FAV 2Q	FAV 1Q	FAV 1P	FAT P	FAV 2Q	FAV 1Q	FAV 2Q

GROUND: Middle Road, Shoreham-by-Sea, West Sussex, BN43 6GA

Nearest Railway Station Shoreham-by-Sea - 1.1km

Bus Route Hammy Lane - stop 150m away

STORRINGTON COMMUNITY

Southern Combination Division One

Founded 1920 Nickname: The Swans **Club Colours:** All blue

Club Contact Details 01903 745 860

HONOURS FA Comps: None

League: Sussex County Division Three 2004-05.

11-12	12-13	13-14	14-15	15-16	16-17	17-18	18-19	19-20	20-21
SxC2 9	SxC2 10	SxC2 15	SxC2 14	SC1 4	SC1 12	SC1 15	SC1 14	SC1 n&v	SC1 n&v
								FAV 1Q	FAV 2Q

GROUND: Recreation Ground, Pulborough Road, Storrington RH20 4HJ

Nearest Railway Station Pulborough - 5.6km

Bus Route Brow Close - stop 238m away

WICK

Southern Combination Division One

Founded 1892 | Nickname: The Wickers | **Club Colours:** Red & black

Club Contact Details 01903 713 535 wickfootballclub@outlook.com

HONOURS FA Comps: None

League: Sussex County Division Two 1981-82, 85-86, 89-90, 93-94.

11-12		12-13		13-14		14-15		15-16		16-17		17-18		18-19		19-20		20-21	
SxC1	14	SxC1	16	SxC2	6	SxC2	3	SCP	16	SCP	19	SC1	5	SC1	9	SC1	n&v	SC1	n&v
FAC	EP									FAC	EP	FAC	EP	FAC	EP				
FAV	1Q	FAV	2Q							FAV	1P	FAV	1Q	FAV	1P	FAV	1Q	FAV	2Q

GROUND: Crabtree Park, Coomes Way, Wick, Littlehampton, W Sussex BN17 7LS

Nearest Railway Station Littlehampton - 1.7km

Bus Route Seaton Road - stop 250 m away

WORTHING UNITED

Southern Combination Division One

Founded 1952 | Nickname: Mavericks | **Club Colours:** Sky blue & white

Club Contact Details 01903 234 466 secretary@worthingunitedfc.co.uk

HONOURS FA Comps: None

League: Sussex County Division Two 1973-74, 2014-15, Division Three 1989-90.

11-12		12-13		13-14		14-15		15-16		16-17		17-18		18-19		19-20		20-21	
SxC1	14	SxC1	22	SxC1	20	SxC2	1	SCP	14	SCP	17	SCP	19	SC1	17	SC1	n&v	SC1	n&v
				FAC	EPr	FAC	EP	FAC	EPr	FAC	EP	FAC	EP	FAC	P				
		FAV	1Qr	FAV	2Q	FAV	2Q	FAV	1P	FAV	1Q	FAV	1Q	FAV	1Q	FAV	2Q	FAV	2P

GROUND: The Robert Albon Memorial Ground, Lyons Way BN14 9JF

Nearest Railway Station East Worthing - 1.9km

Bus Route Lyons Farm Sainsbury's - stop 203m away

BEARSTED

Southern Counties East Premier

Founded 1895 Nickname: The Bears **Club Colours:** White and blue

Club Contact Details 07849 089 875 benton951@aol.com

Previous Names: None

Previous Leagues: Maidstone & District. Kent County 1982-2011. Kent Invicta (Founder Member) 2011-16.

HONOURS

FA Comps: None

League: Maidstone & District Div.6 1961-62, Div.3 73-74, Div.2 74-75, Div.1 77-78, Premier 79-80, 80-81, 81-82.
Kent County WD2 82-83, WD1 83-84, WPrem 87-87, WSen 87-88, D1W 96-97, Prem 2000-01, 01-02. Kent Invicta 2015-16.

11-12		12-13		13-14		14-15		15-16		16-17		17-18		18-19		19-20		20-21	
K_Iv	7	K_Iv	4	K_Iv	6	K_Iv	2	K_Iv	1	SCEP	12	SCEP	14	SCEP	14	SCEP	n&v	SCEP	n&v
												FAC	EP	FAC	P	FAC	EPr	FAC	EP
										FAV	1Q	FAV	1Q	FAV	4P	FAV	2P	FAV	1Q

GROUND: Otham Sports Ground, White Horse Lane, Otham ME15 8RG

Nearest Railway Station Bearsted - 3.2km

Bus Route Arriva No.13

CLUB MOVEMENTS

PREMIER DIVISION - IN: Holmesdale, Kennington and Rusthall (P - SCE1).

OUT: AFC Croydon Athletic, Balham and Beckenham Town (LM - CCPS). Corinthian (P - IsthSE).

CANTERBURY CITY

Southern Counties East Premier

Founded 1904 Nickname: **Club Colours:** Burgundy and white

Club Contact Details 01795 591 900 secretary@cantburycityfc.net

Previous Names: None

Previous Leagues: Kent 1947-59, 94-01, Metropolitan 1959-60, Southern 1960-94, Kent County 2007-11.

HONOURS

FA Comps: None

League: Kent County Division Two East 2007-08, One East 08-09.

11-12		12-13		13-14		14-15		15-16		16-17		17-18		18-19		19-20		20-21	
Kent P	9	Kent P	9	SCE	12	SCE	12	SCE	8	SCEP	9	SCEP	10	SCEP	9	SCEP	n&v	SCEP	n&v
				FAC	EP	FAC	P	FAC	P	FAC	Pr	FAC	EP	FAC	EP	FAC	P	FAC	EP
		FAV	1P	FAV	1Q	FAV	1Q	FAV	3P	FAV	2P	FAV	2P	FAV	SF	FAV	2P	FAV	2Q

GROUND: Shepherd Neame Stadium, Salters Lane, Faversham ME13 8ND

Capacity: 2,500
Seats: 180
Covered: 180

CHATHAM TOWN

Southern Counties East Premier

Founded 1882 Nickname: Chats **Club Colours:** Red & black

Club Contact Details 01634 401 130 secretary@chathamtownfc.com

Previous Names: Chatham FC 1882-1974, Medway FC 1974-79

Previous Leagues: Southern 1894-1900, 1920-21, 27-29, 83-88, 2001-06, Kent 1894-96, 1901-1905, 29-59, 68-83, 88-2001, Aetolian 1959-64, Metropolitan 1964-68, Isthmian 2006-17.

HONOURS

FA Comps: None

League: Kent 1894-95, 1903-04, 04-05, 71-72, 73-74, 75-76, 76-77, 79-80, 2000-01. Aetolian 1963-64.

11-12		12-13		13-14		14-15		15-16		16-17		17-18		18-19		19-20		20-21	
Isth1N	15	Isth1N	13	Isth1N	12	Isth1N	21	Isth1S	19	Isth1S	22	SCEP	16	SCEP	4	SCEP	n&v	SCEP	n&v
FAC	1Q	FAC	1Q	FAC	4Q	FAC	P	FAC	2Q	FAC	Pr	FAC	EPr	FAC	P	FAC	EP	FAC	EP
FAT	P	FAT	1Q	FAT	2Q	FAT	1Qr	FAT	1Q	FAT	P	FAV	2Q	FAV	2P	FAV	4P	FAV	3P

GROUND: The Bauvill Stadium, Maidstone Road, Chatham ME4 6LR

Nearest Railway Station Chatham - 1.4km

Bus Route Bus stops outside the ground.

Capacity: 2,000
Seats: 600
Covered: 600

CROWBOROUGH ATHLETIC

Southern Counties East Premier

Founded 1894 Nickname: The Crows **Club Colours:** Navy blue and sky blue

Club Contact Details 07908 116 778 cafc1sts@outlook.com

Previous Names: None

Previous Leagues: Sussex County 1974-2008. Isthmian 2008-09. Sussex County 2009-14.

HONOURS

FA Comps: None

League: Sussex County Division Two 1992-93, 2004-05, Division Three 2003-04, Division One 2007-08.

11-12	12-13	13-14	14-15	15-16	16-17	17-18	18-19	19-20	20-21
SxC1 13	SxC1 15	SxC1 5	SCE 10	SCE 7	SCEP 2	SCEP 3	SCEP 13	SCEP n&v	SCEP n&v
FAC EP	FAC P	FAC EPr	FAC EPr	FAC EPr	FAC EP	FAC 2Q	FAC EPr	FAC EP	FAC EP
FAV 1Q	FAV 1Q	FAV 2P	FAV 1Q	FAV 1Q	FAV 5P	FAV 4P	FAV 2P	FAV 1P	FAV 1Q

GROUND: Crowborough Co. Stadium, Alderbrook Rec, Fermor Road, TN6 3AN

Capacity: 2,000
Seats: 150
Covered: 150

DEAL TOWN

Southern Counties East Premier

Founded 1908 Nickname: The Hoops **Club Colours:** Black & white

Club Contact Details 01304 375 623 secretary@dealtownfc.co.uk

Previous Names: Deal Cinque Ports FC > 1920

Previous Leagues: Thanet. East Kent. Kent 1894-96, 1900-27, 32-39, 45-59, 72-84, Southern 1894-1901 & 84-90, Aetolian 1959-64, Greater London 1964-65, Metropolitan 1965-71, Metropolitan London 1971-72

HONOURS

FA Comps: FA Vase 1999-2000

League: Kent 1953-54. Southern Counties East 1999-2000.

11-12	12-13	13-14	14-15	15-16	16-17	17-18	18-19	19-20	20-21
Kent P 15	Kent P 12	SCE 13	SCE 13	SCE 9	SCEP 13	SCEP 7	SCEP 11	SCEP n&v	SCEP n&v
FAC P	FAC EP	FAC P	FAC Pr	FAC 2Q	FAC EP	FAC P	FAC EPr	FAC EP	FAC 1Q
FAV 2P	FAV 2P	FAV 1Q	FAV 1Q	FAV 2P	FAV 2Qr	FAV 2P	FAV 1P	FAV 5P	FAV 3P

GROUND: Charles Sports Ground, St Leonards Road, Deal CT14 9AU
Nearest Railway Station Deal - 3/4 mile away

Capacity: 2,500
Seats: 180
Covered: 180

ERITH & BELVEDERE

Southern Counties East Premier

Founded 1922 Nickname: Deres **Club Colours:** Blue & white

Club Contact Details 07890 927 261 brian.spurrell@yahoo.com

Previous Names: Belvedere & District FC (Formed 1918 restructured 1922)

Previous Leagues: Kent 1922-29, 31-39, 78-82. London. Corinthian 1945-63. Athenian 1963-78. Southern. Kent League 2005-13. Isthmian 2013-14.

HONOURS

FA Comps: None

League: Kent Division One / Premier 1981-82 / 2012-13.

11-12	12-13	13-14	14-15	15-16	16-17	17-18	18-19	19-20	20-21
Kent P 2	Kent P 1	Isth1N 24	SCEP 3	SCEP 16	SCEP 20	SCE1 4	SCE1 2	SCEP n&v	SCEP n&v
FAC 1Q	FAC EP	FAC P	FAC Pr	FAC P	FAC EP	FAC P	FAC EPr	FAC P	FAC 1Q
FAV 1Q	FAV 3P	FAT P	FAV QF	FAV 2P	FAV 1Q	FAV 1Pr	FAV 1Q	FAV 1P	FAV 1P

GROUND: Park View Road, Welling DA16 1SY
Nearest Railway Station Welling - 1.1km

Capacity: 4,000
Seats: 1,070
Covered: 1,000

ERITH TOWN

Southern Counties East Premier

Founded 1956 Nickname: The Dockers **Club Colours:** Red & black stripes

Club Contact Details 07877 766 794 secretary@erithtown.co.uk

Previous Names: Woolwich Town 1959-89 and 1990-97.

Previous Leagues: London Metropolitan Sunday. London Spartan.

HONOURS

FA Comps: None

League: London Metropolitan Sunday Senior Section 1965-66, 70-71, 74-75.

11-12		12-13		13-14		14-15		15-16		16-17		17-18		18-19		19-20		20-21	
Kent P	4	Kent P	3	SCE	3	SCE	19	SCE	13	SCEP	17	SCEP	17	SCEP	6	SCEP	n&v	SCEP	n&v
FAC	2Q	FAC	EP	FAC	P	FAC	EP	FAC	P	FAC	P	FAC	1Q	FAC	2Q	FAC	EP	FAC	EP
FAV	2P	FAV	2P	FAV	3P	FAV	2P	FAV	2Q	FAV	1Q	FAV	2P	FAV	3P	FAV	1Qr	FAV	1Q

GROUND: Erith Stadium, Avenue Road, Erith DA8 3AT

Nearest Railway Station Erith

FISHER

Southern Counties East Premier

Founded 1908 Nickname: The Fish **Club Colours:** Black & white stripes

Club Contact Details 07743 499 529 secretary.fisherfc@yahoo.com

Previous Names: Fisher Athletic. Reformed as Fisher F.C. in 2009.

Previous Leagues: Parthenon, Kent Amateur, London Spartan, Southern, Isthmian, Conference.

HONOURS

FA Comps: None

League: Southern Southern Division 1982-83, Premier 86-87, Eastern 2004-05.

11-12		12-13		13-14		14-15		15-16		16-17		17-18		18-19		19-20		20-21	
Kent P	10	Kent P	14	SCEP	14	SCEP	16	SCEP	17	SCEP	19	SCE1	3	SCEP	3	SCEP	n&v	SCEP	n&v
FAC	P	FAC	EPr	FAC	EP	FAC	P	FAC	EP					FAC	EP	FAC	EP	FAC	1Q
FAV	2Q	FAV	2Q	FAV	2Q	FAV	1Pr	FAV	2P			FAV	1P	FAV	1Qr	FAV	2P	FAV	1P

GROUND: St Pauls Sports Ground, Salter Road, Rotherhithe, London SE16 5EF

Nearest Railway Station Rotherhithe, on the London Overground (1 km)

GLEBE

Southern Counties East Premier

Founded 1995 Nickname: **Club Colours:** Red & black

Club Contact Details 07903 274 178 lukejefferies@virginmedia.com

Previous Names: Glebe Wickham Youth Team founded in 1995 with an adult side formed in 2013.

Previous Leagues: Kent Invicta 2013-16.

HONOURS

FA Comps: None

League: Southern Counties east Division One 2016-17.

11-12		12-13		13-14		14-15		15-16		16-17		17-18		18-19		19-20		20-21	
				K_lv	10	K_lv	7	K_lv	3	SCE1	1	SCEP	12	SCEP	8	SCEP	n&v	SCEP	n&v
								FAC	EP	FAC	EP	FAC	2Qr	FAC	EP	FAC	P	FAC	EP
				FAV	2Q	FAV	1Q	FAV	1Q	FAV	3P	FAV	1Qr	FAV	2Q	FAV	4P	FAV	2P

GROUND: Foxbury Avenue, Chislehurst, Bromley BR7 6SD **Capacity:** 1,200

Nearest Railway Station Sidcup - 1.9km

Bus Route Nos. 269 & 260.

HOLLANDS & BLAIR

Southern Counties East Premier

Founded 1967 Nickname: Blair **Club Colours:** All red

Club Contact Details 01634 573 839 secretary@hollandsandblair.co.uk

Previous Names: Hollands & Blair United 1970-74

Previous Leagues: Rochester & District 1970-2004. Kent County 2004-11

HONOURS

FA Comps: None

League: Rochester & District Premier 1989-90, 93-94, 2002-03, 03-04. Kent County Division Two Easy 2004-05, Division One East 05-06, Premier 08-9, 10-11. Kent Invicta 2013-14, 14-15.

11-12	12-13	13-14	14-15	15-16	16-17	17-18	18-19	19-20	20-21
K_lv 3	K_lv 2	K_lv 1	K_lv 1	SCE 2	SCEP 8	SCEP 18	SCEP 18	SCEP n&v	SCEP n&v
					FAC Pr	FAC P	FAC EP	FAC EP	FAC P
				FAV 2Q	FAV 1P	FAV 1P	FAV 1Q	FAV 2Q	FAV 1Q

GROUND: Star Meadow Sports Club, Darland Avenue, Gillingham, Kent ME7 3AN

HOLMESDALE

Southern Counties East Premier

Founded 1956 Nickname: The Dalers **Club Colours:** Green & yellow

Club Contact Details 07912 870 840 mark.hayes2@rjpowergroup.co.uk

Previous Names: None.

Previous Leagues: Thornton Heath & Dist. Surrey Inter. Surrey South Eastern. Kent County.

HONOURS

FA Comps: None

League: Thorton Heath & District Division Six 1956-57, Two 61-62, One 71-72, Premier 86-87. Surrey South Eastern Comb. Prem 92-93. Kent County Div.1W 2005-06, Prem 06-07.

11-12	12-13	13-14	14-15	15-16	16-17	17-18	18-19	19-20	20-21
Kent P 13	Kent P 16	SCE 10	SCE 14	SCE 19	SCE1 6	SCE1 7	SCE1 6	SCE1 n&v	SCE1 n&v
FAC EP	FAC EP	FAC P	FAC P	FAC P	FAC EP	FAC EP			
FAV 1Q	FAV 2Q	FAV 2Q	FAV 1Q	FAV 1Qr	FAV 2Q	FAV 1Q	FAV 1Q	FAV 2Q	FAV 1P

GROUND: Holmesdale Sp.& Soc.Club, 68 Oakley Road, Bromley BR2 8HG
Nearest Railway Station Hayes - 2.1km

K SPORTS

Southern Counties East Premier

Founded 1919 Nickname: The Paperboys **Club Colours:** Black & white

Club Contact Details 07725 941 711 holtam@blueyonder.co.uk

Previous Names: Reeds International. APM. APM Contrast.

Previous Leagues: Kent County >2015.

HONOURS

FA Comps: None

League: Kent Division Two 1929-30, 30-31, 31-32, 46-47.
Kent County Senior Division West 1959-60, 63-64, Premier West 1990-91.

11-12	12-13	13-14	14-15	15-16	16-17	17-18	18-19	19-20	20-21
KC P 6	KC P 6	KC P 3	KC P 4	K_lv 6	SCE1 5	SCE1 2	SCEP 12	SCEP n&v	SCEP n&v
							FAC EPr	FAC EP	FAC EP
						FAV 1P	FAV 2Q	FAV 2Q	FAV 2Q

GROUND: Cobdown Sports & Social Club, Station Road, Ditton, Aylesford, Kent ME20 6AU
Nearest Railway Station Aylesford

KENNINGTON

Southern Counties East Premier

Founded 1888 Nickname: The Ton **Club Colours:** Amber & black

Club Contact Details 01233 611 838 kevin@lab-services.co.uk

Previous Names: None
Previous Leagues: Ashford & District > 1989. Kent County 1989-2018.
HONOURS
FA Comps: None
League: Kent County Eastern Section Premier 1989-90, Division One East 1989-99, 2001-02, Premier 2017-18.

11-12		12-13		13-14		14-15		15-16		16-17		17-18		18-19		19-20		20-21	
KC1E	11	KC1E	4	KC1E	4	KC1E	2	KC P	2	KC P	4	KC P	1	SCE1	3	SCE1	n&v	SCE1	n&v
																		FAC	EP
																		FAV	3P

GROUND: Ashford United FC, Homelands Stadium, Ashford Road, Kingsnorth, Ashford TN26 1NJ **Capacity:** 3,200
Nearest Railway Station Ham Street - 4.2km **Seats:** 500
Bus Route Smithfields Crossroads - stop 600m away **Covered:** Yes

LORDSWOOD

Southern Counties East Premier

Founded 1968 Nickname: Lords **Club Colours:** Orange

Club Contact Details 01634 669 138 slew1953@hotmail.co.uk

Previous Names: None.
Previous Leagues: Rochester & District. Kent County.
HONOURS
FA Comps: None
League: None

11-12		12-13		13-14		14-15		15-16		16-17		17-18		18-19		19-20		20-21	
Kent P	12	Kent P	5	SCE	11	SCE	15	SCE	4	SCEP	16	SCEP	8	SCEP	10	SCEP	n&v	SCEP	n&v
FAC	P	FAC	Pr	FAC	EP	FAC	Pr	FAC	EP	FAC	EPr	FAC	EP	FAC	EP	FAC	EP	FAC	EP
FAV	1P	FAV	4P	FAV	3P	FAV	1P	FAV	3P	FAV	1P	FAV	3P	FAV	2P	FAV	2Q	FAV	2Q

GROUND: Martyn Grove, Northdane Way, Walderslade, ME5 8YE **Capacity:** 600
Nearest Railway Station Chatham - 4.8km **Seats:** 123
Bus Route Lords Wood Leisure Centre - stop 30m away **Covered:** 123

PUNJAB UNITED

Southern Counties East Premier

Founded 2003 Nickname: **Club Colours:** All red with white trim

Club Contact Details 01474 323 817 jindi_banwait@hotmail.com

Previous Names: None
Previous Leagues: Kent County 2016-17.
HONOURS
FA Comps: None
League: Kent County Premier 2016-17. Southern Counties East Division One 2017-18.

11-12		12-13		13-14		14-15		15-16		16-17		17-18		18-19		19-20		20-21	
										KC P	1	SCE1	1	SCEP	17	SCEP	n&v	SCEP	n&v
																FAC	EP	FAC	EP
														FAV	2Q	FAV	1P	FAV	2Q

GROUND: Elite Venue, Hawkins Avenue, Dunkirk Close, Gravesend, Kent DA12 5ND
Nearest Railway Station Gravesend - 2.7km

RUSTHALL

Southern Counties East Premier

Foundec 1899 Nickname: The Rustics **Club Colours:** Green & white

Club Contact Details 07976 386 527 deanjacquin@icloud.com

Previous Names: None

Previous Leagues: Tunbridege Wells 1899-1983. Kent County 1983-2011. Kent Invicta 2011-16.

HONOURS

FA Comps: None

League: Tunbridge Wells 1904-05, 22-23, 23-24, 24-25, 25-26, 29-30, 30-31, 34-35, 37-38, 38-39, 51-52.
Kent county Division Two West 1983-84, Division One West 1984-85, 2004-05.

11-12	12-13	13-14	14-15	15-16	16-17	17-18	18-19	19-20	20-21
K_Iv 11	K_Iv 12	K_Iv 7	K_Iv 13	K_Iv 19	SCE1 2	SCEP 19	SCEP 19	SCE1 n&v	SCE1 n&v
						FAC EPr	FAC Pr	FAC EP	
					FAV 2Q	FAV 1P	FAV 1P	FAV 1P	FAV 1Q

GROUND: Jockey Farm, Nellington Road, Rusthall, Tunbridge Wells TN4 8SH

Nearest Railway Station High Rocks - 1.5km

SHEPPEY UNITED

Southern Counties East Premier

Foundec 1890 Nickname: **Club Colours:** Red & white

Club Contact Details 01795 669 547 jon.longhurst@hotmail.com

Previous Names: AFC Sheppy 2007-2010. Sheppey & Sheerness United after merger 2013-14.

Previous Leagues: Kent County > 2014.

HONOURS

FA Comps: None

League: Kent 1905-06, 06-07, 72-73, 74-75, 78-79, 94-95. Greater London Section B 1964-65.

11-12	12-13	13-14	14-15	15-16	16-17	17-18	18-19	19-20	20-21
KC1E 4	KC P Exp	KC P 2	K_Iv 5	K_Iv 2	SCEP 6	SCEP 11	SCEP 7	SCEP n&v	SCEP n&v
					FAC EP	FAC P	FAC EP	FAC 1Q	FAC 3Q
				FAV 2Q	FAV 2Q	FAV 2P	FAV 3P	FAV 1P	FAV 2P

GROUND: The Total Power Stadium, Holm Park, Queenborough Road ME12 3DB

Capacity: 1,450
Seats: 170
Covered: 470

TOWER HAMLETS

Southern Counties East Premier

Foundec 2000 Nickname: Green Army **Club Colours:** Orange & black

Club Contact Details 07853 660 189 shakilhoque119@gmail.com

Previous Names: Bethnal Green United 2000-2013.

Previous Leagues: Canery Wharf Summer League. Inner London. London Intermediate. Middlesex County >2009. Essex Senior 2009-20.

HONOURS

FA Comps: None

League: Middlesex County Premier Division 2008-09.

11-12	12-13	13-14	14-15	15-16	16-17	17-18	18-19	19-20	20-21
ESen 9	ESen 12	ESen 4	ESen 17	ESen 17	ESen 20	ESen 11	ESen 16	ESen n&v	SCEP n&v
		FAC P	FAC EP	FAC Pr	FAC P	FAC P	FAC EP	FAC P	FAC EP
		FAV 1P	FAV 1P	FAV 1Q	FAV 1Q	FAV 2P	FAV 1Q	FAV 2Q	FAV 1Q

GROUND: Phoenix FC, Mayplace Ground, Mayplace Road East, Barnehurst, Kent DA7 6JT

Capacity: 2,000
Seats: 439

Nearest Railway Station Barnehurst - 1.1km

Bus Route 492 stops at the ground

TUNBRIDGE WELLS

Southern Counties East Premier

Founded 1886 Nickname: The Wells **Club Colours:** All red

Club Contact Details 07966 123 337 secretary@twfcexec.com

Previous Names: None.

Previous Leagues: South Eastern. Southern Amateur 1908-11. Isthminan 1911-13. Spartan 1913-14. Kent.

HONOURS

FA Comps: None

League: Southern Amateur Section B 1909-10. Kent Division One 1984-85.

11-12		12-13		13-14		14-15		15-16		16-17		17-18		18-19		19-20		20-21	
Kent P	5	Kent P	7	SCE	4	SCE	5	SCE	14	SCEP	15	SCEP	15	SCEP	16	SCEP	n&v	SCEP	n&v
FAC	P	FAC	EP	FAC	1Q	FAC	EP	FAC	Pr	FAC	EPr	FAC	2Q	FAC	EPr	FAC	P	FAC	1Q
FAV	4P	FAV	F	FAV	3P	FAV	4Pr	FAV	2P	FAV	1P	FAV	2Qr	FAV	1P	FAV	1Pr	FAV	1Q

GROUND: Culverden Stadium, Culverden Down, Tunbridge Wells TN4 9SG

Nearest Railway Station Tunbridge Wells 1.5km. High Brooms - 1.8km

Capacity: 3,750
Seats: 250
Covered: 1,000

WELLING TOWN

Southern Counties East Premier

Founded 2014 Nickname: The Boots **Club Colours:** Green and black

Club Contact Details 07891 431 735 info@wellingtontown.co.uk

Previous Names: None

Previous Leagues: Kent County 2016-18.

HONOURS

FA Comps: None

League: Kent County Division Two West 2017-18. Southern Counties East Division One 2018-19.

11-12		12-13		13-14		14-15		15-16		16-17		17-18		18-19		19-20		20-21	
										KC3W	2	KC2W	1	SCE1	1	SCEP	n&v	SCEP	n&v
																FAC	EP	FAC	EP
																FAV	3P	FAV	1P

GROUND: Bayliss Avenue, Thamesmead, London SE28 8NJ

Nearest Railway Station Abbey Wood - 2 miles

Bus Route 177, 229 401, 472

CLUB MOVEMENTS

PREMIER DIVISION - IN: Chessington & Hook, Tooting Bec and Westside (LM - CC1).
Faversham Strike Force, Larkfield & New Hythe and Staplehurst Monarchs (P - KC).

OUT: Holmesdale, Kennington and Rusthall (P - SCE1).

BRIDON ROPES

Southern Counties East Division One

Founded 1935 Nickname: The Ropes **Club Colours:** Royal blue

Club Contact Details 0208 856 1923 cburtonsmith@gmail.com

HONOURS FA Comps: None

League: Spartan Division Two 1991-92. Kent County Division One West 2009-10.

11-12	12-13	13-14	14-15	15-16	16-17	17-18	18-19	19-20	20-21
K_lv 4	K_lv 7	K_lv 8	K_lv 10	K_lv 5	SCE1 7	SCE1 5	SCE1 4	SCE1 n&v	SCE1 n&v
					FAC EP			FAC P	
				FAV 1P	FAV 1P	FAV 2Q	FAV 2Qr	FAV 2Q	FAV 1Qr

GROUND: Meridian Sports & Social Club, Charlton Park Lane, Charlton, London SE7 8QS

Nearest Railway Station Charlton - 1.3km

CHESSINGTON & HOOK UNITED

Southern Counties East Division One

Founded 1921 Nickname: Chessey **Club Colours:** Blue

Club Contact Details 07983 027 127 rebecca.woodward@chufc.co.uk

HONOURS FA Comps: None

League: Kingston & District Division Four 1922-23, Division Two 1955-56, Division One 1957-58.

11-12	12-13	13-14	14-15	15-16	16-17	17-18	18-19	19-20	20-21
CCP 20	CCP 17	CCP 22	CC1 3	CCP 21	CC1 5	CC1 13	CC1 9	CC1 n&v	CC1 n&v
FAC P	FAC P	FAC P	FAC 1Q	FAC 1Q	FAC Pr	FAC P			
FAV 1Q	FAV 2Q	FAV 2P	FAV 2P	FAV 1Q	FAV 1Qr	FAV 2Q	FAV 2Q	FAV 1Q	FAV 1Q

GROUND: Chalky Lane, Chessington, Surrey KT9 2NF

Nearest Railway Station Chessington South

Bus Route London United 71, 465

CROYDON

Southern Counties East Division One

Founded 1953 Nickname: The Trams **Club Colours:** Sky & navy blue

Club Contact Details 0208 654 8555 sallycroydonfc@aol.com

HONOURS FA Comps: None

League: Spartan 1963-64. Athenian Division Two 1965-66. Isthmian Division One 1999-00.

11-12	12-13	13-14	14-15	15-16	16-17	17-18	18-19	19-20	20-21
CCP 16	CCP 14	CCP 13	SCE 18	SCE 18	SCEP 11	SCEP 5	SCEP 20	SCE1 n&v	SCE1 n&v
FAC EP	FAC EP	FAC P	FAC 1Q	FAC 2Q	FAC Pr	FAC Pr	FAC P	FAC EP	
FAV 1Q	FAV 3P	FAV 2Q	FAV 1Qr	FAV 1P	FAV 4P	FAV 2P	FAV 1Q	FAV 2Q	FAV 1Q

GROUND: Croydon Sports Arena, Albert Road, South Norwood SE25 4QL

Nearest Railway Station Croydon Tramlink - 1/4 mile

Bus Route No.312

FAVERSHAM STRIKE FORCE

Southern Counties East Division One

Founded 1999 Nickname: **Club Colours:** Royal blue

Club Contact Details 07770 997 329 ruthswillmott@me.com

HONOURS FA Comps: None

League: Kent County 2014-15, 15-16.

11-12	12-13	13-14	14-15	15-16	16-17	17-18	18-19	19-20	20-21
		KC2E 2	KC1E 1	KC P 1	KC P 7	KC P 14	KC P 8	KC P n&v	KC P n&v

GROUND: Rochester United FC, Rede Court Sports Ground, Rede Court Road, Rochester ME2 3TU

Nearest Railway Station Strood - 2.1km

FC ELMSTEAD

Southern Counties East Division One

Founded 1958 Nickname: The Cocks **Club Colours:** Sky blue & red

Club Contact Details 07711 287295 stewartmurphy1001@gmail.com

HONOURS FA Comps: None

League: None

11-12	12-13	13-14	14-15	15-16	16-17	17-18	18-19	19-20	20-21
		KC3W 2	KC2W 2	K_Iv 11	SCE1 11	SCE1 8	SCE1 13	SCE1 n&v	SCE1 n&v
				FAV 1Q	FAV 1P	FAV 1Q	FAV 1Q	FAV 1Q	FAV 1Q

GROUND: Sutton Athletic FC, Lower Road, Hextable, Kent BR8 7RZ

Nearest Railway Station Swanley - 2.4km

FOREST HILL PARK

Southern Counties East Division One

Founded 1992 Nickname: **Club Colours:** All blue

Club Contact Details 07774 294 236 info@fhpfc.co.uk

HONOURS FA Comps: None

League: South London Alliance Division One 2005-06. Kent County Division Two West 2009-10.

11-12	12-13	13-14	14-15	15-16	16-17	17-18	18-19	19-20	20-21
KC P 6	KC P 7	KC1W 10	KC1W 5	K_Iv 13	SCE1 12	SCE1 16	SCE1 7	SCE1 n&v	SCE1 n&v
						FAV 2Q	FAV 2Q	FAV 1Q	FAV 1Q

GROUND: Ladywell Arena, Silvermere Road, Catford, London SE6 4QX

Nearest Railway Station Ladywell and Catford Bridge.

Bus Route 47, 54, 75, 136, 181, 185, 199, 208

GREENWAYS

Southern Counties East Division One

Founded 1965 Nickname: **Club Colours:** Green

Club Contact Details 07889 313 935 greenwaysfc@hotmail.com

HONOURS FA Comps: None

League: Gravesend Premier x7. Kent County Premier 1988-89.

11-12	12-13	13-14	14-15	15-16	16-17	17-18	18-19	19-20	20-21
KC P 8	KC P 7	KC P 5	KC P 7	KC P 8	KC P 2	KC P 2	SCE1 10	SCE1 n&v	SCE1 n&v
								FAV 1Q	FAV 1Q

GROUND: K Sports, Cobdown, Station Road, Ditton, Aylesford, Kent ME20 6AU

KENT FOOTBALL UNITED

Southern Counties East Division One

Founded 2010 Nickname: **Club Colours:** All blue

Club Contact Details 07875 488 856 m.bolton.kfu@gmail.com

HONOURS FA Comps: None

League: None

11-12	12-13	13-14	14-15	15-16	16-17	17-18	18-19	19-20	20-21
K_Iv 13	K_Iv 11	K_Iv 11	K_Iv 15	K_Iv 17	SCE1 4	SCE1 9	SCE1 14	SCE1 n&v	SCE1 n&v
FAV 2Q	FAV 1Q	FAV 1Q					FAV 1Q	FAV 1Q	FAV 1Q

GROUND: Glentworth Club, Lowfield Street, Dartford DA1 1JB

Nearest Railway Station Dartford - 0.8 km

LARKFIELD & NEW HYTHE

Southern Counties East Division One

Founded 1961 Nickname: Club Colours: Yellow & black

Club Contact Details 07920 051 833 adam.handy@albatrossgroup.com

HONOURS FA Comps: None

League: None

11-12	12-13	13-14	14-15	15-16	16-17	17-18	18-19	19-20	20-21
KC2E 9	KC2E 11	KC2E 7	KC2E 10	KC2E 4	KC2E 9	KC2E 10	KC2E 5	KC2E n&v	KC1E n&v

GROUND: Taray Community Stadium, 251a New Hythe Lane, Larkfield, Maidstone ME20 6PU

LEWISHAM BOROUGH

Southern Counties East Division One

Founded 2003 Nickname: The Boro Club Colours: Blue

Club Contact Details 07857 361 185 colin.jarrett@lbcfc.co.uk

HONOURS FA Comps: None

League: Kent County Division One West 2003-04, Premier 2005-06.

11-12	12-13	13-14	14-15	15-16	16-17	17-18	18-19	19-20	20-21
K_lv 8	K_lv 16	K_lv 13	K_lv 16	K_lv 20	SCE1 19	SCE1 18	SCE1 11	SCE1 n&v	SCE1 n&v
						FAV 1Q	FAV 1Q		FAV 1Q

GROUND: Ladywell Arena, Silvermere Road, Catford, London SE6 4QX

Nearest Railway Station Ladywell and Catford Bridge.

Bus Route 47, 54, 75, 136, 181, 185, 199, 208

LYDD TOWN

Southern Counties East Division One

Founded 1885 Nickname: The Lydders Club Colours: Green & red

Club Contact Details 01797 321 904 brucemarchant@hotmail.com

HONOURS FA Comps: None

League: Kent County Premier East 1969-70, 70-71, Senior East 1989-90, 90-91, 91-92, Division One East 92-93, 93-94.

11-12	12-13	13-14	14-15	15-16	16-17	17-18	18-19	19-20	20-21
K_lv 12	K_lv 6	K_lv 2	K_lv 3	K_lv 8	SCE1 9	SCE1 10	SCE1 12	SCE1	SCE1 n&v
						FAV 1Q	FAV 1Q	FAV 1Qr	FAV 2Q

GROUND: The Lindsey Field, Dengemarsh Road, Lydd, Kent TN29 9JH

MERIDIAN VP

Southern Counties East Division One

Founded 1995 Nickname: Club Colours: White & royal blue

Club Contact Details 07791 861 346 stevenbailey@meridianfc.co.uk

HONOURS FA Comps: None

League: None

11-12	12-13	13-14	14-15	15-16	16-17	17-18	18-19	19-20	20-21
K_lv 15	K_lv 15	K_lv 14	K_lv 12	K_lv 12	SCE1 17	SCE1 15	SCE1 18	SCE1 n&v	SCE1 n&v
				FAV 1P	FAV 1Q	FAV 2P	FAV 1Q	FAV 1Q	FAV 1Q

GROUND: Meridian Sports & Social Club, Charlton Park Lane, London SE7 8QS

Nearest Railway Station Charlton - 1.3km

ROCHESTER UNITED

Southern Counties East Division One

Founded 1982 Nickname: **Club Colours:** Red, white & black

Club Contact Details 07775 735 543 toniwalker709@gmail.com

HONOURS FA Comps: None

League: Rochester & District Division One 1997-98. Kent County Division One West 2007-08. Kent Invicta 2011-12.

11-12	12-13	13-14	14-15	15-16	16-17	17-18	18-19	19-20	20-21
K_lv 1	Kent P 13	SCE 15	SCE 20	SCE 15	SCEP 14	SCEP 20	SCE1 17	SCE1 n&v	SCE1 n&v
				FAC 1Q	FAC Pr	FAC EPr	FAC EP		
			FAV 1P	FAV 2Q	FAV 2Q	FAV 1Q	FAV 1Q	FAV 1Q	FAV 2Q

GROUND: Rochester United Sports Ground, Rede Court Road, Strood ME2 3TU

Nearest Railway Station Strood - 2.1km

SNODLAND TOWN

Southern Counties East Division One

Founded 2012 Nickname: **Club Colours:** Royal blue & yellow

Club Contact Details 07999 457 864 terry.reeves55@virginmedia.com

HONOURS FA Comps: None

League: None

11-12	12-13	13-14	14-15	15-16	16-17	17-18	18-19	19-20	20-21
	KC P 11	KC P 4	KC P 9	KC1E 3	SCE1 8	SCE1 6	SCE1 15	SCE1 n&v	SCE1 n&v
						FAV 1Q	FAV 1Q	FAV 1P	FAV 1Q

GROUND: Potyns Field, Paddlesworth Road, Snodland ME6 5DP

Nearest Railway Station Snodland - 1.3km

SPORTING CLUB THAMESMEAD

Southern Counties East Division One

Founded 1900 Nickname: The Acre **Club Colours:** Red & black

Club Contact Details 0208 320 4488 richardleach1979@gmail.com

HONOURS FA Comps: None

League: South London Alliance Division One 2008-09.

11-12	12-13	13-14	14-15	15-16	16-17	17-18	18-19	19-20	20-21
K_lv 10	K_lv 5	K_lv 9	K_lv 6	K_lv 9	SCE1 10	SCE1 12	SCE1 9	SCE1 n&v	SCE1 n&v
				FAC P	FAC EP				
			FAV 1Q	FAV 1Qr	FAV 2P	FAV 2Q	FAV 2Q	FAV 1P	FAV 1Q

GROUND: Sporting Club Thamesmead, Bayliss Avenue, Thamesmead SE28 8NJ

Nearest Railway Station Abbey Wood - 1.8km

STANSFELD

Southern Counties East Division One

Founded 1897 Nickname: Palace **Club Colours:** Yellow & blue stripes

Club Contact Details 07861 885 590 stansfeldfc@hotmail.com

HONOURS FA Comps: None

League: Kent County Division Two (Western) 1958-59, Premier (Western) 62-63, 63-64, 77-78, Senior (Western) 84-85, 86-87, 88-89, 89-90, Premier 94-95, 2009-10.

11-12	12-13	13-14	14-15	15-16	16-17	17-18	18-19	19-20	20-21
KC P 2	KC P 9	KC P 6	KC P 2	KC P 4	KC P 9	SCE1 13	SCE1 8	SCE1 n&v	SCE1 n&v
						FAV 2Q	FAV 1Q	FAV 1Q	FAV 2P

GROUND: Glebe FC, Foxbury Avenue, Chislehurst, Bromley BR7 6HA

Nearest Railway Station Sidcup - 1.9km

STAPLEHURST & MONARCHS UNITED

Southern Counties East Division One

Founded 1893 Nickname: **Club Colours:** Red

Club Contact Details 07536 102 600 ian.humphrey59@gmail.com

HONOURS FA Comps: None

League: Kent County Division Two East 2005-06, Premier 18-19.

11-12	12-13	13-14	14-15	15-16	16-17	17-18	18-19	19-20	20-21
KC P 12	KC P 3	KC P 9	KC P 8	KC P 7	KC P 11	KC P 6	KC P 1	KC P n&v	KC P n&v

GROUND: Jubilee Sports Ground, Headcorn Road, Staplehurst TN12 0DS

SUTTON ATHLETIC

Southern Counties East Division One

Founded 1898 Nickname: **Club Colours:** Green & white

Club Contact Details 07778 053 433 guy.eldridge@btconnect.com

HONOURS FA Comps: None

League: Dartford 1952-53, 53-54, 54-55, 56-57, 58-59, 59-60, 60-61, 61-62, 62-63, 63-64, 64-65.
Kent County D2W 68-69, D1W 69-70, PremW 70-71, SeniorW 76-77.

11-12	12-13	13-14	14-15	15-16	16-17	17-18	18-19	19-20	20-21
K_lv 6	K_lv 8	K_lv 3	K_lv 4	K_lv 4	SCE1 3	SCE1 11	SCE1 5	SCE1 n&v	SCE1 n&v
								FAC 1Q	FAC EP
							FAV 1Q	FAV 1Q	FAV 1P

GROUND: London Hire Stadium, Lower Road, Hextable, Kent BR8 7RZ

Nearest Railway Station Swanley - 2.4km

TOOTING BEC

Southern Counties East Division One

Founded 2004 Nickname: **Club Colours:** Black & white

Club Contact Details 07866 231 469 neil_jack_40@hotmail.com

HONOURS FA Comps: None

League: Surrey Elite Intermediate Division One 2009-10, Premier 2017-18.

11-12	12-13	13-14	14-15	15-16	16-17	17-18	18-19	19-20	20-21
SuEI 13	SuEI 9	SuEI 7	SuEI 10	SuEI 7	SuEI 2	SuEI 1	CC1 3	CC1 n&v	CC1 n&v
								FAC EP	
						FAV 2Q	FAV 1Q	FAV 1Q	FAV 1P

GROUND: Imperial Fields, Bishopsford Road, Morden SM4 6BF

Nearest Railway Station Mitcham Junction - then take the tram to Mitcham Tram stop, ground an 8min walk from there.

WESTSIDE

Southern Counties East Division One

Founded 1996 Nickname: **Club Colours:** Yellow & blue

Club Contact Details 07799 390 339 stevewalters990@gmail.com

HONOURS FA Comps: None

League: Surrey South Eastern Combination Division Two 2014-15, Division One 2015-16.

11-12	12-13	13-14	14-15	15-16	16-17	17-18	18-19	19-20	20-21
SSECI2 5	SSECI2 6	SSECI2 3	SSECI2 1	SSECI1 1	SuEI 6	SuEI 12	SuEI 4	CC1 n&v	CC1 n&v
									FAC P
						FAV 1Q	FAV 1Q	FAV 1P	FAV 1Q

GROUND: Colliers Wood United FC, Wibbandune Sports Ground, Robin Hood Way, Wimbledon SW20 0AA

Nearest Railway Station Raynes Park

Bus Route London Transport 265

ARDLEY UNITED

Spartan South Midlands Premier

Founded 1945 Nickname: None **Club Colours:** All sky blue

Club Contact Details 07467 549 294 natashafeaver@hotmail.co.uk

Previous Names: None

Previous Leagues: Oxford Senior. Volunteered for relegation after 2016-17 season. Hellenic >2021.

HONOURS

FA Comps: None

League: Banbury District & Lord Jersey FA Divion One 1984-85. Oxfordshire Senior Division One 1988-89, Premier 1990-91. Hellenic Division One 1996-97, 97-98, Division One West 2017-18.

11-12	12-13	13-14	14-15	15-16	16-17	17-18	18-19	19-20	20-21
Hel P 3	Hel P 5	Hel P 2	Hel P 8	Hel P 13	Hel P 5	Hel1W 1	Hel P 17	Hel P n&v	Hel P n&v
FAC Pr	FAC P	FAC 1Qr	FAC 2Q	FAC EP	FAC P	FAC EP	FAC P	FAC P	FAC EP
FAV 1P	FAV 3P	FAV 1Q	FAV 1P	FAV 1Q	FAV 2Q	FAV 1Q	FAV 1Q	FAV 1Q	FAV 1Q

GROUND: The Playing Fields, Fritwell Road, Ardley OX27 7PA
Capacity: 1,000
Nearest Railway Station Bicester North - 6.3km
Seats: 100
Bus Route Water Lane stop - 121m away
Covered: 200

CLUB MOVEMENTS

PREMIER DIVISION - IN: Ardley United, Flackwell Heath, and Holmer Green (LM - HLP). Hadley (LM - ESL). Milton Keynes Irish and New Salamis (P - SSM1). Risborough Rangers (P - HL1E).

OUT: Edgware Town, North Greenford United and Wembley (LM - CCPN). Colney Heath (P - SthD1C).

ARLESEY TOWN

Spartan South Midlands Premier

Founded 1891 Nickname: The Blues **Club Colours:** Light & dark blue

Club Contact Details 07910 110 720 chris.sterry@ntlworld.com

Previous Names: None

Previous Leagues: Biggleswade & Dist., Bedfordshire Co. (South Midlands) 1922-26, 27-28, Parthenon, London 1958-60, United Co. 1933-36, 82-92, Spartan South Mid. 1992-2000, Isthmian 2000-04, 06-08, Southern 2004-07, 08-18.

HONOURS

FA Comps: FA Vase 1994-95.

League: South Midlands Premier 1951-52, 52-53, 94-95, 95-96. Spartan South Midlands Premier 1999-2000. United Counties Premier Division 1984-85. Isthmian Division Three 2000-01. Southern Division One Central 2010-11.

11-12	12-13	13-14	14-15	15-16	16-17	17-18	18-19	19-20	20-21
SthP 18	SthP 6	SthP 15	SthP 22	SthC 16	SthC 15	SthC 22	SSM P 8	SSM P n&v	SSM P n&v
FAC 1P	FAC 1P	FAC 3Q	FAC 1Q	FAC 1Q	FAC Pr	FAC 1Q	FAC EP	FAC 1Q	FAC EP
FAT 2Q	FAT 2Qr	FAT 1P	FAT 2Qr	FAT Pr	FAT Pr	FAT 1Q	FAV 2Q	FAV 1Q	FAV 2Q

GROUND: New Lamb Meadow, Hitchin Road, Arlesey SG15 6RS
Capacity: 2,920
Nearest Railway Station Arlesey - 2.6km
Seats: 150
Bus Route Prince of Wales - stop 100m away
Covered: 600

AYLESBURY VALE DYNAMOES

Spartan South Midlands Premier

Founded 1930 Nickname: The Moles **Club Colours:** Red & black

Club Contact Details 07715 772 500 iwillcocks@gmail.com

Previous Names: Negretti & Zambra FC 1930-54, Stocklake 1954-2000, Haywood United 00, Haywood FC 00-06, Aylesbury Vale 06-09, Aylesbury 09-19

Previous Leagues: Aylesbury District. Wycombe & District. Chiltern, Spartan South Midlands >2010. Southern 2010-19.

HONOURS

FA Comps: None

League: Spartan South Midlands Division One 2003-04, Premier Division 2009-10.

11-12	12-13	13-14	14-15	15-16	16-17	17-18	18-19	19-20	20-21
SthC 20	SthC 12	SthC 16	SthC 3	SthC 8	SthC 19	Sth1E 21	SthC 19	SSM P n&v	SSM P n&v
FAC P	FAC P	FAC 1Q	FAC 1Q	FAC 1Qr	FAC P	FAC 1Q	FAC Pr	FAC P	FAC EP
FAT 1Qr	FAT P	FAT 1Q	FAT 1Q	FAT 1Qr	FAT P	FAT 1Qr	FAT P	FAV 1P	FAV 1Q

GROUND: The Greenfleets Stadium, Haywood Way, Aylesbury, Bucks. HP19 9WZ
Nearest Railway Station Aylesbury Vale Parkway - 1.2km
Bus Route O'grady Way - stop 200m away

BALDOCK TOWN

Spartan South Midlands Premier

Founded 1905 Nickname: The Reds **Club Colours:** All red

Club Contact Details 07761 553 566 baldocktownfootballclub@outlook.com

Previous Names: Baldock 1905-21. Folded in 2001 reformed as Baldock 2003-06. Baldock Town 2006-08. Baldock Town Letchworth 2008-11.

Previous Leagues: Herts County 1905-25, 46-47, 2007-13. Beds & Dist/South Midlands 1925-39, 47-54, 64-83. Parthenon 1954-59. London 1959-64. United Counties 1983-87. Southern 1987-2001. North Herts 2003-06. North & Mid Herts (FM) 2006-07.

HONOURS

FA Comps: None

League: Herts Senior County Northern Div. 1920-21, Div.1 2007-08, Premier 11-12.
South Midlands Div.2 47-38, Div.1 49-50, Premier 27-28, 65-66, 67-68, 69-70.

11-12	12-13	13-14	14-15	15-16	16-17	17-18	18-19	19-20	20-21
HertP 1	HertP 2	SSM1 7	SSM1 10	SSM1 3	SSM1 3	SSM1 2	SSM P 5	SSM P n&v	SSM P n&v
			FAC P	FAC EP	FAC EP	FAC 2Q	FAC P	FAC EP	FAC EP
		FAV 1P	FAV 1P	FAV 2Q	FAV 1P	FAV 1P	FAV 2P	FAV 1P	FAV 1P

GROUND: Arlesey Town FC, New Lamb Meadow, Hitchin Road, Arlesey SG15 6RS
Nearest Railway Station Arlesey - 2.6km
Bus Route Prince of Wales - stop 100m away

Capacity: 2,920
Seats: 150
Covered: 600

BROADFIELDS UNITED

Spartan South Midlands Premier

Founded 1993 Nickname: The Fighting Cocks **Club Colours:** Blue and white

Club Contact Details 07944 370 116 websterlocke@aol.com

Previous Names: None

Previous Leagues: Middlesex >2015

HONOURS

FA Comps: None

League: Southern Olympian Division Four 1994-95.
Middlesex County Senior Division 1996-97.

11-12	12-13	13-14	14-15	15-16	16-17	17-18	18-19	19-20	20-21
MidxP 8	MidxP 5	MidxP 15	MidxP 4	SSM1 11	SSM1 11	SSM1 4	SSM1 2	SSM P n&v	SSM P n&v
							FAC P	FAC EP	FAC P
		FAV 2Q	FAV 1Q	FAV 1Q	FAV 2P	FAV 1P	FAV 1P	FAV 1P	FAV 2Q

GROUND: Tithe Farm Sports & Social Club, 151 Rayners Lane, Harrow HA2 0XH

CRAWLEY GREEN

Spartan South Midlands Premier

Founded 1992 Nickname: **Club Colours:** All maroon

Club Contact Details 07762 752 213 alan.clark1351@gmail.com

Previous Names: None

Previous Leagues: None

HONOURS

FA Comps: None

League: Spartan South Midlands Division Two 2004-05.

11-12	12-13	13-14	14-15	15-16	16-17	17-18	18-19	19-20	20-21
SSM1 6	SSM1 4	SSM1 5	SSM1 7	SSM1 2	SSM P 11	SSM P 18	SSM P 10	SSM P n&v	SSM P n&v
FAC EP	FAC EP	FAC P	FAC EP	FAC EP	FAC P	FAC P	FAC P	FAC EP	FAC EP
FAV 2Q	FAV 2Qr	FAV 1Q	FAV 2Q	FAV 2Q	FAV 1P	FAV 2P	FAV 1P	FAV 1P	FAV 1P

GROUND: The Stadium at The Brache, Park Street, Luton LU1 3HH

Capacity: 4,000
Seats: 160

DUNSTABLE TOWN

Spartan South Midlands Premier

Founded 1883 Nickname: The Duns / The Blues **Club Colours:** Blue & white

Club Contact Details 07828 604 170 andrew.madaras@hotmail.com

Previous Names: Dunstable Town 1883-1976. Dunstable FC 1976-98.

Previous Leagues: Metropolitan & District 1950-61, 64-65. United Counties 1961-63. Southern 1965-76, 2004-09, 13-19. Spartan South Midlands 1998-2003, 09-13. Isthmian 2003-04.

HONOURS

FA Comps: None

League: Spartan South Midlands Division One 1999-00, Premier 2002-03, 12-13. Southern Division One Central 2013-14.

11-12		12-13		13-14		14-15		15-16		16-17		17-18		18-19		19-20		20-21	
SSM P	2	SSM P	1	SthC	1	SthP	14	SthP	11	SthP	16	SthP	24	SthC	20	SSM P	n&v	SSM P	n&v
FAC	3Q	FAC	1Qr	FAC	2Q	FAC	2Q	FAC	3Q	FAC	1Q	FAC	1Q	FAC	Pr	FAC	1Q	FAC	1Q
FAV	2P	FAV	3P	FAT	2Q	FAT	1Q	FAT	1Q	FAT	2Q	FAT	1Q	FAT	1Q	FAV	1Q	FAV	1Q

GROUND: Creasey Park Stadium, Brewers Hill Rd, Dunstable LU6 1BB **Capacity:** 3,500

Seats: 350

Bus Route Langridge Court - stop 100m away **Covered:** 1000

FLACKWELL HEATH

Spartan South Midlands Premier

Founded 1907 Nickname: Heathens **Club Colours:** All red.

Club Contact Details 07984 199 878 joparsons19@sky.com

Previous Names: None.

Previous Leagues: High Wycombe & District 1907-50. Great Western Combination 1950-76. Hellenic 1976-82. Athenian 1982-84. Isthmian 1984-2007. Hellenic 2007-21.

HONOURS

FA Comps: None

League: Great Western Combination Division Two 1950-51, Premier 1957-58, 62-63. Hellenic Premier Division 2014-15.

11-12		12-13		13-14		14-15		15-16		16-17		17-18		18-19		19-20		20-21	
Hel P	4	Hel P	10	Hel P	8	Hel P	1	Hel P	3	Hel P	3	Hel P	5	Hel P	8	Hel P	n&v	Hel P	n&v
FAC	EP	FAC	EP	FAC	EPr	FAC	3Q	FAC	EP	FAC	1Q	FAC	P	FAC	EP	FAC	2Q	FAC	P
FAV	3P	FAV	1P	FAV	1Q	FAV	5P	FAV	2P	FAV	1P	FAV	1P	FAV	1P	FAV	1P	FAV	QF

GROUND: Wilks Park, Magpie Lane, Heath End Rd, Flackwell Hth HP10 9EA **Capacity:** 2,000

Nearest Railway Station Bourne End - 3km **Seats:** 150

Bus Route Fernlea Close stop - 106m

HADLEY

Spartan South Midlands Premier

Founded 1882 Nickname: Bricks **Club Colours:** Red and black

Club Contact Details 07748 267 295 gensecretary@hadleyfc.com

Previous Names: None

Previous Leagues: Barnet & Dist. 1922-57, North Suburban 1957-70, Mid-Herts 1970-77, Herts Senior County 1977-85, 99-2007, Southern Olymian 1985-99, West Herts 2007-08. Spartan South Midlands 08-19. Essex Senior 2019-21.

HONOURS

FA Comps: None

League: Mid-Herts Premier 1975-76, 76-77. Hertfordshire Senior County Division Three 1977-78, Division One 2001-02, Premier 2003-04, 04-05. West Hertfordshire 2007-08.

11-12		12-13		13-14		14-15		15-16		16-17		17-18		18-19		19-20		20-21	
SSM P	15	SSM P	12	SSM P	13	SSM P	9	SSM P	6	SSM P	19	SSM P	6	SSM P	3	ESen	n&v	ESen	n&v
FAC	EPr	FAC	P	FAC	P	FAC	EPr	FAC	EP	FAC	3Qr	FAC	1Q	FAC	1Qr	FAC	3Q	FAC	P
FAV	1P	FAV	1Pr	FAV	2P	FAV	2Qr	FAV	1P	FAV	1Q	FAV	2Qr	FAV	2Q	FAV	1P	FAV	5P

GROUND: Hadley Sports Ground, Brickfield Lane, Arkley, Barnet EN5 3LD **Capacity:** 2,000

Nearest Railway Station Elstree & Borehamwood - 2.8km **Seats:** 150

Bus Route Brickfield Lane - stop 70m away **Covered:** 250

HAREFIELD UNITED

Spartan South Midlands Premier

Founded 1868 Nickname: Hares **Club Colours:** Red & black

Club Contact Details 07834 771 212 rayjgreen1@btinternet.com

Previous Names: None

Previous Leagues: Uxbridge & District, Great Western Comb, Panthernon, Middlesex, Athenian & Isthmian.

HONOURS

FA Comps: None

League: Great Western Comb. Division Two 1947-48, Division One 50-51.
Parthenon 1964-65. Spartan South Midlands Division One 2018-19.

11-12	12-13	13-14	14-15	15-16	16-17	17-18	18-19	19-20	20-21
SSM P 18	SSM P 10	SSM P 14	SSM P 4	SSM P 21	SSM1 8	SSM1 9	SSM1 1	SSM P n&v	SSM P n&v
FAC Pr	FAC 2Qr	FAC P	FAC P	FAC EPr	FAC 1Q			FAC P	FAC P
FAV 1Q	FAV 1Q	FAV 1Q	FAV 1P	FAV 1P	FAV 2Q	FAV 1Q	FAV 1P	FAV 2Q	FAV 1Q

GROUND: Preston Park, Breakespeare Road North, Harefield, UB9 6NE **Capacity:** 1,200
Nearest Railway Station Denham - 3km **Seats:** 150
Bus Route Wickham Close - stop 150m away

HARPENDEN TOWN

Spartan South Midlands Premier

Founded 1891 Nickname: The Harps **Club Colours:** Yellow & blue

Club Contact Details 07796 955 197 stephen@hartnup.com

Previous Names: Harpenden FC 1891-1908.

Previous Leagues: Herts Senior County (founder member) 1898-1900, 1908-22, 48-57. Mid-Herts 1900-08. South Midlands 1957-97.

HONOURS

FA Comps: None

League: Herts Senior County Western Division 1910-11, 11-12, 20-21, Premier 50-51, 52-53, 54-55.
South Midlands Division One 1989-90, Premier 61-62, 64-65.

11-12	12-13	13-14	14-15	15-16	16-17	17-18	18-19	19-20	20-21
SSM1 5	SSM1 7	SSM1 8	SSM1 6	SSM1 4	SSM1 2	SSM P 3	SSM P 14	SSM P n&v	SSM P n&v
					FAC P	FAC EP	FAC P	FAC EP	FAC P
				FAV 2Q	FAV 1Q	FAV 1P	FAV 1P	FAV 1Q	FAV 2Q

GROUND: Rothamstead Park, Amenbury Lane, Harpenden AL5 2EF
Nearest Railway Station Harpenden - 0.6km
Bus Route Amenbury Lane - stop 250m away

HOLMER GREEN

Spartan South Midlands Premier

Founded 1908 Nickname: The Greens **Club Colours:** All Green

Club Contact Details 07900 081 814 j.ostinelli@sky.com

Previous Names: None

Previous Leagues: Chesham & District 1908-38, Wycombe Combination 1984-95, Chiltonian 1995-98. Spartan South Midlands 1998-2018. Hellenic 2018-21.

HONOURS

FA Comps: None

League: Wycombe Combination 1971-72, 73-74, 76-77, 80-81. Chiltonian Prmeier 1984-85, 85-86, 93-94.
South Midlands Senior 1995-96. Spartan South Midlands 1998-99, Division One 2009-10.

11-12	12-13	13-14	14-15	15-16	16-17	17-18	18-19	19-20	20-21
SSM P 20	SSM P 22	SSM P 12	SSM P 20	SSM P 7	SSM P 14	SSM P 14	Hel P 12	Hel P n&v	Hel P n&v
FAC EP	FAC EP	FAC EP	FAC Pr	FAC EP	FAC EP	FAC P	FAC EP	FAC EPr	FAC P
FAV 1Q	FAV 2Q	FAV 2Q	FAV 1Pr	FAV 1Q	FAV 2P	FAV 1Q	FAV 1Q	FAV 1Q	FAV 2Q

GROUND: Airedale Park, Watchet Lane, Holmer Green, Bucks HP15 6UF **Capacity:** 1,000
Nearest Railway Station Great Missenden - 4.3km **Seats:** 25
Bus Route Copners Drive - stop 350m away

LEIGHTON TOWN

Spartan South Midlands Premier

Founded 1885 Nickname: Reds **Club Colours:** Red & white

Club Contact Details 07757 720 833 roy.parkerlu4@gmail.com

Previous Names: Leighton United 1922-63

Previous Leagues: Leighton & District. South Midlands 1922-24, 26-29, 46-54, 55-56, 76-92. Spartan 1922-53, 67-74. Isthmian 1992-2004. Southern 2004-16.

HONOURS

FA Comps: None

League: South Midlands 1966-67, 91-92. Isthmian Division Two 2003-04.

11-12	12-13	13-14	14-15	15-16	16-17	17-18	18-19	19-20	20-21
SthC 13	SthC 21	SthC 19	SthC 18	SthC 21	SSM P 16	SSM P 4	SSM P 11	SSM P n&v	SSM P n&v
FAC 3Q	FAC Pr	FAC P	FAC P	FAC 1Q	FAC EP	FAC P	FAC EP	FAC 1Q	FAC 2Q
FAT 1Q	FAT P	FAT P	FAT 1Qr	FAT 1Q	FAV 2Q	FAV QF	FAV 3P	FAV QF	FAV QF

GROUND: Bell Close, Lake Street, Leighton Buzzard, Beds LU7 1RX **Capacity:** 2,800

Nearest Railway Station Leighton Buzzard - 1.3km **Seats:** 400

Bus Route Morrisons (Lake St) - stop 60m away **Covered:** 300

LEVERSTOCK GREEN

Spartan South Midlands Premier

Founded 1895 Nickname: The Green / The Trees **Club Colours:** White and green

Club Contact Details 07747 756 591 deanobradford@gmail.com

Previous Names: None

Previous Leagues: West Herts (pre 1954) & Herts Senior County 1954-91. South Midlands 1991-97.

HONOURS

FA Comps: None

League: Herts Senior County Division One 1978-79.
South Midlands Senior Division 1996-97.

11-12	12-13	13-14	14-15	15-16	16-17	17-18	18-19	19-20	20-21
SSM P 11	SSM P 15	SSM P 20	SSM P 15	SSM P 18	SSM P 12	SSM P 7	SSM P 17	SSM P n&v	SSM P n&v
FAC EP	FAC EP	FAC EP	FAC 2Q	FAC EP	FAC EP	FAC Pr	FAC 2Q	FAC EPr	FAC P
FAV 2Pr	FAV 1Q	FAV 1Q	FAV 2Q	FAV 2Q	FAV 2P	FAV 2Q	FAV 3P	FAV 1Qr	FAV 1Q

GROUND: Pancake Lane, Leverstock Green, Hemel Hempstead, Herts HP2 4NQ **Capacity:** 1,500

Nearest Railway Station Apsley - 3.2km **Seats:** 50

Bus Route Pancake Lane - stop 300m away **Covered:** 100

LONDON COLNEY

Spartan South Midlands Premier

Founded 1907 Nickname: Blueboys **Club Colours:** Royal blue and white

Club Contact Details 07907 658 025 sly.lcfc@gmail.com

Previous Names: None

Previous Leagues: Herts Senior 1955-93.

HONOURS

FA Comps: None

League: Herts Senior County 1956-57, 59-60, 86-87, 88-89. 89-90. South Midlands Senior Division 1994-95.
Spartan South Midlands Premier Division 2001-02, 16-17, Division One 2011-12.

11-12	12-13	13-14	14-15	15-16	16-17	17-18	18-19	19-20	20-21
SSM1 1	SSM P 7	SSM P 7	SSM P 2	SSM P 2	SSM P 1	SSM P 13	SSM P 15	SSM P n&v	SSM P n&v
FAC EP	FAC P	FAC EPr	FAC 1Q	FAC P	FAC 1Q	FAC EPr	FAC EP	FAC 1Q	FAC EP
FAV 1Q	FAV 2Q	FAV 1Q	FAV 3P	FAV 2P	FAV 3P	FAV 1Pr	FAV 1P	FAV 2Q	FAV 2Q

GROUND: Cotlandswick Playing Fields, London Colney, Herts AL2 1DW **Capacity:** 1,000

Nearest Railway Station Park Street - 2.3km **Seats:** Yes

Bus Route Leisure Centre - stop 430m away **Covered:** Yes

MILTON KEYNES IRISH

Spartan South Midlands Premier

Founded 1883 | Nickname: Robins | **Club Colours:** Yellow & blue

Club Contact Details 07724 137 422 cgreenwood@mkirishfc.co.uk

Previous Names: Buckingham Town > Jan 2019. In May 2020 M K Robins, Unite and M K Irish Veterns merged to form today's club.

Previous Leagues: Hellenic (FM) 1953-57. South Midlands 1971-74. United Counties 1974-86, 97-2018. Southern 1986-97.

HONOURS

FA Comps: None

League: Aylesbury & Dist. 1902-03, 67-68. North Bucks 24-25, 28-29, 33-34, 35-36, 36-37, 38-39, 48-49, 49-50. Southern Southern Division 90 -91. United Counties 83-84, 85-86.

11-12	12-13	13-14	14-15	15-16	16-17	17-18	18-19	19-20	20-21
UCL 1 11	UCL 1 15	UCL 1 11	UCL 1 16	UCL 1 17	UCL 1 5	UCL 1 7	SSM1 14	SSM1 n&v	SSM1 n&v
						FAC EP			
FAV 2P		FAV 2Q		FAV 1Q	FAV 1P	FAV 1Q		FAV 2P	FAV 3P

GROUND: Irish Centre, Manor Fields, Bletchley, Milton Keynes MK2 2HX — **Capacity:** 2,500

Nearest Railway Station Fenny Stratford - 0.6km — **Seats:** 600

Bus Route Wharfside - stop 300m away

NEW SALAMIS

Spartan South Midlands Premier

Founded 1971 | Nickname: | **Club Colours:** Red & white

Club Contact Details 07725 040 409 newsalamisofficial@outlook.com

Previous Names:

Previous Leagues: KOPA. Hertfordshire Senior County 2018-19.

HONOURS

FA Comps: Sunday Cup 2015-16.

League: KOPA 1984-85, 93-94, 99-00, 00-01, 08-09, 10-11, 11-12, 12-13, 14-15, 15-16, 16-17, 17-18

11-12	12-13	13-14	14-15	15-16	16-17	17-18	18-19	19-20	20-21
KOPA 1	KOPA 1		KOPA 1	KOPA 1	KOPA 1	KOPA 1	HertP 2	SSM1 n&v	SSM1 n&v
									FAC 1Q
								FAV 1P	FAV 1P

GROUND: Haringey Boro FC, Coles Park, White Hart Lane, Tottenham N17 7JP — **Capacity:** 2,500

Nearest Railway Station White Hart Lane - 1.5km. Wood Green (UG) - 1.5km

Bus Route W3 stops outside the ground (see directions).

OXHEY JETS

Spartan South Midlands Premier

Founded 1972 | Nickname: Jets | **Club Colours:** Blue and white

Club Contact Details 07786 627 659 d.g.fuller@ntlworld.com

Previous Names: None

Previous Leagues: Youth Leagues > 1981. Herts Senior County 1981-2004.

HONOURS

FA Comps: None

League: Herts Senior County Premier 2000-01, 01-02, 02-03. Spartan South Midladns Division One 2004-2005.

11-12	12-13	13-14	14-15	15-16	16-17	17-18	18-19	19-20	20-21
SSM P 17	SSM P 3	SSM P 18	SSM P 12	SSM P 17	SSM P 15	SSM P 19	SSM P 9	SSM P n&v	SSM P n&v
FAC 2Q	FAC P	FAC EPr	FAC EP	FAC EPr	FAC P	FAC EP	FAC EP	FAC EP	FAC P
FAV 1P	FAV 3P	FAV 2P	FAV 2P	FAV 2Q	FAV 1P	FAV 1P	FAV 2Q	FAV 2P	FAV 2Q

GROUND: Boundary Stadium, Altham Way, South Oxhey, Watford WD19 6FW — **Capacity:** 2,000

Nearest Railway Station Carpenders Park - 1km — **Seats:** 150

Bus Route Lytham Avenue - stop 75m away — **Covered:** 100

RISBOROUGH RANGERS

Spartan South Midlands Premier

Founded 1971 Nickname: Rangers or Boro **Club Colours:** All red

Club Contact Details 07855 958 236 nick@lloydlatchford.co.uk

Previous Names:

Previous Leagues: South Midlands 1989-2019. Hellenic 2019-21.

HONOURS

FA Comps: None

League: None

11-12	12-13	13-14	14-15	15-16	16-17	17-18	18-19	19-20	20-21
SSM2 2	SSM2 4	SSM1 14	SSM1 5	SSM1 7	SSM1 6	SSM1 8	SSM1 7	Hel1E n&v	Hel1E n&v
				FAC P	FAC EP	FAC EPr			FAC 2Q
			FAV 2Q	FAV 2Q	FAV 1Q	FAV 1Q	FAV 1Q	FAV 1P	FAV 2P

GROUND: " Windsors" Horsenden Lane, Princes Risborough. Bucks HP27 9NE **Capacity:** 1,500

Nearest Railway Station Princes Rosborough - 0.2km

Bus Route Railway Station - stop 0.2km away

TRING ATHLETIC

Spartan South Midlands Premier

Founded 1958 Nickname: Athletic **Club Colours:** Red and black

Club Contact Details 07825 747 775 davidgblair@gmail.com

Previous Names: Tring Athletic Youth 1958-71.

Previous Leagues: West Herts 1958-88.

HONOURS

FA Comps: None

League: West Herts Division One 1961-62, 64-65, 65-66.
Spartan South Midlands Senior Division 1999-2000.

11-12	12-13	13-14	14-15	15-16	16-17	17-18	18-19	19-20	20-21
SSM P 6	SSM P 22	SSM P 10	SSM P 10	SSM P 12	SSM P 5	SSM P 17	SSM P 2	SSM P n&v	SSM P n&v
FAC P	FAC Pr	FAC P	FAC EP	FAC P	FAC EP	FAC EP	FAC EP	FAC EP	FAC EP
FAV 2P	FAV 1Q	FAV 3P	FAV 3P	FAV 1P	FAV 4P	FAV 5P	FAV 3Pr	FAV 1P	FAV 2Q

GROUND: Grass Roots Stadium, Pendley Sports Centre, Cow Lane, Tring HP23 5NS **Capacity:** 2,000

Nearest Railway Station Tring - 1.5km **Seats:** 125

Bus Route Bus stops at the ground. **Covered:** 100+

CLUB MOVEMENTS

DIVISION ONE - IN: Burton Park Wanderers, Irchester United, Northampton Sileby Rangers, Raunds Town, Rushden & Higham United and Wellingborough Whitworths (LM - UCL1).
Kidlington Reserves, Long Credon, Penn & Tylers Green and Thames Rangers (LM - HL1E).
Letchworth GC Eagles (P - HSL).
Thame United Reserves (formerly Thame Rangers).

OUT: Enfield Borough, Hillingdon Borough, London Lions & Rayners Lane (LM - CC1). Milton Keynes Irish and New Salamis (P - SSMP). St Panteleimon (P - CCPN). Park View (ECD1S).

AMERSHAM TOWN

Spartan South Midlands Division One

Founded 1890 Nickname: The Magpies **Club Colours:** Black & white stripes

Club Contact Details 01494 722 073 bryan.fisher53@yahoo.co.uk

HONOURS FA Comps: None

League: Wycombe & District Combination 1902-03, 19-20, 20.21.
Hellenic Division One 1962-63, Premier 63-64.

11-12	12-13	13-14	14-15	15-16	16-17	17-18	18-19	19-20	20-21
SSM1 20	SSM1 20	SSM1 16	SSM1 21	SSM2 12	SSM2 16	SSM2 6	SSM1 17	SSM1 n&v	SSM1 n&v
FAV 2Q	FAV 2P				FAV 1Q	FAV 1Q	FAV 2Q	FAV 2Q	FAV 1Q

GROUND: Spratleys Meadow, School Lane, Amersham, Bucks HP7 0EL

AMPTHILL TOWN

Spartan South Midlands Division One

Founded 1881 Nickname: The Amps **Club Colours:** Amber and black

Club Contact Details 07887 872 632 789ericturner@gmail.com

HONOURS FA Comps: None

League: South Midlands Premier Division 1959-60.

11-12	12-13	13-14	14-15	15-16	16-17	17-18	18-19	19-20	20-21
SSM1 2	SSM P 5	SSM P 2	SSM P 21	SSM1 14	SSM1 14	SSM1 14	SSM1 10	SSM1 n&v	SSM1 n&v
	FAC EP	FAC P	FAC EP	FAC EP					
FAV 4P	FAV 5P	FAV QF	FAV 2P	FAV 1Q	FAV 1Q	FAV 1P	FAV 1Q	FAV 1Q	FAV 3P

GROUND: Ampthill Park, Woburn Street, Ampthill MK45 2HX

Nearest Railway Station Flitwick - 3.1km. Millbrook - 3.4km

Bus Route Alameda Road - stop 117m away

BEDFORD

Spartan South Midlands Division One

Founded 1957 Nickname: The B's **Club Colours:** Black & white

Club Contact Details 07748 773 011 1967bobfender@gmail.com

HONOURS FA Comps: None

League: None

11-12	12-13	13-14	14-15	15-16	16-17	17-18	18-19	19-20	20-21
SSM1 12	SSM1 5	SSM1 3	SSM1 3	SSM P 22	SSM1 19	SSM1 12	SSM1 5	SSM1 n&v	SSM1 n&v
FAC EP			FAC EP	FAC EP	FAC EP				
FAV 2Q		FAV 1Q	FAV 2Q	FAV 1Q	FAV 1Q	FAV 1Qr	FAV 1Q	FAV 2Q	FAV 2Q

GROUND: McMullen Park, Meadow Lane, Cardington, Bedford, MK44 3SB

Nearest Railway Station Bedford St Johns - 3.8km

Bus Route Meadow Lane - stop 141m away

BUCKINGHAM ATHELTIC

Spartan South Midlands Division One

Founded 1933 Nickname: The Ath **Club Colours:** Sky blue & navy blue

Club Contact Details 07751 659 769 colin@thehowkins.co.uk

HONOURS FA Comps: None

League: North Bucks Premier Division 1984-85. South Midlands Division One 1985-86, 90-91, Spartan South Midlands Division Two 2002-03.

11-12	12-13	13-14	14-15	15-16	16-17	17-18	18-19	19-20	20-21
SSM1 18	SSM1 11	SSM1 13	SSM1 15	SSM1 8	SSM1 10	SSM1 7	SSM1 4	SSM1 n&v	SSM1 n&v
FAV 1Q	FAV 2Q	FAV 2Q	FAV 1Qr	FAV 2Q	FAV 1Q	FAV 1P	FAV 1Pr	FAV 1P	FAV 1Q

GROUND: Stratford Fields, Stratford Road, Buckingham MK18 1NY

Bus Route High Street - stop 206m away

BURTON PARK WANDERERS

Spartan South Midlands Division One

Founded 1961 Nickname: The Wanderers **Club Colours:** Blue & black

Club Contact Details 07794 959 915 daveborrett66@gmail.com

HONOURS FA Comps: None

League: None

11-12	12-13	13-14	14-15	15-16	16-17	17-18	18-19	19-20	20-21
UCL 1 9	UCL 1 19	UCL 1 8	UCL 1 18	UCL 1 19	UCL 1 19	UCL 1	UCL 1 12	UCL 1 n&v	UCL 1 n&v
									FAC EP
			FAV 2Q	FAV 1Qr	FAV 1Q	FAV 2Q	FAV 2Q	FAV 1Q	FAV P

GROUND: Latimer Park, Polwell Lane, Burton Latimer, Northants NN15 5PS

Nearest Railway Station Kettering - 4.1km

Bus Route Station Road - stop 120m away

IRCHESTER UNITED

Spartan South Midlands Division One

Founded 1885 Nickname: The Romans **Club Colours:** Red and black

Club Contact Details 07802 728 736 glynn.cotter@btinternet.com

HONOURS FA Comps: None

League: Rushden & District 1928-29, 29-30, 36-37. Northants / United Counties Division Two 1930-31, 31-32 / United Counties Division One 2009-10.

11-12	12-13	13-14	14-15	15-16	16-17	17-18	18-19	19-20	20-21
UCL P 20	UCL P 21	UCL 1 19	UCL 1 15	UCL 1 16	UCL 1 8	UCL 1 13	UCL 1 10	UCL 1 n&v	UCL 1 n&v
FAC EP	FAC EP	FAC EP							
FAV 2Q	FAV 2Q	FAV 2Q	FAV 1P	FAV 1Q	FAV 2Q	FAV 2Q	FAV 2P	FAV 1Q	FAV 1Q

GROUND: Alfred Street, Irchester NN29 7DR

Nearest Railway Station Wellingborough - 3.1km

Bus Route Alfred Street - stop 100m away

KIDLINGTON RESERVES

Spartan South Midlands Division One

Founded 1909 Nickname: Greens **Club Colours:** All green

Club Contact Details 07903 037 898 a.spence.15@outlook.com

HONOURS FA Comps: None

League: None

11-12	12-13	13-14	14-15	15-16	16-17	17-18	18-19	19-20	20-21
						Hel1W 11	Hel1W 6	Hel1E n&v	Hel1E n&v

GROUND: Yarnton Road, Kidlington, Oxford OX5 1AT

Nearest Railway Station Oxford Parkway - 1.9km

Bus Route Treeground Place stop - 63m away

LANGFORD

Spartan South Midlands Division One

Founded 1908 Nickname: Reds **Club Colours:** Red & white

Club Contact Details 07368 885 679 lisatrinier@gmail.com

HONOURS FA Comps: None

League: Bedford & District 1931-32, 49-50. South Midlands Premier Division 1988-89.

11-12	12-13	13-14	14-15	15-16	16-17	17-18	18-19	19-20	20-21
SSM1 10	SSM1 16	SSM1 19	SSM1 13	SSM1 18	SSM1 4	SSM1 17	SSM1 11	SSM1 n&v	SSM1 n&v
FAC EP						FAC EP			
FAV 1Q	FAV 2Q	FAV 1Q	FAV 1Qr	FAV 1Q	FAV 1Q	FAV 2Q	FAV 2Q	FAV 2Qr	FAV 1Q

GROUND: Forde Park, Langford Road, Henlow, Beds SG16 6AF

Nearest Railway Station Arlesey - 1.9km

Bus Route Newtown (Langford Rd) - stop 24m away

LETCHWORTH GARDEN CITY EAGLES

Spartan South Midlands Division One

Founded 1979 Nickname: **Club Colours:** Black & blue

Club Contact Details 07307 179 945 kevin.bowles71@gmail.com

HONOURS FA Comps: None

League: Herts Senior Division One 2009-10, Premier Division 2018-19.

11-12	12-13	13-14	14-15	15-16	16-17	17-18	18-19	19-20	20-21
HertP 4	HertP 8	HertP 6	HertP 2	HertP 3	HertP 3	HertP 2	HertP 1	HertP n&v	HertP n&v

GROUND: Pixmore Playing Fields, Ledgers Lane, Baldock Road, Letchworth SG6 2EN

LONDON TIGERS

Spartan South Midlands Division One

Founded 1986 Nickname: Tigers **Club Colours:** Amber and black

Club Contact Details sports@londontigers.org

HONOURS FA Comps: None

League: None

11-12	12-13	13-14	14-15	15-16	16-17	17-18	18-19	19-20	20-21
SSM P 14	SSM P 20	SSM P 15	SSM P 17	SSM P 13	SSM P 21	SSM P 15	SSM P 20	SSM1 n&v	SSM1 n&v
		FAC P	FAC 2Q	FAC EPr	FAC EPr			FAC EP	
	FAV 2Q	FAV 1Q	FAV 1Q	FAV 1P	FAV 2Q		FAV 1Q	FAV 2Q	FAV 1Q

GROUND: Spratleys Meadow, School Lane, Amersham HP7 0EJ

LONG CRENDON

Spartan South Midlands Division One

Founded 1886 Nickname: The Robins **Club Colours:** Red and white

Club Contact Details 07432 745 789 tomf@pcjservices.com

HONOURS FA Comps: None

League: Aylesbury & District Division Two 2014-15, Hellenic Division Two East 2018-19

11-12	12-13	13-14	14-15	15-16	16-17	17-18	18-19	19-20	20-21
		AyD2 9	AyD2 1	AyD1 2	AyDP 2	Hel2E 3	Hel2E 1	Hel1E n&v	Hel1E n&v
									FAC P
								FAV 2Q	FAV 2Q

GROUND: Oxford City Stadium, Marsh Lane, Marston, Oxford OX3 0NQ

Nearest Railway Station Oxford - three miles from the ground.

Bus Route 14A from the Station to the ground.

NORTHAMPTON SILEBY RANGERS

Spartan South Midlands Division One

Founded 1968 Nickname: Rangers **Club Colours:** Red and black

Club Contact Details 07783 150 082 daveron51@yahoo.com

HONOURS FA Comps: None

League: Northampton Town 1988-89 89-90. United Counties Division One 1993-94, 2002-03, 04-05, 12-13.

11-12	12-13	13-14	14-15	15-16	16-17	17-18	18-19	19-20	20-21
UCL 1 16	UCL 1 1	UCL P 15	UCL P 18	UCL P 19	UCL P 8	UCL P 22	UCL 1 9	UCL 1 n&v	UCL 1 n&v
			FAC 1Q	FAC P	FAC P	FAC EP	FAC Pr		
		FAV 1P	FAV 1Q	FAV 2P	FAV 2P	FAV 2Q	FAV 2Q	FAV 2Q	FAV 1P

GROUND: Fernie Fields Sports Ground, Moulton, Northampton NN3 6BD

Nearest Railway Station Northampton - 5.5km

Bus Route Booth Rise - stop 205m away

PENN & TYLERS GREEN

Spartan South Midlands Division One

Founded 1905 Nickname: Penn **Club Colours:** Blue & white

Club Contact Details 07904 538 868 hsvlatta1955@yahoo.co.uk

HONOURS FA Comps: None

League: Wycombe Comb. Div.A 1911-12, Div.2 35-36, 56,57, 60-61, North 39-40, Div.1 46-47, Div.3 55-56, Prem 62-63. Wycombe & Dist Sen 83-84. Hellenic D1E 2015-16, 16-17

11-12	12-13	13-14	14-15	15-16	16-17	17-18	18-19	19-20	20-21
Hel1E 12	Hel1E 4	Hel1E 5	Hel1E 9	Hel1E 1	Hel1E 1	Hel1E 3	Hel1E 9	Hel1E n&v	Hel1E n&v
							FAV 1Q		FAV 2Q

GROUND: French School Meadow, Elm Road, Penn HP10 8LG

RAUNDS TOWN

Spartan South Midlands Division One

Founded 1946 Nickname: Shopmates **Club Colours:** Red & black

Club Contact Details 07763 492 184 raundssecretary@gmail.com

HONOURS FA Comps: None

League: United Counties Division One 1982-83.

11-12	12-13	13-14	14-15	15-16	16-17	17-18	18-19	19-20	20-21
UCL 1 13	UCL 1 14	UCL 1 12	UCL 1 9	UCL 1 8	UCL 1 7	UCL 1 4	UCL 1 19	UCL 1 n&v	UCL 1 n&v
FAC EP				FAC P	FAC EP	FAC EPr	FAC EP		
FAV 2Q	FAV 2Q		FAV 1Q	FAV 1P	FAV 1Q	FAV 2Q	FAV 2Q	FAV 2Q	FAV 2Q

GROUND: Kiln Park, London Road, Raunds, Northants NN9 6EQ

Bus Route Bus stops outside the ground.

RUSHDEN & HIGHAM UNITED

Spartan South Midlands Division One

Founded Formed: Nickname: The Lankies **Club Colours:** Red and black

Club Contact Details 07771 727 265 rhufcsec@yahoo.co.uk

HONOURS FA Comps: None

League: None

11-12	12-13	13-14	14-15	15-16	16-17	17-18	18-19	19-20	20-21
UCL 1 5	UCL 1 8	UCL 1 14	UCL 1 13	UCL 1 13	UCL 1 16	UCL 1 9	UCL 1 11	UCL 1 n&v	UCL 1 n&v
FAC EP	FAC EP	FAC EP							
FAV 2Q	FAV 2Q	FAV 1Q		FAV 1Q	FAV 1Q	FAV 1P	FAV 1Q	FAV 1Q	FAV 1Q

GROUND: Hayden Road, Rushden, Northants NN10 9LA

Bus Route Ashwell Road - stop 60m away

SHEFFORD TOWN & CAMPTON

Spartan South Midlands Division One

Founded 2010 Nickname: **Club Colours:** Red & white

Club Contact Details 07885 557 274 sheffordtownandcampton@gmail.com

HONOURS FA Comps: None

League: Bedfordshire County Premier Division 2011-12, 17-18, 18-19.

11-12	12-13	13-14	14-15	15-16	16-17	17-18	18-19	19-20	20-21
BedCP 1	BedCP 7	BedCP 11	BedCP 5	BedCP 9	BedCP 7	BedCP 1	BedCP 1	SSM1 n&v	SSM1 n&v

GROUND: Shefford Sports Club, Hitchin Road, Shefford SG17 5JD

STOTFOLD

Spartan South Midlands Division One

Founded 1904 Nickname: The Eagles **Club Colours:** Amber and black

Club Contact Details 07752 430 493 julie.longhurst46@virginmedia.com

HONOURS FA Comps: None

League: South Midlands 1980-81. United Counties Premier 2007-08.

11-12	12-13	13-14	14-15	15-16	16-17	17-18	18-19	19-20	20-21
SSM P 9	SSM P 14	SSM P 19	SSM P 16	SSM P 15	SSM P 13	SSM P 21	SSM P 19	SSM1 n&v	SSM1 n&v
FAC 1Q	FAC Pr	FAC P	FAC EP	FAC EP	FAC 1Q	FAC EP	FAC EP	FAC P	
FAV 1Q	FAV 1Q	FAV 1P	FAV 2Q	FAV 2P	FAV 1Qr	FAV 1Q	FAV 2Q	FAV 1Q	FAV 1Q

GROUND: The JSJ Stadium, New Roker Park, Arlesey Road, Stotfold SG5 4HW

Nearest Railway Station Arlesey - 2.9km

Bus Route The Green - stop 80m away

THAME UNITED RESERVES

Spartan South Midlands Division One

Founded 1883 Nickname: None **Club Colours:** Red & black

Club Contact Details 07753 502 955 jake@jcpc.org.uk

HONOURS FA Comps: None

League: Wycombe & District Senior Division 2015-16.
Spartan South Midlands Division Two 2016-17.

11-12	12-13	13-14	14-15	15-16	16-17	17-18	18-19	19-20	20-21
				WyDS 1	SSM2 1	Hel1E 8	Hel1E 2	Hel1E n&v	Hel1E n&v
								FAC Pr	FAC EP
							FAV 2P	FAV 1Q	FAV 1Q

GROUND: The ASM Stadium, Meadow View Park, Tythrop Way, Thame OX9 3RN

Nearest Railway Station Haddenham & Thame Parkway - 2.9km

Bus Route Queens Close stop - 309m away

WELLINGBOROUGH WHITWORTH

Spartan South Midlands Division One

Founded 1973 Nickname: Flourmen **Club Colours:** Red & black

Club Contact Details 07776 160 169 victorgoodes@aol.com

HONOURS FA Comps: None

League: Rushden & District 1975-76, 76-77. United Counties Division One 2006-07.

11-12	12-13	13-14	14-15	15-16	16-17	17-18	18-19	19-20	20-21
UCL 1 4	UCL 1 13	UCL 1 17	UCL 1 7	UCL 1 15	UCL 1 2	UCL P 20	UCL P 20	UCL 1 n&v	UCL 1 n&v
	FAC EP			FAC EP	FAC EP	FAC EP	FAC EP	FAC EP	FAC EP
FAV 1Q	FAV 2Q	FAV 2Q	FAV 1Q	FAV 1Q	FAV 2Q	FAV 2Q	FAV 1Q	FAV 1Q	FAV 2Q

GROUND: Victoria Mill Ground, London Road, Wellingborough NN8 2DP

Nearest Railway Station Wellingborough - 1.2km

Bus Route The Dog & Duck Pub - stop 50m away

WINSLOW UNITED

Spartan South Midlands Division One

Founded 1891 Nickname: The Ploughmen **Club Colours:** Yellow and blue

Club Contact Details 07791 598 346 garethrobins75@gmail.com

HONOURS FA Comps: None

League: South Midlands Division One 1974-75.

11-12	12-13	13-14	14-15	15-16	16-17	17-18	18-19	19-20	20-21
SSM2 7	SSM1 14	SSM1 9	SSM1 14	SSM1 19	SSM1 16	SSM1 3	SSM1 3	SSM1 n&v	SSM1 n&v
							FAC EP	FAC EP	FAC P
FAV 1P	FAV 2Q	FAV 2Q	FAV 1Qr	FAV 2Q	FAV 2Q	FAV 1Q	FAV 2Q	FAV 2Q	FAV 1Q

GROUND: The Recreation Ground, Elmfields Gate, Winslow, Bucks MK18 3JG

Bus Route Elmside - stop 210m away

ANSTEY NOMADS

United Counties Premier North

Founded 1947 Nickname: Nomads **Club Colours:** Red & white

Club Contact Details 07946 856 430

Previous Names: None

Previous Leagues: Leicestershire Senior. East Midlands Counties 2009-18.

HONOURS

FA Comps: None

League: Leicestershire Senior 1951-52, 53-54, 81-82, 82-83, 2008-09, Division Two 1973-74.

11-12		12-13		13-14		14-15		15-16		16-17		17-18		18-19		19-20		20-21	
EMC	9	EMC	14	EMC	17	EMC	14	EMC	4	EMC	17	EMC	2	UCL 1	2	UCL P	n&v	UCL P	n&v
FAC	EP	FAC	EP							FAC	EP			FAC	2Q	FAC	EP	FAC	P
FAV	2Q	FAV	2Q	FAV	1Q	FAV	1Q	FAV	1P	FAV	2Q	FAV	1Q	FAV	1Q	FAV	2Q	FAV	5P

GROUND: Calingtons Community Complex, Cropston Road, Anstey, Leicester LE7 7BP **Capacity:** 1000

Nearest Railway Station Leicester - 6.2km **Seats:** 100

CLUB MOVEMENTS

PREMIER DIVISION NORTH - IN: Eastwood CFC and Heanor Town (P - EMCP). Gresley, Heather St John, Long Eaton United, Newark and Selston (LM - MLP). Melton Town (P - UCL1). Skegness Town (P - NCE1).
OUT: Shepshed Dynamo (P - NPLM).

BOSTON TOWN

United Counties Premier North

Founded 1964 Nickname: Poachers **Club Colours:** All blue

Club Contact Details 07704 051 050 btfcsec@hotmail.co.uk

Previous Names: Boston 1964-1994

Previous Leagues: Lincolnshire. Central Alliance 1965-66. Eastern Counties 1966-68. Midland 1968-82. Northern Counties East 1982-87. Central Midlands 1987-91.

HONOURS

FA Comps: None

League: Lincolnshire 1964-65. Central Alliance 1965-65. Midland 1974-75, 78-79, 80-81.
Central Midlands Supreme 1988-89. United Counties League 1994-95, 2000-01.

11-12		12-13		13-14		14-15		15-16		16-17		17-18		18-19		19-20		20-21	
UCL P	14	UCL P	10	UCL P	14	UCL P	12	UCL P	16	UCL P	20	UCL P	13	UCL P	17	UCL P	n&v	UCL P	n&v
FAC	P	FAC	EP	FAC	P	FAC	1Q	FAC	EP	FAC	EP	FAC	3Q	FAC	EP	FAC	2Q	FAC	P
FAV	2P	FAV	3P	FAV	1P	FAV	2Q	FAV	1Q	FAV	2Q	FAV	2Q	FAV	1Q	FAV	1Q	FAV	2Q

GROUND: DWB Stadium, Tattershall Road, Boston, Lincs PE21 9LR **Capacity:** 6,000

Nearest Railway Station Boston - 1.6km **Seats:** 450

Bus Route Bus stops outside the ground **Covered:** 950

DEEPING RANGERS

United Counties Premier North

Founded 1964 Nickname: Rangers **Club Colours:** All claret

Club Contact Details 01778 344 701 drfcsecretary@gmail.com

Previous Names: None

Previous Leagues: Peterborough & District 1966 - 1999.

HONOURS

FA Comps: None

League: United Counties Premier Division 2006-07.

11-12		12-13		13-14		14-15		15-16		16-17		17-18		18-19		19-20		20-21	
UCL P	4	UCL P	5	UCL P	4	UCL P	9	UCL P	10	UCL P	2	UCL P	5	UCL P	2	UCL P	n&v	UCL P	n&v
FAC	2Q	FAC	EP	FAC	EP	FAC	EP	FAC	2Q	FAC	1Q	FAC	2Q	FAC	Pr	FAC	2Q	FAC	EP
FAV	3P	FAV	2P	FAV	2Q	FAV	3P	FAV	2Q	FAV	1Qr	FAV	3P	FAV	5P	FAV	2P	FAV	1P

GROUND: The Haydon Whitham Stadium, Outgang Road, Market Deeping PE6 8LQ **Capacity:** 2,000

Seats: 164

Bus Route Buttercup Court - stop 720m away **Covered:** 250

EASTWOOD COMMUNITY

United Counties Premier North

Founded 2014 Nickname: Red Badgers **Club Colours:** Red

Club Contact Details 01773 432 414

Previous Names: None

Previous Leagues: Central Midlands 2014-18. East Midlands 2018-21.

HONOURS

FA Comps: None

League: Central Midlands South 2017-18.

11-12	12-13	13-14	14-15	15-16	16-17	17-18	18-19	19-20	20-21
			CMSth 13	CMSth 10	CMSth 2	CMSth 1	EMC 6	EMC n&v	EMC n&v
				FAV 1Q	FAV 2Q	FAV 2Q	FAV 2P	FAV 2P	FAV 2Q

GROUND: Halbrooke Stadium, Chewton Street, Eastwood, Notts NG26 3HB

Nearest Railway Station Langley Mill via Chesterfield station. Walk to Acorn Centre to catch bus.

Bus Route Rainbow one bus from Acorn Centre. 11min journey via seven stops to Edward Road, ground 1min walk from there.

GRESLEY

United Counties Premier North

Founded 2009 Nickname: The Moatmen **Club Colours:** Red & white

Club Contact Details 01283 216 315 ian.collins@gresleyrovers.com

Previous Names: Gresley Rovers

Previous Leagues: East Midlands 2009-11. Midland Football Alliance 2011-12. Northern Premier 2012-19. Midland 2019-21.

HONOURS

FA Comps: None

League: East Midlands Counties 2010-11. Midland Alliance 2011-12.

11-12	12-13	13-14	14-15	15-16	16-17	17-18	18-19	19-20	20-21
MidAl 1	NP1S 11	NP1S 9	NP1S 5	NP1S 16	NP1S 18	NP1S 17	NP1E 20	MFLP n&v	MFLP n&v
FAC 1Q	FAC 3Q	FAC 2Qr	FAC Pr	FAC Pr	FAC 2Qr	FAC P	FAC P	FAC P	
FAV 5P	FAT 1Q	FAT 1P	FAT 3Q	FAT 1Q	FAT 1Q	FAT P	FAT P	FAV 1P	

GROUND: The Moat Ground, Moat Street, Church Gresley, Derbyshire DE11 9RE **Capacity:** 2,400

Bus Route Church Street - stop 200m away

HEANOR TOWN

United Counties Premier North

Founded 1883 Nickname: The Lions **Club Colours:** White & black

Club Contact Details 07581 015 868 amanda.jones10@live.co.uk

Previous Names: None

Previous Leagues: Midland 1961-72. Central Midlands 1986-2008. East Midlands Counties 2008-12, 18-21. Northern Counties East 2012-15. Midland Football 2015-18.

HONOURS

FA Comps: None

League: Central Midlands Supreme Division 1994-95, 96-97.
East Midlands Counties 2011-12.

11-12	12-13	13-14	14-15	15-16	16-17	17-18	18-19	19-20	20-21
EMC 1	NCEP 11	NCEP 8	NCEP 6	MFLP 6	MFLP 6	MFLP 13	EMC 4	EMC n&v	EMC n&v
FAC 1Q	FAC P	FAC EP	FAC P	FAC EP	FAC 1Q	FAC EP	FAC EP	FAC P	
FAV 1Q	FAT 1Pr	FAV 1P	FAV 4P	FAV 2P	FAV 1P	FAV 1Q	FAV 1P	FAV 3P	FAV 1P

GROUND: The Town Ground, Mayfield Avenue, Heanor DE75 7EN **Capacity:** 2,700

Nearest Railway Station Langley Mill - 2km **Seats:** 100

Bus Route Sports Ground stop - 132m away **Covered:** 1,000

HEATHER ST. JOHN'S

United Counties Premier North

Founded 1949 Nickname: **Club Colours:** All royal blue

Club Contact Details 01530 263 986 ctissington1962@btinternet.com

Previous Names: Heather Athletic 1949-2007.

Previous Leagues: Midland Combination > 2011. Midland Alliance 2011-14. Midland 2014-21.

HONOURS

FA Comps: None

League: Leicester & District Division One 1965-66., 69-70, 71-72.
Midland Combination Division One 2006-07, Premier 10-11. Midland Division One 2018-19.

11-12	12-13	13-14	14-15	15-16	16-17	17-18	18-19	19-20	20-21
MidAl 19	MidAl 20	MidAl 22	MFL1 16	MFL1 16	MFL1 8	MFL1 7	MFL1 1	MFLP n&v	MFLP n&v
		FAC EP	FAC EP				FAC EP	FAC 1Q	FAC EP
	FAV 1P	FAV 2Q	FAV 2Q	FAV 1Q	FAV 1Q	FAV 1P	FAV 2P	FAV 1P	FAV 1Q

GROUND: St John's Park, Ravenstone Rd, Heather LE67 2QJ

Bus Route Holyoake Drive stop - 160m away

HOLBEACH UNITED

United Counties Premier North

Founded 1929 Nickname: Tigers **Club Colours:** Gold & black

Club Contact Details 01406 424 761 jamesmcmartin3@btinternet.com

Previous Names: None

Previous Leagues: King's Lynn. Peterborough & District 1936-46. United Counties 1946-55, Eastern 1955-62, Midland Counties 1962-63.

HONOURS

FA Comps: None

League: United Counties 1989-90, 02-03, 12-13.

11-12	12-13	13-14	14-15	15-16	16-17	17-18	18-19	19-20	20-21
UCL P 6	UCL P 1	UCL P 11	UCL P 6	UCL P 4	UCL P 7	UCL P 4	UCL P 5	UCL P n&v	UCL P n&v
FAC Pr	FAC 1Q	FAC P	FAC P	FAC 2Qr	FAC 1Q	FAC 1Q	FAC EP	FAC P	FAC P
FAV 1P	FAV 2Q	FAV 1P	FAV 5P	FAV 2P	FAV 2P	FAV 2P	FAV 3P	FAV 1P	FAV 1Q

GROUND: Carters Park, Park Road, Holbeach, Lincs PE12 7EE

Capacity: 4,00
Seats: 20
Covered: 450

Bus Route Carter's Park - stop 70m away

LEICESTER NIRVANA

United Counties Premier North

Founded 2008 Nickname: **Club Colours:** Red and black

Club Contact Details 07710 426 728 nirvanaminisoccer@gmail.com

Previous Names: Thurnby Rangers and Leicester Nirvana merged to form today's club in 2008. Thurnby Nirvana 2008-15.

Previous Leagues: Leicestershire Senior >2010 East Midland Counties 2010-14

HONOURS

FA Comps: None

League: Leicestershire Senior Division One 1997-98, 2000-01, Premier Division 04-05. East Midland Counties 2013-14.

11-12	12-13	13-14	14-15	15-16	16-17	17-18	18-19	19-20	20-21
EMC 7	EMC 3	EMC 1	UCL P 2	UCL P 2	UCL P 17	UCL P 6	UCL P 12	UCL P n&v	UCL P n&v
FAC 1Qr	FAC 1Qr	FAC EPr	FAC P	FAC P	FAC EP	FAC EP	FAC EP	FAC Pr	FAC EP
FAV 1Q	FAV 1Q	FAV 2Q	FAV 4P	FAV 4P	FAV 2Q	FAV 2P	FAV 5P	FAV 2P	FAV 1P

GROUND: Hamilton Park, Sandhills Avenue, Leicester LE5 1LU

Nearest Railway Station Syston - 3.9km

Bus Route Lakeview Chase - stop 70m away

Dunn (Melton) closed down by the West Bridgford defence.

Melton Town v West Bridgford pre-season friendly. Photos Keith Clayton.

LONG EATON UNITED

United Counties Premier North

Founded 1956 Nickname: Blues **Club Colours:** Blue and black

Club Contact Details 01159 735 700 secretary@longeatonutd.co.uk

Previous Names: None

Previous Leagues: Central Alliance 1956-61, Mid Co Football Lge 1961-82, NCE 1982-89, 2002-14. Central Midlands 1989-2002. Midland 2002-21.

HONOURS

FA Comps: None

League: Northern Counties East Division One South 1984-85.

11-12		12-13		13-14		14-15		15-16		16-17		17-18		18-19		19-20		20-21	
NCEP	15	NCEP	12	NCEP	11	MFLP	3	MFLP	18	MFLP	14	MFLP	9	MFLP	15	MFLP	n&v	MFLP	n&v
FAC	EP			FAC	1Q	FAC	EP	FAC	1Q	FAC	P	FAC	EP	FAC	P	FAC	Pr	FAC	1Q
FAV	2P	FAV	3P	FAV	2P	FAV	1P	FAV	2P	FAV	3P	FAV	2Q	FAV	1P	FAV	2Q	FAV	QF

GROUND: Grange Park, Station Road, Long Eaton, Derbys NG10 2EF

Nearest Railway Station Attenborough - 1.9km

Bus Route School stop - 158m away

Capacity: 1,500
Seats: 450
Covered: 500

LOUGHBOROUGH STUDENTS

United Counties Premier North

Founded 1920 Nickname: The Scholars **Club Colours:** Purple

Club Contact Details 07458 126 730 footballsecretary@lboro.ac.uk

Previous Names: Loughborough College, Loughborough University.

Previous Leagues: Leicestershire Senior. Midland Combination. Midland Alliance 2009-14. Midland 2014-19.

HONOURS

FA Comps: None

League: Midland Combination 2008-09.

11-12		12-13		13-14		14-15		15-16		16-17		17-18		18-19		19-20		20-21	
MidAl	5	MidAl	4	MidAl	14	MFLP	20	MFLP	14	MFLP	18	MFLP	18	MFLP	18	UCL P	n&v	UCL P	n&v
FAC	1Q	FAC	P	FAC	1Q	FAC	P	FAC	P	FAC	P	FAC	1Q	FAC	Pr	FAC	P	FAC	EP
FAV	1P	FAV	1Q	FAV	2P	FAV	1Q	FAV	1Pr	FAV	2Q	FAV	2Q	FAV	1P	FAV	2P	FAV	2P

GROUND: Loughborough Uni Stadium, Holywell Sports Complex, Holywell Park LE11 3QF

Nearest Railway Station Loughborough - 4km

Bus Route Wheatsheaf stop - 172m away

Capacity: 3,300

MELTON TOWN

United Counties Premier North

Founded 2004 Nickname: **Club Colours:** Red

Club Contact Details 01664 481 188 secretarymeltonmowbrayfc@hotmail.com

Previous Names: Melton Mowbray >2016.

Previous Leagues: Leicestershire Senior >2016.

HONOURS

FA Comps: None

League: None

11-12		12-13		13-14		14-15		15-16		16-17		17-18		18-19		19-20		20-21	
LeicS1	6	LeicS1	2	LeicSP	2	LeicSP	2	LeicSP	3	UCL 1	9	UCL 1	16	UCL 1	3	UCL 1	n&v	UCL 1	n&v
																FAC	P	FAC	EP
												FAV	2Q	FAV	1Qr	FAV	1Q	FAV	1P

GROUND: Melton Sports Village, Burton Road, Melton Mowbray LE13 1DN

Seats: 135

NEWARK

United Counties Premier North

Founded 1901 Nickname: Highwaymen **Club Colours:** Orange & black

Club Contact Details 07973 702 588 kmpnewark@aol.com

Previous Names: Worthington Simpsons >1998, IDP Newark 1998-2001. Newark Flowserve 2001-20.

Previous Leagues: Nottingham Alliance. Nottinghamshire Senior >2004, 2009-18. Central Midlands 2004-09. East Midlands Counties 2018-19. Midland 2019-21.

HONOURS

FA Comps: None

League: Notts Alliance 1952-53, 65-66. Nottinghamshire Senior Premier Division 2017-18.

11-12	12-13	13-14	14-15	15-16	16-17	17-18	18-19	19-20	20-21
		NottS2 3	NottS1 2	NottSP	NottSP	NottSP 1	EMC 2	MFLP n&v	MFLP n&v
									FAC 2Q
							FAV 1Q	FAV 4P	FAV 3P

GROUND: Mill Street Playing Field, Greenwich Avenue, Basford, Nttingham NG6 0LD

PINCHBECK UNITED

United Counties Premier North

Founded 1935 Nickname: The Knights **Club Colours:** Red

Club Contact Details 07736 909 829 pinbeckunitedfootballclub@gmail.com

Previous Names: None

Previous Leagues: Peterborough & District >2017

HONOURS

FA Comps: None

League: Peterborough & District Premier Division 1989-90, 90-91, 2011-12.
United Counties Division One 2017-18.

11-12	12-13	13-14	14-15	15-16	16-17	17-18	18-19	19-20	20-21
P&D P 1	P&D P 15	P&D P 15	P&D P 7	P&D P 3	P&D P 2	UCL 1 1	UCL P 4	UCL P n&v	UCL P n&v
							FAC EP	FAC EP	FAC EP
						FAV 1Q	FAV 2Q	FAV 1P	FAV 1Q

GROUND: Sir Harley Stewart Field, Winfrey Avenue, Spalding PE11 1DA
Nearest Railway Station Spalding - 0.2km
Bus Route Broad Street - stop 100m away

QUORN

United Counties Premier North

Founded 1924 Nickname: Reds **Club Colours:** All red

Club Contact Details 01509 620 232 secretary@quornfc.co.uk

Previous Names: Quorn Methodists >1952

Previous Leagues: Leicestershire Senior, Midland Alliance > 2007. NPL 2007-2012. United Counties 2012-13. Midland Alliance 2013-14. Midland 2014-19.

HONOURS

FA Comps: None

League: Leicestershire Senior 2000-01

11-12	12-13	13-14	14-15	15-16	16-17	17-18	18-19	19-20	20-21
NP1S 21	UCL P 7	MidAl 5	MFLP 11	MFLP 17	MFLP 11	MFLP 11	MFLP 6	UCL P n&v	UCL P n&v
FAC 2Q	FAC 1Q	FAC Pr	FAC P	FAC EP	FAC EP	FAC P	FAC 1Q	FAC EP	FAC 1Q
FAT P	FAV 1P	FAV 1Q	FAV 2Q	FAV 2P	FAV 3P	FAV 2P	FAV 2P	FAV 2P	FAV 1P

GROUND: Farley Way Stadium, Farley Way, Quorn, Leicestershire LE12 8RB
Nearest Railway Station Quorn & Woodhouse - 1.5km
Bus Route Alexander Road stop - 189m away

Capacity: 1,550
Seats: 350
Covered: 250

SELSTON

United Counties Premier North

Founded 1968 Nickname: The Parishioners **Club Colours:** Blue & black

Club Contact Details adamrovers@hotmail.com

Previous Names: None

Previous Leagues: Midland Regional Alliance >2011. Notts Senior 2011-15. Central Midlands 2015-17. East Midlands Counties 2017-19. Midland 2019-21.

HONOURS

FA Comps: None

League: Midland Regional Alliance Division Two 2007-08. Notts Senior 2013-14. Central Midlands South Division 2015-16, 16-17. East Midlands Counties 2018-19.

11-12	12-13	13-14	14-15	15-16	16-17	17-18	18-19	19-20	20-21
NottSP 11	NottSP 11	NottSP 1	NottSP 4	CMSth 1	CMSth 1	EMC 4	EMC 1	MFLP n&v	MFLP n&v
								FAC EP	FAC EP
							FAV 1P	FAV 2Q	FAV 2Q

GROUND: Parish Hall, Mansfield Road, Selston, Nottinghamshire NG16 6EE

Nearest Railway Station Kirkby in Ashfield - 4.5km

SKEGNESS TOWN

United Counties Premier North

Founded 1947 Nickname: Lilywhites **Club Colours:** White & red

Club Contact Details 07917 861 021 skegnesstownfcsecretary@gmail.com

Previous Names: None

Previous Leagues: Lincolnshire >2018. Northern Counties East 2018-21.

HONOURS

FA Comps: None

League: Lincolnshire 1951-52, 55-56, 2006-07, 07-08, 13-14, 15-16, 16-17.

11-12	12-13	13-14	14-15	15-16	16-17	17-18	18-19	19-20	20-21
Lincs 12	Lincs 8	Lincs 1	Lincs 2	Lincs 1	Lincs 1	Lincs 2	NCE1 15	NCE1 n&v	NCE1 n&v
						FAV 2Q	FAV 2Q	FAV 2Q	FAV 1P

GROUND: Wainfleet Road, Skegness, Lincolnshire PE25 2EL

Nearest Railway Station Skegness ½ mile

SLEAFORD TOWN

United Counties Premier North

Founded 1968 Nickname: Town **Club Colours:** Green and black

Club Contact Details 01529 415 951 jennyorourke@btinternet.com

Previous Names: None

Previous Leagues: Lincolnshire 1968-2003.

HONOURS

FA Comps: None

League: United Counties Division One 2005-06.

11-12	12-13	13-14	14-15	15-16	16-17	17-18	18-19	19-20	20-21
UCL P 19	UCL P 18	UCL P 13	UCL P 19	UCL P 7	UCL P 14	UCL P 18	UCL P 13	UCL P n&v	UCL P n&v
FAC EP	FAC P	FAC 1Q	FAC EP	FAC EP	FAC P	FAC EP	FAC EP	FAC EP	FAC EP
FAV 2Q	FAV 1P	FAV 2Q	FAV 2Q	FAV 4P	FAV 3Pr	FAV 1Q	FAV 1Pr	FAV 1Q	FAV 1Q

GROUND: Eslaforde Park, Boston Road, Sleaford, Lincs NG34 9GH

Nearest Railway Station Sleaford - 1.4km

Bus Route Eslaforde Park - stop 90m away

Capacity: 1,000 **Seats:** 88 **Covered:** 88

BIGGLESWADE UNITED

United Counties Premier South

Founded 1959 Nickname: United **Club Colours:** Red and navy

Club Contact Details 07714 661 827 tracey.james58@btinternet.com

Previous Names: None

Previous Leagues: North Hertfordshire 1959-69. Midlands 1969-84. Hertfordshire Senior County 1984-86. Bedford & District 1986-96. South Midlands 1996-97. Spartan South Midlands 1997-2021.

HONOURS

FA Comps: None

League: Bedford & District Division Two 1990-91, Division One 91-92, Premier 94-95, 95-96. South Midlands Division One 1996-97.

11-12	12-13	13-14	14-15	15-16	16-17	17-18	18-19	19-20	20-21
SSM P 19	SSM P 18	SSM P 17	SSM P 13	SSM P 10	SSM P 9	SSM P 8	SSM P 4	SSM P n&v	SSM P n&v
FAC P	FAC P	FAC 1Q	FAC 1Q	FAC 1Q	FAC 1Q	FAC EPr	FAC EPr	FAC P	FAC 1Q
FAV 1P	FAV 2Q	FAV 1Q	FAV 2Q	FAV 2P	FAV 2Pr	FAV 1P	FAV 1P	FAV 1Pr	FAT 1Q

GROUND: Second Meadow, Fairfield Road, Biggleswade, Beds SG18 0BS **Capacity:** 2,000
Nearest Railway Station Biggleswade - 0.9km **Seats:** 260
Bus Route Fairfield Road - stop 85m away **Covered:** 130

CLUB MOVEMENTS

PREMIER DIVISION SOUTH - IN: Biggleswade United, Eynesbury Town, Newport Pagnell Town and Potton United (LM - SSMP). Bugbrooke St Michael (P - UCL1). Coventry Sphinx and Coventry United (LM - MLP). Easington Sports (LM HLP). Godmanchester Rovers (LM - ECLP). Leicester Road (P - ML1). Long Buckby (P UCL1)

BUGBROOKE ST MICHAELS

United Counties Premier South

Founded 1929 Nickname: Badgers **Club Colours:** White and black

Club Contact Details 01604 839 129 graybags05@btinternet.com

Previous Names: None

Previous Leagues: Central Northants Combination.

HONOURS

FA Comps: None

League: Central Northants Combination 1968-69, 69-70, 71-72, 76-77, 85-86. United Counties Division One 1998-99.

11-12	12-13	13-14	14-15	15-16	16-17	17-18	18-19	19-20	20-21
UCL 1 3	UCL 1 7	UCL 1 18	UCL 1 11	UCL 1 18	UCL 1 3	UCL 1 18	UCL 1 4	UCL 1 n&v	UCL 1 n&v
FAC P	FAC 1Q	FAC EP						FAC P	
FAV 1P	FAV 2Q	FAV 2Q	FAV 1Q	FAV 1Q			FAV 2Qr	FAV 1Q	FAV 1P

GROUND: Birds Close, Gayton Road, Bugbrooke NN7 3PH **Capacity:** 2,500
Seats: 120
Bus Route Bakers Arms Pub - stop 500m away

COGENHOE UNITED

United Counties Premier South

Founded 1967 Nickname: Cooks **Club Colours:** All royal blue

Club Contact Details 01604 890 521 cogenhoeunited@outlook.com

Previous Names: None

Previous Leagues: Central Northants Combination 1967-85.

HONOURS

FA Comps: None

League: Central Northants Combination Division Two 1951-52, Premier 80-81, 82-83, 83-84. United Counties 2004-05.

11-12	12-13	13-14	14-15	15-16	16-17	17-18	18-19	19-20	20-21
UCL P 12	UCL P 8	UCL P 5	UCL P 5	UCL P 5	UCL P 13	UCL P 8	UCL P 7	UCL P n&v	UCL P n&v
FAC P	FAC EP	FAC EPr	FAC P	FAC 2Q	FAC P	FAC P	FAC EP		FAC P
FAV 2P	FAV 2Q	FAV 1Q	FAV 1Q	FAV 1P	FAV 1Q	FAV 4P	FAV 2P		FAV 2P

GROUND: Compton Park, Brafield Road, Cogenhoe NN7 1ND **Capacity:** 5,000
Seats: 100
Bus Route Orchard Way - stop 190m away **Covered:** 200

COVENTRY SPHINX

United Counties Premier South

Founded 1946 Nickname: Sphinx **Club Colours:** Sky blue & white

Club Contact Details 07979 233 845 sharon@coventrysphinx.co.uk

Previous Names: Armstrong Siddeley Motors. Sphinx > 1995.

Previous Leagues: Midland Combination. Midland Alliance 2007-14. Midland 2014-21.

HONOURS

FA Comps: None

League: Midland Combination Premier 2006-07.

11-12		12-13		13-14		14-15		15-16		16-17		17-18		18-19		19-20		20-21	
MidAl	3	MidAl	14	MidAl	7	MFLP	18	MFLP	19	MFLP	10	MFLP	10	MFLP	9	MFLP	n&v	MFLP	n&v
FAC	P	FAC	P	FAC	2Q	FAC	Pr	FAC	P	FAC	EP	FAC	EP	FAC	EP	FAC	P	FAC	1Q
FAV	2Q	FAV	2P	FAV	2P	FAV	2Q	FAV	2P	FAV	2Q	FAV	1Q	FAV	1Qr	FAV	2Q	FAV	3P

GROUND: Sphinx Sports & Social Club, Sphinx Drive, Coventry CV3 1WA **Capacity:** 1,000

Nearest Railway Station Coventry - 2.6km

Bus Route Bulls Head Lane stop - 363m away

COVENTRY UNITED

United Counties Premier South

Founded 2013 Nickname: Cov United **Club Colours:** Red and green

Club Contact Details 024 7623 1001 greywoodkoi@hotmail.co.uk

Previous Names: None

Previous Leagues: Midland Combination 2013-14. Midland 2014-21.

HONOURS

FA Comps: None

League: Midland Football League Division Two 2014-15, Division One 2015-16.

11-12		12-13		13-14		14-15		15-16		16-17		17-18		18-19		19-20		20-21	
				MCm2	2	MFL2	1	MFL1	1	MFLP	8	MFLP	8	MFLP	8	MFLP	n&v	MFLP	n&v
										FAC	1Q	FAC	EP	FAC	EP	FAC	EPr	FAC	P
								FAV	2P	FAV	1P	FAV	3Pr	FAV	4P	FAV	4P	FAV	3P

GROUND: Coventry RFC, Butts Park Arena, The Butts, Coventry CV1 3GE **Capacity:** 3,000

Nearest Railway Station Coventry - 1km

Bus Route Albany Road stop - 156m away

DESBOROUGH TOWN

United Counties Premier South

Founded 1896 Nickname: Ar Tam **Club Colours:** All royal blue

Club Contact Details 01536 761 350 froggerycottage@hotmail.com

Previous Names: None

Previous Leagues: Northamptonshire change name to United Counties in 1934.

HONOURS

FA Comps: None

League: Northamptonshire/United Counties 1900-01, 01-02, 06-07, 20-21, 23-24, 24-25, 27-28 / 48-49, 66-67.

11-12		12-13		13-14		14-15		15-16		16-17		17-18		18-19		19-20		20-21	
UCL P	16	UCL P	11	UCL P	4	UCL P	14	UCL P	15	UCL P	4	UCL P	9	UCL P	9	UCL P	n&v	UCL P	n&v
FAC	EPr	FAC	EPr	FAC	P	FAC	EP	FAC	EP	FAC	P	FAC	P	FAC	P	FAC	EP	FAC	EP
FAV	1P	FAV	2P	FAV	2P	FAV	2Q	FAV	1Q	FAV	1P	FAV	4P	FAV	3P	FAV	1Q	FAV	2Q

GROUND: Waterworks Field, Braybrooke Road, Desborough NN14 2LE **Capacity:** 8,000

Seats: 250

Bus Route Bus stops outside the ground. **Covered:** 500

EASINGTON SPORTS

United Counties Premier South

Founded 1946 Nickname: The Clan **Club Colours:** Red & white

Club Contact Details 07791 681 204 jamiehunter@hotmail.co.uk

Previous Names:

Previous Leagues: Warwick Combination. Hellenic >2021.

HONOURS

FA Comps: None

League: Oxfordshire Senior Premier Division 1957-58, 58-59, Division One 1965-66.
Hellenic Division One West 2018-19.

11-12	12-13	13-14	14-15	15-16	16-17	17-18	18-19	19-20	20-21
Hel1W 6	Hel1W 8	Hel1W 9	Hel1W 4	Hel1W 5	Hel1W 4	Hel1W 3	Hel1W 1	Hel P n&v	Hel P n&v
							FAC P	FAC EP	FAC P
						FAV 1Q	FAV 2Q	FAV 1Q	FAV 2Q

GROUND: Addison Road, Banbury OX16 9DH
Nearest Railway Station Banbury - 1.6km
Bus Route Springfield Avenu stop - 117m away

Capacity: 1,500
Seats: 50

EYNESBURY ROVERS

United Counties Premier South

Founded 1897 Nickname: Rovers **Club Colours:** Royal blue & white

Club Contact Details 07854 950 008 / 07787 567 338 erfcsecretary@gmail.com

Previous Names: None

Previous Leagues: Biggleswade & District. St Neots Junior. Bed & District. South Midlands 1934-39. United Counties 1946-52, 63-2019. Eastern Counties 1952-63. Spartan South Midlands 2019-21.

HONOURS

FA Comps: None

League: St Neots Junior 1910-11. Bedford & District Division Two 1926-27, 30-31, 31-32.
United Counties Division 1 1976-77.

11-12	12-13	13-14	14-15	15-16	16-17	17-18	18-19	19-20	20-21
UCL 1 6	UCL 1 3	UCL 1 2	UCL P 11	UCL P 6	UCL P 5	UCL P 7	UCL P 6	SSM P n&v	SSM P n&v
		FAC EP		FAC EP	FAC 1Q	FAC P	FAC Pr	FAC EPr	FAC P
FAV 1Q	FAV 1P	FAV 2P	FAV 1Qr	FAV 1P	FAV 1Q	FAV 1P	FAV 1Q	FAV 4P	FAV 2P

GROUND: Alfred Hall Memorial Ground, Hall Road, Eynesbury, St Neots PE19 2SF
Nearest Railway Station St Neots - 2.1km
Bus Route Ernulf Academy Forecourt - stop 150m away

GNG OADBY TOWN

United Counties Premier South

Founded 1937 Nickname: The Poachers **Club Colours:** All red

Club Contact Details 07445 102 486 hardipdayal@gmail.com

Previous Names: Oadby Imperial > 1951. Oadby Town 1951-2020.

Previous Leagues: Leicestershire Senior. Midland Alliance > 2011. East Midlands Counties 2011-12.

HONOURS

FA Comps: None

League: Leicestershire Senior Division Two 1951-52, Premier 63-64, 67-68, 68-69, 72-73, 94-95, 96-97, 97-98, 98-99. Midland Alliance 99-00. United Counties Division One 2013-14.

11-12	12-13	13-14	14-15	15-16	16-17	17-18	18-19	19-20	20-21
EMC 3	UCL 1 4	UCL 1 1	UCL P 13	UCL P 21	UCL P 19	UCL P 19	UCL P 10	UCL P n&v	UCL P n&v
FAC Pr	FAC P	FAC EP	FAC EP	FAC 2Q	FAC EP	FAC P	FAC EP	FAC EP	FAC P
FAV 5P	FAV 2P	FAV 2P	FAV 1P	FAV 2Q	FAV 1Q	FAV 1Q	FAV 1Q	FAV 1Q	FAV 1Q

GROUND: Oaks Park, Wigston Road, Oadby LE2 5QG
Nearest Railway Station South Wigston - 3.6km
Bus Route Brabazon Road - stop 35m away

Capacity: 5,000
Seats: 224
Covered: 224

GODMANCHESTER ROVERS

United Counties Premier South

Founded 1911 Nickname: Goody/Rovers **Club Colours:** Royal blue

Club Contact Details 07734 136 419 (Ground) secretary@godmanchesterroversfc.co.uk

Previous Names: None

Previous Leagues: Huntingdonshire County. Cambridgeshire >2002. Eastern Counties 2002-21.

HONOURS

FA Comps: None

League: Eastern Counties League Division One 2011-12.

11-12	12-13	13-14	14-15	15-16	16-17	17-18	18-19	19-20	20-21
EC1 1	ECP 5	ECP 5	ECP 2	ECP 2	ECP 12	ECP 4	ECP 3	ECP n&v	ECP n&v
FAC P	FAC P	FAC P	FAC P	FAC P	FAC Pr	FAC EP	FAC 1Q	FAC Pr	FAC EP
FAV 3P	FAV 1P	FAV 1P	FAV 1Pr	FAV 1Pr	FAV 1P	FAV 2Q	FAV 4P	FAV 2P	FAV 1Q

GROUND: The David Wilson Homes Ground, Godmanchester, Huntingdon PE29 2LQ

Nearest Railway Station Huntingdon - 3.1km

Bus Route 478 & X3

HARBOROUGH TOWN

United Counties Premier South

Founded 1976 Nickname: The Bees **Club Colours:** Yellow and black

Club Contact Details 01858 465 934 p.winston2402@btinternet.com

Previous Names: Harborough Town Juniors 1976-2008. Juniors merged with adult team Spencer United to form today's club.

Previous Leagues: Northants Combination.

HONOURS

FA Comps: None

League: Northants Combination Premier Division 2009-10.

11-12	12-13	13-14	14-15	15-16	16-17	17-18	18-19	19-20	20-21
UCL 1 2	UCL P 19	UCL P 17	UCL P 20	UCL P 11	UCL P 11	UCL P 11	UCL P 11	UCL P n&v	UCL P n&v
		FAC P	FAC EPr	FAC P	FAC P	FAC P	FAC P	FAC EP	FAC P
FAV 1Pr	FAV 2Q	FAV 1P	FAV 1Q	FAV 1Q	FAV 1P	FAV 1Q	FAV 2Q	FAV 2P	FAV 2Q

GROUND: Bowden's Park, Northampton Road, Market Harborough, Leics. LE16 9HF

Nearest Railway Station Market Harborough - 1.5km

Bus Route Leisure Centre - stop 200m away

LEICESTER ROAD

United Counties Premier South

Founded 2013 Nickname: The Knitters **Club Colours:** Blue & red

Club Contact Details 01455 844 444 stumill43@outlook.com

Previous Names: None

Previous Leagues: Midland 2014-21.

HONOURS

FA Comps: None

League: None

11-12	12-13	13-14	14-15	15-16	16-17	17-18	18-19	19-20	20-21
			MFL2 2	MFL1 4	MFL1 3	MFL1 4	MFL1 5	MFL1 n&v	MFL1 n&v
					FAC 1Qr	FAC P	FAC P	FAC P	
				FAV 2Q	FAV 1P	FAV 1Q	FAV 1Qr	FAV 1P	FAV 2Q

GROUND: Leicester Road Stadium, Leicester Road, Hinckley, LE10 3DR

Nearest Railway Station Hinckley - 2.7km

Bus Route Leicester Road stop - 262m away

LONG BUCKBY AFC

United Counties Premier South

Founded 1937 Nickname: Bucks **Club Colours:** All claret

Club Contact Details 07749 393 045 lbafc.dja@gmail.com

Previous Names: Long Buckby Nomads

Previous Leagues: Rugby & District Central, Northants Combination pre 68

HONOURS

FA Comps: None

League: United Counties Division Three 1969-70, Division Two 70-71, 71-72, Premier Division 2011-12.

11-12	12-13	13-14	14-15	15-16	16-17	17-18	18-19	19-20	20-21
UCL P 1	UCL P 16	UCL P 18	UCL P 21	UCL 1 6	UCL 1 13	UCL 1 17	UCL 1 15	UCL 1 n&v	UCL 1 n&v
FAC 3Q	FAC EP	FAC EP	FAC EPr	FAC 1Q					
FAV 3P	FAV 1Pr	FAV 1Q	FAV 2Q	FAV 2Q	FAV 1Q	FAV 1Q	FAV 2Q	FAV 2P	FAV 2Q

GROUND: Station Road, Long Buckby NN6 7PL

Nearest Railway Station Long Buckby - 0.3km

Bus Route Watson Road - stop 70m away

Capacity: 2,000 **Seats:** 200 **Covered:** 200

LUTTERWORTH TOWN

United Counties Premier South

Founded 1955 Nickname: The Swifts **Club Colours:** Orange and black

Club Contact Details 07855 836 489 lutterworthtownfc@hotmail.com

Previous Names: None

Previous Leagues: Leicestershrie Senior 1955-2017

HONOURS

FA Comps: None

League: Leicestershire Senior Division Two 1980-81, Premier 90-91, 2016-17.
United Counties Division One 2018-19.

11-12	12-13	13-14	14-15	15-16	16-17	17-18	18-19	19-20	20-21
LeicS1 14	LeicS1 6	LeicS1 6	LeicS1 7	LeicS1 3	LeicSP 1	UCL 1 3	UCL 1 1	UCL P n&v	UCL P n&v
							FAC EP	FAC 1Q	FAC P
						FAV 1P	FAV 1Q	FAV 4P	FAV 2P

GROUND: Dunley Way, Lutterworth, Leicestershire, LE17 4NP

Bus Route Elizabethan Way - stop 300m away

NEWPORT PAGNELL TOWN

United Counties Premier South

Founded 1963 Nickname: Swans **Club Colours:** All green

Club Contact Details 01908 611 993 steve@nptfc.co.uk

Previous Names: Newport Pagnell Wanderers 1963-72.

Previous Leagues: North Bucks 1963-71. South Midlands 1971-73. United Counties 1973-2019. Spartan South Midlands 2019-21.

HONOURS

FA Comps: None

League: United Counties Division One 1981-82, 2001-02.

11-12	12-13	13-14	14-15	15-16	16-17	17-18	18-19	19-20	20-21
UCL P 5	UCL P 6	UCL P 16	UCL P 10	UCL P 3	UCL P 10	UCL P 3	UCL P 8	SSM P n&v	SSM P n&v
FAC Pr	FAC 1Q	FAC P	FAC EP	FAC Pr	FAC EP	FAC Pr	FAC EP	FAC P	FAC EP
FAV 4P	FAV 2P	FAV 2Q	FAV 2Q	FAV 1Q	FAV QF	FAV 2P	FAV 4P	FAV 3P	FAV 1P

GROUND: Willen Road, Newport Pagnell MK16 0DF

Bus Route Green Park Drive - stop 160m away

Capacity: 2,000 **Seats:** 100 **Covered:** 100

NORTHAMPTON O.N.C.

United Counties Premier South

Founded 1946 Nickname: The Chens **Club Colours:** White and navy

Club Contact Details 01604 634 045 bryanlewin@gmail.com

Previous Names: Chenecks FC 1946-60. ON (Old Northamptonians) Chenecks 1960-

Previous Leagues: Northampton Minor 1946-50. Northampton Town 1950-69.

HONOURS

FA Comps: None

League: United Counties Division One 1977-78, 79-80.

11-12	12-13	13-14	14-15	15-16	16-17	17-18	18-19	19-20	20-21
UCL 1 12	UCL 1 11	UCL 1 6	UCL 1 6	UCL 1 2	UCL P 12	UCL P 17	UCL P 15	UCL P n&v	UCL P n&v
					FAC EPr	FAC P	FAC EP	FAC EP	FAC EP
				FAV 2Q	FAV 1P	FAV 1P	FAV 1Q	FAV 1P	FAV 2Q

GROUND: Old Northamptonians Sports Ground, Billing Road NN1 5RX **Capacity:** 1,000

Nearest Railway Station Northampton - 2.7km

Bus Route School for Boys - stop 80m away

PETERBOROUGH NORTHERN STAR

United Counties Premier South

Founded 1900 Nickname: Star **Club Colours:** Black & white

Club Contact Details 07983 524 742 clubsecretary@pnsfc.co.uk

Previous Names: Eye United 1900-31. Northam Star SC 1931-51. Eye United 1951-2005.

Previous Leagues: Peterborough & District >2003

HONOURS

FA Comps: None

League: Peterborough & District Premier Division (x10) 2002-03 most recently.
United Counties League Division One 2008-09.

11-12	12-13	13-14	14-15	15-16	16-17	17-18	18-19	19-20	20-21
UCL P 7	UCL P 13	UCL P 9	UCL P 7	UCL P 17	UCL P 15	UCL P 16	UCL P 16	UCL P n&v	UCL P n&v
	FAC 1Q	FAC P	FAC P	FAC EP	FAC EP	FAC EP	FAC EP	FAC P	FAC EP
FAV QF	FAV 2P	FAV 2Q	FAV 3P	FAV 2Q	FAV 1P	FAV 2P	FAV 2P	FAV 1P	FAV 1Q

GROUND: Chestnut Avenue, Peterborough, Cambs PE1 4PE **Capacity:** 1,500

Nearest Railway Station Peterborough - 2.6km

Bus Route Hawthorn Road - stop 35m away

POTTON UNITED

United Counties Premier South

Founded 1943 Nickname: Royals **Club Colours:** All blue

Club Contact Details 07703 442 565 bev.strong@iscali.co.uk

Previous Names: None

Previous Leagues: South Midlands 1946-55. United Counties 1961-2018. Spartan South Midlands 2018-21.

HONOURS

FA Comps: None

League: United Counties 1986-87, 88-89, Division One 2003-04.

11-12	12-13	13-14	14-15	15-16	16-17	17-18	18-19	19-20	20-21
UCL 1 15	UCL 1 16	UCL 1 10	UCL 1 3	UCL 1 7	UCL 1 6	UCL 1 2	SSM P 7	SSM P n&v	SSM P n&v
				FAC EP		FAC 1Q	FAC EP	FAC EP	FAC 1Q
FAV 2Q	FAV 2Q	FAV 1Q	FAV 2Q	FAV 2Q	FAV 1Q	FAV 2Q	FAV 2Q	FAV 1Q	FAV 2Q

GROUND: The Hutchinson Hollow, Bigglewade Road, Potton, Beds SG19 2LU **Capacity:** 2,000

Nearest Railway Station Sandy - 4.4km

Bus Route The Ridgewy - stop 11m away

ROTHWELL CORINTHIANS

United Counties Premier South

Founded 1934 Nickname: Corinthians **Club Colours:** Red and black

Club Contact Details 01536 711 706 mbudworth@budworthhardcastle.com

Previous Names: None

Previous Leagues: Kettering & District Amateur/East Midlands Alliance 1934-95.

HONOURS

FA Comps: None

League: None

11-12	12-13	13-14	14-15	15-16	16-17	17-18	18-19	19-20	20-21
UCL 1 8	UCL 1 17	UCL 1 15	UCL 1 2	UCL P 14	UCL P 16	UCL P 15	UCL P 18	UCL P n&v	UCL P n&v
FAC P	FAC EP			FAC EP	FAC EP	FAC EP	FAC P	FAC 1Q	FAC EP
FAV 1Q	FAV 1Q	FAV 1Q	FAV 2Q	FAV 2Qr	FAV 2P	FAV 1Qr	FAV 1Q	FAT 2P	FAV 1P

GROUND: Sergeants Lawn, Desborough Road, Rothwell NN14 6JQ

Nearest Railway Station Kettering - 5.6km

Seats: 50

Covered: 200

RUGBY TOWN

United Counties Premier South

Founded 1956 Nickname: The Valley **Club Colours:** Sky blue

Club Contact Details 01788 844 806 dougwilkins44@hotmail.com

Previous Names: Valley Sports 1956-71, Valley Sport Rugby 1971-73, VS Rugby 1973-2000, Rugby United 2000-05

Previous Leagues: Rugby & District 1956-62, Coventry & Partnership, North Warwickshire 1963-69, United Counties 1969-75 West Midlands 1975-83. Southern 1983-2015. Northern Premier 2015-17. Midland Football 2017-18.

HONOURS

FA Comps: FA Vase 1982-83.

League: Southern Midland Division 1986-87. Midland Combination Division 1 2001-02.

11-12	12-13	13-14	14-15	15-16	16-17	17-18	18-19	19-20	20-21
SthC 6	SthC 2	SthC 2	SthC 6	NP1S 9	NP1S 21	MFLP 6	UCL P 3	UCL P n&v	UCL P n&v
FAC Pr	FAC 1Qr	FAC 3Qr	FAC 2Q	FAC 3Qr	FAC 2Q	FAC P	FAC EP	FAC EP	FAC EP
FAT Pr	FAT 1Qr	FAT P	FAT P	FAT P	FAT Pr	FAV 2Pr	FAV 1P	FAV 2P	FAV 1P

GROUND: Butlin Road, Rugby, Warwicks CV21 3SD

Nearest Railway Station Rugby - 1km

Bus Route Jolly Brewers stop - 127m away

Capacity: 6,000

Seats: 750

Covered: 1,000

WELLINGBOROUGH TOWN

United Counties Premier South

Founded 1867 Nickname: Doughboys **Club Colours:** Yellow & blue

Club Contact Details 01933 441 388 waldenmichael44@gmail.com

Previous Names: Original team (Formed 1867) folded in 2002 reforming in 2004

Previous Leagues: Metropolitan. Southern.

HONOURS

FA Comps: None

League: United Counties 1964-65.

11-12	12-13	13-14	14-15	15-16	16-17	17-18	18-19	19-20	20-21
UCL P 8	UCL P 15	UCL P 8	UCL P 15	UCL P 20	UCL P 9	UCL P 14	UCL P 14	UCL P n&v	UCL P n&v
FAC EP	FAC P	FAC EPr	FAC EP	FAC EP	FAC EP	FAC P	FAC P	FAC P	FAC EP
FAV 1Q	FAV 1Q	FAV 2Q	FAV 2Q	FAV 2Q	FAV 2Q	FAV 1Q	FAV 2P	FAV 3P	FAV 4P

GROUND: Dog and Duck, London Road, Wellingborough NN8 2DP

Nearest Railway Station Wellingborough - 1.2km

Bus Route The Dog & Duck Pub - stop 50m away

Capacity: 2,500

AYLESTONE PARK

United Counties Division One

Founded 1967 Nickname: Club Colours: Red

Club Contact Details 07990 335 830 gary.sheffield@gtssecurity.co.uk

HONOURS FA Comps: None

League: None

11-12	12-13	13-14	14-15	15-16	16-17	17-18	18-19	19-20	20-21
LeicSP 3	EMC 7	EMC 18	EMC 19	EMC 5	EMC 4	EMC 9	UCL 1 8	UCL 1 n&v	UCL 1 n&v
					FAC EP	FAC P			
FAV 2Q		FAV 2Q	FAV 1Q	FAV 2Q	FAV 1Q	FAV 1Q	FAV 1P	FAV 1Q	FAV 2P

GROUND: Gary Lineker Pavillion, Saffron Lane, Leicester LE2 6TG

Nearest Railway Station South Wigston - 1.1km

BARROW TOWN

United Counties Division One

Founded Late Nickname: The Riversiders Club Colours: Red & black

Club Contact Details 01509 620 650 srichards997@gmail.com

HONOURS FA Comps: None

League: Leicester Senior Division One 1992-93.

11-12	12-13	13-14	14-15	15-16	16-17	17-18	18-19	19-20	20-21
EMC 5	EMC 2	EMC 19	EMC 9	EMC 13	EMC 14	EMC 11	EMC 8	EMC n&v	EMC n&v
FAC 3Q	FAC EP	FAC EP	FAC EP	FAC EP					
FAV 2Q	FAV 1Q	FAV 2Q	FAV 2Q	FAV 2Q	FAV 1Q	FAV 1Q	FAV 1P	FAV 1P	FAV 1Q

GROUND: Riverside Park, Quorn Road, Loughborough, Leicestershire LE12 8XJ

Nearest Railway Station Barrow upon Soar - 1.7km

Bus Route 2 - alight at Crossley Close, 6min walk from there.

BELPER UNITED

United Counties Division One

Founded 1920 Nickname: Club Colours: Green and black

Club Contact Details 07977 599 775 johnedwardsbufc@btinternet.com

HONOURS FA Comps: None

League: Midlands Regional Alliance Premier Division 1985-86, 94-95,
Division One 2004-05.

11-12	12-13	13-14	14-15	15-16	16-17	17-18	18-19	19-20	20-21
CMSth 9	CMSth 3	CMSth 10	CMSth 5	CMSth 2	EMC 13	EMC 5	EMC 10	EMC n&v	EMC n&v
						FAC P	FAC EP		
		FAV 1Q	FAV 1P	FAV 1Q	FAV 1Q	FAV 2Q	FAV 1P	FAV 1Q	FAV 1P

GROUND: Christchurch Meadow, Bridge Street, Belper DE56 1BA

Nearest Railway Station Belper

Bus Route Transpeak towards Buxton - alight at Mill, 4min walk from there.

BIRSTALL UNITED SOCIAL

United Counties Division One

Founded 1961 Nickname: Club Colours: White and navy

Club Contact Details 07801 242 406 birstallutdsecretary@gmail.com

HONOURS FA Comps: None

League: Leicester Mutual Division One 1972-73, 73-74, 75-76.
Leicestershire Senior Division Two 1976-77, Premier 2015-16.

11-12	12-13	13-14	14-15	15-16	16-17	17-18	18-19	19-20	20-21
LeicSP 6	LeicSP 11	LeicSP 4	LeicSP 4	LeicSP 1	EMC 3	EMC 8	UCL 1 17	UCL 1 n&v	UCL 1 n&v
						FAC P			
FAV 2Q	FAV 1Q				FAV 2Qr	FAV 1Q	FAV 2Q	FAV 2Q	FAV 2Q

GROUND: Meadow Lane, Birstall LE4 4FN

Nearest Railway Station Syston

BLACKSTONES

United Counties Division One

Founded 1920 Nickname: Stones **Club Colours:** Green and black

Club Contact Details 01780 757 835 imacgilli@outlook.com

HONOURS FA Comps: None

League: Peterborough & District 1918-19, Division Two 1961-62, Division One 75-76.

11-12	12-13	13-14	14-15	15-16	16-17	17-18	18-19	19-20	20-21
UCL P 11	UCL P 20	UCL 1 20	UCL 1 17	UCL 1 10	UCL 1 14	UCL 1 8	UCL 1 5	UCL 1 n&v	UCL 1 n&v
FAC EP	FAC P	FAC EP							FAC EP
FAV 1Q	FAV 2Q	FAV 2Q	FAV 2Q	FAV 1P	FAV 2Q	FAV 1Q	FAV 1Q	FAV 2Q	FAV 1Q

GROUND: Thorne Sports Field, Lincoln Road, Stamford, Lincs PE9 1SH

Nearest Railway Station Stamford - 1.5km

Bus Route Junction with Kesteven Rd - stop 75m away

BORROWASH VICTORIA

United Counties Division One

Founded 1911 Nickname: The Vics **Club Colours:** Red & white stripes

Club Contact Details 07540 938 780 alanure1@gmail.com

HONOURS FA Comps: None

League: Derby & District 1952-53. East Midlands regional Premier 1977-78.
Midland Division One 1980-81. Northern Counties East Div.1 South 1983-84.

11-12	12-13	13-14	14-15	15-16	16-17	17-18	18-19	19-20	20-21
EMC 2	EMC 4	EMC 5	EMC 16	EMC 9	EMC 12	EMC 19	EMC 19	EMC n&v	EMC n&v
FAC P	FAC P	FAC P	FAC EP						
FAV 2Q	FAV 4P	FAV 2P	FAV 2P	FAV 1P	FAV 1Q		FAV 1Q	FAV 1Q	FAV 2Q

GROUND: Borrowash Road, Spondon, Derby DE21 7PH

Nearest Railway Station Spondon - 1.2km

Bus Route I4 & Indigo

BOURNE TOWN

United Counties Division One

Founded 1883 Nickname: Wakes **Club Colours:** Claret

Club Contact Details 07709 785 273 tonyhull2@hotmail.com

HONOURS FA Comps: None

League: Peterborough & District 1933-34, 39-40, 45-46, 46-47. Central Alliance Division One South 59-60. United Counties Premier 65-66, 68-69, 69-70, 71-72, 90-91.

11-12	12-13	13-14	14-15	15-16	16-17	17-18	18-19	19-20	20-21
UCL 1 14	UCL 1 10	UCL 1 21	UCL 1 10	UCL 1 5	UCL 1 15	UCL 1 10	UCL 1 13	UCL 1 n&v	UCL 1 n&v
				FAV 2Q	FAV 1Q	FAV 2Q	FAV 1Q	FAV 2Q	FAV 2Q

GROUND: Abbey Lawn, Abbey Road, Bourne, Lincs PE10 9EN

Bus Route Nowells Lane - stop 105m away

CLIFTON ALL WHITES

United Counties Division One

Founded 1963 Nickname: All Whites **Club Colours:** All white

Club Contact Details 07775 615 237 dwigs61@hotmail.com

HONOURS FA Comps: None

League: Notts Alliance Division One 1998-99. Central Midlands 2013-14.
Notts Senior Premier Division 2016-17.

11-12	12-13	13-14	14-15	15-16	16-17	17-18	18-19	19-20	20-21
NottS1 2	CMSth 4	CMSth 1	CMSth 8	NottSP 6	NottSP 1	EMC 12	EMC 12	EMC n&v	EMC n&v
				FAV 2Q	FAV 2Q	FAV 1Qr	FAV 1Qr	FAV 2Q	FAV 1Q

GROUND: Green Lane, Clifton, Nottingham NG11 9AZ

Nearest Railway Station Beeston - 3.2km

Bus Route Clifton Centre Tram Stop 426m from ground.

DUNKIRK

United Counties Division One

Founded 1946 Nickname: The Boatmen **Club Colours:** Red and black

Club Contact Details 0115 985 0803 philipallen1982@hotmail.co.uk

HONOURS FA Comps: None

League: Notts Alliance Division Two 1981-82, Division One 1984-85.
Central Midlands Supreme Division 2004-05. East Midlands 2009-10, 17-18.

11-12		12-13		13-14		14-15		15-16		16-17		17-18		18-19		19-20		20-21	
MidAl	18	MidAl	10	MidAl	19	MFLP	19	MFLP	20	EMC	5	EMC	1	MFLP	19	EMC	n&v	EMC	n&v
FAC	EP	FAC	P	FAC	1Q	FAC	EP	FAC	3Q	FAC	1Q	FAC	1Q	FAC	EP	FAC	EP	FAC	EP
FAV	2Q	FAV	1P	FAV	2Q	FAV	2Q	FAV	2P	FAV	2Q	FAV	1P	FAV	2Q	FAV	2P	FAV	1Q

GROUND: Ron Steel Spts Ground, Lenton Lane, Clifton Bridge, Nottingham NG7 2SA

Nearest Railway Station Beeston - 2.3km

Bus Route 1, 48X, 49X & 901

GEDLING MINERS WELFARE

United Counties Division One

Founded 1919 Nickname: Miners **Club Colours:** Yellow

Club Contact Details 07976 935 364 norman.hay@virginmedia.com

HONOURS FA Comps: None

League: Notts Alliance 1945-46, 49-50, 50-51, 51–52, 53-54, 55-56, 57-58, 58-59,
59-60, 60-61, Division Two 2000-01.

11-12		12-13		13-14		14-15		15-16		16-17		17-18		18-19		19-20		20-21	
EMC	13	EMC	13	EMC	12	EMC	12	EMC	14	EMC	20	EMC	10	EMC	16	EMC	n&v	EMC	n&v
FAC	EPr																		
FAV	1Q	FAV	2Q	FAV	1Q	FAV	1P	FAV	1Q	FAV	1Q	FAV	1Q	FAV	1Q	FAV	2Q	FAV	2Q

GROUND: Plains Social Club, Plains Road, Mapperley, Nottingham NG3 5RH

Nearest Railway Station Carlton - 3.5km

Bus Route 45

GRAHAM STREET PRIMS

United Counties Division One

Founded 1904 Nickname: Prims **Club Colours:** Red & white

Club Contact Details 07892 151 203 secretary@gspfc.co.uk

HONOURS FA Comps: None

League: Central Alliance Premier Division 1970-71.
East Midlands Regional 1978-79.

11-12		12-13		13-14		14-15		15-16		16-17		17-18		18-19		19-20		20-21	
EMC	14	EMC	8	EMC	10	EMC	18	EMC	11	EMC	19	EMC	16	EMC	7	EMC	n&v	EMC	n&v
				FAC	EP	FAC	EP												
FAV	1Q	FAV	1P	FAV	3P	FAV	1P	FAV	2Q	FAV	1Q	FAV	1Q	FAV	2Q	FAV	1Q	FAV	1Q

GROUND: The Gred Harding Ground, Borrowash Road, Spondon DE21 7PH

Nearest Railway Station Spondon - 1.2km

Bus Route Indigo - alight at Borrowash Road, 3min walk from there.

HARROWBY UNITED

United Counties Division One

Founded 1949 Nickname: The Arrows **Club Colours:** Royal blue

Club Contact Details 07742 077 474 simonjackson670@hotmail.com

HONOURS FA Comps: None

League: Midlands Regional Alliance Premier Division 1989-90.
United Counties Division One 1991-92.

11-12		12-13		13-14		14-15		15-16		16-17		17-18		18-19		19-20		20-21	
		UCL 1	6	UCL 1	3	UCL P	17	UCL P	18	UCL P	21	UCL 1	5	UCL 1	7	UCL 1	n&v	UCL 1	n&v
						FAC	EP	FAC	EP	FAC	P	FAC	EP						
				FAV	1P	FAV	2Q	FAV	1P	FAV	1Q	FAV	1P	FAV	2Q	FAV	2Q	FAV	1P

GROUND: Harrowby Stadium, Dickens Road, Grantham NG31 9QY

Nearest Railway Station Grantham - 2.6km

Bus Route St Wulframs School - stop 100m away

HINCKLEY AFC

United Counties Division One

Founded 2014 Nickname: **Club Colours:** Red & blue

Club Contact Details 07718 541 444 jackson.dh18@gmail.com

HONOURS FA Comps: None

League: None

11-12	12-13	13-14	14-15	15-16	16-17	17-18	18-19	19-20	20-21
			MFL1 3	MFL1 5	MFL1 2	MFL1 6	MFL1 16	MFL1 n&v	MFL1 n&v
				FAC 2Q	FAC EPr	FAC 1Q	FAC EPr		
			FAV 1Q	FAV 1P	FAV 5P	FAV 4P	FAV 3P	FAV 2Q	FAV 1Q

GROUND: *Barwell FC, Kirkby Road Sports Ground, Kirkby Road, Barwell LE9 8FQ

Nearest Railway Station Hinckley - 7 miles away

*Will play their opening 2021-22 games at Heather St Johns whilst pitch work is carried out at Barwell FC.

HOLWELL SPORTS

United Counties Division One

Founded 1902 Nickname: **Club Colours:** Yellow and green

Club Contact Details 07910 879 919 hataylor64@gmail.com

HONOURS FA Comps: None

League: Leic Senior Premier 1911-12, 87-88, 91-92, 92-93, Division One 1984-85.
Leicester & District 1907-08, 08-09. Melton Mowbray & Dist Am 1933-34.

11-12	12-13	13-14	14-15	15-16	16-17	17-18	18-19	19-20	20-21
EMC 11	EMC 5	EMC 9	EMC 8	EMC 16	EMC 16	EMC 18	UCL 1 14	UCL 1 n&v	UCL 1 n&v
	FAC EP	FAC EP	FAC 1Q	FAC 1Qr					
FAV 1P	FAV 1Q	FAV 3P	FAV 2Q	FAV 2Q	FAV 1P	FAV 2Q	FAV 1Q	FAV 1Q	FAV 1Q

GROUND: Welby Road, Asfordby Hill, Melton Mowbray, Leicestershire LE14 3RD

Nearest Railway Station Melton Mowbray - 2.8km

HUCKNALL TOWN

United Counties Division One

Founded 1987 Nickname: The Town **Club Colours:** Yellow and black

Club Contact Details 07572 473 037 pm.henry@btopenworld.com

HONOURS FA Comps: None

League: Central Midlands South Division 2018-19.

11-12	12-13	13-14	14-15	15-16	16-17	17-18	18-19	19-20	20-21
NP1S 11	NP1S 22	CMSth 13	CMSth 4	CMSth 3	CMSth 4	CMSth 3	CMSth 1	EMC n&v	EMC n&v
FAC 1Q	FAC P	FAC EP							
FAT 1Q	FAT 2Q	FAV 1P		FAV 1P	FAV 3P	FAV 2Q	FAV 2P	FAV 1P	FAV 1Q

GROUND: Watnall Road, Hucknall, Notts NG15 6EY

Nearest Railway Station Hucknall

Bus Route 3A, 3C, C1, Connect, Green

INGLES

United Counties Division One

Founded 1972 Nickname: **Club Colours:** Red and white

Club Contact Details 01509 650 992 mslowes@hotmail.com

HONOURS FA Comps: None

League: North Leicestershire Division Three 1973-74, Division Two 74-75, Premier 92-93, 95-96, 2013-14. Leicestershire Senior Premier Division 2017-18.

11-12	12-13	13-14	14-15	15-16	16-17	17-18	18-19	19-20	20-21
		NLeiP 1	LeicSP 3	LeicSP 5	LeicSP 7	LeicSP 1	EMC 11	EMC n&v	EMC n&v
							FAV 2Q	FAV 2Qr	FAV 2Q

GROUND: The Dovecote, Little Haw Lane, Shepshed, Leicestershire LE12 9BN

Nearest Railway Station Loughborough

Bus Route Skylink - alight at the Bull Ring, 6min walk from there.

KIMBERLEY MINERS WELFARE

United Counties Division One

Founded 1926 Nickname: Miners **Club Colours:** Red & black

Club Contact Details 07803 267 825 johnbeeston1775@sky.com

HONOURS FA Comps: None

League: Spartan League 1947-48, 64-65, 65-66. Notts Amateur League 1985-86. Notts Alliance Division Two 1994-95, Division One 95-96.

11-12	12-13	13-14	14-15	15-16	16-17	17-18	18-19	19-20	20-21
NottSP 13	NottSP 5	NottSP 2	EMC 13	EMC 15	EMC 8	EMC 6	EMC 9	EMC n&v	EMC n&v
						FAC P	FAC P		
				FAV 1Q	FAV 2Qr	FAV 2P	FAV 2Q	FAV 1P	FAV 2Q

GROUND: The Stag Ground, Kimberley, Nottingham NG16 2NB

Nearest Railway Station Ilkeston - 3.4km and Bulwell - 3.8km.

Bus Route Rainbow One

KIRBY MUXLOE

United Counties Division One

Founded 1910 Nickname: **Club Colours:** Royal blue

Club Contact Details 07715 403 409 kirbymuxloefc@outlook.com

HONOURS FA Comps: None

League: Leicestershire Senior Premier Division 2007-08.
East Midlands Counties 2008-09.

11-12	12-13	13-14	14-15	15-16	16-17	17-18	18-19	19-20	20-21
MidAl 11	MidAl 12	MidAl 14	MFLP 5	UCL P 9	UCL P 18	UCL P 12	UCL P 19	MFL1 n&v	MFL1 n&v
FAC EP	FAC P	FAC P	FAC P	FAC Pr	FAC 2Q	FAC P	FAC EP	FAC 1Q	FAC EP
FAV 2Q	FAV 1P	FAV 1P	FAV 2Q	FAV 2Q	FAV 1P	FAV 2Q	FAV 1Q	FAV 2Q	FAV 2Q

GROUND: Kirby Muxloe Sports Club, Ratby Lane LE9 2AQ

Bus Route Kirby Corner - stop 55m away

LUTTERWORTH ATHLETIC

United Counties Division One

Founded 1983 Nickname: The Athletic **Club Colours:** Green & white

Club Contact Details 01455 554 046 markwezzy@hotmail.com

HONOURS FA Comps: None

League: Leicester & District Division Two 1994-95, Premier 2004-05.

11-12	12-13	13-14	14-15	15-16	16-17	17-18	18-19	19-20	20-21
LeicSP 2	EMC 13	UCL 1 5	UCL 1 4	UCL 1 11	UCL 1 12	UCL 1 11	UCL 1 6	UCL 1 n&v	UCL 1 n&v
FAV 1P	FAV 2Q	FAV 1Q		FAV 1Q	FAV 1Q	FAV 1Q	FAV 1Q	FAV 1Q	FAV 2Q

GROUND: Hall Park, Hall Lane, Bitteswell, Lutterworth LE17 4LN

Bus Route Manor Farm - stop 1.5km away

RADFORD

United Counties Division One

Founded 1964 Nickname: The Pheasants **Club Colours:** Claret and sky blue

Club Contact Details 0115 942 3250 vote4holt@hotmail.co.uk

HONOURS FA Comps: None

League: East Midlands Regional League 1982-83.

11-12	12-13	13-14	14-15	15-16	16-17	17-18	18-19	19-20	20-21
EMC 17	EMC 19	EMC 15	EMC 3	EMC 2	EMC 7	EMC 7	EMC 5	EMC n&v	EMC n&v
				FAC P	FAC EP	FAC EPr	FAC EP	FAC EP	FAC EP
FAV 2Q	FAV 2Q	FAV 1Q	FAV 1Q	FAV 1P	FAV 2P	FAV 2Q	FAV 1Q	FAV 1Q	FAV 3P

GROUND: Selhurst Street, Off Radford Road, Nottingham NG7 5AN

Nearest Railway Station Nottingham - 2.8km

Bus Route 77, 79B, Medlink & Rainbow One

SAFFRON DYNAMO

United Counties Division One

Founded 1963 Nickname: **Club Colours:** Red and black

Club Contact Details 07957 151 630 bobking1@talktalk.net

HONOURS FA Comps: None

League: None

11-12	12-13	13-14	14-15	15-16	16-17	17-18	18-19	19-20	20-21
LeicSP 13	LeicSP 13	LeicSP 13	LeicSP 3	LeicSP 7	LeicSP 2	LeicSP 5	LeicSP 2	UCL 1 n&v	UCL 1 n&v
FAV 1Q							FAV 2P	FAV 1Q	FAV 1Q

GROUND: King Park, Cambridge Road, Whetstone LE9 1SJ

ST. ANDREWS

United Counties Division One

Founded 1973 Nickname: The Saints **Club Colours:** Black & white

Club Contact Details 0116 283 9298 mark_mcglinchey@outlook.com

HONOURS FA Comps: None

League: Leicestershire City Premier x4. Leicestershire Senior 1989-90, 93-94, 95-96.
East Midlands Counties 2015-16.

11-12	12-13	13-14	14-15	15-16	16-17	17-18	18-19	19-20	20-21
EMC 4	EMC 16	EMC 7	EMC 2	EMC 1	MFLP 9	UCL P 21	UCL 1 16	UCL 1 n&v	UCL 1 n&v
	FAC EP		FAC EPr	FAC EP	FAC EP	FAC EPr	FAC EP		
FAV 2P	FAV EP	FAV SF	FAV 2P	FAV 3P	FAV 1P	FAV 2Q	FAV 1Q	FAV 2Q	FAV 1Q

GROUND: Canal Street, Aylestone, Leicester LE2 8DR

Nearest Railway Station South Wigston - 3km

WEST BRIDGFORD

United Counties Division One

Founded 1990 Nickname: **Club Colours:** Black & red

Club Contact Details 07581 049 797 tim2703@hotmail.co.uk

HONOURS FA Comps: None

League: East Midlands Counties 2016-17.

11-12	12-13	13-14	14-15	15-16	16-17	17-18	18-19	19-20	20-21
NottS2 2	NottS1 5	NottS1 2	NottSP 2	NottSP 3	EMC 1	EMC 15	EMC 13	EMC n&v	EMC n&v
						FAC EP			
					FAV 2Q	FAV 1Q	FAV 1Q	FAV 2P	

GROUND: Regatta Way, Gamston, West Bridgford, Nottingham NG2 5AT

Nearest Railway Station Nottingham

Bus Route Mainline & The Cotgrave

CLUB MOVEMENTS

DIVISION ONE - IN: Barrow Town, Belper United, Borrowash Victoria, Clifton All Whites, Dunkirk, Gedling Miners Welfare, Graham Street Pimms, Hucknall Town, Ingles FC, Kimberley MW, Radford and West Bridgford (LM - EMCP). Hinckley AFC and Kirby Muxloe (LM - ML1).

OUT: Huntingdon Town and Whittlesey Athletic (EC1N).
Burton Park Wanderers, Irchester United, Northampton Sileby Rangers, Raunds Town, Rushden & Higham United and Wellingborough Whitworths (LM - SSM1).
Melton Town (P - UCLPN).
Bugbooke St Michael and Long Buckby (P - UCLPS).

AFC PORTCHESTER

Wessex Premier

Founded 1971 Nickname: Portchy/Royals **Club Colours:** Tangerine

Club Contact Details 01329 233 833 (Clubhouse) secretary@afcportchester.co.uk

Previous Names: Loyds Sports 1971-73. Colourvison Rangers 1973-76. Wilcor Mill 1976-2003.
Previous Leagues: City of Portsmouth Sunday. Portsmouth & District >1998. Hampshire 1998-2004.

HONOURS
FA Comps: None
League: Portsmouth & Football 1997-98. Hampshire Division One 2001-02.

11-12		12-13		13-14		14-15		15-16		16-17		17-18		18-19		19-20		20-21	
Wex1	2	WexP	15	WexP	8	WexP	3	WexP	6	WexP	8	WexP	6	WexP	13	WexP	n&v	WexP	n&v
FAC	Pr	FAC	EP	FAC	2Q	FAC	P	FAC	2Q	FAC	2Q	FAC	2Q	FAC	EPr	FAC	EPr	FAC	P
FAV	2Q	FAV	2Q	FAV	3P	FAV	3P	FAV	1P	FAV	2Q	FAV	1P	FAV	1Q	FAV	2P	FAV	2Q

GROUND: The Crest Finance Stadium, Cranleigh Road, Portchester, Hampshire PO16 9DP
Nearest Railway Station Porchester - 15.km
Bus Route Sandport Grove stop

CLUB MOVEMENTS

PREMIER DIVISION - IN: Alton, Hythe & Dibden and U S Portsmouth (P - WX1). Moneyfields (R - SthS).
OUT: Tadley Calleva (LM - CCPN). Fleet Town (LM - CCPS). Lymington Town (P - Sth1S).

AFC STONEHAM

Wessex Premier

Founded 1919 Nickname: The Purples **Club Colours:** All purple

Club Contact Details 07747 096 943 theosbornes4@sky.com

Previous Names: Ordnance Survey > 2006. Stoneham 2006-07.
Previous Leagues: Hampshire Premier League >2015

HONOURS
FA Comps: None
League: Southampton Senior 1982-83, 92-93, 96-97. Hampshire Premier 2007-08. Wessex Division One 2018-19.

11-12		12-13		13-14		14-15		15-16		16-17		17-18		18-19		19-20		20-21	
HantP	4	HantP	2	HantP	12	HantP	4	Wex1	8	Wex1	8	Wex1	5	Wex1	1	WexP	n&v	WexP	n&v
														FAC	1Q	FAC	Pr	FAC	1Q
										FAV	1P	FAV	1Q	FAV	1P	FAV	1Q	FAV	2Q

GROUND: Stoneham Lane Football Complex, Stoneham Lane, Eastleigh SO16 2PA
Nearest Railway Station Eastleigh - 2 miles
Bus Route Bluestar Bus No.2 from station to Stoneham Lane.

ALRESFORD TOWN

Wessex Premier

Founded 1898 Nickname: The Magpies **Club Colours:** White and black

Club Contact Details 07530 194 722 secretary.alresfordtownfc@gmail.com

Previous Names: None
Previous Leagues: Winchester League, North Hants league, Hampshire League

HONOURS
FA Comps: None
League: North Hampshire 1999-2000.

11-12		12-13		13-14		14-15		15-16		16-17		17-18		18-19		19-20		20-21	
WexP	15	WexP	2	WexP	2	WexP	16	WexP	20	WexP	5	WexP	7	WexP	12	WexP	n&v	WexP	n&v
FAC	P	FAC	P	FAC	EP	FAC	Pr	FAC	EP	FAC	2Q	FAC	P	FAC	EPr	FAC	EPr	FAC	EP
FAV	1P	FAV	2Q	FAV	4P	FAV	3P	FAV	1Q	FAV	2P	FAV	2Q	FAV	2P	FAV	2Q	FAV	1Q

GROUND: Arlebury Park, The Avenue, Alresford, Hants SO24 9EP
Nearest Railway Station Alresford - 620m
Bus Route Bridge Road stop

ALTON

Wessex Premier

Founded 1990 Nickname: The Brewers **Club Colours:** White and black

Club Contact Details 07709 715 322 waynealtonfc@outlook.com

Previous Names: Present club formed in 1990 when Alton Town and Bass Alton merged. Alton Town 1990-2016.

Previous Leagues: Athenian 1973-81. Hampshire League 1981-2002. Wessex 2002-13. Combined Counties 2013-15.

HONOURS

FA Comps: None

League: Hampshire Division One 1998-99, Premier 2001-02.

11-12	12-13	13-14	14-15	15-16	16-17	17-18	18-19	19-20	20-21
WexP 10	WexP 18	CCP 21	CC1 13	Wex1 7	Wex1 12	Wex1 8	Wex1 13	Wex1 n&v	Wex1 n&v
FAC P	FAC P	FAC P	FAC 1Q	FAC EP					
FAV 2Pr	FAV 1P	FAV 1Q	FAV 1Q	FAV 1P	FAV 1P	FAV 1P	FAV 2Q	FAV 2Q	FAV 2Q

GROUND: Anstey Park Enclosure, Anstey Road, Alton, Hants GU34 2NB
Nearest Railway Station Alton - 0.6km
Bus Route Anstey Lane - stop 32m away

Capacity: 2,000
Seats: 200
Covered: 250

AMESBURY TOWN

Wessex Premier

Founded 1904 Nickname: Blues **Club Colours:** Royal blue & white

Club Contact Details 07422 520 818 amesburytownfc@gmail.com

Previous Names: Amesbury FC 1904-1984.

Previous Leagues: Salisbury & District Junior 1904-06. Salisbury & District 1906-56, 97-98. Wiltshire 1956-71. Wiltshire Combination/County 71-. Western 1994-97. Hampshire 1998-2004.

HONOURS

FA Comps: None

League: Salisbury & District Division Two 1954-55, Division One 55-56. Wiltshire Division One 1959-60.
Wiltshire Combination/County 1974-75, 79-80 / Division One 90-91, 91-92. Hampshire Premier 1999-2000.

11-12	12-13	13-14	14-15	15-16	16-17	17-18	18-19	19-20	20-21
Wex1 14	Wex1 14	Wex1 10	Wex1 4	Wex1 2	WexP 19	WexP 20	Wex1 2	WexP n&v	WexP n&v
				FAC EP	FAC P	FAC P	FAC EP	FAC EP	FAC EP
FAV 1Q	FAV 1Q	FAV 1Q	FAV 2Q	FAV 1Q	FAV 1P	FAV 2Q	FAV 1Q	FAV 1Q	FAV 1Q

GROUND: Bonnymead Park Recreation Road Amesbury SP4 7BB
Nearest Railway Station Salisbury - 8 miles
Bus Route Salisbury Reds bus No.8, X4 and X5, Stagecoach South No.8.

BAFFINS MILTON ROVERS

Wessex Premier

Founded 2011 Nickname: None **Club Colours:** All royal blue

Club Contact Details 07980 403 336 yvonne@baffinsmiltonroversfc.co.uk

Previous Names: Formed when Sunday league teams Baffins Milton and Milton Rovers merged.

Previous Leagues: Hampshire Premier >2016

HONOURS

FA Comps: None

League: Portsmouth Saturday Premier Division 2011-12.
Hampshire Premier Senior Division , 2013-14, 15-16.

11-12	12-13	13-14	14-15	15-16	16-17	17-18	18-19	19-20	20-21
PorS P 1	PorS P 2	HantP 1	HantP 2	HantP 1	Wex1 2	WexP 9	WexP 5	WexP n&v	WexP n&v
							FAC P	FAC P	FAC EP
						FAV 3P	FAV 4P	FAV 2P	FAV 1Q

GROUND: Kendall Wharf, Eastern Road, Portsmouth PO3 5LY
Nearest Railway Station Hilsea - 1.3km
Bus Route Robinson Way - stop 420m away

Seats: 120

BASHLEY

Wessex Premier

Founded 1947 Nickname: The Bash **Club Colours:** Gold and black

Club Contact Details 07591 187 663 footballsecretary@bashleyfc.org.uk

Previous Names: None

Previous Leagues: Bournemouth 1953-83, Hampshire 1983-86, Wessex 1986-89, Southern 1989-2004, 06-16. Isthmian 2004-06

HONOURS

FA Comps: None

League: Hampshire Division Three 1984-85. Wessex 1986-87, 87-88, 88-89. Southern Southern Division 1989-90, Division One South & West 2006-07.

11-12	12-13	13-14	14-15	15-16	16-17	17-18	18-19	19-20	20-21
SthP 13	SthP 17	SthP 23	Sthsw 22	Sthsw 22	WexP 14	WexP 14	WexP 9	WexP n&v	WexP n&v
FAC 1Q	FAC 1Qr	FAC 2Q	FAC P	FAC P	FAC EP	FAC EP	FAC EP	FAC EP	FAC P
FAT 1Qr	FAT 1Qr	FAT 1Q	FAT P	FAT 1Q	FAV 2Q	FAV 1P	FAV 1P	FAV 2Q	FAV 2P

GROUND: Bashley Road Ground, Bashley Road, New Milton, Hampshire BH25 5RY **Capacity:** 4,250

Nearest Railway Station New Milton - 1.9km **Seats:** 250

Bus Route Village Store & PO - stop 230m away **Covered:** 1,200

BLACKFIELD & LANGLEY

Wessex Premier

Founded 1935 Nickname: Watersiders **Club Colours:** Green & white

Club Contact Details 07856 118 401 secretarybandlfc@gmail.com

Previous Names: None

Previous Leagues: Southampton Junior. Southampton Senior. Hampshire 1950-2000. Wessex 2000-18. Southern 2018-20 (Took voluntary relegation).

HONOURS

FA Comps: None

League: Southampton Junior Division One 1945-46. Southampton West Division 1946-47. Hampshire Division Three West 1951-52, Division Two 1984-85, Premier Division 97-98. Wessex Premier Division 2012-13, 17-18. Southern D1S 2018-19.

11-12	12-13	13-14	14-15	15-16	16-17	17-18	18-19	19-20	20-21
WexP 16	WexP 1	WexP 6	WexP 5	WexP 3	WexP 4	WexP 1	SthS 1	SthPS n&v	WexP n&v
FAC 1Q	FAC 4Q	FAC EP	FAC 2Qr	FAC 3Q	FAC P	FAC EPr	FAC P	FAC 3Q	FAC EP
FAV 2P	FAV 4P	FAV 4P	FAV 3P	FAV 1P	FAV 3P	FAV 4Pr	FAT P	FAT 2Q	FAV 2Q

GROUND: Gang Warily Rec., Newlands Rd, Southampton SO45 1GA **Capacity:** 2,000

Nearest Railway Station Beaulieu Road - 7.2 miles **Seats:** 180

Bus Route Gang Warily Leisure Centre - stop 50m away

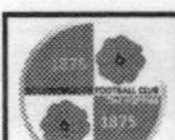

BOURNEMOUTH

Wessex Premier

Founded 1875 Nickname: Poppies **Club Colours:** Red and white

Club Contact Details 07894 948 267 bournemouthwessex@gmail.com

Previous Names: Bournemouth Rovers, Bournemouth Wanderers, Bournemouth Dean Park.

Previous Leagues: Hampshire 1896-98, 1903-39 & 46-86.

HONOURS

FA Comps: None

League: None

11-12	12-13	13-14	14-15	15-16	16-17	17-18	18-19	19-20	20-21
WexP 9	WexP 13	WexP 15	WexP 18	WexP 18	WexP 17	WexP 18	WexP 3	WexP n&v	WexP n&v
FAC 2Qr	FAC EP	FAC P	FAC Pr	FAC EP	FAC EP	FAC EP	FAC P	FAC P	FAC EP
FAV QF	FAV 2P	FAV 1Q	FAV 2Q	FAV 2Q	FAV 1P	FAV 2Q	FAV 2P	FAV 1P	FAV 1P

GROUND: Victoria Park, Namu Road, Winton, Bournemouth BH9 2RA **Capacity:** 3,000

Nearest Railway Station Bournemouth - 2miles **Seats:** 205

Bus Route Morebus No.17 and Yellow Bueses No.6 from rail station. **Covered:** 205

BROCKENHURST

Wessex Premier

Founded 1898 Nickname: The Badgers **Club Colours:** Blue

Club Contact Details 07903 620 495 brockenhurstfcsec@gmail.com

Previous Names: None
Previous Leagues: Hampshire 1924-26, 35-37, 47-86.

HONOURS
FA Comps: None
League: Hampshire Division Three 1959-60, Division Two 70-71, Division One 75-76. Wessex Division One 2012-13.

11-12		12-13		13-14		14-15		15-16		16-17		17-18		18-19		19-20		20-21	
Wex1	5	Wex1	1	WexP	11	WexP	14	WexP	14	WexP	10	WexP	13	WexP	15	WexP	n&v	WexP	n&v
FAC	1Q	FAC	EP	FAC	1Q	FAC	EP	FAC	3Q	FAC	P	FAC	P	FAC	P	FAC	EP	FAC	EP
FAV	1P	FAV	1Q	FAV	2Q	FAV	1Q	FAV	1Q	FAV	2Q	FAV	2P	FAV	2P	FAV	2P	FAV	2P

GROUND: Grigg Lane, Brockenhurst, Hants SO42 7RE
Nearest Railway Station Brockenhurst - 0.5km
Bus Route Brockenhurst College - stop 260m away

Capacity: 2,000
Seats: 200
Covered: 300

CHRISTCHURCH

Wessex Premier

Founded 1885 Nickname: The Church **Club Colours:** All Blue

Club Contact Details 07805 201 032 secretary@christchurchfc.co.uk

Previous Names: None
Previous Leagues: Hampshire

HONOURS
FA Comps: None
League: Hampshire Division Two 1937-38, 47-48, 85-86, Division Three 52-53.
Wessex Division One 2017-18.

11-12		12-13		13-14		14-15		15-16		16-17		17-18		18-19		19-20		20-21	
WexP	3	WexP	3	WexP	16	WexP	21	Wex1	6	Wex1	4	Wex1	1	WexP	16	WexP	n&v	WexP	n&v
FAC	EP	FAC	1Q	FAC	EP	FAC	EPr	FAC	P	FAC	EP	FAC	EP	FAC	EPr	FAC	P	FAC	3Q
FAV	3P	FAV	1P	FAV	1Pr	FAV	2Q	FAV	1Q	FAV	2Q	FAV	3P	FAV	2Q	FAV	4P	FAV	4P

GROUND: Hurn Bridge Sports Ground, Avon Causeway, Christchurch BH23 6DY
Nearest Railway Station Christchurch - 4.6km
Bus Route Post Office - stop 100m away

Capacity: 1,200
Seats: 215
Covered: 265

COWES SPORTS

Wessex Premier

Founded 1881 Nickname: Yachtsmen **Club Colours:** Blue & White

Club Contact Details 07879 445 988 secretary.cowessportsfc@outlook.com

Previous Names: Cowes
Previous Leagues: Hampshire (FM) 1896-98, 1903-94. Southern 1898-99.

HONOURS
FA Comps: None
League: Hampshire Division One 1896-97, 1908-09 (jt), 26-27, 27-28, 30-31, 36-37, 55-56, 93-94, Division Two 1974-75.
Southern Division Two South West 1898-99.

11-12		12-13		13-14		14-15		15-16		16-17		17-18		18-19		19-20		20-21	
Wex1	6	Wex1	4	Wex1	3	Wex1	2	WexP	11	WexP	18	WexP	19	WexP	18	WexP	n&v	WexP	n&v
FAC	EP	FAC	EP	FAC	P	FAC	P	FAC	P	FAC	EP	FAC	EP	FAC	EP	FAC	EP	FAC	1Q
FAV	3P	FAV	2Q	FAV	2Q	FAV	1P	FAV	2Q	FAV	2Q	FAV	1Q	FAV	1Q	FAV	1P	FAV	2Q

GROUND: Westwood Park, Reynolds Close, off Park Road, Cowes, Isle of Wight PO31 7NT

Bus Route Parklands Avenue - stop 100m away

FAREHAM TOWN

Wessex Premier

Founded 1947 Nickname: Creeksiders **Club Colours:** Red & black stripes

Club Contact Details 07794 816 609 secretary@farehamtownfc.co.uk

Previous Names: Formed when Fareham FC, Fareham Brotherhood and Fareham Youth Centre merged.

Previous Leagues: Portsmouth 1946-49. Hampshire 1949-79. Southern 1979-98.

HONOURS

FA Comps: None

League: Hampshire League Division Three East 1949-50, Premier 1959-60, 62-63, 63-64, 64-65, 65-66, 66-67, 72-73, 74-75.

11-12		12-13		13-14		14-15		15-16		16-17		17-18		18-19		19-20		20-21	
WexP	12	WexP	9	WexP	10	WexP	19	WexP	12	WexP	12	WexP	16	WexP	17	WexP	n&v	WexP	n&v
FAC	EP	FAC	2Q	FAC	1Q	FAC	P	FAC	EP	FAC	1Qr	FAC	P	FAC	EP	FAC	1Q	FAC	EP
FAV	1P	FAV	2Q	FAV	2P	FAV	1P	FAV	1Q	FAV	2Q	FAV	2P	FAV	1P	FAV	2Q	FAV	3P

GROUND: Cams Alders, Palmerston Drive, Fareham, Hants PO14 1BJ **Capacity:** 2,000

Nearest Railway Station Fareham - 0.9km **Seats:** 450

Bus Route Fairfield Avenue - stop 250m away **Covered:** 500

HAMBLE CLUB

Wessex Premier

Founded 1969 Nickname: The Monks **Club Colours:** Yellow & black

Club Contact Details 07900 430 115 sharon.betts@hcyfc.co.uk

Previous Names: None

Previous Leagues: Hampshire Premier 1993-2016.

HONOURS

FA Comps: None

League: Hampshire Premier 2014-15. Wessex Division One 2016-17.

11-12		12-13		13-14		14-15		15-16		16-17		17-18		18-19		19-20		20-21	
HantP	15	HantP	Exp	Hant1	2	HantP	1	HantP	3	Wex1	1	WexP	10	WexP	7	WexP	n&v	WexP	n&v
														FAC	P	FAC	P	FAC	P
												FAV	5P	FAV	3Pr	FAV	2Q	FAV	2Q

GROUND: Hamble Community Facility, Hamble Lane SO31 4TS

Nearest Railway Station Hamble - 0.4km

Bus Route Hamble Lane School - stop 500m away

HAMWORTHY UNITED

Wessex Premier

Founded 1926 Nickname: The Hammers **Club Colours:** Maroon & sky blue

Club Contact Details 07702 995 282 hamworthyutdsecretary@gmail.com

Previous Names: Hamworthy St. Michael merged with Trinidad Old Boys 1926

Previous Leagues: Dorset Combination (Founder Member) / Dorset Premier 1957-2004.

HONOURS

FA Comps: None

League: Dorset Premier 2002-03, 03-04.

11-12		12-13		13-14		14-15		15-16		16-17		17-18		18-19		19-20		20-21	
WexP	7	WexP	10	WexP	12	WexP	10	WexP	16	WexP	16	WexP	5	WexP	6	WexP	n&v	WexP	n&v
FAC	EP	FAC	P	FAC	2Q	FAC	EP	FAC	1Q	FAC	1Q	FAC	1Q	FAC	1Qr	FAC	P	FAC	P
FAV	1Q	FAV	2Q	FAV	1P	FAV	2Q	FAV	1Q	FAV	1Q	FAV	2Q	FAV	4P	FAV	3P	FAV	2P

GROUND: The County Ground, Blandford Close, Hamworthy, Poole BH15 4BF **Capacity:** 2,000

Nearest Railway Station Poole - 1.4km

Bus Route Carter School - stop 100m away

HORNDEAN

Wessex Premier

Founded: 1887 Nickname: Deans **Club Colours:** All red

Club Contact Details 07968 349 978 horndeanfc48@gmail.com

Previous Names: None

Previous Leagues: Waterlooville & District. Portsmouth. Hampshire 1972-86, 1995-2004. Wessex 1986-95

HONOURS

FA Comps: None

League: Waterlooville & District 1926-27, 29-30, 30-31, 31-32. Portsmouth Division Two 1953-54, Premier 68-69, 69-70, 70-71. Hampshire Division Four 1974-75, Division Three 75-76, Division Two 79-80.

11-12	12-13	13-14	14-15	15-16	16-17	17-18	18-19	19-20	20-21
WexP 17	WexP 11	WexP 17	WexP 11	WexP 5	WexP 6	WexP 4	WexP 2	WexP n&v	WexP n&v
FAC 1Q	FAC 1Q	FAC 1Q	FAC 1Q	FAC EP	FAC EP	FAC 1Q	FAC 1Q	FAC P	FAC EP
FAV 2Q	FAV 3P	FAV 2Q	FAV 2P	FAV 1P	FAV 1P	FAV 3P	FAV 2P	FAV 1Pr	FAV 2Q

GROUND: Five Heads Park Five Heads Road Horndean Hampshire PO8 9NZ

Nearest Railway Station Rowlands Castle - 4.5km

Bus Route Horndean Com. School - stop 560m away

HYTHE & DIBDEN

Wessex Premier

Founded: 1902 Nickname: The Boatmen **Club Colours:** Green and white

Club Contact Details 07789 266 473 hythedibdenfc@aol.com

Previous Names: Hythe and Power United.

Previous Leagues: Hampshire. Southampton.

HONOURS

FA Comps: None

League: Hampshire Division Three West 1949-50.
Southampton Division Two 1970-71, 75-76.

11-12	12-13	13-14	14-15	15-16	16-17	17-18	18-19	19-20	20-21
Wex1 18	Wex1 16	Wex1 4	Wex1 7	Wex1 11	Wex1 18	Wex1 15	Wex1 3	Wex1 n&v	Wex1 n&v
			FAC EP	FAC EP				FAC 1Q	
	FAV 1Q	FAV 1P	FAV 1Q	FAV 2Q	FAV 1Q	FAV 2Q	FAV 1Q	FAV 2Q	FAV 1Q

GROUND: Clayfields, Claypit Lane, Dibden SO45 5TN

Nearest Railway Station Southampton Town Quay - 3.5km

Bus Route Drapers Copse - stop 200m away

MONEYFIELDS

Wessex Premier

Founded: 1987 Nickname: Moneys **Club Colours:** Yellow and navy

Club Contact Details 07521 961 841 moneyfieldsfcsec@hotmail.com

Previous Names: Portsmouth Civil Service 1987-94.

Previous Leagues: Portsmouth 1987-91. Hampshire 1991-98. Wessex 1998-2017. Southern 2017-21.

HONOURS

FA Comps: None

League: Portsmouth Premier 1990-91.
Hampshire Division Three 1991-92, Division Two 1992-93, Division One 1996-97.

11-12	12-13	13-14	14-15	15-16	16-17	17-18	18-19	19-20	20-21
WexP 4	WexP 4	WexP 9	WexP 4	WexP 8	WexP 2	Sth1E 10	SthS 4	SthS n&v	SthS n&v
FAC 1Qr	FAC P	FAC 1Q	FAC EP	FAC P	FAC 1Q	FAC 1Q	FAC 3Q	FAC 2Q	FAC 2Q
FAV 2Q	FAV 2P	FAV 3P	FAV 2Q	FAV 4P	FAV 2P	FAT 2Qr	FAT P	FAT EP	FAT 1P

GROUND: Moneyfields Sports Ground, Moneyfield Avenue, Portsmouth PO3 6LA

Nearest Railway Station Hilsea - 1.6km

Bus Route Chichester Road - stop 400m away

Capacity: 1,500
Seats: 150
Covered: 150

PORTLAND UNITED

Wessex Premier

Founded 1921 Nickname: Blues **Club Colours:** All royal blue

Club Contact Details 07928 341 060 secretary.portlandutdfc@aol.com

Previous Names: None

Previous Leagues: Western 1925-70. Dorset Combination 1970-76, 77-2001, Dorset Premier 2006-07. Wessex 2001-02.

HONOURS

FA Comps: None

League: Western Division Two 1930-31, 31-32. Dorset Combination 1998-99, 99-2000, Dorset Premier 2007-08, 08-09, 12-13, 13-14. Wessex Division One 2015-16, Premier 2016-17.

11-12		12-13		13-14		14-15		15-16		16-17		17-18		18-19		19-20		20-21	
Dor P	3	Dor P	1	Dor P	1	Dor P	2	Wex1	1	WexP	1	WexP	15	WexP	4	WexP	n&v	WexP	n&v
												FAC	P	FAC	P	FAC	2Q	FAC	EP
										FAV	2P	FAV	2Q	FAV	1Q	FAV	1P	FAV	1Q

GROUND: Weyline Stadium, Grove Road, Portland DT5 1DP **Capacity:** 2,000

Nearest Railway Station Weymouth - 6 miles

Bus Route First Wessex Dorset & South Somerset Bus No.1 from Weymouth to Easton Lane.

SHAFTESBURY

Wessex Premier

Founded 1888 Nickname: The Rockies **Club Colours:** Red & white

Club Contact Details 07706 354 039 secretary@shaftesburyfc.co.uk

Previous Names: Shaftesbury >2012. Shaftesbury Town 2012-17.

Previous Leagues: Dorset Junior. Dorset Senior 1931-57. Dorset Combination (FM) 1957-62, 76-2004. Wessex 2004-11. Dorset Premier 2011-16.

HONOURS

FA Comps: None

League: Dorset Junior 1905-06, 62-63. Dorset Senior 1932-33. Dorset Combination 1988-89, 96-97. Dorset Premier 2015-16. Wessex Division One 2016-17.

11-12		12-13		13-14		14-15		15-16		16-17		17-18		18-19		19-20		20-21	
Dor P	18	Dor P	11	Dor P	14	Dor P	4	Dor P	1	Wex1	3	WexP	12	WexP	14	WexP	n&v	WexP	n&v
												FAC	P	FAC	1Q	FAC	EP	FAC	EP
								FAV	2Q	FAV	2P	FAV	1Q	FAV	1P	FAV	1Q	FAV	1Q

GROUND: Cockrams, Coppice Street, Shaftesbury SP7 8PD **Covered:** 250

Nearest Railway Station Gillingham - 4 3/4 miles

Bus Route Linden Park - stop 100m away

UNITED SERVICES PORTSMOUTH

Wessex Premier

Founded 1962 Nickname: The Navy **Club Colours:** Royal blue & red

Club Contact Details 07887 541 782 usportsmouthfc@hotmail.co.uk

Previous Names: Portsmouth Royal Navy FC 1962-2004.

Previous Leagues: Hampshire 1962-86, 2001-04. Wessex 1986-2001.

HONOURS

FA Comps: None

League: Hampshire Division Two 1967-68, 77-78, 80-81.

11-12		12-13		13-14		14-15		15-16		16-17		17-18		18-19		19-20		20-21	
Wex1	13	Wex1	12	Wex1	7	Wex1	5	Wex1	4	Wex1	9	Wex1	4	Wex1	5	Wex1	n&v	Wex1	n&v
								FAC	EP	FAC	P			FAC	P	FAC	EP		
FAV	2Q	FAV	2Q	FAV	2Q	FAV	2P	FAV	2Qr	FAV	1Q	FAV	1P	FAV	2Q	FAV	1Q	FAV	SF

GROUND: Victory Stadium, HMS Temeraire, Burnaby Road, Portsmouth PO1 2HB

Nearest Railway Station Portsmouth Harbour - 0.7km

Bus Route University - stop 120m away

ANDOVER NEW STREET

Wessex Division One

Founded 1895 Nickname: The Street **Club Colours:** Green & black

Club Contact Details 07976 630 218 andovernewstreetfc@hotmail.co.uk

HONOURS FA Comps: None

League: None

11-12	12-13	13-14	14-15	15-16	16-17	17-18	18-19	19-20	20-21
Wex1 10	Wex1 15	Wex1 15	Wex1 13	Wex1 16	Wex1 19	Wex1 2	WexP 20	Wex1 n&v	Wex1 n&v
							FAC P	FAC P	
FAV 2Q	FAV 1Q			FAV 1Q	FAV 1Q	FAV 1Q	FAV 2Q	FAV 1Q	FAV 1Q

GROUND: Foxcotte Park Charlton Andover Hampshire SP11 0TA

Nearest Railway Station Andover - 2.4km

Bus Route Charlton Cemetery - stop 120m away

ANDOVER TOWN

Wessex Division One

Founded 2013 Nickname: **Club Colours:** All blue

Club Contact Details 07730 590 183 ben.stokes@sparsholt.ac.uk

HONOURS FA Comps: None

League: None

11-12	12-13	13-14	14-15	15-16	16-17	17-18	18-19	19-20	20-21
			WexP 12	WexP 4	WexP 13	WexP 2	Wex1 18	Wex1 n&v	Wex1 n&v
				FAC Pr	FAC 1Q	FAC 1Q	FAC EP		
			FAV 2Q	FAV 1P	FAV 2P	FAV 1Q	FAV 1P	FAV 1Q	

GROUND: Portway Stadium, West Portway Industrial Estate, Andover SP10 3LF

Nearest Railway Station Andover - 1.8km

Bus Route Arkwright Gate - stop 130m away

ASH UNITED

Wessex Division One

Founded 1911 Nickname: Green Army **Club Colours:** Green & red.

Club Contact Details 07908 803 765 graham_w_marshall@tinyworld.co.uk

HONOURS FA Comps: None

League: Combined Counties 1981-82, 86-87, 98-99.

11-12	12-13	13-14	14-15	15-16	16-17	17-18	18-19	19-20	20-21
CCP 13	CCP 20	CCP 1	CC1 10	CC1 10	CC1 12	CC1 10	CC1 7	CC1 n&v	CC1 n&v
FAC EP	FAC EP	FAC EP	FAC EP						
FAV 1Q	FAV 2P	FAV 1Q	FAV 1Q	FAV 1Q	FAV 1P	FAV 1Q	FAV 1Q	FAV 1Q	FAV 2Q

GROUND: Shawfield Stadium, Youngs Drive off Shawfield Road, Ash GU12 6RE.

Nearest Railway Station Ash or Ash Vale

Bus Route Stagecoach 20A, 550

BEMERTON HEATH HARLEQUINS

Wessex Division One

Founded 1989 Nickname: Quins **Club Colours:** Black & white

Club Contact Details 07917 228 708 bhhfc.sec@btinternet.com

HONOURS FA Comps: None

League: None

11-12	12-13	13-14	14-15	15-16	16-17	17-18	18-19	19-20	20-21
WexP 2	WexP 5	WexP 7	WexP 13	WexP 9	WexP 11	WexP 11	WexP 19	Wex1 n&v	Wex1 n&v
FAC EP	FAC EP	FAC EP	FAC 1Q	FAC P	FAC 1Q	FAC EP	FAC 1Q	FAC EPr	FAC P
FAV 3P	FAV 5P	FAV 2P	FAV 2P	FAV 2Q	FAV 3P	FAV 1Q	FAV 2Q	FAV 1Q	FAV 1Q

GROUND: Moon Park, Western Way, Bemerton Heath Salisbury SP2 9DR

Nearest Railway Station Salisbury - 2.1km

Bus Route Winding Way - stop 75m away

CLUB MOVEMENTS **DIVISION ONE - IN:** Ash United and Fleet Spurs (LM - CCL1). Infinity FC (P - HPL). Millbrook FC (N). **OUT:** Alton, Hythe & Dibden and U S Portsmouth (P - WX1)

MILLBROOK

Wessex Division One

Founded 2021 Nickname: Club Colours: Grey & blue

Club Contact Details 07833 255 899 millbrooksecretary@hotmail.com

HONOURS FA Comps: None

League: None

11-12	12-13	13-14	14-15	15-16	16-17	17-18	18-19	19-20	20-21

GROUND: Test Park Sports Facility, Lower Brownhill Road, Millbrook, Southampton SO16 9BP

Bus Route No.18 from Southampton City Centre to Kendall Avenue - alight outside the Saints Public House, then a short walk.

DOWNTON

Wessex Division One

Founded 1905 Nickname: The Robins Club Colours: Red & white

Club Contact Details 07734 206 173 secretary@downtonfc.com

HONOURS FA Comps: None

League: Bournemouth League Division One x5, Senior Division One x7. Wessex League Division One 2010-11.

11-12	12-13	13-14	14-15	15-16	16-17	17-18	18-19	19-20	20-21
WexP 6	WexP 8	WexP 21	Wex1 12	Wex1 10	Wex1 11	Wex1 12	Wex1 7	Wex1 n&v	Wex1 n&v
FAC EPr	FAC EP	FAC EP	FAC EP						
FAV 2P	FAV 3P	FAV 2Q		FAV 1Q	FAV 1Q	FAV 1P	FAV 1Q	FAV 1P	FAV 1Q

GROUND: Brian Whitehead Sports Ground Wick Lane Downton Wiltshire SP5 3NF

Nearest Railway Station Salisbury - 6.5 miles

Bus Route The Bull - stop 180m away

EAST COWES VICTORIA ATHLETIC

Wessex Division One

Founded 1885 Nickname: The Vics Club Colours: Red & white

Club Contact Details 07917 043 152 ecvics@gmail.com

HONOURS FA Comps: None

League: Hampshire Division Two 1947-48, 63-64, 71-72, Division One 85-86, 86-87.

11-12	12-13	13-14	14-15	15-16	16-17	17-18	18-19	19-20	20-21
Wex1 4	Wex1 8	Wex1 16	Wex1 15	Wex1 18	Wex1 20	Wex1 16	Wex1 10	Wex1 n&v	Wex1 n&v
	FAC P	FAC EP							
FAV 1Q	FAV 1Q	FAV 2Q	FAV 2Q	FAV 1Q	FAV 2Q	FAV 1Q	FAV 2Q	FAV 1P	FAV 1Q

GROUND: Beatrice Avenue, East Cowes, Isle of Wight PO32 6PA

Bus Route Osborne House - stop 400m away

FAWLEY AFC

Wessex Division One

Founded 1923 Nickname: Oilers Club Colours: Blue

Club Contact Details 07913 015 292 mahfawleyafc@aol.com

HONOURS FA Comps: None

League: Hampshire Division Three 1994-95.

11-12	12-13	13-14	14-15	15-16	16-17	17-18	18-19	19-20	20-21
WexP 19	WexP 17	WexP 20	WexP 17	WexP 19	WexP 20	Wex1 9	Wex1 11	Wex1 n&v	Wex1 n&v
	FAC EP	FAC EP	FAC EP	FAC EP	FAC EP	FAC EP			FAC P
FAV 2P	FAV 1P	FAV 2Q	FAV 1Q	FAV 1Q	FAV 1Q	FAV 2Q	FAV 2Q	FAV 1Q	FAV 1Q

GROUND: Waterside Spts & Soc. club, 179 Long Lane, Holbury, Soto, SO45 2PA

Nearest Railway Station Netley - 5.3km

Bus Route New Forest Academy - stop 100m away

FLEET SPURS

Wessex Division One

Founded 1948 Nickname: Spurs **Club Colours:** Blue & red

Club Contact Details 07748 373 979 richardwyborn@outlook.com

HONOURS FA Comps: None

League: Surrey Premier A Division 1968-69. Aldershot Senior 1990-91. Hampshire Division Two 1997-98.

11-12	12-13	13-14	14-15	15-16	16-17	17-18	18-19	19-20	20-21
Wex1 7	Wex1 10	Wex1 12	Wex1 9	Wex1 12	Wex1 16	CC1 16	CC1 17	CC1 n&v	CC1 n&v
FAC EP	FAC EP								
FAV 1Q	FAV 2Q	FAV 1Q	FAV 1Qr	FAV 1Q	FAV 2Q	FAV 1Q	FAV 2Q	FAV 2Q	FAV 2Q

GROUND: Southwood Sports Pavilion, Kennels Lane, Farnborough GU14 0ST

Nearest Railway Station Fleet - take No.10 bus towards Farnborough - alight at Trunk Road, 5min walk from there.

Bus Route 10 & 7

FOLLAND SPORTS

Wessex Division One

Founded 1938 Nickname: Planemakers **Club Colours:** All red

Club Contact Details 07770 452 660 colinchamberlain@gmail.com

HONOURS FA Comps: None

League: Hampshire 1941-42, Division Four 79-80, Division Three 80-81. Southampton Senior 1961-62, 67-68. Wessex Division One 2009-10.

11-12	12-13	13-14	14-15	15-16	16-17	17-18	18-19	19-20	20-21
WexP 5	WexP 7	WexP 3	WexP 8	WexP 21	Wex1 17	Wex1 18	Wex1 16	Wex1 n&v	Wex1 n&v
FAC EP	FAC P	FAC P	FAC 2Qr	FAC EP	FAC EP				
FAV 2Q	FAV 3P	FAV 2P	FAV 2P	FAV 2Q	FAV 1Q	FAV 1Q	FAV 1Q	FAV 1Q	FAV 1Q

GROUND: Folland Park, Kings Ave, Hamble, Southampton SO31 4NF

Nearest Railway Station Hamble - 1km

Bus Route Verdon Avenue - stop 300m away

INFINITY

Wessex Division One

Founded 2006 Nickname: **Club Colours:** Yellow & black

Club Contact Details 07931 791 126 infinityfc2006@gmail.com

HONOURS FA Comps: None

League: Hampshire Premier Division One 2014-15.

11-12	12-13	13-14	14-15	15-16	16-17	17-18	18-19	19-20	20-21
		Hant1 3	Hant1 1	HantP 8	HantP 12	HantP 3	HantP 2	HantP n&v	HantP n&v

GROUND: Hythe Garage Stadium, Claypits Lane, Dibden, Southampton SO45 5TN

Nearest Railway Station Southampton Central - 9.5 miles

Bus Route Bluestar Bus No.9 from Rail station to Claypits Lane (Applemore Tesco).

LAVERSTOCK & FORD

Wessex Division One

Founded 1956 Nickname: The Stock **Club Colours:** Green & white

Club Contact Details 07795 665 731 sec.laverstockandfordfc@gmail.com

HONOURS FA Comps: None

League: Hampshire Division Two 2002-03.

11-12	12-13	13-14	14-15	15-16	16-17	17-18	18-19	19-20	20-21
WexP 22	Wex1 13	Wex1 9	Wex1 8	Wex1 5	Wex1 6	Wex1 7	Wex1 9	Wex1 n&v	Wex1 n&v
					FAC EP	FAC P			
	FAV 1Q	FAV 1P	FAV 2Q	FAV 1P	FAV 1Q	FAV 1Q	FAV 1Q	FAV 2Q	FAV 2Q

GROUND: The Dell, Church Road, Laverstock, Salisbury, Wilts SP1 1QX

Nearest Railway Station Salisbury - 2.5km

Bus Route St Andrews School - stop 40m away

NEW MILTON TOWN

Wessex Division One

Founded 1998 Nickname: The Linnets **Club Colours:** Navy and red

Club Contact Details 07588 000 489 secretry@nmtfc.co.uk

HONOURS FA Comps: None

League: Wessex 1998-99, 2004-05.

11-12	12-13	13-14	14-15	15-16	16-17	17-18	18-19	19-20	20-21
WexP 20	WexP 21	Wex1 11	Wex1 6	Wex1 14	Wex1 14	Wex1 10	Wex1 17	Wex1 n&v	Wex1 n&v
FAC EPr	FAC EP			FAC EP					
FAV 2Q	FAV 2P		FAV 2Q	FAV 1P	FAV 1Q	FAV 1Q	FAV 2Q	FAV 1Q	FAV 3P

GROUND: Fawcetts Fields, Christchurch Road, New Milton BH25 6QF

Nearest Railway Station New Milton - 1.1km

Bus Route Old Milton Green - stop 150m away

NEWPORT (I.O.W.)

Wessex Division One

Founded 1888 Nickname: The Port **Club Colours:** Yellow and blue

Club Contact Details 07949 464 905 trackmaster775@gmail.com

HONOURS FA Comps: None

League: Isle of Wight 1907-08, 08-09, 09-10, 23-24. Hampshire 1929-30, 32-33, 38-39, 47-48, 49-50, 52-53, 53-54, 56-57, 79-79, 79 -80, 80-81. Southern Eastern Division 2000-01.

11-12	12-13	13-14	14-15	15-16	16-17	17-18	18-19	19-20	20-21
WexP 13	WexP 6	WexP 4	WexP 7	WexP 10	WexP 15	WexP 21	Wex1 6	Wex1 n&v	Wex1 n&v
FAC 1Q	FAC 2Q	FAC P	FAC 2Qr	FAC EP	FAC EP	FAC EP	FAC P		
FAV 1Q	FAV 5Pr	FAV 2P	FAV 3P	FAV 4P	FAV 2P	FAV 4P	FAV 2P	FAV 1P	FAV 1P

GROUND: East Cowes Vics FC, Beatrice Avenue, Isle of Wight PO32 6PA

Bus Route Island Line No.37 from Ryde Esplanade to Ashey Road.

PETERSFIELD TOWN

Wessex Division One

Founded 1993 Nickname: Rams **Club Colours:** Red & black

Club Contact Details 07949 328 240 secretary.petersfieldtownfc@outlook.com

HONOURS FA Comps: None

League: Wessex Division One 2013-14, Premier Division 2014-15.

11-12	12-13	13-14	14-15	15-16	16-17	17-18	18-19	19-20	20-21
Wex1 12	Wex1 6	Wex1 1	WexP 1	SthC 13	SthC 22	WexP 22	Wex1 15	Wex1 n&v	Wex1 n&v
FAC EP	FAC EPr	FAC P	FAC EP	FAC 3Q	FAC P	FAC EP	FAC P		
FAV 2Q	FAV 1P	FAV 1P	FAV 2Q	FAT P	FAT Pr	FAV 2Q	FAV 2Q	FAV 2P	FAV 1P

GROUND: Love Lane, Petersfield, Hampshire GU31 4BW

Nearest Railway Station Petersfield - 0.8km

Bus Route Madeline Road - stop 140m away

RINGWOOD TOWN

Wessex Division One

Founded 1879 Nickname: The Peckers **Club Colours:** Red and white

Club Contact Details 07732 185 429 sandy.ringwoodtownfc@gmail.com

HONOURS FA Comps: None

League: Hampshire Division three 1995-96.

11-12	12-13	13-14	14-15	15-16	16-17	17-18	18-19	19-20	20-21
Wex1 9	Wex1 9	Wex1 13	Wex1 11	Wex1 13	Wex1 5	Wex1 11	Wex1 12	Wex1 n&v	Wex1 n&v
FAC EP	FAC EP					FAC EP			
FAV 2Q	FAV 1Q	FAV 1Q	FAV 1P	FAV 2Q	FAV 1Q	FAV 2Q	FAV 1Q	FAV 1Q	FAV 1P

GROUND: Long Lane, Ringwood, Hampshire BH24 3BX

Nearest Railway Station Bournemouth - 11 miles

Bus Route Crow Crossroads - stop 100m away

ROMSEY TOWN

Wessex Division One

Founded 1886 | Nickname: Town | **Club Colours:** Red & black

Club Contact Details 07824 323 442 | rtfcclubsecretary@gmail.com

HONOURS FA Comps: None

League: Post War: Southampton West 1951-52, Senior Div.2 72-73, Senior Div.1 73-74, 76-77, Prem 80-81, 83-84. Hampshire Div.4 75-76, Div.2 78-79. Wessex 89-90.

11-12	12-13	13-14	14-15	15-16	16-17	17-18	18-19	19-20	20-21
WexP 8	WexP 20	WexP 22	Wex1 14	Wex1 9	Wex1 13	Wex1 6	Wex1 4	Wex1 n&v	Wex1 n&v
FAC EP	FAC P	FAC EP	FAC EP				FAC EP	FAC EP	
FAV 2Q	FAV 2Q	FAV 2Q	FAV 1Q	FAV 2Q	FAV 1P	FAV 1P	FAV 1Qr	FAV 1P	FAV 2Q

GROUND: The By-Pass Ground, South Front, Romsey SO51 8GJ

Nearest Railway Station Romsey - 0.5km

Bus Route Linden Road - stop 100m away

TOTTON & ELING

Wessex Division One

Founded 1925 | Nickname: The Millers | **Club Colours:** Red & black

Club Contact Details 07876 776 985 | tefcsecretary@gmail.com

HONOURS FA Comps: None

League: Hampshire Division three 1974-75, Division One 1987-88, 88-89. Wessex Division One 2008-09.

11-12	12-13	13-14	14-15	15-16	16-17	17-18	18-19	19-20	20-21
WexP 11	WexP 12	WexP 8	WexP 20	Wex1 15	Wex1 15	Wex1 14	Wex1 19	Wex1 n&v	Wex1 n&v
FAC P	FAC 1Qr	FAC Pr	FAC EP						FAC EP
FAV 1Q	FAV 1Q	FAV 1Q	FAV 1Q				FAV 1P	FAV 1Q	FAV 2Q

GROUND: Millers Park, Salisbury Road, Totton SO40 2RW

Nearest Railway Station Totton - 2.9km

Bus Route Cooks Lane - stop 280m away

VERWOOD TOWN

Wessex Division One

Founded 1920 | Nickname: The Potters | **Club Colours:** Red & black

Club Contact Details 07517 077 566 | secretary@vtfc.co.uk

HONOURS FA Comps: None

League: Wessex Division One 2011-12.

11-12	12-13	13-14	14-15	15-16	16-17	17-18	18-19	19-20	20-21
Wex1 1	WexP 14	WexP 19	WexP 15	WexP 17	WexP 22	Wex1 17	Wex1 8	Wex1 n&v	Wex1 n&v
FAC EP	FAC EP	FAC EP	FAC EP	FAC P	FAC Pr	FAC EPr			
FAV 1Q	FAV 1Qr	FAV 2P	FAV 3P	FAV 2Q	FAV 1Q	FAV 1Q	FAV 2Qr	FAV 2Q	FAV 2Q

GROUND: Potterne Park Potterne Way Verwood Dorset BH21 6RS

Nearest Railway Station Poole - 13.5 miles

Bus Route Potterne Bridge - stop 280m away

WHITCHURCH UNITED

Wessex Division One

Founded 1903 | Nickname: Jam Boys | **Club Colours:** Red & white stripes

Club Contact Details 07870 341 729 | secretary.wufc@gmail.com

HONOURS FA Comps: None

League: Hampshire Division Two 1989-90.

11-12	12-13	13-14	14-15	15-16	16-17	17-18	18-19	19-20	20-21
Wex1 8	Wex1 2	WexP 13	WexP 6	WexP 15	WexP 21	Wex1 13	Wex1 14	Wex1 n&v	Wex1 n&v
FAC 2Q	FAC EP	FAC EPr	FAC EPr	FAC EPr	FAC P	FAC EP			FAC EP
FAV 2Q	FAV 2Q	FAV 1Q	FAV 2Q	FAV 1Pr	FAV 2Q	FAV 2Q	FAV 1Q	FAV 1Q	FAV 1P

GROUND: Longmeadow, Winchester Road, Whitchurch, Hampshire RG28 7RB

Nearest Railway Station Whitchurch - 1.7km

Bus Route Charcot Close - stop 100m away

ASHTON & BACKWELL UNITED

Western League Premier

Founded 2010 Nickname: The Stags **Club Colours:** Maroon & blue

Club Contact Details 07866 024 499 ashtonbackwellsecretary@gmail.com

Previous Names: Formed when Backwell United merged with Ashton Boys.
Previous Leagues: None
HONOURS
FA Comps: None
League: None

11-12	12-13	13-14	14-15	15-16	16-17	17-18	18-19	19-20	20-21
SomP 3	SomP 3	West1 14	West1 8	West1 8	West1 7	West1 18	West1 4	West1 n&v	West1 n&v
				FAC EP	FAC EP				
FAV 2Q	FAV 2Q	FAV 1P	FAV 2Q	FAV 2Q	FAV 2Q	FAV 2Q	FAV 2Q	FAV 2Q	FAV 1P

GROUND: The Lancer Scott Stadium, West Town Road, Backwell. BS48 3HQ **Capacity:** 1,000
Nearest Railway Station Nailsea & Backwell - 0.9km **Seats:** 151
Bus Route Spar (Rodney Rd) - stop 150m away

CLUB MOVEMENTS

PREMIER DIVISION - IN: Ashton & Backwell United (P - WL1). Helston Athletic, Mousehole and Saltash United (P - SWPW). Ilfracombe Town (P - SWPE).
OUT: Bradford Town, Chipping Sodbury Town, Cribbs, Hallen, Roman Glass St George and Westbury United (LM - HLP). Plymouth Parkway (P - Sth1S). Odd Down (R - WL1).

BITTON

Western League Premier

Founded 1892 Nickname: The Ton **Club Colours:** Red & white

Club Contact Details 01179 323 222 binner1966@hotmail.com

Previous Names: None
Previous Leagues: Avon Premier Combination, Gloucestershire County 1995-97.
HONOURS
FA Comps: None
League: Western League Premier Division 2008-09.

11-12	12-13	13-14	14-15	15-16	16-17	17-18	18-19	19-20	20-21
WestP 2	WestP 7	WestP 6	WestP 7	WestP 14	WestP 19	WestP 10	WestP 3	WestP n&v	WestP n&v
FAC EPr	FAC P	FAC P	FAC EP	FAC P	FAC P	FAC EPr	FAC 2Q	FAC P	FAC 1Q
FAV 4P	FAV 4P	FAV 3P	FAV 1Q	FAV 2Q	FAV 2Q	FAV 1Q	FAV 1P	FAV SF	FAV 2P

GROUND: Bath Road, Bitton, Bristol BS30 6HX **Capacity:** 1,000
Nearest Railway Station Bitton - 500m **Seats:** 48
Bus Route Cherry Garden Road - stop 50m away **Covered:** 200

BRIDGWATER UNITED

Western League Premier

Founded 1984 Nickname: The Robins **Club Colours:** Red & white

Club Contact Details 01278 446 899 kerrymiller100@hotmail.com

Previous Names: Bridgwater Town 1984-21. Merged with Yeovil United Women's FC to form Bridgwater United.
Previous Leagues: Somerset Senior 1984-94. Western 1994-2007. Southern 2007-2017.
HONOURS
FA Comps: None
League: Somerset Senior Division One 1986-87, Premier 89-90, 90-91, 91-92. Western Division One 1995-96.

11-12	12-13	13-14	14-15	15-16	16-17	17-18	18-19	19-20	20-21
Sthsw 15	Sthsw 19	Sthsw 14	Sthsw 12	Sthsw 19	Sthsw 22	WestP 8	WestP 4	WestP n&v	WestP n&v
FAC 1Q	FAC P	FAC 3Q	FAC 2Q	FAC P	FAC P	FAC 1Q	FAC EP	FAC 1Q	FAC P
FAT P	FAT 2Q	FAT 1Q	FAT P	FAT Pr	FAT Pr	FAV 3Pr	FAV 2Q	FAV 3P	FAV 4P

GROUND: Fairfax Park, College Way, Bath Road, Bridgwater, Somerset TA6 4TZ **Capacity:** 2,500
Nearest Railway Station Bridgwater - 0.7km **Seats:** 128
Covered: 500

BRIDPORT

Western League Premier

Founded 1885 Nickname: Bees **Club Colours:** Red and black

Club Contact Details 01308 423 834 sevie@tiscali.co.uk

Previous Names: None

Previous Leagues: Dorset. South Dorset. West Dorset. Perry Street. Dorset Combination (Founding Memeber) 1957-61, 84-88. Western 1961-84.

HONOURS

FA Comps: None

League: Dorset Combination 1985-86, 86-87, 87-88.

11-12		12-13		13-14		14-15		15-16		16-17		17-18		18-19		19-20		20-21	
WestP	14	WestP	14	WestP	12	WestP	14	WestP	16	WestP	16	WestP	7	WestP	13	WestP	n&v	WestP	n&v
FAC	P	FAC	EP	FAC	P	FAC	EP	FAC	1Q	FAC	EP	FAC	3Q	FAC	1Q	FAC	EP	FAC	EP
FAV	1P	FAV	2Q	FAV	1Q	FAV	2P	FAV	1P	FAV	1Q	FAV	1Q	FAV	1P	FAV	1Q	FAV	2Q

GROUND: St Mary's Field, Bridport, Dorset DT6 5LN **Capacity:** 2,000 **Seats:** 150

Bus Route Leisure Centre - stop 20m away

BRISLINGTON

Western League Premier

Founded 1956 Nickname: Bris **Club Colours:** Red & black

Club Contact Details 01179 774 030 kevinhazell@me.com

Previous Names: Formed as an U16 team.

Previous Leagues: Bristol Church of England. Bristol & Suburban. Somerset Senior until 1991.

HONOURS

FA Comps: None

League: Somerset Senior 1988-89. Western Division One 1994-95.

11-12		12-13		13-14		14-15		15-16		16-17		17-18		18-19		19-20		20-21	
WestP	7	WestP	2	WestP	10	WestP	10	WestP	11	WestP	10	WestP	16	WestP	18	WestP	n&v	WestP	n&v
FAC	1Q	FAC	EP	FAC	4Q	FAC	P	FAC	EP	FAC	2Q	FAC	P	FAC	EP	FAC	P	FAC	EP
FAV	1Q	FAV	1P	FAV	2P	FAV	1P	FAV	1Q	FAV	2Q	FAV	2Q	FAV	1Q	FAV	1Q	FAV	2Q

GROUND: Ironmould Lane, Brislington, Bristol BS4 4TZ **Capacity:** 2,000 **Seats:** 144 **Covered:** 1,500

Nearest Railway Station Keynsham - 3km

Bus Route Ironmould Lane - stop 100m away

BUCKLAND ATHLETIC

Western League Premier

Founded 1977 Nickname: The Bucks **Club Colours:** Yellow with black trim

Club Contact Details 01626 361 020 bafcsec@gmail.com

Previous Names: None

Previous Leagues: Torbay Pioneer 1977-87. Devon & Exeter 1987-2000. Devon County 2000-07. South West Peninsula 2007-12.

HONOURS

FA Comps: None

League: Devon & Exeter Senior Third Division 1987-88, Premier 94-95, 99-00.
South West Peninsula Premier 2009-10, 10-11.

11-12		12-13		13-14		14-15		15-16		16-17		17-18		18-19		19-20		20-21	
SWPP	2	WestP	10	WestP	11	WestP	2	WestP	4	WestP	4	WestP	5	WestP	9	WestP	n&v	WestP	n&v
FAC	Pr	FAC	2Q	FAC	EP	FAC	EP	FAC	P	FAC	EP	FAC	EP	FAC	1Q	FAC	EP	FAC	EP
FAV	1P	FAV	2P	FAV	2P	FAV	3P	FAV	3P	FAV	QF	FAV	2P	FAV	2Q	FAV	4P	FAV	3P

GROUND: Homers Heath, South Quarry, Kingskerswell Road, Newton Abbot TQ12 5JU **Capacity:** 1,000

Nearest Railway Station Newton Abbot approx 2 miles from the ground.

CADBURY HEATH

Western League Premier

Founded 1894 Nickname: The Heathens **Club Colours:** Red

Club Contact Details 07971 399 268 martinbristol1955@hotmail.com

Previous Names: None

Previous Leagues: Bristol & District. Bristol Premier Combination. Gloucestershire County 1968-75, 80-2000. Midland Combination 1975-77.

HONOURS

FA Comps: None

League: Gloucestershire County 1970-71, 71-72, 72-73, 73-74, 93-94, 97-98, 98-99.
Western League Division One 2011-12.

11-12	12-13	13-14	14-15	15-16	16-17	17-18	18-19	19-20	20-21
West1 1	WestP 4	WestP 13	WestP 11	WestP 12	WestP 11	WestP 18	WestP 14	WestP n&v	WestP n&v
FAC 2Q	FAC P	FAC EP	FAC EP	FAC EP	FAC 3Q	FAC 2Qr	FAC 1Q	FAC EP	FAC P
FAV 2P	FAV 2P	FAV 1P	FAV 2Q	FAV 2P	FAV 2Q	FAV 1P	FAV 3P	FAV 2Q	FAV 2Q

GROUND: Springfield, Cadbury Heath Road, Bristol BS30 8BX **Capacity:** 2,000

Nearest Railway Station Oldland - 1.2km

Bus Route The King William IV - stop 100m away

CLEVEDON TOWN

Western League Premier

Founded 1880 Nickname: Seasiders **Club Colours:** Blue & white

Club Contact Details 01275 871 600 erichowe@hotmail.co.uk

Previous Names: Clevedon FC and Ashtonians merged in 1974

Previous Leagues: Western (Founder Members 1892), 1945-58, 73-93. Bristol & District. Bristol Suburban. Somerset Senior. Southern 1993-2015.

HONOURS

FA Comps: None

League: Bristol & Suburban 1925-26, 27-28, 28-29. Somerset Senior 36-37. Bristol Charity 37-38, 40-41. Western 92-93. Southern Midland Division 98-99, Divions 1W 2005-06.

11-12	12-13	13-14	14-15	15-16	16-17	17-18	18-19	19-20	20-21
Sthsw 20	Sthsw 15	Sthsw 17	Sthsw 18	WestP 19	WestP 14	WestP 12	WestP 6	WestP n&v	WestP n&v
FAC 2Q	FAC 2Q	FAC 3Qr	FAC P	FAC 3Q	FAC P	FAC P	FAC EP	FAC P	FAC 1Q
FAT P	FAT Pr	FAT 2Q	FAT P	FAV 1Q	FAV 2P	FAV 2Q	FAV 2Q	FAV 1Q	FAV 4P

GROUND: Everyone Active Stadium, Davis Lane, Clevedon BS21 6TG **Capacity:** 3,500

Nearest Railway Station Yatton - 4km **Seats:** 300

Bus Route Sercombe Park - stop 400m away **Covered:** 1,600

EXMOUTH TOWN

Western League Premier

Founded 1933 Nickname: The Town **Club Colours:** All royal blue

Club Contact Details 01395 263 348 chardtapp1@hotmail.co.uk

Previous Names: None

Previous Leagues: Western 1973-2006. South West Peninsula (FM) 2007-19.

HONOURS

FA Comps: None

League: Western 1983-84, 85-86.
South West Peninsula Division One East 2012-13.

11-12	12-13	13-14	14-15	15-16	16-17	17-18	18-19	19-20	20-21
SW1E 5	SW1E 1	SWPP 2	SWPP 8	SWPP 12	SWPP 5	SWPP 16	SWPP 2	WestP n&v	WestP n&v
						FAC EP		FAC 1Q	FAC P
	FAV 1P	FAV 2Q		FAV 2Q	FAV 5P	FAV 2P	FAV 2P	FAV 2P	FAV 2Q

GROUND: King George V, Exmouth EX8 3EE

Nearest Railway Station Exmouth - 0.6km **Seats:** 50

Bus Route Exeter Road - stop 143m away

HELSTON ATHLETIC

Western League Premier

Founded 1896 Nickname: The Blues **Club Colours:** Blue & white

Club Contact Details 01326 573 742 (Clubhouse) paul.m.hendy@btinternet.com

Previous Names: None

Previous Leagues: Cornwall Combination >2011. South West Peninsula 2011-21.

HONOURS

FA Comps: None

League: Cornwall Senior 1936-37, 37-38, 39-40. Cornwall Comb. 87-88, 2000-01, 10-11. South West Peninsula Division One West 2014-15.

11-12		12-13		13-14		14-15		15-16		16-17		17-18		18-19		19-20		20-21	
SW1W	2	SW1W	2	SW1W	3	SW1W	1	SWPP	10	SWPP	16	SWPP	9	SWPP	11	SWPW	n&v	SWPW	n&v
																		FAC	P
										FAV	1P	FAV	1Q	FAV	1Q	FAV	1P	FAV	2P

GROUND: Kellaway Park, Helston TR13 8PJ

Bus Route Tesco - stop 101m away

ILFRACOMBE TOWN

Western League Premier

Founded 1902 Nickname: Bluebirds **Club Colours:** All blue

Club Contact Details 01271 865 939 afalcock@aol.com

Previous Names:

Previous Leagues: North Devon, East Devon Premier, Exeter & District, Western, South West Peninsula >2021.

HONOURS

FA Comps:

League: North Devon Premier Division 2016-17.

11-12		12-13		13-14		14-15		15-16		16-17		17-18		18-19		19-20		20-21	
WestP	11	WestP	16	WestP	18	NDevP	6	NDevP	6	NDevP	1	SW1E	7	SW1E	8	SWPE	n&v	SWPE	n&v
FAC	EP	FAC	EP	FAC	P														
FAV	3Pr	FAV	1Q	FAV	1Q	FAV	2Q							FAV	1Q	FAV	1Q	FAV	1P

GROUND: Marlborough Park, Ilfracombe, Devon EX34 8PD

Nearest Railway Station Barnstaple

Capacity: 2,000
Seats: 60
Covered: 450

KEYNSHAM TOWN

Western League Premier

Founded 1895 Nickname: K's **Club Colours:** Amber and black

Club Contact Details jules1233@live.com

Previous Names: None

Previous Leagues: East Bristol & District >late 1950s. Bristol Premier Combination >1967. Somerset County 1967-73.

HONOURS

FA Comps: None

League: Bristol & District Division Three 1898-99, Division Two 1948-49. Western Division One 1977-78, 2018-19.

11-12		12-13		13-14		14-15		15-16		16-17		17-18		18-19		19-20		20-21	
West1	13	West1	13	West1	19	West1	17	West1	9	West1	4	West1	3	West1	1	WestP	n&v	WestP	n&v
										FAC	EP	FAC	EP	FAC	EPr	FAC	EP	FAC	EP
FAV	2Q	FAV	1Q	FAV	2Q	FAV	2Q	FAV	2Qr	FAV	2Q	FAV	1Q	FAV	1Q	FAV	1Q	FAV	1P

GROUND: AJN Stadium, Bristol Road, Keynsham BS31 2BE

Capacity: 3,000

Nearest Railway Station Keynsham - 0.7km

Bus Route Rugby Club - stop 50m away

MILLBROOK AFC

Western League Premier

Founded 1888 Nickname: Magpies / Brook **Club Colours:** Black & white

Club Contact Details 01752 822 113 greenanne@hotmail.co.uk

Previous Names: None

Previous Leagues: Plymouth & District. South Western 1980-07. South West Peninsula (FM) 2007-10, 14-21. East Cornwall 2010-14.

HONOURS

FA Comps: None

League: South West Peninsula Division One West 2017-18.

11-12	12-13	13-14	14-15	15-16	16-17	17-18	18-19	19-20	20-21
EC1 2	ECP 6	ECP 3	SW1W 15	SW1W 13	SW1W 4	SW1W 1	SWPP 10	SWPE n&v	SWPE n&v
									FAC EP
								FAV 1Q	FAV 3P

GROUND: Jenkins Park, Mill Road, Millbrook PL10 1EN

MOUSEHOLE

Western League Premier

Founded 1923 Nickname: The Seagulls **Club Colours:** White and green

Club Contact Details 01736 731 518 darrwoodard@gmail.com

Previous Names: None

Previous Leagues: South West Peninsula >2021.

HONOURS

FA Comps: None

League: South West Peninsula League Division One West 2015-16.

11-12	12-13	13-14	14-15	15-16	16-17	17-18	18-19	19-20	20-21
SW1W 17	SW1W 15	SW1W 2	SW1W 7	SW1W 1	SW1W 6	SW1W 4	SW1W 2	SWPW n&v	SWPW n&v
									FAV 1Q

GROUND: Trungle Parc, Paul, Penzance TR19 6UG

SALTASH UNITED

Western League Premier

Founded 1945 Nickname: The Ashes **Club Colours:** Red & white

Club Contact Details 01752 845 746 secretary.saltashunited@gmail.com

Previous Names: None

Previous Leagues: South West Peninsula >2021.

HONOURS

FA Comps: None

League: South Western 1953-54, 75-76. Western Division One 1976-77, Premier 1984-85, 86-87, 88-89.

11-12	12-13	13-14	14-15	15-16	16-17	17-18	18-19	19-20	20-21
SWPP 4	SWPP 6	SWPP 3	SWPP 3	SWPP 6	SWPP 2	SWPP 4	SWPP 4	SWPW n&v	SWPW n&v
FAC EP	FAC EP	FAC EP	FAC 1Q	FAC EP			FAC P	FAC EP	FAC 2Q
FAV 2P	FAV 1P	FAV 3P	FAV 1P	FAV 1Q		FAV 2Q	FAV 3P	FAV 2P	FAV 1Q

GROUND: Kimberley Stadium, Callington Road, Saltash PL12 6DX

Nearest Railway Station Saltash - 0.9km

Bus Route Callington Road St Annes - stop 40m away

SHEPTON MALLET

Western League Premier

Founded 1986 Nickname: The Mallet **Club Colours:** Black & white

Club Contact Details 01749 344 609 sally.robertson757@gmail.com

Previous Names: None
Previous Leagues: Somerset Senior.
HONOURS
FA Comps: None
League: Somerset Senior League 2000-01.

11-12		12-13		13-14		14-15		15-16		16-17		17-18		18-19		19-20		20-21	
West1	16	West1	7	West1	2	WestP	9	WestP	10	WestP	12	WestP	6	WestP	11	WestP	n&v	WestP	n&v
				FAC	EPr	FAC	Pr	FAC	EP	FAC	P	FAC	EP	FAC	EPr	FAC	1Qr	FAC	1Q
FAV	1Q	FAV	1Q	FAV	2P	FAV	3P	FAV	2Q	FAV	1Q	FAV	2Q	FAV	1Q	FAV	1P	FAV	1P

GROUND: Playing Fields, Old Wells Road, West Shepton, Shepton Mallet BA4 5XN
Capacity: 2,500
Seats: 120
Bus Route West Lodge - stop 180m away

STREET

Western League Premier

Founded 1880 Nickname: The Cobblers **Club Colours:** All green

Club Contact Details 01458 445 987 streetfootballclub@outlook.com

Previous Names: None
Previous Leagues: Somerset Senior 1880-1911, 22-30, 60-98. Western 1911-22, 30-39, 46-60, 98-2018. Southern 2018-19.
HONOURS
FA Comps: None
League: Somerset Senior 1892-93, 95-96, 97-98, 98-99, 1909-10, 63-64, 65-66, 1996-97, Division Three 93-94.
Western Premier 2017-18.

11-12		12-13		13-14		14-15		15-16		16-17		17-18		18-19		19-20		20-21	
WestP	10	WestP	6	WestP	5	WestP	13	WestP	7	WestP	2	WestP	1	SthS	8	WestP	n&v	WestP	n&v
FAC	EP	FAC	EP	FAC	1Q	FAC	EPr	FAC	P	FAC	1Q	FAC	P	FAC	1Qr	FAC	P	FAC	EP
FAV	1Q	FAV	1P	FAV	2Q	FAV	2Q	FAV	1Q	FAV	1P	FAV	1P	FAT	2Qr	FAV	2Q	FAV	1P

GROUND: The Tannery Ground, Middlebrooks, Street BA16 0TA
Capacity: 1,000
Seats: 150
Covered: 25
Bus Route Green Lane Ave - stop 220m away

TAVISTOCK

Western League Premier

Founded 1888 Nickname: The Lambs **Club Colours:** Red & black

Club Contact Details 01822 614 447 secretary@tavistockfc.com

Previous Names:
Previous Leagues: South Western 1952-61, 68-2007. South West Peninsula 2007-19.
HONOURS
FA Comps: None
League: Devon 1900-01. Plymouth Combination Division One 1950-51.
South West Peninsula League Division One East 2014-15, Premier 16-17, 18-19.

11-12		12-13		13-14		14-15		15-16		16-17		17-18		18-19		19-20		20-21	
SWPP	10	SWPP	10	SWPP	19	SW1E	1	SWPP	3	SWPP	1	SWPP	2	SWPP	1	WestP	n&v	WestP	n&v
FAC	1Q	FAC	EP	FAC	EP							FAC	2Q	FAC	EP	FAC	3Q	FAC	1Q
FAV	1P	FAV	1Q	FAV	2P	FAV	1Q			FAV	1P	FAV	2P	FAV	2P	FAV	3P	FAV	5P

GROUND: Langsford Park, Red & Black Club, Crowndale Road, Tavistock PL19 8JR
Nearest Railway Station Gunnislake - 4.9km
Bus Route Canons Way - stop 694m away

WELLINGTON AFC

Western League Premier

Founded 1892 Nickname: Wellie **Club Colours:** Orange and black

Club Contact Details 01823 664 810 jeffandjane@talktalk.net

Previous Names: None

Previous Leagues: Taunton Saturday, Somerset Senior.

HONOURS

FA Comps: None

League: Western Division One 2007-08, 16-17.

11-12		12-13		13-14		14-15		15-16		16-17		17-18		18-19		19-20		20-21	
West1	18	West1	18	West1	8	West1	6	West1	12	West1	1	WestP	15	WestP	16	WestP	n&v	WestP	n&v
FAC	EP											FAC	EP	FAC	EPr	FAC	EP	FAC	EP
FAV	2Q	FAT	2Q			FAV	2Q			FAV	1Q	FAV	2P	FAV	1Q	FAV	1Q	FAV	1Q

GROUND: Wellington Playing Field, North Street, Wellington TA21 8NE

Capacity: 1,500
Seats: 200
Covered: 200

Bus Route Nth St Police Station - stop 150m away

CLUB MOVEMENTS

DIVISION ONE - IN: AEK Boco (P - GCL).
Gillingham Town (P - DPL).
Tytherington Rocks (LM - HL1W).

OUT: Ashton & Backwell United (P - WL1).
Calne Town and Corsham Town (P - HLP).

AEK BOCO

Western League Division One

Founded 2003 Nickname: **Club Colours:** Sky blue and navy

Club Contact Details 01179 477 331 contact@aekboco.co.uk

HONOURS FA Comps: None

League: Gloucestershire 2015-16.

11-12	12-13	13-14	14-15	15-16	16-17	17-18	18-19	19-20	20-21
BrPC1 2	BrPCP 7	BrPCP 2	GlCo 2	GlCo 1	GlCo 7	GlCo 6	GlCo 12	GlCo n&v	GlCo n&v

GROUND: LA Clark Pavilion, Greenbank Road, Hanham, Bristol BS15 3RZ

ALMONDSBURY

Western League Division One

Founded 1969 Nickname: The Almonds **Club Colours:** Green & white

Club Contact Details 01454 612 240 doug2004.coles@blueyonder.co.uk

HONOURS FA Comps: None

League: Bristol Suburban Premier Division 1990-91. Gloucestershire County 2003-04.

11-12	12-13	13-14	14-15	15-16	16-17	17-18	18-19	19-20	20-21
West1 9	West1 10	West1 9	West1 5	West1 11	West1 22	West1 13	Hel1W 7	West1 n&v	West1 n&v
FAC EP	FAC 1Q		FAC EP	FAC 1Q					
FAV 1Q	FAV 1Q	FAV 1P	FAV 1Q	FAV 2Q	FAV 2Q	FAV 1Q	FAV 2P	FAV 1Q	FAV 1Q

GROUND: The Field, Gloucester Road, Almondsbury, Bristol BS32 4AA

Nearest Railway Station Patchway - 2.9km

Bus Route Over Lane - stop 70m away

BISHOP SUTTON

Western League Division One

Founded 1977 Nickname: Bishops **Club Colours:** All blue

Club Contact Details 01275 332 855 bishopsuttonafcsecretary@hotmail.co.uk

HONOURS FA Comps: None

League: Western Division One 1997-98, Premier Division 2012-13.

11-12	12-13	13-14	14-15	15-16	16-17	17-18	18-19	19-20	20-21
WestP 6	WestP 1	WestP 9	WestP 19	West1 21	West1 16	West1 12	West1 17	West1 n&v	West1 n&v
FAC 1Q	FAC Pr	FAC P	FAC EP	FAC EP					
FAV 2P	FAV 2Q	FAV 1P	FAV 1Q	FAV 1P	FAV 2Q	FAV 2Q	FAV 1Q	FAV 1Q	FAV 1Q

GROUND: Lakeview, Wick Road, Bishops Sutton, Bristol BS39 5XN.

Bus Route Butchers Arms Pub - stop 50m away

BISHOPS LYDEARD

Western League Division One

Founded 1912 Nickname: **Club Colours:** Red & black stripes/

Club Contact Details itspeebee@gmail.com

HONOURS FA Comps: None

League: Somerset County Division One 2004-05, Premier Division 15-16.

11-12	12-13	13-14	14-15	15-16	16-17	17-18	18-19	19-20	20-21
SomP 11	SomP 13	SomP 10	SthP 6	SomP 1	West1 6	West1 14	West1 12	West1 n&v	West1 n&v
							FAV 2Q	FAV 1Q	FAV 1Q

GROUND: Cottlestone Road, Bishops Lydeard, Taunton, TA4 3BA

Nearest Railway Station Bishops Lydeard - 1.5km

Bus Route Darby Way - 80m away

BRISTOL TELEPHONES

Western League Division One

Founded 1948 Nickname: The Phones **Club Colours:** All pale blue

Club Contact Details 01275 891 776 steve.watkins56@talktalk.net

HONOURS FA Comps: None

League: Bristol & Suburban Premier Division 2010-11, 12-13.
Gloucestershire County 2016-17.

11-12	12-13	13-14	14-15	15-16	16-17	17-18	18-19	19-20	20-21
Br&SuP1 3	Br&SuP1 1	GlCo 3	GlCo 8	GlCo 10	GlCo 1	West1 16	West1 20	West1 n&v	West1 n&v
							FAV 1Q	FAV 1Q	FAV 2Q

GROUND: BTRA Sports Ground, Stockwood Lane, Stockwood, Bristol BS14 8SJ

Nearest Railway Station Keynsham - 3.6km

Bus Route Battson Road - stop 50m away

CHEDDAR

Western League Division One

Founded 1892 Nickname: The Cheesemen **Club Colours:** Yellow and black

Club Contact Details 01934 708 586 harvs360@hotmail.co.uk

HONOURS FA Comps: None

League: Cheddar Valley 1910-11.
Somerset Senior Division One 2003-04.

11-12	12-13	13-14	14-15	15-16	16-17	17-18	18-19	19-20	20-21
SomP 2	West1 11	West1 17	West1 10	WestP 5	West1 3	West1 4	West1 2	West1 n&v	West1 n&v
					FAC EPr	FAC EP	FAC P	FAC EP	
		FAV 1Q	FAV 1Q	FAV 1Q	FAV 2Q	FAV 1Q	FAV 2P	FAV 2Q	FAV 2P

GROUND: Bowdens Park, Draycott Road, Cheddar BS27 3RL

Bus Route Church Street - stop 400m away

DEVIZES TOWN

Western League Division One

Founded 1885 Nickname: The Town **Club Colours:** Red & white stripes

Club Contact Details 01380 825 545 neil@hallmarkflooringltd.co.uk

HONOURS FA Comps: None

League: Wiltshire Senior 1895-96, 89-99, 35-36, 48-49, 51-52, 53-54, Premier 61-62, 63-64. Western Premier Division 1972-73, Division One 99-2000.

11-12	12-13	13-14	14-15	15-16	16-17	17-18	18-19	19-20	20-21
West1 19	West1 21	West1 11	West1 18	West1 19	West1 11	West1 5	West1 11	West1 n&v	West1 n&v
FAC EP									
FAV 1P	FAV 1Q	FAV 1Q	FAV 1Q	FAV 1Q	FAV 1P	FAV 1Q	FAV 1Q	FAV 2Q	FAV 1Q

GROUND: Nursteed Road, Devizes, Wiltshire SN10 3DX

Bus Route Eastleigh Road - stop 80m away

GILLINGHAM TOWN

Western League Division One

Founded 1879 Nickname: The Gills **Club Colours:** All tangerine

Club Contact Details 07545 650 808 secretary@gtfc.one

HONOURS FA Comps: None

League: None

11-12	12-13	13-14	14-15	15-16	16-17	17-18	18-19	19-20	20-21
West1 3	WestP 3	WestP 3	WestP 15	WestP 9	WestP 9	Dor P 3	Dor P 5	Dor P n&v	Dor P n&v

GROUND: Woodwater Lane, Gillingham, Dorset SP8 4HX

HENGROVE ATHLETIC

Western League Division One

Founded 1948 Nickname: The Grove **Club Colours:** Green & white

Club Contact Details 07884 492 217 secretary@hengroveathletic.com

HONOURS FA Comps: None

League: Somerset County Premier Division 2005-06.

11-12		12-13		13-14		14-15		15-16		16-17		17-18		18-19		19-20		20-21	
West1	10	West1	2	WestP	21	West1	12	West1	7	West1	2	WestP	9	WestP	19	West1	n&v	West1	n&v
FAC	EP	FAC	P	FAC	EP	FAC	EP			FAC	EPr	FAC	P	FAC	EP	FAC	EP		
FAV	2Q	FAV	2Q	FAV	2Q	FAV	2Q	FAV	3P	FAV	1P	FAV	2P	FAV	1Q	FAV	1Q	FAV	2Q

GROUND: Norton Lane, Whitchurch, Bristol BS14 0BT

Nearest Railway Station Bedminster - 2.5km

Bus Route Wooton Park - stop 100m away

LEBEQ UNITED

Western League Division One

Founded 2008 Nickname: **Club Colours:** Red

Club Contact Details Lebequnited@hotmail.com

HONOURS FA Comps: None

League: Bristol & Suburban Division Three 2009-10, Division Two 11-12, Premier Division One 15-16.
Gloucestershire County 2018-19.

11-12		12-13		13-14		14-15		15-16		16-17		17-18		18-19		19-20		20-21	
Br&Su2	1	Br&Su1	4	Br&SuP2	3	Br&SuP1	8	Br&SuP1	1	GlCo	10	GlCo	2	GlCo	1	West1	n&v	West1	n&v

GROUND: Oaklands Park, Almondsbury, Bristol BS32 4AG

LONGWELL GREEN SPORTS

Western League Division One

Founded 1966 Nickname: The Green **Club Colours:** Blue & white

Club Contact Details 01179 323 722 dauncey t@blueyonder.co.uk

HONOURS FA Comps: None

League: Bristol & District Division Four 1982-83.

11-12		12-13		13-14		14-15		15-16		16-17		17-18		18-19		19-20		20-21	
WestP	13	WestP	15	WestP	14	WestP	16	WestP	18	WestP	17	WestP	19	West1	5	West1	n&v	West1	n&v
FAC	P	FAC	EPr	FAC	Pr	FAC	1Q	FAC	P	FAC	EP	FAC	EP	FAC	EPr				
FAV	1Qr	FAV	2Pr	FAV	1P	FAV	1P	FAV	2Qr	FAV	2Q	FAV	2Q	FAV	1P	FAV	1Q	FAV	1P

GROUND: Longwell Green Com. Centre, Shellards Road BS30 9DU

Nearest Railway Station Bitton - 1.4km

Bus Route Sally Barn Close - stop 500m away

ODD DOWN

Western League Division One

Founded 1901 Nickname: The Down **Club Colours:** All blue

Club Contact Details 01225 832 491 sbraders43@googlemail.com

HONOURS FA Comps: None

League: Western Division One 1992-93, Premier Division 2015-16.

11-12		12-13		13-14		14-15		15-16		16-17		17-18		18-19		19-20		20-21	
WestP	9	WestP	8	WestP	4	WestP	5	WestP	1	WestP	7	WestP	14	WestP	15	WestP	n&v	WestP	n&v
FAC	P	FAC	P	FAC	EPr	FAC	P	FAC	P	FAC	P	FAC	1Q	FAC	EP	FAC	EP	FAC	EP
FAV	2Q	FAV	2P	FAV	2P	FAV	3P	FAV	2P	FAV	2P	FAV	1P	FAV	1P	FAV	1Q	FAV	1Q

GROUND: Lew Hill Memorial Ground, Combe Hay Lane, Odd Down BA2 8PA

Nearest Railway Station Oldfield Park - 2.9km

Bus Route St Gregory's School - stop 50m away

OLDLAND ABBOTONIANS

Western League Division One

Founded 1910 Nickname: The O's **Club Colours:** Blue & white

Club Contact Details 01179 328 263 secretary@oldlandfootball.com

HONOURS FA Comps: None

League: Somerset County Division One 2004-05.

11-12	12-13	13-14	14-15	15-16	16-17	17-18	18-19	19-20	20-21
West1 11	West1 5	West1 21	West1 14	West1 4	West1 17	West1 7	West1 18	West1 n&v	West1 n&v
		FAC EP			FAC P				
	FAV 1Q	FAV 1Q	FAV 1Q	FAV 2Q	FAV 2Q	FAV 2Q	FAV 1Q		FAV 2Q

GROUND: Aitchison Playing Field, Castle Road, Oldland Common, Bristol BS30 9SZ

Nearest Railway Station Oldland - 400m

Bus Route The Clamp - stop 130m away

PORTISHEAD TOWN

Western League Division One

Founded 1912 Nickname: Posset **Club Colours:** White and black

Club Contact Details 01275 817 600 andy.carling@yahoo.co.uk

HONOURS FA Comps: None

League: Somerset County 1993-94, 94-95, 95-96, 97-98.

11-12	12-13	13-14	14-15	15-16	16-17	17-18	18-19	19-20	20-21
West1 12	West1 14	West1 22	West1 21	West1 6	West1 14	West1 21	West1 16	West1 n&v	West1 n&v
					FAC 1Q				
FAV 1Q	FAV 1Q	FAV 1Q	FAV 2Q	FAV 1P	FAV 2Q	FAV 2Q	FAV 1Q	FAV 2Q	FAV 1Q

GROUND: Bristol Road, Portishead, Bristol BS20 6QG

Nearest Railway Station Avonmouth - 5.1km

Bus Route Glebe Road - stop 50m away

RADSTOCK TOWN

Western League Division One

Founded 1895 Nickname: The Miners **Club Colours:** Red and black

Club Contact Details 01761 435 004 ianlanning9@gmail.com

HONOURS FA Comps: None

League: Somerset Senior Division One 1996-97.

11-12	12-13	13-14	14-15	15-16	16-17	17-18	18-19	19-20	20-21
WestP 16	WestP 17	WestP 1	West1 13	West1 13	West1 5	West1 6	West1 15	West1 n&v	West1 n&v
FAC P	FAC EP	FAC EP	FAC EP						
FAV 1Q	FAV 2Q	FAV 2Q	FAV 1P	FAV 2Q	FAV 1Q	FAV 1P	FAV 2Q	FAV 2Q	FAV 1Q

GROUND: Southfields Recreation Ground, Southfields, Radstock BA3 3NZ

Bus Route Withies Park - stop 80m away

SHERBORNE TOWN

Western League Division One

Founded 1894 Nickname: **Club Colours:** Black & white

Club Contact Details 01935 816 110 secretary@sherbornetownfc.com

HONOURS FA Comps: None

League: Dorset Premier 1981-82. Western Division One 2012-13.

11-12	12-13	13-14	14-15	15-16	16-17	17-18	18-19	19-20	20-21
WestP 17	West1 1	WestP 9	WestP 12	WestP 13	WestP 20	WestP 19	West1 13	West1 n&v	West1 n&v
FAC EP	FAC 1Q	FAC P	FAC 1Q	FAC Pr	FAC EP	FAC EP			FAC P
FAV 2Q	FAV 2P	FAV 2Q	FAV 1P	FAV 1Q	FAV 1P	FAV 1Q	FAV 2Q	FAV 2Qr	FAV 1P

GROUND: Raleigh Grove, Terrace Playing Field, Sherborne DT9 5NS

Nearest Railway Station Sherborne - 0.5km

Bus Route Sherborne Station - stop 0.5km away

TYTHERINGTON ROCKS

Western League Division One

Founded 1896 Nickname: The Rocks **Club Colours:** Amber & black

Club Contact Details clonwithy@talktalk.net

HONOURS FA Comps: None

League: Iron Acton & District 1944-45. Bristol & Suburban Div.3 1949-50, Prem Div.2 93-94, Prem Div.1 96-97, Prem Div.1 97-98. Hellenic Div.1W 2011-12, 13-14.

11-12	12-13	13-14	14-15	15-16	16-17	17-18	18-19	19-20	20-21
Hel1W 1	Hel1W 3	Hel1W 1	Hel1W 15	Hel1W 14	Hel1W 15	Hel1W 14	Hel1W 11	Hel1W n&v	Hel1W n&v
				FAV 2Qr	FAV 1Q	FAV 2Q	FAV 1Q	FAV 1Q	FAV 1Q

GROUND: Hardwicke Playing Field, Woodlands Road, Tytherington GL12 8UQ

Bus Route Stowell Hill Road stop - 102m away

WARMINSTER TOWN

Western League Division One

Founded 1878 Nickname: The Red & Blacks **Club Colours:** Red & black stripes

Club Contact Details 01985 217 828 davidw.parry58@gmail.com

HONOURS FA Comps: None

League: None

11-12	12-13	13-14	14-15	15-16	16-17	17-18	18-19	19-20	20-21
Wex1 16	West1 15	West1 18	West1 16	West1 17	West1 18	West1 22	West1 6	West1 n&v	West1 n&v
	FAV 2Q	FAV 1P	FAV 1Q	FAV 2Q	FAV 1Q	FAV 2Q	FAV 2Q	FAV 4P	

GROUND: Weymouth Street, Warminster BA12 9NS

Nearest Railway Station Warminster - 0.9km

Bus Route Glebe Field - stop 80m away

WELLS CITY

Western League Division One

Founded 1890 Nickname: **Club Colours:** All blue

Club Contact Details 01749 679 971 daveg55@hotmail.co.uk

HONOURS FA Comps: None

League: Western Division One 1949-50, 2009-10.

11-12	12-13	13-14	14-15	15-16	16-17	17-18	18-19	19-20	20-21
WestP 12	WestP 19	West1 6	West1 19	West1 2	WestP 15	WestP 20	West1 10	West1 n&v	West1 n&v
FAC 2Q	FAC P	FAC 1Q			FAC EPr	FAC P	FAC EP		FAC P
FAV 1P	FAV 2Q	FAV 1Q	FAV 1Q	FAV 1P	FAV 2Q	FAV 1Q	FAV 2Q	FAV 2Q	FAV 2P

GROUND: Athletic Ground, Rowdens Road, Wells, Somerset BA5 1TU

Bus Route The Police Station - stop 20m away

WELTON ROVERS

Western League Division One

Founded 1887 Nickname: Rovers **Club Colours:** Green & white

Club Contact Details 07970 791 644 garethpaisey@outlook.com

HONOURS FA Comps: None

League: Western 1911-12, 64-65, 65-66, 66-67, 73-74, Division One 59-60, 87-88.

11-12	12-13	13-14	14-15	15-16	16-17	17-18	18-19	19-20	20-21
West1 7	West1 16	West1 6	West1 2	WestP 20	West1 20	West1 8	West1 9	West1 n&v	West1 n&v
FAC EP	FAC EP		FAC EP	FAC EP	FAC EP				
FAV 1Q	FAV 2Q	FAV 1Q	FAV 2P	FAV 3P	FAV 1Q	FAV 1Q	FAV 2Q	FAV 1Q	FAV 1P

GROUND: West Clewes, North Road, Midsomer Norton, Bath BA3 2QD

Bus Route Elm View - 50m away

WINCANTON TOWN

Western League Division One

Founded 1890 Nickname: Winky **Club Colours:** Yellow & black

Club Contact Details 01963 31815 cmartin10101981@gmail.com

HONOURS FA Comps: None

League: Yeovil & District Division Two 1988-89, Division One 89-90, Premier 90-91.
Dorset Senior Division 2006-07.

11-12	12-13	13-14	14-15	15-16	16-17	17-18	18-19	19-20	20-21
Dor P 4	Dor P 2	West1 4	West1 4	West1 16	West1 13	West1 10	West1 14	West1 n&v	West1 n&v
				FAC P					
			FAV 1Q	FAV EP	FAV 1Q	FAV 2Q	FAV 1Q	FAV 2Q	

GROUND: Wincanton Sports Ground, Moor Lane, Wincanton. BA9 9EJ

Nearest Railway Station Templecombe - 4.9km

Bus Route Balsam Lane - stop 1.2km away

Harris (Melton) gets his shot in against West Bridgford.

Benjamin (Melton) heads the ball against the West Bridgford crossbar during this pre-season friendly. Photos Keith Clayton.

GROUNDS OF GREAT BRITAIN

A small selection of some of the grounds our photographers have visited during the season

AFC Mansfield 2020. Photo Bill Wheatcroft.

Alfreton Town 2020. Photo Bill Wheatcroft.

CLUB INDEX

The National League System Clubs as they line up for the 2021-22 season

Club	League	Page
1874 NORTHWICH	NPL WEST	590
ABBEY HEY	NORTH WEST COUNTIES DIVISION 1S	721
ABBEY HULTON UNITED	NORTH WEST COUNTIES DIVISION 1S	721
ABBEY RANGERS	COMBINED COUNTIES PREMIER NORTH	644
ABINGDON UNITED	HELLENIC DIVISION ONE	693
AEK BOCO	WESTERN LEAGUE DIVISION ONE	838
AFC ALDERMASTON	COMBINED COUNTIES DIVISION ONE	657
AFC BLACKPOOL	NORTH WEST COUNTIES DIVISION 1N	717
AFC BRIDGNORTH	MIDLAND FOOTBALL LEAGUE DIVISION ONE	705
AFC CROYDON ATHLETIC	COMBINED COUNTIES PREMIER SOUTH	650
AFC DARWEN	NORTH WEST COUNTIES DIVISION 1N	717
AFC DUNSTABLE	SOUTHERN D1 CENTRAL	624
AFC FYLDE	NATIONAL NORTH	494
AFC HAYES	COMBINED COUNTIES DIVISION ONE	657
AFC LIVERPOOL	NORTH WEST COUNTIES PREMIER	710
AFC MANSFIELD	NORTHERN COUNTIES EAST PREMIER	727
AFC PORTCHESTER	WESSEX PREMIER	819
AFC RUSHDEN & DIAMONDS	SOUTHERN PREMIER CENTRAL	602
AFC ST. AUSTELL	SOUTH WEST PENINSULA PREMIER WEST	758
AFC STONEHAM	WESSEX PREMIER	819
AFC SUDBURY	ISTHMIAN NORTH	527
AFC SUDBURY RESERVES	EASTERN COUNTIES DIVISION ONE SOUTH	674
AFC TELFORD UNITED	NATIONAL NORTH	494
AFC TOTTON	SOUTHERN D1 SOUTH	634
AFC UCKFIELD TOWN	SOUTHERN COMBINATION PREMIER	763
AFC VARNDEANIANS	SOUTHERN COMBINATION PREMIER	763
AFC WULFRUNIANS	MIDLAND FOOTBALL LEAGUE PREMIER	698
ALBION SPORTS	NORTHERN COUNTIES EAST PREMIER	727
ALDERSHOT TOWN	NATIONAL LEAGUE	482
ALFOLD	SOUTHERN COMBINATION PREMIER	763
ALFRETON TOWN	NATIONAL NORTH	494
ALMONDSBURY	WESTERN LEAGUE DIVISION ONE	838
ALRESFORD TOWN	WESSEX PREMIER	819
ALSAGER TOWN	NORTH WEST COUNTIES DIVISION 1S	721
ALTON	WESSEX PREMIER	819
ALTRINCHAM	NATIONAL LEAGUE	482
ALVECHURCH	SOUTHERN PREMIER CENTRAL	602
AMERSHAM TOWN	SPARTAN SOUTH MIDLANDS DIVISION ONE	794
AMESBURY TOWN	WESSEX PREMIER	819
AMPTHILL TOWN	SPARTAN SOUTH MIDLANDS DIVISION ONE	794
ANDOVER NEW STREET	WESSEX DIVISION ONE	826
ANDOVER TOWN	WESSEX DIVISION ONE	826
ANSTEY NOMADS	UNITED COUNTIES PREMIER NORTH	799
ARDLEY UNITED	SPARTAN SOUTH MIDLANDS PREMIER	787
ARLESEY TOWN	SPARTAN SOUTH MIDLANDS PREMIER	787

Armthorpe Welfare. Photos Bill Wheatcroft.

ARMTHORPE WELFARE	NORTHERN COUNTIES EAST DIVISION ONE	734
ARUNDEL	SOUTHERN COMBINATION DIVISION ONE	770
ASCOT UNITED	COMBINED COUNTIES PREMIER NORTH	644
ASH UNITED	WESSEX DIVISION ONE	826
ASHBY IVANHOE	MIDLAND FOOTBALL LEAGUE DIVISION ONE	705
ASHFORD TOWN (MIDDX)	ISTHMIAN SOUTH CENTRAL	537
ASHFORD UNITED	ISTHMIAN SOUTH EAST	547
ASHINGTON	NORTHERN LEAGUE DIVISION ONE	740
ASHTON & BACKWELL UNITED	WESTERN LEAGUE PREMIER	831
ASHTON ATHLETIC	NORTH WEST COUNTIES PREMIER	710
ASHTON TOWN	NORTH WEST COUNTIES DIVISION 1N	717
ASHTON UNITED	NPL PREMIER DIVISION	558
ATHERSLEY RECREATION	NORTHERN COUNTIES EAST PREMIER	727
ATHERSTONE TOWN	MIDLAND FOOTBALL LEAGUE DIVISION ONE	705
ATHERTON COLLIERIES	NPL PREMIER DIVISION	558
ATHERTON LABURNUM ROVERS	NORTH WEST COUNTIES DIVISION 1N	717
ATHLETIC NEWHAM	ESSEX SENIOR	679
AVELEY	ISTHMIAN NORTH	527
AVRO	NORTH WEST COUNTIES PREMIER	710
AXMINSTER TOWN	SOUTH WEST PENINSULA PREMIER EAST	753
AYLESBURY UNITED	SOUTHERN D1 CENTRAL	624
AYLESBURY VALE DYNAMOES	SPARTAN SOUTH MIDLANDS PREMIER	787
AYLESTONE PARK	UNITED COUNTIES DIVISION ONE	815
BACUP BOROUGH	NORTH WEST COUNTIES DIVISION 1N	717
BADSHOT LEA	COMBINED COUNTIES PREMIER SOUTH	650
BAFFINS MILTON ROVERS	WESSEX PREMIER	819
BAGSHOT	COMBINED COUNTIES DIVISION ONE	657
BALDOCK TOWN	SPARTAN SOUTH MIDLANDS PREMIER	787
BALHAM	COMBINED COUNTIES PREMIER SOUTH	650
BAMBER BRIDGE	NPL PREMIER DIVISION	558
BANBURY UNITED	SOUTHERN PREMIER CENTRAL	602
BANSTEAD ATHLETIC	COMBINED COUNTIES PREMIER SOUTH	650
BARKING	ISTHMIAN NORTH	527
BARKINGSIDE	EASTERN COUNTIES DIVISION ONE SOUTH	674
BARNET	NATIONAL LEAGUE	482
BARNOLDSWICK TOWN	NORTH WEST COUNTIES PREMIER	710
BARNSTAPLE TOWN	SOUTHERN D1 SOUTH	634
BARNTON	NORTH WEST COUNTIES DIVISION 1S	721
BARROW TOWN	UNITED COUNTIES DIVISION ONE	815
BARTON ROVERS	SOUTHERN D1 CENTRAL	624
BARTON TOWN	NORTHERN COUNTIES EAST PREMIER	727
BARWELL	SOUTHERN PREMIER CENTRAL	602
BASFORD UNITED	NPL PREMIER DIVISION	558
BASHLEY	WESSEX PREMIER	819
BASILDON UNITED	ISTHMIAN NORTH	527
BASINGSTOKE TOWN	ISTHMIAN SOUTH CENTRAL	537
BATH CITY	NATIONAL SOUTH	505
BEACONSFIELD TOWN	SOUTHERN PREMIER SOUTH	613
BEARSTED	SOUTHERN COUNTIES EAST PREMIER	775

Ashover 2021. Photo Bill Wheatcroft.

Boston Town Main Stand. Photo Keith Clayton.

BECKENHAM TOWN	COMBINED COUNTIES PREMIER SOUTH	650
BEDFONT & FELTHAM	COMBINED COUNTIES DIVISION ONE	657
BEDFONT SPORTS	ISTHMIAN SOUTH CENTRAL	537
BEDFORD	SPARTAN SOUTH MIDLANDS DIVISION ONE	794
BEDFORD TOWN	SOUTHERN D1 CENTRAL	624
BEDLINGTON TERRIERS	NORTHERN LEAGUE DIVISION TWO	747
BEDWORTH UNITED	NPL MIDLANDS	580
BELPER TOWN	NPL MIDLANDS	580
BELPER UNITED	UNITED COUNTIES DIVISION ONE	815
BEMERTON HEATH HARLEQUINS	WESSEX DIVISION ONE	826
BENFLEET	EASTERN COUNTIES DIVISION ONE SOUTH	674
BERKHAMSTED	SOUTHERN D1 CENTRAL	624
BERKS COUNTY	COMBINED COUNTIES DIVISION ONE	657
BEWDLEY TOWN	MIDLAND FOOTBALL LEAGUE PREMIER	698
BEXHILL UNITED	SOUTHERN COMBINATION PREMIER	763
BIDEFORD	SOUTHERN D1 SOUTH	634
BIGGLESWADE FC	SOUTHERN D1 CENTRAL	624
BIGGLESWADE TOWN	SOUTHERN PREMIER CENTRAL	602
BIGGLESWADE UNITED	UNITED COUNTIES PREMIER SOUTH	806
BILLERICAY TOWN	NATIONAL SOUTH	505
BILLINGHAM SYNTHONIA	NORTHERN LEAGUE DIVISION TWO	747
BILLINGHAM TOWN	NORTHERN LEAGUE DIVISION ONE	740
BILLINGSHURST	SOUTHERN COMBINATION DIVISION ONE	770
BILSTON TOWN COMMUNITY	MIDLAND FOOTBALL LEAGUE DIVISION ONE	705
BINFIELD	ISTHMIAN SOUTH CENTRAL	537
BIRSTALL UNITED SOCIAL	UNITED COUNTIES DIVISION ONE	815
BIRTLEY TOWN	NORTHERN LEAGUE DIVISION TWO	747
BISHOP AUCKLAND	NORTHERN LEAGUE DIVISION ONE	740
BISHOP SUTTON	WESTERN LEAGUE DIVISION ONE	838
BISHOP'S CLEEVE	HELLENIC PREMIER	686
BISHOP'S STORTFORD	ISTHMIAN PREMIER	516
BISHOPS LYDEARD	WESTERN LEAGUE DIVISION ONE	838
BITTON	WESTERN LEAGUE PREMIER	831
BLACKFIELD & LANGLEY	WESSEX PREMIER	819
BLACKSTONES	UNITED COUNTIES DIVISION ONE	815
BLYTH SPARTANS	NATIONAL NORTH	494
BLYTH TOWN	NORTHERN LEAGUE DIVISION TWO	747
BODMIN TOWN	SOUTH WEST PENINSULA PREMIER WEST	758
BOGNOR REGIS TOWN	ISTHMIAN PREMIER	516
BOLDMERE ST. MICHAELS	MIDLAND FOOTBALL LEAGUE PREMIER	698
BOLDON C.A.	NORTHERN LEAGUE DIVISION TWO	747
BOOTLE	NPL WEST	590
BOREHAM WOOD	NATIONAL LEAGUE	482
BORROWASH VICTORIA	UNITED COUNTIES DIVISION ONE	815
BOSTON TOWN	UNITED COUNTIES PREMIER NORTH	799
BOSTON UNITED	NATIONAL NORTH	494
BOTTESFORD TOWN	NORTHERN COUNTIES EAST PREMIER	727
BOURNE TOWN	UNITED COUNTIES DIVISION ONE	815
BOURNEMOUTH	WESSEX PREMIER	819

Main Stand Bottesford Town. Photo Keith Clayton.

Main Stand Bury Town. Photo Keith Clayton.

BOURTON ROVERS	HELLENIC DIVISION ONE	693
BOVEY TRACEY	SOUTH WEST PENINSULA PREMIER EAST	753
BOWERS & PITSEA	ISTHMIAN PREMIER	516
BRACKLEY TOWN	NATIONAL NORTH	494
BRACKNELL TOWN	ISTHMIAN SOUTH CENTRAL	537
BRADFORD (PARK AVENUE)	NATIONAL NORTH	494
BRADFORD TOWN	HELLENIC PREMIER	686
BRAINTREE TOWN	NATIONAL SOUTH	505
BRANDON UNITED	NORTHERN LEAGUE DIVISION TWO	747
BRANTHAM ATHLETIC	EASTERN COUNTIES PREMIER	663
BRENTWOOD TOWN	ISTHMIAN NORTH	527
BRIDGWATER UNITED	WESTERN LEAGUE PREMIER	831
BRIDLINGTON TOWN	NPL EAST	570
BRIDON ROPES	SOUTHERN COUNTIES EAST DIVISION ONE	782
BRIDPORT	WESTERN LEAGUE PREMIER	831
BRIGG TOWN	NORTHERN COUNTIES EAST DIVISION ONE	734
BRIGHOUSE TOWN	NPL EAST	570
BRIGHTLINGSEA REGENT	ISTHMIAN PREMIER	516
BRIMSCOMBE & THRUPP	HELLENIC PREMIER	686
BRIMSDOWN	EASTERN COUNTIES DIVISION ONE SOUTH	674
BRISLINGTON	WESTERN LEAGUE PREMIER	831
BRISTOL MANOR FARM	SOUTHERN D1 SOUTH	634
BRISTOL TELEPHONES	WESTERN LEAGUE DIVISION ONE	838
BRITISH AIRWAYS	COMBINED COUNTIES DIVISION ONE	657
BRIXHAM AFC	SOUTH WEST PENINSULA PREMIER EAST	753
BROADBRIDGE HEATH	SOUTHERN COMBINATION PREMIER	763
BROADFIELDS UNITED	SPARTAN SOUTH MIDLANDS PREMIER	787
BROCKENHURST	WESSEX PREMIER	819
BROCTON	NORTH WEST COUNTIES DIVISION 1S	721
BROMLEY	NATIONAL LEAGUE	482
BROMSGROVE SPORTING	SOUTHERN PREMIER CENTRAL	602
BUCKHURST HILL	EASTERN COUNTIES DIVISION ONE SOUTH	674
BUCKINGHAM ATHELTIC	SPARTAN SOUTH MIDLANDS DIVISION ONE	794
BUCKLAND ATHLETIC	WESTERN LEAGUE PREMIER	831
BUGBROOKE ST MICHAELS	UNITED COUNTIES PREMIER SOUTH	806
BURGESS HILL TOWN	ISTHMIAN SOUTH EAST	547
BURNHAM	COMBINED COUNTIES PREMIER NORTH	644
BURNHAM RAMBLERS	EASTERN COUNTIES DIVISION ONE SOUTH	674
BURSCOUGH	NORTH WEST COUNTIES PREMIER	710
BURTON PARK WANDERERS	SPARTAN SOUTH MIDLANDS DIVISION ONE	794
BURY AFC	NORTH WEST COUNTIES DIVISION 1N	717
BURY TOWN	ISTHMIAN NORTH	527
BUXTON	NPL PREMIER DIVISION	558
CADBURY HEATH	WESTERN LEAGUE PREMIER	831
CALLINGTON TOWN	SOUTH WEST PENINSULA PREMIER WEST	758
CALNE TOWN	HELLENIC PREMIER	686
CAMBERLEY TOWN	COMBINED COUNTIES PREMIER SOUTH	650
CAMBRIDGE CITY	NPL MIDLANDS	580
CAMELFORD	SOUTH WEST PENINSULA PREMIER WEST	758

Cathedral End Bury Town. Photo Keith Clayton.

Cleethorpes Town 2020. Photo Bill Wheatcroft.

CAMMELL LAIRD 1907	NORTH WEST COUNTIES DIVISION 1S	721
CAMPION	NORTH WEST COUNTIES DIVISION 1N	717
CANTERBURY CITY	SOUTHERN COUNTIES EAST PREMIER	775
CANVEY ISLAND	ISTHMIAN NORTH	527
CARLISLE CITY	NORTHERN LEAGUE DIVISION TWO	747
CARLTON TOWN	NPL MIDLANDS	580
CARSHALTON ATHLETIC	ISTHMIAN PREMIER	516
CB HOUNSLOW UNITED	COMBINED COUNTIES PREMIER NORTH	644
CHADDERTON	NORTH WEST COUNTIES DIVISION 1N	717
CHALFONT ST PETER	ISTHMIAN SOUTH CENTRAL	537
CHALVEY SPORTS	COMBINED COUNTIES DIVISION ONE	657
CHARNOCK RICHARD	NORTH WEST COUNTIES PREMIER	710
CHASETOWN	NPL MIDLANDS	580
CHATHAM TOWN	SOUTHERN COUNTIES EAST PREMIER	775
CHEADLE HEATH NOMADS	NORTH WEST COUNTIES DIVISION 1S	721
CHEADLE TOWN	NORTH WEST COUNTIES DIVISION 1S	721
CHEDDAR	WESTERN LEAGUE DIVISION ONE	838
CHELMSFORD CITY	NATIONAL SOUTH	505
CHELMSLEY TOWN	MIDLAND FOOTBALL LEAGUE DIVISION ONE	705
CHELTENHAM SARACENS	HELLENIC DIVISION ONE	693
CHERTSEY TOWN	ISTHMIAN SOUTH CENTRAL	537
CHESHAM UNITED	SOUTHERN PREMIER SOUTH	613
CHESHUNT	ISTHMIAN PREMIER	516
CHESSINGTON & HOOK UNITED	SOUTHERN COUNTIES EAST DIVISION ONE	782
CHESTER	NATIONAL NORTH	494
CHESTER-LE-STREET TOWN	NORTHERN LEAGUE DIVISION TWO	747
CHESTERFIELD	NATIONAL LEAGUE	482
CHICHESTER CITY	ISTHMIAN SOUTH EAST	547
CHIPPENHAM TOWN	NATIONAL SOUTH	505
CHIPPING SODBURY TOWN	HELLENIC PREMIER	686
CHIPSTEAD	ISTHMIAN SOUTH CENTRAL	537
CHORLEY	NATIONAL NORTH	494
CHRISTCHURCH	WESSEX PREMIER	819
CINDERFORD TOWN	SOUTHERN D1 SOUTH	634
CIRENCESTER TOWN	SOUTHERN D1 SOUTH	634
CIRENCESTER TOWN DEV.	HELLENIC DIVISION ONE	693
CITY OF LIVERPOOL	NPL WEST	590
CLANFIELD 85	HELLENIC DIVISION ONE	693
CLAPTON	ESSEX SENIOR	679
CLEATOR MOOR CELTIC	NORTH WEST COUNTIES DIVISION 1N	717
CLEETHORPES TOWN	NPL EAST	570
CLEVEDON TOWN	WESTERN LEAGUE PREMIER	831
CLIFTON ALL WHITES	UNITED COUNTIES DIVISION ONE	815
CLIPSTONE	NORTHERN COUNTIES EAST DIVISION ONE	734
CLITHEROE	NPL WEST	590
COALVILLE TOWN	SOUTHERN PREMIER CENTRAL	602
COBHAM	COMBINED COUNTIES PREMIER SOUTH	650
COCKFOSTERS	ESSEX SENIOR	679
COGENHOE UNITED	UNITED COUNTIES PREMIER SOUTH	806

Eastwood Community 2020-21. Photos Bill Wheatcroft.

COGGESHALL TOWN	ISTHMIAN NORTH	527
COGGESHALL UNITED	EASTERN COUNTIES DIVISION ONE SOUTH	674
COLESHILL TOWN	NPL MIDLANDS	580
COLLIERS WOOD UNITED	COMBINED COUNTIES PREMIER SOUTH	650
COLNE	NPL WEST	590
COLNEY HEATH	SOUTHERN D1 CENTRAL	624
CONCORD RANGERS	NATIONAL SOUTH	505
CONGLETON TOWN	NORTH WEST COUNTIES PREMIER	710
CONSETT	NORTHERN LEAGUE DIVISION ONE	740
CORBY TOWN	NPL MIDLANDS	580
CORINTHIAN	ISTHMIAN SOUTH EAST	547
CORINTHIAN-CASUALS	ISTHMIAN PREMIER	516
CORNARD UNITED	EASTERN COUNTIES DIVISION ONE SOUTH	674
CORSHAM TOWN	HELLENIC PREMIER	686
COVE	COMBINED COUNTIES DIVISION ONE	657
COVENTRY COPSEWOOD	MIDLAND FOOTBALL LEAGUE DIVISION ONE	705
COVENTRY SPHINX	UNITED COUNTIES PREMIER SOUTH	806
COVENTRY UNITED	UNITED COUNTIES PREMIER SOUTH	806
COWES SPORTS	WESSEX PREMIER	819
CRADLEY TOWN	MIDLAND FOOTBALL LEAGUE DIVISION ONE	705
CRAWLEY DOWN GATWICK	SOUTHERN COMBINATION PREMIER	763
CRAWLEY GREEN	SPARTAN SOUTH MIDLANDS PREMIER	787
CRAY VALLEY PAPER MILLS	ISTHMIAN SOUTH EAST	547
CRAY WANDERERS	ISTHMIAN PREMIER	516
CREDITON UNITED	SOUTH WEST PENINSULA PREMIER EAST	753
CRIBBS	HELLENIC PREMIER	686
CROOK TOWN	NORTHERN LEAGUE DIVISION ONE	740
CROWBOROUGH ATHLETIC	SOUTHERN COUNTIES EAST PREMIER	775
CROYDON	SOUTHERN COUNTIES EAST DIVISION ONE	782
CULLOMPTON RANGERS	SOUTH WEST PENINSULA PREMIER EAST	753
CURZON ASHTON	NATIONAL NORTH	494
DAGENHAM & REDBRIDGE	NATIONAL LEAGUE	482
DAISY HILL	NORTH WEST COUNTIES DIVISION 1N	717
DARLASTON TOWN (1874)	MIDLAND FOOTBALL LEAGUE DIVISION ONE	705
DARLINGTON 1883	NATIONAL NORTH	494
DARTFORD	NATIONAL SOUTH	505
DARTMOUTH AFC	SOUTH WEST PENINSULA PREMIER EAST	753
DAVENTRY TOWN	NPL MIDLANDS	580
DEAL TOWN	SOUTHERN COUNTIES EAST PREMIER	775
DEBENHAM LC	EASTERN COUNTIES DIVISION ONE NORTH	670
DEEPING RANGERS	UNITED COUNTIES PREMIER NORTH	799
DEREHAM TOWN	ISTHMIAN NORTH	527
DESBOROUGH TOWN	UNITED COUNTIES PREMIER SOUTH	806
DEVIZES TOWN	WESTERN LEAGUE DIVISION ONE	838
DIDCOT TOWN	SOUTHERN D1 CENTRAL	624
DISS TOWN	EASTERN COUNTIES DIVISION ONE NORTH	670
DOBWALLS	SOUTH WEST PENINSULA PREMIER WEST	758
DORCHESTER TOWN	SOUTHERN PREMIER SOUTH	613
DORKING WANDERERS	NATIONAL SOUTH	505

Gainsborough Trinity 2020. Photo Bill Wheatcroft.

DORKING WANDERERS RESERVES	SOUTHERN COMBINATION DIVISION ONE	770
DOVER ATHLETIC	NATIONAL LEAGUE	482
DOWNHAM TOWN	EASTERN COUNTIES DIVISION ONE NORTH	670
DOWNTON	WESSEX DIVISION ONE	826
DRONFIELD TOWN	NORTHERN COUNTIES EAST DIVISION ONE	734
DUDLEY SPORTS	MIDLAND FOOTBALL LEAGUE DIVISION ONE	705
DUDLEY TOWN	MIDLAND FOOTBALL LEAGUE DIVISION ONE	705
DULWICH HAMLET	NATIONAL SOUTH	505
DUNKIRK	UNITED COUNTIES DIVISION ONE	815
DUNSTABLE TOWN	SPARTAN SOUTH MIDLANDS PREMIER	787
DUNSTON	NPL EAST	570
DURHAM CITY	NORTHERN LEAGUE DIVISION TWO	747
EASINGTON COLLIERY	NORTHERN LEAGUE DIVISION TWO	747
EASINGTON SPORTS	UNITED COUNTIES PREMIER SOUTH	806
EAST COWES VICTORIA ATHLETIC	WESSEX DIVISION ONE	826
EAST GRINSTEAD TOWN	ISTHMIAN SOUTH EAST	547
EAST PRESTON	SOUTHERN COMBINATION PREMIER	763
EAST THURROCK UNITED	ISTHMIAN PREMIER	516
EASTBOURNE BOROUGH	NATIONAL SOUTH	505
EASTBOURNE TOWN	SOUTHERN COMBINATION PREMIER	763
EASTBOURNE UNITED ASSOCIATION	SOUTHERN COMBINATION PREMIER	763
EASTLEIGH	NATIONAL LEAGUE	482
EASTWOOD COMMUNITY	UNITED COUNTIES PREMIER NORTH	799
EBBSFLEET UNITED	NATIONAL SOUTH	505
ECCLESHALL	NORTH WEST COUNTIES DIVISION 1S	721
ECCLESHILL UNITED	NORTHERN COUNTIES EAST PREMIER	727
EDGWARE TOWN	COMBINED COUNTIES PREMIER NORTH	644
EGHAM TOWN	COMBINED COUNTIES PREMIER NORTH	644
ELBURTON VILLA	SOUTH WEST PENINSULA PREMIER EAST	753
ELLESMERE RANGERS	NORTH WEST COUNTIES DIVISION 1S	721
ELMORE	SOUTH WEST PENINSULA PREMIER EAST	753
ELY CITY	EASTERN COUNTIES PREMIER	663
EMLEY AFC	NORTHERN COUNTIES EAST PREMIER	727
ENFIELD 1893 FC	ESSEX SENIOR	679
ENFIELD BOROUGH	COMBINED COUNTIES DIVISION ONE	657
ENFIELD TOWN	ISTHMIAN PREMIER	516
EPSOM & EWELL	SOUTHERN COMBINATION DIVISION ONE	770
ERITH & BELVEDERE	SOUTHERN COUNTIES EAST PREMIER	775
ERITH TOWN	SOUTHERN COUNTIES EAST PREMIER	775
ESH WINNING	NORTHERN LEAGUE DIVISION TWO	747
EVERSLEY & CALIFORNIA	COMBINED COUNTIES DIVISION ONE	657
EVESHAM UNITED	SOUTHERN D1 SOUTH	634
EXMOUTH TOWN	WESTERN LEAGUE PREMIER	831
EYNESBURY ROVERS	UNITED COUNTIES PREMIER SOUTH	806
FAIRFORD TOWN	HELLENIC PREMIER	686
FAKENHAM TOWN	EASTERN COUNTIES PREMIER	663
FALMOUTH TOWN	SOUTH WEST PENINSULA PREMIER WEST	758
FAREHAM TOWN	WESSEX PREMIER	819

Main Stand Irlam. Photo Keith Clayton.

Leighton Town 20-21.. Photos Bill Wheatcroft.

FARNBOROUGH	SOUTHERN PREMIER SOUTH	613
FARNHAM TOWN	COMBINED COUNTIES PREMIER SOUTH	650
FARSLEY CELTIC	NATIONAL NORTH	494
FAVERSHAM STRIKE FORCE	SOUTHERN COUNTIES EAST DIVISION ONE	782
FAVERSHAM TOWN	ISTHMIAN SOUTH EAST	547
FAWLEY AFC	WESSEX DIVISION ONE	826
FC CLACTON	ESSEX SENIOR	679
FC DEPORTIVO GALICIA	COMBINED COUNTIES DIVISION ONE	657
FC ELMSTEAD	SOUTHERN COUNTIES EAST DIVISION ONE	782
FC HALIFAX TOWN	NATIONAL LEAGUE	482
FC HUMBER UNITED	NORTHERN COUNTIES EAST DIVISION ONE	734
FC ISLE OF MAN	NORTH WEST COUNTIES DIVISION 1S	721
FC PARSON DROVE	EASTERN COUNTIES DIVISION ONE NORTH	670
FC ROMANIA	SOUTHERN D1 CENTRAL	624
FC STRATFORD	HELLENIC DIVISION ONE	693
FC UNITED OF MANCHESTER	NPL PREMIER DIVISION	558
FELIXSTOWE & WALTON UNITED	ISTHMIAN NORTH	527
FISHER	SOUTHERN COUNTIES EAST PREMIER	775
FLACKWELL HEATH	SPARTAN SOUTH MIDLANDS PREMIER	787
FLEET SPURS	WESSEX DIVISION ONE	826
FLEET TOWN	COMBINED COUNTIES PREMIER SOUTH	650
FOLKESTONE INVICTA	ISTHMIAN PREMIER	516
FOLLAND SPORTS	WESSEX DIVISION ONE	826
FOREST HILL PARK	SOUTHERN COUNTIES EAST DIVISION ONE	782
FOREST ROW	SOUTHERN COMBINATION DIVISION ONE	770
FRAMLINGHAM TOWN	EASTERN COUNTIES DIVISION ONE NORTH	670
FRENFORD	EASTERN COUNTIES DIVISION ONE SOUTH	674
FRICKLEY ATHLETIC	NPL EAST	570
FRIMLEY GREEN	COMBINED COUNTIES PREMIER SOUTH	650
FROME TOWN	SOUTHERN D1 SOUTH	634
GAINSBOROUGH TRINITY	NPL PREMIER DIVISION	558
GARFORTH TOWN	NORTHERN COUNTIES EAST PREMIER	727
GARSTANG	NORTH WEST COUNTIES DIVISION 1N	717
GATESHEAD	NATIONAL NORTH	494
GEDLING MINERS WELFARE	UNITED COUNTIES DIVISION ONE	815
GILLINGHAM TOWN	WESTERN LEAGUE DIVISION ONE	838
GLASSHOUGHTON WELFARE	NORTHERN COUNTIES EAST DIVISION ONE	734
GLEBE	SOUTHERN COUNTIES EAST PREMIER	775
GLOSSOP NORTH END	NPL WEST	590
GLOUCESTER CITY	NATIONAL NORTH	494
GNG OADBY TOWN	UNITED COUNTIES PREMIER SOUTH	806
GODALMING TOWN	SOUTHERN COMBINATION DIVISION ONE	770
GODMANCHESTER ROVERS	UNITED COUNTIES PREMIER SOUTH	806
GODOLPHIN ATLANTIC (NEWQUAY)	SOUTH WEST PENINSULA PREMIER WEST	758
GOLCAR UNITED	NORTH WEST COUNTIES DIVISION 1N	717
GOOLE AFC	NORTHERN COUNTIES EAST PREMIER	727
GORLESTON	EASTERN COUNTIES PREMIER	663
GOSPORT BOROUGH	SOUTHERN PREMIER SOUTH	613
GRAHAM STREET PRIMS	UNITED COUNTIES DIVISION ONE	815

Loughborough University 2020. Photos Bill Wheatcroft.

GRANTHAM TOWN	NPL PREMIER DIVISION	558
GRAYS ATHLETIC	ISTHMIAN NORTH	527
GREAT WAKERING ROVERS	ISTHMIAN NORTH	527
GREAT YARMOUTH TOWN	EASTERN COUNTIES DIVISION ONE NORTH	670
GREENWAYS	SOUTHERN COUNTIES EAST DIVISION ONE	782
GRESLEY	UNITED COUNTIES PREMIER NORTH	799
GRIMSBY BOROUGH	NORTHERN COUNTIES EAST PREMIER	727
GRIMSBY TOWN	NATIONAL LEAGUE	482
GUERNSEY	ISTHMIAN SOUTH CENTRAL	537
GUILDFORD CITY	COMBINED COUNTIES PREMIER SOUTH	650
GUISBOROUGH TOWN	NORTHERN LEAGUE DIVISION ONE	740
GUISELEY	NATIONAL NORTH	494
HACKNEY WICK	EASTERN COUNTIES DIVISION ONE SOUTH	674
HADLEIGH UNITED	EASTERN COUNTIES PREMIER	663
HADLEY	SPARTAN SOUTH MIDLANDS PREMIER	787
HAILSHAM TOWN	SOUTHERN COMBINATION DIVISION ONE	770
HALESOWEN TOWN	NPL MIDLANDS	580
HALL ROAD RANGERS	NORTHERN COUNTIES EAST DIVISION ONE	734
HALLAM	NORTHERN COUNTIES EAST DIVISION ONE	734
HALLEN	HELLENIC PREMIER	686
HALSTEAD TOWN	EASTERN COUNTIES DIVISION ONE SOUTH	674
HAMBLE CLUB	WESSEX PREMIER	819
HAMPTON & RICHMOND BOROUGH	NATIONAL SOUTH	505
HAMWORTHY UNITED	WESSEX PREMIER	819
HANDSWORTH	NORTHERN COUNTIES EAST PREMIER	727
HANLEY TOWN	MIDLAND FOOTBALL LEAGUE PREMIER	698
HANWELL TOWN	ISTHMIAN SOUTH CENTRAL	537
HANWORTH VILLA	COMBINED COUNTIES PREMIER NORTH	644
HARBOROUGH TOWN	UNITED COUNTIES PREMIER SOUTH	806
HAREFIELD UNITED	SPARTAN SOUTH MIDLANDS PREMIER	787
HARINGEY BOROUGH	ISTHMIAN PREMIER	516
HARLESTON TOWN	EASTERN COUNTIES DIVISION ONE NORTH	670
HARLOW TOWN	SOUTHERN D1 CENTRAL	624
HARPENDEN TOWN	SPARTAN SOUTH MIDLANDS PREMIER	787
HARROGATE RAILWAY ATHLETIC	NORTHERN COUNTIES EAST DIVISION ONE	734
HARROW BOROUGH	SOUTHERN PREMIER SOUTH	613
HARROWBY UNITED	UNITED COUNTIES DIVISION ONE	815
HARTLEY WINTNEY	SOUTHERN PREMIER SOUTH	613
HARWICH & PARKESTON	EASTERN COUNTIES DIVISION ONE SOUTH	674
HASHTAG UNITED	ISTHMIAN NORTH	527
HASSOCKS	SOUTHERN COMBINATION PREMIER	763
HASTINGS UNITED	ISTHMIAN SOUTH EAST	547
HAUGHMOND	MIDLAND FOOTBALL LEAGUE PREMIER	698
HAVANT AND WATERLOOVILLE	NATIONAL SOUTH	505
HAVERHILL BOROUGH	EASTERN COUNTIES DIVISION ONE SOUTH	674
HAVERHILL ROVERS	EASTERN COUNTIES PREMIER	663
HAYES & YEADING UNITED	SOUTHERN PREMIER SOUTH	613
HAYWARDS HEATH TOWN	ISTHMIAN SOUTH EAST	547
HEANOR TOWN	UNITED COUNTIES PREMIER NORTH	799

Melton Town FC. Photo Keith Clayton.

Main Stand Nantwich Town. Photo Keith Clayton.

HEATH HAYES	MIDLAND FOOTBALL LEAGUE DIVISION ONE	705
HEATHER ST. JOHN'S	UNITED COUNTIES PREMIER NORTH	799
HEATON STANNINGTON	NORTHERN LEAGUE DIVISION TWO	747
HEBBURN TOWN	NPL EAST	570
HEDNESFORD TOWN	SOUTHERN PREMIER CENTRAL	602
HELSTON ATHLETIC	WESTERN LEAGUE PREMIER	831
HEMEL HEMPSTEAD TOWN	NATIONAL SOUTH	505
HEMSWORTH MINERS WELFARE	NORTHERN COUNTIES EAST PREMIER	727
HENDON	SOUTHERN PREMIER SOUTH	613
HENGROVE ATHLETIC	WESTERN LEAGUE DIVISION ONE	838
HEREFORD	NATIONAL NORTH	494
HEREFORD LADS CLUB	HELLENIC PREMIER	686
HEREFORD PEGASUS	HELLENIC DIVISION ONE	693
HERNE BAY	ISTHMIAN SOUTH EAST	547
HERTFORD TOWN	SOUTHERN D1 CENTRAL	624
HEYBRIDGE SWIFTS	ISTHMIAN NORTH	527
HIGHGATE UNITED	MIDLAND FOOTBALL LEAGUE PREMIER	698
HIGHWORTH TOWN	SOUTHERN D1 SOUTH	634
HILLINGDON BOROUGH	COMBINED COUNTIES DIVISION ONE	657
HILLTOP	COMBINED COUNTIES DIVISION ONE	657
HINCKLEY AFC	UNITED COUNTIES DIVISION ONE	815
HISTON	NPL MIDLANDS	580
HITCHIN TOWN	SOUTHERN PREMIER CENTRAL	602
HODDESDON TOWN	ESSEX SENIOR	679
HOLBEACH UNITED	UNITED COUNTIES PREMIER NORTH	799
HOLKER OLD BOYS	NORTH WEST COUNTIES DIVISION 1N	717
HOLLAND	EASTERN COUNTIES DIVISION ONE SOUTH	674
HOLLANDS & BLAIR	SOUTHERN COUNTIES EAST PREMIER	775
HOLMER GREEN	SPARTAN SOUTH MIDLANDS PREMIER	787
HOLMESDALE	SOUTHERN COUNTIES EAST PREMIER	775
HOLSWORTHY AFC	SOUTH WEST PENINSULA PREMIER EAST	753
HOLWELL SPORTS	UNITED COUNTIES DIVISION ONE	815
HOLYPORT	COMBINED COUNTIES PREMIER NORTH	644
HONITON TOWN	SOUTH WEST PENINSULA PREMIER EAST	753
HORDEN COMMUNITY WELFARE	NORTHERN LEAGUE DIVISION TWO	747
HORLEY TOWN	COMBINED COUNTIES PREMIER SOUTH	650
HORNCHURCH	ISTHMIAN PREMIER	516
HORNDEAN	WESSEX PREMIER	819
HORSHAM	ISTHMIAN PREMIER	516
HORSHAM YMCA	SOUTHERN COMBINATION PREMIER	763
HUCKNALL TOWN	UNITED COUNTIES DIVISION ONE	815
HULLBRIDGE SPORTS	ISTHMIAN NORTH	527
HUNGERFORD TOWN	NATIONAL SOUTH	505
HUNTINGDON TOWN	EASTERN COUNTIES DIVISION ONE NORTH	670
HYDE UNITED	NPL PREMIER DIVISION	558
HYTHE & DIBDEN	WESSEX PREMIER	819
HYTHE TOWN	ISTHMIAN SOUTH EAST	547
ILFORD	ESSEX SENIOR	679
ILFRACOMBE TOWN	WESTERN LEAGUE PREMIER	831

North Ferriby 20-21. . Photos Bill Wheatcroft.

ILKESTON TOWN	NPL MIDLANDS	580
ILKLEY TOWN	NORTH WEST COUNTIES DIVISION 1N	717
INFINITY	WESSEX DIVISION ONE	826
INGLES	UNITED COUNTIES DIVISION ONE	815
IPSWICH WANDERERS	EASTERN COUNTIES DIVISION ONE SOUTH	674
IRCHESTER UNITED	SPARTAN SOUTH MIDLANDS DIVISION ONE	794
IRLAM	NORTH WEST COUNTIES PREMIER	710
IVYBRIDGE TOWN	SOUTH WEST PENINSULA PREMIER EAST	753
JARROW	NORTHERN LEAGUE DIVISION TWO	747
JERSEY BULLS	COMBINED COUNTIES PREMIER SOUTH	650
K SPORTS	SOUTHERN COUNTIES EAST PREMIER	775
KEMPSTON ROVERS	SOUTHERN D1 CENTRAL	624
KENDAL TOWN	NPL WEST	590
KENNINGTON	SOUTHERN COUNTIES EAST PREMIER	775
KENSINGTON & EALING BOROUGH	COMBINED COUNTIES DIVISION ONE	657
KENT FOOTBALL UNITED	SOUTHERN COUNTIES EAST DIVISION ONE	782
KETTERING TOWN	NATIONAL NORTH	494
KEYNSHAM TOWN	WESTERN LEAGUE PREMIER	831
KHALSA FOOTBALL FEDERATION	MIDLAND FOOTBALL LEAGUE DIVISION ONE	705
KIDDERMINSTER HARRIERS	NATIONAL NORTH	494
KIDLINGTON	SOUTHERN D1 CENTRAL	624
KIDLINGTON RESERVES	SPARTAN SOUTH MIDLANDS DIVISION ONE	794
KIDSGROVE ATHLETIC	NPL WEST	590
KIMBERLEY MINERS WELFARE	UNITED COUNTIES DIVISION ONE	815
KING'S LANGLEY	SOUTHERN PREMIER SOUTH	613
KING'S LYNN TOWN	NATIONAL LEAGUE	482
KINGSTONIAN	ISTHMIAN PREMIER	516
KIRBY MUXLOE	UNITED COUNTIES DIVISION ONE	815
KIRKLEY & PAKEFIELD	EASTERN COUNTIES PREMIER	663
KNAPHILL	COMBINED COUNTIES PREMIER SOUTH	650
KNARESBOROUGH TOWN	NORTHERN COUNTIES EAST PREMIER	727
LAKENHEATH	EASTERN COUNTIES PREMIER	663
LANCASTER CITY	NPL PREMIER DIVISION	558
LANCING	ISTHMIAN SOUTH EAST	547
LANGFORD	SPARTAN SOUTH MIDLANDS DIVISION ONE	794
LANGLEY	COMBINED COUNTIES DIVISION ONE	657
LARKFIELD & NEW HYTHE	SOUTHERN COUNTIES EAST DIVISION ONE	782
LARKHALL ATHLETIC	SOUTHERN D1 SOUTH	634
LAUNCESTON	SOUTH WEST PENINSULA PREMIER WEST	758
LAVERSTOCK & FORD	WESSEX DIVISION ONE	826
LEAMINGTON	NATIONAL NORTH	494
LEATHERHEAD	ISTHMIAN PREMIER	516
LEBEQ UNITED	WESTERN LEAGUE DIVISION ONE	838
LEEK TOWN	NPL WEST	590
LEICESTER NIRVANA	UNITED COUNTIES PREMIER NORTH	799
LEICESTER ROAD	UNITED COUNTIES PREMIER SOUTH	806
LEIGHTON TOWN	SPARTAN SOUTH MIDLANDS PREMIER	787
LEISTON	SOUTHERN PREMIER CENTRAL	602
LEISTON RESERVES	EASTERN COUNTIES DIVISION ONE NORTH	670

. Photos Bill Wheatcroft.

LETCHWORTH GARDEN CITY EAGLES	SPARTAN SOUTH MIDLANDS DIVISION ONE	794
LEVERSTOCK GREEN	SPARTAN SOUTH MIDLANDS PREMIER	787
LEWES	ISTHMIAN PREMIER	516
LEWISHAM BOROUGH	SOUTHERN COUNTIES EAST DIVISION ONE	782
LICHFIELD CITY	MIDLAND FOOTBALL LEAGUE PREMIER	698
LINCOLN UNITED	NPL EAST	570
LINGFIELD	SOUTHERN COMBINATION PREMIER	763
LISKEARD ATHLETIC	SOUTH WEST PENINSULA PREMIER WEST	758
LITHERLAND REMYCA	NORTH WEST COUNTIES PREMIER	710
LITTLE COMMON	SOUTHERN COMBINATION PREMIER	763
LITTLE OAKLEY	ESSEX SENIOR	679
LITTLEHAMPTON TOWN	SOUTHERN COMBINATION PREMIER	763
LITTLETON	HELLENIC DIVISION ONE	693
LIVERSEDGE	NPL EAST	570
LONDON COLNEY	SPARTAN SOUTH MIDLANDS PREMIER	787
LONDON LIONS	COMBINED COUNTIES DIVISION ONE	657
LONDON SAMURAI ROVERS	COMBINED COUNTIES DIVISION ONE	657
LONDON TIGERS	SPARTAN SOUTH MIDLANDS DIVISION ONE	794
LONG BUCKBY AFC	UNITED COUNTIES PREMIER SOUTH	806
LONG CRENDON	SPARTAN SOUTH MIDLANDS DIVISION ONE	794
LONG EATON UNITED	UNITED COUNTIES PREMIER NORTH	799
LONG MELFORD	EASTERN COUNTIES PREMIER	663
LONGLEVENS AFC	HELLENIC PREMIER	686
LONGRIDGE TOWN	NORTH WEST COUNTIES PREMIER	710
LONGWELL GREEN SPORTS	WESTERN LEAGUE DIVISION ONE	838
LORDSWOOD	SOUTHERN COUNTIES EAST PREMIER	775
LOUGHBOROUGH DYNAMO	NPL MIDLANDS	580
LOUGHBOROUGH STUDENTS	UNITED COUNTIES PREMIER NORTH	799
LOWER BRECK	NORTH WEST COUNTIES PREMIER	710
LOWESTOFT TOWN	SOUTHERN PREMIER CENTRAL	602
LOXWOOD	SOUTHERN COMBINATION PREMIER	763
LUTTERWORTH ATHLETIC	UNITED COUNTIES DIVISION ONE	815
LUTTERWORTH TOWN	UNITED COUNTIES PREMIER SOUTH	806
LYDD TOWN	SOUTHERN COUNTIES EAST DIVISION ONE	782
LYDNEY TOWN	HELLENIC PREMIER	686
LYE TOWN	MIDLAND FOOTBALL LEAGUE PREMIER	698
LYMINGTON TOWN	SOUTHERN D1 SOUTH	634
MACCLESFIELD FC	NORTH WEST COUNTIES PREMIER	710
MAIDENHEAD UNITED	NATIONAL LEAGUE	482
MAIDSTONE UNITED	NATIONAL SOUTH	505
MAINE ROAD	NORTH WEST COUNTIES DIVISION 1S	721
MALDON & TIPTREE	ISTHMIAN NORTH	527
MALMESBURY VICTORIA	HELLENIC DIVISION ONE	693
MALTBY MAIN	NORTHERN COUNTIES EAST PREMIER	727
MALVERN TOWN	HELLENIC PREMIER	686
MANGOTSFIELD UNITED	SOUTHERN D1 SOUTH	634
MARCH TOWN UNITED	EASTERN COUNTIES PREMIER	663
MARGATE	ISTHMIAN PREMIER	516
MARINE	NPL WEST	590

Rowsley FC. Photo Bill Wheatcroft.

Selston 2020. Photos Bill Wheatcroft.

MARKET DRAYTON TOWN	NPL WEST	590
MARLOW	ISTHMIAN SOUTH CENTRAL	537
MARSKE UNITED	NPL EAST	570
MATLOCK TOWN	NPL PREMIER DIVISION	558
MAY & BAKER E.C.	EASTERN COUNTIES DIVISION ONE SOUTH	674
MELKSHAM TOWN	SOUTHERN D1 SOUTH	634
MELTON TOWN	UNITED COUNTIES PREMIER NORTH	799
MERIDIAN VP	SOUTHERN COUNTIES EAST DIVISION ONE	782
MERSTHAM	ISTHMIAN PREMIER	516
MERTHYR TOWN	SOUTHERN PREMIER SOUTH	613
METROPOLITAN POLICE	SOUTHERN PREMIER SOUTH	613
MICKLEOVER	NPL PREMIER DIVISION	558
MIDHURST & EASEBOURNE	SOUTHERN COMBINATION DIVISION ONE	770
MILDENHALL TOWN	EASTERN COUNTIES PREMIER	663
MILE OAK	SOUTHERN COMBINATION DIVISION ONE	770
MILLBROOK	WESSEX DIVISION ONE	826
MILLBROOK AFC	WESTERN LEAGUE PREMIER	831
MILTON KEYNES IRISH	SPARTAN SOUTH MIDLANDS PREMIER	787
MILTON UNITED	HELLENIC DIVISION ONE	693
MOLESEY	COMBINED COUNTIES PREMIER SOUTH	650
MONEYFIELDS	WESSEX PREMIER	819
MONTPELIER VILLA	SOUTHERN COMBINATION DIVISION ONE	770
MORETON RANGERS	HELLENIC DIVISION ONE	693
MORPETH TOWN	NPL PREMIER DIVISION	558
MOSSLEY	NPL WEST	590
MOUSEHOLE	WESTERN LEAGUE PREMIER	831
MULBARTON WANDERERS	EASTERN COUNTIES PREMIER	663
NANTWICH TOWN	NPL PREMIER DIVISION	558
NEEDHAM MARKET	SOUTHERN PREMIER CENTRAL	602
NEEDHAM MARKET RESERVES	EASTERN COUNTIES DIVISION ONE NORTH	670
NELSON	NORTH WEST COUNTIES DIVISION 1N	717
NEW MILLS	NORTH WEST COUNTIES DIVISION 1S	721
NEW MILTON TOWN	WESSEX DIVISION ONE	826
NEW SALAMIS	SPARTAN SOUTH MIDLANDS PREMIER	787
NEWARK	UNITED COUNTIES PREMIER NORTH	799
NEWBURY FOREST	EASTERN COUNTIES DIVISION ONE SOUTH	674
NEWCASTLE BENFIELD	NORTHERN LEAGUE DIVISION ONE	740
NEWCASTLE TOWN	NPL WEST	590
NEWCASTLE UNIVERSITY	NORTHERN LEAGUE DIVISION TWO	747
NEWENT TOWN AFC	HELLENIC DIVISION ONE	693
NEWHAVEN	SOUTHERN COMBINATION PREMIER	763
NEWMARKET TOWN	EASTERN COUNTIES PREMIER	663
NEWPORT (I.O.W.)	WESSEX DIVISION ONE	826
NEWPORT PAGNELL TOWN	UNITED COUNTIES PREMIER SOUTH	806
NEWQUAY	SOUTH WEST PENINSULA PREMIER WEST	758
NEWTON ABBOT SPURS	SOUTH WEST PENINSULA PREMIER EAST	753
NEWTON AYCLIFFE	NORTHERN LEAGUE DIVISION ONE	740
NORTH FERRIBY	NORTHERN COUNTIES EAST DIVISION ONE	734
NORTH GREENFORD UNITED	COMBINED COUNTIES PREMIER NORTH	644

Stafford Town 2020-21. Photo Bill Wheatcroft.

Teversal 2020-21. Photos Bill Wheatcroft.

NORTH LEIGH	SOUTHERN D1 CENTRAL	624
NORTH SHIELDS	NORTHERN LEAGUE DIVISION ONE	740
NORTHALLERTON TOWN	NORTHERN LEAGUE DIVISION ONE	740
NORTHAMPTON O.N.C.	UNITED COUNTIES PREMIER SOUTH	806
NORTHAMPTON SILEBY RANGERS	SPARTAN SOUTH MIDLANDS DIVISION ONE	794
NORTHWICH VICTORIA	NORTH WEST COUNTIES PREMIER	710
NORTHWOOD	ISTHMIAN SOUTH CENTRAL	537
NORWICH CBS	EASTERN COUNTIES DIVISION ONE NORTH	670
NORWICH UNITED	EASTERN COUNTIES PREMIER	663
NOSTELL MINERS WELFARE	NORTHERN COUNTIES EAST DIVISION ONE	734
NOTTS COUNTY	NATIONAL LEAGUE	482
NUNEATON BOROUGH	SOUTHERN PREMIER CENTRAL	602
NUNEATON GRIFF	MIDLAND FOOTBALL LEAGUE DIVISION ONE	705
OAKWOOD	SOUTHERN COMBINATION DIVISION ONE	770
ODD DOWN	WESTERN LEAGUE DIVISION ONE	838
OJM BLACK COUNTRY RANGERS	MIDLAND FOOTBALL LEAGUE DIVISION ONE	705
OKEHAMPTON ARGYLE	SOUTH WEST PENINSULA PREMIER EAST	753
OLDLAND ABBOTONIANS	WESTERN LEAGUE DIVISION ONE	838
OLLERTON TOWN	NORTHERN COUNTIES EAST DIVISION ONE	734
OSSETT UNITED	NPL EAST	570
OTTERY ST MARY	SOUTH WEST PENINSULA PREMIER EAST	753
OXFORD CITY	NATIONAL SOUTH	505
OXHEY JETS	SPARTAN SOUTH MIDLANDS PREMIER	787
PADIHAM	NORTH WEST COUNTIES PREMIER	710
PAGET RANGERS	MIDLAND FOOTBALL LEAGUE DIVISION ONE	705
PAGHAM	SOUTHERN COMBINATION PREMIER	763
PARK VIEW	EASTERN COUNTIES DIVISION ONE SOUTH	674
PARKGATE	NORTHERN COUNTIES EAST DIVISION ONE	734
PAULTON ROVERS	SOUTHERN D1 SOUTH	634
PEACEHAVEN & TELSCOMBE	SOUTHERN COMBINATION PREMIER	763
PENISTONE CHURCH	NORTHERN COUNTIES EAST PREMIER	727
PENN & TYLERS GREEN	SPARTAN SOUTH MIDLANDS DIVISION ONE	794
PENRITH	NORTHERN LEAGUE DIVISION ONE	740
PENRYN ATHLETIC	SOUTH WEST PENINSULA PREMIER WEST	758
PENZANCE	SOUTH WEST PENINSULA PREMIER WEST	758
PERSHORE TOWN	HELLENIC DIVISION ONE	693
PETERBOROUGH NORTH END SPORTS	EASTERN COUNTIES DIVISION ONE NORTH	670
PETERBOROUGH NORTHERN STAR	UNITED COUNTIES PREMIER SOUTH	806
PETERBOROUGH SPORTS	SOUTHERN PREMIER CENTRAL	602
PETERSFIELD TOWN	WESSEX DIVISION ONE	826
PHOENIX SPORTS	ISTHMIAN SOUTH EAST	547
PICKERING TOWN	NPL EAST	570
PILKINGTON	NORTH WEST COUNTIES DIVISION 1N	717
PINCHBECK UNITED	UNITED COUNTIES PREMIER NORTH	799
PLYMOUTH MAJON	SOUTH WEST PENINSULA PREMIER EAST	753
PLYMOUTH PARKWAY AFC	SOUTHERN D1 SOUTH	634
PONTEFRACT COLLIERIES	NPL EAST	570
POOLE TOWN	SOUTHERN PREMIER SOUTH	613
PORTHLEVEN	SOUTH WEST PENINSULA PREMIER WEST	758

Walsall Wood 20-21. Photos Bill Wheatcroft.

PORTISHEAD TOWN	WESTERN LEAGUE DIVISION ONE	838
PORTLAND UNITED	WESSEX PREMIER	819
POTTERS BAR TOWN	ISTHMIAN PREMIER	516
POTTON UNITED	UNITED COUNTIES PREMIER SOUTH	806
PRESCOT CABLES	NPL WEST	590
PRESTWICH HEYS	NORTH WEST COUNTIES PREMIER	710
PUNJAB UNITED	SOUTHERN COUNTIES EAST PREMIER	775
QUORN	UNITED COUNTIES PREMIER NORTH	799
RACING CLUB WARWICK	MIDLAND FOOTBALL LEAGUE PREMIER	698
RADCLIFFE	NPL PREMIER DIVISION	558
RADFORD	UNITED COUNTIES DIVISION ONE	815
RADSTOCK TOWN	WESTERN LEAGUE DIVISION ONE	838
RAINWORTH MINERS WELFARE	NORTHERN COUNTIES EAST DIVISION ONE	734
RAMSBOTTOM UNITED	NPL WEST	590
RAMSGATE	ISTHMIAN SOUTH EAST	547
RAUNDS TOWN	SPARTAN SOUTH MIDLANDS DIVISION ONE	794
RAYNERS LANE	COMBINED COUNTIES DIVISION ONE	657
RAYNES PARK VALE	COMBINED COUNTIES PREMIER SOUTH	650
READING CITY	COMBINED COUNTIES PREMIER NORTH	644
REDBRIDGE	ESSEX SENIOR	679
REDCAR ATHLETIC	NORTHERN LEAGUE DIVISION ONE	740
REDCAR TOWN	NORTHERN LEAGUE DIVISION TWO	747
REDDITCH UNITED	SOUTHERN PREMIER CENTRAL	602
REDHILL	COMBINED COUNTIES PREMIER SOUTH	650
RETFORD	NORTHERN COUNTIES EAST DIVISION ONE	734
RINGWOOD TOWN	WESSEX DIVISION ONE	826
RISBOROUGH RANGERS	SPARTAN SOUTH MIDLANDS PREMIER	787
ROCESTER	NORTH WEST COUNTIES DIVISION 1S	721
ROCHESTER UNITED	SOUTHERN COUNTIES EAST DIVISION ONE	782
ROFFEY	SOUTHERN COMBINATION DIVISION ONE	770
ROMAN GLASS ST GEORGE	HELLENIC PREMIER	686
ROMFORD	ISTHMIAN NORTH	527
ROMSEY TOWN	WESSEX DIVISION ONE	826
ROMULUS	MIDLAND FOOTBALL LEAGUE PREMIER	698
ROSSINGTON MAIN	NORTHERN COUNTIES EAST DIVISION ONE	734
ROTHWELL CORINTHIANS	UNITED COUNTIES PREMIER SOUTH	806
ROYAL WOOTTON BASSETT	HELLENIC PREMIER	686
ROYSTON TOWN	SOUTHERN PREMIER CENTRAL	602
RUGBY TOWN	UNITED COUNTIES PREMIER SOUTH	806
RUNCORN LINNETS	NPL WEST	590
RUNCORN TOWN	NORTH WEST COUNTIES PREMIER	710
RUSHALL OLYMPIC	SOUTHERN PREMIER CENTRAL	602
RUSHDEN & HIGHAM UNITED	SPARTAN SOUTH MIDLANDS DIVISION ONE	794
RUSTHALL	SOUTHERN COUNTIES EAST PREMIER	775
RYTON & CRAWCROOK ALBION	NORTHERN LEAGUE DIVISION TWO	747
SAFFRON DYNAMO	UNITED COUNTIES DIVISION ONE	815
SAFFRON WALDEN TOWN	ESSEX SENIOR	679
SALISBURY	SOUTHERN PREMIER SOUTH	613
SALTASH UNITED	WESTERN LEAGUE PREMIER	831

Warrington Rylands 2021. Photos Bill Wheatcroft.

SALTDEAN UNITED	SOUTHERN COMBINATION PREMIER	763
SANDBACH UNITED	NORTH WEST COUNTIES DIVISION 1S	721
SANDHURST TOWN	COMBINED COUNTIES DIVISION ONE	657
SAWBRIDGEWORTH TOWN	ESSEX SENIOR	679
SCARBOROUGH ATHLETIC	NPL PREMIER DIVISION	558
SEAFORD TOWN	SOUTHERN COMBINATION DIVISION ONE	770
SEAHAM RED STAR	NORTHERN LEAGUE DIVISION ONE	740
SELBY TOWN	NORTHERN COUNTIES EAST DIVISION ONE	734
SELSEY	SOUTHERN COMBINATION DIVISION ONE	770
SELSTON	UNITED COUNTIES PREMIER NORTH	799
SEVENOAKS TOWN	ISTHMIAN SOUTH EAST	547
SHAFTESBURY	WESSEX PREMIER	819
SHAWBURY UNITED	MIDLAND FOOTBALL LEAGUE DIVISION ONE	705
SHEERWATER	COMBINED COUNTIES PREMIER SOUTH	650
SHEFFIELD	NPL EAST	570
SHEFFORD TOWN & CAMPTON	SPARTAN SOUTH MIDLANDS DIVISION ONE	794
SHEPPEY UNITED	SOUTHERN COUNTIES EAST PREMIER	775
SHEPSHED DYNAMO	NPL MIDLANDS	580
SHEPTON MALLET	WESTERN LEAGUE PREMIER	831
SHERBORNE TOWN	WESTERN LEAGUE DIVISION ONE	838
SHERINGHAM	EASTERN COUNTIES DIVISION ONE NORTH	670
SHERWOOD COLLIERY	NORTHERN COUNTIES EAST PREMIER	727
SHIFNAL TOWN	MIDLAND FOOTBALL LEAGUE PREMIER	698
SHILDON	NPL EAST	570
SHIREBROOK TOWN	NORTHERN COUNTIES EAST DIVISION ONE	734
SHOLING	SOUTHERN D1 SOUTH	634
SHOREHAM	SOUTHERN COMBINATION DIVISION ONE	770
SHORTWOOD UNITED	HELLENIC DIVISION ONE	693
SHRIVENHAM	HELLENIC PREMIER	686
SIDMOUTH TOWN	SOUTH WEST PENINSULA PREMIER EAST	753
SILSDEN	NORTHERN COUNTIES EAST PREMIER	727
SITTINGBOURNE	ISTHMIAN SOUTH EAST	547
SKEGNESS TOWN	UNITED COUNTIES PREMIER NORTH	799
SKELMERSDALE UNITED	NORTH WEST COUNTIES PREMIER	710
SLEAFORD TOWN	UNITED COUNTIES PREMIER NORTH	799
SLIMBRIDGE	SOUTHERN D1 SOUTH	634
SLOUGH TOWN	NATIONAL SOUTH	505
SNODLAND TOWN	SOUTHERN COUNTIES EAST DIVISION ONE	782
SOHAM TOWN RANGERS	NPL MIDLANDS	580
SOLIHULL MOORS	NATIONAL LEAGUE	482
SOUTH LIVERPOOL	NORTH WEST COUNTIES DIVISION 1N	717
SOUTH PARK	ISTHMIAN SOUTH CENTRAL	537
SOUTH SHIELDS	NPL PREMIER DIVISION	558
SOUTHALL	COMBINED COUNTIES PREMIER NORTH	644
SOUTHEND MANOR	ESSEX SENIOR	679
SOUTHEND UNITED	NATIONAL LEAGUE	482
SOUTHPORT	NATIONAL NORTH	494
SPALDING UNITED	NPL MIDLANDS	580
SPELTHORNE SPORTS	COMBINED COUNTIES PREMIER NORTH	644

Wellingborough Town Main Stand 2020. Photo Keith Clayton.

Main Stand Winterton Rangers. Photo Keith Clayton.

SPENNYMOOR TOWN	NATIONAL NORTH	494
SPORTING BENGAL UNITED	ESSEX SENIOR	679
SPORTING CLUB THAMESMEAD	SOUTHERN COUNTIES EAST DIVISION ONE	782
SPORTING KHALSA	NPL MIDLANDS	580
SQUIRES GATE	NORTH WEST COUNTIES PREMIER	710
ST ALBANS CITY	NATIONAL SOUTH	505
ST HELENS TOWN	NORTH WEST COUNTIES DIVISION 1N	717
ST MARGARETSBURY	ESSEX SENIOR	679
ST MARTINS	NORTH WEST COUNTIES DIVISION 1S	721
ST PANTELEIMON	COMBINED COUNTIES PREMIER NORTH	644
ST. ANDREWS	UNITED COUNTIES DIVISION ONE	815
ST. BLAZEY	SOUTH WEST PENINSULA PREMIER WEST	758
ST. DENNIS	SOUTH WEST PENINSULA PREMIER WEST	758
ST. IVES TOWN	SOUTHERN PREMIER CENTRAL	602
ST. NEOTS TOWN	SOUTHERN D1 CENTRAL	624
STAFFORD RANGERS	NPL PREMIER DIVISION	558
STAFFORD TOWN	NORTH WEST COUNTIES DIVISION 1S	721
STAINES TOWN	ISTHMIAN SOUTH CENTRAL	537
STALYBRIDGE CELTIC	NPL PREMIER DIVISION	558
STAMFORD	NPL MIDLANDS	580
STANSFELD	SOUTHERN COUNTIES EAST DIVISION ONE	782
STANSTED	ESSEX SENIOR	679
STANWAY ROVERS	ESSEX SENIOR	679
STAPENHILL	MIDLAND FOOTBALL LEAGUE DIVISION ONE	705
STAPLEHURST & MONARCHS UNITED	SOUTHERN COUNTIES EAST DIVISION ONE	782
STAVELEY MINERS WELFARE	NORTHERN COUNTIES EAST PREMIER	727
STEETON	NORTH WEST COUNTIES DIVISION 1N	717
STEYNING TOWN	SOUTHERN COMBINATION PREMIER	763
STICKER	SOUTH WEST PENINSULA PREMIER WEST	758
STOCKPORT COUNTY	NATIONAL LEAGUE	482
STOCKPORT TOWN	NORTH WEST COUNTIES DIVISION 1S	721
STOCKSBRIDGE PARK STEELS	NPL EAST	570
STOCKTON TOWN	NPL EAST	570
STOKE GABRIEL & TORBAY POLICE	SOUTH WEST PENINSULA PREMIER EAST	753
STONE OLD ALLEYNIANS	MIDLAND FOOTBALL LEAGUE PREMIER	698
STONEHOUSE TOWN	HELLENIC DIVISION ONE	693
STORRINGTON COMMUNITY	SOUTHERN COMBINATION DIVISION ONE	770
STOTFOLD	SPARTAN SOUTH MIDLANDS DIVISION ONE	794
STOURBRIDGE	SOUTHERN PREMIER CENTRAL	602
STOURPORT SWIFTS	MIDLAND FOOTBALL LEAGUE PREMIER	698
STOWMARKET TOWN	ISTHMIAN NORTH	527
STRATFORD TOWN	SOUTHERN PREMIER CENTRAL	602
STREET	WESTERN LEAGUE PREMIER	831
STUDLEY	HELLENIC DIVISION ONE	693
SUNDERLAND R.C.A.	NORTHERN LEAGUE DIVISION ONE	740
SUNDERLAND RYHOPE C.W.	NORTHERN LEAGUE DIVISION ONE	740
SUNDERLAND WEST END	NORTHERN LEAGUE DIVISION TWO	747
SUTTON ATHLETIC	SOUTHERN COUNTIES EAST DIVISION ONE	782
SUTTON COLDFIELD TOWN	NPL MIDLANDS	580

CLUB INDEX

SUTTON COMMON ROVERS	ISTHMIAN SOUTH CENTRAL	537
SWAFFHAM TOWN	EASTERN COUNTIES PREMIER	663
SWALLOWNEST	NORTHERN COUNTIES EAST DIVISION ONE	734
SWINDON SUPERMARINE	SOUTHERN PREMIER SOUTH	613
TADCASTER ALBION	NPL EAST	570
TADLEY CALLEVA	COMBINED COUNTIES PREMIER NORTH	644
TAKELEY	ESSEX SENIOR	679
TAMWORTH	SOUTHERN PREMIER CENTRAL	602
TAUNTON TOWN	SOUTHERN PREMIER SOUTH	613
TAVISTOCK	WESTERN LEAGUE PREMIER	831
TEVERSAL	NORTHERN COUNTIES EAST DIVISION ONE	734
THACKLEY	NORTHERN COUNTIES EAST PREMIER	727
THAME UNITED	SOUTHERN D1 CENTRAL	624
THAME UNITED RESERVES	SPARTAN SOUTH MIDLANDS DIVISION ONE	794
THATCHAM TOWN	ISTHMIAN SOUTH CENTRAL	537
THETFORD TOWN	EASTERN COUNTIES PREMIER	663
THORNABY	NORTHERN LEAGUE DIVISION ONE	740
THORNBURY TOWN	HELLENIC PREMIER	686
THREE BRIDGES	ISTHMIAN SOUTH EAST	547
TILBURY	ISTHMIAN NORTH	527
TIVERTON TOWN	SOUTHERN PREMIER SOUTH	613
TIVIDALE	MIDLAND FOOTBALL LEAGUE PREMIER	698
TONBRIDGE ANGELS	NATIONAL SOUTH	505
TOOTING & MITCHAM UNITED	ISTHMIAN SOUTH CENTRAL	537
TOOTING BEC	SOUTHERN COUNTIES EAST DIVISION ONE	782
TORPOINT ATHLETIC	SOUTH WEST PENINSULA PREMIER EAST	753
TORQUAY UNITED	NATIONAL LEAGUE	482
TORRIDGESIDE	SOUTH WEST PENINSULA PREMIER EAST	753
TORRINGTON	SOUTH WEST PENINSULA PREMIER EAST	753
TOTTON & ELING	WESSEX DIVISION ONE	826
TOW LAW TOWN	NORTHERN LEAGUE DIVISION TWO	747
TOWER HAMLETS	SOUTHERN COUNTIES EAST PREMIER	775
TRAFFORD	NPL WEST	590
TRING ATHLETIC	SPARTAN SOUTH MIDLANDS PREMIER	787
TRURO CITY	SOUTHERN PREMIER SOUTH	613
TUFFLEY ROVERS	HELLENIC PREMIER	686
TUNBRIDGE WELLS	SOUTHERN COUNTIES EAST PREMIER	775
TYTHERINGTON ROCKS	WESTERN LEAGUE DIVISION ONE	838
UEA	EASTERN COUNTIES DIVISION ONE NORTH	670
UNITED SERVICES PORTSMOUTH	WESSEX PREMIER	819
UTTOXETER TOWN	MIDLAND FOOTBALL LEAGUE PREMIER	698
UXBRIDGE	ISTHMIAN SOUTH CENTRAL	537
VAUXHALL MOTORS	NORTH WEST COUNTIES PREMIER	710
VCD ATHLETIC	ISTHMIAN SOUTH EAST	547
VERWOOD TOWN	WESSEX DIVISION ONE	826
VIRGINIA WATER	COMBINED COUNTIES PREMIER NORTH	644
WADEBRIDGE TOWN	SOUTH WEST PENINSULA PREMIER WEST	758
WALLINGFORD TOWN	COMBINED COUNTIES DIVISION ONE	657
WALSALL WOOD	MIDLAND FOOTBALL LEAGUE PREMIER	698

WALSHAM LE WILLOWS	EASTERN COUNTIES PREMIER	663
WALTHAM ABBEY	SOUTHERN D1 CENTRAL	624
WALTHAMSTOW	ESSEX SENIOR	679
WALTON & HERSHAM	COMBINED COUNTIES PREMIER SOUTH	650
WALTON CASUALS	SOUTHERN PREMIER SOUTH	613
WANTAGE TOWN	SOUTHERN D1 CENTRAL	624
WARE	SOUTHERN D1 CENTRAL	624
WARMINSTER TOWN	WESTERN LEAGUE DIVISION ONE	838
WARRINGTON RYLANDS	NPL WEST	590
WARRINGTON TOWN	NPL PREMIER DIVISION	558
WASHINGTON	NORTHERN LEAGUE DIVISION TWO	747
WEALDSTONE	NATIONAL LEAGUE	482
WEDNESFIELD	MIDLAND FOOTBALL LEAGUE DIVISION ONE	705
WELLING TOWN	SOUTHERN COUNTIES EAST PREMIER	775
WELLING UNITED	NATIONAL SOUTH	505
WELLINGBOROUGH TOWN	UNITED COUNTIES PREMIER SOUTH	806
WELLINGBOROUGH WHITWORTH	SPARTAN SOUTH MIDLANDS DIVISION ONE	794
WELLINGTON	HELLENIC DIVISION ONE	693
WELLINGTON AFC	WESTERN LEAGUE PREMIER	831
WELLS CITY	WESTERN LEAGUE DIVISION ONE	838
WELTON ROVERS	WESTERN LEAGUE DIVISION ONE	838
WELWYN GARDEN CITY	SOUTHERN D1 CENTRAL	624
WEMBLEY	COMBINED COUNTIES PREMIER NORTH	644
WENDRON UNITED	SOUTH WEST PENINSULA PREMIER WEST	758
WEST ALLOTMENT CELTIC	NORTHERN LEAGUE DIVISION ONE	740
WEST AUCKLAND TOWN	NORTHERN LEAGUE DIVISION ONE	740
WEST BRIDGFORD	UNITED COUNTIES DIVISION ONE	815
WEST DIDSBURY & CHORLTON	NORTH WEST COUNTIES DIVISION 1S	721
WEST ESSEX	ESSEX SENIOR	679
WESTBURY UNITED	HELLENIC PREMIER	686
WESTFIELD	ISTHMIAN SOUTH CENTRAL	537
WESTFIELDS	HELLENIC PREMIER	686
WESTON-SUPER-MARE	SOUTHERN PREMIER SOUTH	613
WESTSIDE	SOUTHERN COUNTIES EAST DIVISION ONE	782
WEYMOUTH	NATIONAL LEAGUE	482
WHICKHAM	NORTHERN LEAGUE DIVISION ONE	740
WHITBY TOWN	NPL PREMIER DIVISION	558
WHITCHURCH ALPORT	MIDLAND FOOTBALL LEAGUE PREMIER	698
WHITCHURCH UNITED	WESSEX DIVISION ONE	826
WHITE ENSIGN	ESSEX SENIOR	679
WHITEHAWK	ISTHMIAN SOUTH EAST	547
WHITLEY BAY	NORTHERN LEAGUE DIVISION ONE	740
WHITSTABLE TOWN	ISTHMIAN SOUTH EAST	547
WHITTLESEY ATHLETIC	EASTERN COUNTIES DIVISION ONE NORTH	670
WHITTON UNITED	EASTERN COUNTIES PREMIER	663
WICK	SOUTHERN COMBINATION DIVISION ONE	770
WIDNES	NPL WEST	590
WILLAND ROVERS	SOUTHERN D1 SOUTH	634
WILLINGTON	NORTHERN LEAGUE DIVISION TWO	747

WIMBORNE TOWN	SOUTHERN PREMIER SOUTH	613
WINCANTON TOWN	WESTERN LEAGUE DIVISION ONE	838
WINCHESTER CITY	SOUTHERN D1 SOUTH	634
WINDSOR	COMBINED COUNTIES PREMIER NORTH	644
WINGATE & FINCHLEY	ISTHMIAN PREMIER	516
WINSFORD UNITED	NORTH WEST COUNTIES PREMIER	710
WINSLOW UNITED	SPARTAN SOUTH MIDLANDS DIVISION ONE	794
WINTERTON RANGERS	NORTHERN COUNTIES EAST PREMIER	727
WISBECH ST MARY	EASTERN COUNTIES DIVISION ONE NORTH	670
WISBECH TOWN	NPL MIDLANDS	580
WITHAM TOWN	ISTHMIAN NORTH	527
WITTON ALBION	NPL PREMIER DIVISION	558
WIVENHOE TOWN	EASTERN COUNTIES DIVISION ONE SOUTH	674
WOKING	NATIONAL LEAGUE	482
WOKINGHAM & EMMBROOK	COMBINED COUNTIES PREMIER NORTH	644
WOLVERHAMPTON CASUALS	MIDLAND FOOTBALL LEAGUE PREMIER	698
WOLVERHAMPTON SPORTING COMM'	MIDLAND FOOTBALL LEAGUE DIVISION ONE	705
WOODBRIDGE TOWN	EASTERN COUNTIES PREMIER	663
WOODFORD TOWN	ESSEX SENIOR	679
WOODLEY UNITED	COMBINED COUNTIES DIVISION ONE	657
WORCESTER CITY	MIDLAND FOOTBALL LEAGUE PREMIER	698
WORCESTER RAIDERS	HELLENIC DIVISION ONE	693
WORKINGTON	NPL WEST	590
WORKSOP TOWN	NPL EAST	570
WORMLEY ROVERS	EASTERN COUNTIES DIVISION ONE SOUTH	674
WORSBROUGH BRIDGE ATHLETIC	NORTHERN COUNTIES EAST DIVISION ONE	734
WORTHING	ISTHMIAN PREMIER	516
WORTHING UNITED	SOUTHERN COMBINATION DIVISION ONE	770
WREXHAM	NATIONAL LEAGUE	482
WROXHAM	EASTERN COUNTIES PREMIER	663
WYTHENSHAWE AMATEURS	NORTH WEST COUNTIES DIVISION 1S	721
WYTHENSHAWE TOWN	NORTH WEST COUNTIES PREMIER	710
YATE TOWN	SOUTHERN PREMIER SOUTH	613
YAXLEY	NPL MIDLANDS	580
YEOVIL TOWN	NATIONAL LEAGUE	482
YORK CITY	NATIONAL NORTH	494
YORKSHIRE AMATEUR	NPL EAST	570